ALGEBRA TWO
AND TRIGONOMETRY

Isidore Dressler

Formerly Chairman, Department of Mathematics
Bayside High School, New York City

Adjunct Assistant Professor
Pace College, New York City

Barnett Rich

Formerly Chairman, Department of Mathematics
Brooklyn Technical High School, New York City

Adjunct Assistant Professor
The City College
The City University of New York

Algebra Two and Trigonometry

(Eleventh Year Mathematics)

A Modern Integrated Course

Dedicated to serving

AMSCO

our nation's youth

When ordering this book, please specify: either **R 104 P** or **Algebra Two and Trigonometry Paperback Edition**

Amsco School Publications, Inc.
315 Hudson Street   New York, N.Y. 10013

ISBN 0-87720-220-6

PRINTED IN THE UNITED STATES OF AMERICA

PREFACE

Algebra Two and Trigonometry presents a modern integrated course in intermediate algebra and trigonometry, including a thorough review of elementary algebra. Each unit of work included in the text is fully in accord with second courses in algebra throughout the United States and with the eleventh year mathematics syllabus of the State of New York.

The book emphasizes an understanding of the structure and processes of mathematics, as well as the acquisition of the necessary manipulative skills. In short, the major objective of the text is to fuse the "why" and the "how" by presenting each topic from a modern point of view. To make mathematics teaching more effective, the book stresses broad, basic, and unifying mathematical concepts such as those of sets and function. For example, function is treated at length in a wide variety of topics such as linear functions, quadratic functions, polynomial functions, exponential functions, logarithmic functions, trigonometric functions, and inverse trigonometric functions.

To meet the ever-increasing demands of today's mathematics classroom, the authors have made consistent use of the laws of algebra and the application of reasoning to mathematical operations and processes. However, while presenting a modern structural approach, the authors have used an informal treatment that avoids undue rigor.

Each reader is urged to note the simplicity of language and the informal style. Students should have little or no difficulty reading and understanding the text. Note further the organization and exposition of the materials in a self-teaching order, meaningfully and pedagogically developed.

The book provides for the integration of intermediate algebra and trigonometry, thus meeting a major objective of many second courses in algebra and in eleventh year mathematics. Trigonometric content is presented at a very early stage and is then carried along simultaneously with the content in algebra. However, the organization of the book is such that it can also be used for courses which lay less emphasis on integration, as well as for courses in which intermediate algebra and trigonometry are dealt with separately.

To help students make a smooth transition from working with algebraic expressions and equations to working with trigonometric expressions and equations, Chapter VIII is devoted entirely to the integration of algebra and trigonometry. To accomplish this, *each practice exercise is presented in two parallel forms, the algebraic form on the left half of the page and the related trigonometric form on the right half.* Each model problem is solved both in an algebraic form as well as in its analogous trigonometric form. If a student has difficulty with the lengthier trigonometric form, the model problems reveal how a problem can be revised into the shorter and simpler algebraic form. This integration technique is continued in later chapters with each new trigonometric unit of work. See, for example, the integrative technique in Chapter XV, which deals with identities and equations.

The text fully covers the units of work customarily contained in second courses in algebra and in eleventh year mathematics.

Included in the text are the following features:

1. The employment of the theory and uses of *sets* as a unifying theme.
2. The comprehensive treatment of the *function concept* as a unifying theme by a full coverage of functions, inverses of functions, relations, and one-to-one correspondence.
3. The clear and precise statement and uses of the *laws of algebra* and the *properties of a field.*
4. The exhibiting of *algebra as a deductive system* in which undefined terms, definitions, and postulates are used in the proof of theorems.
5. The presentation of *coordinate geometry* as a most effective means of integrating intermediate algebra and trigonometry, emphasizing as it does the graphs of linear functions, the graphs of quadratic functions and the conic sections, and the graphs of trigonometric functions.
6. The development of *inequalities* both from an algebraic and a graphic point of view.
7. The presentation and development of *logarithmic and exponential properties and their applications.*
8. The treatment of *verbal problem-solving* and the provision of a generous supply of problems necessary for the proper development of this unit of work.
9. The early introduction and wide use of the subject of *absolute values.*
10. The inclusion of challenging *honor units for the superior student:* (1) complex numbers; (2) conic sections; (3) types of variation; (4) sequences and series, including infinite series; (5) binomial theorem; and (6) systems of equations involving three variables.

Chapters I to VI enable teachers to make a thorough review of elementary algebra, a review which is indispensable to any understanding of intermediate algebra. Because of the inadequate exposure of many students in previous courses, their lack of understanding of basic principles, and their weaknesses in manipulative skills, the early chapters of the text afford valuable remedial opportunities. Chapter VII provides for an effective review of elementary trigonometric principles and techniques.

An important feature of the text is the character of its organization:
1. Each chapter is divided into related and sequential learning units which, with proper application, a student can readily master.
2. The basic concepts and principles of each unit are carefully developed using precise, yet simple, language and symbolism.
3. New terms are clearly defined.
4. Explanations and problems suitable for teaching purposes lead to the statement of the general principles and procedures involved in a unit.
5. Model problems, whose solutions are accompanied by detailed step-by-step explanations, are most helpful in showing students how to apply the related principles and how to follow the necessary procedures.
6. A set of expertly selected and carefully graded exercises covering types of problems appropriate for a second course in algebra or a course in eleventh year mathematics enables a student to understand thoroughly the basic concepts and related procedures of each unit. The exercises enable him to test the extent of his mastery of the unit.
7. Each chapter includes exercises of more-than-average difficulty, as well as enrichment materials to challenge the superior student.
8. The last two chapters are devoted completely to the proofs, derivations, and a summary of the important trigonometric and algebraic formulas.

In summary, *Algebra Two and Trigonometry* serves either as a textbook or as a supplement to the class textbook. It makes available to both students and teachers an abundance of teaching and practice materials suitable for use as a source for refresher and remedial work on both the secondary school level and college level.

The authors are deeply grateful to Mr. Harry Schor, Chairman of the Mathematics Department of Abraham Lincoln High School, N.Y.C.; Mr. Melvin Klein, Chairman of the Mathematics Department of Brooklyn Technical High School, N.Y.C.; Mr. Murray Navon, Chairman of the Mathematics Department of James Madison High School, N.Y.C.; and Dr. Robert E. Dressler, Assistant Professor of Mathematics at Kansas State University, for their many valuable suggestions and criticisms.

Isidore Dressler
Barnett Rich

CONTENTS

CHAPTER I

THE REAL NUMBER SYSTEM

1. Numbers and Sets of Numbers

In the study of geometry, we deal with collections, or *sets*, of points, sets of lines, etc. In the study of arithmetic and algebra, we deal with sets of numbers, the properties of sets of numbers, and operations on numbers. Understanding sets is a basic requirement in the study of mathematics.

SETS

Originally, *number* meant one of the counting numbers: 1, 2, 3, 4, 5, ... (the three dots are read "and so on"). Today, however, the inventiveness of mathematicians has given us many other collections or sets of numbers for our study and use. In this chapter, the following sets of numbers are emphasized:

1. The set of *natural numbers,* or *counting numbers.*
2. The set of *whole numbers,* which consists of 0 and the natural numbers.
3. The set of *integers,* which consists of 0, the positive integers, and the negative integers.
4. The set of *rational numbers,* which consists of those numbers expressible as fractions whose numerator is an integer and whose denominator is a nonzero integer.
5. The set of *real numbers,* which consists of the first four sets and also the set of irrational numbers.

The branch of mathematics that studies sets is scarcely a century old. The study of sets and their properties provides a foundation for mathematics, finds application in many important fields of knowledge, and serves as a powerful aid to logical reasoning and mathematical analysis. Think of the common words we use to refer to sets, words such as *club, class, team, squad, group, regiment, family, congress, pair, trio,* and *quartet.*

Since we shall make frequent reference to collections and to objects that belong to them, we shall in the future refer to a collection as a *set* and to the objects in the collection as the **members,** or **elements,** of the set.

For the most part in our study of sets, the sets which we shall consider are **sets of numbers.**

Number and Numeral

A "number" is an abstract idea which may be represented by means of a symbol or expression called a **numeral.** Many different numerals may represent the same number.

For example, the numerals 5, V, ⊢⊣⊣ , and five all name the same number.

In mathematics, we perform operations on numbers, not on numerals. At times, however, to avoid awkward and cumbersome expressions, we will use the word *number* when we should really use the word *numeral.* For example, we may say, for the sake of brevity and simplicity, "write the number" instead of saying "write the numeral that represents the number." This is commonly accepted practice when the context clearly indicates whether we are referring to the number or the numeral.

Similarly, when discussing sets whose members are not numbers, we may say "write the elements of the set" rather than "write the names that represent the elements of the set."

METHODS OF DEFINING A SET

If a set is designated adequately, it is possible to determine whether a particular object does or does not belong to that set. A set is *defined* if we can identify an object as an element of that set. To designate a set and its elements, we use braces to enclose the elements; we generally use a capital letter to refer to the set.

A set may be defined in the following ways:
1. by roster or listing
2. by rule or description
3. by set-builder notation

The Roster Method

Using the **roster method,** a set is defined by listing its elements within braces. For example, we may indicate the set of seasons by writing $S = \{$spring, summer, fall, winter$\}$; the set of natural numbers by writing $N = \{1, 2, 3, 4, \ldots\}$; the set of whole numbers by writing $W = \{0, 1, 2, 3, 4, \ldots\}$; and the set of integers by writing $I = \{\ldots, -4, -3, -2, -1, 0, 1, 2, 3, 4, \ldots\}$.

To indicate that an element belongs to a set, we use the symbol ∈. To show that an element does not belong to a set, we use the symbol ∉. For example, if N represents the set of natural numbers, $3 \in N$ and $3\frac{1}{2} \notin N$.

Three dots are used in the roster method when it is impossible to list all the members, as in the case of an infinite set. Note this use in the case of the infinite set of natural numbers:

$$N = \{1, 2, 3, 4, 5, \ldots\}$$

Three dots are also used in the roster method when it is needless to list all the members, as in the case of a finite set with a large number of elements. For example, we may define the set of positive odd integers less than 1000 as $\{1, 3, 5, 7, \ldots, 995, 997, 999\}$. When using three dots to define a set, be sure to list enough elements of the set to make the pattern clear.

The elements of a set may be listed in any order, and each element should be listed only once. For example, the set of digits in 1,000,000 should be listed as $\{1, 0\}$ or $\{0, 1\}$.

The Rule Method

Using the *rule method,* a set may be defined by stating a rule or a condition that makes it possible to determine whether or not a given object belongs to the set. For example, if $S = \{1, 2, 3, 4, 5\}$, we may use a rule to define S as the set of the first five counting numbers, or $S = \{$the first five counting numbers$\}$. The braces are read "the set of." Using the rule method, we may define the set of rational numbers as $R = \{$numbers that may be expressed in the form of $\frac{a}{b}$ where a and b are integers and $b \neq 0\}$.

The Set-Builder Notation

A notation called the *set-builder notation* may be used to define a set. For example, if $A = \{$all natural numbers greater than 5$\}$, we may use set-builder notation to denote A as follows:

$$A = \{x \,|\, x > 5, x \text{ is a natural number}\}$$

or

$$A = \{x : x > 5, x \text{ is a natural number}\}$$

The following indicates the manner in which set A is read compared with the way in which it is written (note that the vertical bar, and also the colon, is read "such that"):

Write: A $=$ $\underbrace{\{x}$ $|$ $\underbrace{x > 5,}$ $\overbrace{x \text{ is a natural number}\}}$

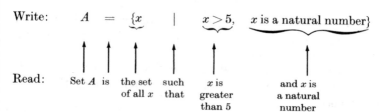

Read: Set A is   the set   such x is   and x is
                    of all x that   greater   a natural
                                        than 5   number

The set-builder notation for $S = \{x \mid x$ is a single-digit positive odd integer$\}$ is read "S is the set of all x such that x is a single-digit positive odd integer." Using the roster method, we write $S = \{1, 3, 5, 7, 9\}$.

Exercises

In 1–4, tell whether or not the set is adequately defined. If the set is not adequately defined, state the reason why it is not.

1. $\{1, 8, 27, 64\}$
2. $\{$large numbers$\}$
3. $\{$natural numbers less than 12$\}$
4. $\{$non-negative integers$\}$

In 5–8, tell whether the statement is *true* or *false*.

5. $0 \in \{$whole numbers$\}$
6. $-3 \notin \{$natural numbers$\}$
7. $7 \in \{$positive odd integers$\}$
8. $123 \in \{13, 23, 33\}$

In 9–13, use the roster method to define the set. Use three dots when necessary or convenient.

9. the set of days of the week that begin with the letter S
10. the set of natural numbers greater than 10 and less than 15
11. the set of odd integers greater than 100
12. the set of factors of 24 greater than 1 and less than 10
13. the set of numbers that differ from 10 by 2

In 14–19, use the rule method to define the set.

14. $\{$Tuesday, Thursday$\}$
15. $\{7, 14, 21, 28\}$
16. $\{\ldots, -7, -5, -3, -1\}$
17. $\{50, 51, 52, \ldots, 97, 98, 99\}$
18. $\{1, 4, 9, 16, 25, 36, 49\}$
19. $\{100, 200, 300, \ldots, 700, 800, 900\}$

In 20–22, use the roster method to list the elements of the set.

20. $\{x \mid x$ is a single-digit natural number$\}$
21. $\{x \mid x$ is a prime number greater than 9 and less than 25$\}$
22. $\{x \mid x^2 = 25, x$ is an integer$\}$

In 23–25, state whether the listed sets are the same set or two different sets.

23. $\{x \mid x$ is a negative integer less than $-5\}$ and $\{-4, -3, -2, -1\}$
24. $\{x \mid x$ is a natural number and a perfect square$\}$ and $\{1, 4, 9, 16, 25, \ldots\}$
25. $\{$natural numbers less than $4\frac{1}{4}\}$ and $\{4, 3, 2, 1, 0\}$

2. Subsets

Consider the set $U = \{3, 5, 7\}$ and the set $B = \{3, 5\}$. Notice that every member of set B is also a member of set U. We say that set B is a **subset** of set U. We express this statement with the symbolism $B \subset U$.

In general, set A is a subset of set B ($A \subset B$) if every member of A is also a member of B.

Consider the set $U = \{3, 5, 7\}$ and the set $T = \{1, 3\}$. Observe that not every member of set T is a member of set U. Therefore, we say that set T is not a subset of set U. We express this statement with the symbolism $T \not\subset U$.

A **universal set,** or **universe,** in a discussion is a set from which elements are chosen to form subsets. A **Venn diagram** may be used to show the relationship between a subset of a set and the set itself. The Venn diagram at the right pictures the statement made earlier that the set $B = \{3, 5\}$ is a subset of the set $U = \{3, 5, 7\}$.

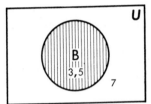

A **proper subset** of a set is one that does not contain all the elements of that set. For example, proper subsets of set $U = \{3, 5, 7\}$ are $B = \{3, 5\}$, $C = \{3, 7\}$, $D = \{5, 7\}$, $E = \{3\}$, $F = \{5\}$, and $G = \{7\}$.

An **improper subset** of a set is one that contains all the elements of that set. For example, the set $A = \{3, 5, 7\}$ is an improper subset of the set $U = \{3, 5, 7\}$. It is obvious that every set is a subset of itself.

The **empty set,** or **null set,** is the set that has no elements. An example of the empty set is the set of all women who have been president of the United States. Either the symbol $\varnothing$ or the symbol $\{\ \}$ may be used to represent the empty set. Mathematicians have agreed:

1. There is only one empty set $\varnothing$.
2. The empty set $\varnothing$ is a subset of every set.

THE NUMBER OF SUBSETS OF A SET THAT CONTAINS *n* ELEMENTS

In our previous discussion of the subsets of a set, we saw that set $U = \{3, 5, 7\}$, which has 3 elements, has 8, or 2^3 subsets. They are the following:

$A = \{3, 5, 7\}$	$B = \{3, 5\}$	$C = \{3, 7\}$	$D = \{5, 7\}$
$E = \{3\}$	$F = \{5\}$	$G = \{7\}$	$H = \varnothing$

Rule. If a set contains n elements, the number of subsets that this set has is 2^n.

Exercises

In 1–8, tell whether the statement is *true* or *false*.
1. {cat, dog} is a subset of {dog, horse, cat}
2. {3, 4, 5, 6} is a subset of {4, 5, 6, 7}
3. {cows} ⊂ {animals}
4. {natural numbers} ⊄ {whole numbers}
5. $\varnothing \not\subset \{1\}$ 6. $\{1\} \subset \varnothing$ 7. $\varnothing \subset \{0\}$ 8. $\{0\} \not\subset \varnothing$

In 9 and 10, tell whether the statement is *true* or *false*. Justify your answer using a Venn diagram.
9. If $A \subset B$ and $B \subset D$, then $A \subset D$
10. If $R \subset S$ and $T \subset S$, then $R \subset T$

11. If $U = \{r, w, b\}$, list all the subsets of U that have (a) one element, (b) two elements, (c) three elements, and (d) no elements.

In 12–15, (a) list all the subsets (including the empty set) of the given set and (b) state the number of subsets that the given set has.
12. {7}   13. {Tom, Harry}   14. {2, 4, 6}   15. {a, b, c, d}

16. Without writing the subsets of set U, determine the number of subsets (including the empty set) of U if the number of elements in U is:
    a. 1   b. 2   c. 3   d. 4   e. n

3. Comparing Sets

ONE-TO-ONE CORRESPONDENCE

Suppose that, in a classroom, each seat is occupied by one and only one student and each student in the class occupies one and only one seat. In this situation, each member of the set of students in the class has been paired with one and only one member of the set of seats in the room; and each member of the set of seats in the room has been paired with one and only one member of the set of students in the class. When the elements of two sets can be paired in this way, the pairing is called a ***one-to-one correspondence.*** Two such sets have the same number of elements. The number of elements that a set contains is called its ***cardinal number.***

FINITE SETS AND INFINITE SETS

A ***finite set*** is a set whose cardinal number is a natural number or zero. When the number of elements of a finite set is counted, the counting comes to an end.

For example, $A = \{2, 4, 6, 8, 10\}$ is a finite set. It has 5 elements. The cardinal number of set A is 5. Also, $B = \{$odd integers that are multiples of 2$\}$ is a finite set because B is the empty set $\varnothing$ which has zero members.

An *infinite set* is a set whose cardinal number is not a natural number or zero. When we attempt to count the number of elements of an infinite set, the counting process never comes to an end. For example, $C = \{$odd natural numbers$\}$, which may be written $\{1, 3, 5, 7, 9, \ldots\}$, is an infinite set.

EQUIVALENT SETS AND EQUAL SETS

Equivalent sets are sets whose elements can be paired so that there is a one-to-one correspondence.

For example, if $A = \{a, b, c\}$ and $B = \{1, 2, 3\}$, we can set up a one-to-one correspondence by pairing the elements of set A and set B as shown below. Then we say, "Set A is equivalent to set B," which may be written as "$A \leftrightarrow B$" or "$A \sim B$."

$$A = \{a, b, c\}$$
$$\updownarrow \updownarrow \updownarrow$$
$$B = \{1, 2, 3\}$$

Since equivalent sets must have the same number of elements, a simple way to determine whether or not two finite sets which have few elements are equivalent is to count the number of elements in each set. Note that two equivalent sets must have the same number of elements, but need not have the same elements.

Sometimes it is possible to match two infinite sets. For example, the set of natural numbers and the set of positive even integers may be matched in a one-to-one correspondence to show that the sets are equivalent. See how this is done.

$$N = \{1, 2, 3, 4, 5, 6, 7, 8, \ldots\}$$
$$\updownarrow \updownarrow \updownarrow \updownarrow \updownarrow \updownarrow \updownarrow \updownarrow$$
$$E = \{2, 4, 6, 8, 10, 12, 14, 16, \ldots\}$$

Since the elements of set N and the elements of set E are paired in a one-to-one correspondence, then $N \leftrightarrow E$; that is, the set of natural numbers is equivalent to the set of positive even integers.

Equal sets are sets that have exactly the same elements. Recall that the order in which the elements of a set are listed does not matter. For example, if $A = \{n, o, w\}$ and $B = \{o, w, n\}$ then set A and set B are equal sets, written "$A = B$." Also, if $C = \{1, 3, 5\}$ and $D = \{5, 1, 3\}$, then $C = D$.

If two sets are equal sets, each set is an improper subset of the other.

Equivalent sets are equal sets if and only if they have the same elements. For example, if $C = \{1, 2, 3, 4, 5\}$ and $D = \{1, 2, 3, 4, 10\}$, then set C is equivalent to set D, but set C is not equal to set D, written "$C \leftrightarrow D$ but $C \neq D$."

Exercises

In 1–4, tell whether or not there is a one-to-one correspondence between the two sets.

1. $\{1, 3, 5, 7, 9\}$ and $\{0, 2, 4, 6, 8\}$
2. $\{T, A, B\}$ and $\{B, A, T\}$
3. $\{1, 2, 3, 4\}$ and $\{-1, -2, -3, -4, \ldots\}$
4. {positive odd integers} and {positive even integers}

In 5–8, state whether the set is a finite set or an infinite set. (An empty set is a finite set.)

5. the set of men 20 feet tall
6. the set of all integers less than 1
7. $\{0\}$
8. the set of rectangles having three diagonals

In 9–11, (*a*) tell whether or not the sets are equivalent sets and (*b*) tell whether or not the sets are equal sets.

9. {Jack, Harry, Ted, Martin} and {Ruth, Hilda, Rose, Sarah}
10. $\{T, E, A\}$ and $\{E, A, T\}$
11. $\{5, 6, 7, 8, 9\}$ and {natural numbers greater than 4 and less than 10}

12. Specify two finite sets that are equivalent sets but are not equal sets.
13. Specify two finite sets that are not equivalent sets.
14. Specify two infinite sets that are equivalent sets.
15. Is it possible to specify two equal sets that are not equivalent sets? Why?
16. Is it possible to specify two equivalent sets that are not equal sets? Why?

4. Using a Number Line To Graph Real Numbers and Sets of Real Numbers

GRAPHING NATURAL NUMBERS AND WHOLE NUMBERS

It is useful to associate numbers with points on a line called a **number line.** To do this, we select any two convenient points on the line. We label the point on the left "0" and call it

the **origin;** we label the point on the right "1." Using the distance between 0 and 1 as a unit of measure, we find points to the right of 1. We label the new points consecutively 2, 3, 4, ..., as shown in the figure above.

On the preceding number line, which extends to the right without ending, every whole number and natural number can be associated with a point on the line. On a number line, the number associated with a point is called the **coordinate** of the point, and the point is the **graph** of the number. Hence, point A is the graph of 2; also, 5 is the coordinate of point B.

GRAPHING INTEGERS

To graph integers on a number line, we begin with a number line on which points have been associated with the set of whole numbers (natural numbers and zero). Then we use the distance between 0 and 1 as a unit of measure and find points to the *left* of 0. We label the new points consecutively $-1, -2, -3$, etc.

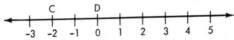

The set of integers consists of the *positive integers, zero,* and the *negative integers.* The side of the number line to the right of 0 is the positive side and contains the graphs of the positive integers. The side to the left of 0 is the negative side and contains the graphs of the negative integers. Hence, point C is the graph of -2 and point D is the graph of 0.

GRAPHING RATIONAL NUMBERS

The set of *rational numbers* consists of numbers that can be expressed in the form $\frac{a}{b}$ where a and b are integers and $b \neq 0$. (Think of a *rational* number as a *ratio* number, the ratio of a to b.) Any integer a is a rational number since it can be written in the form of $\frac{a}{1}$. For example, the integer 5, which may be written $\frac{5}{1}$, is a rational number. Other examples of rational numbers are $\frac{7}{3}$ or $2\frac{1}{3}$, $\frac{13}{10}$ or 1.3, and $\frac{-8}{+5}$ or $-1\frac{3}{5}$. Since division by 0 is impossible, $\frac{3}{0}$ is meaningless.

To graph the set of rational numbers on a number line, we begin with a number line on which points have been associated with the members of the set of integers. Then, we divide the intervals between integers into halves, thirds, quarters, etc. Now we can associate every member of the set of rational numbers with one of these points, as shown in the following figure:

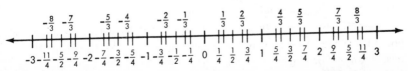

In order to graph a particular rational number whose denominator is 7, such as $\frac{18}{7}$ or $2\frac{4}{7}$, we would divide the interval between 2 and 3 into 7 equal parts.

GRAPHING REAL NUMBERS: COMPLETING THE NUMBER LINE

The graph of the set of rational numbers is a set of closely spaced points, as shown in the figure at the right. However, no

matter how close to each other two points on the number line may be, there is always an infinite number of points between them. We say that between any two rational numbers there is an infinite number of rational numbers.

For example, using two-place decimals, $\frac{1}{10}$ may be expressed as .10 and may be expressed as .20. Between .10 and .20 are the rational numbers $\{.11, .12, .13, \ldots, .18, .19\}$. Using three-place decimals, $\frac{1}{10}$ may be expressed as .100 and $\frac{1}{5}$ may be expressed as .200. Between .100 and .200 are the rational numbers $\{.101, .102, .103, \ldots, .198, .199\}$. Thus, by increasing the number of decimal places, we can obtain an infinite number of rational numbers between $\frac{1}{10}$ and $\frac{1}{5}$.

A *dense set* is any set in which there is at least one element between any two given elements of the set. In the case of the set of rational numbers, as shown above, there is not only one, but an infinite number of rational numbers between any two given rational numbers. Hence, the set of rational numbers is a dense set.

From our previous discussion, we see that every rational number can be associated with a point on the number line. It might also appear that every point on the number line can be associated with some rational number. However, this is not true. On a number line, no matter how closely packed the points which are associated with rational numbers may be, there are always points that are not associated with rational numbers. These points are associated with *irrational numbers*, numbers that are not rational numbers. Examples of irrational numbers are $\sqrt{2}, \frac{\sqrt{3}}{3}$, and π.

The number $\sqrt{2}$ is not a rational number. It cannot be expressed as a fraction whose numerator is an integer and whose denominator is a nonzero integer. Yet, the point that is the graph of $\sqrt{2}$ can be located on the number line by constructing a right triangle so that the length

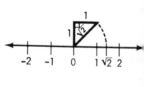

of each leg is 1 unit. According to the theorem of Pythagoras, the length of the hypotenuse is $\sqrt{2}$. As shown in the preceding figure, the length of the hypotenuse is laid off on a number line.

The set of real numbers consists of all the rational numbers and all the irrational numbers. When the set of real numbers is graphed on a number line, each point on the line can be associated with one and only one real number, and each real number can be associated with one and only one point. There are no longer any "holes" in the line. The number line for the set of real numbers is now completely filled in.

Below, we see the graphs of some members of the set of real numbers. Note the graphs of irrational numbers such as $-2\sqrt{3}$, $-\sqrt{6}$, π, and $3+\sqrt{2}$ on this number line.

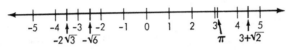

By using advanced mathematics, it can be demonstrated that there is a *one-to-one correspondence* between the set of real numbers and the set of points on a number line. This statement implies two very important ideas:

1. Each real number corresponds to a unique (one and only one) point on the number line.
2. Each point on the number line corresponds to a unique real number.

COMPARING THE GRAPHS OF SUBSETS OF THE SET OF REAL NUMBERS

Following are the graphs of sets of numbers that are subsets of the set of real numbers. Notice that the sets of natural numbers, whole numbers, integers, and rational numbers are represented by sets of points that do not fill in the entire number line. However, the graph of the set of real numbers does fill in the entire number line.

Name of Set　　　　　　　　　　　　　*Graph of Set*

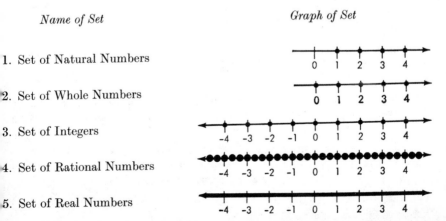

1. Set of Natural Numbers
2. Set of Whole Numbers
3. Set of Integers
4. Set of Rational Numbers
5. Set of Real Numbers

THE REAL NUMBER SYSTEM

The following diagram and the accompanying remarks will help you understand the structure of the real number system by showing you the relationships among the set of real numbers and its number subsets. Beginning at the top, note that the set of real numbers consists of the elements of two sets, the set of rational numbers and the set of irrational numbers. Continue downward and note the other relationships.

In the chart, note the following:

REAL NUMBERS

RATIONAL   IRRATIONAL
NUMBERS   NUMBERS

INTEGERS   NONINTEGRAL
            RATIONALS

POSITIVE   ZERO   NEGATIVE
INTEGERS   INTEGERS

NONZERO
WHOLE NUMBERS

NATURAL
NUMBERS

1. Each *real number* is either a rational number or it is an irrational number. Thus, the real number 2 is rational, while the real number $\sqrt{2}$ is irrational.

2. Each *rational number* is either an integer or it is a nonintegral rational number. Thus, the rational number 3 (which may be expressed as $\frac{3}{1}$) is an integer, while the rational number $\frac{3}{4}$ is a nonintegral rational number.

3. Each *integer* is either a positive integer, a negative integer, or zero. Thus, the integer 3 is a positive integer, while the integer -3 is a negative integer. The integer 0 is neither positive nor negative.

4. Each *whole number* is either a natural number or zero.

5. Each *natural number* is a nonzero whole number and also corresponds to a positive integer. Thus, in counting, 3 is a natural number or a nonzero whole number. If 3 is considered as the opposite of -3, then 3 is a positive integer.

Exercises

In 1 and 2, give the coordinate of each of the labeled points on the number line.

1.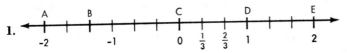

2.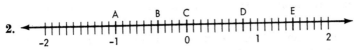

3. Draw a number line and on it locate the points whose coordinates are:

a. $-\frac{8}{5}, -\frac{2}{5}, \frac{5}{5}, \frac{7}{5}, 1\frac{4}{5}$

b. $-\frac{16}{8}, -\frac{7}{8}, \frac{5}{8}, \frac{8}{8}, \frac{15}{8}$

c. $-1.7, -.5, .3, 1.4, 1.8$

d. $-1\frac{1}{2}, -.25, \frac{3}{4}, 1\frac{1}{8}, \frac{15}{8}$

4. Express the coordinate of each labeled point on the following number line as the ratio of two integers.

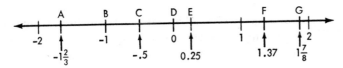

5. The distance between 0 and 1 on the following number line is a unit.

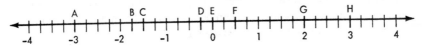

Find the coordinate of:

a. the point 3 units to the right of point E

b. each point that is 3 units from point E

c. the point $\frac{1}{4}$ of a unit to the right of point C

d. the point midway between point A and point H

In 6–9, write the rational number that is the average of the pair of given numbers.

6. 3 and 4   7. 2 and $2\frac{1}{2}$ 8. $\frac{1}{2}$ and $\frac{1}{3}$ 9. 1.2 and 1.3

In 10–13, (a) indicate whether or not the given set of numbers is dense and (b) give a reason for your answer.

10. rational numbers   11. rational numbers between 1 and 2

12. integers   13. natural numbers

5. Using a Number Line To Order Real Numbers

The statement $3 \neq 5$ is read "3 is not equal to 5." On a number line, the graphs of 3 and 5 are different points. In general, if a and b are real numbers, $a \neq b$ is read "a is not equal to b"; and on a number line, the graphs of a and are different points.

We assume that we can arrange the set of real numbers in a definite order. For example, the statement "-2 is less than 4," symbolized by "$-2 < 4$," expresses an order relation between -2 and 4. By convention, on a number line, the graph of the smaller number, -2, is to the left of the graph of the greater number, 4. The same order relation can be expressed by the statement "4 is greater than -2," symbolized by "$4 > -2$." Observe, in the figure below, that the graph of the greater number, 4, is to the right of the graph of the smaller number, -2.

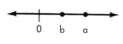

In general, if a and b are two real numbers, then $a > b$ if and only if the graph of a is to the right of the graph of b on the number line, as shown in the figure.

Note that when we use the inequality symbols $>$ and $<$ to express a true order relation between two real numbers, the narrow part of the symbol points to the numeral that represents the smaller number.

The inequalities $1 < 3$ and $3 < 5$ can be written in the compact form $1 < 3 < 5$. Similarly, $a < b$ and $b < c$ can be written $a < b < c$.

On the number line, since $1 < 3 < 5$, the graph of 1 is to the left of the graph of 3, which in turn is to the left of the graph of 5, as shown in the figure. Therefore, we say that "3 is between 1 and 5." In general, if a, b, and c are real numbers, then $a < b < c$ can be read "b is between a and c."

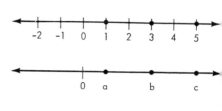

The meanings of other compact inequality symbols follow:

$a \leq b$ means $a < b$ or $a = b$. Read $a \leq b$ as "a is less than or equal to b."

$a \geq b$ means $a > b$ or $a = b$. Read $a \geq b$ as "a is greater than or equal to b."

$a < b \leq c$ means $a < b$ and $b \leq c$. Read $a < b \leq c$ as "a is less than b, and b is less than or equal to c."

Exercises

In 1–5, use a number line to determine whether the statement is *true* or *false*.
1. $3 < 5$ **2.** $3 < -2$ **3.** $-5 > -2$ **4.** $-\frac{3}{4} < \frac{1}{2}$ **5.** $-1\frac{1}{2} > -3\frac{1}{3}$

In 6–10, arrange the numbers in proper order so that they will appear from left to right on a number line.
6. $5, -2$ **7.** $-5, -8$ **8.** $3, 0, -4$ **9.** $-1, 3, -4$ **10.** $1\frac{1}{2}, -1, 2\frac{3}{4}$

In 11–13, use the symbol $<$ to write the sentence in compact form.
11. 13 is between 10 and 15.   **12.** n is between -2 and 2.
13. x is between y and w, where w is greater than y.

In 14–17, order the given numbers and use the symbol $<$ to write your result in compact form.
14. $3, 5, 2$ **15.** $-6, 7, 4$ **16.** $-1, 3, -2$ **17.** $-3, -1, -6$

6. Open Sentences, Statements, Variables, and Solution Sets

Consider the sentence: It is the capital of the United States.

This sentence cannot be described as true or false until the particular city to which " It " refers is known. Such a sentence, one that is neither true nor false as it stands, is called an ***open sentence.*** Now suppose that " It " is replaced by an element of the set {London, Paris, Washington, Rome}. The resulting sentence is is called a ***statement.*** A statement is a meaningful assertion that is either true or false, but not both true and false. If " It " is replaced by Washington, the resulting statement " Washington is the capital of the United States " is true. If " It " is replaced by London, Paris, or Rome, the resulting statements are false.

A ***variable*** is a symbol that holds a place for, or represents, any one of the elements of a specified set that has more than one element. In the sentence " It is the capital of the United States," " It " is a variable. In mathematics, a letter such as x may be the variable, as in the case of $x + 5 = 8$.

The ***replacement set*** of a variable, or the ***domain*** of a variable, is the specified set whose elements may be used as replacements for the variable. In the previous discussion, {London, Paris, Washington, Rome} is the replacement set, or the domain, of the variable " It." The elements of the replacement set of a variable are called the ***values*** of the variable.

The ***truth set,*** or ***solution set,*** of an open sentence over the domain of the variable is the subset of the domain that consists of those elements for which the open sentence is true. Each element of the solution set is called a ***solution*** or a ***root*** of the open sentence and is said to ***satisfy*** the open sentence.

To solve an open sentence over a stated domain means to determine its solution set in that domain.

For example, if the domain, or replacement set, of x is $U = \{2, 3, 4, 5\}$, then the root, or solution, of $x + 5 = 8$ is 3. Hence, the solution set of $x + 5 = 8$ is $\{3\}$. In set-builder notation, we can write this result as

$$\{x \mid x \in U \text{ and } x + 5 = 8\} = \{3\}$$

This is read " the set of all x such that x is a member of U and $x + 5 = 8$ equals the set whose member is 3."

A change in the domain of the variable can change the solution set of an open sentence.

For example, if the replacement set of x were changed to $U = \{4, 5, 6, 7\}$, no element of this set would make the sentence $x + 5 = 8$ a true statement. As a result, the solution set of $x + 5 = 8$ would now be the empty set, $\varnothing$. To show this, we would write

$$\{x \mid x \in U \text{ and } x + 5 = 8\} = \varnothing$$

A **constant** is a symbol representing the one element of a set that has only a single element. Examples of a constant are 5 and π.

Exercises

In 1–8, tell whether or not the sentence is an open sentence.
1. Lyndon Johnson was a president of the United States.
2. He is 6 feet tall.
3. Henry Ford discovered radium.
4. X holds the all-time record for hitting home runs.
5. $6 + 1 = 9$ **6.** $x - 1 = 4$ **7.** $2 + 4 < 9$ **8.** $2x > 3$

In 9–12, use roster notation to write the solution set of the sentence when the domain of the variable is $\{0, 1, 2, 3, 4, 5\}$. If the solution set is empty, write $\varnothing$ as the answer.
9. $3x + 1 = 10$ **10.** $3 = 8 - 2y$ **11.** $x + 2 > 5$ **12.** $4 \leq 2x - 2$

In 13–16, use roster notation to write the solution set of the open sentence when the domain of the variable is the set of natural numbers. If the solution set is empty, write $\varnothing$ as the answer.
13. $x + 5 = 9$ **14.** $2y + 4 = 10$ **15.** $2y + 4 \geq 10$ **16.** $2y + 4 < 9$

In 17–19, use roster notation to represent the set when the domain of the variable is the set of single-digit positive integers. If the given set is empty, write $\varnothing$ as the answer.
17. $\{x \mid 2x + 1 = 7\}$ **18.** $\{w \mid 4w - 1 > 25\}$ **19.** $\{y \mid 2y - 1 \leq 4\}$

In 20–23, write the set in roster notation.

20. $\{n \mid n$ is less than 5 and n is a natural number$\}$

21. $\{x \mid x > 5, x$ is a natural number$\}$

22. $\{y \mid 8 < y < 18, y$ is an odd integer$\}$

23. $\{x \mid x^2 - 9 = 0, x$ is a natural number$\}$

In 24–27, using set-builder notation, write the solution set of the open sentence.

24. $x + 4 = 10$ and $x \in \{5, 6, 7, 8\}$ **25.** $2y + 6 = 14$ and $y \in \{$even integers$\}$

26. $x \geq 4$ and $x \in \{$real numbers$\}$ **27.** $40 < n < 100; n \in \{$natural numbers$\}$

7. Graphing Sets of Numbers and Solution Sets of Open Sentences

The **graph of a set of numbers** is the set of points on a number line that are associated with the numbers of the set.

The **graph of the solution set of an open sentence in one variable** is the set of points on a number line that are associated with the members of the solution set. This graph is called the **graph of the open sentence.**

When we make such a graph, we use:

1. A darkened circle ● to represent a point on the number line that is associated with a number in the set.
2. A non-darkened circle ○ to represent a point that does not belong to the graph.
3. A darkened line ▬▬▬ to indicate that every point on the line is associated with a number in the set. Parts of the line that are not darkened show points that do not belong to the graph.

〰〰〰〰〰〰 *MODEL PROBLEMS* 〰〰〰〰〰〰

1. Using a number line, draw the graph of each set.

   a. $\{-2, 1, 3\}$

   Answer: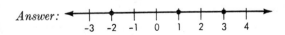

   b. $\{$real numbers between 1 and 4$\}$

   Answer: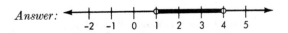

c. {real numbers greater than or equal to $-1\frac{1}{2}$}

Answer:

2. If $x \in \{0, 1, 2, 3, 4, 5\}$, (*a*) find the solution set of the open sentence $3x + 1 = 13$ and (*b*) using a number line, graph the solution set.

Solution:

a. To find the solution set, replace the variable x in the open sentence $3x + 1 = 13$ by each member of the replacement set. The number 4 is the only replacement for x that results in a true sentence, $3 \times 4 + 1 = 13$. Therefore, the solution set of $3x + 1 = 13$ is {4}.

Answer: {4}

b.

3. Graph $\{x \,|\, -1 < x \le 3\}$.

Solution:

1. $\{x \,|\, -1 < x \le 3\}$ is the set of real numbers greater than -1 and also less than or equal to 3. Hence, the solution set of the open sentence includes 3 and also all the real numbers greater than -1 and less than 3.
2. Graph the solution set. Note that the non-darkened circle at -1 indicates that -1 is not a member of the solution set; also, the darkened circle at 3 indicates that 3 is a member of the solution set.

Answer:

Exercises

In 1–8, using a number line, draw the graph of the set of numbers.
1. $\{-2, 0, 3\}$ **2.** $\{-3, 1, 2\frac{1}{2}\}$ **3.** $\{-2, -1, 0, 1, \ldots 6, 7\}$ **4.** $\{0\}$
5. {whole numbers between 1 and 8}
6. {integers between 4 and 6}
7. {real numbers between 4 and 6}
8. {real numbers except -1 and 1}

In 9–12, if $R = \{-3, -1, 0, 2\}$ and $S = \{-2, -1, 0, 1, 2\}$, using a number line, graph the indicated set.
9. the set whose members are elements of set R and also of set S

10. the set of elements of set R or of set S

11. {elements of set R but not of set S}

12. {elements of set S but not of set R}

In 13–21, using a number line, draw the graph of the set of numbers.

13. $\{x \mid x + 2 = 6\}$ $x \in \{1, 2, 3, 4, 5\}$

14. $\{y \mid 5 - y = 2\}$ $y \in \{\text{positive integers}\}$

15. $\{y \mid y > 4\}$ $y \in \{\text{positive integers less than 10}\}$

16. $\{t \mid t \leq 1\}$ $t \in \{-3, -2, -1, 0, 1, 2, 3\}$

17. $\{x \mid x > -1\}$ $x \in \{\text{real numbers}\}$

18. $\{x \mid x > -1\}$ $x \in \{\text{integers}\}$

19. $\{x \mid x < 4\}$ $x \in \{\text{real numbers}\}$

20. $\{x \mid x \leq 2\}$ $x \in \{\text{negative real numbers}\}$

21. $\{x \mid x + 2 > 5\}$ $x \in \{\text{real numbers}\}$

In 22–25, using $\{-3, -2, -1, 0, 1, 2, 3\}$ as the domain of the variable, (a) find the solution set of the open sentence and (b) use a number line to graph the solution set.

22. $3x - 2 = 4$ **23.** $y > -2$ **24.** $2t + 1 < 3$ **25.** $3r - 1 \leq 5$

In 26–37, using a number line, graph the open sentence when the domain of the variable is the set of real numbers.

26. $x - 3 = 4$ **27.** $3x + 1 = 7$ **28.** $4x = -8$

29. $x > 1$ **30.** $x < -2$ **31.** $3x > 12$

32. $x \leq -2$ **33.** $1 < x < 4$ **34.** $-2 \leq x \leq 3$

35. $x + 2 = 2 + x$ **36.** $x + 2x = 3x$ **37.** $x + 1 = x + 2$

38. Using a number line, graph $x \leq 4$ when the domain of x is the set of (a) natural numbers, (b) positive odd integers, and (c) real numbers.

8. Postulates of the Real Number System and of a Field

BINARY OPERATIONS

In your previous study of algebra, you have learned how to perform the operations of addition, subtraction, multiplication, and division on numbers. These operations are called **binary operations.** In a binary operation, a correspondence is set up between two numbers of a given set of numbers, taken in a certain order, and another number of that set. For example, when we add the real numbers 4 and 5, we assign to those numbers the real number 9. When we multiply 4 and 5, we assign to those numbers the number 20.

In general, when any two real numbers a and b are added, the real number $a + b$ is assigned to them; when any two real numbers a and b are multiplied, the real number ab is assigned to them. In addition, the numbers a and b are called the **addends,** and $a + b$ is called the **sum;** in multiplication, the numbers a and b are called the **factors,** and ab is called the **product.**

POSTULATES FOR ADDITION AND MULTIPLICATION

In dealing with real numbers, we assume the truth of some basic statements dealing with the properties of addition and multiplication. Such statements, whose truth we assume, are called **postulates** or **axioms.**

CLOSURE POSTULATES FOR ADDITION AND MULTIPLICATION

Closure Postulate for Addition, A_1. The sum of any two real numbers is a unique (one and only one) real number.

For example, the real number 15 is the unique sum of 10 and 5.

In general, for any two real numbers a and b,

$$a + b \text{ is a unique real number}$$

We call this statement the **closure postulate for addition of real numbers.**

Closure Postulate for Multiplication, M_1. The product of any two real numbers is a unique real number.

For example, the real number 50 is the unique product of 10 and 5.

In general, for any two real numbers a and b,

$$ab \text{ is a unique real number}$$

We call this statement the **closure postulate for multiplication of real numbers.**

We also say that the set of real numbers is closed under addition and under multiplication.

COMMUTATIVE POSTULATES FOR ADDITION AND MULTIPLICATION

Commutative Postulate for Addition, A_2. The sum of any two real numbers remains the same if the numbers are interchanged.

For example, $4 + 5 = 5 + 4$.

In general, for any two real numbers a and b,

$$a + b = b + a$$

We call this statement the ***commutative postulate for addition.***

Commutative Postulate for Multiplication, M_2. The product of any two real numbers remains the same if the numbers are interchanged.

For example, $4 \times 5 = 5 \times 4$.

In general, for any two real numbers a and b,

$$ab = ba$$

We call this statement the ***commutative postulate for multiplication.***

We also say that, in the set of real numbers, *both addition and multiplication are commutative operations.* The word "commutative" is appropriate because it refers to "change."

ASSOCIATIVE POSTULATES FOR ADDITION AND MULTIPLICATION

Associative Postulate for Addition, A_3. The sum of any three real numbers remains the same regardless of the way in which they are grouped when their sum is found.

For example, $(3 + 4) + 5 = 3 + (4 + 5)$.

In general, for any three real numbers a, b, and c,

$$(a + b) + c = a + (b + c)$$

We call this statement the ***associative postulate for addition.***

Associative Postulate for Multiplication, M_3. The product of any three real numbers remains the same regardless of the way in which they are grouped when their product is found.

For example, $(3 \cdot 4) \cdot 5 = 3 \cdot (4 \cdot 5)$.

In general, for any three real numbers a, b, and c,

$$(ab)c = a(bc)$$

We call this statement the ***associative postulate for multiplication.***

We also say that, in the set of real numbers, *both addition and multiplication are associative operations.* The word "associative" is appropriate because it refers to "grouping."

IDENTITY POSTULATES FOR ADDITION AND MULTIPLICATION

Identity Postulate for Addition, A_4. The sum of 0 and any given real number is identical with that given number.

For example, $0 + 157 = 157$ and $157 + 0 = 157$.

In general, for each real number a,

$$0 + a = a \text{ and } a + 0 = a$$

The number 0 is called the ***identity element for addition,*** or the ***additive identity.***

Identity Postulate for Multiplication, M_4. The product of 1 and any given real number is identical with that given number.

For example, $1 \cdot 157 = 157$ and $157 \cdot 1 = 157$.

In general, for each real number a,

$$1 \cdot a = a \text{ and } a \cdot 1 = a$$

The number 1 is called the ***identity element for multiplication,*** or the ***multiplicative identity.***

INVERSE ELEMENT POSTULATES FOR ADDITION AND MULTIPLICATION

Inverse Element Postulate for Addition, A_5. For each real number a, there exists a unique real number $-a$, such that the sum $a + (-a) = 0$, the additive identity. The real number $-a$ is called the ***additive inverse*** of a. It is also true that a is the additive inverse of $-a$.

For example, the additive inverse of $+2$ is -2, since $(+2) + (-2) = 0$; the additive inverse of -2 is $+2$, since $(-2) + (+2) = 0$. Observe that if we are given a signed number (a number that is positive or negative), we can obtain its additive inverse by simply changing its sign.

Rule. To form the additive inverse of a signed number, change its sign.

Since $0 + 0 = 0$, we say that 0 is its own additive inverse.

Note, on the number line, the way in which a real number and its additive inverse may be paired.

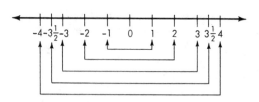

The sum of every pair of real numbers connected by the arrows is 0; that is, $(+4) + (-4) = 0$, $(+3\frac{1}{2}) + (-3\frac{1}{2}) = 0$, $(+3) + (-3) = 0$, $(-2) + (+2) = 0$, $(-1) + (+1) = 0$. Observe that each number in every pair is the *negative* of the other or the *opposite* of the other.

In general, for each real number a, there exists a unique real number $-a$ such that

$$a + (-a) = 0 \text{ and } (-a) + a = 0$$

Inverse Element Postulate for Multiplication, M_5. For each nonzero real number a, there exists a unique real number $\frac{1}{a}$ such that the product of a and $\frac{1}{a}$ is 1, the multiplicative identity. The real numbers a and $\frac{1}{a}$ are called **multiplicative inverses**, or **reciprocals**, of each other.

For example, the multiplicative inverse of 2 is $\frac{1}{2}$ since $2 \cdot \frac{1}{2} = 1$; the multiplicative inverse of $\frac{3}{4}$ is $\frac{1}{\frac{3}{4}}$, or $\frac{4}{3}$, since $\frac{3}{4} \cdot \frac{4}{3} = 1$.

Since $1 \cdot 1 = 1$, we say that 1 is its own multiplicative inverse.

In general, for each nonzero real number a, there exists a unique real number $\frac{1}{a}$ such that

$$a \cdot \frac{1}{a} = 1 \text{ and } \frac{1}{a} \cdot a = 1$$

The reason that 0 does not have a multiplicative inverse is that $\frac{1}{0}$ is not defined; $\frac{1}{0}$ is meaningless.

DISTRIBUTIVE POSTULATE FOR MULTIPLICATION WITH RESPECT TO ADDITION

In the set of real numbers, one property involves both multiplication and addition. For example, since $2(3 + 4) = 2(7) = 14$ and $2 \cdot 3 + 2 \cdot 4 = 6 + 8 = 14$, we know that $2(3 + 4) = 2 \cdot 3 + 2 \cdot 4$ is a true statement. This example illustrates the **distributive postulate for multiplication with respect to addition**. The word "distributive" is appropriate because we "distribute" the multiplier 2 to each of the addends 3 and 4.

In general, we postulate that for any real numbers a, b, and c,

$$a(b + c) = ab + ac$$

By making use of the commutative property for multiplication, we can also show that

$$(b + c)a = ba + ca$$

We say that, in the set of real numbers, *multiplication is distributive with respect to addition.*

The distributive postulate may be extended to involve four or more real numbers:

$$\boldsymbol{a(b + c + d + \cdots) = ab + ac + ad + \cdots}$$

FIELD POSTULATES FOR ADDITION AND MULTIPLICATION

We have considered eleven postulates of the real number system. They are properties of a mathematical system called a **field.** The following chart summarizes the eleven field postulates:

FIELD POSTULATES FOR ADDITION AND MULTIPLICATION OF REAL NUMBERS

(a, b, and c represent any members of a set of real numbers.)	
A_1	Closure postulate for addition $a + b$ is a unique element of the set of real numbers
A_2	Commutative postulate for addition $a + b = b + a$
A_3	Associative postulate for addition $(a + b) + c = a + (b + c)$
A_4	Additive identity postulate There exists a unique number 0 such that for each a $a + 0 = a$ and $0 + a = a$
A_5	Additive inverse postulate For each real number a, there exists a unique number $-a$ such that $a + (-a) = 0$ and $(-a) + a = 0$
M_1	Closure postulate for multiplication ab is a unique member of the set of real numbers
M_2	Commutative postulate for multiplication $ab = ba$
M_3	Associative postulate for multiplication $(ab)c = a(bc)$

M_4	Multiplicative identity postulate
	There exists a unique number 1 such that for each a
	$a \cdot 1 = a$ and $1 \cdot a = a$

M_5	Multiplicative inverse postulate
	For every real nonzero number a, there exists a unique number $\dfrac{1}{a}$ such that
	$a \cdot \dfrac{1}{a} = 1$ and $\dfrac{1}{a} \cdot a = 1$

	Distributive postulate for multiplication with respect to addition
	$a(b + c) = ab + ac$

SUMMARY OF THE FIELD POSTULATES AS THEY APPLY TO THE SET OF REAL NUMBERS AND ITS SUBSETS

The diagram at the right shows the development of the real number system. The system of natural numbers was extended to the system of whole numbers; the system of whole numbers was extended to the system of integers; the system of integers was extended to the system of rational numbers; the system of rational numbers was extended to the system of real numbers.

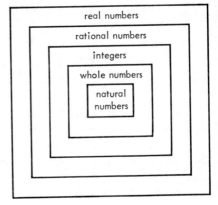

The addition and multiplication postulates of each number system are also postulates of the new number system to which it was extended. For example, the addition and multiplication postulates of the system of natural numbers are also postulates of the system of whole numbers to which the system of natural numbers was extended.

The following chart shows how the eleven field postulates for addition and multiplication apply to the set of real numbers and its subsets. A "✓" in a column naming a number system means that the set of numbers in the system satisfies the field postulate that is checked. A "No" means that the set of numbers in the system does not satisfy the postulate.

Postulate	Natural Numbers	Whole Numbers	Integers	Rational Numbers	Real Numbers
1. Closure under addition	✓	✓	✓	✓	✓
2. Closure under multiplication	✓	✓	✓	✓	✓
3. Commutative under addition	✓	✓	✓	✓	✓
4. Commutative under multiplication	✓	✓	✓	✓	✓
5. Associative under addition	✓	✓	✓	✓	✓
6. Associative under multiplication	✓	✓	✓	✓	✓
7. Distributive	✓	✓	✓	✓	✓
8. Multiplicative identity	✓	✓	✓	✓	✓
9. Additive identity	No	✓	✓	✓	✓
10. Additive inverse	No	No	✓	✓	✓
11. Multiplicative inverse	No	No	No	✓	✓

Note in the chart that the first eight postulates apply to each of the sets of numbers. The last three postulates do not apply to the set of natural numbers.

Since the set of whole numbers consists of 0 as well as the natural numbers, the ninth postulate, the additive identity postulate, applies to the set of whole numbers.

Since the set of integers consists of the negative integers as well as 0 and the positive integers, the tenth postulate, the additive inverse postulate, applies to the set of integers.

Since the set of rational numbers consists of numbers expressible as a fraction whose numerator is an integer and whose denominator is a nonzero integer, the eleventh postulate, the multiplicative inverse postulate, applies to the set of rational numbers. Note that the set of rational numbers and the set of real numbers are the only ones of the listed sets to which all eleven postulates apply. Hence, the sets of rational numbers and real numbers are the only fields among the listed sets.

ADDING OR MULTIPLYING THREE OR MORE NUMBERS

If we wish to add 3, 4, and 5, we define $3 + 4 + 5$ as $(3 + 4) + 5$. In general, we define $a + b + c$ to be $(a + b) + c$; that is, $a + b + c = (a + b) + c$. Likewise, we define $a + b + c + d$ to be $(a + b + c) + d$. In fact, because of the commutative and associative properties of addition, we may add the addends in a sum in any desirable groups of two numbers. For example,

$$865 + 739 + 135 + 261 = (865 + 135) + (739 + 261)$$
$$= 1000 + 1000 = 2000$$

If we wish to multiply 3, 4, and 5, we define $3 \cdot 4 \cdot 5$ as $(3 \cdot 4) \cdot 5$. In general, we define abc to be $(ab)c$; that is, $abc = (ab)c$. Likewise, we define $abcd$ to be $(abc)d$. In fact, because of the commutative and associative properties of multiplication, we can multiply the factors in a product in any convenient groups of two numbers. For example,

$$125 \cdot 25 \cdot 8 \cdot 4 = (125 \cdot 8) \cdot (25 \cdot 4) = 1000 \cdot 100 = 100,000$$

PROPERTIES OF EQUALITY

In our study of the real number system, we will make use of the following properties of equality, which are concerned with the use of the symbol $=$.

REFLEXIVE PROPERTY

The *reflexive property of equality* states that any number is equal to itself. For example, $2 = 2$ and $8 = 8$.

In general, for each real number a,

$$a = a$$

SYMMETRIC PROPERTY

The *symmetric property of equality* states that the sides of an equality may be interchanged. For example, if $3 + 6 = 5 + 4$, then $5 + 4 = 3 + 6$.

In general, for each real number a and each real number b,

$$\text{if } a = b, \text{ then } b = a$$

TRANSITIVE PROPERTY

The *transitive property of equality* states that if one number is equal to a second number, and the second number is equal to a third number, then the first number is equal to the third number. For example, if $7 + 3 = 6 + 4$, and $6 + 4 = 8 + 2$, then $7 + 3 = 8 + 2$.

In general, for each real number a, each real number b, and each real number c,

if $a = b$ and $b = c$, then $a = c$

The transitive property of equality is useful in the following ways:

If $a = b$ and $b = c$, the transitive property of equality makes it possible for us to replace b by c in the first equality, thus obtaining $a = c$. We call this process of replacing a number by an equal number **substitution.**

Also, the transitive property of equality allows us to state that two numbers are equal if each of them is equal to a third number. For example, if $x = y$ and $y = 5$, then $x = 5$.

Observe that we are making use of the substitution principle when we write $(5 \cdot 10) + 25 = 50 + 25$, or 75, because $5 \cdot 10 = 50$. Also, $76(85 + 15) = 76(100)$, or 7600, because $85 + 15 = 100$.

ADDITION PROPERTY

The **addition property of equality** states that if the same number is added to each of two equal numbers, the resulting numbers are equal. For example, if $5 + 2 = 6 + 1$, then $(5 + 2) + 3 = (6 + 1) + 3$.

In general, for each real number a, each real number b, and each real number c,

if $a = b$, then $a + c = b + c$

MULTIPLICATION PROPERTY

The **multiplication property of equality** states that if each of two equal numbers is multiplied by the same number, the resulting numbers are equal. For example, if $5 + 4 = 7 + 2$, then $(5 + 4) \cdot 3 = (7 + 2) \cdot 3$.

In general, for each real number a, each real number b, and each real number c,

if $a = b$, then $ac = bc$

SUMMARY OF PROPERTIES OF EQUALITY

(a, b, and c are members of the set of real numbers.)	
Reflexive property	$a = a$
Symmetric property	If $a = b$, then $b = a$.
Transitive property	If $a = b$, and $b = c$, then $a = c$.
Addition property	If $a = b$, then $a + c = b + c$.
Multiplication property	If $a = b$, then $ac = bc$.

~~~~~~~~~~~~~~ *MODEL PROBLEM* ~~~~~~~~~~~~~~

Name the property of the real number system illustrated in each sentence.

   a. $5 + 8 = 8 + 5$ *Ans.* Commutative property for addition (A_2)

   b. $(7 \times r) \times s = 7 \times (r \times s)$ *Ans.* Associative property for multiplication (M_3)

   c. $(y) + (-y) = 0$ *Ans.* Additive inverse property (A_5)

   d. $7 \times (a + b) = (7 \times a) + (7 \times b)$ *Ans.* Distributive property for multiplication with respect to addition

~~~~~~

Exercises

In this set of exercises, assume that no denominator is 0.

In 1–12, name the property of the real number system illustrated in the statement.

1. $6 + 4 = 4 + 6$

2. $8 \cdot (\frac{1}{8}) = 1$

3. $7 \times (9 \times 5) = (7 \times 9) \times 5$

4. $(3) + (-3) = 0$

5. $(\frac{1}{2} + \frac{1}{3}) + \frac{1}{4} = \frac{1}{2} + (\frac{1}{3} + \frac{1}{4})$

6. $\frac{2}{3}(6 + 9) = (\frac{2}{3} \times 6) + (\frac{2}{3} \times 9)$

7. $x + 3 = 3 + x$

8. $2y + (-2y) = 0$

9. $(5 + 2x) + 3x = 5 + (2x + 3x)$

10. $8 \times (\frac{1}{2} \times y) = (8 \times \frac{1}{2}) \times y$

11. $\frac{1}{4}(8x + 4y) = (\frac{1}{4} \times 8x) + (\frac{1}{4} \times 4y)$

12. $8 \times 100 = (8 \times 77) + (8 \times 23)$

In 13–18, (*a*) give a replacement for the question mark which makes the sentence true for all real values of the variable and (*b*) name the property illustrated in the sentence that is formed when the replacement is made.

13. $r \times 9 = 9 \times ?$

14. $(7 + ?) + 5 = 7 + (x + 5)$

15. $\frac{9}{4} + ? = d + \frac{9}{4}$

16. $t + ? = 0$

17. $w \times ? = w$

18. $x + (\frac{5}{9} + ?) = x + \frac{5}{9}$

In 19–27, name the property of equality that is illustrated.

19. $8 + 9 = 8 + 9$

20. If $9 + 8 = 12 + 5$, then $12 + 5 = 9 + 8$.

21. If $5 + 2 = 6 + 1$, then $(5 + 2) + 7 = (6 + 1) + 7$.

22. If $(7 + 3) = (6 + 4)$, then $(7 + 3) \times 8 = (6 + 4) \times 8$.

23. If $x = y$ and $y = 15$, then $x = 15$.

24. If $24 = 3x + 6$, then $3x + 6 = 24$.

25. If $a = b$, then $a \cdot 10 = b \cdot 10$.

26. If $a = b$, then $a + 7 = b + 7$.

27. If $40x = 200$, then $(40x) \cdot \frac{1}{40} = (200) \cdot \frac{1}{40}$.

In 28–31, find the value of the numerical expression by using the properties of the real number system to simplify the computation.

28. $125 \times 197 \times 8$ **29.** $.69 + .94 + .31$

30. $978 \times 8 + 978 \times 2$ **31.** $\frac{1}{3} \times 620 + \frac{1}{3} \times 280$

In 32–36, if r and s are elements of the given set of numbers, state whether or not each of the following must represent an element of the given set of numbers: (a) $r + s$ (b) $r - s$ (c) rs (d) $r \div s, s \neq 0$

32. {natural numbers}   **33.** {whole numbers}   **34.** {integers}

35. {rational numbers}   **36.** {real numbers}

In 37–51, state whether or not the given set is closed under   (a) addition (b) multiplication   (c) subtraction   (d) division.
If the answer is *no*, give an example justifying this answer.

37. {1, 3, 5}   **38.** {2, 4, 6}   **39.** {−1, 0, 1}

40. {1, 0}   **41.** {1}   **42.** {0}

43. $\{0, \frac{1}{3}, \frac{1}{9}, \frac{1}{27}, \frac{1}{81}, \ldots\}$

44. {natural numbers}

45. {even natural numbers}

46. {whole numbers}   **47.** {integers}

48. {integers divisible by 3}   **49.** {rational numbers}

50. {real numbers}   **51.** {irrational numbers}

52. List the eleven properties of both the set of rational numbers and the set of real numbers which are postulates for a field.

53. From the eleven field postulates, name those that are satisfied by each of the following sets:

    a. {the set of natural numbers}

    b. {the set of whole numbers}

    c. {the set of integers}

9. Deductive Reasoning and Proof in Algebra

In recent years, mathematicians have organized algebra into a logical structure. In this organization, as in geometry, we begin with ***undefined terms,*** which are used to define additional terms, and ***postulates*** or ***axioms,*** which are assumptions. By a process of logical reasoning, we can make use of the undefined terms, the defined terms, and the postulates to deduce additional number properties. Statements about numbers which have been proved are called ***theorems.*** Theorems, in turn, are used in proving other theorems. When we prove a theorem, we reason from the ***hypothesis,*** which is the given information, to the ***conclusion.*** This is done by using a sequence of statements, each of which is supported by the hypothesis or a definition or a postulate or a previously proved theorem.

Although we may not have realized it, the techniques which we have used in working with algebraic expressions are justified by the postulates that were assumed and the theorems that were proved.

Note. In the following model problems and exercises, the variables represent real numbers.

~~~~~~~~~~~~~ *MODEL PROBLEMS* ~~~~~~~~~~~~~

1. Prove: $8x + x = 9x$

Solution: *Method* 1

Statements	*Reasons*
1. $x = 1x$	1. Multiplicative identity property.
2. $8x + x = 8x + 1x$	2. Substitution principle.
3. $8x + 1x = (8 + 1)x$	3. Distributive property.
4. $8 + 1 = 9$	4. Number fact.
5. $(8 + 1)x = 9x$	5. Substitution principle.
6. $8x + x = 9x$	6. Transitive property of equality.

Method 2

Statements	*Reasons*
1. $8x + x = 8x + 1x$	1. Multiplication property of 1.
2. $8x + 1x = (8 + 1)x$	2. Distributive property.
3. $(8 + 1)x = 9x$	3. Number fact.
4. $8x + x = 9x$	4. Transitive property of equality.

Note. In the shortened version, Method 2, we have omitted steps 1 and 4 of Method 1. Also, we have not stated the substitution principle.

Method 3

Statements	*Reasons*
1. $8x + x = 8x + 1x$	1. Multiplication property of 1.
2. $= (8 + 1)x$	2. Distributive property.
3. $= 9x$	3. Number fact.

Note. In Method 3 we have omitted step 4 of Method 2, and have not stated the transitive property of equality. We have also omitted the rewriting of the right member of an equation as the left member in the next equation.

2. Prove: $r(x + y) = yr + xr$

Solution:

Statements	Reasons
1. $r(x + y) = rx + ry$	1. Distributive property.
2. $\quad\quad\quad = ry + rx$	2. Commutative property of addition.
3. $\quad\quad\quad = yr + xr$	3. Commutative property of multiplication.

3. Prove: $(5x) \cdot (7y) = 35xy$

Solution:

Statements	Reasons
1. $(5x) \cdot (7y) = [(5x) \cdot 7] \cdot y$	1. Associative property of multiplication.
2. $\quad\quad\quad = [5 \cdot (x \cdot 7)] \cdot y$	2. Associative property of multiplication.
3. $\quad\quad\quad = [5 \cdot (7 \cdot x)] \cdot y$	3. Commutative property of multiplication.
4. $\quad\quad\quad = [(5 \cdot 7) \cdot x] \cdot y$	4. Associative property of multiplication.
5. $\quad\quad\quad = (35 \cdot x) \cdot y$	5. Number fact.
6. $\quad\quad\quad = 35xy$	6. Definition of multiplication.

Exercises

In 1–4, state the property that justifies the statement.

1. $x \cdot 8 = 8 \cdot x$ **2.** $(x + 8) + 0 = x + 8$

3. $1(x + 8) = x + 8$ **4.** $8 + x = x + 8$

In 5–12, prove the statement.

5. $(x + 8) + y = x + (y + 8)$ **6.** $x(8y) = (8x)y$

7. $(8 + x)y = y(x + 8)$ **8.** $y(x + 8) = xy + 8y$

9. $xy + 8y = y(x + 8)$ **10.** $y(8x) = (8y)x$

11. $(y + 2)(x + 8) = x(y + 2) + 8(y + 2)$

12. $(y + 2)(x + 8) = 2x + xy + 8y + 16$

In 13–18, state the property that justifies the statement.

13. $px + qx = qx + px$ **14.** $(px + qx) + rx = px + (qx + rx)$

15. $px + [-(px)] = 0$ **16.** $px \cdot \dfrac{1}{px} = 1$

17. $px + x = px + 1x$ **18.** $(px + qx) + 0 = px + qx$

In 19–24, prove the statement.

19. $(px)\left(\dfrac{1}{x}\right) = p$ **20.** $px(qx \cdot rx) = (rx \cdot qx)px$

21. $p(qx + rx) = prx + pqx$

22. $xp + x = x(p + 1)$

23. $p[qx + (-qx)] = 0$

24. $p + [qx + (-qx)] = p$

In 25–27, the statements in the proof are given. Supply the reason for each statement.

25. Prove: $r(3x + 3y + 3z) = 3(yr + xr + zr)$

1. $r(3x + 3y + 3z) = (3x + 3y + 3z)r$
2. $\qquad\qquad = (3x)r + (3y)r + (3z)r$
3. $\qquad\qquad = 3(xr) + 3(yr) + 3(zr)$
4. $\qquad\qquad = 3(xr + yr + zr)$
5. $\qquad\qquad = 3(yr + xr + zr)$

26. Prove: $p(qx + rx) = x(pr + pq)$

1. $p(qx + rx) = p(qx) + p(rx)$
2. $\qquad\qquad = (pq)x + (pr)x$
3. $\qquad\qquad = (pq + pr)x$
4. $\qquad\qquad = x(pq + pr)$
5. $\qquad\qquad = x(pr + pq)$

27. Prove: $7y + 2y + x = x + 9y$

1. $7y + 2y + x = (7y + 2y) + x$
2. $\qquad\qquad = (7 + 2)y + x$
3. $\qquad\qquad = 9y + x$
4. $\qquad\qquad = x + 9y$

In 28–35, prove the statement.

28. $4x + 10x = 14x$

29. $(x + 8) + (-8) = x$

30. $5x(3) = 15x$

31. $(d + 7) + 2d = 3d + 7$

32. $4x(x + 5) + 10x = 4x^2 + 30x$

33. $(x + 4)(x + 5) = x^2 + 9x + 20$

34. $(ab)c = (ca)b$

35. $a(b + c + d) = ca + ba + da$

CHAPTER II

OPERATIONS ON REAL NUMBERS, POLYNOMIALS, AND ALGEBRAIC EXPRESSIONS

1. Using Signed Numbers To Represent Opposite Situations

In our daily life we frequently talk about "opposite situations." For example, we may travel east or west from a starting point; we have a profit or a loss; latitude is north or south of the Equator. We see, therefore, that there is need for a number which represents both direction and size. The positive and negative real numbers, called the *signed numbers,* or *directed numbers,* meet this need.

To represent quantities that are "opposites," we use the positive (+) numbers, which are usually to the right of 0, the starting point on the real number line; and we use the negative (−) numbers, which are usually to the left of 0. Examples of positive numbers are $+4$, $+\frac{1}{2}$, $+1\frac{4}{5}$; examples of negative numbers are -2, $-\frac{2}{3}$, $-1\frac{1}{2}$. A positive number may be written without a sign. For example, $+6$ may be written as 6. Zero (0) is neither a positive number nor a negative number.

USES OF THE SYMBOL "+"

The symbol "+" may be used in two ways:

1. In $7 + 5$, the "+" indicates the operation of *addition.*
2. In $+8$, the "+" indicates that the number is *positive.*

Exercises

In 1–6, give the opposite of:

1. a rise in price   **2.** below sea level   **3.** north of the Equator
4. traveling east   **5.** a loss in weight   **6.** increasing speed

7. If $+5$ means a profit of \$5, what does -5 mean?
8. If -10 means 10 miles west, what does $+10$ mean?
9. If $+30$ means 30° north of the Equator, what does -30 mean?
10. If -2.50 means taking \$2.50 from a bank, what does $+2.50$ mean?

In 11–16, represent the stated expression by a signed number or by zero.

11. 100° above zero   **12.** $10\frac{1}{2}$° below zero   **13.** sea level
14. a fall of 30 feet   **15.** a height of 1000 feet   **16.** a profit of $25.75

2. The Additive Inverse of a Real Number

We have assumed that every real number a, whether it is a positive number or a negative number, has an *additive inverse* represented by $-a$, such that $a + (-a) = 0$. Observe that when a is a positive number, its additive inverse, $-a$, is a negative number. For example, the additive inverse of $+9$ is -9 because $(+9) + (-9) = 0$. When a is a negative number, its additive inverse is a positive number. For example, the additive inverse of -7 is $+7$ because $(-7) + (+7) = 0$. The additive inverse of 0 is 0 because $0 + 0 = 0$.

The additive inverse of a given number is also the *negative of the given number* as well as the *opposite of the given number*. For example,

$-(+9) = -9$ is read "the additive inverse of positive 9 is negative 9."
$-(-7) = +7$ is read "the additive inverse of negative 7 is positive 7."

The additive inverse of the additive inverse of a given real number is the given number itself. For example,

$-[-(+7)] = +7$ is read "the additive inverse of the additive inverse of $+7$ is $+7$."

In general, if a is a real number, then

$$-(-a) = a$$

MODEL PROBLEMS

In 1–3, write the additive inverse of the given number in simplest form.
1. $(3 + 6)$ *Ans.* -9 **2.** $-(-5)$ *Ans.* -5
3. $-(8 - 2)$ *Ans.* 6 or $+6$

4. Graph the solution set of $-a > 0$ when the domain of a is $\{-2, -1, 0, 1, 2\}$.

Solution:
1. The open sentence $-a > 0$ means, "The additive inverse of a is a positive number." Hence, the number a must be negative.
   Therefore, the solution set of $-a > 0$ is $\{-2, -1\}$.

2. Graph the solution set $\{-2, -1\}$.

Exercises

In 1–8, write the additive inverse of the given number in simplest form.
1. $+4.5$ 2. $-1\frac{2}{3}$ 3. $(8+7)$ 4. $(9-9)$
5. $-(+7)$ 6. $-(-\frac{3}{4})$ 7. $-[-(+3)]$ 8. $-[-(-15)]$

In 9–16, graph the solution set of the open sentence if the domain of the variable is $\{-5, -4, -3, -2, -1, 0, 1, 2, 3, 4, 5\}$.
9. $-x > 1$ 10. $-a < 2$ 11. $-r \leq 0$ 12. $-y < -2$
13. $-t \geq -1$ 14. $-b \leq 2\frac{1}{2}$ 15. $-3 < -x < 5$ 16. $-3 \leq -x \leq 4$

In 17–20, graph the solution set of the open sentence if the domain of the variable is the set of real numbers.
17. $-x > 2$ 18. $-y \leq -1$ 19. $-6 < -m \leq 2$ 20. $-5 \leq -x \leq 0$

In 21 and 22, graph the indicated set of numbers.
21. $\{x \mid -x < 4\}$, $x \in \{\text{real numbers}\}$
22. $\{x \mid -7 < -x \leq 5\}$, $x \in \{\text{real numbers}\}$

In 23–25, tell whether the statement is *true* or *false*.
23. If a is a positive real number, $-a$ is always a negative real number.
24. If a is a negative real number, $-a$ is always a negative real number.
25. The additive inverse of a real number is always a different real number.

3. The Absolute Value of a Real Number

In performing operations on real numbers, we will find it useful to make use of the concept of the *absolute value* of a number.

On the real number line, a pair of opposite numbers is represented by points that are equally distant from the point associated with zero. For example, the points associated with the pair of opposites $+5$ and -5 are each 5 units from 0 on the number line shown below. The real number which represents this common distance 5 is called the ***absolute value*** of both $+5$ and -5.

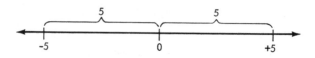

In general, the absolute value of a real number x, symbolized $|x|$, is the real number representing the non-directed distance on the number line between the zero point and the point associated with the number. For example, the absolute value of $+3$ is 3, symbolized $|+3| = 3$. The absolute value of -2 is 2, symbolized $|-2| = 2$. The absolute value of 0 is 0, symbolized $|0| = 0$.

Observe that the absolute value of a real number x, $|x|$, is a nonnegative number. Observe also that:

1. The absolute value of either a given positive number or zero is that number itself.
2. The absolute value of a given negative number is the opposite of that negative number.

In general, if x is a real number, we define $|x|$ as follows:

$$|x| = x \text{ when } x \geq 0 \qquad |x| = -x \text{ when } x < 0$$

~~~~~~~~~~~~~~~ *MODEL PROBLEM* ~~~~~~~~~~~~~~~

Find the value of the number expression $|15| + |-4|$.

Solution: $|15| + |-4| = 15 + 4 = 19$ *Answer:* 19

~~~~~~

Exercises

In 1–5, (*a*) give the absolute value of the given number and (*b*) give another number—if there is such a number—that has the same absolute value as the given number.

1. $+10$ **2.** -5 **3.** 0 **4.** $6\frac{1}{2}$ **5.** -6.82

In 6–9, select the number that has the smaller absolute value.

6. $+8, +4$ **7.** $3, -20$ **8.** $-15.6, +15.06$ **9.** $-5\frac{1}{4}, 5\frac{1}{3}$

In 10–12, state whether the sentence is *true* or *false*.

10. $|-15| = -15$ **11.** $|-7| = |+7|$ **12.** $|-12| > |4|$

In 13–15, find the value of the number expression.

13. $|+7| + |-2|$ **14.** $|+8| \times |-5|$ **15.** $|+12| + |0| - |-7|$

In 16–19, state whether the sentence is *true* or *false*.

16. $|+3| + |-3| = 0$ **17.** $|5| - |-5| = 0$
18. $|+4| \times |-4| = |+16|$ **19.** $|+8| + |-8| = |+4| \times |-4|$

4. Adding Signed Numbers

ADDING SIGNED NUMBERS ON A NUMBER LINE

A sequence of directed movements on a real number line can be used to define the operation of addition for signed numbers. A positive number will be interpreted as a "movement to the right," a negative number as a "movement to the left," and 0 as "no movement at all."

~~~~~~~~~~~~~~~~ **MODEL PROBLEMS** ~~~~~~~~~~~~~~~~

1. Add $+2$ and $+4$.

Solution:

1. Start at 0 and move 2 units to the right.

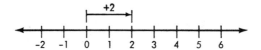

2. Move 4 more units to the right.

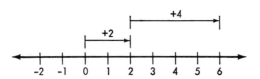

3. Read the coordinate of the point that was last reached, $+6$.

Answer: $(+2) + (+4) = +6$

2. Add $+2$ and -4.

Solution:

1. Start at 0 and move 2 units to the right.

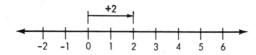

2. Then move 4 units to the left.

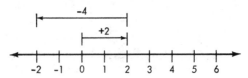

3. Read the coordinate of the point that was last reached, -2.

Answer: $(+2) + (-4) = (-2)$

Procedure. To add two signed numbers on a number line:
1. Graph the first number on the number line.
2. From this point, move to the right or to the left a number of units equal to the absolute value of the second number. If the second number is positive, move to the right (model problem 1); if the second number is negative, move to the left (model problem 2); if the second number is zero, do not move at all.
3. Read the coordinate of the point that was last reached. This coordinate represents the sum of the two numbers.

Exercises

In 1–6, use a real number line to find the sum of the real numbers.

1. $(+4) + (+3)$ **2.** $(-5) + (-1)$ **3.** $(-6) + (+8)$

4. $(+3) + (-8)$ **5.** $(+7) + (0)$ **6.** $(0) + (-5)$

In 7 and 8, use a number line to find the sum of the real numbers; state the relationship between the two results; and state the property of real numbers that is illustrated.

7. *a.* $(-3) + (-5)$ *b.* $(-5) + (-3)$

8. *a.* $[(-5) + (+6)] + (-4)$ *b.* $(-5) + [(+6) + (-4)]$

In 9 and 10, (*a*) use a number line to find the sum of the real numbers and (*b*) state the property of real numbers that is illustrated.

9. $(-5) + (0)$ **10.** $(+8) + [-(+8)]$

USING RULES FOR ADDING REAL NUMBERS

Now we will define the operation of addition for real numbers, without the use of a number line, in such a way that all the properties of addition will be satisfied. Remember that we have postulated:

If a is a real number, then $a + 0 = a$ and $0 + a = a$.

ADDITION OF TWO POSITIVE NUMBERS OR TWO NEGATIVE NUMBERS

By making use of a number line, we find that $(+4) + (+5) = +9$ and $-4) + (-5) = -9$. These examples illustrate the following rules:

Rule 1. The sum of two positive numbers is a positive number whose absolute value is found by adding the absolute values of the numbers.
In general, if a and b are both positive numbers,

$$a + b = |a| + |b|$$

Rule 2. The sum of two negative numbers is a negative number whose absolute value is found by adding the absolute values of the numbers.

In general, if a and b are both negative numbers,

$$a + b = -(|a| + |b|)$$

〰〰〰〰〰〰〰 **MODEL PROBLEMS** 〰〰〰〰〰〰〰

In 1–6, add.

1. $+8$
    $+7$
    ――
    $+15$

2. 0
    $+9$
    ――
    $+9$

3. -8
    -5
    ――
    -13

4. -9.1
    -7.5
    ――
    -16.6

5. $(-5\frac{1}{2}) + (-3\frac{1}{4}) = -8\frac{3}{4}$

6. $(-15) + (0) = -15$

〰〰〰〰〰〰〰〰〰〰〰〰〰〰〰〰〰〰〰〰〰〰〰〰〰〰

ADDITION OF A POSITIVE NUMBER AND A NEGATIVE NUMBER

By making use of a number line, we find that $(+5) + (-2) = +3$ and $(-5) + (+2) = -3$. These examples illustrate the following rule:

Rule 3. The sum of two numbers, one of which is positive or 0 and the other negative, is a number whose absolute value is found by subtracting the smaller of the absolute values of the numbers from the greater.

(1) The sum is positive if the positive number has the greater absolute value.
(2) The sum is negative if the negative number has the greater absolute value.
(3) The sum is 0 if both numbers have the same absolute value.

In general, if a is a positive number and b is a negative number:

> **(1) If $|a| > |b|$, then $a + b = |a| - |b|$.**
> **(2) If $|b| > |a|$, then $a + b = -(|b| - |a|)$.**
> **(3) If $|a| = |b|$, then $a + b = 0$.**

〰〰〰〰〰〰〰 **MODEL PROBLEMS** 〰〰〰〰〰〰〰

In 1–6, add.

1. $+8$
    -2
    ――
    $+6$

2. -9
    $+5$
    ――
    -4

3. -7
    $+9$
    ――
    $+2$

4. $+3$
    -7
    ――
    -4

5. $-8\frac{3}{4}$
    $+5\frac{1}{4}$
    ――
    $-3\frac{1}{2}$

6. $+2.8$
    -2.8
    ――
    0

ADDING MORE THAN TWO NUMBERS

Since the commutative and associative properties of addition hold for signed numbers, these numbers may be rearranged in any order when they are being added.

Thus, $a + b + c = a + c + b = b + a + c = b + c + a = c + a + b = c + b + a$.

A useful method of adding signed numbers is to add all the positive numbers first, all the negative numbers second, and then add the two results. In the following example, this method is used after the terms have been rearranged in the desired order:

$$(+8) + (-3) + (+6) + (-2) = \underbrace{(+8) + (+6)} + \underbrace{(-3) + (-2)}$$

$$= \quad (+14) \quad + \quad (-5) \quad = 9$$

In any future proof, if addends or terms are being added in a desired order, *Rearranging terms* may be used as the reason.

Exercises

In 1–36, add.

1. $+13$ $+5$	**2.** -8 -12	**3.** -14 -10	**4.** $+9$ $+15$	**5.** $+7$ 0	**6.** -19 -28
7. $+36$ -14	**8.** -50 $+33$	**9.** $+14$ -32	**10.** -25 $+25$	**11.** -15 $+35$	**12.** $+12$ -12
13. $+1.3$ $+6.4$	**14.** -6.8 $+4.7$	**15.** -8.3 $+5.9$	**16.** -3.8 -9.7	**17.** $+6.4$ -6.4	**18.** $+9.6$ -2.8
19. $+\frac{3}{8}$ $+\frac{4}{8}$	**20.** $-\frac{3}{10}$ $-\frac{2}{10}$	**21.** $+\frac{1}{4}$ $-\frac{3}{4}$	**22.** $+4\frac{1}{2}$ $-7\frac{3}{4}$	**23.** $+9\frac{2}{3}$ $-3\frac{5}{6}$	**24.** $-6\frac{3}{4}$ $-5\frac{5}{6}$

25. $(+15) + (+9)$

26. $(-13) + (-12)$

27. $(-12) + (+18)$

28. $(-16) + (+16)$

29. $|-15| + (-7)$

30. $|20| + (-|-20|)$

31. $(+15) + (-17) + (+8)$

32. $(-23) + (+11) + (-14)$

33. $(+8) + (+6) + (-3) + (-2)$

34. $(+9) + (-4) + (-6) + (+3)$

35. $|-5| + |0| + (-15)$

36. $|-19| + |8| + (-|-25|)$

USEFUL PROPERTIES OF ADDITION

Now we will present several theorems that state useful properties of addition of signed numbers. These theorems can be proved by deducing them from defi-

nitions that we have agreed upon, from postulates that we have assumed to b
true, and from other theorems that have been proved previously.

Addition Theorem 1. If a and b are real numbers, then $(a + b) + (-b) = a$.
For example, $(7 + 3) + (-3) = 7$ and $[y + (-3)] + (+3) = y$.
The proof of this theorem is shown in exercise 8 on page 43.

Addition Theorem 2 (*Cancellation Property of Addition*). If a, b, and c are re&
numbers, and if $a + c = b + c$, or $c + a = c + b$, then $a = b$.
For example, if $x + y = 5 + y$, then $x = 5$. And, if $y + (-5) = x + (-5)$, the&
$y = x$.
The proof of this theorem is shown in exercise 12 on page 43.

Addition Theorem 3 (*Property of the Opposite of a Sum*). If a and b are re&
numbers, the opposite of their sum is equal to the sum of their opposite&
$-(a + b) = (-a) + (-b)$.
For example, $-(5 + 4) = (-5) + (-4)$ and $-[5 + (-4)] = (-5) + [-(-4)]$
The proof of this theorem is shown in exercise 13 on page 43.

MODEL PROBLEM

Prove: If c and y are real numbers, then $(-c) + (y + c) = y$.

Solution:

Statements	*Reasons*
1. If c and y are real numbers, then $(y + c)$ is a real number.	1. Closure property of addition.
2. If c is a real number, then $-c$ is a real number.	2. Additive inverse property of rea& numbers.
3. $(-c) + (y + c) = (y + c) + (-c)$	3. Commutative property of addition.
4. $(y + c) + (-c) = y$	4. Addition Theorem 1: If a and are real numbers, then $(a + b) + (-b) = a$.

Note. This proof is a condensed or shortened version of the complete proof
To understand methods which are used to shorten proofs, see page 31.

Exercises

In 1–4, the variables represent real numbers. Give a replacement for the
question mark that will make the resulting sentence true for all values of the
variable.

1. $(x + 20) + (-20) = ?$ **2.** $(-y) + (a + y) = ?$
3. $(-5 + y) + 5 = ?$ **4.** $-[(-8) + (-y)] = ?$

In 5–7, give the value of the expression.

5. $-[13 + (-25)]$ **6.** $-[(+4) + (-4)]$ **7.** $-[(-7) + (-17)]$

In exercise 8, give the reason that justifies each statement in the proof.

8. Prove: If a and b are real numbers, $(a + b) + (-b) = a$.

Statements
1. If a and b are real numbers, $(a + b)$ is a real number.
2. $(a + b) + (-b) = a + [b + (-b)]$
3. $\qquad\qquad\quad = a + 0$
4. $\qquad\qquad\quad = a$

In 9–11, c is a real number. Prove that the statement is true.

9. $(c + 7) + (-7) = c$ **10.** $(c + 5) + (-c) = 5$ **11.** $(-c) + (5 + c) = 5$

In 12 and 13, give the reason that justifies each statement in the proof. The variables represent real numbers.

12. Prove: If a, b, and c are real numbers and $a + c = b + c$, then $a = b$.

Statements
1. If a, b, and c are real numbers, then $(a + c)$ and $(b + c)$ are real numbers.
2. $(-c)$ is a real number.
3. $a = (a + c) + (-c)$
4. $\quad = (b + c) + (-c)$
5. $\quad = b$

13. Prove: If a and b are real numbers, then $-(a + b) = (-a) + (-b)$.

Statements
1. If a and b are real numbers, then $(a + b)$ is a real number.
2. $(-a)$, $(-b)$, and $-(a + b)$ are real numbers.
3. $(a + b) + [(-a) + (-b)] = [(a + b) + (-a)] + (-b)$
4. $\qquad\qquad\qquad\quad = [(-a) + (a + b)] + (-b)$
5. $\qquad\qquad\qquad\quad = [(-a) + (a)] + [b + (-b)]$
6. $\qquad\qquad\qquad\quad = \quad\; 0 \;\; + \;\; 0$
7. $\qquad\qquad\qquad\quad = 0$
8. $\qquad\qquad\qquad\quad = (a + b) + [-(a + b)]$
9. $(a + b) + [(-a) + (-b)] = (a + b) + [-(a + b)]$
10. $\qquad (-a) + (-b) = -(a + b)$

Note. Using "Rearranging terms" as a reason, statement 3 could have been written as follows, thus saving two steps:

$$3.\ (a + b) + [(-a) + (-b)] = [(-a) + a] + [b + (-b)]$$

In 14–17, prove that the sentence is true if the variables represent real numbers. Give a reason that justifies each statement of the proof.

14. $(-a) + (x + a) = x$

15. $r + [y + (-r)] = y$

16. $x + y = -[(-x) + (-y)]$

17. $(x + y) + [(-x) + (-y)] = 0$

5. Subtracting Signed Numbers

Subtraction of real numbers is defined in terms of addition. To subtract 5 from 8, symbolized $8 - 5$, we ask, "Which number added to 5 gives 8?" That number is 3. Since $5 + 3 = 8$, we write $8 - 5 = 3$. The number 8 is the **minuend**, 5 is the **subtrahend**, and 3 is the **difference.**

In general, if a and b are real numbers, the expression $a - b$ represents a real number c (that is, $a - b = c$) such that $b + c = a$.

Thus, to find $(+3) - (-2)$, ask $(-2) + $ (what number) $= (+3)$. That number is $+5$, since $(-2) + (+5) = (+3)$. Hence, $(+3) - (-2) = +5$.

If we compare the two examples at the right, we observe that when we subtract (-2) from $(+3)$, we obtain the same result as when we add $(+2)$, the opposite or additive inverse of (-2), to $(+3)$. This example illustrates the following definition of subtraction:

If a and b are real numbers, $a - b = a + (-b)$.

Subtract:	*Add:*
$(+3)$	$(+3)$
(-2) $\longrightarrow$	$(+2)$
$(+5)$	$(+5)$

Procedure. To subtract one real number from another, add the opposite (additive inverse) of the subtrahend to the minuend.

For example, $8 - 2 = 8 + (-2) = 6$.

Since $8 - 2 = 8 + (-2)$, we may simplify the writing of $8 + (-2)$ by writing $8 - 2$. Similarly, $(+7) + (-3) + (-1)$ can be written as $7 - 3 - 1$ and $(-3) + (-4) + (-2)$ can be written as $-3 - 4 - 2$.

USES OF THE SYMBOL "−"

In the expression $9 - (-6)$, the symbol "−" is used in two different ways:

1. Between 9 and (-6), the "−" indicates the operation of *subtraction*.
2. As the sign of (-6), the "−" indicates the *negative* of 6.

Hence, when $8 + (-2)$ is written in the simplified form $8 - 2$, we may think of $8 - 2$ as $8 + (-2)$, in which case the symbol "−" indicates the *negative* of 2. Or, we may think of $8 - 2$ as $8 - (+2)$, in which case the symbol "−" indicates the *subtraction* of 2.

~~~~~~~~~~~~~~~~~~~ *MODEL PROBLEMS* ~~~~~~~~~~~~~~~~~~~

In 1–7, subtract the lower number from the upper number.

1. $+25$	**2.** $+30$	**3.** -13	**4.** -15	**5.** -12	**6.** $+9$	**7.** 0
$+10$	-10	$+12$	-8	-12	0	-3
$+15$	$+40$	-25	-7	0	$+9$	$+3$

Note. In each problem, the signed number is subtracted by adding its opposite to the minuend. To check the answer (difference) in subtraction, add it to the subtrahend to see whether you obtain the minuend.

~~~~~~

Exercises

In 1–12, subtract the lower number from the upper number.

1. $+35$	**2.** $+10$	**3.** $+24$	**4.** $+7$	**5.** -48	**6.** -32
$+25$	$+17$	-12	-7	$+13$	$+19$

7. $-14\frac{1}{2}$	**8.** $-5\frac{1}{4}$	**9.** $+5.8$	**10.** $+9.2$	**11.** -7.4	**12.** -8.6
$-12\frac{1}{2}$	$-5\frac{1}{4}$	$+7.6$	-5.1	-9.3	-8.6

In 13–18, perform the indicated subtraction.

13. $(+12) - (+17)$ **14.** $(-13) - (-20)$ **15.** $(-25) - (+3)$
16. $(+18) - (-2)$ **17.** $(0) - (-4)$ **18.** $(+12) - 0$

In 19–21, subtract.

19. $(+14)$ from $(+8)$ **20.** (-9) from (-15) **21.** (-12) from $(+5)$

In 22–25, find the value of the given expression.

22. $(+8) + (+12) - (-5)$ **23.** $(-9) - (+3) + (+12)$
24. $(+12.4) - (+3.8) - (-2.5)$ **25.** $42 - 9 - 20$

In 26–31, state whether or not the set of numbers is closed under subtraction. If your answer is *no*, give an example to show that the difference of two members of the set is not a unique member of the set.

26. natural numbers   **27.** integers   **28.** positive integers
29. negative integers   **30.** odd integers   **31.** even integers

32. Give an example showing that $x - y \neq y - x$ for all real numbers x and y.
33. Give an example showing that $(x - y) - z \neq x - (y - z)$ for all real values of x, y, and z.
34. Prove: If x and y are real numbers, then $x - y = -(y - x)$.
35. *a.* Prove: If x, y, and z are real numbers, then $x(y - z) = xy - xz$.
    b. What property of multiplication has been proved in part *a*?

6. Multiplying Signed Numbers

We will define multiplication of real numbers in such a way that all the properties of multiplication will be satisfied. In order to do this, we will find the following two theorems useful. Remember we have assumed the postulate that if a is a real number, then $a \times 1 = a$ and $1 \times a = a$.

Multiplication Theorem 1 (*Multiplication Property of Zero*). The multiplication property of zero states that the product of any given real number and 0 is 0. If a is a real number, then $a \times 0 = 0$ and $0 \times a = 0$.

For example, $(12) \times (0) = 0$ and $(0) \times (12) = 0$; also, $(-15) \times (0) = 0$ and $(0) \times (-15) = 0$.

The proof of this theorem is shown in exercise 20 on page 50.

Multiplication Theorem 2 [*Multiplication Property of* (-1)]. The multiplication property of (-1) states that the product of any given real number a and (-1) is the opposite of a. If a is a real number, then $a(-1) = -a$ and $(-1)(a) = -a$.

For example, $(-1)(3) = -3$; $3(-1) = -3$; and $(-1)(-3) = -(-3)$ or $+3$.

The proof of this theorem is shown in exercise 21 on page 50.

Note that since $(-1)(-1) = 1$, the reciprocal of -1 is -1; that is, $-1 = \dfrac{1}{-1}$.

Now we are ready to multiply any real numbers. For example:

$(4)(2) = 8$

$(-4)(2) = [(-1)4](2) = -1[(4)(2)] = -1(8) = -8$

$(2)(-4) = 2[(4)(-1)] = [(2)(4)](-1) = 8(-1) = -8$

$(-2)(-4) = [(-1)(2)][(-1)(4)] = [(-1)(-1)][(2)(4)] = [-(-1)](8) = (1)(8) = 8$

These four examples illustrate the following rules for multiplying real numbers:

Rule 1. The product of two positive numbers or of two negative numbers is a positive number whose absolute value is the product of the absolute values of the numbers.

In general, if a and b are both positive or both negative, then

$$ab = |a| \cdot |b|$$

Rule 2. The product of a positive number and a negative number is a negative number whose absolute value is the product of the absolute values of the numbers.

In general, if one of the two numbers a and b is positive and the other is negative, then

$$ab = -(|a| \cdot |b|)$$

Rule 3. The product of a real number and 0 is equal to 0. If a is a real number, then

$$0 \cdot a = a \cdot 0 = 0$$

The statements for the proofs of the rules for multiplying signed numbers are shown in exercises 15–17 on page 49.

〰〰〰〰〰〰〰〰 *MODEL PROBLEMS* 〰〰〰〰〰〰〰〰〰

In 1–6, multiply.

1. $+10$	**2.** -12	**3.** $+15$	**4.** -18	**5.** $+7$	**6.** 0
$+3$	-4	-3	$+5$	$+1$	-7
$+30$	$+48$	-45	-90	$+7$	0

〰〰〰〰〰〰〰〰〰〰〰〰〰〰〰〰〰〰〰〰〰〰〰〰〰〰〰〰〰〰

MULTIPLYING MORE THAN TWO NUMBERS

Since the commutative and associative properties of multiplication hold for signed numbers, these numbers may be rearranged in any order when they are being multiplied.

Thus, $abc = acb = bac = bca = cab = cba$.

For example, $(-2)(+5)(-3)(+6) = (-2)(-3)(+5)(+6)$

$$= (+6) \times (+30) = 180$$

In any future proof, if factors are being multiplied in a desired order, "Rearranging factors" may be used as the reason.

```
┌──────────── KEEP IN MIND ────────────┐
│  1. If, in an indicated product that has no zero factor, │
│     there is an even number of negative factors, the pro- │
│     duct is a positive number.                            │
│  2. If, in an indicated product that has no zero factor,  │
│     there is an odd number of negative factors, the pro-  │
│     duct is a negative number.                            │
└───────────────────────────────────────┘
```

Exercises

In 1–21, multiply.

1. $+6$	**2.** -8	**3.** $+10$	**4.** -9	**5.** $+8$	**6.** 0
$+5$	-4	-7	$+5$	$+1$	-9

7. $+7$ by $+4$ **8.** -25 by -8 **9.** $+6$ by -3 **10.** $+15$ by 0

11. $(+4)(+3)$ **12.** $(-2)(-9)$ **13.** $(-7)(+4)$ **14.** $(+8)(-9)$

15. $(+2)(+5)(+3)$

16. $(-1)(-6)(-9)$

17. $(-2)(+4)(-7)$

18. $(-5)(-5)$

19. $(-3)(-3)(-3)(-3)$

20. $(-5)(-1)(-2)(-10)(+4)$

21. $|+5| \cdot |-4| \cdot (6)$

In 22 and 23, state the property of real numbers that justifies the statement.

22. $(-7) \times (-4) = (-4) \times (-7)$

23. $[(-5) \cdot 2] \cdot 7 = (-5) \cdot (2 \cdot 7)$

24. Use the distributive property to find the result mentally.

    a. $35 \times 73 + 35 \times 27$

    b. $97 \times (-8) + 97 \times (-2)$

ADDITIONAL PROPERTIES OF MULTIPLICATION

The following theorems can be proved using the definitions we have agreed upon and the postulates we have assumed.

Multiplication Theorem 3. If a is a real number and b is a nonzero real number, then $(ab)\dfrac{1}{b} = a$. For example, $(5 \times 7) \times \dfrac{1}{7} = 5$.

The statements for the proof of this theorem are shown in exercise 18 on page 49.

Multiplication Theorem 4 (*Cancellation Property of Multiplication*). If a and b are real numbers, and c is a nonzero real number, and if $ac = bc$ or $ca = cb$, then $a = b$. For example, if $9x = 9y$, then $x = y$.

The statements for the proof of this theorem are shown in exercise 19 on page 49.

Multiplication Theorem 5. If a and b are nonzero real numbers, the reciprocal of their product is the product of their reciprocals: $\dfrac{1}{ab} = \dfrac{1}{a} \cdot \dfrac{1}{b}$, $a \neq 0, b \neq 0$. For example, $\dfrac{1}{5 \times 3} = \dfrac{1}{5} \cdot \dfrac{1}{3}$.

The statements for the proof of this theorem are shown in exercise 22 on page 50.

Multiplication Theorem 6. If a is a nonzero real number, the reciprocal of the negative of a is the negative of the reciprocal of a: $\dfrac{1}{-a} = -\dfrac{1}{a}$, $a \neq 0$. For example, $\dfrac{1}{-9} = -\dfrac{1}{9}$.

The statements for the proof of this theorem are shown in exercise 23 on page 50.

Exercises

In 1–6, give the reciprocal of the number.

1. 7 **2.** -4 **3.** $-\frac{1}{8}$ **4.** $\frac{2}{3}$ **5.** $-\frac{3}{4}$ **6.** $-.5$

In 7–10, give the simplest replacement for the question mark that will make the resulting sentence true. The variables represent real numbers.

7. $\frac{1}{5}(5x) = ?$

8. $(-3y) \cdot (-\frac{1}{3}) = ?$

9. $(ax)\dfrac{1}{a} = ?, \ a \neq 0$

10. $\dfrac{1}{7} \cdot \dfrac{1}{x} = \dfrac{1}{?}, \ x \neq 0$

In 11–14, multiply the numbers.

11. $(\frac{1}{2})(8)$ **12.** $(35)(-\frac{1}{5})$ **13.** $(\frac{1}{3})(-\frac{1}{4})$ **14.** $18(-\frac{1}{3})(+\frac{1}{6})$

In 15–23, give a reason that justifies each statement in the proof. The variables represent real numbers. Assume that all products and all additive and multiplicative inverses involved are real numbers.

15. Prove: $a(-b) = -ab$

Statements
1. $a(-b) = a[(-1)b]$
2. $\quad = (-1)(ab)$
3. $\quad = -ab$

16. Prove: $(-a)b = -ab$

Statements
1. $(-a)b = [(-1)a]b$
2. $\quad = (-1)ab$
3. $\quad = -ab$

17. Prove: $(-a)(-b) = ab$

Statements
1. $(-a)(-b) = [(-1)a][(-1)b]$
2. $\quad = (-1)(-1)ab$
3. $\quad = 1 \cdot ab$
4. $\quad = ab$

18. Prove: $(ab)\dfrac{1}{b} = a, \ (b \neq 0)$

Statements
1. $ab\left(\dfrac{1}{b}\right) = a\left(b \cdot \dfrac{1}{b}\right)$
2. $\quad = a \cdot 1$
3. $\quad = a$

19. Prove: If $ac = bc$, then $a = b, \ (c \neq 0)$

Statements
1. $\quad ac = bc$
2. $(ac) \cdot \dfrac{1}{c} = (bc) \cdot \dfrac{1}{c}$
3. $\quad a = b$

20. Prove that $a \cdot 0 = 0$
and that $0 \cdot a = 0$.

    Statements

1. $a + 0 = a$
2. $ = a \cdot 1$
3. $ = a(1 + 0)$
4. $ = a \cdot 1 + a \cdot 0$
5. $ = a + a \cdot 0$ Hence,
6. $a + 0 = a + a \cdot 0$
7. $ 0 = a \cdot 0$
8. $ a \cdot 0 = 0$
9. $ 0 \cdot a = 0$

21. Prove that $a(-1) = -a$
and that $(-1)a = -a$.

    Statements

1. $[a(-1) + a] = [a(-1) + a \cdot 1]$
2. $ = a[(-1) + 1]$
3. $ = a \cdot 0$
4. $ = 0$
5. $ = (-a + a)$ Hence,
6. $[a(-1) + a] = (-a + a)$
7. $ a(-1) = -a$
8. $ (-1)a = -a$

22. Prove: $\dfrac{1}{ab} = \dfrac{1}{a} \cdot \dfrac{1}{b}$, $(a \neq 0, \, b \neq 0)$

    Statements

1. $ab\left(\dfrac{1}{a} \cdot \dfrac{1}{b}\right) = \left(a \cdot \dfrac{1}{a}\right)\left(b \cdot \dfrac{1}{b}\right)$

2. $\phantom{ab\left(\dfrac{1}{a} \cdot \dfrac{1}{b}\right)} = 1 \cdot 1$

3. $\phantom{ab\left(\dfrac{1}{a} \cdot \dfrac{1}{b}\right)} = 1$

4. $\phantom{ab\left(\dfrac{1}{a} \cdot \dfrac{1}{b}\right)} = ab\left(\dfrac{1}{ab}\right)$ Hence,

5. $ab\left(\dfrac{1}{a} \cdot \dfrac{1}{b}\right) = ab\left(\dfrac{1}{ab}\right)$

6. $\dfrac{1}{a} \cdot \dfrac{1}{b} = \dfrac{1}{ab}$

7. $\dfrac{1}{ab} = \dfrac{1}{a} \cdot \dfrac{1}{b}$

23. Prove: $\dfrac{1}{-a} = -\dfrac{1}{a}$, $(a \neq 0)$

    Statements

1. $\dfrac{1}{-a} = \dfrac{1}{(-1)(a)}$

2. $\phantom{\dfrac{1}{-a}} = \dfrac{1}{-1} \cdot \dfrac{1}{a}$

3. $\phantom{\dfrac{1}{-a}} = (-1)\dfrac{1}{a}$

4. $\phantom{\dfrac{1}{-a}} = -\dfrac{1}{a}$

In 24 and 25, prove the theorem if a and b are nonzero real numbers.

24. If $a = b$, then $\dfrac{1}{a} = \dfrac{1}{b}$.

25. $a \cdot \dfrac{1}{ab} = \dfrac{1}{b}$

7. Dividing Signed Numbers

Division of real numbers is defined in terms of multiplication.

To divide 8 by 4, symbolized $8 \div 4$ or $\frac{8}{4}$, we ask, "Which number multiplied by 4 gives 8?" That number is 2. Since $2 \times 4 = 8$, we write $8 \div 4 = 2$. The number 8 is the **dividend,** 4 is the **divisor,** and 2 is the **quotient.**

It is impossible to divide a real number by 0. For example, to divide 8 by 0, we ask, "Which number multiplied by 0 gives 8?" There is no such number because the product of any real number and 0 is 0. Hence, $8 \div 0$ is **undefined** or meaningless.

To divide 0 by 0, we ask, "Which number multiplied by 0 gives 0?" The answer is any number. Hence, $0 \div 0$ is meaningless.

In general, for all real numbers a and b ($b \neq 0$), to divide a by b, symbolized $a \div b$ or $\frac{a}{b}$, means to find a number c such that $bc = a$. Also if $a \neq 0$, then $\frac{1}{a}$, the reciprocal of a, may represent $1 \div a$.

This definition of division leads to the following results:

$$\frac{+8}{+4} = +2 \qquad \frac{-8}{-4} = +2 \qquad \frac{-8}{+4} = -2 \qquad \frac{+8}{-4} = -2 \qquad \frac{0}{+8} = 0 \qquad \frac{0}{-8} = 0$$

These examples illustrate the following rules for dividing real numbers:

Rule 1. The quotient of two positive numbers or of two negative numbers is a positive number whose absolute value is the absolute value of the dividend divided by the absolute value of the divisor.

In general, if a and b are both positive or both negative numbers, then

$$\frac{a}{b} = \frac{|a|}{|b|}$$

Rule 2. The quotient of two numbers, one of which is a positive number and the other a negative number, is a negative number whose absolute value is the absolute value of the dividend divided by the absolute value of the divisor.

In general, if one of the numbers a and b is positive and the other is negative, then

$$\frac{a}{b} = -\left(\frac{|a|}{|b|}\right)$$

Rule 3. Zero divided by a nonzero number is zero.
In general, if a is a nonzero real number, then

$$\frac{0}{a} = 0$$

MODEL PROBLEMS

In 1–5, perform the indicated division.

1. $(+35) \div (+5) = +7$ **2.** $(-64) \div (-16) = +4$

3. $(+40) \div (-8) = -5$ **4.** $\dfrac{-36}{+4} = -9$ **5.** $\dfrac{0}{-2} = 0$

Note. To check the answer (quotient) in division, multiply the quotient by the divisor to see whether you obtain the dividend.

USING RECIPROCALS IN DIVIDING SIGNED NUMBERS

Recall that, for every nonzero real number a, $a \neq 0$, there is a unique real number called the *reciprocal* or *multiplicative inverse* of a such that $a \cdot \dfrac{1}{a} = 1$.

Using the reciprocal of a number, we can demonstrate the following relationship between multiplication and division.

For every real number a and every nonzero real number b, $b \neq 0$, a divided by b is equal to a multiplied by the reciprocal of b.

$$\frac{a}{b} = a \cdot \frac{1}{b}, \ b \neq 0$$

The statements for the proof of this sentence are shown in exercise 33 on page 53.

Rule. To divide a real number (the dividend) by a nonzero real number (the divisor), multiply the dividend by the reciprocal of the divisor.

MODEL PROBLEMS

In 1–3, perform the indicated division.

1. $\dfrac{-35}{-5} = (-35)\left(-\dfrac{1}{5}\right) = +(35)\dfrac{1}{5} = +7$ **2.** $\dfrac{0}{-6} = (0)\left(-\dfrac{1}{6}\right) = 0$

3. $(+27) \div (-\tfrac{1}{3}) = (+27)(-3) = -(27)(3) = -81$

Exercises

In 1–6, name the reciprocal of the given number.

1. 8 **2.** -7 **3.** 1 **4.** $\frac{1}{4}$ **5.** $-\frac{3}{2}$ **6.** y $(y \neq 0)$

In 7–24, perform the indicated division.

7. $\dfrac{-12}{-4}$ **8.** $\dfrac{-10}{+5}$ **9.** $\dfrac{-16}{+4}$ **10.** $\dfrac{-36}{-6}$ **11.** $\dfrac{+40}{+10}$ **12.** $\dfrac{0}{-2}$

13. $\dfrac{+8.4}{-4}$ **14.** $\dfrac{-.25}{+5}$ **15.** $\dfrac{-9.6}{-.3}$ **16.** $\dfrac{-3.6}{+1.2}$ **17.** $\dfrac{+.4}{-.8}$ **18.** $\dfrac{0}{+.7}$

19. $(+50) \div (+10)$ **20.** $(-14) \div (-7)$ **21.** $(+48) \div (-12)$

22. $(-64) \div (+16)$ **23.** $(-12) \div (+\frac{2}{3})$ **24.** $(+\frac{6}{8}) \div (-\frac{1}{4})$

25. Given the fraction $\dfrac{6}{y-x}$. Which of the following substitutions leads to an impossible operation?   (1) 1 for x, -1 for y (2) 2 for x, 3 for y (3) -2 for x, -3 for y (4) 3 for x, 3 for y

In 26–29, give the multiplicative inverse of the expression and state the value of x for which the multiplicative inverse is not defined.

26. $x - 7$ **27.** $x + 5$ **28.** $3x - 1$ **29.** $2x + 1$

In 30–32, state whether or not the set of numbers is closed under division (division by zero is excluded). If your answer is *no*, give an example to show that the quotient of two members in the set is not a unique member of the set.

30. positive integers **31.** even integers **32.** rational numbers

33. Following are the statements in the proof of the sentence "If a and b are real numbers, and $b \neq 0$, then $\dfrac{a}{b} = a \cdot \dfrac{1}{b}$." Give a reason that justifies each statement in the proof.

Statements

1. If $\dfrac{a}{b} = c$, then $bc = a$.

2. If b is a real number, then $\dfrac{1}{b}$ is a real number.

3. $a \cdot \dfrac{1}{b} = a \cdot \dfrac{1}{b}$

4. $\quad = bc\left(\dfrac{1}{b}\right)$

5. $\quad = \left(b \cdot \dfrac{1}{b}\right)c$

6. $\quad = 1 \cdot c$

7. $\quad = c$

8. $a \cdot \dfrac{1}{b} = \dfrac{a}{b}$

9. $\dfrac{a}{b} = a \cdot \dfrac{1}{b}$

34. State whether the following sentences are *true* or *false*:

    a. $(18 + 6) \div 3 = (18 \div 3) + (6 \div 3)$

    b. $[(+35) - (-15)] \div (+5) = [(+35) \div (+5)] - [(-15) \div (+5)]$

35. Prove that the operation of division is distributive over addition. That is, $(x + y) \div z = x \div z + y \div z$ for all real numbers x, y, and z, $z \neq 0$.

36. Prove that the operation of division is distributive over subtraction. That is, $(x - y) \div z = x \div z - y \div z$ for all real numbers x, y, and z, $z \neq 0$.

37. Prove that the reciprocal of $\frac{x}{y}$ is $\frac{y}{x}$ for all nonzero real numbers x and y.

8. Understanding the Meanings of Important Mathematical Terms

BASE, EXPONENT, POWER

The product $2 \times 2 \times 2 \times 2 \times 2 \times 2$ may be written 2^6 to show that the same number, 2, is a factor 6 times. The value of 2^6 is 64. In $2^6 = 64$, 2 is the **base**, 6 is the **exponent** of the base, and 64 is the sixth **power** of the base.

The Sixth Power of 2
$$2^6 = 2 \times 2 \times 2 \times 2 \times 2 \times 2 = 64$$

base $\longrightarrow$ $2 = 64$ $\longleftarrow$ power, $6 \longleftarrow$ exponent

For any real number b, the powers of b are defined as follows:

first power: $b^1 = b$

second power: $b^2 = b \cdot b$, read "b-squared," or "b-second," or "b to the second."

third power: $b^3 = b \cdot b \cdot b$, read "b-cubed," or "b-cube," or "b-third," or "b to the third."

fourth power: $b^4 = b \cdot b \cdot b \cdot b$, read "$b$-fourth," or "$b$ to the fourth."

nth power: $b^n = b \cdot b \cdot b \cdots$ (n times), read "b-nth," or "b to the nth."

In general, if n is a positive integer more than 1, then b^n, the nth power of b, represents the product of n factors, each factor equal to b.

  In b^n: b is the base, n is the exponent, and b^n is the power.

For example, in 10^3, the base is 10, the exponent is 3, and 10^3 or 1000 is the power.

Caution. Distinguish between expressions such as $5y^2$ and $(5y)^2$. The expression $5y^2 = 5(y \cdot y)$. In $(5y)^2$, the entire expression is the second power of $5y$; that is, $(5y)^2 = (5y)(5y) = 25(y \cdot y) = 25y^2$.

TERM AND EXPRESSION

Understanding the meanings of *term* and *expression* and the distinction between them is important to an understanding of many of the most important ideas in mathematics. Let us begin by noting that an expression such as $6xy + \dfrac{5}{x}$, which does not contain parentheses, consists of two terms, one of which is $6xy$ and the other is $\dfrac{5}{x}$.

A ***term*** may be a number, a variable, a product of numbers and variables, a quotient of numbers and variables, or a combination of products and quotients. Examples of terms are 6, x, $6xy$, $\dfrac{5}{x}$, $\dfrac{2z}{3v}$, and $.75x^2y$.

An ***expression*** may be one term, or the sum or difference of terms. Examples of expressions are 6, $6xy$, $\dfrac{5}{x}$, $6xy + \dfrac{5}{x}$, and $6xy - 6$.

FACTOR OF A TERM

A ***factor of a term*** is any one of the numbers or variables whose product forms the term, or any product of these numbers or variables.

For example, the factors of $6xy$ are $1, 2, 3, 6, x, y, 2x, 2y, 3x, 3y, 6x, 6y, xy, 2xy, 3xy,$ and $6xy$. Note that the factors of 6 are 1, 2, 3, and 6 for the reason that, in factoring an integer such as 6, factoring is restricted to integers. Otherwise, any number except 0 could be a factor of 6; for example, $\frac{1}{2}$ and 12.

A ***literal factor of a term*** is the product of all the literal or variable factors. For example, the literal factor of $6xy$ is xy; the literal factor of $25c^2d$ is c^2d.

COEFFICIENT

In any product consisting of two factors, each factor is the ***coefficient*** of the other factor. Hence, if $6xy$ is separated into the factors 6 and xy, then 6 is the numerical coefficient of xy. In future problems, a numerical coefficient of a literal factor shall be referred to simply as the coefficient. In a term such as x^2y, the coefficient is understood to be 1, the multiplicative identity.

LIKE TERMS

Like terms or *similar terms* are terms having the identically same literal factor.

For example, $6x^2y$ and $-2x^2y$ are like terms, but $6x^2y$ and $-2xy^2$ are not like terms.

MONOMIAL

A monomial may be a number, or a variable, or the product of numbers and variables.

For example, 6, x, $6xy$, and $.75x^2y$ are monomials.

A *monomial in one variable* is of the form ax^n where n is a positive integer or zero. The degree of a monomial in one variable is n if the coefficient a is not equal to zero. The degree of a monomial that is a number is 0.

For example, the monomial $5x^2$ is a monomial in x of degree 2; the monomial $\frac{1}{4}y^5$, or $\frac{y^5}{4}$, is a monomial in y of degree 5. Since 15 may be written as $15x^0$, as will be shown in a later chapter, the monomial 15 is of degree 0. The number 0 has no degree since it may be written as $0x^2$, $0x^3$, and so on. By definition, $x = x^1$, a monomial of degree 1.

The *degree of a monomial* in more than one variable is the sum of the exponents of the variables. For example, the degree of the monomial $5x^2y^3z$ is $2 + 3 + 1$, or 6.

POLYNOMIAL

A *polynomial* may be a monomial, or the sum or difference of monomials. For example, 4, $7y + 4$, and $y^2 - 7y + 4$ are polynomials.

A *binomial* is a polynomial of two terms. For example, $7y^3 + 4$ is a binomial. Also, $\frac{x^2}{3} + \frac{x}{2}$, or $\frac{1}{3}x^2 + \frac{1}{2}x$, is a binomial.

A *trinomial* is a polynomial of three terms. For example, $x^3 - 4x + 10$ and $y^2 - 7y + 4$ are trinomials.

The *degree of a polynomial* is the degree of the monomial term of highest degree. For example, the degree of $x^2 + 5x$ is 2; the degree of $x^2 + 5xy^2$ is 3, since the degree of $5xy^2$ is 3.

Exercises

In 1–6, state the factors of the product.

1. cd **2.** $4m$ **3.** $7t$ **4.** $6mn$ **5.** $20cd$ **6.** $7xy$

In 7–12, state the base and exponent of the power.

7. c^2 **8.** e^3 **9.** x^4 **10.** 8^2 **11.** 3^5 **12.** 10^8

In 13–18, state the coefficient and the exponent.

13. $6x^2$ **14.** $2d^4$ **15.** $\frac{2}{3}t^2$ **16.** m^3 **17.** $6y^5$ **18.** $\frac{1}{8}e^3$

In 19–23, write the expression using exponents.

19. $x \cdot x \cdot x \cdot x$ **20.** $e \cdot e \cdot e \cdot e \cdot e$ **21.** $7 \cdot y \cdot y \cdot y$

22. $x \cdot x \cdot y \cdot y \cdot y$ **23.** $3 \cdot r \cdot r \cdot r \cdot s$

In 24–29, write the expression without using exponents.

24. m^3 **25.** x^4y^2 **26.** $4x^2$ **27.** $4c^2d^3$ **28.** $10x^3y^2z$ **29.** $(4x)^2$

In 30–41, find the value of the power.

30. 6^2 **31.** 2^4 **32.** 5^3 **33.** 10^5 **34.** 12^2 **35.** 1^6

36. $(\frac{1}{2})^4$ **37.** $(-2)^5$ **38.** $(-1)^4$ **39.** $(-1)^{13}$ **40.** $(-3)^4$ **41.** $(-.3)^4$

In 42–47, state the degree of the polynomial and tell whether the polynomial is a monomial, a binomial, or a trinomial.

42. $5x + 7$ **43.** $8y$ **44.** $a^2 + 4a - 5$

45. $x^2 + y^2 + z^2$ **46.** $6a - 7b$ **47.** $5x^2y^3z + 10x^2y^2z$

9. Expressing Verbal Phrases Algebraically

The verbal phrase "one more than twice a number" may be expressed algebraically as $2n + 1$, using n as a variable to represent "a number." In $2n + 1$, if the domain or replacement set of the variable n is the set of integers, then n is a *placeholder* for any integer. This means that n may be replaced by any number in the set of integers.

〰〰〰〰〰〰〰 *MODEL PROBLEMS* 〰〰〰〰〰〰〰

In 1–7, express the verbal phrase algebraically.

1. x increased by 5   *Ans.* $x + 5$

2. y decreased by 4   *Ans.* $y - 4$

3. t multiplied by 40   *Ans.* $40t$

4. d divided by r *Ans.* $d \div r$ or $\dfrac{d}{r}$

5. 10 times t, increased by u *Ans.* $10t + u$

6. 2 less than $3x$ *Ans.* $3x - 2$

7. twice the sum of x and y *Ans.* $2(x + y)$

Exercises

In 1–16, express the verbal phrase algebraically.
1. the sum of (a) c and d (b) x and 2   (c) $3a$ and $2b$
2. the difference between (a) x and y (b) m and 1   (c) $6x$ and $4y$
3. the product of (a) m and n (b) 100 and h (c) $5r$ and s
4. the quotient of (a) s and t (b) d and 20   (c) $3p$ and $2q$

5. b plus 5
6. 6 more than x
7. x more than y
8. f increased by g
9. t decreased by 7
10. 9 decreased by w
11. 6 less than x
12. d subtracted from 7
13. 8 times x
14. the product of $3a$ and b
15. 6 divided by x
16. A divided by L

In 17–22, using the letter n to represent the variable "a number," write the phrase as an algebraic expression.
17. the number increased by 10
18. the number decreased by 7
19. two-thirds of the number
20. 25% of the number
21. 6 more than, 4 times the number
22. 20 less than, 5 times the number

In 23–27, represent the phrase as an algebraic expression using h to represent the greater number and b to represent the smaller number.
23. the product of the two numbers
24. three times the sum of the two numbers
25. twice the greater number, increased by twice the smaller number
26. the sum of twice the greater and half the smaller
27. twice the greater, decreased by 3 times the smaller

28. A coat costs \$60. Represent the cost of c coats.
29. A pencil costs c cents. Represent the cost of a dozen pencils.
30. Represent the cost of x oranges at y cents each.
31. Bill is a years old now. Represent his age 9 years from now.
32. Arthur is n years old now. Represent his age 5 years ago.
33. Margaret is 20 years old. Represent her age y years ago.
34. Helen is y years old. Her brother Jack is twice as old as Helen. Represent Jack's age d years ago.
35. Walter is t years old. His mother is 25 years older than he is. Represent his mother's age 10 years ago.
36. The length of a rectangle is s feet. Represent the width of the rectangle if it exceeds twice the length by 4 feet.
37. Represent the diameter of a circle if its radius is represented by r yards.

In 38–43, express algebraically the number of:
38. inches in f feet
39. yards in f feet
40. cents in n nickels
41. cents in q quarters
42. ounces in p pounds
43. days in w weeks

44. If n represents the smallest of three consecutive odd integers, express their sum in terms of n.

45. If N represents an even integer, which of the following represents an odd integer? (1) $3N$ (2) N^3 (3) $3N + 2$ (4) $3N + 1$

46. If n is an odd integer, which of the following represents an even integer? (1) $3n$ (2) n^3 (3) $n^2 + 1$ (4) $n + 2$

47. The units digit of a two-digit number is a and the tens digit is b. Represent the number in terms of a and b.

48. If the tens digit of a two-digit number is 5 and the units digit is represented by x, the number may be represented by (1) $5x$ (2) $50x$ (3) $50 + x$

49. A man bought n articles, each of which cost d cents. Represent the number of cents he spent.

50. A boy bought n articles, each of which cost c cents. Express, in cents, his change from a five-dollar bill.

51. If n pencils cost c cents, represent the cost of r pencils in cents.

52. If r apples cost t cents, represent the cost of m of these apples.

53. A boy was x years old 5 years ago. Represent his age 7 years from now.

54. A girl will be y years old 3 years from now. Represent her age 4 years ago.

10. Order of Operations in Evaluating Numerical Expressions

PARENTHESES MAY BE USED TO CHANGE THE ORDER OF OPERATIONS

To find the value of $(2 + 3) \times 4$, do the addition first, since it is within parentheses. Hence, the value of $(2 + 3) \times 4$ is 5×4 or 20. Similarly, to find the value of $10 - (4 + 3)$, do the addition first, since it is within parentheses. Hence, the value of $10 - (4 + 3)$ is $10 - 7$, or 3.

To find the value of a numerical expression, the order of operations that has been agreed upon by mathematicians must be observed. The correct order of operations is the order set forth in the following procedure:

Procedure. To find the value of a numerical expression:
1. Evaluate within parentheses or within other symbols of grouping.
2. Evaluate the powers and the roots.
3. Evaluate the multiplications and divisions in order from left to right.
4. Evaluate the additions and subtractions in order from left to right.

~~~~~~~~~~~~~~ *MODEL PROBLEMS* ~~~~~~~~~~~~~

1. Evaluate: $8 + 4 \times 7$

Solution: Multiply before adding.

$$8 + 4 \times 7 = 8 + 28 = 36 \quad Ans.$$

2. Evaluate: $27 \div 3^2 \times 2$

Solution: Evaluate the power first.

$$27 \div 3^2 \times 2 = 27 \div 9 \times 2$$

Operate in order, from left to right, doing the division first.

$$= 3 \times 2 = 6 \quad Ans.$$

3. Evaluate: $12 - \sqrt{9} + 5$

Solution: Evaluate the root first.

$$12 - \sqrt{9} + 5 = 12 - 3 + 5$$

Operate in order, from left to right, doing the subtraction first.

$$= 9 + 5 = 14 \quad Ans.$$

4. Evaluate: $5(6 - 7)^3 + (-3)^2(-5)$

Solution: Evaluate within parentheses.

$$5(6 - 7)^3 + (-3)^2(-5) = 5(-1)^3 + (-3)^2(-5)$$

Evaluate the powers.

$$= 5(-1) + 9(-5)$$

Evaluate the multiplications; then add.

$$= (-5) + (-45) = -50 \quad Ans.$$

~~~~~~

Exercises

In 1–24, find the value of the numerical expression.

1. $6 + 5 \times 9$	**2.** $12 + 9 \div 3$	**3.** $30 - 15 \div 5$
4. $13 \times 3 - 2$	**5.** $81 \div 9 - 6$	**6.** $7 \times 5 - 9 \times 3$
7. $20 + 20 \div 5 + 5$	**8.** $15 + 3 \times 2 - 8$	**9.** $(3 + 2) \times 4$

10. $(18 - 12) \div 3$ **11.** $(10 - 5) + 6$ **12.** $10 - (10 \div 10)$
13. $2(8 + 6) - 4$ **14.** $2(7 + 3)(7 - 3)$ **15.** $5(3)^2 + 2$
16. $12 + (4 + 5)^2$ **17.** $12 + (-2)(-3)$ **18.** $7 - 3(4 - 6)$
19. $(-5)(+3) + (-2)(-6)$ **20.** $16 - (-3)^2$
21. $3(+5)^2 - 2(-4)^2$ **22.** $20 - 2^3(-3)^2$
23. $20(-1)^2 - 2^2(-3)^3$ **24.** $30 - \sqrt{169 - 25}$

11. Evaluating an Algebraic Expression

To evaluate an algebraic expression means to find the number that the expression represents for given values of its variables.

～～～～～～ *MODEL PROBLEMS* ～～～～～～

1. Evaluate $6x - 3y$ when $x = 5$ and $y = -4$.

2. Evaluate $c^2 - 2d^2$ when $c = -5$ and $d = 4$.

3. Evaluate $4x^2 + 3x - 5$ when $x = -2$.

How To Proceed	*Solution*	*Solution*	*Solution*
1. Replace the variables by their given values.	$6(5) - 3(-4)$	$(-5)^2 - 2(4^2)$	$4(-2)^2 + 3(-2) - 5$
2. Follow the correct order of operations.	$30 + 12$ 42 *Ans.*	$25 - 2(16)$ $25 - 32$ -7 *Ans.*	$4(4) + 3(-2) - 5$ $16 - 6 - 5$ $10 - 5$ 5 *Ans.*

Exercises

In 1–32, find the value of the expression when $a = 1$, $b = -2$, $c = -3$, $d = 3$, $x = 4$, $y = 5$, and $z = -1$.

1. $5a$ **2.** bx **3.** $2abz$ **4.** $\frac{1}{2}x$
5. $\frac{2}{3}b$ **6.** $\frac{1}{9}bdy$ **7.** $-d^2$ **8.** $(-d)^2$
9. y^3 **10.** $2y^2$ **11.** $-3x^2$ **12.** $4d^3$
13. $\frac{1}{2}x^2$ **14.** $\frac{2}{3}d^3$ **15.** $-\frac{1}{5}y^3$ **16.** $3y - b$
17. $b - 4z$ **18.** $5x + 2y$ **19.** $y^2 - 4y$ **20.** $a^2 - b^2$
21. $b^3 - z^3$ **22.** $2y^2 - y$ **23.** $7y - y^2$ **24.** $5z - 3z^2$

25. $x^2 + 3x + 5$ **26.** $a^2 - 5a - 3$ **27.** $-a^2 + 4a + 6$ **28.** $-b^2 + 3b - 2$
29. $15 + 5z - z^2$ **30.** $2x^2 - 5x + 15$ **31.** $4b^2 - 2b + 3$ **32.** $-2c^2 + 5c - 6$

In 33–36, find the value of the expression when $a = 12$, $b = -6$, and $c = -4$.

33. $\dfrac{a - b}{a + b}$ **34.** $\dfrac{3a + 2b}{3c}$ **35.** $\dfrac{3a - 2b}{3b + a}$ **36.** $\dfrac{a^2 + 3b^2}{c^2}$

In 37–42, find the value of the expression when $x = 8$, $y = 5$, and $z = -2$.

37. $2(x + y)$ **38.** $3(5y - 2z)$ **39.** $\frac{1}{2}x(y + 3z)$
40. $3y - (x - z)$ **41.** $2(x + z) - 5$ **42.** $4z - 5(z - x)$

12. Expressing Verbal Statements as Formulas

A *formula* is an equation that expresses one variable in terms of other variables. For example, the formula $A = bh$ expresses the variable A in terms of the variables b and h.

MODEL PROBLEM

Write a formula for the relationship: The surface, S, of a sphere is equal to the product of 4π and the square of the radius, r.

Solution: $S = 4\pi r^2$ *Ans.*

Exercises

In 1–11, write the formula that expresses the stated relationship.

1. The selling price of an article, s, is equal to its cost, c, plus the profit, p.
2. The median of a trapezoid, M, is equal to one-half the sum of the bases, b and c.
3. The number of diagonals, d, that can be drawn from one vertex of a polygon to all the other vertices is three less than the number of sides of the polygon, n.
4. The average, M, of three numbers a, b, c is their sum divided by 3.
5. The number of degrees, d, in the central angle of a regular polygon is 360 divided by the number of sides of the polygon, n.
6. The volume of a rectangular solid, V, is equal to the product of the length, l, width, w, and height, h.
7. The surface of a cube, S, is equal to six times the square of its edge, e.
8. The volume of a sphere, V, is equal to four-thirds of the product of π and the cube of its radius, r.

9. The geometric mean, G, between two numbers, a and b, is equal to the square root of their product.

10. The Fahrenheit temperature, F, is $32°$ more than nine-fifths of the centigrade temperature, C.

11. The distance, s, which a body will fall from rest is one-half the product of the gravitational constant, g, and the square of the time, t.

12. Represent the cost, C, in cents, of sending a telegram of n words, n being greater than 10, if the cost of sending the first 10 words is a cents and each additional word costs b cents.

13. Represent the cost, C, in cents, of a telephone conversation lasting 8 minutes if the charge for the first 3 minutes is x cents and the cost for each additional minute is y cents.

14. Represent the charge, C, in cents, for borrowing a book from a lending library for 12 days if the cost for the first 3 days is a cents and the cost for each additional day is b cents.

13. Evaluating the Subject of a Formula

In a formula, the variable that is expressed in terms of the remaining variables is called the **subject of the formula.** We can evaluate the subject of a formula, that is, find its value, when the values of the remaining variables in the formula are given.

~~~~~~~~~ *MODEL PROBLEMS* ~~~~~~~~~

1. Evaluate

$$S = \frac{n}{2}(a + l)$$

when $n = 9$,
$a = -2, l = 22.$

2. Evaluate

$$S = \frac{n}{2}[2a + (n-1)d]$$

when $a = 5, n = 10$,
$d = 7.$

How To Proceed	*Solution*	*Solution*
1. Replace the variables by their given values.	$S = \dfrac{9}{2}(-2 + 22)$	$S = \dfrac{10}{2}[2(5) + (10-1)7]$
2. Follow the correct order of operations.	$= \dfrac{9}{2}(20)$	$= 5(10 + 63)$
	$= 90 \ Ans.$	$= 5(73) = 365 \ Ans.$

~~~~~~~~~~~~~~~~~~~~~~~~~~~~~~~~~~~~

Exercises

1. Using the formula $P = 2l + 2w$, find P when $l = 13$ and $w = 5$.
2. If $A = p + prt$, find A when $p = 500$, $r = .06$, and $t = 8$.
3. If $C = \frac{5}{9}(F - 32)$, find C when $F = -40$.
4. If $A = \pi r^2$, find A when $r = 20$ and $\pi = 3.14$.
5. Using the formula $V = \frac{1}{3}\pi r^2 h$, find V when $\pi = \frac{22}{7}$, $r = 3$, and $h = 2.1$.
6. If $V = \frac{4}{3}\pi r^3$, find V when $\pi = \frac{22}{7}$ and $r = 21$.

7. If $S = \dfrac{a}{1 - r}$, find S when $a = 4$ and $r = \frac{1}{2}$.

8. If $F = \dfrac{9}{5}C + 32$, find F when $C = -30°$.

9. If $v = \dfrac{MV}{M + m}$, find v when $M = 1.5$, $V = 600$, and $m = 28.5$.

10. If $C = \dfrac{nE}{R + nr}$, find C when $n = 50$, $E = 1.3$, $R = 400$, and $r = 5$.

11. If $S = \dfrac{n}{2}[2a + (n - 1)d]$, find S when $a = -4$, $n = 8$, and $d = 9$.

14. Adding Like Monomials or Like Terms

We have learned that we can transform $7x + 2x$ by using the distributive property of multiplication as follows:

$$7x + 2x = (7 + 2)x = 9x$$

Since the distributive property of multiplication guarantees that $7x + 2x = 9x$ is true for every replacement of the variable x, $7x + 2x$ and $9x$ are called *equivalent expressions.*

The previous example illustrates the following:

Procedure. To add like monomials:
1. Find the sum of their coefficients.
2. Multiply the sum by the common literal factor.

When we add like terms, we say that we *combine like terms.*
The indicated sum of two unlike terms cannot be expressed as a single term. For example, $4x + 5y$ and $2ac - bd$ cannot be simplified.

~~~~~~~~~~~~~~~~~ *MODEL PROBLEMS* ~~~~~~~~~~~~~~~~

In 1–6, add.

1. $+8a$ **2.** $-4x^2$ **3.** $+15x^2y$ **4.** $-9abc$ **5.** $-8x^a$ **6.** $-5(a+b)$
$\quad\ +3a$ $\quad\ +6x^2$ $\quad\ -3x^2y$ $\quad\ +8abc$ $\quad\ +7x^a$ $\quad\ -6(a+b)$
$\quad\ \overline{+11a}$ $\quad\ \underline{-8x^2}$ $\quad\ \underline{-x^2y}$ $\quad\ \underline{+abc}$ $\quad\ \overline{-x^a}$ $\quad\ \underline{+8(a+b)}$
$\qquad\qquad\overline{-6x^2}$ $\qquad\ \overline{+11x^2y}$ $\qquad\ \overline{0}$ $\qquad\qquad\quad\overline{-3(a+b)}$

~~~~~~

Exercises

In 1–9, add.

1. $+6a$ $\qquad\qquad$ **2.** $-3b$ $\qquad\qquad$ **3.** $+6x^2$
$\quad\ \underline{+4a}$ $\qquad\qquad\quad\ -b$ $\qquad\qquad\qquad\ +9x^2$
$\qquad\qquad\qquad\qquad\ \underline{-7b}$ $\qquad\qquad\qquad\ \underline{-4x^2}$

4. $-12y^2$ $\qquad\quad$ **5.** $-1.5x$ $\qquad\qquad$ **6.** $-8cd$
$\quad\ +\ 8y^2$ $\qquad\qquad\ +.4x$ $\qquad\qquad\qquad\ +5cd$
$\quad\ \underline{+\ 4y^2}$ $\qquad\qquad\ \underline{-1.1x}$ $\qquad\qquad\qquad\ \underline{+3cd}$

7. $+6xyz$ $\qquad\qquad$ **8.** $+8z^b$ $\qquad\qquad$ **9.** $-7(m+n)$
$\quad\ -4xyz$ $\qquad\qquad\quad\ -2z^b$ $\qquad\qquad\qquad\ -9(m+n)$
$\quad\ \underline{-7xyz}$ $\qquad\qquad\quad\ \underline{-3z^b}$ $\qquad\qquad\qquad\ \underline{+8(m+n)}$

In 10–15, combine like terms.

10. $(+9y)+(-3y)$ $\qquad\qquad$ **11.** $(-4x^2)+(-8x^2)$
12. $8r+5r$ $\qquad\qquad\qquad\qquad$ **13.** $10t+(-8t)$
14. $6b^2+(-4b^2)+(-2b^2)$ $\qquad$ **15.** $(9d)+(-d)$

15. Adding Polynomials

A *polynomial in x* is an expression that can be formed from the variable x and numerical coefficients using only the operations of addition, subtraction, and multiplication. All exponents of the variable must be positive integers. The variable is never in the denominator of a fraction. For example, $5x^2-2x+7$ is a polynomial in x; however, $\dfrac{8}{x}+7$ is not a polynomial because the variable x is in the denominator of a fraction.

The degree of a polynomial in one variable is the same as the greatest exponent that appears in it. For example, $3x^2+7x+4$ is a polynomial of degree 2; $9x-24$ is a polynomial of degree 1.

The polynomials $3x^2 + 7x + 4$ and $9x - 24$, or $9x + (-24)$, are written in **standard form**. The standard form of a polynomial of the second degree in x, such as $3x^2 + 7x + 4$, is $ax^2 + bx + c$, $a \neq 0$. The standard form of a polynomial of the first degree in x, such as $9x - 24$, is $ax + b$, $a \neq 0$. Note that when a polynomial in one variable is written in standard form, the term having the greatest exponent of the variable is written first and the remaining terms are written in descending powers of the variable.

The polynomial $x^2 + 2xy + 3y^2$ is a polynomial of the second degree in two variables. As it is written, $x^2 + 2xy + 3y^2$ is arranged in descending powers of x and in ascending powers of y.

A polynomial is in **simple form** if there are no like terms in it. A polynomial such as $5x^2 + 3x - x^2 - 2x + 10$ can be put in simple form by **combining like terms** or **collecting like terms.** The resulting polynomial, $4x^2 + x + 10$, is in simple form.

To add two polynomials, we use the commutative, associative, and distributive properties of real numbers to combine like terms. For example, let us add $3x + 2$ and $5x + 4$:

Statements	*Reasons*
1. $(3x + 2) + (5x + 4)$ $= (3x + 5x) + (2 + 4)$	1. Rearranging terms by means of the commutative and associative properties.
2. $= (3 + 5)x + (2 + 4)$	2. Distributive property.
3. $= 8x + 6$	3. Substitution.

This example illustrates the following:

Procedure. To add polynomials, combine like terms. For convenience, arrange the polynomials in descending or ascending powers of a particular variable so that like terms are arranged in vertical columns. Then, add each column separately.

Addition may be checked by adding again in the opposite direction.

~~~~~~~~~~ *MODEL PROBLEMS* ~~~~~~~~~~

1. Add: $(5x^2 - 6x + 3) + (4x^2 + 5x - 4) + (-3x^2 - x + 8)$

Solution: $\begin{aligned} 5x^2 - 6x + 3 \\ 4x^2 + 5x - 4 \\ \underline{-3x^2 - x + 8} \end{aligned}$

Answer: $6x^2 - 2x + 7$ *Check* by adding in the opposite direction.

2. Simplify: $7b + [6b + (8 - 4b)]$

Solution: When one grouping symbol appears within another grouping symbol, first perform the operation involving the expression within the innermost grouping symbol.

$$7b + [6b + (8 - 4b)] = 7b + (6b + 8 - 4b)$$
$$= 7b + (2b + 8)$$
$$= 9b + 8 \quad Ans.$$

Exercises

In 1–4, simplify the polynomials.
1. $8x + 7y + 6x + y$ **2.** $x^2 - 5x + 3 - 2x^2 + 3x - 3$
3. $c^2 - 3cd + 8d^2 - 4c + 8cd - 8d^2$ **4.** $\frac{1}{4}y^2 + \frac{2}{3}y - 5 - \frac{5}{6}y + 1\frac{1}{2}y^2 - 4\frac{1}{2}$

In 5–7, add the polynomials.

5.
$$5a + 6b - 7$$
$$3a - 4b + 2$$
$$-4a + 3b - 4$$

6.
$$y^2 - 4y - 5$$
$$3y^2 - 6y + 4$$
$$-8y^2 + 10y - 7$$

7.
$$4r^2 - 6rs + 2s^2$$
$$-8r^2 \quad\quad + 7s^2$$
$$-2r^2 + 6rs$$

8. Combine: $8y^2 + 6y - 3, -4y^2 - 7y - 2, -9y^2 + y + 7$

In 9–14, simplify the expression.
9. $9b + (3b - 5)$ **10.** $(-4m^2 + 7) + (8m^2)$
11. $(-7a + 4) + (4a - 8)$ **12.** $(y^2 + y - 7) + (-2x^2 - 7x + 2)$
13. $(x^2 + 8x - 3) + (-4x^2 + 5)$ **14.** $9 + [3 + (7 + y)]$

15. Find the sum of $6p - 3q + z, -3p - z + 9q,$ and $-p + q$.
16. A boy's savings for four weeks are represented by $3x + 4y, 9y - 2x, 5x - 3y,$ and $7x - y$. Represent his total savings.

16. Subtracting Monomials or Like Terms

We can subtract monomials in the same way that we subtracted real numbers:

$$(+9) - (-2) = (+9) + (+2) = +11$$
$$(9x) - (-2x) = (+9x) + (+2x) = +11x$$
$$(17y) - (-5x) = (17y) + (+5x) = 17y + 5x$$

Procedure. To subtract one monomial from another like monomial, add the opposite (additive inverse) of the subtrahend to the minuend.

~~~~~~~~~~~~~~~ *MODEL PROBLEMS* ~~~~~~~~~~~~~~~

In 1–5, subtract the lower number from the upper number.

1. $+7a$
$\underline{+4a}$
$+3a$

2. $+4x^2$
$\underline{+9x^2}$
$-5x^2$

3. $-4y^2z$
$\underline{+y^2z}$
$-5y^2z$

4. $-5abc$
$\underline{-5abc}$
0

5. $-6(a+b)$
$\underline{-4(a+b)}$
$-2(a+b)$

~~~~~~

Exercises

In 1–12, subtract the lower number from the upper number.

1. $+10b$
$\underline{+7b}$

2. $+7xy$
$\underline{+xy}$

3. $+5x^2y^2$
$\underline{+3x^2y^2}$

4. $+7(m+n)$
$\underline{+5(m+n)}$

5. $-8b$
$\underline{-3b}$

6. $-6rs$
$\underline{-9rs}$

7. $-6a^2b^2$
$\underline{-8a^2b^2}$

8. $-7(x-y)$
$\underline{-4(x-y)}$

9. $-8m$
$\underline{+2m}$

10. $-8cd$
$\underline{+3cd}$

11. $-7cd^2$
$\underline{+7cd^2}$

12. $+4(a+b)$
$\underline{+7(a+b)}$

In 13–18, perform the indicated subtraction.

13. $(+12x^2)-(-4x^2)$ **14.** $(-9y^2)-(-9y^2)$ **15.** $(+7ab)-(+2ab)$

16. $(-5xy)-(-12xy)$ **17.** $(-6xy^2)-(2xy^2)$ **18.** $(+8a^2b^2)-(+8a^2b^2)$

19. Subtract $-3x$ from $-9x$.

20. From the sum of $+6w^2$ and $-8w^2$, subtract the sum of $-5w^2$ and $-w^2$.

17. Subtracting Polynomials

Procedure. To subtract one polynomial from another, add the opposite (additive inverse) of the subtrahend to the minuend.

The opposite of a given polynomial is formed by writing another polynomial whose terms are the opposites of the terms of the given polynomial. For example, the opposite of $3x^2+8x-4$ is $-3x^2-8x+4$. Thus:

$$(8x^2-6x-9)-(3x^2+8x-4)=(8x^2-6x-9)+(-3x^2-8x+4)$$
$$=5x^2-14x-5$$

For convenience, as shown at the right, we can arrange the polynomials vertically so that like terms are in the same vertical column. Then we mentally add the opposite of each term of the subtrahend to the corresponding term of the minuend.

Subtract:
$8x^2-\ 6x-9$
$\underline{3x^2+\ 8x-4}$
$5x^2-14x-5$

~~~~~~~~~~~~~~~~ *MODEL PROBLEMS* ~~~~~~~~~~~~~~~~

In 1 and 2, subtract the lower polynomial from the upper polynomial.

1. $7y^2 - 5y$
　　$\underline{-2y^2\qquad + 8}$
　　$9y^2 - 5y - 8$

2. $-4a^2 + 3ab + \ 8b^2$
　　$\underline{\ 3a^2 + 9ab - \ 4b^2}$
　　$-7a^2 - 6ab + 12b^2$

~~~~~~

Exercises

In 1–4, write the opposite (additive inverse) of the expression.

1. $7x - 4$ **2.** $-3ab - xy$ **3.** $-a^2 + a - 5$ **4.** $x^2 - 3xy + 2y^2$

In 5–14, subtract the lower polynomial from the upper polynomial.

5. $12a + 10b$
　$\underline{\ 5a + \ 6b}$

6. $4x + 2y$
　$\underline{3x - \ y}$

7. $8x - 3y$
　$\underline{-4x + 8y}$

8. $4c - 7d$
　$\underline{5c - 7d}$

9. $x^2 - 7x + 3$
　$\underline{4x^2 - 2x - 4}$

10. $3y^2 - 2y - 1$
　$\underline{-5y^2 - 2y + 6}$

11. $-6ab + 2cd$
　$\underline{\ 3ab - 4cd}$

12. $-6x^2 + 3y^2$
　$\underline{\ \ x^2 - 3y^2}$

13. $3x^2 - 5xy - y^2$
　$\underline{-5x^2 + 3xy - y^2}$

14. $-5x^2\qquad\ \ - 9y^2$
　$\underline{-3x^2 + 4xy + 6y^2}$

In 15–22, simplify the expression.

15. $7y - (2y - 3)$

16. $8r - (-4s - 8r)$

17. $-4d - (3c - 4d)$

18. $(3x - 7) - (8 - 9x)$

19. $(2x + 3y) - (-7x - 4y)$

20. $(5x^2 + 3x - 4) - (-2x^2 + 7x)$

21. $12a - [-5 + (6a - 9)]$

22. $3x^2 - [9x - (4x - x^2) + 8]$

23. Subtract $2x^2 + 3x - 6$ from $5x^2 - 10x - 4$.

24. From the sum of $6xy - 5yz$ and $-2xy - 3yz$, subtract $-4xy + 7yz$.

25. By how much does $a + d$ exceed $a - d$?

26. Subtract $3x^2 - y^2$ from the sum of $5xy - 2x^2 + y^2$ and $3y^2 - 4xy$.

18. Multiplying a Monomial by a Monomial

MULTIPLYING POWERS THAT HAVE THE SAME BASE

Since x^2 means $x \cdot x$ and x^4 means $x \cdot x \cdot x \cdot x$,

$$x^2 \cdot x^4 = \overbrace{x \cdot x}^{2} \cdot \overbrace{x \cdot x \cdot x \cdot x}^{4} = \overbrace{x \cdot x \cdot x \cdot x \cdot x \cdot x}^{6} = x^6$$

Observe that 6, the exponent in the product, is equal to $2 + 4$, the sum of the exponents in the factors.

In general, when x is a real number and a and b are positive integers,

$$x^a \cdot x^b = x^{a+b}$$

RULE FOR MULTIPLYING POWERS OF THE SAME BASE

When multiplying powers of the same base, find the exponent of the product by adding the exponents of the factors. The base of the power which is the product is the same as the base of the factors.

Observe that the rule for multiplying powers of the same base does not apply to $x^2 \cdot y^3$ because the powers x^2 and y^3 have different bases. The product $x^2 \cdot y^3$ represents $x \cdot x \cdot y \cdot y \cdot y$, an expression which does not have five identical factors.

To multiply a monomial by a monomial, rearrange and group the factors by making use of the commutative and associative properties of multiplication. For example,

$$(7x) \cdot (3y) = (7)(x)(3)(y) = (7 \cdot 3) \cdot (x \cdot y) = 21xy$$

$$(-2x^3)(+5x^5) = (-2)(x^3)(+5)(x^5) = [(-2) \cdot (+5)][(x^3) \cdot (x^5)] = -10x^8$$

Procedure. To multiply a monomial by a monomial:
1. Rearrange and group the factors mentally.
2. Multiply the coefficients.
3. Multiply the factors that are powers of the same base.
4. Multiply the products obtained in steps 2 and 3.

〰〰〰〰〰〰〰 *MODEL PROBLEMS* 〰〰〰〰〰〰〰

In 1–8, multiply.
1. $x^5 \cdot x^2 = x^7$ **2.** $c^3 \cdot c = c^4$ **3.** $a^b \cdot a^{2b} = a^{3b}$
4. $10^3 \cdot 10^2 = 10^5$ **5.** $r^{2x} \cdot r^3 = r^{2x+3}$ **6.** $3x^2 \cdot 4x^3 = 12x^5$
7. $(+2a^3b^2)(-3ab^4c^2) = -6a^4b^6c^2$ **8.** $(-4a^{3m})(+2a^2) = -8a^{3m+2}$

〰〰〰〰〰〰〰〰〰〰〰〰〰〰〰〰〰〰〰〰〰〰〰

Exercises

In 1–26, simplify the indicated product.
1. $c^3 \cdot c^4$ **2.** $x \cdot x$ **3.** $x^3 \cdot x$ **4.** $2^5 \cdot 2^2$
5. $10^6 \cdot 10$ **6.** $c^r \cdot c^s$ **7.** $x^{2r} \cdot x^{3r}$ **8.** $m^{2y} \cdot m$
9. $s^{t-1} \cdot s^{t+1}$ **10.** $x^3 \cdot x^2 \cdot x^5$ **11.** $2^3 \cdot 2^2 \cdot 2^4$ **12.** $10^2 \cdot 10^2 \cdot 10$

13. $x^a \cdot x^{2a} \cdot x$ **14.** $6(-5x)$ **15.** $x^2(3x^3)$ **16.** $(2d^2)(4d^3)$
17. $(3x)(7x)$ **18.** $(-9y)(-2y)$ **19.** $(7e^2)(9e)$ **20.** $(-m)(+2m^3)$
21. $(3x)(4x^2)(5x)$ **22.** $(-2x)(-2x)(-2x)$ **23.** $(5x)(3y)$ **24.** $(-5m)(+3n)$
25. $(7r)(2st)$ **26.** $(-a^2)(+3a)(-5a^3)$

In 27–36, multiply.

27. $-3rs$ by $+2rs$ **28.** $-7ab^2$ by $+4a^2$ **29.** $2xy$ by $-4yz$
30. $9xz$ by $-3x^2yz$ **31.** $-2b$ by $+5a^2c^2$ **32.** $-6y^b$ by $-2y^{4b}$
33. $7a^x$ by $-4a^2$ **34.** $-3x^{2b+5}$ by $-2x^{b+1}$ **35.** $7y^{a+5}$ by $-4y^{3a}$
36. $-8b^{2d-1}$ by $+3b$

In 37–39, simplify the indicated power.

37. $(x^4)^3$ **38.** $(-3a^2)^3$ **39.** $[(x^2)^3]^4$

In 40–42, simplify the indicated product.

40. $3x(4x)^2$ **41.** $(-2x)^3(3x^2)^2$ **42.** $(x^n)^4(-5x^n)^3$

43. Select the correct answer:
   $x^m \cdot x^3$ equals   (1) x^{3m} (2) $2x^{3m}$ (3) x^{m+3} (4) $2x^{m+3}$
44. The product of 4^y and 4^y is   (1) 4^{y^2} (2) 4^{2y} (3) 16^{2y}

19. Multiplying a Polynomial by a Monomial

The distributive property of multiplication states:

$$a(b+c) = ab + ac$$

For example, $x(3x+7) = (x)(3x) + (x)(7) = 3x^2 + 7x$.
This property of multiplication justifies the following:

Procedure. To multiply a polynomial by a monomial, multiply each term of the polynomial by the monomial and add the resulting products.

~~~~~~~~~~ *MODEL PROBLEMS* ~~~~~~~~~~

In 1–4, multiply.
1. $8(2x-3) = 16x - 24$
2. $-3x(x^2 - 4x + 2) = -3x^3 + 12x^2 - 6x$
3. $-5c^2d^2(4cd^2 - 2c^3) = -20c^3d^4 + 10c^5d^2$
4. $5a^{2x}(2a^{3x} - a^x) = 10a^{5x} - 5a^{3x}$

Exercises

In 1–17, multiply.

1. $8(c + d)$ **2.** $-5(x - 3y)$ **3.** $10(2x - \frac{1}{2}y)$

4. $-\frac{1}{3}(6x - 3y + 12z)$ **5.** $8c(2c - 5)$ **6.** $-5d(d^2 - 3d)$

7. $xy(x - y)$ **8.** $2cd(c^2 + d^2)$ **9.** $-3xy(4x^2y^2 - 6xy)$

10. $3x^2 - 5x + 2$ by $3x$ **11.** $x^2 - 7x - 3$ by $-5x^2$

12. $9c^2 - 3cd + 2d^2$ by $3cd$ **13.** $c^2 + d^2$ by $-8cd$

14. $-2ab - 5ac + 3bc$ by $a^2b^2c^2$ **15.** $y^2 + y^3$ by $-y^{2c}$

16. $z^b - 7$ by z **17.** $y^{3b} + y^{2b} - y^b$ by $-5y^2$

18. Represent the area of a rectangle whose base is $\frac{2}{3}x$ and whose height is $(9x - 6)$.

19. A car travels $(3y + 10)$ miles per hour. Express the distance it travels in (*a*) 4   (*b*) 10   (*c*) y (*d*) h hours.

20. Multiplying a Polynomial by a Polynomial

We can find the product $(x + 5)(x + 2)$ as follows:

$$
\begin{aligned}
(x + 5)(x + 2) &= (x + 5)(x) + (x + 5)(2) && \text{Distributive property.} \\
&= x^2 + 5x + 2x + 10 && \text{Distributive property.} \\
&= x^2 + 7x + 10 && \text{Combining like terms.}
\end{aligned}
$$

In general, for all real numbers, a, b, c, and d,

$$
\begin{aligned}
(a + b)(c + d) &= (a + b)c + (a + b)d \\
&= ac + bc + ad + bd
\end{aligned}
$$

Notice that each term of the first polynomial is multiplied by each term of the second polynomial. In the model problems that follow, for convenience, we use a vertical arrangement for performing the multiplication.

Procedure. To multiply a polynomial by a polynomial:

1. **Arrange the multiplicand and the multiplier according to descending or ascending powers of a common variable.**

2. **Using the distributive property, multiply each term of the multiplicand by each term of the multiplier.**

3. **Add the like terms in the partial products.**

~~~~~~~~~~~~~ *MODEL PROBLEMS* ~~~~~~~~~~~~~

In 1 and 2, multiply.

1. $2x + 5$ multiplicand | **2.** $a^2 - 3ab + 2b^2$

$2x + 5$ multiplicand	**2.** $a^2 - 3ab + 2b^2$
$\underline{x - 3}$ multiplier	$\underline{a \quad - 2b}$
$\overline{2x^2 + 5x}$ partial product	$a^3 - 3a^2b + 2ab^2$
$\underline{\quad\quad - 6x - 15}$ partial product	$\underline{\quad - 2a^2b + 6ab^2 - 4b^3}$
$2x^2 - \; x - 15$ product	$a^3 - 5a^2b + 8ab^2 - 4b^3$

Exercises

In 1–12, multiply.

1. $x + 2$ by $x + 3$ **2.** $5r - 1$ by $6r + 7$ **3.** $(6 - c)(5 + c)$

4. $(4x + 3)(4x - 3)$ **5.** $(a + 2b)(a + 3b)$ **6.** $(r^2 + 5)(r^2 - 2)$

7. $(x^2 + y^2)(x^2 - y^2)$ **8.** $y^2 - 3y + 4$ by $2y - 3$

9. $2x^3 - 3x + 4$ by $2x + 1$ **10.** $m^a - 2$ by $m^a + 2$

11. $x^a + y^b$ by $x^a - y^b$ **12.** $2x^a + 1$ by $3x^a - 5$

In 13–16, perform the indicated operation and simplify the result.

13. $(3x + 4)^2$ **14.** $7a(3a + 2)^2$

15. $(x^a + y^b)^2$ **16.** $(x - y)^3$

In 17 and 18, simplify the expression.

17. $(x + 5)(x - 1) - x^2$ **18.** $(x + 3)^2 - (x - 4)^2$

19. A boy worked $(3x - 2)$ hours and earned $(4x + 1)$ dollars per hour. Represent as a polynomial the total amount he earned.

21. Using Multiplication To Simplify Algebraic Expressions Containing Symbols of Grouping

USING THE DISTRIBUTIVE PROPERTY OF MULTIPLICATION

To simplify the expression $5x + 3(2x + 7)$, (that is, to transform it to an equivalent expression that does not contain parentheses), we use the distributive property of multiplication and then combine like terms:

$$5x + 3(2x + 7) = 5x + 3(2x) + 3(7)$$
$$= 5x + 6x + 21 = 11x + 21$$

USING THE MULTIPLICATION PROPERTIES OF 1 AND (-1)

Since the multiplication property of 1 states that $1 \cdot x = x$, then $1 \cdot (3x - 7) = 3x - 7$. Hence, we can simplify $4 + (3x - 7)$ as follows:

$$4 + (3x - 7) = 4 + 1 \cdot (3x - 7) = 4 + 3x - 7 = 3x - 3$$

Since the multiplication property of (-1) states that $-x = (-1) \cdot x$, then $-(5 - 3x) = -1(5 - 3x) = -5 + 3x$. Hence, we can simplify $9x - (5 - 3x)$ as follows:

$$9x - (5 - 3x) = 9x - 1 \cdot (5 - 3x) = 9x - 5 + 3x = 12x - 5$$

~~~~~~~~~~ *MODEL PROBLEMS* ~~~~~~~~~~

In 1–4, find a polynomial in simple form that is equivalent to the given expression. [In 1 and 2, use multiplication properties of 1 and (-1).]

1. $5c + (2 - 7c)$
$= 5c + 1 \cdot (2 - 7c)$
$= 5c + 2 - 7c$
$= -2c + 2$ *Ans.*

2. $10d - (d - 2)$
$= 10d - 1 \cdot (d - 2)$
$= 10d - d + 2$
$= 9d + 2$ *Ans.*

3. $x^2 - (x - 3)(x - 2)$
$= x^2 - 1 \cdot (x - 3)(x - 2)$
$= x^2 - 1(x^2 - 5x + 6)$
$= x^2 - x^2 + 5x - 6$
$= 5x - 6$ *Ans.*

4. $x[x^2 - 4(x - 1)]$
$= x[x^2 - 4x + 4]$
$= x^3 - 4x^2 + 4x$ *Ans.*

~~~~~~~~~~

Exercises

In 1–15, find a polynomial in simple form that does not contain symbols of grouping and that is equivalent to the given expression. [In 1–5, use multiplication properties of 1 and (-1).]

1. $9 + (4x - 3)$ **2.** $-5x + (6 - 9x)$ **3.** $2x^2 + (5 - 3x - 2x^2)$
4. $15 - (10 + 3c)$ **5.** $6x^2 - (4x^2 - 7x - 5)$ **6.** $3y + 4(-8y + 7)$
7. $2x(2x - 1) + 6x$ **8.** $9m - 3(4 + m)$ **9.** $5a^2 - 3a(2a - 1)$
10. $3(a + 9) + 2(a - 6)$ **11.** $\frac{1}{2}(4x + 3y) - 2(6x - 4y)$
12. $m^2 - (m - 6)(m - 2)$ **13.** $5[20 + 3(n - 1)]$
14. $5\{2x - [4 - 5(2 - x)]\}$ **15.** $10y - 2\{4 - 3[y - 5(2 - 3y)]\}$

22. **Dividing a Monomial by a Monomial**

DIVIDING POWERS THAT HAVE THE SAME BASE

Since $x^2 \cdot x^3 = x^5$, then $x^5 \div x^3 = x^2$.

Since $x^3 \cdot x = x^4$, then $x^4 \div x = x^3$. (Remember that $x = x^1$.)

Observe that the exponent in each quotient is the difference between the exponent in the dividend and the exponent in the divisor.

In general, when x is a nonzero real number and a and b are positive integers with $a > b$,

$$x^a \div x^b = x^{a-b}$$

RULES FOR DIVIDING POWERS OF THE SAME BASE

Rule 1. In dividing powers of the same nonzero real base, find the exponent of the quotient by subtracting the exponent of the divisor from the exponent of the dividend. The base of the power which is the quotient is the same as the base of the dividend and the base of the divisor.

Since $(-7x^4)(+3x^3) = -21x^7$, then $(-21x^7) \div (+3x^3) = -7x^4$. Observe that -21 divided by $+3$ equals -7, and that x^7 divided by $x^3 = x^4$.

Rule 2. The quotient of any positive integral power of a nonzero real number divided by itself is 1.

Since $1 \cdot x = x$, then $x \div x = 1$. Also, since $1 \cdot x^3 = x^3$, then $x^3 \div x^3 = 1$.

In general, when x is a nonzero real number and a is a positive integer,

$$x^a \div x^a = 1$$

Procedure. To divide a monomial by a monomial:

1. **Divide their numerical coefficients.**
2. **Divide the factors that are powers of the same base.**
3. **Multiply the quotients previously obtained.**

~~~~~~~~~~ *MODEL PROBLEMS* ~~~~~~~~~~

In 1–9, perform the indicated division.

1. $y^8 \div y^2 = y^6$

2. $b^4 \div b = b^3$

3. $x^2 \div x^2 = 1$

4. $10^5 \div 10^3 = 10^2$

5. $x^{5a} \div x^{2a} = x^{3a}$

6. $(+8y^9) \div (+2y^2) = +4y^7$

7. $(+15x^5y^4) \div (-5x^3y^2) = -3x^2y^2$

8. $(-18x^3y^2z^2) \div (-3x^2y^2) = +6xz^2$

9. $(-24a^{3b}) \div (+6a^3) = -4a^{3b-3}$

Exercises

In 1–26, divide.

1. a^7 by a^3 **2.** b^6 by b^5 **3.** c^4 by c **4.** x^5 by x^5
5. $(-r)^8$ by $(-r)^2$ **6.** 10^5 by 10^2 **7.** 10^4 by 10^3 **8.** 4^3 by 4
9. 2^6 by 2^6 **10.** a^{5b} by a^{3b} **11.** x^{3y} by x^{2y}
12. x^{3a} by x **13.** y^3 by y^a **14.** $18c^6$ by $-9c^5$
15. $-30x^3$ by $-3x$ **16.** $-5y^4$ by $-5y^4$ **17.** $36x^3y^2$ by $6xy$
18. $+56x^3y^4b$ by $-7x^3y^2$ **19.** $13a^4b^4c$ by $13ab^3$ **20.** $-28xyz$ by $-28xyz$
21. $27r^2s^2t$ by $9r^2s^2t$ **22.** $-16y^{4b}$ by $-8y^b$ **23.** $-20a^{3c}$ by $5a^3$
24. $-10b^{c+1}$ by $5b$ **25.** $5x^{3a}$ by $-x^a$ **26.** $-9x^cy^{3c}$ by xy

27. The result of dividing x^{2m} by x is   (1) x^m (2) 1^{2m} (3) x^{2m-1}
28. Divide a^{3m} by a^m.
29. Divide a^{6m} by a^{2m}.
30. $4^{2x} \div 4^x$ is (1) 1^x (2) 4^2 (3) 4^x
31. How many times $-5x^2y^3$ is $+20x^6y^9$?
32. If 10 suits cost $60y$ dollars, represent the cost of one suit.
33. If the area of a rectangle is represented by $64x^6$ and the length is represented by $16x^2$, represent the width of the rectangle.

23. Dividing a Polynomial by a Monomial

Since division is distributive over addition and subtraction,

$$(8x + 6y) \div 2 = \frac{8x}{2} + \frac{6y}{2} = 4x + 3y$$

Observe that the quotient $(4x + 3y)$ is obtained by dividing each term of $(8x + 6y)$ by 2.

In general, for all real numbers a, x, and y $(a \neq 0)$,

$$\frac{ax + ay}{a} = \frac{ax}{a} + \frac{ay}{a} = x + y \quad \text{and} \quad \frac{ax - ay}{a} = \frac{ax}{a} - \frac{ay}{a} = x - y$$

The middle steps $\dfrac{ax}{a} + \dfrac{ay}{a}$ and $\dfrac{ax}{a} - \dfrac{ay}{a}$ may be done mentally.

Procedure. To divide a polynomial by a monomial:
1. Divide each term of the polynomial by the monomial.
2. Combine the resulting quotients.

~~~~~~~~~~~~~~ *MODEL PROBLEMS* ~~~~~~~~~~~~~~

In 1 and 2, perform the indicated division.

1. $(10x^5 - 25x^4 + 5x^3) \div (-5x^3) = -2x^2 + 5x - 1$

2. $(24x^3y^2 - 36xy^2z) \div (6xy^2) = 4x^2 - 6z$

~~~~~~

Exercises

In 1–12, divide.

1. $12r + 27s$ by 3 **2.** $18x^2 - 24y^2$ by -6 **3.** $c^2 + c$ by c

4. $16x^2 - 8x$ by $-4x$ **5.** $6r^4 + 12r^3$ by $3r^2$ **6.** $24c^3 - 2c^2$ by $-2c^2$

7. $16a^4 - 8a^3 - 24a^2$ by $-4a^2$ **8.** $6a^2b - 12ab^2$ by $2ab$

9. $a^{3x} - a^{2x}$ by a^x **10.** $-9x^{2a+4} - 3x^{3a+5}$ by $-3x^{2a+1}$

11. $9x^{2a+2} - 4x^2$ by x^2 **12.** $-8b^{2c+2} + 4b^{2c+1}$ by $-b$

In 13–18, perform the indicated division.

13. $\dfrac{8x^2 - 10x}{2x}$ **14.** $\dfrac{ab^2 - 2a^2b}{ab}$ **15.** $\dfrac{8x^2 - 16x - 4}{4}$

16. $\dfrac{x^{2a} - 3x^a}{x^a}$ **17.** $\dfrac{30(a+b)^2 - 50(a+b)}{2(a+b)}$ **18.** $\dfrac{d^3(c-d) - d^2(c-d)}{d^2(c-d)}$

19. If $20x^2 + 10x$ represents the distance traveled by a man in $10x$ hours, represent the number of miles he travels in 1 hour.

24. Dividing a Polynomial by a Polynomial

The algebraic process of dividing a polynomial by a polynomial is very much like the arithmetic process used in the division of 1087 by 25, shown at the right. Understanding the steps used in this arithmetic process will help you understand the following steps used to divide a polynomial by a polynomial.

$$43\frac{12}{25}$$
$$25\overline{\smash{)}1087}$$
$$\underline{100}$$
$$87$$
$$\underline{75}$$
$$12$$

Procedure. To divide a polynomial by a polynomial:

1. **Arrange the terms of both the divisor and the dividend according to descending or ascending powers of one variable.**
2. **Divide the first term of the dividend by the first term of the divisor to obtain the first term of the quotient.**
3. **Multiply the complete divisor by the first term of the quotient.**
4. **Subtract this product from the dividend.**
5. **Use the remainder as the new dividend.**

6. Repeat steps 2 to 5 until the remainder is 0 or until the degree of the remainder is less than the degree of the divisor.

7. If the remainder is not 0, write the division as:

$$\frac{\text{dividend}}{\text{divisor}} = \text{quotient} + \frac{\text{remainder}}{\text{divisor}}$$

8. To check, use the principle:
divisor × quotient + remainder = dividend

~~~~~~~~~~~ *MODEL PROBLEM* ~~~~~~~~~~~

Divide $t^2 + 4t - 45$ by $t + 9$. Check the answer.

Solution:

$$\begin{array}{r} t - 5 \\ t + 9 \overline{\smash{\big)}\ t^2 + 4t - 45} \\ \underline{t^2 + 9t} \\ -5t - 45 \\ \underline{-5t - 45} \end{array}$$

Divide t into t^2 to get t.
Multiply $t + 9$ by t.
Subtract.
Divide t into $-5t$ to get -5;
multiply $t + 9$ by -5.
Subtract.

Check:

$$\begin{array}{r} t + 9 \\ t - 5 \\ \hline t^2 + 9t \\ -5t - 4\! \\ \hline t^2 + 4t - 4\! \end{array}$$

Answer: Quotient is $t - 5$.

~~~~~~

Exercises

In 1–13, divide. (Check each answer.)

1. $x^2 + 8x + 12$ by $x + 2$
2. $66 + 17x + x^2$ by $6 + x$
3. $6x^2 - 13x + 6$ by $3x - 2$
4. $2a^2 - ab - 6b^2$ by $a - 2b$
5. $4a^2 - 6 + 5a$ by $4a - 3$
6. $10y^{2c} + y^c - 3$ by $5y^c + 3$
7. $3x^3 - 19x^2 + 27x + 4$ by $x - 4$
8. $6a^3 + 27a - 19a^2 - 15$ by $3a - 5$
9. $4x^3 + 7x + 5$ by $2x + 1$
10. $x^3 + 1$ by $x + 1$
11. $y^3 + 27$ by $y + 3$
12. $a^3 - 64$ by $a - 4$
13. $8b^3 - 1$ by $2b - 1$

14. Find the dividend when the quotient is $x - 3$, the remainder is -5, and the divisor is $3x - 1$.

CHAPTER III

FACTORING AND OPERATIONS ON RATIONAL EXPRESSIONS

1. Factoring Polynomials Whose Terms Have a Common Factor

Because $4 \times 7 = 28$, the integer 28 is a multiple of two integral factors, 4 and 7; also $28 \div 7 = 4$, and $28 \div 4 = 7$. This example illustrates that over the set of integers:

1. A factor of an integer is an exact divisor of the integer.
2. When the product of two integers is divided by one of its factors, the quotient is the other factor.

Factoring a number is the process of finding those numbers whose product is the given number. When we factor an integer, we deal with integral factors only. For example, although $\frac{1}{2} \times 24 = 12$, we do not say that $\frac{1}{2}$ and 24 are the factors of 12.

Because $(2x + 1)(3x - 7) = 6x^2 - 11x - 7$, we say that $(2x + 1)$ and $(3x - 7)$ are factors of the polynomial $6x^2 - 11x - 7$.

Factoring a polynomial over a specified set of numbers means to express it as a product of polynomials whose coefficients are members of that set of numbers. In future problems, if no set of numbers is specified, it is to be understood the factoring of a polynomial will be with respect to the set of integers. Exceptions will be made where there are simple nonintegral coefficients, such as in the factoring of $\frac{1}{2}x + \frac{1}{2}y$, $\sqrt{2}x - \sqrt{2}y$, and $\pi x^2 + \pi y^2$.

For polynomials, it is also true that:

1. A factor of a polynomial is an exact divisor of the polynomial.
2. When the product of two polynomials is divided by one of its factors, the quotient is the other factor.

For example, since 5 and $x^2 + 7$ are the factors of $5x^2 + 35$, then:
1. 5 and $x^2 + 7$ are exact divisors of $5x^2 + 35$.
2. When $5x^2 + 35$ is divided by 5, the quotient is $x^2 + 7$; when $5x^2 + 35$ is divided by $x^2 + 7$, the quotient is 5.

A positive integer is called a **_prime number_** if it is greater than 1 and it has no factors other than itself and 1. For example, 2, 3, 5, 7, and 11 are the first five prime numbers.

A **_prime polynomial_** is a polynomial other than 1 that has no factors except itself and 1 with respect to a specified set of numbers. For example, $2x + 3$ is a prime polynomial with respect to the set of integers.

Using the distributive property, $10x^2(x + 3) = 10x^3 + 30x^2$. Hence, $10x^3 + 30x^2 = 10x^2(x + 3)$. The monomial $10x^2$ is the product of 10, which is the greatest common factor of the coefficients of the polynomial $10x^3 + 30x^2$, and x^2, which is the variable factor of highest degree that is a common factor of all terms of this polynomial. Therefore, we call $10x^2$ the highest common monomial factor, or H.C.F., of the polynomial $10x^3 + 30x^2$.

The **_highest common monomial factor of a polynomial, or H.C.F.,_** is the product of the greatest common factor of its coefficients and the highest power of each variable that is a common factor of each of its terms.

For example, to factor $12x^2y^2 + 18xy^3$, first we obtain the H.C.F., which is $6xy^2$. Then, we divide $12x^2y^2 + 18xy^3$ by $6xy^2$ and obtain the quotient, $2x + 3y$, which is the other factor of $12x^2y^2 + 18xy^3$. Therefore, we see that by factoring, $12x^2y^2 + 18xy^3 = 6xy^2(2x + 3y)$.

Procedure. To factor a polynomial whose terms have a common monomial factor:
1. **Find the highest monomial that is a factor of each term of the polynomial.**
2. **Divide the polynomial by the monomial factor. The quotient is the other factor.**
3. **Express the polynomial as the indicated product of the two factors.**
4. **Check by multiplying the factors to obtain the polynomial.**

~~~~~~~~~~ *MODEL PROBLEMS* ~~~~~~~~~~

In 1–5, factor.

1. $3x - 3y$ *Ans.* $3x - 3y = 3(x - y)$

2. $\frac{1}{2}na + \frac{1}{2}nl$ *Ans.* $\frac{1}{2}na + \frac{1}{2}nl = \frac{1}{2}n(a + l)$

3. $35a^2 - 7a$ *Ans.* $35a^2 - 7a = 7a(5a - 1)$

4. $25a^2b - 35ab^2$ *Ans.* $25a^2b - 35ab^2 = 5ab(5a - 7b)$

5. $x^{n+2} - 5x^n$ *Ans.* $x^{n+2} - 5x^n = x^n(x^2 - 5)$

Note. In problem 2, we are factoring over the set of rational numbers. The given polynomial is prime over the set of integers.

~~~~~~

Exercises

In 1–36, factor the polynomial.

1. $6a + 6b$

2. $7l - 7n$

3. $xc - xd$

4. $5x^2 + 5y^2$

5. $bc^2 - 2b$

6. $16a + 4b$

7. $25x^2 - 15y^2$

8. $16x + x^2$

9. $5y - 15y^3$

10. $5y^4 + 5y^2$

11. $ax + ax^3$

12. $3ab^2 - 6a^2b$

13. $21c^3d^2 - 7c^2d$

14. $12x^2y^3 - 18xy^4$

15. $40xy^2 - 32x^2y$

16. $2x^2 + 8x + 4$

17. $ay - 4aw - 12a$

18. $c^3 - c^2 + 2c$

19. $ax^3 - a^2x^2 + ax$

20. $p + prt$

21. $\pi r^2 + \pi R^2$

22. $\frac{1}{2}hb + \frac{1}{2}hc$

23. $\pi r^2 + 2\pi rh$

24. $y^{n+2} + y^2$

25. $x^{a+1} - x$

26. $x^{2a+1} - x^{2a}$

27. $z^{1+2b} + z$

28. $x^{r+5} + x^3$

29. $cdy^r - dy^r$

30. $x^{2a+2} + x^{2a+1} + x^{2a}$

31. $a^{2b+1} + 4a^{b+1} + a$

32. $x(a+b) + y(a+b)$

33. $x(2b+1) + y(2b+1)$

34. $ax + ay + bx + by$

35. $xv - xw + yv - yw$

36. $mr + nr - ms - ns$

37. Write the polynomials whose factors are:
   a. 5 and $(v + 2w)$ *b.* $4xy^2$ and $(5x - 3y^2)$ *c.* $3x$ and $(6x^2 - 5)$

38. Use factoring to find mentally the value of:
   a. $59 \times 37 + 41 \times 37$ *b.* $64 \times 81 + 64 \times 19$

2. Multiplying the Sum and Difference of Two Terms

In the examples at the right, we have found the binomial which is the product of the sum of two terms and the difference of the same two terms. The procedure that follows will enable us to find such products mentally.

$$
\begin{array}{ll}
a + b & 3x^2 + 5y \\
\underline{a - b} & \underline{3x^2 - 5y} \\
a^2 + ab & 9x^4 + 15x^2y \\
\underline{\quad - ab - b^2} & \underline{\quad - 15x^2y - 25y^2} \\
a^2 \quad\quad - b^2 & 9x^4 \quad\quad\quad - 25y^2
\end{array}
$$

Procedure. To multiply the sum of two terms by the difference of the same two terms:

1. Square the first term.

2. From this result, subtract the square of the second term.

┌─ *KEEP IN MIND* ─┐
$$(a+b)(a-b) = a^2 - b^2$$
└──────────────────┘

〜〜〜〜 *MODEL PROBLEMS* 〜〜〜〜

In 1–3, find the product mentally.

	Problem	*Think*	*Write*
1.	$(x+9)(x-9)$	$=(x)^2-(9)^2$	$=x^2-81$ *Ans.*
2.	$(2x+7y)(2x-7y)$	$=(2x)^2-(7y)^2$	$=4x^2-49y^2$ *Ans.*
3.	$(a^3-5b^2)(a^3+5b^2)$	$=(a^3)^2-(5b^2)^2$	$=a^6-25b^4$ *Ans.*

Exercises

In 1–16, find the product mentally.

1. $(x+4)(x-4)$ **2.** $(n-9)(n+9)$ **3.** $(6+b)(6-b)$

4. $(x-y)(y+x)$ **5.** $(3x+2)(3x-2)$ **6.** $(8-3x)(8+3x)$

7. $(3m+7n)(3m-7n)$ **8.** $(2-5y^2)(5y^2+2)$ **9.** $(b+\frac{1}{3})(b-\frac{1}{3})$

10. $(.7+d)(.7-d)$ **11.** $(rs+6)(rs-6)$ **12.** $(x^2-8)(x^2+8)$

13. $(2ab+3)(2ab-3)$ **14.** $(m+3)(m-3)(m^2+9)$

15. $(a^x+2)(a^x-2)$ **16.** $(2c^{3x}-3d^y)(2c^{3x}+3d^y)$

In 17–20, first express the factors as the sum and difference of the same two numbers. Then multiply mentally.

17. 23×17 **18.** 49×51

19. 36×44 **20.** 88×92

3. Factoring the Difference of Two Squares

An expression of the form a^2-b^2 is called a *difference of two squares.* Since the product of $(a+b)$ and $(a-b)$ is a^2-b^2, the factors of a^2-b^2 are $(a+b)$ and $(a-b)$. Therefore, $a^2-b^2=(a+b)(a-b)$.

~~~~~~~~~~~~~~ *MODEL PROBLEMS* ~~~~~~~~~~~~~~

1. Factor: $x^2 - 100$

How To Proceed	*Solution*
1. Express each term as the square of a monomial.	$x^2 - 100 = (x)^2 - (10)^2$
2. Apply the rule: $a^2 - b^2 = (a + b)(a - b)$	$x^2 - 100 = (x + 10)(x - 10)$ *Ans.*

In 2 and 3, factor the polynomial in the set of rational numbers.

2. Factor: $25a^2 - \frac{1}{9}b^2c^2$

Solution: $25a^2 - \frac{1}{9}b^2c^2 = (5a)^2 - (\frac{1}{3}bc)^2$
$25a^2 - \frac{1}{9}b^2c^2 = (5a + \frac{1}{3}bc)(5a - \frac{1}{3}bc)$ *Ans.*

3. Factor: $x^2 - .64y^2$

Solution: $x^2 - .64y^2 = (x)^2 - (.8y)^2$
$x^2 - .64y^2 = (x + .8y)(x - .8y)$ *Ans.*

Note. The polynomials in problems 2 and 3 are not factorable in the set of integers. They are factorable in the set of rational numbers.

In 4 and 5, factor the polynomial mentally.

Problem	*Think*	*Write*
4. $a^6 - b^4$	$= (a^3)^2 - (b^2)^2$	$= (a^3 + b^2)(a^3 - b^2)$ *Ans.*
5. $x^{2a} - y^{2b}$	$= (x^a)^2 - (y^b)^2$	$= (x^a + y^b)(x^a - y^b)$ *Ans.*

~~~~~~

Exercises

In 1–21, factor the polynomial.

1. $y^2 - 64$ **2.** $x^2 - 81$ **3.** $144 - a^2$ **4.** $4x^2 - 25y^2$

5. $49a^2 - 64b^2$ **6.** $10^2 - 81d^2$ **7.** $r^2s^2 - 144$ **8.** $a^2 - .49$

9. $36 - .49d^2$ **10.** $25x^2 - \frac{1}{9}$ **11.** $\frac{1}{4}r^2 - \frac{25}{9}s^2$ **12.** $x^2y^2 - 121a^2b^2$

13. $a^4 - c^2$ **14.** $4x^6 - 9y^4$ **15.** $x^{2c} - y^{2d}$

16. $a^{2m} - b^{4n}$ **17.** $x^{2a} - 1$ **18.** $9 - a^{2c}$

19. $\frac{1}{4}y^{2d} - .81$ **20.** $9x^{4a} - 16y^{2b}$ **21.** $(x + y)^2 - z^2$

22. Write the polynomial whose factors are:

a. $(7x + 3y)$ and $(7x - 3y)$ *b.* $(x^m + 1)$ and $(x^m - 1)$

4. Finding the Product of Two Binomials

Let us learn how to find, mentally, the product of two binomials of the form $ax + b$ and $cx + d$.

Study the multiplication of the two binomials at the right.

Note:

1. $8x^2$, the first term in the product, is equal to the product of $2x$ and $4x$, the first terms of the binomials.
2. -15, the last term in the product, is equal to the product of $+3$ and -5, the last terms of the binomials.
3. $+2x$, the middle term, is obtained by adding the cross-products, that is, by multiplying the first term of each binomial by the second term of the other and adding these products, $(+12x) + (-10x) = +2x$.

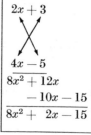

$$2x + 3$$
$$4x - 5$$
$$8x^2 + 12x$$
$$- 10x - 15$$
$$\overline{8x^2 + 2x - 15}$$

~~~~~~~~~~~ **MODEL PROBLEM** ~~~~~~~~~~~

Multiply: $(3x - 4)(5x + 9)$

How To Proceed	*Solution*
1. Multiply the first terms.	$(3x)(5x) = 15x^2$
2. Add the cross-products.	$(-20x) + (+27x) = +7x$
3. Multiply the last terms.	$(-4)(+9) = \underline{-36}$
4. Combine the products obtained.	*Ans.* $15x^2 + 7x - 36$

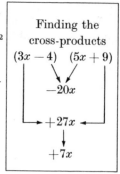

Finding the cross-products

$(3x - 4) \quad (5x + 9)$

$-20x$

$+27x$

$+7x$

~~~~~~

Exercises

In 1–19, multiply the binomials mentally.

1. $(x + 7)(x + 2)$
2. $(a - 1)(a - 5)$
3. $(z - 2)(z - 2)$
4. $(12 - d)(4 - d)$
5. $(x + 9)(x - 2)$
6. $(5 - a)(3 + a)$
7. $(6 - m)(7 + m)$
8. $(c - 5)(3c + 1)$
9. $(5z - 7)(4z + 3)$
10. $(3x + 2)(3x + 2)$
11. $(5 - 3d)^2$
12. $(2t - 5r)(3t - r)$
13. $(7x + 5y)(7x + 5y)$
14. $(a^2 + 5)(a^2 - 2)$
15. $(2x^2 - 7)(x^2 - 9)$
16. $(x^a + 7)(x^a - 5)$
17. $(y^b - 4)(2y^b + 1)$
18. $(c^{2d} - 4)(c^{2d} - 9)$
19. $(x^{3n} + 5)(2x^{3n} - 1)$

20. Represent the area of a square whose side is represented by $(2x - 3)$.

5. Factoring Quadratic Trinomials of the Form $ax^2 + bx + c$

Because $(x + 2)(x + 3) = x^2 + 5x + 6$, the factors of $x^2 + 5x + 6$ are $(x + 2)$ and $(x + 3)$. Factoring a quadratic trinomial of the form $ax^2 + bx + c$ (a, b, and $c \neq 0$) is the reverse of multiplying binomials of the form $(ax + b)$ and $(cx + d)$. When we factor a trinomial of this form, we list the possible pairs of factors and test them one by one until we find the correct result.

For example, let us factor $2x^2 + 7x - 15$.

1. Since the product of the first terms of the binomials must be $2x^2$, one of these terms must be $2x$, the other x. We write:

$$2x^2 + 7x - 15 = (2x \qquad)(x \qquad)$$

2. Since the product of the last terms of the binomials must be -15, one of these last terms must be positive, the other negative. The pairs of integers whose product is -15 are $(+1)$ and (-15), (-1) and $(+15)$, $(+3)$ and (-5), (-3) and $(+5)$.

3. Because of the results obtained in steps 1 and 2, the possible pairs of factors are:

$(2x + 1)(x - 15)$	$(2x - 1)(x + 15)$
$(2x + 15)(x - 1)$	$(2x - 15)(x + 1)$
$(2x + 3)(x - 5)$	$(2x - 3)(x + 5)$
$(2x + 5)(x - 3)$	$(2x - 5)(x + 3)$

4. To discover the product in which the middle term is $+7x$, we test the middle term of each of the trinomial products. We find that only the pair $(2x - 3)(x + 5)$ yields a middle term of $+7x$.

5. Hence, $2x^2 + 7x - 15 = (2x - 3)(x + 5)$.

KEEP IN MIND

In factoring a trinomial of the form $ax^2 + bx + c$, when a is a positive integer ($a > 0$):

1. If the last term, the constant c, is positive, the last terms of the binomial factors must be either both positive or both negative.
2. If the last term, the constant c, is negative, one of the last terms in the binomial factors must be positive, the other negative.

~~~~~~~~~~~~~~~~ *MODEL PROBLEMS* ~~~~~~~~~~~~~~~~

In 1 and 2, factor.

1. $x^2 + 6x + 8$ **2.** $3x^2 - 2x - 5$

How To Proceed	*Solution*	*Solution*
	$x^2 + 6x + 8$	$3x^2 - 2x - 5$
1. Factor the first term and the last term.	$x(x) \quad (+1)(+8)$ $(+2)(+4)$ $(-1)(-8)$ $(-2)(-4)$	$(3x)x \quad (+1)(-5)$ $(-1)(+5)$
2. Write the possible pairs of binomial factors.	$(x+1)(x+8)$ $(x+2)(x+4)$ $(x-1)(x-8)$ $(x-2)(x-4)$	$(3x+1)(x-5)$ $(3x-1)(x+5)$ $(3x+5)(x-1)$ $(3x-5)(x+1)$
3. Test to find which trinomial product has the given middle term.	$(x+2) \qquad (x+4)$ $+2x$ $+4x$ $+6x$ $(x+2)(x+4)$ *Ans.*	$(3x-5) \qquad (x+1)$ $-5x$ $+3x$ $-2x$ $(3x-5)(x+1)$ *Ans.*

In 3 and 4, factor.
3. $x^2 + 5xy - 6y^2 = (x + 6y)(x - y)$ *Ans.*
4. $m^4 - m^2 - 56 = (m^2 - 8)(m^2 + 7)$ *Ans.*

~~~~~~

Exercises

In 1–24, factor the trinomial.

1. $a^2 + 8a + 12$ **2.** $r^2 - 6r + 8$ **3.** $a^2 - 14a + 24$
4. $c^2 + c - 6$ **5.** $36 + 13x + x^2$ **6.** $c^2 - 16 - 6c$
7. $3x^2 - 16x + 5$ **8.** $16 - 8d + d^2$ **9.** $5x^2 - 13x + 6$
10. $12 + 7y - 10y^2$ **11.** $6y^2 + 19y - 20$ **12.** $-12 + 5x^2 - 4x$
13. $x^2 + 5xy + 4y^2$ **14.** $2a^2 - 7ab + 6b^2$ **15.** $4x^2 - 13xy + 3y^2$
16. $2x^2 - 7xy - 15y^2$ **17.** $a^4 - 7a^2 + 10$ **18.** $18 + 3y^2 - y^4$
19. $x^{2a} + 6x^a + 8$ **20.** $x^{2a} - 6x^a + 5$ **21.** $y^{2b} - 14y^b + 45$
22. $x^{2a} + 6x^a - 16$ **23.** $5x^{2a} - 11x^a - 12$ **24.** $3x^{2n} - 11x^n + 6$

6. Factoring a Polynomial Completely

To *factor a polynomial completely* means to find the ***prime factors*** of the polynomial with respect to a specified set of numbers. Therefore, whenever we factor a polynomial, we will continue the process of factoring until all factors other than monomial factors are prime factors with respect to the specified sets of numbers.

Procedure. To factor a polynomial completely:
1. **Factor the given polynomial. First find the H.C.F., if there is one. Then examine each factor.**
2. **Continue factoring the factors obtained in step 1 until all factors other than monomial factors are prime.**

~~~~~~~~~~~ *MODEL PROBLEMS* ~~~~~~~~~~~

In 1–4, factor completely.

1. Factor: $5x^3 - 45x$

Solution

$$5x^3 - 45x$$
$$= 5x(x^2 - 9)$$
$$= 5x(x + 3)(x - 3) \quad Ans.$$

2. Factor: $3x^2 - 6x - 24$

Solution

$$3x^2 - 6x - 24$$
$$= 3(x^2 - 2x - 8)$$
$$= 3(x - 4)(x + 2) \quad Ans.$$

3. Factor: $x^4 - 16$

Solution

$$x^4 - 16$$
$$= (x^2 + 4)(x^2 - 4)$$
$$= (x^2 + 4)(x + 2)(x - 2) \quad Ans.$$

4. Factor: $4x^{n+2} - x^n$

Solution

$$4x^{n+2} - x^n$$
$$= x^n(4x^2 - 1)$$
$$= x^n(2x + 1)(2x - 1) \quad Ans.$$

~~~~~~

Exercises

In 1–16, factor the polynomial completely.

1. $5x^2 - 5$ **2.** $3x^2 - 75$ **3.** $y - 9y^3$ **4.** $25x^3 - x$

5. $4 - 16x^2$ **6.** $xy - x^3y^3$ **7.** $\pi R^2 - \pi r^2$ **8.** $16x - x^3$

9. $ax^2 - 9a$ **10.** $x^3 - x$ **11.** $c^4 - d^4$ **12.** $x^3 + 7x^2 + 12x$

13. $5x^2 + 4x + x^3$ **14.** $x^4 + x^2 - 2x^3$ **15.** $x^{2a+2} - x^{2a}$ **16.** $ay^{2+2b} - ay^2$

17. Express as the product of three factors:

a. $x^3 - a^2x$ b. $4x^{2a} - 100y^{4b}$ c. $by^{2x+1} - 5by^{x+1} - 6by$

7. Transforming Rational Expressions Into Equivalent Rational Expressions

Recall that a rational number, such as $\frac{5}{8}$, is expressible in the form

$$\frac{a}{b} \text{ where } a \text{ and } b \text{ are integers and } b \neq 0$$

The role that integers play in the study of rational numbers is very much like the role that polynomials play in the study of rational expressions, as can be seen from the following definition of a rational expression:

A ***rational expression*** is an expression that is expressible in the form

$$\frac{P}{Q} \text{ where } P \text{ and } Q \text{ are polynomials and } Q \neq 0$$

Examples of rational expressions are $\frac{5}{8}, \frac{5}{x}, \frac{5x}{8y}, \frac{x+5}{8y}, \frac{x^2+5x}{8-y}, \frac{5x^2+xy}{16y-8x}$.

Note that, since division by zero is an impossible operation, a fraction whose denominator is zero is meaningless. For example, the fraction $\frac{5}{x}$ has no meaning when $x = 0$. In this book, to avoid meaningless fractions, we will assume that the values of the variables are such that the denominators of rational expressions are nonzero. For example, in the case of $\frac{x^2+5x}{8-x}$, it is understood that $x \neq 8$; in the case of $\frac{x-5}{(x-3)(x+2)}$, $x \neq 3$ and $x \neq -2$.

Because of the close parallel between rational numbers and rational expressions, we shall find that the laws and properties we have used to deal with rational numbers can often be used to deal with rational expressions.

THE PRODUCT OF RATIONAL EXPRESSIONS

The example $\frac{3}{4} \times \frac{5}{7} = \frac{3 \times 5}{4 \times 7}$ illustrates the following rule involving the product of two rational numbers:

If a and c are real numbers, and b and d are nonzero real numbers,

$$\frac{a}{b} \cdot \frac{c}{d} = \frac{ac}{bd} \quad \text{and} \quad \frac{ac}{bd} = \frac{a}{b} \cdot \frac{c}{d}$$

The product of two rational expressions is found in the same way. For example,

$$\frac{x+5}{x-3} \cdot \frac{x+3}{x+5} = \frac{(x+5)(x+3)}{(x-3)(x+5)}$$

FUNDAMENTAL PROPERTY OF A FRACTION OR A RATIONAL EXPRESSION

Since $\dfrac{a}{b} = \dfrac{a}{b} \cdot 1$, then $\dfrac{a}{b} = \dfrac{a}{b} \cdot \dfrac{x}{x}$, or $\dfrac{a}{b} = \dfrac{ax}{bx}$.

Since $\dfrac{a}{b} = \dfrac{a}{b} \cdot 1$, then $\dfrac{a}{b} = \dfrac{a}{b} \cdot \dfrac{\frac{1}{x}}{\frac{1}{x}}$ or $\dfrac{a}{b} = \dfrac{a\left(\frac{1}{x}\right)}{b\left(\frac{1}{x}\right)}$, or $\dfrac{a}{b} = \dfrac{a \div x}{b \div x}$.

Therefore, we have proved the following fundamental property of a fraction:

If the numerator and the denominator of a fraction are either multiplied or divided by the same nonzero number, the resulting fraction is equivalent to the original fraction.

Thus, $\dfrac{35}{25} = \dfrac{35 \div 5}{25 \div 5} = \dfrac{7}{5}$, and $\dfrac{\frac{1}{3}}{\frac{1}{4}} = \dfrac{\frac{1}{3} \times 12}{\frac{1}{4} \times 12} = \dfrac{4}{3}$.

Also, $\dfrac{6(x-2)}{2(x+2)} = \dfrac{6(x-2) \div 2}{2(x+2) \div 2} = \dfrac{3(x-2)}{x+2}$.

~~~~~~~~~~~~~~~ *MODEL PROBLEM* ~~~~~~~~~~~~~~~

Find the value of x for which $\dfrac{3x+9}{2x-8}$ is not defined.

Solution: $\dfrac{3x+9}{2x-8}$ is not defined when the denominator $2x-8$ is equal to 0.

$2x - 8 = 0$ when $x = 4$. *Ans.* 4

Exercises

In 1–3, represent the rational expression as a fraction and give the value(s) of the variable for which the fraction is not defined.

1. $9 \div 3x$ **2.** $10 \div (x - 8)$ **3.** $4y \div (3y + 1)$

In 4–8, find the value(s) of the variable for which the fraction is not defined.

4. $\dfrac{3}{x}$ **5.** $\dfrac{7}{y^2}$ **6.** $\dfrac{a^2 - 25}{2a - 1}$ **7.** $\dfrac{3m + 2}{4m + 2}$ **8.** $\dfrac{7b - 1}{b^2 - 81}$

In 9–14, replace the question mark with a number or a polynomial that will make the fractions equivalent.

9. $\dfrac{3}{5} \cdot \dfrac{7}{8} = \dfrac{3 \times 7}{5 \times ?}$ **10.** $\dfrac{c}{d} \cdot \dfrac{x}{y} = \dfrac{c \cdot ?}{d \cdot y}$

11. $\dfrac{3}{5} = \dfrac{3 \times 4}{5 \times ?}$ **12.** $\dfrac{10}{5} = \dfrac{10 \div 5}{5 \div ?}$

13. $\dfrac{4(x - 1)}{5(x - 1)} = \dfrac{4(x - 1) \div (?)}{5(x - 1) \div (x - 1)}$ **14.** $\dfrac{x + 1}{1 - x} = \dfrac{?}{x - 1}$

15. Write the fraction $\dfrac{6}{1 - x}$ as an equivalent fraction whose denominator is $x - 1$.

16. The fraction $\dfrac{b - a}{2}$ is *not* equal to (1) $-\dfrac{a - b}{2}$ (2) $\dfrac{a - b}{-2}$ (3) $\dfrac{a - b}{2}$ (4) $\dfrac{-a + b}{2}$

17. Prove: If a and c are real numbers, and b and d are nonzero real numbers, $\dfrac{ac}{bd} = \dfrac{a}{b} \cdot \dfrac{c}{d}$. $\left(Hint\text{: Use } \dfrac{ac}{bd} = (ac) \cdot \dfrac{1}{bd}.\right)$

18. Prove: If $\dfrac{a}{b}$ and $\dfrac{c}{d}$ are rational numbers, then $\dfrac{a}{b} \times \dfrac{c}{d} = \dfrac{c}{d} \times \dfrac{a}{b}$. That is, multiplication of rational numbers is commutative.

19. Prove: If $\dfrac{a}{b}, \dfrac{c}{d}$, and $\dfrac{e}{f}$ are rational numbers, then $\left(\dfrac{a}{b} \times \dfrac{c}{d}\right) \times \dfrac{e}{f} = \left(\dfrac{a}{b}\right) \times \left(\dfrac{c}{d} \times \dfrac{e}{f}\right)$. That is, multiplication of rational numbers is associative.

8. Reducing a Fraction or Rational Expression to Its Lowest Terms

A fraction is in its ***lowest terms*** or in its ***simplest form*** when its numerator and denominator have no common factor other than 1.

To reduce a fraction to its lowest terms, we make use of the division property of a fraction, $\dfrac{x}{y} = \dfrac{x \div a}{y \div a}$. For example,

$$\frac{12}{18} = \frac{12 \div 6}{18 \div 6} = \frac{2}{3} \qquad \frac{20x^3}{15x^2} = \frac{20x^3 \div 5x^2}{15x^2 \div 5x^2} = \frac{4x}{3}$$

In the following problem, observe the two ways that may be used to indicate that the numerator and the denominator of the fraction are divided by $x + 3$.

$$\frac{5(x+3)}{7(x+3)} = \frac{5(x+3) \div (x+3)}{7(x+3) \div (x+3)} = \frac{5}{7} \qquad \frac{5(x+3)}{7(x+3)} = \frac{5\overset{1}{\cancel{(x+3)}}}{7\underset{1}{\cancel{(x+3)}}} = \frac{5}{7}$$

We sometimes deal with fractions in which a factor of the numerator is the negative of a factor in the denominator. In such a case, remember that any expression divided by its negative gives the quotient -1. For example,

$$\frac{a-b}{b-a} = \frac{(a-b) \div (a-b)}{(b-a) \div (a-b)} = \frac{1}{-1} = -1 \quad \text{or} \quad \frac{a-b}{b-a} = \frac{\overset{1}{\cancel{(a-b)}}}{\underset{-1}{\cancel{(b-a)}}} = -1$$

~~~~~~~~~ *MODEL PROBLEMS* ~~~~~~~~~

In 1 and 2 reduce the fraction to its lowest terms.

1. $\dfrac{5x^2 + 10xy}{15xy + 30y^2}$ **2.** $\dfrac{2x - 4}{4 - x^2}$

How To Proceed

1. Factor both the numerator and the denominator completely.
2. Divide both the numerator and the denominator by their highest common factor.

Solution

$$\frac{5x^2 + 10xy}{15xy + 30y^2}$$

$$= \frac{5x(x+2y)}{15y(x+2y)}$$

$$= \frac{\overset{1}{\cancel{5x}}\overset{1}{\cancel{(x+2y)}}}{\underset{3}{\cancel{15y}}\underset{1}{\cancel{(x+2y)}}}$$

$$= \frac{x}{3y} \ Ans.$$

Solution

$$\frac{2x - 4}{4 - x^2}$$

$$= \frac{2(x-2)}{(2+x)(2-x)}$$

$$= \frac{2\overset{-1}{\cancel{(x-2)}}}{(2+x)\underset{1}{\cancel{(2-x)}}}$$

$$= \frac{-2}{2+x} \ Ans.$$

Exercises

In 1–24, reduce the fraction to its lowest terms.

1. $\dfrac{27a}{36b}$ 2. $\dfrac{12y^2}{18y^2}$ 3. $\dfrac{18c}{36c^2}$ 4. $\dfrac{8xy^2}{24x^2y}$

5. $\dfrac{18rs^2}{45s^2}$ 6. $\dfrac{3(x+3)}{5(x+3)}$ 7. $\dfrac{20(y-2)}{15(y-2)}$ 8. $\dfrac{6a^2(a-5)}{3a(5-a)}$

9. $\dfrac{2b(x+y)}{4b^2}$ 10. $\dfrac{3x(x+1)}{3x}$ 11. $\dfrac{9b-18}{4b-8}$ 12. $\dfrac{y^2-9}{3y+9}$

13. $\dfrac{5a^2-20}{(a-2)^2}$ 14. $\dfrac{5m}{15m^2-5m}$ 15. $\dfrac{8a-4}{1-4a^2}$ 16. $\dfrac{x^3-x}{2x+2}$

17. $\dfrac{3-3x}{x^2-1}$ 18. $\dfrac{2x-2y}{3y-3x}$ 19. $\dfrac{1-4x^2}{6x-3}$ 20. $\dfrac{(x-5)^2}{10-2x}$

21. $\dfrac{y^2-3y}{y^2-4y+3}$ 22. $\dfrac{r^2-25}{r^2-2r-15}$ 23. $\dfrac{3-3y}{(y-1)^2}$ 24. $\dfrac{6-m-m^2}{m^2-9}$

25. The fraction $\dfrac{t-1}{2-3t^2}$ is equivalent to (1) $\dfrac{1-t}{3t^2-2}$ (2) $\dfrac{t-1}{3t^2-2}$ (3) $\dfrac{1-t}{2-3t^2}$

26. The fraction that is equivalent to $\dfrac{2x+4}{2x}$ is (1) 4 (2) $\dfrac{2x+2}{x}$ (3) $\dfrac{x+2}{x}$

27. When the fraction $\dfrac{5x+15}{5x}$ is reduced to its lowest terms, the result is

   (1) $\dfrac{5}{x}$ (2) $\dfrac{x+3}{3}$ (3) 15 (4) none of these

28. The fraction $\dfrac{8x}{8x+16}$ is equivalent to (1) $\dfrac{1}{16}$ (2) $\dfrac{1}{17}$ (3) $\dfrac{x}{8x+2}$ (4) $\dfrac{x}{x+2}$

29. If r, s, and t are positive real numbers, no two of which are equal, then $\dfrac{r+s}{s+t}$ is (1) always (2) sometimes (3) never equal to $\dfrac{r}{t}$.

In 30–35, explain why the indicated method which was used by a student in reducing the fraction is *incorrect*.

30. $\dfrac{\overset{1}{\cancel{3x}}}{\underset{1}{\cancel{3}}+y}=\dfrac{x}{1+y}$ 31. $\dfrac{2\overset{1}{\cancel{x}}+y}{\cancel{x}}=2+y$ 32. $\dfrac{2a+\overset{1}{\cancel{b}}}{a+\underset{1}{\cancel{b}}}=2$

33. $\dfrac{\frac{1}{x+y+z}}{\frac{x+y}{1}} = 1 + z$ **34.** $\dfrac{\frac{x^2+y^2}{x}}{1} = x + y^2$ **35.** $\dfrac{\frac{a}{a^2+b^2}}{\frac{a+b}{1}\ \frac{b}{1}} = a + b$

9. Multiplying Fractions or Rational Expressions

Since $\dfrac{a}{b} \cdot \dfrac{c}{d} = \dfrac{ac}{bd}$ when a and c are real numbers and b and d are nonzero real numbers, we can state the following rule:

The product of two fractions is a fraction whose numerator is the product of the numerators of the given fractions and whose denominator is the product of the denominators of the given fractions.

Study the following two methods that may be used to multiply $\dfrac{2a^2}{3b}$ by $\dfrac{15b^2}{4a^3}$.

Method 1

$$\frac{2a^2}{3b} \cdot \frac{15b^2}{4a^3} = \frac{2a^2 \cdot 15b^2}{3b \cdot 4a^3} = \frac{30a^2b^2}{12a^3b} = \frac{30a^2b^2 \div 6a^2b}{12a^3b \div 6a^2b} = \frac{5b}{2a}$$

Method 2

$$\frac{2a^2}{3b} \cdot \frac{15b^2}{4a^3} = \frac{\overset{1}{\cancel{2a^2}}}{\underset{1}{\cancel{3b}}} \cdot \frac{\overset{5b}{\cancel{15b^2}}}{\underset{2a}{\cancel{4a^3}}} = \frac{5b}{2a}$$

Observe that method 2 requires less computation than method 1 because the reduced form of the product was obtained by dividing the numerator and the denominator by a common factor before the product was found.

~~~~~~~~~~ *MODEL PROBLEM* ~~~~~~~~~~

Multiply $\dfrac{4x+8}{4x^2-25}$ by $\dfrac{6x+15}{2x^2+4x}$ and express the product in reduced form.

How To Proceed	*Solution*
1. Factor the numerators and denominators of the fractions.	$\dfrac{4x+8}{4x^2-25} \cdot \dfrac{6x+15}{2x^2+4x}$ $= \dfrac{4(x+2)}{(2x+5)(2x-5)} \cdot \dfrac{3(2x+5)}{2x(x+2)}$
2. Divide both the numerator and denominator by all common factors.	$= \dfrac{\overset{2}{\cancel{4}}\overset{1}{\cancel{(x+2)}}}{\underset{1}{\cancel{(2x+5)}}(2x-5)} \cdot \dfrac{\overset{1}{3}\cancel{(2x+5)}}{\underset{1}{2}x\underset{1}{\cancel{(x+2)}}}$
3. Multiply the remaining factors of the numerator; then multiply the remaining factors of the denominator.	$= \dfrac{2 \cdot 3}{x(2x-5)} = \dfrac{6}{x(2x-5)} \quad Ans.$

〰〰〰〰〰〰〰〰〰〰〰〰〰〰〰〰〰〰〰〰〰〰〰〰〰

Exercises

In 1–15, perform the multiplication and express the product in its simplest form.

1. $\dfrac{36}{30} \cdot \dfrac{12}{8}$ **2.** $\dfrac{5}{d} \cdot d^2$ **3.** $\dfrac{3x}{7y} \cdot \dfrac{7a}{3b}$

4. $\dfrac{30a^2}{18b} \cdot \dfrac{6b}{5a}$ **5.** $\dfrac{24x^3y^2}{7z} \cdot \dfrac{21z^2}{12xy}$ **6.** $\dfrac{12x}{(5y)^2} \cdot \dfrac{15y^2}{36x^2}$

7. $\dfrac{5x}{x^2-9} \cdot \dfrac{6x+18}{15x^3}$ **8.** $\dfrac{3a-6}{6a+12} \cdot \dfrac{3a^2-12}{a^2-5a+6}$ **9.** $\dfrac{4x-6}{4x+8} \cdot \dfrac{6x+12}{4x^2-9}$

10. $\dfrac{b^2+b-2}{b^2-7b} \cdot \dfrac{b^2-13b+42}{b+2}$ **11.** $\dfrac{4x+8y}{6x+18y} \cdot \dfrac{5x+15y}{x^2-4y^2}$

12. $\dfrac{a^2-7ab+12b^2}{a^2-4b^2} \cdot \dfrac{2a+4b}{a-3b}$ **13.** $\dfrac{4-2x}{6x+30} \cdot \dfrac{x^2-25}{x^2-7x+10}$

14. $\dfrac{4y^3}{8-2y-y^2} \cdot \dfrac{3y+12}{6y}$ **15.** $\dfrac{b-a}{a+b} \cdot \dfrac{a^2-b^2}{a^2-2ab+b^2}$

16. Multiply $\dfrac{x^2-y^2}{2xy}$ by $\dfrac{x^2}{x-y}$. Express the result in simplest form.

17. Express the product $\dfrac{6}{3x-1} \cdot (1-3x)$ in simplest form.

10. Dividing Fractions or Rational Expressions

Since we have defined $a \div b$ as $a \times \dfrac{1}{b}$, a quotient may be expressed as the product of the dividend and the multiplicative inverse, or reciprocal, of the divisor. Thus, $9 \div 5 = 9 \times \dfrac{1}{5} = \dfrac{9}{5}$ and $\dfrac{4}{5} \div \dfrac{3}{7} = \dfrac{4}{5} \times \dfrac{1}{\frac{3}{7}} = \dfrac{4}{5} \times \dfrac{7}{3} = \dfrac{28}{15}$.

In general, if a is a real number and b, c, and d are nonzero real numbers,

$$\frac{a}{b} \div \frac{c}{d} = \frac{a}{b} \cdot \frac{d}{c} = \frac{ad}{bc}$$

The quotient of two rational expressions can be found in exactly the same way.

~~~~~~~~~~ MODEL PROBLEMS ~~~~~~~~~~

In 1 and 2, perform the division and represent the quotient in its simplest form.

1. $\dfrac{8x^3}{27y^2} \div \dfrac{20x^4}{9y^3}$ 2. $\dfrac{5x + 15}{x^2 - 9} \div \dfrac{10x^2 + 10x}{4x - 12}$

How To Proceed	Solution	Solution
1. Find the reciprocal of the divisor.	The reciprocal of $\dfrac{20x^4}{9y^3}$ is $\dfrac{9y^3}{20x^4}$.	The reciprocal of $\dfrac{10x^2 + 10x}{4x - 12}$ is $\dfrac{4x - 12}{10x^2 + 10x}$.
2. Multiply the dividend by the reciprocal of the divisor.	$\dfrac{8x^3}{27y^2} \div \dfrac{20x^4}{9y^3}$ $= \dfrac{8x^3}{27y^2} \cdot \dfrac{9y^3}{20x^4}$ $= \dfrac{\overset{2}{\cancel{8x^3}}}{\underset{3}{\cancel{27y^2}}} \cdot \dfrac{\overset{y}{\cancel{9y^3}}}{\underset{5x}{\cancel{20x^4}}}$ $= \dfrac{2y}{15x}$ *Ans.*	$\dfrac{5x + 15}{x^2 - 9} \div \dfrac{10x^2 + 10x}{4x - 12}$ $= \dfrac{5x + 15}{x^2 - 9} \cdot \dfrac{4x - 12}{10x^2 + 10x}$ $= \dfrac{\overset{1}{\cancel{5}}(x \overset{1}{\cancel{+ 3}})}{(x \cancel{+ 3})(x \cancel{- 3})} \cdot \dfrac{\overset{2}{\cancel{4}}(x \overset{1}{\cancel{- 3}})}{\underset{\underset{1}{2}}{\cancel{10}}x(x + 1)}$ $= \dfrac{2}{x(x + 1)}$ *Ans.*

Exercises

In 1–19, perform the division and represent the quotient in its simplest form.

1. $\dfrac{12}{35} \div \dfrac{4}{7}$ **2.** $15 \div \frac{1}{3}$ **3.** $\dfrac{6}{y^2} \div \dfrac{6}{y}$ **4.** $\dfrac{21x}{20y} \div \dfrac{3x}{5y}$

5. $\dfrac{7xy^2}{10rs} \div \dfrac{14y^2}{5r^2s^2}$ **6.** $\dfrac{ab^2}{a^2b} \div \dfrac{a}{b^3}$ **7.** $8xy \div \dfrac{24x}{y}$ **8.** $\dfrac{a-5}{a} \div \dfrac{a^2-25}{a^2}$

9. $\dfrac{4-b^2}{b^2} \div \dfrac{2+b}{b}$ **10.** $\dfrac{12+6a}{15-3a} \div \dfrac{4-a^2}{25-a^2}$ **11.** $\dfrac{x^2-9y^2}{8x+4y} \div \dfrac{3x-9y}{12x+6y}$

12. $\dfrac{y^2-49}{(y+7)^2} \div \dfrac{3y-21}{2y+14}$ **13.** $\dfrac{25a^2}{(a-b)^2} \div \dfrac{5a}{a-b}$ **14.** $\dfrac{-3}{2-x} \div \dfrac{9}{x-2}$

15. $\dfrac{x^2-1}{x^2+1} \div \dfrac{1-x}{3}$ **16.** $\dfrac{r^2-3rs-10s^2}{r^2-25s^2} \div \dfrac{10r+20s}{2r+10s}$

17. $\dfrac{x-7}{3x^2-8x+4} \div \dfrac{3x-21}{6x^2-24}$ **18.** $\dfrac{3x^2+2y}{x-y} \cdot \dfrac{x^2-y^2}{9x^4-4y^2} \div \dfrac{2x+2y}{12x^2-8y}$

19. $\dfrac{x^2-4}{2x+14} \cdot \dfrac{x^2+10x+21}{6x-12} \div \dfrac{x^2+5x+6}{12x}$

20. If the area of a rectangle is represented by $\dfrac{x+y}{x^2-xy}$ and the length is represented by $\dfrac{1}{x^2-y^2}$, what expression represents the width?

11. Adding or Subtracting Fractions or Rational Expressions That Have the Same Denominator

When we add two fractions that have the same denominator, we make use of the definition of division and the distributive property of multiplication over addition. For example,

$$\frac{3}{11} + \frac{4}{11} = 3 \cdot \left(\frac{1}{11}\right) + 4 \cdot \left(\frac{1}{11}\right) = (3+4) \cdot \frac{1}{11} = \frac{3+4}{11} = \frac{7}{11}$$

In general, if a and b are real numbers and x is a nonzero real number,

$$\frac{a}{x} + \frac{b}{x} = \frac{a+b}{x}$$

Rational expressions that have the same divisor are added in the same way.

~~~~~~~~~~~~~~~~~ *MODEL PROBLEMS* ~~~~~~~~~~~~~~~~~

In 1 and 2, add or subtract as indicated. Reduce answers to lowest terms.

1. $\dfrac{5a}{8} - \dfrac{2a}{8} + \dfrac{3a}{8}$ **2.** $\dfrac{5}{2x-2} - \dfrac{2x-1}{2-2x}$

How To Proceed	*Solution*	*Solution*
	$\dfrac{5a}{8} - \dfrac{2a}{8} + \dfrac{3a}{8}$	$\dfrac{5}{2x-2} - \dfrac{2x-1}{2-2x}$
1. Write a fraction whose numerator is the sum (or difference) of the numerators and whose denominator is the denominator of the given fractions.	$= \dfrac{5a - 2a + 3a}{8}$ $= \dfrac{6a}{8}$	$= \dfrac{5}{2x-2} - \dfrac{-2x+1}{2x-2}$ $= \dfrac{5-(-2x+1)}{2x-2}$ $= \dfrac{5+2x-1}{2x-2}$ $= \dfrac{2x+4}{2x-2}$
2. Reduce the resulting fraction to its lowest terms.	$= \dfrac{\overset{3}{\cancel{6}}a}{\underset{4}{\cancel{8}}}$ $= \dfrac{3a}{4}$ *Ans.*	$= \dfrac{\overset{1}{\cancel{2}}(x+2)}{\underset{1}{\cancel{2}}(x-1)}$ $= \dfrac{x+2}{x-1}$ *Ans.*

~~~~~~

Exercises

In 1–15, add or subtract (combine) the fractions as indicated. Reduce answers to lowest terms.

1. $\frac{3}{4} + \frac{5}{4} + \frac{1}{4}$ **2.** $\frac{7}{12} - \frac{1}{12} - \frac{2}{12}$ **3.** $\dfrac{5x}{4} + \dfrac{x}{4} + \dfrac{3x}{4}$

4. $\dfrac{11r}{6} - \dfrac{r}{6} - \dfrac{7r}{6}$ **5.** $\dfrac{9}{8x} + \dfrac{3}{8x} - \dfrac{2}{8x}$ **6.** $\dfrac{a}{5y} + \dfrac{b}{5y} + \dfrac{c}{5y}$

7. $\dfrac{x}{x+1} + \dfrac{1}{x+1}$ **8.** $\dfrac{a}{a^2-b^2} - \dfrac{b}{a^2-b^2}$ **9.** $\dfrac{3}{x-4} + \dfrac{1}{4-x}$

10. $\dfrac{x}{x-3} + \dfrac{3}{3-x}$ **11.** $\dfrac{4x}{2x-5} + \dfrac{10}{5-2x}$ **12.** $\dfrac{5a}{a^2-b^2} - \dfrac{5b}{b^2-a^2}$

13. $\dfrac{3r+6}{2} + \dfrac{2r+1}{2}$ **14.** $\dfrac{12x-15}{12x} - \dfrac{9x-6}{12x}$ **15.** $\dfrac{6r-5}{r^2-1} - \dfrac{5r-6}{r^2-1}$

12. Adding or Subtracting Fractions or Rational Expressions That Have Different Denominators

If we wish to add (or subtract) fractions that have different denominators, we first transform them into equivalent fractions that have the same denominator by using the fundamental multiplication property of a fraction. Then we add (or subtract) the resulting equivalent fractions.

For example, to add $\frac{7}{24}$ and $\frac{11}{36}$, we first transform them to equivalent fractions which have a common denominator. Any integer which has both 24 and 36 as factors could become a common denominator. To simplify our work, we use the lowest common denominator (L.C.D.), which can be found in the following manner:

1. Express each denominator as a product of prime factors.

$$24 = 2 \cdot 2 \cdot 2 \cdot 3 = 2^3 \cdot 3 \qquad 36 = 2 \cdot 2 \cdot 3 \cdot 3 = 2^2 \cdot 3^2$$

2. Write the product of the highest power of each of the different prime factors of the denominators.

$$\text{L.C.D.} = 2^3 \cdot 3^2 = 8 \cdot 9 = 72$$

We now can add $\frac{7}{24}$ and $\frac{11}{36}$ as follows:

$$\frac{7}{24} + \frac{11}{36} = \frac{7 \cdot 3}{24 \cdot 3} + \frac{11 \cdot 2}{36 \cdot 2} = \frac{21}{72} + \frac{22}{72} = \frac{21+22}{72} = \frac{43}{72}$$

Rational expressions written as fractions are added in the same manner.

Procedure. To add (or subtract) fractions that have different denominators:
1. **Factor each denominator in order to find the lowest common denominator, L.C.D.**
2. **Transform each fraction to an equivalent fraction by multiplying its numerator and its denominator by the quotient that is obtained when the L.C.D. is divided by the denominator of the fraction.**
3. **Write a fraction whose numerator is the sum (or difference) of the numerators of the new fractions and whose denominator is the L.C.D.**
4. **Reduce the resulting fraction to its lowest terms.**

See how these steps are used in the following two model problems:

~~~~~~~~~~~~~~ *MODEL PROBLEMS* ~~~~~~~~~~~~~~

In 1 and 2, combine (add or subtract) the fractions.

1. $\dfrac{3x+4}{4} + \dfrac{x-3}{6}$

2. $\dfrac{3}{x^2-4} - \dfrac{4}{2-x}$

Solution:

Step 1

$$4 = 2 \cdot 2 = 2^2; \; 6 = 2 \cdot 3$$

$$\text{L.C.D.} = 2^2 \cdot 3 = 12$$

$$12 \div 4 = 3$$
$$12 \div 6 = 2$$

$$\frac{3}{x^2-4} - \frac{4}{2-x}$$

$$= \frac{3}{x^2-4} - \frac{-4}{x-2}$$

$$x^2 - 4 = (x-2)(x+2)$$
$$x - 2 = 1 \cdot (x-2)$$
$$\text{L.C.D.} = (x-2)(x+2)$$
$$(x-2)(x+2) \div (x-2) = (x+2)$$

Step 2

$$\frac{3x+4}{4} + \frac{x-3}{6}$$

$$= \frac{3(3x+4)}{3 \cdot 4} + \frac{2(x-3)}{2 \cdot 6}$$

$$= \frac{9x+12}{12} + \frac{2x-6}{12}$$

$$\frac{3}{x^2-4} - \frac{-4}{x-2}$$

$$= \frac{3}{(x-2)(x+2)} - \frac{-4}{(x-2)}$$

$$= \frac{3}{(x-2)(x+2)} - \frac{-4(x+2)}{(x-2)(x+2)}$$

Step 3

$$= \frac{(9x+12)+(2x-6)}{12}$$

$$= \frac{9x+12+2x-6}{12}$$

$$= \frac{3-(-4x-8)}{(x-2)(x+2)}$$

$$= \frac{3+4x+8}{(x-2)(x+2)}$$

Step 4

$$= \frac{11x+6}{12} \; Ans.$$

$$= \frac{4x+11}{(x-2)(x+2)} \text{ or } \frac{4x+11}{x^2-4} \; Ans.$$

~~~~~~

Exercises

In 1–4, find the L.C.D. for two fractions whose denominators are:

1. $12x^2y^3$; $18xy^2$ **2.** x; $x+5$ **3.** $5x+15$; $4x+12$ **4.** y^2-4; $3y+6$

In 5–8, transform the given fractions into equivalent fractions that have the L.C.D. as their denominators.

5. $\dfrac{7y}{12} ; \dfrac{3y}{90}$ **6.** $\dfrac{5}{4x^2} ; \dfrac{7}{xy^2}$ **7.** $\dfrac{5}{d} ; \dfrac{d-2}{d+2}$ **8.** $\dfrac{2y+1}{y^2-9} ; \dfrac{-7}{y+3}$

In 9–36, combine the fractions.

9. $\frac{1}{2} + \frac{3}{4} + \frac{7}{8}$ **10.** $\frac{3}{4} - \frac{2}{3} + \frac{5}{6}$ **11.** $\frac{1}{2} - \frac{3}{4} + \frac{4}{5}$

12. $\dfrac{9x}{4} + \dfrac{x}{2} + \dfrac{3x}{8}$ **13.** $\dfrac{5a}{6} - \dfrac{3a}{4} + \dfrac{a}{12}$ **14.** $\dfrac{7}{4y} - \dfrac{2}{6y} - \dfrac{1}{9y}$

15. $\dfrac{5}{x} - \dfrac{6}{y}$ **16.** $\dfrac{n}{s} - \dfrac{m}{t}$ **17.** $\dfrac{3}{y^2} - \dfrac{2}{y}$

18. $\dfrac{1}{5x^2} + \dfrac{3}{10xy} - \dfrac{4}{x^2y^2}$ **19.** $\dfrac{y-2}{3} + \dfrac{y+1}{6}$ **20.** $\dfrac{2a+1}{5a} - \dfrac{4a-2}{4a}$

21. $\dfrac{x-2}{4x} + \dfrac{2x-3}{3x}$ **22.** $\dfrac{r+x}{r^2x} - \dfrac{r-2x}{rx^2}$ **23.** $\dfrac{3}{x-1} - \dfrac{1}{x}$

24. $\dfrac{4}{x-3} - \dfrac{3}{x}$ **25.** $\dfrac{4}{x+1} + \dfrac{2}{x-1}$ **26.** $\dfrac{1}{a+b} - \dfrac{1}{a-b}$

27. $\dfrac{5}{x^2-4} + \dfrac{3}{x-2}$ **28.** $\dfrac{m}{a^2-ab} - \dfrac{m}{b^2-ab}$ **29.** $\dfrac{3}{x^2-25} + \dfrac{4}{5-x}$

30. $\dfrac{2}{y^2-4} + \dfrac{1}{2y-y^2}$ **31.** $\dfrac{1+x}{1-x} + \dfrac{1-x}{1+x}$ **32.** $\dfrac{a+b}{a-b} + \dfrac{a-b}{a+b}$

33. $\dfrac{3}{x^2-3x+2} - \dfrac{2}{x^2-1}$ **34.** $\dfrac{x}{x^2-3x-10} - \dfrac{2}{x^2-6x+5}$

35. $\dfrac{4}{x^2-x-6} + \dfrac{5}{4-x^2}$ **36.** $\dfrac{5}{x+2} + \dfrac{5}{2-x} - \dfrac{6}{x^2-4}$

13. Multiplying and Dividing Mixed Expressions

The mixed number $2\frac{1}{4}$, which means the sum of the integer 2 and the fraction $\frac{1}{4}$, $2 + \frac{1}{4}$, can be expressed as the fraction $\frac{9}{4}$.

A *mixed expression* is the indicated sum or difference of a polynomial and a rational expression written as a fraction. For example, $x + \dfrac{2}{x}$ is a mixed expression. A mixed expression can be transformed into an equivalent fraction. For example,

$$x + \frac{2}{x} = \frac{x}{1} + \frac{2}{x} = \frac{x \cdot x}{x \cdot 1} + \frac{2}{x} = \frac{x^2}{x} + \frac{2}{x} = \frac{x^2+2}{x}$$

~~~~~~~~~~~~~~~~~ *MODEL PROBLEM* ~~~~~~~~~~~~~~~~~

Simplify: $\left(2 + \dfrac{a}{b}\right) \div \left(4 - \dfrac{a^2}{b^2}\right)$

How To Proceed	*Solution*
	$\left(2 + \dfrac{a}{b}\right) \div \left(4 - \dfrac{a^2}{b^2}\right)$
1. Combine the terms in each mixed expression into a single fraction.	$= \left(\dfrac{2 \cdot b}{1 \cdot b} + \dfrac{a}{b}\right) \div \left(\dfrac{4 \cdot b^2}{1 \cdot b^2} - \dfrac{a^2}{b^2}\right)$
	$= \dfrac{2b + a}{b} \div \dfrac{4b^2 - a^2}{b^2}$
2. Perform the indicated division.	$= \dfrac{2b + a}{b} \cdot \dfrac{b^2}{4b^2 - a^2}$
	$= \dfrac{\overset{1}{\cancel{(2b + a)}}}{\cancel{b}} \cdot \dfrac{\overset{b}{\cancel{b^2}}}{\cancel{(2b + a)}(2b - a)}$
	$= \dfrac{b}{2b - a}$ *Ans.*

~~~~~~

Exercises

In 1–12, perform the indicated operations on the mixed expressions. Express the result in its simplest form.

1. $\left(\dfrac{x}{y} + 2\right)\left(\dfrac{x}{y} - 2\right)$

2. $\left(1 + \dfrac{a}{b}\right)\left(\dfrac{b^2}{b^2 - a^2}\right)$

3. $\left(1 - \dfrac{a}{a + b}\right)\left(\dfrac{a^2}{b^2} - 1\right)$

4. $\left(1 - \dfrac{x}{y}\right) \div \left(y - \dfrac{x^2}{y}\right)$

5. $\left(5 + \dfrac{5}{3x}\right) \div \left(\dfrac{1}{9x} - x\right)$

6. $\left(1 - \dfrac{5}{x^2 - 4}\right) \div (x + 3)$

7. $\left(r - 4 + \dfrac{3}{r}\right)\left(\dfrac{r^2}{r - 3}\right)$

8. $\left(x + 5 - \dfrac{14}{x}\right) \div \left(x - 4 + \dfrac{4}{x}\right)$

9. $\left(\dfrac{1}{y} - \dfrac{1}{x}\right) \div \left(1 - \dfrac{x}{y}\right)$

10. $\left(\dfrac{r^2}{s^2} - \dfrac{a^2}{b^2}\right) \div \left(\dfrac{a}{b} - \dfrac{r}{s}\right)$

11. $\left(1 - \dfrac{2}{x^2 + 1}\right) \div (x - 1)$

12. $\left(x - 1 - \dfrac{x^2 - 1}{x}\right) \times \left(1 + \dfrac{1}{x - 1}\right)$

14. Simplifying Complex Fractions

A *complex fraction* is a fraction that contains one or more fractions in either its numerator or denominator or in both its numerator and denominator. Thus, each of the following is a complex fraction:

$$\frac{\frac{1}{2}}{\frac{1}{3}} \qquad \frac{\frac{1}{y}}{2y} \qquad \frac{x}{1+\frac{1}{x}} \qquad \frac{1+\frac{4}{x}}{1-\frac{16}{x^2}}$$

A complex fraction may be simplified using either of the two methods shown in the following model problems.

~~~~~~~~~ *MODEL PROBLEMS* ~~~~~~~~~

METHOD 1

Simplify:

1. $\dfrac{\dfrac{a}{b}+1}{\dfrac{a}{b}-1}$

2. $\dfrac{x+\frac{1}{2}}{x^2-\frac{1}{4}}$

How To Proceed	*Solution*	*Solution*
1. Find the L.C.D. of all fractions that appear in the complex fraction.	L.C.D. for $\frac{a}{b}$ and $\frac{a}{b}$ is b.	L.C.D. for $\frac{1}{2}$ and $\frac{1}{4}$ is 4.
2. Multiply the numerator and the denominator of the complex fraction by this L.C.D.	$\dfrac{\dfrac{a}{b}+1}{\dfrac{a}{b}-1}$ $=\dfrac{b\left(\dfrac{a}{b}+1\right)}{b\left(\dfrac{a}{b}-1\right)}$	$\dfrac{x+\frac{1}{2}}{x^2-\frac{1}{4}}$ $=\dfrac{4(x+\frac{1}{2})}{4(x^2-\frac{1}{4})}=\dfrac{4x+2}{4x^2-1}$ $=\dfrac{2\overset{1}{\cancel{(2x+1)}}}{\underset{1}{\cancel{(2x+1)}}(2x-1)}$
3. Simplify and reduce the resulting simple fraction.	$=\dfrac{a+b}{a-b}$ *Ans.*	$=\dfrac{2}{2x-1}$ *Ans.*

METHOD 2

Simplify:

1. $\dfrac{\dfrac{a}{b}+1}{\dfrac{a}{b}-1}$ **2.** $\dfrac{x+\frac{1}{2}}{x^2-\frac{1}{4}}$

How To Proceed	*Solution*	*Solution*
	$\dfrac{\dfrac{a}{b}+1}{\dfrac{a}{b}-1}$	$\dfrac{x+\frac{1}{2}}{x^2-\frac{1}{4}}$
1. Combine the terms in the numerator into a single fraction, and do the same in the denominator.	$=\dfrac{\dfrac{a}{b}+\dfrac{b}{b}}{\dfrac{a}{b}-\dfrac{b}{b}}$ $=\dfrac{\dfrac{a+b}{b}}{\dfrac{a-b}{b}}$	$=\dfrac{\dfrac{2x}{2}+\dfrac{1}{2}}{\dfrac{4x^2}{4}-\dfrac{1}{4}}$ $=\dfrac{\dfrac{2x+1}{2}}{\dfrac{4x^2-1}{4}}$
2. Divide the numerator of the resulting fraction by its denominator.	$=\dfrac{(a+b)}{b}\div\dfrac{(a-b)}{b}$ $=\dfrac{(a+b)}{\cancel{b}}\cdot\dfrac{\overset{1}{\cancel{b}}}{(a-b)}$ $=\dfrac{a+b}{a-b}$ *Ans.*	$=\dfrac{2x+1}{2}\div\dfrac{4x^2-1}{4}$ $=\dfrac{\cancel{(2x+1)}^{\,1}}{\cancel{2}}\cdot\dfrac{\cancel{4}^{\,2}}{\cancel{(2x+1)}(2x-1)}$ $=\dfrac{2}{2x-1}$ *Ans.*

Exercises

In 1–20, simplify the complex fraction.

1. $\dfrac{4}{1-\frac{1}{2}}$ **2.** $\dfrac{3-\frac{1}{2}}{10}$ **3.** $\dfrac{2+\frac{1}{4}}{1+\frac{1}{2}}$ **4.** $\dfrac{5-\frac{1}{5}}{3-\frac{3}{10}}$

5. $\dfrac{\dfrac{b^2}{y}}{\dfrac{b}{y^2}}$

6. $\dfrac{\dfrac{x}{x+y}}{\dfrac{y}{x+y}}$

7. $\dfrac{\dfrac{r^2-4s^2}{s^2}}{\dfrac{r+2s}{s}}$

8. $\dfrac{x+\frac{1}{4}}{x^2-\frac{1}{16}}$

9. $\dfrac{3-\dfrac{1}{x}}{3+\dfrac{1}{x}}$

10. $\dfrac{1-\dfrac{3}{y}}{1-\dfrac{9}{y^2}}$

11. $\dfrac{\dfrac{1}{x}-\dfrac{1}{y}}{\dfrac{1}{x}+\dfrac{1}{y}}$

12. $\dfrac{\dfrac{x}{y}+\dfrac{y}{x}}{\dfrac{1}{xy}}$

13. $\dfrac{\dfrac{1}{a^2}+\dfrac{1}{b^2}}{\dfrac{2}{ab}}$

14. $\dfrac{\dfrac{y}{y+3}}{1-\dfrac{y}{y+3}}$

15. $\dfrac{\frac{1}{9}-x^2}{x-\frac{1}{3}}$

16. $\dfrac{5+\dfrac{5}{2x}}{\dfrac{1}{4x}-x}$

17. $\dfrac{1-\dfrac{6}{x}+\dfrac{9}{x^2}}{\dfrac{3}{x}-1}$

18. $\dfrac{\dfrac{r}{s}-\dfrac{s}{r}}{\dfrac{s}{r}-1}$

19. $\dfrac{1-\dfrac{5}{x}+\dfrac{6}{x^2}}{1-\dfrac{6}{x}+\dfrac{8}{x^2}}$

20. $\dfrac{\dfrac{2}{a+b}-\dfrac{2}{a-b}}{\dfrac{4}{a^2-b^2}}$

In 21–24, write in simplest form the reciprocal of the given expression.

21. $\left(\dfrac{1}{x}+5\right)$

22. $\dfrac{c+\dfrac{c}{b}}{b-\dfrac{1}{b}}$

23. $\dfrac{\dfrac{1}{a}-b}{\dfrac{1}{b}-a}$

24. $\dfrac{\dfrac{a}{b}-\dfrac{b}{a}}{\dfrac{a}{b}-1}$

CHAPTER IV

FIRST-DEGREE EQUATIONS AND INEQUALITIES IN ONE VARIABLE

1. Understanding the Meaning of Solving an Equation

An equation is a sentence which states that two expressions have the same value. We use the symbol $=$, read "equals" or "is equal to," to indicate that two expressions have the same value. For example $5 + 4 = 7 + 2$ is an equation in which $5 + 4$ is called the **left side** or **left member** and $7 + 2$ is called the **right side** or **right member**.

An equation may be a true sentence, such as $5 + 4 = 9$, or a false sentence, such as $5 - 4 = 2$. As we know, an equation may be an *open sentence*, such as $x + 4 = 9$. If x is replaced by a number, a new sentence is formed which is true or false depending on the selected number.

Consider the equation $x + 4 = 9$ when the *replacement set* or *domain* of x is the set of real numbers. Only when x is replaced by 5 does $x + 4 = 9$ become a true sentence: $5 + 4 = 9$. The number 5, which *satisfies* the equation $x + 4 = 9$, is called a *root* or a *solution* of the equation. The set consisting of all the solutions of an equation is called its *solution set* or *truth set*. Thus, the solution set of $x + 4 = 9$ is $\{5\}$.

The solution set of an equation is a subset of the domain of the variable. Hence, the solution set of an equation depends on the domain of the variable. When the domain of x is {real numbers}, the solution set of $x + 4 = 9$ is $\{5\}$. However, when the domain of x is {even integers}, the solution set of $x + 4 = 9$ is the empty set, $\varnothing$, because there is no even integer that can replace x in $x + 4 = 9$ and make the resulting statement true.

To **solve an equation** means to find its solution set.

An **identity** is an equation that becomes a true statement for every value of the variable over the domain of the variable. For example, $9 + x = x + 9$ is an identity if the domain of x is the set of real numbers.

A **conditional equation** or, more simply, an **equation** is an equation that becomes a true statement for some but not for every value of the variable over the domain of the variable. For example, if the domain of x is {real numbers}, $x + 4 = 9$ is a conditional equation because it is true only when $x = 5$.

There are some equations which are not satisfied by any element of the domain. For example, $x = x + 1$ is never true if the domain of x is the set of real numbers. The solution set of such an equation is the empty set, $\varnothing$.

Exercises

In 1–3, tell whether the number in parentheses is a root of the given equation.

1. $2x + 5 = 13$ (4)   **2.** $20 = 4x - 8$ (3)   **3.** $\frac{1}{2}x = 36$ (18)

In 4–6, using the domain {1, 2, 3, 4, 5, 6}, find the solution set of the equation. If the equation has no roots, indicate the solution set as the empty set, $\varnothing$.

4. $4x + 5 = 21$ **5.** $6 - 3x = 0$ **6.** $\frac{1}{2}x + 8 = 20$

7. Find the solution set of $2x + 4 = 6$ when the domain of x is (a) {positive integers} and (b) {negative integers}.

8. What might be the domain of x in order that the solution set of $x + 5 = 4$ be the empty set?

9. What is the solution set of $2x + 5 = 7 + 2x$ when the domain of x is {real numbers}?

10. What is the solution set of $4x + 2 = 2(2x + 1)$ when the domain of x is {natural numbers}?

In 11–16, using the domain {0, 1, 2, 3, 4, 5}, tell whether the equation is a conditional equation or an identity.

11. $2x + 1 = 11$ **12.** $2x + 1 = 1 + 2x$ **13.** $r - 2 - 3 = r - 5$

14. $7b = b \times 7$ **15.** $7b = 56 - 7b$ **16.** $3 \times 2 \times t = t \times 2 \times 3$

2. Solving Simple First-Degree Equations

In this chapter, we will study only **first-degree equations** in one variable that are expressible in the form $ax + b = c$, $a \neq 0$, such as $2x + 3 = 5$. If the domain of the variable is not stated, we will assume it to be {real numbers}.

Equivalent equations are equations that have the same solution set. For example, $x + 4 = 9$ and $x = 5$ are equivalent equations because the solution set of each equation is {5}.

When we solve the equation $x + 4 = 9$, we obtain the equivalent equation $x = 5$. In general, when we solve an equation, we transform it into a simpler equivalent equation of the form $x = n$ whose solution set, $\{n\}$, is also the solution set of the original given equation. In order to transform an equation of the form $ax + b = c$ into an equivalent equation of the form $x = n$ whose solution set is $\{n\}$, we will make use of certain postulates.

POSTULATES INVOLVING EQUIVALENT EQUATIONS

We will assume five postulates, which correspond to the addition, subtraction, multiplication, and division properties of equality.

Postulate 1. Substituting an equivalent expression for an expression in an equation results in an equation that is equivalent to the given equation.

Thus, $2x + 3x = 10$ and $5x = 10$ are equivalent equations.

Postulate 2. If the same number or expression is added to both members of an equation, the resulting equation is equivalent to the original equation.

Thus, if $x - 4 = 5$, then $(x - 4) + 4 = 5 + 4$, and $x = 5 + 4$. Hence, $x - 4 = 5$ has been transformed into $x = 5 + 4$ by Postulate 2. In this way, *the operation of subtraction is undone by addition*, its inverse operation. Therefore, the solution set of $x - 4 = 5$ is $\{9\}$.

Postulate 3. If the same number or expression is subtracted from both members of an equation, the resulting equation is equivalent to the original equation.

Thus, if $x + 8 = 14$, then $(x + 8) - 8 = 14 - 8$, and $x = 14 - 8$. Hence, $x + 8 = 14$ has been transformed into $x = 14 - 8$ by Postulate 3. In this way, *the operation of addition is undone by subtraction*, its inverse operation. Therefore, the solution set of $x + 8 = 14$ is $\{6\}$.

Postulate 4. If both members of an equation are multiplied by the same non-zero number or expression, the resulting equation is equivalent to the original equation.

Thus, if $\dfrac{x}{2} = 4$, then $2\left(\dfrac{x}{2}\right) = 2\,(4)$ and $x = 2(4)$. Hence, $\dfrac{x}{2} = 4$ has been transformed into $x = 2(4)$ by Postulate 4. In this way, *the operation of division has been undone by multiplication*, its inverse operation. Therefore, the solution set of $\dfrac{x}{2} = 4$, or $\frac{1}{2}x = 4$, is $\{8\}$.

Postulate 5. If both members of an equation are divided by the same nonzero number or expression, the resulting equation is equivalent to the original equation.

Thus, if $3x = 15$, then $\dfrac{3x}{3} = \dfrac{15}{3}$ and $x = \dfrac{15}{3}$. Hence, $3x = 15$ has been trans-

formed into $x = \dfrac{15}{3}$ by Postulate 5. In this way, *the operation of multiplication has been undone by division*, its inverse operation. Therefore, the solution set of $3x = 15$ is $\{5\}$.

In the examples in which Postulates 2–5 were applied, notice that the inverse operation of the operation associated with the variable was used to transform the given simple equation into an equivalent equation of the form $x = a$. In this respect, the four fundamental operations are paired as follows:

Addition and subtraction are inverse operations of each other.

That is, addition undoes subtraction, and subtraction undoes addition.

Multiplication and division are inverse operations of each other.

That is, multiplication undoes division, and division undoes multiplication.

Exercises

In 1–28, solve for the variable and check.

1. $y + 5 = 6$ **2.** $x - 3 = 9$ **3.** $36 = y + 10$ **4.** $x - 5 = -8$
5. $5 + r = -7$ **6.** $-3 = s - 7$ **7.** $3 = c + 12$ **8.** $.6 + m = .9$
9. $x + 2\frac{1}{2} = 6$ **10.** $x - 1\frac{1}{5} = -8$ **11.** $-\frac{3}{4} = x - 1\frac{1}{4}$ **12.** $4\frac{1}{2} = x + 6\frac{3}{4}$
13. $5a = 40$ **14.** $12x = -48$ **15.** $-63 = 9t$ **16.** $-x = -3$
17. $.7b = 84$ **18.** $.01x = 25$ **19.** $.002y = .4$ **20.** $1.4 = .5t$
21. $\frac{1}{4}x = 8$ **22.** $\frac{3}{5}b = 21$ **23.** $\frac{5}{8}x = -20$ **24.** $-\frac{3}{4}x = 36$
25. $-\frac{3}{2}y = -1\frac{1}{2}$ **26.** $\frac{2}{3}x = -1.8$ **27.** $\dfrac{y}{3} = -12$ **28.** $\dfrac{2x}{3} = \dfrac{4}{9}$

In 29–34, determine the elements of the set if $x \in \{\text{real numbers}\}$.

29. $\{x \mid x - 4 = 7\}$ **30.** $\{x \mid x + 15 = -9\}$ **31.** $\{x \mid 15 = x + 15\}$
32. $\{x \mid 4x = 28\}$ **33.** $\{x \mid \frac{1}{5}x = -5\}$ **34.** $\left\{x \mid \dfrac{x}{3} = -6\right\}$

3. Solving Equations by Using Several Operations

Procedure. To solve an equation by performing several operations upon a variable, use inverse operations to obtain an equivalent equation of the form $x = a$.

~~~~~~~~~~~~~~ *MODEL PROBLEMS* ~~~~~~~~~~~~~~

1. Solve and check: $\frac{2}{3}x + 5 = 11$

How To Proceed	*Solution*
	$\frac{2}{3}x + 5 = 11$
1. To undo addition, subtract the same number from each side. (*Note.* S_5 means "subtract 5 from each side.")	$S_5: (\frac{2}{3}x + 5) - 5 = (11) - 5$ $\frac{2}{3}x = 6$
2. To undo multiplication, divide each side by the same number. (*Note.* $D_{\frac{2}{3}}$ means "divide each side by $\frac{2}{3}$.")	$D_{\frac{2}{3}}: \frac{2}{3}x \div \frac{2}{3} = 6 \div \frac{2}{3}$ $x = 6 \times \frac{3}{2}$ $x = 9$
	Check $\frac{2}{3}x + 5 = 11$ Let $x = 9$: $\frac{2}{3}(9) + 5 \overset{?}{=} 11$ $6 + 5 \overset{?}{=} 11$ $11 = 11$ (true)

Answer: $x = 9$, or solution set is $\{9\}$.

In model problems, if the check is not included, it is left to the student to perform the check.

2. Solve and check: $5x - 4 = 3x + 10$

How To Proceed	*Solution*
	$5x - 4 = 3x + 10$
1. To undo addition, subtract the same number from each side.	$S_{3x}: (5x - 4) - 3x = (3x + 10) - 3x$ $2x - 4 = 10$
2. To undo subtraction, add the same number to each side. (*Note.* A_4 means "add 4 to each side.")	$A_4: (2x - 4) + 4 = (10) + 4$ $2x = 14$
3. To undo multiplication, divide each side by the same number.	$D_2: \dfrac{2x}{2} = \dfrac{14}{2}$ $x = 7$

Answer: $x = 7$, or solution set is $\{7\}$.

Exercises

In 1–30, solve the equation and check.

1. $11y + 12 = 39$ **2.** $5s - s = 36$ **3.** $2m - \frac{1}{2} = 3\frac{1}{2}$

4. $.8z - 5 = .6$ **5.** $90 = 4x - 10$ **6.** $3y - 8 = 25$

7. $6x + x = 49$ **8.** $8b - b - 2 = 18$ **9.** $38 = 9x + x + 3$

10. $\dfrac{a}{4} - 3 = 5$ **11.** $\frac{1}{2}c + \frac{1}{4}c = 6$ **12.** $3n + 4n - 5 = 30$

13. $\dfrac{3x}{5} + 4 = 34$ **14.** $\dfrac{m}{5} + 3\frac{1}{2} = 6\frac{1}{2}$ **15.** $5x - 3x + 5 = 21$

16. $.4c - 4 = 3.6$ **17.** $\dfrac{b}{4} - \dfrac{5}{2} = 4\frac{1}{2}$ **18.** $21 = \dfrac{4x}{9} - 7$

19. $\dfrac{x}{10} + \dfrac{3x}{5} = 14$ **20** $\dfrac{3y}{2} = 16\frac{1}{2}$ **21.** $5b + 3 - b = 22$

22. $17 = \frac{1}{3}x + 5$ **23.** $\dfrac{3a}{4} - 3 = 9$ **24.** $7x - 3 = 5x + 7$

25. $5x = 48 - x$ **26.** $3y + 12 = 7y$ **27.** $4y + 5 = y + 35$

28. $2m = 5m - 30$ **29.** $8c - 21 = c$ **30.** $3b - 3 = 37 - 2b$

In 31–33, determine the elements of the set if $x \in \{\text{real numbers}\}$.

31. $\{x \mid 3x + 5 = -7\}$ **32.** $\{x \mid 5x = 3x + 4\}$ **33.** $\{x \mid 5x - 8 = 7x - 4\}$

4. Solving Equations by Using Transposition

By using the addition postulate to solve $5x - 3 = 10$, we obtain an equivalent equation $5x = 10 + 3$. If we compare the two equations, we notice that -3 has disappeared from the left member of the original equation, and its opposite, $+3$, now appears in the right member of the equivalent equation.

By using the subtraction postulate to solve $4y = 20 + 2y$, we obtain an equivalent equation $4y - 2y = 20$. If we compare the two equations, we notice that $+2y$ has disappeared from the right member of the original equation and its opposite, $-2y$, now appears in the left member of the equivalent equation.

These examples illustrate that we can make a term disappear from one member of an equation by making the opposite of that term appear in the other member of the equation. In this way, we obtain an equation that is equivalent to the original equation. This process is called ***transposition***. It must be kept in mind that transposition is not a mathematical operation. Transposition is merely a short-cut device for transforming an equation into an equivalent equation by using the postulates involving the inverse operations of addition and subtraction (postulates 2 and 3).

~~~~~~~~~~~~~~ *MODEL PROBLEM* ~~~~~~~~~~~~~~

Solve the equation $9x - 4 = 12 + 5x$.

How To Proceed	*Solution*
	$9x - 4 = 12 + 5x$
1. Transpose.	$9x - 5x = 12 + 4$
2. Collect like terms.	$4x = 16$
3. Solve the resulting equation.	$D_4: \dfrac{4x}{4} = \dfrac{16}{4}$
	$x = 4$

Check: The check, which is performed by substituting 4 for x in the given equation, is left to the student.

Answer: $x = 4$, or the solution set is $\{4\}$.

~~~~~~~~~~~~~~~~~~~~~~~~~~~~~~~~~~~~~~

Exercises

In 1–26, solve the equation and check.

1. $5x + 3 = 23$ 2. $6x - 5 = 31$ 3. $4c = 5 - 6c$
4. $7d = d - 12$ 5. $-3x - 5 = 10$ 6. $3x + 2\frac{1}{2} = 5\frac{1}{2}$
7. $19 = 4x - 6.5$ 8. $2x + \frac{1}{4} = \frac{3}{4}$ 9. $1.4x = .49 - .7x$
10. $.9x = .6x - 3$ 11. $15 = 20 + 15n$ 12. $5n = 7n - 12$
13. $9x - 5 = 7x + 3$ 14. $11y - 7 = 6y - 22$ 15. $14x + 3 = 8 - x$
16. $5y - 1 = 15y + 4$ 17. $5 - 4c = c + 20$ 18. $7x - 4 + 3x = 26$
19. $25 + 7x - 1 = 4x$ 20. $1.4x - 7 = 5 - .6x$
21. $1.2x - 3.6 + .3x = 2.4$ 22. $3.7y = 4.5y - 10 - 5.8y$
23. $2\frac{1}{2}x - 5 + 1\frac{1}{4}x = 10 - \frac{3}{4}x$ 24. $2x - 1\frac{2}{3} = 8\frac{1}{3} + 7x$
25. $10x - 5 + 12 = 7x + 21 - 4x$
26. $8x - 9 + x - 17 = 3x + 4 + 8x - 12$

5. Solving Equations That Contain Parentheses

To solve an equation that contains parentheses, such as $2(x + 3) - 5 = 17 - (4x - 2)$, transform it into an equivalent equation that does not have parentheses. Note how this is done in the following model problem:

~~~~~~~~~~~ *MODEL PROBLEM* ~~~~~~~~~~~

Solve for x: $2(x + 3) - 5 = 17 - (4x - 2)$

How To Proceed	*Solution*
	$2(x + 3) - 5 = 17 - (4x - 2)$
1. Transform the equation by performing the indicated operations.	$2x + 6 - 5 = 17 - 4x + 2$
2. Collect like terms.	$2x + 1 = 19 - 4x$
3. Solve the resulting equation.	$6x = 18$
	$D_6: \dfrac{6x}{6} = \dfrac{18}{3}$
	$x = 3$

Answer: $x = 3$, or solution set is $\{3\}$.

~~~~~~

Exercises

In 1–18, solve the equation and check.

1. $3(x - 5) = 6$
2. $3(2x + 1) = -15$
3. $4(3 - x) = 2x$
4. $7(a + 2) = 5(a + 4)$
5. $5x + (x - 2) = 1$
6. $6 = 5 - (3x - 4)$
7. $4(x - 3) + 3x = 16$
8. $6x - 3(x - 4) = 6$
9. $13 + 2(3x + 1) = 9x + 12$
10. $10 - y = 3 - 6(y - 2)$
11. $17 - 8(2 + 3x) = 5$
12. $4x = 11 - 3(4x + 5)$
13. $3y + (2y - 5) = 13 - 2(y + 2)$
14. $2(y - 3) - 17 = 13 - 3(y + 2)$
15. $3(x - 2) - 2 = 5(x + 3) - 7(x - 1)$
16. $(x + 3)(x + 2) = x(x + 7)$
17. $(4 - c)(6 + c) = 40 - (c^2 - 4c - 18)$
18. $(x - 1)^2 - 3x(x - 2) = 19 - 2x(x + 1)$

In 19–22, determine the element of the set if the domain of the variable is {real numbers}.

19. $\{x \mid 3x + (2x - 1) = 4\}$
20. $\{y \mid 8y = 15 - (2y + 35)\}$
21. $\{c \mid 5c - 2(c - 5) = 17\}$
22. $\{z \mid 6z = 10 + 4(2z - 6)\}$

6. Graphing the Solution Set of a First-Degree Equation

〰〰〰〰〰〰〰〰 *MODEL PROBLEMS* 〰〰〰〰〰〰〰〰

In 1 and 2, using the set of real numbers as the domain, (*a*) find the solution set of the equation and (*b*) graph the solution set. The checks are left to the student.

1. $4x - 1 = 5$

Solution:

a. $4x - 1 = 5$

$\quad 4x = 5 + 1$

$\quad 4x = 6$

$\quad x = 1.5$

Answer: Solution set is {1.5}.

b.

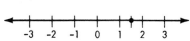

2. $\dfrac{x}{2} + 1 = 3$

Solution:

a. $\dfrac{x}{2} + 1 = 3$

$\quad \dfrac{x}{2} = 3 - 1$

$\quad \dfrac{x}{2} = 2$

$\quad x = 4$

Answer: Solution set is {4}.

b.

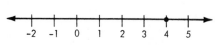

〰〰〰〰〰〰〰〰〰〰〰〰〰〰〰〰〰〰〰〰〰〰〰〰

Exercises

In 1–18, find and graph the solution set. Use the set of real numbers as the domain.

1. $x - 3 = 2$

2. $x + 12 = 8$

3. $y - 1\frac{1}{2} = 2\frac{1}{2}$

4. $-3m = 6$

5. $\frac{1}{2}x = -2$

6. $3y + 4 = 13$

7. $2x + 18 = 8$

8. $5x - 2 = -22$

9. $\frac{1}{5}y - 3 = -4$

10. $8y = 90 - 2y$

11. $5a - 14 = 3a$

12. $y = 9y - 72$

13. $6y - 7 = 4y + 3$

14. $11x + 7 = 4x - 21$

15. $2(10 - 3c) = 22$

16. $3(x - 5) = 2(2x + 1)$

17. $5x - 2(x - 5) = 10$

18. $15y - 4(3y + 2) = -14$

In 19–24, graph the element of the set if $x \in$ {real numbers}.

19. $\{x \mid 3x + 2 = 20\}$

20. $\{x \mid 5x + 2x = -21\}$

21. $\{x \mid 5x = 7x + 8\}$

22. $\{x \mid 7x - (9x + 1) = -5\}$

23. $\{x \mid 4x + 2(x - 1) = 7\}$

24. $\{x \mid 2(4x + 3) = 3(3x + 3)\}$

7. Solving Equations Containing Fractions

The following are examples of equations that contain fractions:

$$\tfrac{1}{2}x + 20 = \tfrac{3}{4}x \qquad \frac{x}{2} + 20 = \frac{3x}{4} \qquad \frac{6}{x-1} = 3$$

To solve such equations, we transform the equation that contains fractions into a simpler equivalent equation that does not contain fractions. We can do this by multiplying both members of the equation by the least common denominator, L.C.D., of its denominators. This process is called *clearing the equation of fractions*.

EQUATIONS CONTAINING FRACTIONS WITH NUMERICAL DENOMINATORS

~~~~~~~~~~~~~~~~~~ *MODEL PROBLEM* ~~~~~~~~~~~~~~~~~~

Solve: $\dfrac{4x+1}{7} - \dfrac{2x-1}{6} = \dfrac{3}{2}$

How To Proceed	*Solution*
	$\dfrac{4x+1}{7} - \dfrac{2x-1}{6} = \dfrac{3}{2}$
1. Find the L.C.D.	L.C.D. $= 42$
2. Clear the equation of fractions by multiplying both of its members by the L.C.D.	$M_{42}\!: 42\left(\dfrac{4x+1}{7} - \dfrac{2x-1}{6}\right) = 42\left(\dfrac{3}{2}\right)$
3. Solve the resulting equation.	$\overset{6}{\cancel{42}}\left(\dfrac{4x+1}{\cancel{7}}\right) - \overset{7}{\cancel{42}}\left(\dfrac{2x-1}{\cancel{6}}\right) = \overset{21}{\cancel{42}}\left(\dfrac{3}{\cancel{2}}\right)$
	$\quad\; 1 \qquad\qquad\quad 1 \qquad\qquad 1$
	$6(4x+1) - 7(2x-1) = 63$
	$24x + 6 - 14x + 7 = 63$
	$10x + 13 = 63$
	$10x = 50$
	$x = 5$

Check: Substituting 5 for x in the given equation results in the true statement
$3 - 1\tfrac{1}{2} = \tfrac{3}{2}$, or $1\tfrac{1}{2} = 1\tfrac{1}{2}$.

Answer: $x = 5$, or solution set is $\{5\}$.

~~~~~~

Exercises

In 1–22, solve and check.

1. $\dfrac{5x}{7} = 35$ **2.** $\dfrac{3a - 1}{4} = 2$ **3.** $\dfrac{1 - 2x}{5} = 1$

4. $\dfrac{y}{4} + \dfrac{y}{3} = \dfrac{7}{12}$ **5.** $\dfrac{a}{3} - \dfrac{a}{4} = \dfrac{2}{3}$ **6.** $\dfrac{17}{4} + \dfrac{3a}{8} = \dfrac{4a}{5}$

7. $\dfrac{x}{2} + \dfrac{x}{3} + \dfrac{x}{4} = 26$ **8.** $\frac{5}{8}x - \frac{1}{3}x = \frac{5}{6}x - 13$ **9.** $y + 1 - \frac{3}{4}y = \frac{1}{5}y$

10. $\dfrac{x}{6} + \dfrac{3x}{8} = \dfrac{5x}{8} - 5\frac{1}{4}$ **11.** $\dfrac{y}{4} - \dfrac{1}{2} = \dfrac{5}{12} - \dfrac{2y}{3}$ **12.** $\dfrac{4y}{15} + 2\dfrac{5}{12} = 3 - \dfrac{y}{5}$

13. $\dfrac{3y + 1}{4} = \dfrac{13 - y}{2}$ **14.** $\dfrac{4y + 6}{5} = \dfrac{8y + 5}{3}$ **15.** $\dfrac{a + 3}{3} + \dfrac{a - 3}{6} = 5$

16. $\dfrac{4}{3} + \dfrac{x - 3}{4} = \dfrac{3x - 1}{6}$ **17.** $\dfrac{x + 2}{4} - \dfrac{x - 3}{3} = \dfrac{1}{2}$ **18.** $\dfrac{3x + 1}{4} = 2 - \dfrac{3 - 2x}{6}$

19. $\dfrac{x + 4}{4} - \dfrac{3x - 9}{7} = \dfrac{1}{2}$ **20.** $\dfrac{7x + 5}{8} - \dfrac{3x + 15}{10} = 2$

21. $\frac{2}{3}(4x - 1) - \frac{3}{5}(x + 1) = 7$ **22.** $\frac{3}{2}(2x + 1) - \frac{1}{3}(4x - 1) = -3\frac{1}{6}$

SOLVING FRACTIONAL EQUATIONS

A *fractional equation* is an equation that contains at least one fraction with the variable in the denominator. To solve such an equation, we use the same methods as those used in solving equations that contain fractions with numerical denominators. (See the model problems on the following page.)

EXTRANEOUS ROOTS OF A FRACTIONAL EQUATION

Sometimes, when we multiply both members of an equation by a polynomial that is the L.C.D. of the denominators of the equation, the resulting equation is not equivalent to the given equation. Consider the solution of the following equation:

$$\frac{m}{m - 2} - \frac{m + 4}{3(m - 2)} = \frac{1}{3}$$

Multiply by the L.C.D., $3(m - 2)$.

$$3(m - 2)\left[\frac{m}{m - 2} - \frac{m + 4}{3(m - 2)}\right] = 3(m - 2)(\tfrac{1}{3})$$
$$3m - (m + 4) = m - 2$$
$$3m - m - 4 = m - 2$$
$$m = 2$$

~~~~~~~~~~~~~ *MODEL PROBLEMS* ~~~~~~~~~~~~~

1. *Solve:* $\dfrac{x+5}{2x} = \dfrac{15}{x} - 2$

Solution:

$$\frac{x+5}{2x} = \frac{15}{x} - 2$$

L.C.D. $= 2x$

$$2x\left(\frac{x+5}{2x}\right) = 2x\left(\frac{15}{x} - 2\right)$$

$$\overset{1}{\cancel{2x}}\left(\frac{x+5}{\cancel{2x}}\right) = \overset{2}{\cancel{2x}}\left(\frac{15}{\cancel{x}}\right) - 2x(2)$$

$$1(x+5) = 2(15) - 4x$$
$$x+5 = 30 - 4x$$
$$x+4x = 30 - 5$$
$$5x = 25$$
$$x = 5$$

Check: $\dfrac{x+5}{2x} = \dfrac{15}{x} - 2$

Let $x = 5$: $\dfrac{5+5}{2(5)} \overset{?}{=} \dfrac{15}{5} - 2$

$$\frac{10}{10} \overset{?}{=} 3 - 2$$

$$1 = 1 \text{ (true)}$$

Answer: $x = 5$, or solution set is $\{5\}$.

2. *Solve:* $\dfrac{7c-4}{c^2-c} = \dfrac{5}{c-1}$

Solution:

$$\frac{7c-4}{c^2-c} = \frac{5}{c-1}$$

L.C.D. $= c(c-1)$

$$\overset{1}{\cancel{c(c-1)}}\left(\frac{7c-4}{\underset{1}{\cancel{c(c-1)}}}\right) = c\overset{1}{\cancel{(c-1)}}\left(\frac{5}{\underset{1}{\cancel{(c-1)}}}\right)$$

$$1(7c-4) = c(5)$$
$$7c - 4 = 5c$$
$$2c = 4$$
$$c = 2$$

Check:

$$\frac{7c-4}{c^2-c} = \frac{5}{c-1}$$

Let $c = 2$: $\dfrac{7(2)-4}{(2)^2-2} \overset{?}{=} \dfrac{5}{2-1}$

$$\frac{14-4}{4-2} \overset{?}{=} \frac{5}{1}$$

$$\frac{10}{2} \overset{?}{=} 5$$

$$5 = 5 \text{ (true)}$$

Answer: $c = 2$, or solution set is $\{2\}$.

~~~~~~

If we now check the solution by letting $m = 2$ in the given equation, on the preceding pages, we obtain:

$$\frac{2}{2-2} - \frac{2+4}{3(2-2)} \overset{?}{=} \frac{1}{3} \quad \text{or} \quad \frac{2}{0} - \frac{6}{0} \overset{?}{=} \frac{1}{3}$$

Since division by 0 is not defined, $\frac{2}{0}$ and $\frac{6}{0}$ are meaningless. Therefore, $m = 2$ is not a root of the given equation. However, $m = 2$ is a root of the *derived* equation $3m - (m+4) = m - 2$. Such a number, which is a root of the derived equation but is not a root of the original given equation, is called an **extraneous root**.

The equation $\dfrac{m}{m-2} - \dfrac{m+4}{3(m-2)} = \dfrac{1}{3}$ has no roots. Therefore, its solution set is the empty set, $\varnothing$.

We see that when we transform a fractional equation by multiplying both of its members by a polynomial multiplier which represents zero, the resulting derived equation and the original equation may not be equivalent equations.

KEEP IN MIND

When solving a fractional equation, check each solution of the derived equation in the original equation to see whether or not it belongs to the solution set of the original equation.

Exercises

In 1–27, solve and check.

1. $\dfrac{18}{x} - 4 = 2$

2. $\dfrac{30}{x} - \dfrac{18}{2x} = 7$

3. $\dfrac{3x-1}{4x} = \dfrac{2x+3}{3x}$

4. $\dfrac{2+x}{6x} = \dfrac{3}{5x} + \dfrac{1}{30}$

5. $\dfrac{9}{2b+1} = 3$

6. $\dfrac{6}{3a-1} = \dfrac{3}{4}$

7. $\dfrac{3}{5-3t} = \dfrac{1}{2}$

8. $\dfrac{x}{x+2} = \dfrac{2}{3}$

9. $\dfrac{4x}{7+5x} = \dfrac{1}{3}$

10. $\dfrac{3}{x} = \dfrac{2}{5-x}$

11. $\dfrac{4}{3c} = \dfrac{3}{2c-1}$

12. $\dfrac{x+3}{x+1} = \dfrac{x+2}{x+4}$

13. $\dfrac{d-2}{d+1} = \dfrac{d+1}{d-2}$

14. $\dfrac{3x+2}{2x-3} = \dfrac{3x-2}{2x-5}$

15. $\dfrac{3r}{3r-1} = \dfrac{r+3}{r+2}$

16. $\dfrac{4}{x-1} = \dfrac{5}{x^2-x}$

17. $\dfrac{x^2+6x}{x^2-4} = \dfrac{x+3}{x-2}$

18. $\dfrac{7}{x-1} = 5 + \dfrac{7}{x-1}$

19. $\dfrac{4m}{m-2} - \dfrac{13}{3m-6} = \dfrac{1}{3}$

20. $\dfrac{1}{t-5} + \dfrac{1}{t+5} = \dfrac{8}{t^2-25}$

21. $\dfrac{w+1}{w-3} - \dfrac{2w-4}{w^2-9} = 1$

22. $\dfrac{6}{x^2-1} = \dfrac{-3}{x+1} + \dfrac{5}{x-1}$

23. $\dfrac{8}{x^2-1} = \dfrac{7}{x-1} - \dfrac{4}{x+1}$

24. $\dfrac{3}{2b+4} - \dfrac{4}{b-2} = \dfrac{3}{2b^2-8}$

25. $\dfrac{t+1}{2t+6} - \dfrac{t-2}{2t-6} = \dfrac{9}{t^2-9}$

26. $\dfrac{20}{y^2-4} = \dfrac{1}{y-2} - \dfrac{5}{y+2}$

27. $\dfrac{30}{9-y^2} = \dfrac{5}{3+y} + \dfrac{2}{3-y}$

8. Solving Verbal Problems Using One Variable and a First-Degree Equation

Now we are ready to solve verbal problems algebraically.

To solve a verbal problem by using a first-degree equation involving one variable, first read the problem carefully until you understand what is given in the problem and what is to be found. Then use the following:

Procedure. **To solve a verbal problem:**
1. **Represent the unknowns in terms of a variable.**
2. **Translate the relationships stated in the problem into an equation.**
3. **Solve the equation to find its root.**
4. **Check the answer by testing it in the word statement of the original problem to see that it satisfies all the required conditions.**

NUMBER PROBLEMS

~~~~~~~~~~~~~~ *MODEL PROBLEM* ~~~~~~~~~~~~~~

Five times a number, decreased by 18, equals three times the number, increased by 6. Find the number.

How To Proceed	*Solution*
1. *Represent* the unknown by a variable.	Let $x =$ the number.
2. *Translate* the relationship involving the unknown into an equation.	Five times the number, decreased by 18 · equals · three times the number, increased by six.
	$5x - 18 \qquad = \qquad 3x + 6$
3. *Solve* the equation.	$5x - 18 = 3x + 6$ $2x = 24$ $x = 12$
4. *Check* in the original problem.	Does 12 check in the original problem? $5(12) - 18 \overset{?}{=} 3(12) + 6$ $42 = 42$ (true)

Answer: The number is 12.

~~~~~~

Exercises

1. The larger of two numbers is twice the smaller. If the sum of the numbers is 120, find the numbers.
2. The larger of two numbers is 1 less than three times the smaller. The difference between the two numbers is 9. Find the numbers.
3. The larger of two numbers exceeds twice the smaller by 6. If the sum of the numbers is 30, find the numbers.
4. If 10 times a number is increased by 4, the result is 12 more than 9 times the number. Find the number.
5. If 14 is added to a certain number and the sum is multiplied by 2, the result is equal to 8 times the number, decreased by 14. Find the number.
6. The larger of two numbers is 1 more than 3 times the smaller. If 8 times the smaller is decreased by 2 times the larger, the result is 10. Find the numbers.
7. The larger of two numbers is 1 more than twice the smaller. Three times the larger exceeds 5 times the smaller by 10. Find the numbers.
8. Separate 144 into two parts such that one part will be 12 less than twice the other.

CONSECUTIVE INTEGER PROBLEMS

PREPARING TO SOLVE CONSECUTIVE INTEGER PROBLEMS

An **integer** is a member of set I where $I = \{\ldots, -3, -2, -1, 0, 1, 2, 3, \ldots\}$.

An **even integer** is an integer which is twice another integer. For example, 4 and -12 are even integers.

An **odd integer** is an integer which is not an even integer. For example, 3 and -9 are odd integers.

Consecutive integers are integers which differ by 1. Each of the following is a set of three consecutive integers arranged in increasing order from left to right:

$$\{2, 3, 4\} \qquad \{-7, -6, -5\}$$

In general, a set of three consecutive integers may be represented by:

$$\{n, n + 1, n + 2\} \text{ if } n \in \{\text{integers}\}$$

Consecutive even integers are even integers which differ by 2. Each of the following is a set of three consecutive even integers arranged in increasing order from left to right:

$$\{4, 6, 8\} \qquad \{-6, -4, -2\}$$

In general, a set of three consecutive even integers may be represented by:

$$\{n, n + 2, n + 4\} \text{ if } n \in \{\text{even integers}\}$$

Consecutive odd integers are odd integers which differ by 2. Each of the following is a set of three consecutive odd integers arranged in increasing order from left to right:

$$\{1, 3, 5\} \qquad \{-9, -7, -5\}$$

In general, a set of three consecutive odd integers may be represented by:

$$\{n, n + 2, n + 4\} \text{ if } n \in \{\text{odd integers}\}$$

KEEP IN MIND

1. Consecutive integers differ by 1.
2. Consecutive even integers and also consecutive odd integers differ by 2.

SOLVING CONSECUTIVE INTEGER PROBLEMS

〜〜〜〜〜〜〜〜 *MODEL PROBLEM* 〜〜〜〜〜〜〜〜

Find 3 consecutive odd integers such that 5 times the first, decreased by the second exceeds twice the third by 16.

Solution:

Let $n =$ the first consecutive odd integer.

Then $n + 2 =$ the second consecutive odd integer.

And $n + 4 =$ the third consecutive odd integer.

Five times the first, decreased by the second	is	16 more than twice the third.

$$5n - (n + 2) = 2(n + 4) + 16$$
$$5n - n - 2 = 2n + 8 + 16$$
$$4n - 2 = 2n + 24$$
$$2n = 26$$
$$n = 13$$
$$n + 2 = 15, \ n + 4 = 17$$

Check in the original problem: The integers 13, 15, 17 are consecutive odd integers. They satisfy the condition in the given problem, 5(13), or 65, decreased by 15, that is, 50, does exceed 2(17), or 34, by 16.

Answer: The odd integers are 13, 15, and 17.

〜〜〜〜〜〜〜〜〜〜〜〜〜〜〜〜〜〜〜〜〜〜〜〜〜〜〜〜〜〜

Exercises

1. Find three consecutive integers whose sum is (*a*) 99 and (*b*) —57.
2. Find three consecutive even integers whose sum is (*a*) 48 and (*b*) —60.
3. Find four consecutive odd integers whose sum is (*a*) 112 and (*b*) —136.
4. Find three consecutive even integers such that the sum of the smallest and twice the second is 20 more than the third.
5. Find three consecutive integers such that the first increased by twice the second exceeds the third by 24.
6. Find three consecutive even integers such that twice the sum of the second and the third exceeds 3 times the first by 34.
7. Find three consecutive odd integers such that the product of the second and third exceeds the square of the first by 50.
8. Prove that the sum of 3 consecutive even integers cannot be 40.
9. Prove that the sum of 3 consecutive odd integers cannot be 40.
10. Prove that the sum of three consecutive integers is equal to 3 times the middle integer.

COIN OR STAMP PROBLEMS

PREPARING TO SOLVE COIN OR STAMP PROBLEMS

The total value, T, of a number of coins or stamps of the same kind equals the number of the coins or stamps, N, multiplied by the value of each coin or stamp, V.

This relationship may be expressed by the formula $T = NV$.

Thus, 6 nickels have a total value of $6(5) = 30$ cents.

Twelve 6-cent stamps have a total value of $12(6) = 72$ cents.

Note. In $T = NV$, T and V must be expressed in the same unit of money; that is, if V is in dollars, then T must be in dollars.

In solving problems which deal with groups of coins or stamps of different denominations—for example, nickels, dimes, and quarters—it is often helpful to represent the values of the different groups of coins or stamps in terms of the same unit of money. In the following examples, the unit of money is cents:

The value of 7 nickels in cents is $7(5)$, or 35 cents.

The value of d dimes in cents is $d(10)$, or $10d$ cents.

The value of $(3q + 1)$ quarters in cents in $(3q + 1)25$, or $(75q + 25)$ cents.

The relationship involving the number of coins, N, each having the same value, V, and the total value of all the coins, T, may be expressed as $NV = T$.

KEEP IN MIND

Number of coins $\times$ Value of each $=$ Total value of all
in the group   coin in cents   the coins in cents
(N) (V) (T)

$$NV = T \qquad V = \frac{T}{N} \qquad N = \frac{T}{V}$$

SOLVING COIN OR STAMP PROBLEMS

~~~~~~~~~~~~ *MODEL PROBLEM* ~~~~~~~~~~~~

In a child's bank, there is a collection of nickels, dimes, and quarters which
amounts to \$4.15. There are 4 times as many dimes as nickels, and there
are 3 less quarters than nickels. How many coins of each kind are there?

Solution:

Let $n =$ the number of nickels.

	Number of coins $\times$	(¢) Value of each coin $=$	(¢) Total value
Nickel	n	5	$5n$
Dime	$4n$	10	$10(4n)$
Quarter	$n-3$	25	$25(n-3)$

The total value of all the coins is 415 cents.

$$5n + 10(4n) + 25(n-3) = 415$$
$$5n + 40n + 25n - 75 = 415$$
$$70n - 75 = 415$$
$$70n = 490$$
$$n = 7$$
$$4n = 28$$
$$n - 3 = 4$$

Answer: There are 7 nickels, 28 dimes, and 4 quarters.

~~~~~~

Exercises

1. Bill has $2.05 in dimes and quarters. He has 4 more quarters than dimes. Find the number he has of each kind of coin.
2. Harry has $2.30 in nickels and dimes. The number of dimes is 7 less than the number of nickels. Find the number he has of each kind of coin.
3. Hilda deposited in her savings account $4.50 in nickels, quarters, and dimes. The number of dimes exceeded the number of nickels by 5, and the number of quarters was 16 less than the number of nickels. Find the number of each kind of coin she deposited.
4. A class contributed $3.50 in dimes and nickels to the Red Cross. In all, there were 45 coins. How many coins of each kind were there?
5. A purse contains $4.70 in nickels and quarters. There are 30 coins in all. How many coins of each kind are there?
6. A postal clerk sold 75 stamps for $4.80. Some were 5-cent stamps and some were 8-cent stamps. How many of each kind of stamp did he sell?
7. In Robert's bank, there is $2.60 in pennies, nickels, and dimes. In all, there are 45 coins. If there are twice as many nickels as pennies, how many coins of each kind are there in the bank?
8. Rose counted her money and found that her 25 coins which were nickels, dimes, and quarters were worth $3.20. The number of dimes exceeded the number of nickels by 4. How many coins of each kind did she have?
9. Prove that it is impossible to have $4.50 in dimes and quarters with the number of quarters being twice the number of dimes.

AGE PROBLEMS

PREPARING TO SOLVE AGE PROBLEMS

If Paul is 15 years old now, 2 years from now he will be $15 + 2$, or 17 years old; 2 years ago, Paul was $15 - 2$, or 13 years old.

KEEP IN MIND

1. To represent a person's age a number of years hence, add that number of years to his present age.
2. To represent a person's age a number of years ago, subtract that number of years from his present age.

~~~~~~~~~~~~~~~~~~~~ *MODEL PROBLEMS* ~~~~~~~~~~~~~~~~~~~~

Represent the age of a person in years:

a. 5 years hence if his present age is x years   *Ans.* $x + 5$

b. 5 years ago if his present age is x years   *Ans.* $x - 5$

c. in y years if his present age is 25 years   *Ans.* $25 + y$

d. y years ago if his present age is 25 years   *Ans.* $25 - y$

e. y years ago if his present age is n years   *Ans.* $n - y$

SOLVING AGE PROBLEMS

~~~~~~~~~~~~~~~~~~~~ *MODEL PROBLEM* ~~~~~~~~~~~~~~~~~~~~

Ray is 20 years older than Bill. Five years ago, Ray was 5 times as old as Bill was then. Find the present age of both Ray and Bill.

Solution:

Let $x =$ Bill's present age in years.

Then $x + 20 =$ Ray's present age in years.

And $x - 5 =$ Bill's age 5 years ago.

And $x + 15 =$ Ray's age 5 years ago.

Ray was 5 times as old as Bill was 5 years ago.

$x + 15 = 5(x - 5)$	*Check* in the original problem:
$x + 15 = 5x - 25$	Is Ray 20 years older than Bill?
$40 = 4x$	$30 \overset{?}{=} 10 + 20,\ 30 = 30$ (true)
$10 = x$	Was Ray 5 times as old as Bill 5 years ago?
$x + 20 = 30$	$30 - 5 \overset{?}{=} 5(10 - 5),\ 25 = 25$ (true)

Answer: Bill's age is 10 years. Ray's age is 30 years.

Exercises

1. Walter is 3 times as old as Martin. Ten years from now, Walter will be twice as old as Martin will be then. How old is each now?

2. Harriet is 3 times as old as Lillian. Ten years from now, Harriet's age will exceed twice Lillian's age at that time by 1 year. Find the present age of both Lillian and Harriet.

3. Sarah's age exceeds Judy's age by 16 years. Four years ago, Sarah was twice as old as Judy was then. Find the present age of each.

4. The sum of Carl's age and Ellen's age is 40 years. Carl's age 10 years from

now will be 1 year less than 4 times Ellen's age 6 years ago. Find their present ages.

5. Sidney is 30 years old and Edward is 15 years old. In how many years will Sidney be $1\frac{1}{2}$ times as old as Edward will be then?

RATIO PROBLEMS

PREPARING TO SOLVE RATIO PROBLEMS

Two numbers whose ratio is $5:2$ may be represented by $5x$ and $2x$ because the ratio of $5x$ to $2x$ may be written $5x:2x$, or $\dfrac{5x}{2x}$, which, simplified, becomes $\frac{5}{2}$, or $5:2$.

In general, if a, b, and x are numbers ($b \neq 0$ and $x \neq 0$), ax and bx represent two numbers whose ratio is $a:b$.

Likewise, three numbers whose continued ratio is $3:2:1$ may be represented by $3x$, $2x$, and $1x$. This is so because the ratio $3x:2x = 3:2$, and the ratio $2x:1x = 2:1$. The separate ratios $3:2$ and $2:1$ may be written as the continued ratio $3:2:1$.

SOLVING RATIO PROBLEMS

~~~~~~~~~~ *MODEL PROBLEM* ~~~~~~~~~~

An angle whose degree measure is 120 is divided into three angles in the ratio $2:3:7$. Find the degree measure of each angle.

Solution:

Let $2x =$ the degree measure of the first angle.

Then $3x =$ the degree measure of the second angle.

And $7x =$ the degree measure of the third angle.

The sum of the degree measures of the three angles is 120.

$$2x + 3x + 7x = 120$$
$$12x = 120$$
$$x = 10$$

$$2x = 20,\ 3x = 30,\ 7x = 70$$

Check in the original problem:

Is the sum of the degree measures of the three angles 120?

$20 + 30 + 70 = 120$ (true)

Is the ratio of the degree measures of the three angles $2:3:7$?

$20:30:70 = 2:3:7$ (true)

Answer: The degree measures of the three angles are 20, 30, 70.

~~~~~~

Exercises

1. Two numbers have the ratio 5 : 3. Their sum is 88. Find the numbers.
2. Find two positive numbers whose ratio is 4 : 1 and whose difference is 36.
3. A line segment 64 inches in length is divided into two parts which are in the ratio 1 : 7. Find the length of each part.
4. The ratio of Paul's age to Saul's age is 2 : 3. The sum of their ages is 35 years. Find the age of each one.
5. Divide $3300 into three parts whose ratio is 1 : 3 : 7.
6. An angle, whose degree measure is 180, is divided into three angles. The degree measures of the first two angles are in the ratio 2 : 3. The degree measure of the third angle is equal to the sum of the degree measures of the first two angles. Find the degree measure of each angle.
7. The ratio of the amount of money Carl has to the amount of money Donald has is 7 : 3. If Carl gives Donald $20, the two will then have equal amounts. Find the original amount that each one has.
8. Two positive numbers have the ratio 2 : 3. The larger number is 30 more than one-half of the smaller number. Find the numbers.
9. Three positive numbers are in the ratio 7 : 3 : 2. The sum of the smallest number and the largest number exceeds twice the remaining number by 30. Find the three numbers.
10. John's age and Helen's age are in the ratio 3 : 5. Two years ago, Helen was twice as old as John was then. Find their present ages.
11. The ratio of Lou's age to Joe's age is 4 : 1. Twenty years from now, Lou will be twice as old as Joe will be then. Find their present ages.
12. Four years ago, the ratio of Grace's age to Martha's age was 5 : 2. At present, Grace's age exceeds twice Martha's age by 2 years. How old were Grace and Martha 4 years ago?

UNIFORM MOTION PROBLEMS

PREPARING TO SOLVE UNIFORM MOTION PROBLEMS

If a car traveled at the rate of 40 miles per hour, in 3 hours it traveled 3(40), or 120 miles. In this case, the three related quantities are:

1. The *distance* traveled, 120 miles (mi.).
2. The rate of speed, or *rate*, 40 miles per hour (mph).
3. The *time* traveled, 3 hours (hr.).

The relation involving the distance, D, the rate, R, and the time, T, may be expressed in the following ways:

$$D = RT \qquad T = \frac{D}{R} \qquad R = \frac{D}{T}$$

In our work, *rate* will represent either of the following:

1. The ***uniform rate of speed***, which represents a rate of speed that does not change throughout a trip.

2. The ***average rate of speed***, which represents the total distance traveled divided by the total time traveled. Thus, a car which traveled 100 miles in 2 hours was traveling at an average rate of $100 \div 2$, or 50 miles per hour.

Note that the rate, time, and distance must be expressed in corresponding units. For example, if the rate is measured in miles per hour, the time must be measured in hours and the distance must be measured in miles.

KEEP IN MIND

$$D = RT \qquad T = \frac{D}{R} \qquad R = \frac{D}{T}$$

SOLVING UNIFORM MOTION PROBLEMS

In solving a uniform motion problem, we can use a chart to organize the facts in the problem and to make the relationships more evident. It is also helpful to draw a diagram to show the relationship of the distances which are involved in the problem.

MODEL PROBLEMS

1. Two trains whose rates differ by 6 miles per hour start at the same time from stations which are 273 miles apart. They meet in $3\frac{1}{2}$ hours. Find the rate of each train.

Solution: Let $r =$ the rate of the slow train.
    Then $r + 6 =$ the rate of the fast train.
First fill in the time and rate of each train.
Then represent the distance for each train.

	(mph) Rate ×	(hr.) Time =	(mi.) Distance
Slow train	r	3.5	$3.5r$
Fast train	$r + 6$	3.5	$3.5(r+6)$

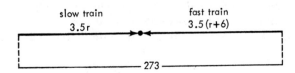

The total distance between the stations was 273 miles.

$$3.5r + 3.5(r + 6) = 273$$
$$3.5r + 3.5r + 21 = 273$$
$$7r = 252$$
$$r = 36$$
$$r + 6 = 42$$

Check in the original problem:

The distance the slow train traveled was 3.5(36) or 126 miles.

The distance the fast train traveled was 3.5(42) or 147 miles.

Was the total distance traveled $\overline{273}$ miles? (true)

Answer: The rate of the slow train is 36 mph. The rate of the fast train is 42 mph.

2. How far can a man drive out into the country at an average rate of 50 mph and return over the same road at the average rate of 40 mph if he travels a total of 9 hours.

Solution: Let $h =$ the number of hours he spent traveling out.

Then $9 - h =$ the number of hours he spent traveling back.

First fill in the rate and time for each trip.

Then represent the distance for each trip.

	(mph) Rate ×	(hr.) Time =	(mi.) Distance
Trip out	50	h	$50h$
Trip back	40	$9 - h$	$40(9 - h)$

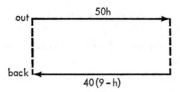

The distance out is the same as the distance back.

$$50h = 40(9 - h)$$
$$50h = 360 - 40h$$
$$50h + 40h = 360$$
$$90h = 360$$
$$h = 4$$

The distance out is $50h = 200$

Check in the original problem:
The distance traveled out is 50(4), or 200 miles.
The distance traveled back is 40(5), or 200 miles.
Are the distances the same? $200 = 200$ (true)
Is the total time 9 hours? $4 + 5 = 9$ (true)

Answer: He can travel 200 miles out into the country.

Exercises

1. Two automobiles start at the same time and travel in opposite directions. The first averages 28 miles per hour and the second averages 35 miles per hour. In how many hours are they 189 miles apart?

2. Two planes start at 9 A.M. at two airports which are 2100 miles apart and fly toward each other at average rates of 150 mph and 200 mph. At what time will they pass each other?

3. A passenger train and a freight train start from the same point at the same time and travel in opposite directions. The passenger train traveled 3 times as fast as the freight train. In 5 hours, they were 360 miles apart. Find the rate of each train.

4. Marie and Anne start from the same point at the same time and travel in the same direction at rates which are in the ratio of 3 : 2. In $2\frac{1}{2}$ hours, they are 30 miles apart. Find the rate of each girl.

5. Arthur and Jim are 292 miles apart. At 10 A.M., they start toward each other; and at 1 P.M., they are 40 miles apart. If Arthur's average rate exceeds Jim's average rate by 8 mph., find the rate of each.

6. Two cars start from the same place at the same time and travel in opposite directions. At the end of 5 hours, they are 340 miles apart. If the average rate of the slower car exceeds $\frac{1}{2}$ of the average rate of the faster car by 11 mph, find the rate of each car.

7. Mr. Atkins spent 7 hours in driving from his home to Albany, a distance of 238 miles. Before noon, he averaged 32 miles per hour. After noon, he averaged 39 miles per hour. Find the number of hours he traveled at each rate of speed.

8. James and Thomas are in two cities which are 186 miles apart and travel toward each other. James' average rate was 32 mph and Thomas' average rate was 36 mph. If James started at 9:00 A.M. and Thomas started at 9:30 A.M., at what time did they meet?

9. Two trains, starting at the same time from stations 396 miles apart, meet in $4\frac{1}{2}$ hours. How far has the faster train traveled when it meets the slower one, if the difference in their rates is 8 miles per hour?

10. Terry leaves a place 3 hours before Harry. Both travel on the same road and in the same direction. If Terry travels 20 miles per hour and Harry travels 25 miles per hour, in how many hours will Harry overtake Terry?

11. Mr. Jackson leaves on a trip planning to travel 24 miles per hour. How fast must his son James travel to overtake him in 5 hours if he starts $2\frac{1}{2}$ hours after his father?

12. A speedboat traveling at 30 miles per hour traveled the length of a lake in 20 minutes less time than when traveling at 24 miles per hour. Find the length of the lake.

13. A man hiked a distance of 9 miles into the country. He rode back in a car at the rate of 27 miles per hour. If the entire trip took 3 hours and 20 minutes, find his rate while walking.

14. Mr. Fox drove from his home to his factory at the rate of 25 miles per hour and returned by a different route at the rate of 30 miles per hour. The route by which he returned was 5 miles longer than the route by which he went. The return trip took 10 minutes less than the trip out. Find the distance Mr. Fox traveled each way.

15. A man walked from A to B at the rate of $3\frac{1}{3}$ miles per hour and returned by a different route at the rate of 4 miles per hour. The route by which he returned was one mile shorter than the route by which he went and the return trip took 45 minutes less time. Find the distance between A and B by the shorter route.

SOLVING UNIFORM MOTION PROBLEMS INVOLVING FRACTIONS

~~~~~~~~~~~~~ *MODEL PROBLEM* ~~~~~~~~~~~~~

A man traveled 150 miles at a certain average rate. By increasing his average rate by 20 mph, he traveled 250 miles in the same time that he spent on the 150-mile trip. Find his average rate on the first trip.

Solution:

Let $r =$ the average rate on the first trip in miles per hour.
Then $r + 20 =$ the average rate on the second trip in miles per hour.

	(mi.) Distance	$\div$ (mph) Rate	$=$ (hr.) Time
First Trip	150	r	$\dfrac{150}{r}$
Second Trip	250	$r + 20$	$\dfrac{250}{r + 20}$

$$\text{Time} = \frac{\text{Distance}}{\text{Rate}}$$

The time for the first trip was the same as the time for the second trip.

$$\frac{150}{r} = \frac{250}{r + 20}$$

Multiply both members of the equation by $r(r + 20)$.

$$r(r + 20)\left(\frac{150}{r}\right) = r(r + 20)\left(\frac{250}{r + 20}\right)$$

$$150(r + 20) = 250r$$
$$150r + 3000 = 250r$$
$$3000 = 100r$$
$$30 = r$$
$$r + 20 = 50$$

Answer: Average rate on the first trip was 30 mph.

Exercises

1. On a trip, a motorist drove 150 miles in the morning and 50 miles in the afternoon. His average rate in the morning was twice his average rate in the afternoon. He spent 5 hours in driving. Find his average rate on each part of the trip.

2. Mr. Bliss traveled 150 miles at a certain average rate. By increasing his rate 15 mph, he traveled 225 miles in the same time that he spent on the 150-mile trip. Find his average rate on the first trip.

3. How far can Mr. Rabin drive into the country at the average rate of 30 mph and return over the same road at the rate of 40 mph if he travels a total of 7 hours.

4. Carl rode away from home at the rate of 32 mph. He walked back on the same road at the rate of 4 mph. The round trip required $2\frac{1}{4}$ hours. How far did Carl walk?

5. A pilot plans to make a flight lasting 2 hours and 30 minutes. How far can he fly from his base at the rate of 300 mph and return over the same route at the rate of 200 mph?

6. Mr. Sawyer drove his car from his home to New York at the rate of 45 mph and returned over the same road at the rate of 40 mph. If his time returning exceeded his time going by 30 minutes, find his time going and his time returning.

7. The rate of a passenger train exceeds the rate of a freight train by 20 mph. It takes the passenger train $\frac{1}{2}$ as much time to travel 160 miles as it does the freight train. Find the rate of each train.

8. Stanley drove 240 miles at a certain rate of speed. If he had traveled 15 mph faster, he would have been able to travel 30 miles further in $\frac{3}{4}$ of the time that he spent on his trip. What was Stanley's rate on the trip?

9. Each of two cars, whose average rates are in the ratio of 4:5, travels a distance of 160 miles. If the fast car travels $\frac{1}{2}$ hour less than the slow car, find the average rate of each car.

STREAM AND WIND MOTION PROBLEMS
(MOTION PROBLEMS INVOLVING CURRENTS)

PREPARING TO SOLVE STREAM AND WIND MOTION PROBLEMS

Let us suppose that the motors of a boat supply enough power for the boat to travel at the rate of 25 mph in a body of still water, where there is no current. When the boat travels in a body of water where there is a current, the boat will move faster than 25 mph when it is traveling downstream with the current. It will move slower than 25 mph when it is traveling upstream against the current. For example, if the boat is traveling in a river that flows at the rate of 3 mph, the rate of the boat traveling downstream with the current will be 25 + 3, or 28 mph. Its rate traveling upstream against the current will be 25 − 3, or 22 mph.

The rate of speed of an airplane is similarly affected by an air current. Suppose the motors of the plane supply enough power for it to travel at the rate of 400 mph in still air, and there is a wind blowing at the rate of 20 mph. When flying with the wind, the plane will be traveling at the rate of 400 + 20, or 420 mph. When flying against the wind, the plane will be traveling at the rate of 400 − 20, or 380 mph.

KEEP IN MIND

If $r =$ the rate in still water or still air,
and $c =$ the rate of the water current or air current,
then $r + c =$ the rate traveling with the current,
and $r - c =$ the rate traveling against the current.

SOLVING STREAM AND WIND MOTION PROBLEMS

∿∿∿∿∿∿∿∿∿ MODEL PROBLEM ∿∿∿∿∿∿∿∿∿

A ship can travel at the rate of 15 mph in still water. To travel 60 miles downstream in a river, the ship requires $\frac{2}{3}$ of the time that it requires to travel the same distance upstream in the same river. Find the rate of the river's current.

Solution:

Note. When a ship can sail r mph in still water and it is sailing in a stream whose current is flowing at the rate of c mph, then:

1. The ship can sail *downstream*, with the current, at the rate of $(r + c)$ mph.

2. The ship can sail *upstream*, against the current, at the rate of $(r - c)$ mph.

Let $c =$ the rate of the current.
Then $15 + c =$ the rate of the ship downstream.
And $15 - c =$ the rate of the ship upstream.

	(mi.) Distance	(mph) ÷ Rate	(hr.) = Time
Upstream	60	$15 - c$	$\dfrac{60}{15 - c}$
Downstream	60	$15 + c$	$\dfrac{60}{15 + c}$

$$\text{Time} = \frac{\text{Distance}}{\text{Rate}}$$

Time downstream equals $\frac{2}{3}$ of the time upstream.

$$\frac{60}{15 + c} = \frac{2}{3}\left(\frac{60}{15 - c}\right)$$

$$\frac{60}{15 + c} = \frac{40}{15 - c} \qquad (\tfrac{2}{3} \times 60 = 40)$$

Multiply both members of the equation by $(15 + c)(15 - c)$.

$$(15 - c)60 = (15 + c)40$$
$$900 - 60c = 600 + 40c$$
$$300 = 100c$$
$$3 = c$$

Check: Is the time downstream equal to $\frac{2}{3}$ of the time upstream?

Time downstream is $\dfrac{60}{15 + 3} = \dfrac{60}{18} = \dfrac{10}{3}$ hours.

Time upstream is $\dfrac{60}{15 - 3} = \dfrac{60}{12} = 5$ hours.

Since $\frac{2}{3} \times 5 = \frac{10}{3}$, then $\frac{10}{3}$ is $\frac{2}{3}$ of 5. (true)

Answer: The rate of the river's current is 3 mph.

Exercises

1. Mr. Sweeney has a motorboat that can travel 14 mph in still water. He wishes to make a trip on a river whose current flows at a rate of 2 mph. If he has 7 hours at his disposal, how far can he travel up the river and return?
2. A man traveled 20 miles upstream in a river, whose current flowed at 3 miles per hour, in $2\frac{1}{2}$ times as much time as he required to return downstream. Find the man's rate in still water.

3. A boat can travel 8 miles an hour in still water. If it can travel 15 miles down a stream in the same time that it can travel 9 miles up the stream, what is the rate of the stream?

4. A plane which can fly 100 miles an hour in still air can fly 500 miles with a wind which is blowing at a certain rate in $\frac{5}{8}$ of the time it would require to fly 500 miles against a wind blowing at the same rate. What was the rate of the wind?

5. A light plane can fly 120 mph in still air. Flying with the wind, it can fly 700 miles in a certain time. Flying against the wind, it can fly only $\frac{5}{7}$ of this distance in the same time. Find the rate of the wind.

PER CENT AND PERCENTAGE PROBLEMS

PREPARING TO SOLVE PER CENT AND PERCENTAGE PROBLEMS

Per cent means *per hundred* or *hundredths*. For example, 15% means $\frac{15}{100}$ or .15;   6% means $\frac{6}{100}$ or .06; $2\frac{1}{2}$% means $\frac{2\frac{1}{2}}{100}$, or .025;   100% means $\frac{100}{100}$ or 1;   125% $= \frac{125}{100}$ or 1.25.

Various types of business problems frequently involve per cents. For example, to find the amount of tax when $80 is taxed at the rate of 5%, we multiply $80 by 5%. Since .05 × 80 = 4, we get $4 as the result. In this case, the three related quantities are:

1. The sum of money being taxed, the ***base***, which is $80.
2. The rate of tax, the ***rate***, which is 5% or .05.
3. The amount of tax, the ***percentage***, which is $4.

The relation involving base, B, rate, R, and percentage, P, may be expressed as $P = BR$.

Note. In $P = BR$, P and B must be expressed in the same unit of money; that is, if B is in dollars, then P must be in dollars.

$$\boxed{\textit{KEEP IN MIND} \qquad P = BR \qquad R = \frac{P}{B} \qquad B = \frac{P}{R}}$$

SOLVING PER CENT AND PERCENTAGE PROBLEMS

~~~~~~~~~~~~~~~~~~ *MODEL PROBLEM* ~~~~~~~~~~~~~~~

Of 150 planes at an airbase, 135 took off on a mission. What per cent of the planes took off?

Solution:

Let $\dfrac{x}{100}$ = the per cent of the planes that took off.

$P = BR$ where $P = 135$, $B = 150$

$$135 = 150\left(\frac{x}{100}\right)$$

M_{100}: $100 \cdot 135 = 100 \cdot 150\left(\dfrac{x}{100}\right)$

$$13,500 = 150x$$
$$90 = x$$
$$\frac{x}{100} = \frac{90}{100} = 90\%$$

Check in the original problem:
Is 90% of 150 equal to 135?
.90(150) = 135 (true)

Answer: 90% of the planes took off.

~~~~~~

Exercises

1. The price of a new car is $3600. Mr. Sawyer made a down payment of 25% of the price of the car when he bought it. How much was his down payment?
2. How much pure copper is in 80 pounds of an alloy which is 8% copper?
3. How much pure iodine is in 12 ounces of a solution which is $2\frac{1}{2}\%$ pure iodine?
4. Sally bought a dress at a "20% off" sale and saved $4. What was the marked price of the dress originally?
5. A businessman is required to collect a 6% sales tax. One day he collected $144 in taxes. Find the total amount of sales he made that day.
6. A merchant sold a radio for $60, which was 25% above its cost to him. Find the cost of the radio set to the merchant.
7. After Mr. Karp lost 12% of his investment, he had $4400 left. How much did he invest originally?
8. Mr. Crowley bought a $60 sport jacket. He had to pay $3 as a sales tax. What per cent of the price of the jacket is the tax?
9. The marked price of a coat is $70. What was the cost of the coat if the marked price represents a profit of 40%?

10. A dealer paid \$24 for a chair. At what price should he mark it for sale if he expects to allow a discount of 20% and wishes to make a profit of $33\frac{1}{3}\%$ on the cost price?

MIXTURE PROBLEMS

PREPARING TO SOLVE MIXTURE PROBLEMS

Many problems deal with the mixing of ingredients which have different costs. In solving these problems, it is helpful to express the total value of each ingredient in the same unit of money, such as cents. For example:

The value of 5 pounds of coffee at 70 cents per pound is 5(70), or 350 cents.

The value of x pounds of nuts at 90 cents per pound is $x(90)$, or $90x$ cents.

The value of $(40 - x)$ gallons of oil at 35 cents per gallon is $(40 - x)35$, or $35(40 - x)$ cents.

The relationship involving the number of units, N, each having the same value, V, and the total value of all the units, T, can be expressed as $NV = T$.

KEEP IN MIND

Number of units of × Value of = Total value of all
the same kind   each unit   the units
(N) (V) (T)

$$NV = T \qquad V = \frac{T}{N} \qquad N = \frac{T}{V}$$

SOLVING MIXTURE PROBLEMS

In solving mixture problems, we can use a chart to organize the facts of the problem compactly.

~~~~~~~~~~ *MODEL PROBLEM* ~~~~~~~~~~

A dealer wishes to mix candy worth 70 cents per pound with candy worth 90 cents per pound to produce a mixture of 40 pounds of candy which he can sell for 85 cents per pound. How many pounds of each type should he use?

Solution:

Let n = the number of pounds of 90-cent candy.

Then $40 - n$ = the number of pounds of 70-cent candy.

	(lb.) Number	×	(¢) Price per pound	=	¢ Total value
90-cent	n		90		$90n$
70-cent	$40 - n$		70		$70(40 - n)$
Mixture	40		85		$40(85)$

*The total value of the 90-cent candy and the 70-cent candy
equals the value of the mixture.*

$$90n + 70(40 - n) = 40(85)$$
$$90n + 2800 - 70n = 3400$$
$$20n + 2800 = 3400$$
$$20n = 600$$
$$n = 30$$
$$40 - n = 10$$

Check in the original problem:
Is the total number of pounds in the
 mixture 40?
$30 + 10 = 40$ (true)
Does the total value of the ingredients
 equal the value of the mixture?
Value of 30 lb. at 90¢ per lb. = $27.00
Value of 10 lb. at 70¢ per lb. =   7.00
Total value   = $34.00
Value of 40 lb. at $.85 per lb. = $34.00

Answer: 30 lb. of the 90-cent candy; 10 lb. of the 70-cent candy.

Exercises

1. A merchant mixed nuts worth 50 cents per pound with nuts worth 80 cents per pound. If he wishes to make a mixture of 30 pounds to sell at 75 cents per pound, how many pounds of each should he use?
2. How many pounds of 80-cent nuts and how many pounds of 50-cent nuts must a dealer use to produce a mixture of 90 pounds to sell at 75 cents per pound?
3. A seedman has seeds worth $.70 per pound and seeds worth $.90 per pound. How many pounds of each must he use to make 300 pounds to sell at $.75 per pound?
4. How many pounds of nuts worth 70 cents per pound must be mixed with 12 pounds of nuts worth 50 cents per pound to produce a mixture which can be sold for 65 cents per pound?

5. How many pounds of candy worth $1.10 per pound must be mixed with 36 pounds of candy worth $1.60 per pound to produce a mixture worth $1.50 per pound?

6. At a matinee performance, orchestra seats are sold for $5 each and balcony seats for $3 each. Explain why it is impossible to sell 700 tickets for this performance with the total receipts amounting to $2975.

PER CENT MIXTURE PROBLEMS

PREPARING TO SOLVE PER CENT MIXTURE PROBLEMS

The quantity of salt in 50 oz. of a 10% solution of salt and water is 10% of 50, which is equal to .10(50), or 5 oz.

The quantity of butterfat in x lb. of milk containing 6% butterfat can be represented by .06(x), or .06x lb.

The quantity of pure acid in $(30 - x)$ oz. of a 20% solution of acid in water may be represented by .20$(30 - x)$ oz.

The number of units, S, of a solution (mixture) that contains a given pure substance $\times$ the part, R, of the solution (mixture) which is that pure substance = the quantity, Q, of that pure substance in the solution (mixture).

This relationship can be expressed by the formula $SR = Q$.

$$\boxed{\quad \textbf{\textit{KEEP IN MIND}} \quad \\[6pt] SR = Q \qquad S = \frac{Q}{R} \qquad R = \frac{Q}{S} \quad}$$

SOLVING PER CENT MIXTURE PROBLEMS

〰〰〰〰 *MODEL PROBLEMS* 〰〰〰〰

1. How much pure acid must be added to 30 ounces of an acid solution which is 40% acid in order to produce a solution which is 50% acid?

Solution:

Let $n =$ the number of ounces of pure acid to be added.

Then $30 + n =$ the number of ounces that the new solution weighs.

	(oz.) Solution	(%) × Part pure acid	(oz.) = Quantity of pure acid
Original solution	30	.40	.40(30)
Pure acid to be added	n	100% = 1.00	1(n)
New solution	30 + n	.50	.50(30 + n)

The amount of pure acid in the original solution
+ the amount of pure acid added = the amount
of pure acid in the new solution.

$.40(30) + 1(n) = .50(30 + n)$
$12 + n = 15 + .50n$
$n - .50n = 15 - 12$
$.50n = 3$
$n = 6$

Check in the original problem:
If 6 oz. of pure acid are added to the original
solution, will the new solution be 50%
acid?
40% of 30 = .40(30) = 12
12 + 6 = 18
50% of (30 + 6) = .50(36) = 18 (true)

Answer: 6 ounces of pure acid must be added.

2. A chemist has 160 pints of a solution which is 20% acid. How much water
must be evaporated to make a solution which is 40% acid?

Solution:

Let n = the number of pints of water to be evaporated.
Then 160 − n = the number of pints in the new solution.

	(pt.) Solution	(%) × Part pure acid	(pt.) = Quantity of pure acid
Original solution	160	.20	.20(160)
Water evaporated	n	0	0(n)
New solution	160 − n	.40	.40(160 − n)

The amount of pure acid in the original solution — the amount of pure acid in the water that was evaporated = the amount of pure acid in the new solution.

$.20(160) - 0(n) = .40(160 - n)$	*Check* in the original problem:
$32 - 0 = 64 - .40n$	If 80 pints of water are evaporated from
$.40n = 64 - 32$	the original solution, will the result-
$.40n = 32$	ing solution be 40% acid?
$n = 80$	20% of $160 = .20(160) = 32$
	$32 - 0 = 32$
	$160 - 80 = 80$
	40% of $80 = .40(80) = 32($ true$)$

Answer: 80 pints of water must be evaporated.

Exercises

1. A chemist has one solution that is 30% pure salt and another solution that is 60% pure salt. How many ounces of each solution must he use to produce 60 ounces of a solution that is 50% pure salt?

2. A farmer has some cream that is 24% butterfat and some cream that is 18% butterfat. How many quarts of each must he use to produce 90 quarts of cream that is 22% butterfat?

3. A chemist has one solution that is 40% pure acid and another solution that is 75% pure acid. How many pints of each solution must he use to produce 60 pints of a solution that is 50% pure acid?

4. How many pints of a solution that is 30% alcohol must be mixed with 21 pints of a solution that is 80% alcohol to produce a mixture that is 60% alcohol?

5. How many ounces of a silver alloy that is 30% silver must be mixed with 18 ounces of a silver alloy that is 12% silver to produce a new alloy that is 18% silver?

6. How many quarts of a solution that is 75% acid must be mixed with 16 quarts of a solution that is 30% acid to produce a solution that is 55% acid?

7. How many pounds of pure salt must be added to 60 pounds of a 2% solution of salt and water to increase it to a 10% solution?

8. An alloy of copper and tin is 20% copper. How many pounds of copper must be added to 80 pounds of the alloy in order that the resulting alloy be 50% copper?

9. A certain grade of gun metal that is a mixture of tin and copper contains 16% tin. How much tin must be added to 820 pounds of this gun metal to make a mixture that is 18% tin?

10. Fifteen gallons of alcohol are mixed with 60 gallons of water. How much alcohol must be added to make a solution that is 55% alcohol?

11. How much water must be added to 40 ounces of a 10% solution of boric acid to reduce it to a 4% solution?

12. How many pounds of water must be added to 24 pounds of a 10% solution of salt to reduce it to a 6% solution?

13. How much water must be evaporated from 32 pounds of a 4% solution of salt and water to make the result a solution that is 6% salt?

14. How much water must be evaporated from 240 pounds of a solution that is 3% salt to make a solution that is 5% salt?

SOLVING PER CENT MIXTURE PROBLEMS USING FRACTIONAL EQUATIONS

If 20 ounces of a solution of salt in water contains 5 ounces of pure salt, then $\frac{5}{20}$ or $\frac{1}{4}$ is the fractional part of the mixture which is pure salt. In general,

$$\frac{\text{number of units of pure substance}}{\text{number of units in the mixture}} = \frac{\text{fractional part of the mixture}}{\text{that is pure substance}}$$

~~~~~~~~~~ *MODEL PROBLEM* ~~~~~~~~~~

How much pure acid must be added to 30 ounces of an acid solution which is 40% acid in order to produce a solution which is 50% acid?

Solution:

Part pure acid × Weight of solution = Weight of pure acid

The number of ounces of pure acid in the given solution is .40(30) = 12.
Let n = the number of ounces of pure acid to be added.
Then $12 + n$ = the number or ounces of pure acid in the new solution.
And $30 + n$ = the number of ounces that the new solution weighs.

Also $\dfrac{12 + n}{30 + n}$ = the fractional part of the new solution which is pure acid.

The fractional part of the new solution that is pure acid is $\frac{50}{100}$ or $\frac{1}{2}$.

$$\mathrm{M}_{2(30+n)}: \frac{12+n}{30+n} = \frac{1}{2}$$

$$2(12 + n) = 1(30 + n)$$
$$24 + 2n = 30 + n$$
$$n = 6$$

Answer: 6 ounces of pure acid must be added.

Note. See alternate solution and check on pages 139–140.

〰〰〰〰〰〰〰〰〰〰〰〰〰〰〰〰〰〰〰〰〰

Exercises

1. Of 24 pounds of salt water, 8% is salt. Of another mixture, 4% is salt. How many pounds of the second mixture should be added to the first mixture in order to get a mixture that is 5% salt?
2. Thirteen ounces of a solution of iodine in alcohol contain 1 ounce of pure iodine. How many ounces of pure iodine must be added to make a solution that is 25% iodine?
3. How much salt must be added to 40 pounds of a 5% salt solution to make a 24% salt solution?
4. A chemist has 20 pints of a solution of iodine and alcohol that is 15% iodine. How much iodine must be added to make a solution that is 20% iodine?
5. A certain alloy of copper and silver weighs 50 pounds and is 10% silver. How much silver must be added to produce a metal that is 25% silver?
6. One solution is 20% pure salt and another solution is 13% pure salt. How many ounces of each solution must be used to produce 35 ounces of a solution that is 15% pure salt?
7. A beaker contains 40 cubic centimeters (cc.) of a 20% solution of acid. How many cc. of this solution must be drawn off and replaced by pure acid so that the resulting solution will be 60% pure acid?

INVESTMENT PROBLEMS

PREPARING TO SOLVE INVESTMENT PROBLEMS

Mr. Field invests $700 at 8%. His annual income is 8% of $700, which equals .08(700), or $56. In finding the annual income, we make use of the *annual interest formula* $I = PR$. In this formula, P represents the **principal,** or amount invested, $700; R represents the **annual rate of interest,** 8%; and I represents the **annual interest,** or **annual income,** $56.

```
┌──────── KEEP IN MIND ────────┐
│                              │
│   I = PR      R = I/P    P = I/R │
│                              │
└──────────────────────────────┘
```

$$I = PR \qquad R = \frac{I}{P} \qquad P = \frac{I}{R}$$

SOLVING INVESTMENT PROBLEMS

In solving investment problems, we can use a chart to organize the facts of the problem compactly.

~~~~~~~~~~~~~~ *MODEL PROBLEM* ~~~~~~~~~~~~~~

Mr. Rabin invested a part of $2000 at 6% and the remainder at $4\frac{1}{2}\%$. The annual income from the $4\frac{1}{2}\%$ investment exceeded the annual income on the 6% investment by $27. Find the amount he invested at each rate.

Solution:

Let $p =$ the amount invested at $4\frac{1}{2}\%$.

Then $2000 - p =$ the amount invested at 6%.

First fill in the principal and rate of interest for each investment. Then represent the annual income for each investment.

	($) Principal	$\times$ Annual rate of interest	($) = Annual income
$4\frac{1}{2}\%$ investment	p	.045	$.045p$
6% investment	$2000 - p$	.06	$.06(2000 - p)$

Principal $\times$ Annual rate of interest $=$ Annual income

The annual income from the $4\frac{1}{2}\%$ investment is $27 more than the annual income from the 6% investment.

$.045p = .06(2000 - p) + 27$	*Check* in the original problem:
$.045p = 120 - .06p + 27$	Is the sum of both investments $2000?
$.045p + .06p = 147$	$1400 + 600 = 2000$ (true)
$.105p = 147$	Does the annual income from the $4\frac{1}{2}\%$
$M_{1000}:\ 105p = 147{,}000$	investment exceed the annual in-
$p = 1400$	come from the 6% investment by
$2000 - p = 600$	$27?
	$.045(1400) = 63$
	$.06(600) = 36$
	$63 exceeds $36 by $27. (true)

Answer: $1400 was invested at $4\frac{1}{2}\%$; $600 was invested at 6%.

~~~~~~

Exercises

1. Mr. Carter invested a sum of money at 4%. He invested a second sum, $250 more than the first sum, at 6%. If his total annual income was $90, how much did he invest at each rate?

2. Mr. Hernandez has invested a sum of money at 6%. A second sum, $400 more than the first sum, is invested at 3%. A third sum, 4 times as much as the first sum, is invested at 4%. The total annual income is $237. How much has he invested at each rate?

3. Mr. Baum invested $8000, part at 4% and the rest at 9%. The total annual income is $495. Find the amount invested at each rate.

4. Mr. Banks invested $\frac{1}{3}$ of his capital at 5%, $\frac{1}{4}$ of his capital at 6%, and the remainder at 3%. The total annual income was $530. Find his capital.

5. Mr. Harvey invested a sum of money at 4%. He invested a second sum, $1000 greater than the first sum, at 3%. The annual income on the first investment was equal to the annual income on the second investment. Find the amount invested at each rate.

6. Mr. Rose invested $3500 in two business enterprises. In one enterprise, he made a profit of 6%; in the other, he suffered a loss of 4%. His net profit for the year was $160. Find the amount invested at each rate.

7. A sum of $2200 is invested, part at 5% and the remainder at 3%. The annual income on the 3% investment is $46 less than the annual income on the 5% investment. How much was invested at each rate?

8. A sum of $3800 is invested, part at 4% and the remainder at 6%. The annual interest on the 6% investment is $98 more than the annual income on the 4% investment. Find the sum invested at each rate.

9. Mr. Roscoe invested $9000, part at 4% and the remainder at 7%. If his total annual income was 5% of his total investment, how much did he invest at each rate?

10. Miss Green invested $1000 at 2% and $6000 at 4%. How much must she invest at 8% to make her total annual income 5% of her total investment?

11. Mr. Sable invested $5000 in a mortgage that pays 5% interest annually. He bought bonds paying $2\frac{1}{2}$% interest annually. His total annual income is 3% of his total investment. How much did he invest in the bonds?

GEOMETRIC PROBLEMS

PREPARING TO SOLVE GEOMETRIC PROBLEMS

Recall the following geometric relationships:

1. The perimeter of a geometric plane figure is the sum of the lengths of all its sides.
2. The area of a rectangle = base × altitude.
3. The area of a triangle = $\frac{1}{2}$ × base × altitude.

Note. In referring to rectangles, the words *length* and *width* are commonly used in place of the words *base* and *altitude*.

SOLVING GEOMETRIC PROBLEMS

In solving problems dealing with geometric figures, it is helpful to draw the figures.

~~~~~~~~~~~~~~~ *MODEL PROBLEM* ~~~~~~~~~~~~~~~

The base of a rectangle exceeds its altitude by 11 feet. If the base is decreased by 5 feet and the altitude is increased by 2 feet, a new rectangle is formed whose area is equal to the area of the original rectangle. Find the dimensions of the original rectangle.

Solution:

Let x = the altitude if the original rectangle in feet.
Then $x + 11$ = the base of the original rectangle in feet.

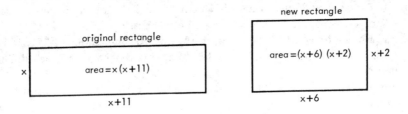

	(ft.) Base	× (ft.) Altitude =	(sq. ft.) Area
Old rectangle	$x + 11$	x	$x(x + 11)$
New rectangle	$x + 6$	$x + 2$	$(x + 6)(x + 2)$

Base × Altitude = Area of rectangle

The areas of the rectangles are equal.

$$x(x + 11) = (x + 6)(x + 2)$$
$$x^2 + 11x = x^2 + 8x + 12$$
$$3x = 12$$
$$x = 4$$
$$x + 11 = 15$$

Check in the original problem:
Does the area of the original rectangle = the area of the new rectangle?
Area of original rectangle = 15(4) = 60 sq. ft.
In new rectangle, base = 10 ft., altitude = 6 ft.
Area of new rectangle = 10(6) = 60 sq. ft.
The areas of the rectangles are equal.

Answer: The base of the original rectangle is 15 feet; the altitude is 4 feet.

Exercises

1. The length of a rectangle exceeds twice its width by 1 inch. The perimeter of the rectangle is 32 inches. Find the dimensions of the rectangle.

2. The base of a rectangle is 5 feet less than $\frac{2}{3}$ of its width. The perimeter of the rectangle is 80 feet. Find the dimensions of the rectangle.

3. The length of a rectangle exceeds its width by 4 inches. If the width is doubled and its length is diminished by 2 inches, a new rectangle is formed whose perimeter is 8 feet more than the perimeter of the original rectangle. Find the dimensions of the original rectangle.

4. If the length of one side of a square is increased by 3 feet and the length of the adjacent side is decreased by 2 feet, a rectangle is formed whose area is equal to the area of the square. Find the length of a side of the square.

5. The base of a rectangle exceeds 3 times its altitude by 1 foot. If the base is decreased by 5 feet and the altitude is increased by 2 feet, a new rectangle is formed whose area is the same as the area of the original rectangle. Find the dimensions of the original rectangle.

6. The width of a rectangle is 2 inches less than its length. If its width is increased by 4 inches and its length is decreased by 2 inches, the area of the rectangle will be increased by 8 square inches. Find the length and width of the original rectangle.

7. If the length of one side of a square is increased by 2 feet and the length of an adjacent side is decreased by 3 feet, a rectangle is formed whose area is 14 sq. ft. less than the area of the square. Find the length of a side of the square.

8. The base of a rectangle exceeds twice its altitude by 2 inches. If the base is increased by 5 inches and the altitude is decreased by 1 inch, a new rectangle is formed whose area exceeds the area of the original rectangle by 20 square inches. Find the dimensions of the original rectangle.

9. The base of a triangle is 10 inches more than its altitude. If the base is increased by 5 inches and the altitude is decreased by 2 inches, the area of

the new triangle is the same as the area of the original triangle. Find the base and altitude of the original triangle.

WORK PROBLEMS

PREPARING TO SOLVE WORK PROBLEMS

If Ted can mow a lawn in 4 hours, then in 1 hour he will complete $\frac{1}{4}$ of the job. The part of the job that can be completed in 1 unit of time is called the **rate of work**. In general, if the job can be completed in x units of time, the rate of work is $\frac{1}{x}$. Notice that the rate of work is the reciprocal of the number of units of time required to complete the job. Therefore, Ted's rate of work is $\frac{1}{4}$. In 2 hours, Ted will complete $2(\frac{1}{4})$ or $\frac{2}{4}$ of the job; in x hours, Ted will complete $x(\frac{1}{4})$ or $\frac{x}{4}$ of the job. Thus we see that:

Rate of work, R, × amount of time worked, T, = part of the work done, W.

The relation involving R, T, and W may be expressed as $RT = W$.

Ted and Sam work on a job together. If Ted finishes $\frac{1}{4}$ of the job while Sam finishes $\frac{3}{4}$ of the job, then together they finish $\frac{1}{4} + \frac{3}{4}$ or $\frac{4}{4}$ of the job. Notice that in order for Ted and Sam to complete the whole job, the sum of the fractional part of the job that Ted finished and the fractional part of the job that Sam finished must be a fraction whose value is 1.

— KEEP IN MIND —

$$RT = W \qquad T = \frac{W}{R} \qquad R = \frac{W}{T}$$

SOLVING WORK PROBLEMS

〰〰〰 MODEL PROBLEM 〰〰〰

It takes Fred twice as long to paint a fence as it takes Harry to paint the same fence. If the two boys work together, they can paint the fence in 2 hours. How many hours would each boy, working alone, need to paint the fence?

Solution:

Let x = number of hours Harry needs to do the job alone.

Then $2x$ = number of hours Fred needs to do the job alone.

	(part of job per hr.) Rate of work	×	(hr.) Time of work	=	(part of job) Work done
Harry	$\dfrac{1}{x}$		2		$\dfrac{2}{x}$
Fred	$\dfrac{1}{2x}$		2		$\dfrac{2}{2x}$

Rate of work × Amount of time worked = Part of work done

If the job is finished, the sum of the fractional part of the job finished by Harry and the fractional part finished by Fred must equal 1.

$$\frac{2}{x} + \frac{2}{2x} = 1$$

$$\text{M}_{2x}: \ 2x\left(\frac{2}{x} + \frac{2}{2x}\right) = 2x(1)$$

$$4 + 2 = 2x$$
$$6 = 2x$$
$$3 = x$$
$$2x = 6$$

Check in the original problem:
Will the boys paint the whole fence if they work
   together for 2 hours?
In 2 hours Harry will paint $2(\frac{1}{3})$ or $\frac{2}{3}$ of the fence.
In 2 hours Fred will paint $2(\frac{1}{6})$ or $\frac{1}{3}$ of the
   fence.
In 2 hours, together, they will paint $\frac{2}{3} + \frac{1}{3} = \frac{3}{3}$,
   or the whole fence.

Answer: Harry requires 3 hours; Fred requires 6 hours.

Exercises

1. Sam can mow a lawn in 20 minutes and Robert can mow the same lawn in 30 minutes. If they worked together, how long would it take them to do the job?

2. A printing press can print 300,000 cards in 12 hours. An older press requires 18 hours to print 300,000 copies of a card. How long would it take for both presses working together to print 300,000 copies?

3. A farmer working together with his son needs 3 hours to plow a field. The farmer working alone can plow the field in 4 hours. How long would it take the son working alone to plow the field?

4. One pipe can fill a tank in 20 minutes. A second pipe can fill the tank in 30 minutes. If the tank is empty, how long would be required for the two pipes operating together to fill it?

5. A farmer working with his son needs 3 hours to plow a field. Working alone, the farmer can plow the field in 12 hours. How long would it take the son working alone to plow the field?

6. A farmer can milk his cows in $\frac{2}{3}$ of an hour, and his son can do the job in 1 hour. How long would it take them to milk the cows together?

7. An inlet pipe can fill a tank in 3 hours. An outlet pipe can empty the tank in 6 hours. If the tank is empty and both pipes are opened, how many hours will it take to fill the tank?

8. A tank can be filled by one pipe in 20 minutes, and it can be filled by a second pipe in 10 minutes. It can be drained by a third pipe in 12 minutes. If the tank is empty and the inlet pipes and the drain are opened, in how many hours will the tank be filled?

9. John working alone can mow a lawn in 20 minutes; Cary can mow the same lawn in 30 minutes. They mow the lawn together for 10 minutes, after which John leaves the job. How much longer will it take Cary to finish the job?

10. A clerk is assigned a job that she can complete in 8 hours. After she has been working 2 hours, another clerk, who is able to do this job in 10 hours, is assigned to help her. In how many hours will the clerks working together complete the job?

11. A man can do a piece of work in 9 hours. After he worked 3 hours alone, he was joined by his son, and they finished the job in $4\frac{1}{2}$ hours. How many hours would it take the son to do the job alone?

12. Leo finished $\frac{2}{3}$ of a job in 12 hours. When he was joined by Ed, they completed the job in 2 hours. How many hours would it take Ed to do the job alone?

13. A mechanic's helper requires twice as long as the mechanic to do the same amount of work. On a particular job, they work together for 2 hours. Then the mechanic is called away, and the helper finishes it in 1 hour. How many hours would it take the helper to do the entire job?

14. It takes a man 8 hours to do a certain job and a boy 12 hours to do the same job. If 2 men and 3 boys work on the job, how many hours does it take them to finish it?

NUMBER PROBLEMS INVOLVING FRACTIONS

~~~~~~~~~~~~~ *MODEL PROBLEMS* ~~~~~~~~~~~~~

1. Two numbers are in the ratio 4 : 5. If 10 is added to each number, the resulting numbers will be in the ratio 5 : 6. Find the original numbers.

Solution:
      Let $4x =$ the first number.
      Then $5x =$ the second number.

Then $4x + 10 =$ the first number increased by 10.
And $5x + 10 =$ the second number increased by 10.

The new numbers are in the ratio 5 : 6.

$$\frac{4x + 10}{5x + 10} = \frac{5}{6}$$

Multiply both members
of the equation
by $6(5x + 10)$.

$6(4x + 10) = 5(5x + 10)$
$24x + 60 = 25x + 50$
$10 = x$
$4x = 40$
$5x = 50$

Check in the original problem:
Is the ratio of the two numbers 4 : 5?

$$\frac{40}{50} = \frac{4}{5} \text{ (true)}$$

If 10 is added to each number, will the ratio of
the resulting numbers be 5 : 6?

$40 + 10 = 50$
$50 + 10 = 60$

$$\frac{50}{60} = \frac{5}{6} \text{ (true)}$$

Answer: The first number is 40; the second number is 50.

2. The larger of two numbers exceeds twice the smaller by 17. When the larger number is divided by the smaller number, the quotient is 3 and the remainder is 7. Find the two numbers.

Solution:

Note. When 23 is divided by 5, the quotient is 4 and the remainder is 3. This may be written as follows: $\frac{23}{5} = 4 + \frac{3}{5}$. Similarly, " when D is divided by d, the quotient is Q and the remainder is R " may be written as $\frac{D}{d} = Q + \frac{R}{d}$.

Let $x =$ the smaller number.
Then $2x + 17 =$ the larger number.

When the larger number is divided by the smaller number, the quotient is 3 and the remainder is 7.

$$\frac{2x + 17}{x} = 3 + \frac{7}{x}$$

M_x:

$2x + 17 = 3x + 7$
$10 = x$
$2x + 17 = 37$

Check in the original problem:
The larger number, 37, is 17 more than 2 times the smaller number, 10. When 37 is divided by 10, the quotient is 3 and the remainder is 7.

Answer: The larger number is 37; the smaller number is 10.

3. The denominator of a fraction is 1 less than 4 times the numerator. If the numerator is doubled and the denominator is increased by 6, the value of the resulting fraction is $\frac{2}{5}$. Find the original fraction.

Solution:

Let n = the numerator of the original fraction.

Then $4n - 1$ = the denominator of the original fraction.

Then $\dfrac{2n}{(4n - 1) + 6}$ = the resulting fraction.

The value of the resulting fraction is $\frac{2}{5}$.

$$\frac{2n}{(4n - 1) + 6} = \frac{2}{5}$$

$$\frac{2n}{4n + 5} = \frac{2}{5}$$

$M_{5(4n+5)}$:

$$5(2n) = 2(4n + 5)$$
$$10n = 8n + 10$$
$$2n = 10$$
$$n = 5$$
$$4n - 1 = 19$$

Check in the original problem:

Is the denominator of the fraction 1 less than 4 times the numerator?

19 is 1 less than 4 times 5. (true)

Is the value of the resulting fraction $\frac{2}{5}$?

The resulting fraction is $\dfrac{2(5)}{19 + 6} = \dfrac{10}{25} = \dfrac{2}{5}$ (true)

Answer: The original fraction is $\dfrac{5}{19}$.

Exercises

1. If one-half of a number is subtracted from three-fifths of that number, the difference is 10. Find the number.

2. The larger of two numbers is 12 less than 5 times the smaller. If the smaller number is equal to $\frac{1}{3}$ of the larger number, find the numbers.

3. One-fifth of the result obtained when a number is increased by 12, is equal to one-fourth of the result that is obtained when that number is increased by 2. Find the number.

4. One of two positive numbers exceeds 4 times the other number by 4. One-third of the larger exceeds one-half of the smaller by 8. Find both numbers.

5. Find three consecutive even numbers such that the sum of the first and the third exceeds one-half of the second by 54.

6. The numerator of a fraction exceeds 8 times the denominator by 2. The value of the fraction is $\frac{17}{2}$. Find the fraction.

7. The numerator of a fraction is 7 less than the denominator. If 3 is added to the numerator and 9 is subtracted from the denominator, the resulting fraction is equal to $\frac{3}{2}$. Find the original fraction.

8. What number must be added to both the numerator and denominator of the fraction $\frac{5}{23}$ to give a fraction equal to $\frac{1}{3}$.

9. The larger of two numbers exceeds the smaller by 8. When the smaller is divided by the larger, the quotient is equal to $\frac{5}{7}$. Find the numbers.

10. The difference between two numbers is 24. If the larger is divided by the smaller, the quotient is 4 and the remainder is 3. Find the numbers.

11. Two numbers are in the ratio of 3 : 5. One-half of the smaller exceeds $\frac{1}{5}$ of the larger by 6. Find the numbers.

12. What number must be added to 12 and 18 respectively so that the new numbers will be in the ratio of 3 : 4?

13. The numerator and the denominator of a fraction are in the ratio of 5 : 4. If 5 is added to the numerator and 12 is subtracted from the denominator, the value of the resulting fraction is $\frac{5}{2}$. Find the original fraction.

14. The larger of two numbers exceeds twice the smaller by 1. If 2 is added to the larger and 1 is subtracted from the smaller, the resulting numbers are in the ratio of 3 : 1. Find the numbers.

15. One-fourth of the reciprocal of a number exceeds one-fifth of the reciprocal of the number by 1. Find the number.

9. Solving Equations Involving More Than One Variable

An equation may contain more than one variable. Examples of such equations are $ax = b$, $x + y = 7$, and $ax + bx = a^2 - b^2$.

To solve such an equation for one of its variables means to express this particular variable in terms of the other variables. In order to plan the steps in the solution, it may be helpful to compare the equation with a similar equation which contains only the variable being solved for. The same operations are used in solving both equations. Note how these ideas are applied in the following model problems:

~~~~~~~~~ *MODEL PROBLEMS* ~~~~~~~~~

1. Solve for x: $a(x - a) = b(x - b)$ [Compare with $7(x - 7) = 5(x - 5)$.]

How To Proceed	*Solution*

1. Transform the equation into an equivalent equation in which all terms involving the variables being solved for are collected on one side of the equation and all the other terms are collected on the other side.

$$a(x-a)=b(x-b)$$
$$ax-a^2=bx-b^2$$
$$ax-bx=a^2-b^2$$

2. Find the coefficient of the variable being solved for.

$$(a-b)x=a^2-b^2$$

3. Divide by the coefficient of the variable being solved for.

$$\frac{(a-b)x}{(a-b)}=\frac{a^2-b^2}{a-b}$$

4. Simplify the equation obtained in step **3**.

$$x=\frac{(a-b)(a+b)}{(a-b)}$$
$$x=a+b \quad \textit{Ans.}$$

Check by substituting $a+b$ for x in the given equation.

2. Solve for x: $\dfrac{1}{a}+\dfrac{1}{b}=\dfrac{1}{x}$ $\left[\text{Compare with } \dfrac{1}{2}+\dfrac{1}{3}=\dfrac{1}{x}\right]$

Solution:

$$\frac{1}{a}+\frac{1}{b}=\frac{1}{x}$$

L.C.D. $=abx$

$$\text{M}_{abx}: \quad abx\left(\frac{1}{a}+\frac{1}{b}\right)=abx\left(\frac{1}{x}\right)$$

$$abx\left(\frac{1}{a}\right)+abx\left(\frac{1}{b}\right)=abx\left(\frac{1}{x}\right)$$

$$bx+ax=ab$$
$$(b+a)x=ab$$

$$\text{D}_{b+a}: \quad \frac{(b+a)x}{b+a}=\frac{ab}{b+a}$$

$$x=\frac{ab}{b+a} \quad \textit{Ans.}$$

Check in the original problem:

$$\frac{1}{a}+\frac{1}{b}=\frac{1}{x}$$

Let $x=\dfrac{ab}{b+a}$

$$\frac{1}{a}+\frac{1}{b}\overset{?}{=}\frac{1}{\dfrac{ab}{b+a}}$$

$$\frac{b+a}{ab}=\frac{b+a}{ab} \quad \text{(true)}$$

Note. Division by $b+a$ is undefined if $b+a=0$. Hence, $b\neq(-a)$.

Exercises

In 1–40, solve for x or y in terms of the other variables.

1. $3x = a$

2. $rx = 10$

3. $ax = b$

4. $x + 2 = a$

5. $x + a = b$

6. $y - 4 = m$

7. $y + r = s$

8. $\dfrac{y}{10} = a$

9. $\dfrac{y}{b} = 7$

10. $3x - 4e = 5e$

11. $bx + b^2 = 5b^2 - 3bx$

12. $\dfrac{ax}{b} = \dfrac{c}{d}$

13. $\dfrac{m}{x} = \dfrac{m^2}{r}$

14. $\dfrac{g}{h} = \dfrac{g^2}{x}$

15. $cy - 3 = d$

16. $tx + r = s$

17. $\dfrac{sx}{t} + a = b$

18. $m = \dfrac{ny}{r} - s$

19. $\dfrac{5}{x} - \dfrac{4}{x} = t$

20. $\dfrac{a}{x} + c = \dfrac{b}{x}$

21. $\dfrac{m}{y} = \dfrac{n}{y} + p$

22. $3x + 2a = x + 4a$

23. $my - m^2 = 5m^2 - 2my$

24. $y - 5 = 5r - ry$

25. $ey + f^2 = e^2 + fy$

26. $(x - r)(x - s) = x^2$

27. $(c - d)x = c^2 - cd$

28. $c(c + x) = b(b + x)$

29. $3cx + 8d^2 = 2d(2x + 3c)$

30. $\dfrac{x}{a} + \dfrac{x}{b} = 1$

31. $\dfrac{c}{x} - c^2 = \dfrac{b}{x} - b^2$

32. $\dfrac{x}{r} + \dfrac{x}{s} + \dfrac{x}{t} = 1$

33. $\dfrac{3}{x - c} = \dfrac{4}{x - d}$

34. $\dfrac{y - r}{y - s} = \dfrac{e}{f}$

35. $\dfrac{y - m}{y + n} = \dfrac{y + n}{y - m}$

36. $\dfrac{y}{y - r} - \dfrac{y}{y + r} = \dfrac{6r}{y^2 - r^2}$

37. $\dfrac{x}{a^2 - 4} = \dfrac{b}{a - 2} - \dfrac{b}{a + 2}$

38. $\dfrac{x}{a^2 - a} = \dfrac{b}{a - 1} - \dfrac{b}{a}$

39. $\dfrac{y - 2}{a^2 - 5a + 6} = \dfrac{a + 1}{a - 3} - \dfrac{a + 2}{a - 2}$

10. Problems Involving Literal Numbers

〜〜〜〜〜〜〜〜〜 *MODEL PROBLEM* 〜〜〜〜〜〜〜〜〜

Marie and Anne start from the same place at the same time and travel in opposite directions. Marie travels r miles per hour and Anne travels s miles per hour. In how many hours will the girls be t miles apart?

Solution:
   Let $x =$ the required number of hours.
Then $rx =$ the distance Marie travels.
 And $sx =$ the distance Anne travels.

The total distance is t miles.

$$rx + sx = t$$
$$(r + s)x = t$$
$$x = \frac{t}{r + s}$$

Answer: The time required is $\dfrac{t}{r + s}$ hours.

Exercises

1. It took m army engineers h hours to build a pontoon bridge. If r more engineers had been assigned to the work and they had worked at the same rate, how many hours would it have taken?
2. A man travels m miles per hour for t hours and then changes his rate to s miles per hour for h hours. Find his average rate.
3. If a pounds of coffee worth c cents a pound are mixed with b pounds of coffee worth d cents a pound, find how much the resulting mixture is worth per pound.
4. If a piece of work can be done by one machine in p hours and by another machine in q hours, find how many hours both machines working together require to do the job.
5. A woman is r times as old as her daughter. In s years she will be t times as old as her daughter will be then. Find the daughter's present age.
6. A boy is c years old. His father is m times as old as he is. How many years ago was the father d times as old as the boy was then?
7. In a purse which contains quarters and dimes, there are w coins whose value is c cents. Find the number of quarters.
8. A man invested p dollars, part at $c\%$ and part at $d\%$. If his annual income is I dollars, find the amount he invested at $c\%$.
9. How far can a man ride out into the country at the rate of w miles per hour and return at the rate of z miles per hour if he travels h hours on the entire trip?
10. Traveling at the rate of r miles per hour, a motorist leaves a town. Another

motorist leaves the same town h hours later and travels on the same road at the rate of s miles per hour. In how many hours will the second motorist overtake the first motorist?

11. A patrol plane flies at r miles an hour in still air. On a certain day, the plane flew a distance of d miles from its base against a headwind of w miles an hour. It returned immediately over the same route, the round trip taking t hours. The rate and the direction of the wind remained the same during the entire trip.

   a. Express in terms of r, d, and w the time required for the flight (1) away from the base (2) back to the base.

   b. Write an equation that can be used to solve for d in terms of r, t, and w.

   c. Solve for d the equation written in answer to *b*.

12. *a.* A solution of water and alcohol is 90% alcohol. Express in terms of n the amount of water that must be added to n gallons of this solution to make it 80% alcohol.

   b. A solution of water and alcohol is 80% alcohol. Express in terms of n the amount of alcohol that must be added to n gallons of this solution to make it 90% alcohol.

13. A mixture of m pounds of sand and cement is c per cent cement.

   a. Express the number of pounds of cement in the mixture in terms of c and m.

   b. If x pounds of sand are added to this mixture, it will then be d per cent cement. Express the number of pounds of cement in the new mixture in terms of d, m, and x.

   c. Find x in terms of c, d, and m.

14. A motorist finds that if he travels r miles per hour, he can cover a certain distance in h hours. By how many miles must he increase his rate per hour if he is to cover the same distance in one hour less time?

15. In a certain solution, there are a pints of acid and w pints of water. How many pints of pure acid must be added to the solution to make a mixture which is p% pure acid?

11. Finding the Value of a Variable in a Formula by Solving an Equation

Procedure. To find the value of an indicated variable in a formula by solving an equation:

1. Replace all variables in the formula except the one that is being evaluated by their specified values.
2. Solve the resulting equation.

~~~~~~~~~~~~~~~ *MODEL PROBLEM* ~~~~~~~~~~~~~~~

If $V = \frac{1}{3}BH$, find H when $V = 24$ and $B = 8$.

Solution:

Substitute the given values.

$$V = \tfrac{1}{3}BH$$
$$24 = \tfrac{1}{3}(8)H$$
$$24 = \tfrac{8}{3}H$$
$$9 = H \quad Ans.$$

Check

$$V = \tfrac{1}{3}BH$$
$$24 \stackrel{?}{=} \tfrac{1}{3}(8)(9)$$
$$24 = 24 \quad (\text{true})$$

~~~~~~

Exercises

1. If $A = \frac{1}{2}bh$, find h when $A = 30$ and $b = 15$.

2. If $F = \frac{9}{5}C + 32$, find C when $F = -13$.

3. If $S = \dfrac{n}{2}(a + l)$, find n when $S = 40$, $a = 7$, and $l = 13$.

4. If $C = \frac{5}{9}(F - 32)$, find F when $C = 15$.

5. If $T = 2\pi r(r + h)$, find h when $T = 1408$, $\pi = \dfrac{22}{7}$, and $r = 14$.

6. If $S = \dfrac{a}{1 - r}$, find r when $a = 2$ and $S = 4$.

7. In the formula $F = \frac{9}{5}C + 32$, find the temperature reading at which $F = C$.

8. If $\dfrac{1}{f} = \dfrac{1}{D} + \dfrac{1}{d}$, find d when $f = 4$ and $D = 12$.

12. Transforming Formulas

A formula may be expressed in more than one form. Sometimes it is desirable to solve a formula for a variable which is different from the one for which it is solved. This is called **transforming** the formula or **changing the subject** of the formula. For example, the formula $D = RT$ can be transformed into the formula $\dfrac{D}{R} = T$ by dividing both of its members by R. Originally D was expressed in terms of R and T; now T is expressed in terms of D and R.

Procedure. To transform a formula:

1. Consider the formula as an equation with several variables.

2. Solve the equation for the indicated variable in terms of the other variables.

The value of a variable in a formula may be found by first transforming the equation so that it is solved for that variable and then by substituting the given values for the other variables.

Thus, to find the value of K in the formula $\dfrac{K}{d^2} = F$ when $F = 120$ and $d = \frac{1}{2}$:

1. Transform $\dfrac{K}{d^2} = F$ to $K = Fd^2$.

2. Substitute and solve $K = 120(\frac{1}{2})^2 = 120(\frac{1}{4}) = 30$.

∿∿∿∿∿∿∿ *MODEL PROBLEMS* ∿∿∿∿∿∿∿

1. Solve the formula $a = p(1 + rt)$ for t in terms of a, p, and r.

How To Proceed	*Solution*
1. Consider the formula as an equation with several variables.	$a = p(1 + rt)$
2. Solve for the indicated variable.	$a = p + prt$
	$\mathrm{S}_p:\ a - p = prt$
	$\mathrm{D}_{pr}:\ \dfrac{a - p}{pr} = \dfrac{\cancel{prt}}{\cancel{pr}}$
	$\dfrac{a - p}{pr} = t \quad Ans.$

2. If $u = \dfrac{MV}{M + V}$, express M in terms of u and V.

Solution:

$$u = \frac{MV}{M + V}$$

$$\mathrm{M}_{M+V}:\quad (M + V)u = (M + V) \cdot \frac{MV}{M + V}$$

$$uM + uV = MV$$

$$\mathrm{S}_{uM}:\quad uV = MV - uM$$

$$uV = (V - u)M$$

$$\mathrm{D}_{V-u}:\quad \frac{uV}{(V - u)} = \frac{(\cancel{V - u})M}{(\cancel{V - u})}$$

$$\frac{uV}{V - u} = M \quad Ans.$$

Exercises

In 1–24, transform the formula by solving for the indicated variable.

1. $A = bh$ for h

2. $C = \pi d$ for d

3. $E = ir$ for i

4. $A = lw$ for l

5. $V = lwh$ for h

6. $i = prt$ for p

7. $A = \frac{1}{2}bh$ for h

8. $C = \dfrac{360}{N}$ for N

9. $I = \dfrac{E}{R}$ for E

10. $v = \dfrac{s}{t}$ for t

11. $F = \dfrac{mv^2}{gr}$ for r

12. $S = \frac{1}{2}at^2$ for a

13. $S = c + g$ for g

14. $p = 2l + 2w$ for w

15. $F = \frac{9}{5}C + 32$ for C

16. $A = \frac{1}{2}h(b + c)$ for b

17. $A = p + prt$ for t

18. $\dfrac{D}{d} = q + \dfrac{r}{d}$ for d

19. $S = vt - \frac{1}{2}gt^2$ for v

20. $A = p + prt$ for p

21. $\dfrac{1}{f} = \dfrac{1}{p} + \dfrac{1}{q}$ for p

22. $R = \dfrac{gs}{g + s}$ for s

23. $S = \dfrac{a}{1 - r}$ for r

24. $C = \dfrac{nE}{R + nr}$ for n

25. Solve for h: $V = \dfrac{\pi r^2 h}{3}$

26. Solve for k: $n = \dfrac{a - k}{5k}$

27. Using the formula $A = P(1 + rt)$, express r in terms of A, P, and t.

In 28–33, (a) transform the given formula by solving for the variable to be evaluated, and (b) substitute the given values in the result obtained in part (a) to evaluate this variable.

28. Find h if $V = 250$, $r = 5$, $\pi = \frac{22}{7}$: $V = \dfrac{\pi r^2 h}{3}$.

29. Find W if $A = 27$, $t = 3$: $t = \dfrac{6W}{A - W}$.

30. Find r if $A = 2000$, $P = 1000$, $t = 10$: $A = P(1 + rt)$.

31. Find I if $E = 42$, $R = 4$, $r = 3$: $E = IR + Ir$.

32. Find t if $V = 1200$, $k = 850$, $g = 7$: $V = k + gt$.

33. Find F if $g = \frac{1}{2}$, $h = \frac{2}{5}$: $\dfrac{1}{F} = \dfrac{1}{g} + \dfrac{1}{h}$.

34. The formula for the area of a triangle is $A = \frac{1}{2}bh$. Rewrite this formula if $h = 8b$; that is, express A in terms of b.

35. The formula for the total surface of a cylinder is $S = 2\pi R(R + H)$. Express S in terms of H if $R = 2H$.

13. Solving Equations Involving Absolute Values

The absolute value of a, $|a|$, has been defined as follows:

$$|a| = a \text{ when } a \geq 0, \ |a| = -a \text{ when } a < 0.$$

If we apply the absolute value definition to $|x+1| = 5$, we see that $x + 1 = 5$ or $x + 1 = -5$. Hence, the roots of $|x+1| = 5$ are $x = 4$, the root of $x + 1 = 5$, together with $x = -6$, the root of $x + 1 = -5$. Therefore, the solution set of $|x+1| = 5$ is $\{4, -6\}$.

Check in the original equation:

$\|x+1\| = 5$	$\|x+1\| = 5$
Let $x = 4$: $\|4+1\| \overset{?}{=} 5$	Let $x = -6$: $\|-6+1\| \overset{?}{=} 5$
$\|5\| \overset{?}{=} 5$	$\|-5\| \overset{?}{=} 5$
$5 = 5$	$5 = 5$

We refer to $x + 1 = 5$ and $x + 1 = -5$ as the *derived equations* of $|x+1| = 5$. In this case, these two equations together are equivalent to $|x+1| = 5$.

It is most important to check the roots of the derived equations in the original absolute value equation because a root of a derived equation may not satisfy the absolute value equation. For example, in the case of $|x| = -5$, the roots of the derived equations $x = 5$ and $x = -5$ do not satisfy $|x| = -5$ since the absolute value of a number cannot be negative. Hence, the solution set of $|x| = -5$ is the empty set, $\varnothing$.

Likewise, in the case of the equation $|2x + 5| = x + 1$, the derived equations are $2x + 5 = x + 1$ and $2x + 5 = -(x + 1)$. Neither $x = -4$, which is the root of $2x + 5 = x + 1$, nor $x = -2$, which is the root of $2x + 5 = -(x + 1)$, satisfies $|2x + 5| = x + 1$. Therefore, the solution set of $|2x + 5| = x + 1$ is the empty set, $\varnothing$.

Procedure. To solve equations involving absolute values:
1. Write the derived equations.
2. Solve each equation.

KEEP IN MIND

When solving an absolute value equation, check to see whether the roots of the derived equations satisfy the given absolute value equation.

~~~~~~~~~~~~~~~ *MODEL PROBLEM* ~~~~~~~~~~~~~~~

a. Solve and check: $|3x + 2| = 4x + 5$

b. Graph the solution set of $|3x + 2| = 4x + 5$

a. *How To Proceed*	*Solution*
	$|3x + 2| = 4x + 5$
1. Write the derived equations.	$3x + 2 = 4x + 5 \qquad 3x + 2 = -(4x + 5)$
2. Solve each equation.	$3x - 4x = 5 - 2 \qquad 3x + 2 = -4x - 5$
	$-x = 3 \qquad\qquad 7x = -7$
	$x = -3 \qquad\qquad\ x = -1$

Check in the original equation:

$$|3x + 2| = 4x + 5 \qquad\qquad\qquad |3x + 2| = 4x + 5$$

Let $x = -3: |-9 + 2| \stackrel{?}{=} -12 + 5 \qquad$ Let $x = -1: |-3 + 2| \stackrel{?}{=} -4 + 5$

$$|-7| \stackrel{?}{=} -7 \qquad\qquad\qquad\qquad |-1| \stackrel{?}{=} 1$$

$$7 \neq -7 \qquad\qquad\qquad\qquad\qquad 1 = 1 \text{ (true)}$$

Answer: $x = -1$, or the solution set is $\{-1\}$.

b. Graph the solution set $\{-1\}$.

Answer:

~~~~~~

Exercises

In 1–8, write two derived equations that do not contain the absolute value symbol and that together are equivalent to the given equation.

1. $|x| = 8$ **2.** $|4x| = 16$ **3.** $|m + 5| = 7$

4. $|2y - 4| = 6$ **5.** $|5 - 3x| = 11$ **6.** $\left|\dfrac{3t + 1}{4}\right| = 7$

7. $|3x - 20| = 2x$ **8.** $|3x - 7| = 2x - 3$

In 9–27, find the solution set of the equation.

9. $|x| = 12$ **10.** $|y| = -6$ **11.** $|2y| = 24$

12. $3|x| = 27$ **13.** $|x + 9| = 25$ **14.** $|4t - 1| = 27$

15. $|6 - 3y| = -9$ **16.** $\left|\dfrac{x}{4}\right| = 8$ **17.** $3\left|\dfrac{d}{4}\right| = 20$

18. $\left|\dfrac{2x}{3}\right| = -12$ **19.** $\left|\dfrac{4x - 1}{3}\right| = 15$ **20.** $\left|\dfrac{2(y + 1)}{7}\right| = 6$

21. $\left|\dfrac{4(3x - 1)}{5}\right| = 4$ **22.** $|5x - 4| = 3x$ **23.** $|3x + 1| = 4x$

24. $|4x + 8| = 2x$ **25.** $|4x - 2| = 3x + 2$ **26.** $|6x - 8| = 5x - 2$

27. $|8x + 20| = 7x + 10$

14. Properties of Inequalities

THE ORDER PROPERTY OF NUMBER

If x and y are real numbers, then one and only one of the following sentences is true:

$$x < y \qquad x = y \qquad x > y$$

The following graphs illustrate this *order property of number:*

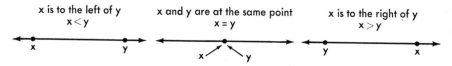

THE TRANSITIVE PROPERTY OF INEQUALITIES

If x, y, and z are real numbers:

$$\text{if } x < y \text{ and } y < z, \text{ then } x < z$$
$$\text{if } z > y \text{ and } y > x, \text{ then } z > x$$

The following graph illustrates the *transitive property of inequalities*:

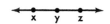

THE ADDITION PROPERTY OF INEQUALITIES

If x, y, and z are real numbers:

$$\text{if } x > y, \text{ then } x + z > y + z$$
$$\text{if } x < y, \text{ then } x + z < y + z$$

The following examples illustrate the *addition property of inequalities*:

$$\text{if } 10 > 7, \text{ then } 10 + 5 > 7 + 5$$
$$\text{if } 6 < 8, \text{ then } 6 + (-4) < 8 + (-4)$$

Since subtracting a real number from both members of an inequality means adding its opposite to both members of the inequality, we can say:

When the same number is added to or subtracted from both members of an inequality, the order of the inequality remains unchanged.

THE MULTIPLICATION PROPERTY OF INEQUALITIES

If x, y, and z are real numbers, then:

if $x > y$, then $xz > yz$ when z is positive $(z > 0)$

if $x < y$, then $xz < yz$ when z is positive $(z > 0)$

if $x > y$, then $xz < yz$ when z is negative $(z < 0)$

if $x < y$, then $xz > yz$ when z is negative $(z < 0)$

The following examples illustrate the *multiplication property of inequalities*:

if $5 > 3$, then $5(7) > 3(7)$

if $6 < 9$, then $6(\frac{1}{3}) < 9(\frac{1}{3})$

if $5 > 3$, then $5(-7) < 3(-7)$

if $6 < 9$, then $6(-\frac{1}{3}) > 9(-\frac{1}{3})$

Note that the order of the inequality is reversed in the last two examples.

Since dividing both members of an inequality by a nonzero number means to multiply by the reciprocal of the number, we can say:

When both members of an inequality are multiplied or divided by a positive number, the order of the inequality remains unchanged; when both members are multiplied or divided by a negative number, the order of the inequality is reversed.

Exercises

In 1–16, replace the question mark with the symbol $>$ or the symbol $<$ so that the resulting sentence will be true. All variables are nonzero real numbers.

1. If $x < 7$ and $7 < y$, then x ? y.

2. If $r > -5$ and $-5 > q$, then r ? q.

3. If $y < 8$ and $z > 8$, then y ? z.

4. If $d > e$ and $g < e$, then d ? g.

5. If $5 < 7$, then $5 - 12$? $7 - 12$.

6. If $12 > 9$, then $12(4)$? $9(4)$.

7. If $15 > 10$, then $15(-2)$? $10(-2)$.

8. If $36 < 42$, then $36 \div 6$? $42 \div 6$.

9. If $24 > 18$, then $24 \div (-2)$? $18 \div (-2)$.

10. If $35 > 20$, then $35 \div 5$? $20 \div 5$.

11. If $x + 5 > 7$, then $x + 5 + (-5)$? $7 + (-5)$ or x ? 2.

12. If $x - 3 < 15$, then $x - 3 + 3$? $15 + 3$ or x ? 18.

13. If $4x > 20$, then $\dfrac{4x}{4}$? $\dfrac{20}{4}$ or x ? 5.

14. If $\frac{1}{2}y > 5$, then $2 \times \frac{1}{2}y$? 2×5 or y ? 10.

15. If $-3x < 27$, then $\dfrac{-3x}{-3}$? $\dfrac{27}{-3}$ or x ? -9.

16. If $\dfrac{-x}{4} > 16$, then $-4\left(\dfrac{-x}{4}\right)$? $-4(16)$ or x ?-64.

15. Solving First-Degree Inequalities

To *solve an inequality* means to find its solution set. Consider the inequality $3x > 6$, the domain of the variable being the set of real numbers.

If $x = 1.9$, then $3(1.9) > 6$, or $5.7 > 6$ is a false sentence.
If $x = 2$, then $3(2) > 6$, or $6 > 6$ is a false sentence.
If $x = 2.1$, then $3(2.1) > 6$, or $6.3 > 6$ is a *true* sentence.

Notice that if x is replaced by any real number greater than 2, the resulting sentence is true. Therefore, the solution set of $3x > 6$ is the set of all real numbers greater than 2, which may be represented by $x > 2$ or $\{x \mid x > 2\}$.

Equivalent inequalities are inequalities that have the same solution set. Therefore, $3x > 6$ and $x > 2$ are equivalent inequalities because they have the same solution set.

If the domain of x is the set of real numbers, the inequality $3x > 6$ is called a **conditional inequality** because it is true for at least one, but not all members of the domain. Other examples of conditional inequalities are $x + 7 > 9$ and $3x - 2 < 7$, $x \in \{\text{real numbers}\}$.

If $x \in \{\text{real numbers}\}$, the inequality $x + 8 > x$ is true for every element of the domain. Such an inequality is called an **absolute inequality**, or an **unconditional inequality**. Other examples of absolute inequalities are $5x + 8 > 5x$ and $x - 4 < x$.

To find the solution set of an inequality, we will solve the inequality using methods similar to those used in solving an equation. We will transform the inequality into a simpler equivalent inequality of the form $x > a$, or $x < a$, making use of the following four postulates, which correspond to the addition, subtraction, multiplication, and division properties of inequalities.

POSTULATES INVOLVING EQUIVALENT INEQUALITIES

Postulate 1. If an equivalent expression is substituted for an expression in an inequality, then the result is an inequality that is equivalent to the original inequality. Thus, $6x + 2x > 4$ and $8x > 4$ are equivalent inequalities.

Postulate 2. If the same number is added to or subtracted from both members of an inequality, the resulting inequality is equivalent to the original inequality.

Thus, if $x - 5 > 2$, then $(x - 5) + 5 > 2 + 5$, and $x > 7$. Therefore, the solution set of $x - 5 > 2$ is $\{x \mid x > 7\}$.

Also, if $x + 3 < 9$, then $(x + 3) - 3 < 9 - 3$, and $x < 6$. Therefore, the solution set of $x + 3 < 9$ is $\{x \mid x < 6\}$.

Postulate 3. If both members of an inequality are multiplied by or divided by the same positive number, the resulting inequality is equivalent to the original inequality.

Thus, if $\frac{x}{5} < 3$, then $5\left(\frac{x}{5}\right) < 5(3)$, and $x < 15$. Therefore, the solution set of $\frac{x}{5} < 3$ is $\{x \mid x < 15\}$.

Also, if $4x > 12$, then $\frac{4x}{4} > \frac{12}{4}$, and $x > 3$. Therefore, the solution set of $4x > 12$ is $\{x \mid x > 3\}$.

Postulate 4. If both members of an inequality are multiplied by or divided by the same negative number, and the order of the inequality is reversed, the resulting inequality is equivalent to the original inequality.

Thus, if $\frac{x}{-4} > 3$, then $(-4)\left(\frac{x}{-4}\right) < (-4)(3)$, and $x < -12$. Therefore, the solution set of $\frac{x}{-4} > 3$ is $\{x \mid x < -12\}$.

Also, if $-3x < 6$, then $\frac{-3x}{-3} > \frac{6}{-3}$, and $x > -2$. Therefore, the solution set of $-3x < 6$ is $\{x \mid x > -2\}$.

~~~~~~~~~~ *MODEL PROBLEMS* ~~~~~~~~~~

In 1 and 2 (*a*) solve and (*b*) graph the solution sets of the inequalities.
1. $8x - 3 < 5x + 12$

Solution:

$$8x - 3 < 5x + 12$$
$$8x - 3 + 3 < 5x + 12 + 3$$
$$8x < 5x + 15$$
$$8x - 5x < 5x + 15 - 5x$$
$$3x < 15$$
$$\frac{3x}{3} < \frac{15}{3}$$
$$x < 5$$

Answer: a. $\{x \mid x < 5\}$

b.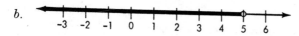

2. $4(2x - 6) - 10x \leq -28$

Solution:

$$4(2x - 6) - 10x \leq -28$$
$$8x - 24 - 10x \leq -28$$
$$-2x - 24 \leq -28$$
$$-2x - 24 + 24 \leq -28 + 24$$
$$-2x \leq -4$$
$$\frac{-2x}{-2} \geq \frac{-4}{-2}$$
$$x \geq 2$$

Answer: a. $\{x \mid x \geq 2\}$.

b.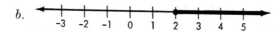

Exercises

In 1–24, find and graph the solution set of the inequality.

1. $x - 3 > 4$

2. $10 \leq 1 + y$

3. $4y > 20$

4. $12 \geq 2x$

5. $-3x > -12$

6. $-4c \leq -8$

7. $\frac{x}{2} > 4$

8. $8 \geq \frac{d}{4}$

9. $\frac{x}{-2} < 5$

10. $-4 \leq \frac{x}{-3}$

11. $4t - 3 < 17$

12. $-8 \leq 3y - 2$

13. $2x + 6x - 12 > 4$

14. $3x + 5 > 4x$

15. $3x + 2 > 2x + 7$

16. $\frac{x}{3} - 2 < \frac{x}{2} - 1$

17. $3(2x - 1) < 21$

18. $7y > 2(2y + 3)$

19. $4\left(\frac{1}{2} - \frac{3y}{4}\right) \geq -7$

20. $10x - 4(2x + 1) \geq 0$

21. $2y^2 - 24 \leq 2y(6 + y)$

22. $5t \leq 8 + 3(2t - 2)$

23. $2(2x + 3) > -3(4x - 8)$

24. $-2(2c - 9) \geq 4 - 5(c - 2)$

In 25–28, state whether the inequality is a conditional inequality or an absolute inequality. $x \in \{\text{real numbers}\}$.

25. $5x + 6 > 5x$

26. $5x + 6 > 11$

27. $2x + 6x - 10 < 8x$

28. $2(3x + 5) > 4x - (6 - x)$

In 29–32, find the set of numbers that satisfy the condition.

29. A number decreased by 4 is greater than 6.

30. Twice a number increased by 8 is less than −4.

31. Three times a number decreased by 10 is less than 2 times the number.

32. Five times a number decreased by 12 is greater than 2 times the number increased by 6.

In 33 and 34, x and $y \in$ {real numbers}.

33. *a.* If $x > y$, prove that $x - y > 0$.   *b.* If $x - y > 0$, prove that $x > y$.

34. *a.* If $x - y < 0$, prove that $x < y$.   *b.* If $x < y$, prove that $x - y < 0$.

In 35 and 36, a, b, x, and $y \in$ {real numbers}.

35. If $a < b$ and $x < y$, prove that $a + x < b + y$.

36. If a, b, x, and y are positive numbers, and $a > b$ and $x > y$, prove that $ax > by$.

In 37–39, a and $b \in$ {real numbers}.

37. If $a > 0$ and $b > 0$, prove that $ab > 0$.

38. If $a > 0$ and $b < 0$, prove that $ab < 0$.

39. If $a < 0$ and $b < 0$, prove that $ab > 0$.

16. Solving Inequalities Involving Absolute Values

On a number line, the absolute value of a real number may represent the non-directed distance between the graph of the number and the origin.

To find the solution set of $|x| < 3$, we must find the set of points such that, on a number line, the distance between the graph of every one of these points and the  origin is less than 3. The graph at the right shows us that the distance between the origin and the graph of any number x between −3 and 3 is less than 3. Hence, x is any real number greater than −3 and less than 3; that is, $-3 < x$ and $x < 3$. These two inequalities may be written as $-3 < x < 3$. Therefore, the solution set of $|x| < 3$ is $\{x \mid -3 < x < 3\}$. This example illustrates the truth of the following:

Principle 1. If a is a positive number ($a > 0$), then the solution set of $|x| < a$ is $\{x \mid -a < x < a\}$.

Note. As shown in the figure at the right, the graph of the solution set of $|x| < a$ is the heavy line 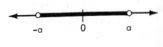 segment between −a and a, not including its endpoints.

If we wish to find the solution set of $|x| > 3$, we must find the set of points such that, on a number line, the distance between the graph of every one of these points and the origin is greater than 3.

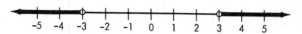

The preceding graph shows us that the distance between the origin and the graph of any number x which is greater than 3, also, the distance between the origin and the graph of any number x which is less than -3, must be greater than 3. Therefore, $|x| > 3$ for $x < -3$ or $x > 3$. Hence, the solution set of $|x| > 3$ is $\{x \mid x < -3 \text{ or } x > 3\}$. This example illustrates the following principle:

Principle 2. If a is a positive number ($a > 0$), then the solution set of $|x| > a$ is $\{x \mid x < -a \text{ or } x > a\}$.

Note. As shown in the figure at the right, the graph of the solution set of $|x| > a$ is the union of the heavy ray to the right of a and the heavy ray to the left of $-a$, not including the endpoints a and $-a$.

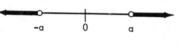

~~~~~~~~~ *MODEL PROBLEMS* ~~~~~~~~~

1. Solve $|4x - 8| < 12$ and graph the solution set.

How To Proceed	*Solution*
1. Write the inequality.	$|4x - 8| < 12$
2. Apply Principle 1.	$-12 < 4x - 8 < 12$
3. Add 8 to each member of the inequality.	$-4 < 4x < 20$
4. Divide each member of the inequality by 4.	$-1 < x < 5$

Answer: Solution set is $\{x \mid -1 < x < 5\}$.

2. Solve $\left| \dfrac{x}{3} - 2 \right| \geq 1$ and graph the solution set.

How To Proceed	*Solution*
1. Write the inequality.	$\left\| \dfrac{x}{3} - 2 \right\| \geq 1$

2. Apply Principle 2. $\dfrac{x}{3} - 2 \le -1$ or $\dfrac{x}{3} - 2 \ge 1$

3. Add 2 to each member of the $\dfrac{x}{3} \le 1$ $\dfrac{x}{3} \ge 3$
   inequality.

4. Multiply each member of the $x \le 3$ $x \ge 9$
   inequality by 3.

Answer: Solution set is $\{x \mid x \le 3 \text{ or } x \ge 9\}$.

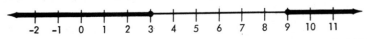

Exercises

In 1–12, solve the inequality and graph the solution set.

1. $|x| > 5$ **2.** $\left|\dfrac{x}{3}\right| \ge 2$ **3.** $|3x| < 9$

4. $|-2r| \le 10$ **5.** $|x - 2| > 4$ **6.** $\left|\dfrac{3 + d}{2}\right| \le 2$

7. $|2x - 1| < 7$ **8.** $\left|\dfrac{3x}{4} - 1\right| \ge 2$ **9.** $|2y + 5| \ge 9$

10. $13 \ge |6x + 1|$ **11.** $|6 - x| \le 18$ **12.** $\left|\dfrac{4 - 2x}{3}\right| \ge 4$

In 13–16, select the inequality whose solution set is pictured in the graph.

13. (1) $|x| > 4$ (2) $|x| < 4$ (3) $|x| \ge 4$ (4) $|x| \le 4$

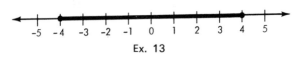

Ex. 13

14. (1) $|x| \le 2$ (2) $|x| > 2$ (3) $|x| < 2$ (4) $|x| \ge 2$

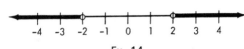

Ex. 14

15. (1) $|x - 2| > 3$ (2) $|x + 2| \le 3$ (3) $|x + 2| \ge 3$ (4) $|x - 2| < 3$

Ex. 15

16. (1) $|x + 3| < 4$ (2) $|x - 3| < 4$ (3) $|x - 3| \leq 2$ (4) $|x + 3| \geq 4$

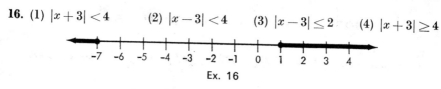

Ex. 16

17. Solving Problems Involving Inequalities

PREPARING TO SOLVE PROBLEMS INVOLVING INEQUALITIES

The following examples illustrate how to represent algebraically sentences that involve relationships of inequality.

Sentence	*Meaning*	*Representation*
1. x is at least 25.	x is equal to 25, or x is greater than 25.	$x \geq 25$
2. The minimum value of x is 25.	x is equal to 25, or x is greater than 25.	$x \geq 25$
3. x is at most 25.	x is equal to 25, or x is less than 25.	$x \leq 25$
4. The maximum value of x is 25.	x is equal to 25, or x is less than 25.	$x \leq 25$
5. x is at least 25 and at most 30.	x is equal to 25 or x is greater than 25 and x is equal to 30 or x is less than 30.	$x \geq 25$ and $x \leq 30$; or $25 \leq x \leq 30$

Exercises

In 1–10, represent the sentence as an algebraic inequality.

1. y is at least 100.

2. The least possible value of x is 18.

3. x is at most 69.

4. The greatest possible value of $5y$ is 150.

5. The sum of $5x$ and $2x$ is at least 77.

6. 8 more than $2y$ is at most 24.

7. The maximum value of $6x - 4$ is 48.

8. The minimum value of the sum of y and $y + 2$ is 62.

9. y is at least 30 and at most 40.

10. The sum of twice x and three times $(x - 5)$ is at least 70 and at most 85.

SOLVING PROBLEMS INVOLVING INEQUALITIES

~~~~~~~~~~~~~~~~ *MODEL PROBLEMS* ~~~~~~~~~~~~~~~~

1. In a town, the number of adults exceeds 3 times the number of children by 80. If the town has at most 3560 persons, find the greatest possible number of adults and the greatest possible number of children there can be in the town.

   Solution: If the town has at most 3560 persons, the sum of the number of adults and the number of children either is equal to 3560 or is less than 3560.

   Let $x =$ the possible number of children in the town.
   Then $3x + 80 =$ the possible number of adults in the town.

   *The possible number of children plus the possible number
   of adults is equal to 3560 or is less than 3560.*

$$x + 3x + 80 \leq 3560$$
$$4x + 80 \leq 3560$$
$$4x \leq 3480$$
$$x \leq 870 \qquad \text{Hence, there are at most 870 children.}$$
$$3x + 80 \leq 2690 \qquad \text{Hence, there are at most 2690 adults.}$$

   Answer: There are at most 2690 adults and at most 870 children in the town.

2. Elliot is 5 times as old as Sid. Ten years from now, Elliot will be at least 3 times as old as Sid will be then. At least how old is each person now?

   Solution: If 10 years from now Elliot will be at least 3 times as old as Sid will be then, Elliot's age at that time either will be equal to or greater than 3 times Sid's age at that time.

   Let $x =$ the possible number of years in Sid's age now.

	Age now	Age 10 years hence
Sid	x	$x + 10$
Elliot	$5x$	$5x + 10$

   *Ten years from now, Elliot's age will be equal to or
   greater than 3 times Sid's age then.*

$$5x + 10 \geq 3(x + 10)$$
$$5x + 10 \geq 3x + 30$$
$$2x \geq 20$$
$$x \geq 10 \qquad \text{Hence, Sid is at least 10 years old now.}$$
$$5x \geq 50 \qquad \text{Hence, Elliot is at least 50 years old now.}$$

Answer: Sid is at least 10 years old now; Elliot is at least 50 years old now.

~~~~~~

Exercises

1. Mr. Freed and his helper, Mr. Standish, work together on a job. Mr. Freed earns twice as much as Mr. Standish. If they receive at least $840 for doing the job, find the least amount that each would receive.

2. Three times a number increased by 8 is at most 40 more than the number. Find the greatest value of the number.

3. The length of a rectangle is 8 inches less than 5 times its width. If the perimeter of the rectangle is at most 104 inches, find the maximum length of the rectangle.

4. Mr. Gold is 8 years younger than Mr. Breen, and Mr. Carney is half as old as Mr. Breen. The sum of Mr. Gold's age and Mr. Breen's age is at least 58 years more than Mr. Carney's age. At least, how old is Mr. Breen now?

5. Mr. Taylor has $15,000. He wishes to invest part of his money in bonds which pay 5% interest and the rest of his money in a business loan which pays 8% interest. Find the maximum amount that he may invest at 5% if his annual income from these investments is to be at least $1050.

6. The smaller of two consecutive even integers is greater than 49 more than one-fourth of the larger. Find the least possible values for the integers.

7. Mr. Gray can drive from his home out into the country traveling at the rate of 30 mph and return traveling at the rate of 40 mph. What is the greatest distance that he can drive out and then return to his home if he has at most 7 hours to spend on the trip?

8. A chemist has 40 quarts of an acid solution which is 20% pure acid. At least, how many quarts of pure acid must he add to this solution to obtain a solution which is at least 50% pure acid?

9. A shoemaker can fix a pair of heels in 10 minutes and a pair of soles in 20 minutes. The number of pairs of heels he fixes is 5 times the number of pairs of soles he fixes. In a week, he works a minimum of 42 hours and a maximum of 49 hours. Find the minimum and the maximum number of pairs of heels that he can fix in a week.

10. Mr. Green would like to save between $250 and $310 a month. He can do this if in a month he will save $50 less than 3 times the amount that he saves a month now. In what range is the amount he saves a month now?

CHAPTER V

LINEAR RELATIONS AND FUNCTIONS

1. Finding Solution Sets of Open Sentences in Two Variables

An example of an open sentence in two variables is $x + 2y = 6$, which is neither true nor false. If x is replaced by 1 and y is replaced by 4, the resulting sentence $1 + 8 = 6$ is *false*. If x is replaced by 4 and y is replaced by 1, the resulting sentence $4 + 2 = 6$ is *true*. Therefore, the pair of numbers $x = 4$ and $y = 1$ satisfies the open sentence $x + 2y = 6$. Such a pair of numbers is called a ***root*** or ***solution*** of $x + 2y = 6$. We can write the solution $x = 4$ and $y = 1$ as an ***ordered pair*** of numbers using the symbol $(4, 1)$ if we agree that the first number in the pair, called the ***first coordinate*** or the ***first component***, represents a value of the variable x, and the second number of the pair, called the ***second coordinate*** or the ***second component***, represents a value of the variable y. We saw that the pair of numbers $x = 1$, $y = 4$ does not satisfy the sentence $x + 2y = 6$. Therefore, the ordered pair $(1, 4)$ is not a solution of $x + 2y = 6$.

Observe that the ordered pair $(4, 1)$ is not the same as the ordered pair $(1, 4)$; that is, $(4, 1) \neq (1, 4)$. When dealing with ordered pairs of numbers, we must be careful not to interchange their coordinates.

Two ordered pairs of numbers are equal if and only if their first coordinates are equal and their second coordinates are equal. For example, $(4, 1) = (\frac{8}{2}, \frac{3}{3})$ because $4 = \frac{8}{2}$ and $1 = \frac{3}{3}$.

In general, for all real numbers a, b, c, d,

$$(a, b) = (c, d) \text{ when } a = c \text{ and } b = d$$

When the domain, or replacement set for x and for y, is $\{1, 2, 3, 4, 5, 6, 7, 8, 9\}$, the solutions of $x + 2y = 6$ are the ordered pairs $(2, 2)$ and $(4, 1)$. We call this set of ordered pairs $\{(2, 2), (4, 1)\}$ the *solution set* of the sentence $x + 2y = 6$. The ***solution set of an open sentence in two variables*** is the set of ordered pairs of numbers that are members of the replacement set of the variables and that also satisfy the open sentence. If there are no ordered pairs that are solutions of the sentence, we say that the solution set is the empty set, $\varnothing$.

If the replacement set for both x and y is the set of real numbers, the solution set of $x + 2y = 6$ has an infinite number of members, some of which are $(1, 2.5)$,

$(2, 2)$, $(0, 3)$, $(-1, 3.5)$. It is impossible to list all the members of the solution set. In such a case, we can describe the solution set as $\{(x, y) \mid x + 2y = 6\}$, which is read "the set of all ordered pairs (x, y) such that $x + 2y = 6$."

When the replacement set of both x and y is $\{1, 2, 3, 4\}$, the solution set of the open sentence $x + 2y < 6$ is the set of ordered pairs $\{(1, 1), (1, 2), (2, 1), (3, 1)\}$. To verify, for example, that $(1, 2)$ is a solution of $x + 2y < 6$, we replace x by 1 and y by 2. We obtain $1 + 4 < 6$, which is a true sentence.

If the replacement set of both x and y is the set of real numbers, the solution set of $x + 2y < 6$ has an infinite number of members, some of which are $(5, 0)$, $(\frac{1}{2}, 2)$, $(0, 1)$, $(-1, 3)$. It is impossible to list all the members of the solution set. In such a case, we can describe the solution set as $\{(x, y) \mid x + 2y < 6\}$, which is read "the set of all ordered pairs (x, y) such that $x + 2y < 6$."

~~~~~~~~~~~~~ *MODEL PROBLEMS* ~~~~~~~~~~~~~

1. Find the solution set of $y - 3x = 2$ when the replacement set of x is $R = \{1, 2, 3, 4, 5\}$ and the replacement set of y is $S = \{8, 9, 10, 11, 12\}$.

How To Proceed	*Solution*
1. Transform the sentence into an equivalent sentence which expresses y in terms of x.	1. $y - 3x = 2$ $y = 3x + 2$

Step 2 | Step 3

2. Replace x by each member of R, the replacement set of x. Then compute each of the corresponding y-values.
3. Determine whether or not each y-value in step 2 is a member of S, the replacement set of y.

$x \in R$	$3x + 2 = y$	Does $y \in S$?
1	$3(1) + 2 = 5$	$5 \notin S$
2	$3(2) + 2 = 8$	$8 \in S$
3	$3(3) + 2 = 11$	$11 \in S$
4	$3(4) + 2 = 14$	$14 \notin S$
5	$3(5) + 2 = 17$	$17 \notin S$

4. List the ordered pairs (x, y), $x \in R$, and $y \in S$, which are solutions of the given open sentence.

4. $(2, 8)$, $(3, 11)$

Answer: Solution set is $\{(2, 8), (3, 11)\}$.

2. Find the solution set of $y + 1 \geq 2x$ when the domain of x is $R = \{1, 2, 3, 4\}$ and the domain of y is $S = \{2, 4, 6\}$.

How To Proceed	*Solution*
1. Transform the sentence into an equivalent sentence which expresses y in terms of x.	1. $y + 1 \geq 2x$ $y \geq 2x - 1$

2. Replace x in the expression found in step 1 by each member of R, the domain of x. Then compute each corresponding value of the expression.

Step 2

$x \in R$	$2x - 1$
1	$2(1) - 1 = 1$
2	$2(2) - 1 = 3$
3	$2(3) - 1 = 5$
4	$2(4) - 1 = 7$

3. Determine whether or not the y-value(s), found by making use of the results obtained in step 2 are members of S, the domain of y.

Step 3

$y \geq 2x - 1$	$y \in S$
$y \geq 1$	2, 4, 6
$y \geq 3$	4, 6
$y \geq 5$	6
$y \geq 7$	no values

4. List the ordered pairs (x, y), $x \in R$, and $y \in S$, which are solutions of the given open sentence.

4. $(1, 2), (1, 4), (1, 6), (2, 4), (2, 6), (3, 6)$

Answer: Solution set is $\{(1, 2), (1, 4), (1, 6), (2, 4), (2, 6), (3, 6)\}$.

~~~~~~

Exercises

In 1–4, find the value for x and the value for y for which the ordered pairs of numbers are equal.

1. $(4, y)$ and $(x, 7)$

2. $(2x, -9)$ and $(6, 3y)$

3. $(\frac{1}{3}x, 8)$ and $(6, \frac{3}{4}y)$

4. $(2x - 6, y + 2)$ and $(6x, 3y + 5)$

In 5–8, state whether or not the given ordered pair of numbers is a solution of the sentence. The replacement set for x and for y is the set of integers.

5. $y = 2x + 1$, $(3, 7)$

6. $5x - 3y = 0$, $(3, 5)$

7. $3y > 2x$, $(3, 4)$

8. $5y - 2x \leq 18$, $(5, 1)$

In 9–12, state whether or not the given ordered pair of numbers is a solution of the sentence. The replacement set for x and for y is the set of real numbers.

9. $4x + 5y = 2$, $(\frac{1}{4}, \frac{1}{5})$

10. $3x < 4y$, $(-4, -2)$

11. $y \geq 4 - 3x$, $(-1, \frac{1}{3})$

12. $4y - 3x \leq 13$, $(-2, -\frac{1}{2})$

In 13–15, find the solution set of the sentence.

13. $y = 3x$ when the replacement set of x is $\{1, 2, 3\}$ and the replacement set of y is $\{5, 6, 7, 8, 9\}$.

14. $2x + 3y = 11$ when the domain of x is $\{1, 2, 3, 4, 5, 6\}$ and the domain of y is $\{0, 1, 2, 3, 4\}$.

15. $x + y \geq 8$ when the domain of x is $\{-6, 8, 10\}$ and the domain of y is $\{-2, 2, 6, 10\}$.

16. If the replacement set of x and of y is {natural numbers}, find three ordered pairs that satisfy the sentence $x + 2y = 20$.

17. If the domain of x and of y is the set of odd integers, find three ordered pairs that are members of the solution set of the sentence $y + 3x > 8$.

In 18–21, use set notation to describe the solution set when the replacement set of x and of y is {real numbers}.

18. $y = 8x$ **19.** $4x + y = 8$ **20.** $y < 2x - 3$ **21.** $y - 2x \leq 6$

2. Graphing Ordered Number Pairs in a Plane

An ordered pair of numbers can be associated with a particular point in a plane. We begin with two lines, called **coordinate axes,** drawn at right angles to each other. The horizontal line is called the **x-axis.** The vertical line is called the **y-axis.** In a **coordinate plane**, or **Cartesian plane**, the point O at which the two axes intersect is called the **origin.**

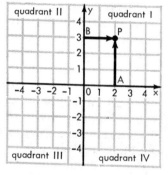

Fig. 1

The x-axis and the y-axis divide the plane into four regions called **quadrants,** which are numbered I, II, III, and IV in a counterclockwise order, as shown in Fig. 1. To determine the ordered pair of numbers that is associated with point P, we draw, through P, a line that is perpendicular to the x-axis and that intersects it at 2. This number 2 is called the **x-coordinate**, or **abscissa,** of point P. We also draw, through P, a line that is perpendicular to the y-axis and that intersects it at 3. This number 3 is called the **y-coordinate,** or **ordinate,** of point P. The x-coordinate, 2, and the y-coordinate, 3, are called the **coordinates** of point P. The coordinates of a point may be written as an ordered pair of numbers in which the first number is always the x-coordinate, and the second number is always the y-coordinate. Thus, the coordinates of point P in Fig. 1 may be written $(2, 3)$. In general, the coordinates of a point may be represented by (x, y).

To find a point, given an ordered pair, we merely reverse the previous procedure. For example, to find the point associated with the ordered pair (3, 2), we draw a line perpendicular to the x-axis at 3; we draw a line perpendicular to the y-axis at 2. The point, P_1, at which these lines intersect (see Fig. 2), is the point associated with the ordered pair (3, 2). Point P_1 is called the **graph** of the ordered number pair (3, 2). The point associated with $(-2, 4)$ is point P_2 in quadrant II. The point associated with $(-3, -4)$ is point P_3 in quadrant III. The point associated with $(4, -2)$ is point P_4 in quadrant IV. When we graph the point associated with an ordered number pair, we are *plotting the point*.

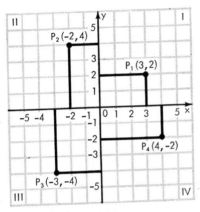

Fig. 2

Each ordered pair of real numbers corresponds to one and only one point in the plane. Also, each point in the plane corresponds to one and only one ordered pair of real numbers. This system, which sets up a one-to-one correspondence between the set of all ordered pairs of real numbers and the set of all points in a plane, is called the **Cartesian coordinate system,** or **rectangular coordinate system.**

If one of the coordinates of a point is zero, the point lies on one of the axes. In Fig. 3, points such as $A(3, 0)$ and $C(-4, 0)$, whose ordinate is 0, lie on the x-axis. Points such as $B(0, 2)$ and $D(0, -3)$, whose abscissa is 0, lie on the y-axis. The origin, $O(0, 0)$, lies on both axes.

The signs and zero values of the coordinates of points in the four quadrants and between the quadrants may be summarized as follows:

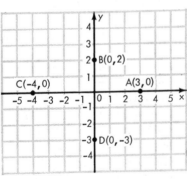

Fig. 3

	Quadrant				Between Quadrants			
	I	II	III	IV	IV & I	I & II	II & III	III & IV
Abscissa, (x)	+	−	−	+	+	0	−	0
Ordinate, (y)	+	+	−	−	0	+	0	−

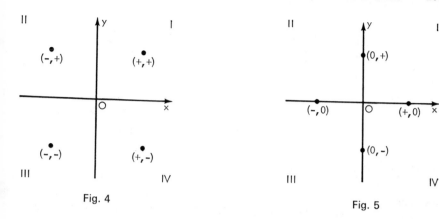

Fig. 4

Fig. 5

Exercises

1. Write as ordered number pairs the coordinates of points $A, B, C, D, E, F, G, H, K, L, M, N$, and O in the graph at the right.

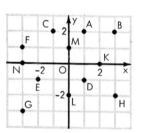

In 2–13, draw a pair of coordinate axes on a sheet of graph paper and plot the point associated with the ordered number pair.

2. $(3, 5)$ **3.** $(-4, 2)$ **4.** $(3, -5)$ **5.** $(-5, -4)$

6. $(3, 6\frac{1}{2})$ **7.** $(-2\frac{1}{2}, 5)$ **8.** $(4, 0)$ **9.** $(-2, 0)$

10. $(-9, 0)$ **11.** $(0, 6)$ **12.** $(0, -4)$ **13.** $(|3|, |5|)$

In 14–16, graph each member of the set.

14. $\{(1, 3), (2, 5), (3, 7)\}$

15. $\{(0, 5), (2, 4), (4, 3)\}$

16. $\{(0, 0), (-1, 1), (-3, 3)\}$

17. Graph several points on the x-axis. What is the value of the ordinate for every point in the set of points on the x-axis?

18. Graph several points on the y-axis. What is the value of the abscissa for every point in the set of points on the y-axis?

19. Name the quadrant in which the graph of $P(x, y)$ lies when:

     a. $x > 0, y > 0$ *b.* $x > 0, y < 0$ *c.* $x < 0, y > 0$ *d.* $x < 0, y < 0$

20. Name the quadrant in whose interior the graph of the point $P(|x|, |y|)$ lies when x and y are members of the set of nonzero real numbers.

3. Graphing a Linear Equation in Two Variables by Using Its Solutions

If we wish to discover pairs of numbers which satisfy, that is, are solutions of, the equation $x + 2y = 6$, we can proceed in either of the following two ways:

Method 1

In the equation $x + 2y = 6$ replace one variable, for example x, by a convenient value. Then solve the resulting equation for the corresponding value of the other variable, y.

Let $x = 4$. Then
$$4 + 2y = 6$$
$$2y = 2$$
$$y = 1$$
$(4, 1)$ is a solution of $x + 2y = 6$.

Method 2

Transform $x + 2y = 6$ into an equivalent equation which has y as one of its members. Then we can assign a value to x and find the corresponding y-value.

For example,
$$x + 2y = 6$$
$$2y = 6 - x$$
$$y = 3 - \tfrac{1}{2}x$$
Let $x = 4$. Then
$$y = 3 - \tfrac{1}{2}(4)$$
$$y = 3 - 2$$
$$y = 1$$
$(4, 1)$ is a solution of $x + 2y = 6$.

Note. When several ordered pairs are to be found, method 2 is preferable since, in this method, y is expressed in terms of x.

We have seen that if the domain of both x and y is the set of real numbers, there is an infinite number of ordered pairs that are solutions of $x + 2y = 6$. Some of these solutions are shown in the following table:

x	-2	0	2	4	6	8
y	4	3	2	1	0	-1

When we graph the number pairs in the table, as shown in the figure below, the points that are associated with these number pairs lie on a straight line; that is, they are called *collinear points*. In fact, any point that is the graph of an ordered pair that is a solution of $x + 2y = 6$ must lie on this same line. Furthermore, any point that is the graph of an ordered pair that is not a solution of $x + 2y = 6$ does not lie on this same line.

The graph of $x + 2y = 6$ is the line which is the set of all those points and only those points whose coordinates satisfy $x + 2y = 6$. In turn, $x + 2y = 6$ is

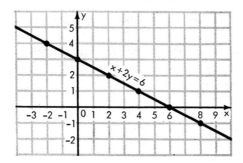

called the ***equation of the line.*** This line is also the graph of every equation which is equivalent to $x + 2y = 6$. Examples of such equations are $x = 6 - 2y$ and $y = \dfrac{6 - x}{2}$.

The equation $x + 2y = 6$ is in the form $Ax + By = C$.

Any first-degree equation in two variables such as $x = 6 - 2y$ or $y = \dfrac{6 - x}{2}$ may be transformed into the form $Ax + By = C$.

The following theorems, which can be proved, apply to first-degree equations transformable into $Ax + By = C$ where the replacement set of x, y, A, B, and C is the set of real numbers and A and B are not both 0:

Theorem 1. The graph of every first-degree equation is a straight line. For this reason, we call such an equation a ***linear equation.***

Theorem 2. Any straight line in a Cartesian plane is the graph of a first-degree equation.

Note. When we graph a linear equation, unless otherwise indicated, the replacement set of the variables is understood to be the set of real numbers.

KEEP IN MIND

1. The graph of an open sentence in two variables is the set of those points that are the graphs of the ordered pairs of real numbers (x, y) for which the sentence becomes a true statement.
2. Each ordered pair of real numbers that satisfies an equation represents the coordinates of a point on the graph of the equation.
3. Each point on the graph of an equation has as its coordinates an ordered pair of real numbers that satisfies the equation.

~~~~~~~~~~~~~~~ *MODEL PROBLEMS* ~~~~~~~~~~~~~~~

1. *a.* Write the following verbal sentence as an equation: "The sum of twice the abscissa of a point and 3 times the ordinate of that point is 6."

   b. Graph the equation written in part *a*.

Solution:

a. Let $x =$ the abscissa of the point.
   Let $y =$ the ordinate of the point.
   Then $2x + 3y = 6$ *Ans.*

b.   *How To Proceed*   *Solution*

1. Transform the equation into an   1. $2x + 3y = 6$
   equivalent equation that expresses $3y = 6 - 2x$
   y in terms of x. $y = 2 - \frac{2}{3}x$

2. Determine three solutions of this   2.
   equation by assuming convenient
   values for x and computing the cor-

x	$2 - \frac{2}{3}x$	$= y$
-3	$2 - \frac{2}{3}(-3) =$	4
0	$2 - \frac{2}{3}(0) \ \ =$	2
3	$2 - \frac{2}{3}(3) \ \ =$	0

   responding values for y. (In this case,
   if we choose multiples of 3 as our
   x-values, we will avoid y-values that
   are fractions.)

3. Plot the points which are associated   Steps 3 and 4
   with the three solutions found in step
   2.

4. Draw a straight line which passes
   through the three points. This is the
   required graph.

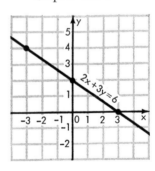

2. If the graph of $4x = 3y + 1$ passes through a point whose ordinate is -3, find the abscissa of the point.

Solution:
   Let $y = -3$ in the equation $4x = 3y + 1$. Then, $4x = 3(-3) + 1$.
   $4x = -8$, or $x = -2$. Hence, the abscissa is -2.   *Answer:* -2

~~~~~~

Exercises

In 1–6, solve the equation for y in terms of x.

1. $2x + y = 3$

2. $3x - y = 9$

3. $2x + 5y = 10$

4. $3x + 4y = 12$

5. $4x - 2y = 8$

6. $2x + 3y - 12 = 0$

In 7–15, graph the equation.

7. $y = 3x$

8. $3y = 4x$

9. $y = -2x$

10. $2x = -5y$

11. $x + y = 5$

12. $y - x = 6$

13. $2x + y = 8$

14. $3x - 4y = 12$

15. $5y - 3x + 15 = 0$

In 16–21, state whether or not the point whose coordinates are given is on the graph of the given equation.

16. $x + y = 8$, $(6, 2)$

17. $x - y = 4$, $(8, -4)$

18. $2x + 3y = -2$, $(5, -4)$

19. $2x = -5y + 2$, $(6, -2)$

20. $y = 5$, $(1, 5)$

21. $x = -2$, $(-2, -1)$

In 22–27, a point is to lie on the graph of the equation. Find its abscissa if its ordinate is the number indicated in the parentheses.

22. $x + 3y = 5$, (2)

23. $3x - y = 8$, (-1)

24. $2x + 3y = 8$, (4)

25. $2y + x = -10$, (6)

26. $4x - 3y = -9$, (0)

27. $y = -2x + 5$, (-3)

In 28–33, a point is to lie on the graph of the equation. Find its ordinate if its abscissa is the number indicated in the parentheses.

28. $x + y = 7$, (5)

29. $2x - y = 11$, (-1)

30. $3x + 2y = 5$, (-5)

31. $4y + x = 10$, (2)

32. $5x - 4y = 8$, (0)

33. $y = -3x - 5$, (4)

In 34–38, find a value that can replace k so that the graph of the resulting equation will pass through the point whose coordinates are given.

34. $x + y = k$, $(1, 3)$

35. $x - y = k$, $(2, -4)$

36. $3x + y = k$, $(-2, -4)$

37. $2x + 3y = k$, $(5, 3)$

38. $3x + 4y = k$, $(4, -3)$

39. If the graph of $y = -3x + b$ passes through the point $(-2, 3)$, find the value of b.

40. If the graph of the equation $Ax + By = 12$ passes through the point $(4, 0)$, find the value of A.

41. Without drawing a graph, find the coordinates of a point on the graph of $x + 4y = 18$ such that the ordinate of the point is twice its abscissa.

In 42–44, (a) write the verbal sentence as an equation, and (b) graph the equation.

42. The abscissa of a point is equal to the ordinate of the point.

43. The ordinate of a point exceeds twice its abscissa by 3.
44. The sum of the abscissa of a point and the ordinate of the point is 7.

4. Graphing a Linear Equation in Two Variables by the Intercept Method

The *x*-intercept of a line is the *x*-coordinate of the point at which the line intersects the *x*-axis. The graph of $2x - 3y = 6$, shown in the figure, intersects the *x*-axis at $A(3, 0)$. Therefore, the *x*-intercept of the graph of $2x - 3y = 6$ is 3. Notice that the value of *y* at point *A* must be zero, since *A* is on the *x*-axis.

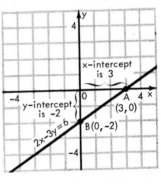

The *y*-intercept of a line is the *y*-coordinate of the point at which the line intersects the *y*-axis. The graph of $2x - 3y = 6$ intersects the *y*-axis at $B(0, -2)$. Therefore, the *y*-intercept of the graph of $2x - 3y = 6$ is -2. Notice that the value of *x* at point *B* must be zero, since *B* is on the *y*-axis.

Procedure. To find the x- and y-intercepts of a line:
1. **To find the x-intercept of a line, substitute 0 for y in the equation of the line. Then solve the resulting equation for x.**
2. **To find the y-intercept of a line, substitute 0 for x in the equation of the line. Then solve the resulting equation for y.**

~~~~~~~~~~~~ *MODEL PROBLEM* ~~~~~~~~~~~~

a. Find the *x*- and *y*-intercepts of the line $x - 2y = 4$.
b. Graph the equation using the intercepts.

How To Proceed	*Solution*	
1. Find the *x*-intercept by substituting 0 for *y*; find the *y*-intercept by substituting 0 for *x*.	1. Find the *x*-intercept: $x - 2y = 4$ $x - 2(0) = 4$ $x = 4$	Find the *y*-intercept: $x - 2y = 4$ $0 - 2y = 4$ $y = -2$

The points $(4, 0)$ and $(0, -2)$ lie on the graph.

2. On the x-axis, graph a point whose abscissa is the x-intercept. On the y-axis, graph a point whose ordinate is the y-intercept.

3. Draw a line through these points.

Steps 2 and 3

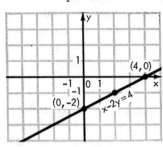

4. To check, find a third ordered pair of numbers that satisfies the given equation. The graph of this ordered pair must be a point in the line.

4. *Check* in the original equation:
$$x - 2y = 4$$
Let $x = 2$: $2 - 2y = 4$
$$-2y = 2$$
$$y = -1$$
The point $(2, -1)$ is on the graph of the line $x - 2y = 4$.

~~~~~~

Exercises

In 1–6, find the x- and y-intercepts of the line that is the graph of the equation.

1. $x + y = 6$
2. $x - 4y = 8$
3. $y = 3x - 12$
4. $y = 4x$
5. $3x - 5y = 15$
6. $3x + 4y = 6$

In 7–12, draw the graph of the equation by the intercept method.

7. $x + y = 4$
8. $x - 3y = 12$
9. $y = 3x + 2$
10. $x = 4y - 8$
11. $2x + 5y = 10$
12. $4x - 6y = 6$

13. *a.* Find the x-intercept and y-intercept for the graph of the equation $y = 2x$.
    b. Is it possible to graph the equation $y = 2x$ by the intercept method?
    c. Draw the graph of $y = 2x$ using another method.

5. Graphing Lines Parallel to the *x*-Axis or *y*-Axis

LINES PARALLEL TO THE *x*-AXIS

If we wish to graph the equation $y = 2$ in a Cartesian plane, we can write this equation in the form $0x + y = 2$.

Every ordered pair in the solution set of this equation has an x-coordinate which is any real number and a y-coordinate which must be 2. Note in Fig. 1 the points $(-2, 2)$, $(0, 2)$, $(2, 2)$, etc. When the graph of $y = 2$ is drawn, it consists of the set of all points and only those points whose ordinate is 2. This set of points is a line parallel to the x-axis and whose y-intercept is 2. Similarly, $y = -2$ represents an equation of a line whose graph is parallel to the x-axis and whose y-intercept is -2.

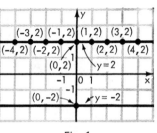

Fig. 1

In general, for any nonzero real number a, the graph of the equation $y = a$ in a Cartesian plane is a line parallel to the x-axis and whose y-intercept is a. Note that when $a = 0$, the graph of $y = a$ in a Cartesian plane is the x-axis itself. Hence, an equation of the x-axis is $y = 0$.

LINES PARALLEL TO THE y-AXIS

If we wish to graph the equation $x = 2$ in a Cartesian plane, we can write this equation in the form $x + 0y = 2$.

The solution set of this equation will be an infinite number of ordered pairs whose x-coordinate is 2 and whose y-coordinate is any real number. Note in Fig. 2 the points $(2, -1)$, $(2, 0)$, $(2, 1)$. The graph of the solution set of $x = 2$ is a line parallel to the y-axis and whose x-intercept is 2. Similarly, $x = -2$ represents the equation of a line whose graph is parallel to the y-axis and whose x-intercept is -2.

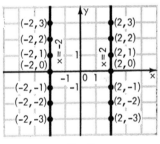

Fig. 2

In general, for any nonzero real number a, the graph of the equation $x = a$ in a Cartesian plane is a line parallel to the y-axis and whose x-intercept is a. Note that when $a = 0$, the graph of the equation $x = a$ in a Cartesian plane is the y-axis itself. Hence, an equation for the y-axis is $x = 0$.

On a number line, there is only one point that has the coordinate a. Therefore, on a number line, the graph of $\{x \mid x = a\}$ is a single point, a.

However, in a Cartesian plane, there is an infinite number of collinear points whose x-coordinate is equal to a. Hence, the graph of $x = a$ in a Cartesian plane is a line, each of whose points has a as its x-coordinate. Therefore, in a Cartesian plane, the graph of $\{(x, y) \mid x = a\}$ is a line, each of whose points is the graph of an ordered pair (x, y) whose x-coordinate is a.

Exercises

In 1–10, draw the graph of the equation in a Cartesian plane.

1. $x = 1$ **2.** $x = \frac{5}{2}$ **3.** $x = 0$ **4.** $x = -4$ **5.** $x + 6 = 0$

6. $y = 3$ **7.** $y = 1.5$ **8.** $y = 0$ **9.** $y = -5$ **10.** $y + 6 = 0$

In 11–13, draw the graph of the set in a Cartesian plane.

11. $\{(x, y) \mid x = 3\}$ **12.** $\{(x, y) \mid y = 1\}$ **13.** $\{(x, y) \mid y + 3 = 0\}$

14. Write an equation of a line that is parallel to the x-axis and whose y-intercept is (a) 4 and (b) -8.

15. Write an equation of a line that passes through all points whose:

　$a.$ abscissa is 4.　　　　　　$b.$ ordinate is 5.

　$c.$ abscissa is -9.　　　　　$d.$ ordinate is -6.

6. The Slope of a Line

LINE REPRESENTATION

In discussions that are to come, we will be dealing with lines. The meanings of the symbols that we will use to represent lines are as follows:

In Fig. 1, $\overleftrightarrow{AB}$ represents a straight line passing through points A and B, extending infinitely far in both directions.

In Fig. 2. $\overline{AB}$ represents line segment AB, or simply segment AB. $\overline{AB}$ is the set of points containing A, B, and all points lying between A and B.

AB represents the length of $\overline{AB}$. AB is a number, the distance between A and B.

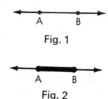

Fig. 1

Fig. 2

MEANING OF THE SLOPE OF A LINE

In triangle ABC (Fig. 3), $\overline{AB}$ represents a section of a straight road. Using $\overline{AC}$ and $\overline{BC}$, we can tell that as a person moves along the road, he will go up a vertical distance

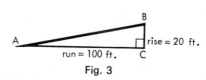

Fig. 3

of 20 feet whenever he travels a horizontal distance of 100 feet. The change in the vertical distance, BC, is called the **rise** and the change in the horizontal distance, AC, is called the **run**.

We may measure the steepness of the road by finding the *slope* of $\overline{AB}$, which is defined as follows:

$$\text{Slope of } \overline{AB} = \frac{\text{change in the vertical distance}}{\text{change in the horizontal distance}} = \frac{\text{rise}}{\text{run}} = \frac{CB}{AC} = \frac{20 \text{ feet}}{100 \text{ feet}} = \frac{1}{5}$$

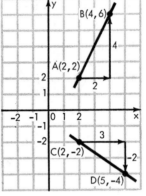

Hence, when we say that the slope of a road is $\frac{1}{5}$, we mean that the road rises 1 foot in each run of 5 feet, or the road rises $\frac{1}{5}$ foot in each run of 1 foot.

Procedure. To find the slope of a line that passes through two points:
1. **Find the horizontal change, the difference in the x-values, in going from the point on the left to the point on the right.**
2. **Find the vertical change, the difference in the y-values, in going from the point on the left to the point on the right.**
3. **Divide the vertical change by the horizontal change.**

Fig. 4

For example, in Fig. 4:

$$\text{slope of } \overleftrightarrow{AB} = \frac{\text{vertical change}}{\text{horizontal change}} = \frac{6-2}{4-2} = \frac{4}{2} = 2$$

$$\text{slope of } \overleftrightarrow{CD} = \frac{\text{vertical change}}{\text{horizontal change}} = \frac{(-4)-(-2)}{5-2} = \frac{-2}{3} = -\frac{2}{3}$$

In general, the slope m of a line that passes through two points $P_1(x_1, y_1)$ and $P_2(x_2, y_2)$, $x_2 \neq x_1$, is the ratio of the difference of the y-values, $y_2 - y_1$, to the difference of the corresponding x-values, $x_2 - x_1$. Thus, as shown in Fig. 5, we may indicate the slope of a line passing through (x_1, y_1) and (x_2, y_2) as

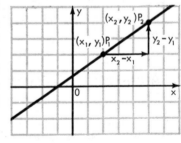

$$m = \frac{y_2 - y_1}{x_2 - x_1}$$

Fig. 5

The expression "difference in x-values, $x_2 - x_1$" may be represented by the symbol Δx, read "delta x." Similarly, "the difference in y-values, $y_2 - y_1$" may be represented by Δy, read "delta y." Therefore, we may indicate the slope of the line passing through (x_1, y_1) and (x_2, y_2) as

$$m = \frac{\Delta y}{\Delta x}$$

Note that in finding the slope of a line passing through two points, it does not matter which point is represented by (x_1, y_1) and which point is represented by (x_2, y_2) since $\frac{y_2 - y_1}{x_2 - x_1} = \frac{y_1 - y_2}{x_1 - x_2}$. Hence, we may write that slope $m = \frac{y_1 - y_2}{x_1 - x_2}$.

The slope of a line that passes through points $A(3, 1)$ and $B(5, 4)$, as in Fig 6, can be found as follows:

$$m = \frac{\Delta y}{\Delta x} = \frac{y_2 - y_1}{x_2 - x_1} = \frac{4 - 1}{5 - 3} = \frac{3}{2}$$

Since this line also passes through points $B(5, 4)$ and $C(9, 10)$, its slope can also be found as follows:

$$m = \frac{\Delta y}{\Delta x} = \frac{10 - 4}{9 - 5} = \frac{6}{4} = \frac{3}{2}$$

Notice that in both cases, the slope of the line was found to be $\frac{3}{2}$. This example illustrates the following:

Principle 1. The slope of a line can be found by using the coordinates of any two of its points.

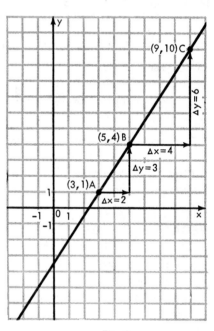

Fig. 6

In Fig. 7, points A, B, C, and D are on the given line. Through A and B, draw lines that are parallel to the x-axis and y-axis respectively, meeting in F. Draw corresponding lines through C and D, meeting in E. Since $\overline{AF}$ and $\overline{CE}$ are both horizontal segments, they are parallel, making $\angle A \cong \angle C$. Therefore, right $\triangle AFB \sim$ right $\triangle CED$ and $\frac{BF}{AF} = \frac{DE}{CE}$. Since the slope of the line, $m = \frac{BF}{AF} = \frac{DE}{CE}$, we see that the slope of the line can be found by using any two points.

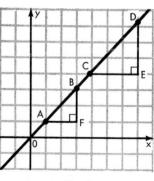

Fig. 7

POSITIVE SLOPES

As a point moves along $\overleftrightarrow{LM}$ from left to right, for example from A to B in Fig. 8, the line is "rising." As the x-values increase, the y-values also increase. Between point A and point B, $y_2 - y_1$, or Δy is a positive number $(+4)$; $x_2 - x_1$ or Δx is also a positive number $(+2)$. Since both Δy and Δx are positive numbers, the slope of $\overleftrightarrow{LM}$, $\dfrac{\Delta y}{\Delta x}$, must be a positive number. In this case,

$$\text{slope} = m = \frac{\Delta y}{\Delta x} = \frac{+4}{+2} = 2$$

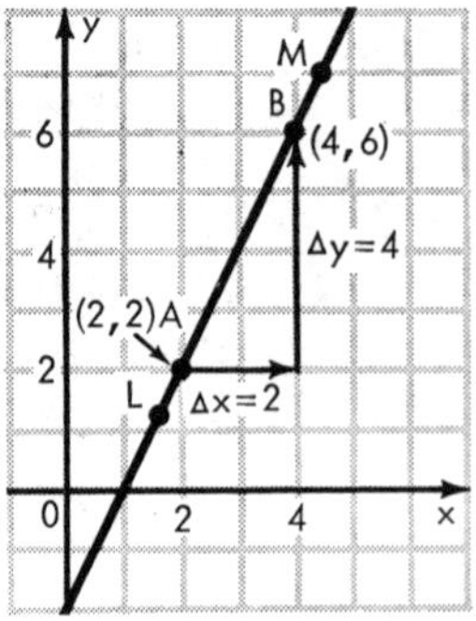

Fig. 8

Thus, we have illustrated the truth of the following:

Principle 2. As a point moves from left to right along a line that is rising, y increases as x increases, and the slope of the line is positive.

NEGATIVE SLOPES

As a point moves along $\overleftrightarrow{RS}$ from left to right, for example from A to B in Fig. 9, the line is "falling." As the x-values increase, the y-values decrease. Between point A and point B, $y_2 - y_1$ or Δy is a negative number (-3); $x_2 - x_1$ or Δx is a positive number (2). Since Δy is a negative number and Δx is a positive number, the slope of $\overleftrightarrow{RS}$, $\dfrac{\Delta y}{\Delta x}$, must be a negative number. In this case,

$$\text{slope} = m = \frac{\Delta y}{\Delta x} = \frac{-3}{2} = -\frac{3}{2}$$

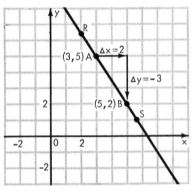

Fig. 9

Thus, we have illustrated the truth of the following:

Principle 3. As a point moves from left to right along a line that is falling, y decreases as x increases, and the slope of the line is negative.

ZERO SLOPE

$\overleftrightarrow{CD}$ is parallel to the x-axis. Consider a point moving
along $\overleftrightarrow{CD}$ from left to right, for example from A to B
in Fig. 10. As the x-values increase, the y-values are
unchanged. Between A and B, $y_2 - y_1$ or Δy is 0; and
$x_2 - x_1$ or Δx is a positive number ($+3$). Since Δy is 0
and Δx is a positive number, the slope of $\overleftrightarrow{CD}$, $\dfrac{\Delta y}{\Delta x}$, must
be 0. In this case,

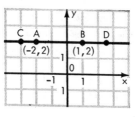

Fig. 10

$$\text{slope} = m = \frac{\Delta y}{\Delta x} = \frac{0}{+3} = 0$$

Thus, we have illustrated the truth of the following:

Principle 4. The slope of a line parallel to the x-axis is 0. (*Note.* The slope of
the x-axis itself is also 0.)

NO SLOPE

$\overleftrightarrow{EF}$ is parallel to the y-axis. Consider a point moving upward along $\overleftrightarrow{EF}$, for example from A to B in Fig. 11. The
x-values are unchanged, but the y-values increase. Between
point A and point B, $y_2 - y_1$ or Δy is a positive number (4)
and $x_2 - x_1$ or Δx is 0. Since the slope of $\overleftrightarrow{EF} = \dfrac{\Delta y}{\Delta x}$, and
$\Delta x = 0$, $\overleftrightarrow{EF}$ has no defined slope because a number cannot
be divided by 0.

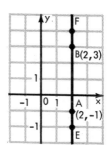

Fig. 11

Thus, we have illustrated the truth of the following:

Principle 5. If a line is parallel to the y-axis, it has no
defined slope. (*Note.* The y-axis itself has no defined slope.)

SLOPES OF PARALLEL LINES

If two lines are vertical, they are parallel to the y-axis and as a result they
have no slope.

If two lines are horizontal, they are parallel to the x-axis. Therefore, the
slopes of these lines are equal, the slope of each line being 0. Also, if the slope
of each of two lines is 0, each of the lines is horizontal and the two lines must be
parallel.

By making use of similar triangles, we can prove the truth of the following:

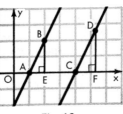

Fig. 12

Principle 6. If two nonvertical lines are parallel, their slopes are equal.

Thus, if $\overleftrightarrow{AB} \parallel \overleftrightarrow{CD}$, then slope of $\overleftrightarrow{AB}$ = slope of $\overleftrightarrow{CD}$.

Principle 7. If two nonvertical lines have the same slope they are parallel lines.

Thus, if the slope of $\overleftrightarrow{AB}$ = slope of $\overleftrightarrow{CD}$, then $\overleftrightarrow{AB} \parallel \overleftrightarrow{CD}$.

Note. Use Fig. 12 to prove principle 6 and principle 7. First prove that right triangle $AEB \sim$ right triangle CFD.

For example (principle 6), if $\overleftrightarrow{AB} \parallel \overleftrightarrow{CD}$ and the slope of $\overleftrightarrow{AB} = \frac{5}{2}$, then the slope of $\overleftrightarrow{CD}$ is also $\frac{5}{2}$. Also (principle 7), if the slope of $\overleftrightarrow{AB}$ is $\frac{5}{2}$ and the slope of $\overleftrightarrow{CD}$ is also $\frac{5}{2}$, then $\overleftrightarrow{AB} \parallel \overleftrightarrow{CD}$.

SLOPES OF PERPENDICULAR LINES

By using the theorem of Pythagoras and its converse, or using principles that we will develop in later chapters, we can prove the truth of the following:

Principle 8. If two nonvertical lines are perpendicular, then the product of their slopes is -1. That is, the slope of one line is the *negative reciprocal* of the slope of the other.

Thus, if $\overleftrightarrow{AB} \perp \overleftrightarrow{CD}$ and the slope of $\overleftrightarrow{AB}$ is m_1 and the slope of $\overleftrightarrow{CD}$ is m_2, then

$$m_1 m_2 = -1, \text{ or } m_2 = -\frac{1}{m_1}.$$

Principle 9. If the product of the slopes of two nonvertical lines is -1 (that is, the slope of one line is the negative reciprocal of the slope of the other line), then the lines are perpendicular to each other. (See the proof, pages 743–744.)

Thus, if the slope of $\overleftrightarrow{AB}$ is m_1 and the slope of $\overleftrightarrow{CD}$ is m_2, and $m_1 m_2 = -1$, then $\overleftrightarrow{AB} \perp \overleftrightarrow{CD}$.

Study the following:

Example 1. If $\overleftrightarrow{AB} \perp \overleftrightarrow{CD}$, and the slope of $\overleftrightarrow{AB} = m_1 = \frac{2}{3}$, find the slope of $\overleftrightarrow{CD}$, m_2. Find the slope of $\overleftrightarrow{CD}$ by applying principle 8: Since $\overleftrightarrow{AB} \perp \overleftrightarrow{CD}$, the slope of $\overleftrightarrow{CD}$ is the negative reciprocal of $\frac{2}{3}$, the slope of $\overleftrightarrow{AB}$. Hence, the slope of $\overleftrightarrow{CD} = -\frac{3}{2}$.

Example 2. If the slope of $\overleftrightarrow{AB} = m_1 = 5$ and the slope of $\overleftrightarrow{CD} = m_2 = -\frac{1}{5}$, show that $\overleftrightarrow{AB} \perp \overleftrightarrow{CD}$. Reason as follows: Since the slope of $\overleftrightarrow{AB} = m_1 = 5$ and the slope of $\overleftrightarrow{CD} = m_2 = -\frac{1}{5}$, then $m_1 m_2 = 5(-\frac{1}{5}) = -1$. Applying principle 9, since $m_1 m_2 = -1$, then $\overleftrightarrow{AB} \perp \overleftrightarrow{CD}$.

~~~~~~~~~~~~~~ *MODEL PROBLEMS* ~~~~~~~~~~~~~~

1. *a.* Graph the straight line that passes through the points $(-2, 3)$ and $(4, 6)$.
   b. Find the slope of the line.

   Solution:
   a. Plot $P_1(-2, 3)$ and $P_2(4, 6)$ as shown. Draw $\overleftrightarrow{P_1 P_2}$.
   b. Complete right triangle $P_1 A P_2$ as shown.

   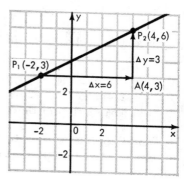

   At $P_2(4, 6) \to x_2 = 4,\ y_2 = 6$
   At $P_1(-2, 3) \to x_1 = -2,\ y_1 = 3$

   $\overleftrightarrow{P_1 P_2}$ passes through $P_1(x_1, y_1)$ and $P_2(x_2, y_2)$.

   $$\text{Slope of } \overleftrightarrow{P_1 P_2} = \frac{y_2 - y_1}{x_2 - x_1}$$
   $$= \frac{6 - 3}{4 - (-2)}$$
   $$= \tfrac{3}{6} = \tfrac{1}{2}\ Ans.$$

2. Show that the line which joins the point $A(1, 1)$ and the point $B(2, 4)$ is parallel to the line which connects the point $C(3, -2)$ and the point $D(4, 1)$.

   Plan: We can prove that $\overleftrightarrow{AB}$ is parallel to $\overleftrightarrow{CD}$ if we can show that the slope of line $\overleftrightarrow{AB}$ is equal to the slope of line $\overleftrightarrow{CD}$.

   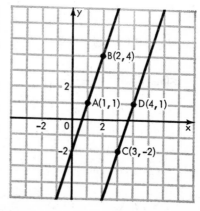

Solution:

Let A be $P_1(x_1, y_1)$.
Let B be $P_2(x_2, y_2)$.
At $B(2, 4) \to x_2 = 2, y_2 = 4$
At $A(1, 1) \to x_1 = 1, y_1 = 1$

Let C be $P_1(x_1, y_1)$.
Let D be $P_2(x_2, y_2)$.
At $D(4, 1) \to x_2 = 4, y_2 = 1$
At $C(3, -2) \to x_1 = 3, y_1 = -2$

Slope of a line passing through (x_1, y_1) and $(x_2, y_2) = \dfrac{y_2 - y_1}{x_2 - x_1}$.

Slope of $\overleftrightarrow{AB} = \dfrac{4-1}{2-1}$

$\qquad = \dfrac{3}{1}$

Slope of $\overleftrightarrow{CD} = \dfrac{1-(-2)}{4-3}$

$\qquad = \dfrac{3}{1}$

Since slope of $\overleftrightarrow{AB}$ = slope of $\overleftrightarrow{CD}$, then $\overleftrightarrow{AB}$ is parallel to $\overleftrightarrow{CD}$.

3. Show that the line which passes through the points $A(-1, 4)$ and $B(2, -2)$ is perpendicular to the line which passes through the points $C(-1, 0)$ and $D(3, 2)$.

Plan: We can prove that $\overleftrightarrow{AB}$ is perpendicular to $\overleftrightarrow{CD}$ if we can show that the product of the slopes of these lines is -1.

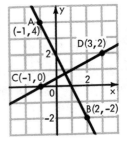

Solution:

Let A be $P_1(x_1, y_1)$.
Let B be $P_2(x_2, y_2)$.
At $B(2, -2) \to x_2 = 2, y_2 = -2$
At $A(-1, 4) \to x_1 = -1, y_1 = 4$

Let C be $P_1(x_1, y_1)$.
Let D be $P_2(x_2, y_2)$.
At $D(3, 2) \to x_2 = 3, y_2 = 2$
At $C(-1, 0) \to x_1 = -1, y_1 = 0$

Slope of a line passing through (x_1, y_1) and $(x_2, y_2) = \dfrac{y_2 - y_1}{x_2 - x_1}$.

Slope of $\overleftrightarrow{AB} = \dfrac{(-2)-4}{2-(-1)}$

$\qquad = \dfrac{-6}{3} = \dfrac{-2}{1}$

Slope of $\overleftrightarrow{CD} = \dfrac{2-0}{3-(-1)}$

$\qquad = \dfrac{2}{4} = \dfrac{1}{2}$

Since the slopes of $\overleftrightarrow{AB}$ and $\overleftrightarrow{CD}$ are negative reciprocals of each other, then $\overleftrightarrow{AB}$ is perpendicular to $\overleftrightarrow{CD}$.

Exercises

1. In *a-f*, tell whether the line has a positive slope, a negative slope, a slope of 0, or no slope.

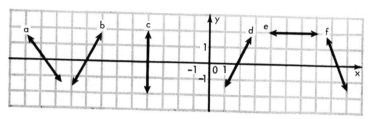

In 2–7, find the slope of the line.

2.
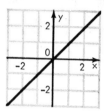

3.
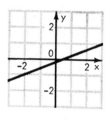

4.
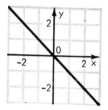

5.
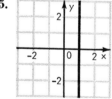

6.
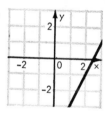

7.
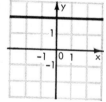

In 8–16, plot both points, draw the straight line that joins them, and find the slope of this line.

8. (0, 0) and (3, 3)   **9.** (0, 0) and (2, 5)   **10.** (0, 0) and (10, 5)
11. (0, 2) and (0, 5)   **12.** (2, 3) and (4, 15)   **13.** (4, 6) and (10, 4)
14. (−3, 8) and (−1, 12)   **15.** (3, −4) and (8, −4)   **16.** (−1, 2) and (6, −3)

In 17–25, through the given point, draw a line with the given slope *m*.

17. $(0, 0), m = \frac{1}{2}$ **18.** $(-2, 4), m = \frac{4}{3}$ **19.** $(0, 0), m = 2$
20. $(-2, -3), m = 1$ **21.** $(0, 0), m = -\frac{2}{3}$ **22.** $(-3, -4), m = -\frac{1}{4}$
23. $(0, 0), m = -3$ **24.** $(0, 5), m = -2$ **25.** $(0, -2), m = -1$

26. Find the value of *y* so that the slope of the line passing through the points (4, *y*) and (8, 12) will be (*a*) 1, (*b*) 3, (*c*) $-\frac{1}{2}$, and (*d*) 0.

27. The straight line which passes through the points (5, 4) and (2, 4)   (1) has a slope of 3   (2) has a slope of zero   (3) has no slope

28. Show that the line which joins the points $(2, 4)$ and $(6, 7)$ is parallel to the line which joins the point $(6, 2)$ and $(10, 5)$.

29. Show that the line whose y-intercept is 2 and which passes through the point $(-2, 1)$ is parallel to the line whose y-intercept is -1 and which passes through the point $(4, 1)$.

In 30–33, use the definition of the slope of a line to determine whether or not the points lie on the same straight line (are collinear).

30. $(1, 2)$, $(4, 5)$, $(6, 7)$ **31.** $(-2, 6)$, $(0, 2)$, $(1, 0)$

32. $(0, 0)$, $(-8, -2)$, $(4, 1)$ **33.** $(-3, 4)$, $(-1, 1)$, $(1, -3)$

In 34–39, find the slope of a line which is perpendicular to the line with the given slope.

34. $m = \frac{3}{4}$ **35.** $m = 2$ **36.** $m = \frac{1}{3}$

37. $m = -\frac{3}{5}$ **38.** $m = -4$ **39.** $m = -1$

In 40–42, show that the line which passes through the first pair of points is perpendicular to the line which passes through the second pair of points.

40. $(7, 3)$ and $(4, 1)$; $(8, 12)$ and $(6, 15)$

41. $(-2, 6)$ and $(1, 1)$; $(9, 2)$ and $(4, -1)$

42. the origin and $(4, 4)$; $(-1, 1)$ and $(-4, 4)$

43. The vertices of parallelogram $ABCD$ have the following coordinates: $A(-2, 4)$, $B(2, 6)$, $C(7, 2)$, $D(x, 0)$.

    a. Find the slope of $\overline{AB}$.

    b. Express the slope of $\overline{DC}$ in terms of x.

    c. Using the results found in answer to *a* and *b*, find the value of x.

44. Show that the triangle whose vertices are the points $(8, 6)$, $(4, 2)$, and $(6, 0)$ is a right triangle.

7. The Slope-Intercept Form of a Linear Equation

Let us determine the equation of a line whose slope is m and whose y-intercept is b.

Since the y-intercept is b, the line passes through $A(0, b)$, as shown in the figure at the right. Let $P(x, y)$ be any other point on this line $(x \neq 0)$ whose slope is m.

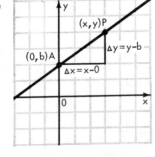

Since $\dfrac{\Delta y}{\Delta x} = $ slope of the line $= m$,

$$\frac{y - b}{x - 0} = m$$

Multiply both members of the equation by x, $x \neq 0$.

$y - b = mx$

Hence, $y = mx + b$.

Therefore, if a line has a slope m and a y-intercept b, the equation of the line is

$$y = mx + b$$

It can also be shown that, conversely, if a line has a slope and its equation is in the form $y = mx + b$, then m represents the slope of the line and b represents the y-intercept of the line.

MODEL PROBLEMS

1. Write an equation of a line whose slope is $\frac{1}{2}$ and whose y-intercept is -1.
   Solution: Substitute $\frac{1}{2}$ for m and -1 for b in the slope-intercept form.

   $$y = mx + b \quad m = \tfrac{1}{2},\, b = -1$$
   $$y = \tfrac{1}{2}x - 1, \text{ or } 2y = x - 2 \quad Ans.$$

2. Find the slope and y-intercept of the line whose equation is $6x + 2y = 8$.
   Solution: Transform the equation into the slope-intercept form $y = mx + b$.

   $$6x + 2y = 8$$
   $$2y = -6x + 8$$
   $$y = -3x + 4$$

   Hence, the slope of the line, $m = -3$; the y-intercept, $b = 4$.
   Answer: Slope is -3; y-intercept is $+4$.

3. Show that the graph of $y = -2x + 3$ is parallel to the graph of $4x + 2y = 5$.
   Solution: The equation $y = -2x + 3$ is in the slope-intercept form $y = mx + b$. Hence, the slope of $y = -2x + 3$ is -2. Transform $4x + 2y = 5$ into the slope-intercept form $y = mx + b$.
   Since $4x + 2y = 5$, $2y = -4x + 5$ and $y = -2x + \frac{5}{2}$.
   Therefore, the slope of $4x + 2y = 5$ is -2. Since the slopes of the two lines are equal and their y-intercepts are not equal, the lines are parallel.

Exercises

In 1–8, write an equation of a straight line, with integral coefficients, whose slope and y-intercept are respectively:

1. 3 and 4
2. -5 and 1
3. -7 and -5
4. 0 and 2
5. 6 and 0
6. 0 and 0
7. $\frac{3}{4}$ and 4
8. $-\frac{5}{6}$ and $-\frac{2}{3}$

In 9–20, find the slope and y-intercept of the graph of the equation.

9. $y = 2x + 1$ **10.** $y = -4x + 2$ **11.** $y = -x - 7$ **12.** $y = 5x$

13. $y = \frac{1}{4}x + 5$ **14.** $y = -\frac{3}{5}x + 2$ **15.** $y = -\frac{2}{3}x$ **16.** $y - 4x = 7$

17. $3y = 6x + 4$ **18.** $2y = -x + 6$ **19.** $3x + 5y = 15$ **20.** $\frac{1}{3}x + \frac{3}{4} = \frac{1}{2}y$

21. The slope of the graph of $2x + 3y = 5$ is   (1) -2 (2) $\frac{5}{3}$ (3) $-\frac{2}{3}$ (4) $\frac{2}{3}$

In 22 and 23, state whether or not the graphs of the two lines are parallel. Give a reason for your answer.

22. $y = 2x + 5,\ y = 2x + 9$ **23.** $2x - y = 6,\ y - 2x = 6$

In 24 and 25, state whether or not the graphs of the two lines are perpendicular to each other. Give a reason for your answer.

24. $2x + 3y = 7,\ 3x - 2y = 9$ **25.** $2x = 7y + 2,\ 4 - 2y = 7x$

26. Write an equation of a line whose slope is 2 and which passes through the point $(0, -3)$.

27. Write an equation of a line which passes through the origin and has a slope of -4.

28. How are the graphs of $y = mx + b$ affected when m is always replaced by the same number and b is replaced by different numbers?

29. How are the graphs of $y = mx + b$ affected when b is always replaced by the same number and m is replaced by different numbers?

30. Find the value of a if the graph of $6x + 9y = 13$ is perpendicular to the graph of $ax + 2y = 8$.

In 31 and 32: Is the line which is the graph of the first set of points parallel to the line which is the graph of the second set of points? Give a reason for your answer.

31. $\{(x, y)\,|\,2x + 4y = 7\};\ \{(x, y)\,|\,3x + 9y = 8\}$

32. $\{(x, y)\,|\,6x + 9y = 4\};\ \{(x, y)\,|\,3y = 5 - 2x\}$

In 33 and 34: Is the line which is the graph of the first set of points perpendicular to the line which is the graph of the second set of points? Give a reason for your answer.

33. $\{(x, y)\,|\,4x + 3y = 24\};\ \{(x, y)\,|\,3x - 4y = 18\}$

34. $\{(x, y)\,|\,2x + 3y = 15\};\ \{(x, y)\,|\,4y - 3 = -6x\}$

35. Write an equation of a line which passes through the point $(d, 4d)$ and has $\frac{3}{4}$ as its slope.

36. Find the value of d for which the graph of $\{(x, y)\,|\,x - 4y = 9\}$ will be perpendicular to the graph of $\{(x, y)\,|\,dx - 12y = 14\}$.

GRAPHING A LINEAR EQUATION BY THE SLOPE-INTERCEPT METHOD

Procedure. To graph a first-degree equation in two variables by the slope-intercept method:

1. Transform the equation into an equivalent equation in the slope-intercept form, $y = mx + b$.
2. Then graph this resulting equation, making use of the slope m and y-intercept b.

Exercises

In 1–12, using the slope-intercept method, graph the line described by the equation.

1. $y = 2x + 3$
2. $y = 2x$
3. $y = -3x$
4. $y = -x - 4$
5. $y = \frac{2}{3}x$
6. $y = -\frac{4}{3}x - 2$
7. $y - 2x = 4$
8. $2y = 3x + 2$
9. $5x + 2y = 10$
10. $4x - y = 5$
11. $2x = 3y + 8$
12. $2x - 3y - 12 = 0$

In 13–15, using the slope-intercept method, graph the line described by the set of points.

13. $\{(x, y) \mid y = 3x - 2\}$
14. $\{(x, y) \mid 2y = x + 4\}$
15. $\{(x, y) \mid 3x - 2y = 6\}$

WRITING A LINEAR EQUATION BY USING THE SLOPE-INTERCEPT FORM

Procedure. To write an equation of a line that satisfies a given set of conditions:
1. Determine the slope of the line, m, and its y-intercept, b.
2. Then use the values found for m and b in the slope-intercept formula $y = mx + b$.

~~~~~~~~~~~~ *MODEL PROBLEMS* ~~~~~~~~~~~~

1. Write an equation of a line whose slope is 4 and which passes through the point $(-1, 2)$.

How To Proceed	*Solution*
1. In the slope-intercept form, $y = mx + b$, find b by substituting the given values for m, x, and y.	1. It is given that the slope, $m = 4$. Since the line passes through the point $(-1, 2)$, $x = -1$ and $y = 2$ satisfy the equation of the line. Substitute in $y = mx + b$.

$$2 = 4(-1) + b$$
$$2 = -4 + b$$
$$6 = b$$

| 2. In $y = mx + b$, substitute the value given for m and the value found for b in step 1. | 2. $y = mx + b$
$y = 4x + 6$ *Ans.* |

2. Using integral coefficients, write an equation of a line that is parallel to the graph of $2y - 3x = 8$ and whose y-intercept is 5.

Solution:

1. Transform the equation $2y - 3x = 8$ into the slope-intercept form, $y = mx + b$.

$$2y - 3x = 8$$
$$2y = 3x + 8$$
$$y = \tfrac{3}{2}x + 4$$

The slope of the line $2y - 3x = 8$ is $\tfrac{3}{2}$.

2. Since parallel lines have the same slope, the slope of a line parallel to the line $2y - 3x = 8$ is also $\tfrac{3}{2}$.

3. The y-intercept of the required line is 5. Substitute $\tfrac{3}{2}$ for m and 5 for b in $y = mx + b$.

$$y = mx + b$$
$$y = \tfrac{3}{2}x + 5$$
$$2y = 3x + 10 \quad Ans.$$

Exercises

In 1–6, using integral coefficients, write an equation of a line which has the given slope m and which passes through the given point.

1. $m = 2$, $(1, 4)$ **2.** $m = 3$, $(-1, 5)$ **3.** $m = -2$, $(-1, -4)$
4. $m = \tfrac{1}{2}$, $(-2, 3)$ **5.** $m = -\tfrac{3}{4}$, $(0, 0)$ **6.** $m = -\tfrac{3}{2}$, $(-2, -3)$

In 7–12, write an equation of the line that passes through the given points.

7. $(2, 4)$, $(4, 8)$ **8.** $(2, 1)$, $(5, 4)$ **9.** $(2, 4)$, $(10, 9)$
10. $(4, 7)$, $(2, 10)$ **11.** $(-2, 7)$, $(2, 10)$ **12.** $(0, 0)$, $(4, -2)$

In 13–16, write a linear equation that expresses the relation between the two variables in the table. Use this equation to find the replacements for the question marks.

13.

x	0	1	2	3	?
y	0	2	4	?	10

14.

x	1	3	5	7	?
y	5	9	13	?	23

15.

a	0	2	3	5	?
b	3	9	12	?	24

16.

c	0	-1	-2	4	?
w	5	7	9	?	-5

In 17–23, write an equation of a line that is:

17. parallel to $y = -\frac{2}{3}x + 5$ and whose y-intercept is -3.

18. parallel to $y = 3x - 1$ and passes through the point (2, 4).

19. parallel to $y = 2x + 3$ and has the same y-intercept as $y + 5 = 4x$.

20. perpendicular to $y = \frac{2}{3}x + 5$ and whose y-intercept is -4.

21. perpendicular to $y = 2x - 3$ and passes through the point (5, 7).

22. perpendicular to $x + 3y = 9$ and passes through the origin.

23. perpendicular to the line which passes through the points (0, 0) and (-2, 4) and whose y-intercept is the same as the y-intercept of $3x - 4y = 24$.

24. Show that an equation of a line whose nonzero x-intercept is a and whose nonzero y-intercept is b is:

$$\frac{x}{a} + \frac{y}{b} = 1$$

(This is called the ***intercept form*** of the equation.)

In 25–28, use the intercept form to write an equation of a line whose x- and y-intercepts are, respectively, the given numbers.

25. 3 and 4   **26.** 5 and -2 **27.** -4 and 6   **28.** -3 and -5

8. The Point-Slope Form of a Linear Equation

Let us discover an equation of a line which passes through a point P_1, with given coordinates (x_1, y_1), and whose slope is m.

Let $P(x, y)$ be any other point on the given line which passes through P_1, as shown in the figure at the right. Hence, $x \neq x_1$.

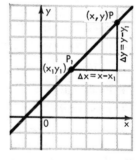

The slope of the line $= m = \dfrac{\Delta y}{\Delta x}$, or

$$m = \frac{y - y_1}{x - x_1}$$

Since $x \neq x_1$, $x - x_1 \neq 0$. Multiply both members of the equation by $x - x_1$ to obtain

$$y - y_1 = m(x - x_1)$$

The equation $y - y_1 = m(x - x_1)$ is called the ***point-slope form*** of a linear equation.

~~~~~~~~~~~~~~~~~~~~ *MODEL PROBLEM* ~~~~~~~~~~~~~~~~~~~~

Write, in the form $y = mx + b$, an equation of a line whose slope is 2 and which
  passes through the point $(-1, 3)$.

How To Proceed	*Solution*
1. In the point-slope form of the equation, $y - y_1 = m(x - x_1)$, substitute the coordinates of the given point for x_1 and y_1 and the value of the slope for m.	1. At $P_1(-1, 3) \rightarrow x_1 = -1, y_1 = 3$. The slope $m = 2$. Substitute: $y - y_1 = m(x - x_1)$ $y - 3 = 2[x - (-1)]$
2. Simplify the resulting equation.	2. $y - 3 = 2(x + 1)$ $y - 3 = 2x + 2$ $y = 2x + 5$

Answer: $y = 2x + 5$

~~~~~~

Exercises

In 1–9, write an equation of a line that has the given slope, m, and passes
through the given point.

1. $m = 4$, $(2, 3)$ **2.** $m = 3$, $(0, 0)$ **3.** $m = -2$, $(6, 1)$
4. $m = 2$, $(4, -1)$ **5.** $m = -1$, $(-2, -3)$ **6.** $m = \frac{1}{2}$, $(8, 6)$
7. $m = \frac{2}{3}$, $(4, 2)$ **8.** $m = -\frac{1}{2}$, $(-1, 5)$ **9.** $m = -\frac{3}{4}$, $(-2, -4)$

In 10–12, write an equation of a line that is:
10. parallel to $y = 4x + 5$ and passes through the point $(4, 2)$.
11. parallel to $2x + 3y = 6$ and passes through the point $(0, -3)$.
12. perpendicular to $y = -\frac{2}{3}x + 4$ and passes through the point $(3, 5)$.

In 13–18, write an equation of a line which passes through the points:

13. $(0, 0)$ and $(4, 8)$ **14.** $(1, 3)$ and $(4, 12)$ **15.** $(-1, 2)$ and $(2, 5)$
16. $(-3, -2)$ and $(5, 2)$ **17.** $(-5, 1)$ and $(-2, 5)$ **18.** $(-1, 3)$ and $(-4, 9)$

19. Write an equation of a line which passes through the point $(-3, 7)$ and is
parallel to the graph of $\{(x, y) \mid x - 2y = 5\}$.
20. Write an equation of a line which passes through the point $(2, -5)$ and is
perpendicular to the graph of $\{(x, y) \mid y + 3x = 8\}$.
21. Show that an equation of a line which passes through two different points
$P_1(x_1, y_1)$ and $P_2(x_2, y_2)$, $(x_1 \neq x_2)$ is:

$$y - y_1 = \frac{y_2 - y_1}{x_2 - x_1}(x - x_1)$$

(This is called the **two-point form** of the equation.)

In 22–25, use the two-point form to write an equation of a line which passes through the two given points.

22. (3, 5), (5, 12)

23. (6, 2), (4, 10)

24. (−1, 3), (2, −6)

25. (0, −5), (−2, −7)

9. Graphing a First-Degree Inequality in the Cartesian Plane

The line which is the graph of the first-degree equation $y = 2x - 1$ (Fig. 1) is the set of all points whose ordinate y, *equals* "1 less than twice its abscissa, x." For example, at point $A(1, 1)$, the ordinate, 1, is 1 less than twice the abscissa, 1. That is, $1 = 2(1) - 1$. This line divides the Cartesian plane into two regions called **half-planes.**

Graph of $y = 2x - 1$

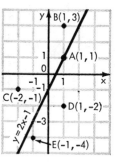

Fig. 1

The half-plane above the line $y = 2x - 1$ (Fig. 1) is the set of all points whose ordinate, y, *is greater than* "1 less than twice its abscissa, x"; that is, $y > 2x - 1$. For example, at point $B(1, 3)$, the ordinate, 3, is greater than "1 less than twice the abscissa, 1." That is, $3 > 2(1) - 1$ is a true statement. The coordinates of point $C(-2, -1)$ also satisfy $y > 2x - 1$ because $-1 > 2(-2) - 1$ is a true sentence. The graph of $y > 2x - 1$ is the shaded half-plane above the line $y = 2x - 1$ (Fig. 2). Notice that the line which is the plane-divider is drawn dashed to indicate that it is not part of the graph. To graph $y \geq 2x - 1$ (Fig. 3), we draw the plane-divider as a solid line to indicate that the line $y = 2x - 1$ is part of the graph.

Graph of $y > 2x - 1$

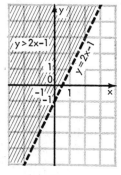

Fig. 2

Graph of $y \geq 2x - 1$

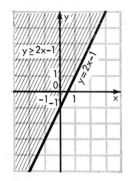

Fig. 3

The half-plane below the line $y = 2x - 1$ (Fig. 1) is the set of all points at which the ordinate, y, *is less than* "1 less than twice the abscissa, x"; that is, $y < 2x - 1$. For example, at point $D(1, -2)$, the ordinate, -2, is less than "1 less than twice the abscissa, 1." That is, $-2 < 2(1) - 1$ is a true sentence. The coordinates of point $E(-1, -4)$ also satisfy $y < 2x - 1$ because the sentence $-4 < 2(-1) - 1$ is true. The graph of $y < 2x - 1$ is the shaded half-plane below the line $y = 2x - 1$ (Fig. 4). Notice that the line which is the plane-divider is drawn dashed to indicate that it is not part of the graph. To graph $y \le 2x - 1$ (Fig. 5), we draw the plane-divider as a solid line to indicate that the line $y = 2x - 1$ is part of the graph.

Graph of $y < 2x - 1$ Graph of $y \le 2x - 1$

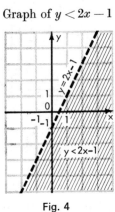

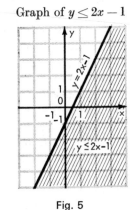

Fig. 4   Fig. 5

From the study of the graphs of $y = 2x - 1$, $y > 2x - 1$, and $y < 2x - 1$ we see that the line which is the graph of $y = 2x - 1$ acts as a ***plane-divider***. It divides the Cartesian plane into two regions. The region above the line is the graph of $y > 2x - 1$; the region below it is the graph of $y < 2x - 1$.

In general, the graph of $y = mx + b$ is a line which divides the coordinate plane into three sets of points:

1. *The set of points on the line.* Each ordered pair that describes a member of this set of points is a solution of $y = mx + b$. The line is the graph of the equation $y = mx + b$; also, the line is the graph of the solution set of $y = mx + b$.

2. *The set of points in the half-plane above the line.* Each ordered pair that describes a member of this set of points is a solution of $y > mx + b$. The half-plane is the graph of the inequality $y > mx + b$; also, the half-plane is the graph of the solution set of the inequality $y > mx + b$.

3. *The set of points in the half-plane below the line.* Each ordered pair that describes a member of this set of points is a solution of $y < mx + b$. The half-plane is the graph of the inequality $y < mx + b$; also, the half-plane is the graph of the solution set of the inequality $y < mx + b$.

KEEP IN MIND

To graph $Ax + By > C$ or $Ax + By < C$, $B \neq 0$, transform the inequality into an equivalent inequality whose left member is y alone: $y > mx + b$ or $y < mx + b$. This enables us first to graph the plane divider $y = mx + b$.

~~~~~~~~~~~~ **MODEL PROBLEMS** ~~~~~~~~~~~~

1. Graph the inequality $2x - y \geq -2$ in the coordinate plane.

How To Proceed	*Solution*
1. Transform the inequality into an equivalent inequality having y as its left member. Remember that when we multiply by -1 or any negative number, we reverse the order of the inequality.	$2x - y \geq -2$ $-y \geq -2x - 2$ $y \leq 2x + 2$
2. Graph the resulting inequality by first graphing the plane-divider $y = 2x + 2$.	$y = 2x + 2$

	x	y
A	-1	0
B	0	2
C	1	4

3. Shade the half-plane below the plane-divider. The required graph is the union of the shaded half-plane, which is the graph of $2x - y > -2$, and the line, which is the graph of $2x - y = -2$. Note that the line is drawn solid to show that it is part of the graph.

Graph of $2x - y \geq -2$

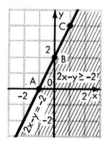

2. Graph each of the following in the coordinate plane: *a.* $x > 1$ *b.* $y \leq 1$

How To Proceed	*Solution*
1. Graph the plane-divider, using either a dotted line or a solid line, whichever the question requires. 2. Shade the proper half-plane.	*a.* Graph of $x > 1$ *b.* Graph of $y \leq 1$

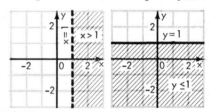

3. Graph $\{(x, y) \mid x < 1\}$.

Solution: $\{(x, y) \mid x < 1\}$ is the set of points whose abscissa is less than 1 and whose ordinate is any real number. Examples of such points are:

$(0, 1)$, $(0, -3)$, $(-1, 5)$, $(-2, -4)$.

The graph of $\{(x, y) \mid x < 1\}$ is the half-plane to the left of the plane-divider $x = 1$.

Graph of $\{(x, y) \mid x < 1\}$

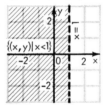

~~~~~~

Exercises

In 1–6, transform the inequality into an equivalent inequality whose left member is y.

1. $y - x < 0$ **2.** $5x \geq 2y$ **3.** $y - x \leq 5$
4. $3x - y \leq 6$ **5.** $2x > 6 + 2y$ **6.** $8 \leq 2x + 3y$

In 7–18, graph the inequality in the coordinate plane.

7. $y > 2x$ **8.** $y < 4x + 2$ **9.** $y > \frac{1}{2}x - 1$
10. $x + y > 6$ **11.** $y - x \geq 4$ **12.** $x - y > 4$
13. $x - y \leq -2$ **14.** $x - 2y \leq 3$ **15.** $3x + y - 4 \leq 0$
16. $2x + 3y - 6 \leq 0$ **17.** $6 \leq 3x + 2y$ **18.** $x \geq -3$

In 19–24, graph the set in the coordinate plane.

19. $\{(x, y) \mid y \geq 2x + 4\}$ **20.** $\{(x, y) \mid 3x + y \leq -2\}$ **21.** $\{(x, y) \mid 2x \geq 4 - y\}$
22. $\{(x, y) \mid 4x < 8 + y\}$ **23.** $\{(x, y) \mid x \geq 6\}$ **24.** $\{(x, y) \mid y \leq -4\}$

In 25–27, (a) write the verbal sentence as an open sentence involving x and y and (b) graph the open sentence in the coordinate plane.

25. The ordinate of a point is less than 3 times its abscissa.

26. The sum of the abscissa and ordinate of a point is greater than or equal to 5.

27. The abscissa of a point decreased by the ordinate of the point is less than 2.

10. Comparing the Graphs of Open Sentences in Two Variables When the Replacement Set Changes

The graph of an open sentence in two variables is the set of points whose coordinates must have the following characteristics:

1. Both coordinates must be members of the replacement sets of the variables.
2. Both coordinates must satisfy the open sentence.

For example: If the replacement set of both x and y is the set of real numbers, the ordered number pair $(5, -6)$ is a member of the solution set of $x - y = 11$ and the graph of $(5, -6)$ is a point in the graph of $x - y = 11$ because (1) both 5 and -6 are members of the replacement set of the variables and (2) $(5, -6)$ satisfies $x - y = 11$. However, should the replacement set of both x and y be the set of positive integers, the point which is the graph of $(5, -6)$ would not be a point in the graph of $x - y = 11$. This would be so because in spite of the fact that $(5, -6)$ satisfies $x - y = 11$, the coordinate -6 is not a member of the replacement set of y.

In Figs. 1–4, we see how the graph of an open sentence in two variables changes when the replacement sets of the variables change.

Graph of $y = x - 1$.
Replacement set for x
and y: {integers}

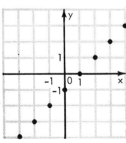

Fig. 1

Graph of $y = x - 1$.
Replacement set for x
and y: {real numbers}

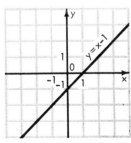

Fig. 2

In Fig. 1, we see the graph of $y = x - 1$ when the replacement set for both x and y is the set of integers. The graph is a set of distinct, individual points, all of which lie on a straight line whose equation is $y = x - 1$, but the graph *does not include all the points on that line.*

In Fig. 2, we see the graph of $y = x - 1$ when the replacement set for both x and y is the set of real numbers. Now the graph is a line, the same line that was referred to in the discussion of Fig. 1. Observe that the graph *includes all the points on this line.*

Graph of $y < x - 1$.
Replacement set for x
and y: {integers}

Graph of $y < x - 1$.
Replacement set for x
and y: {real numbers}

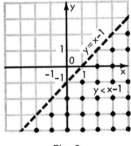

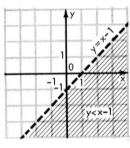

Fig. 3   Fig. 4

In Fig. 3, we see the graph of $y < x - 1$ when the replacement set of both x and y is the set of integers. The graph is a set of distinct individual points, all of which lie in the half-plane below the plane-divider $y = x - 1$, but the graph *does not include all the points in this half-plane.*

In Fig. 4, we see the graph of $y < x - 1$ when the replacement set of both x and y is the set of real numbers. Now the graph is the half-plane below the plane-divider $y = x - 1$, the same half-plane that was referred to in the discussion of Fig. 3. Observe that the graph *includes all the points in the half-plane.*

Exercises

In 1–15, draw the graph of the open sentence when the replacement set of both variables is (*a*) the set of real numbers, (*b*) the set of integers, and (*c*) the set of positive integers.

1. $y = 2x$	**2.** $y = x + 2$	**3.** $y = 2x - 1$
4. $y > 2x$	**5.** $y < x + 2$	**6.** $y > 2x - 1$
7. $y \leq 2x$	**8.** $y \geq x + 2$	**9.** $y \leq 2x - 1$
10. $y = \frac{1}{2}x + 4$	**11.** $y < \frac{1}{2}x + 4$	**12.** $y \geq \frac{1}{2}x + 4$
13. $x + 2y = 6$	**14.** $3x + y > 4$	**15.** $2x - y \leq 0$

11. Understanding Relations and Functions

RELATIONS

DOMAIN AND RANGE OF A RELATION

Mr. Dale is a salesman. In the table at the right, we find the amounts he earned and saved during each of the first four weeks of January. The pairings in this table may be written as a set of ordered pairs in which the first coordinate represents the amount earned during a week and the second coordinate represents the amount saved during that week:

($) Earnings	($) Savings
150	30
165	32
140	35
150	25

$A = \{(150, 30), (165, 32), (140, 35), (150, 25)\}$

A set of ordered pairs is called a ***relation.*** The set consisting of the first members of the ordered pairs is called the ***domain*** of the relation. Thus, the domain of relation A is $\{150, 165, 140\}$.

The set consisting of the second members of the ordered pairs is called the ***range*** of the relation. Thus, the range of relation A is $\{30, 32, 35, 25\}$.

In general, a relation involves:

1. A set of first members, the domain.
2. A set of second members, the range.
3. A pairing of a member of the domain with a member of the range to define the relation.

The pairing can be shown in several ways.

METHODS OF DEFINING A RELATION

1. *Using a mapping diagram to define a relation.*
   On a block, there is a set of children, $C = \{$Alice, Robert, Martha, Walter$\}$ and there is a set of houses, $H = \{X, Y, Z\}$. Fig. 1 at the right shows how the members of the set of children, C, are paired with the members of the set of houses, H, to define a relation R.

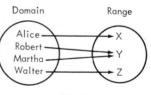

Fig. 1

$R = \{($Alice, $X), ($Robert, $Y), ($Martha, $Y), ($Walter, $Z)\}$

The arrow is used to show the element of the range that is paired with a particular element of the domain. We call this a *mapping diagram* and say that the domain is mapped into the range.

2. *Using a table to define a relation.*
The table at the right shows how the numbers x and y are paired to define the relation $R = \{(1,4),(2,8),(3,12)\}$.

x	y		(x, y)
1	4		$(1, 4)$
2	8	or	$(2, 8)$
3	12		$(3, 12)$

3. *Using a rule to define a relation.*
A relation may be defined by a rule which makes it possible to determine how the member or members of the range are to be paired with each member of the domain. For example the solution set of an open sentence such as $y = 4x$ is a relation in which the second member of each ordered pair is 4 times the first member. We can define this relation as follows:

$$R = \{(x, y) \,|\, y = 4x, x \text{ and } y \text{ are real numbers}\}$$

We can omit " x and y are real numbers" from the rule defining the relation by assuming that the domain and range include only real numbers. In the case of the relation $\{(x, y) \,|\, y = \dfrac{1}{x}\}$ we assume that the domain is the set of real numbers, and also that $x \neq 0$, since $\dfrac{1}{x}$ is not defined if $x = 0$.

4. *Using graphs to define a relation by means of a picture.*
When we draw the graphs of first-degree equalities and first-degree inequalities, we are picturing sets of ordered pairs, or relations.

Observe that $\{(x, y) \,|\, x + y = 2, x \text{ and } y \text{ are integers}\}$, whose graph is shown in Fig. 2, and $\{(x, y) \,|\, x + y = 2, x \text{ and } y \text{ are real numbers}\}$, whose graph is shown in Fig. 3, are different relations.

Graph of $\{(x, y) \,|\, x + y = 2\}$
Domain: {integers}

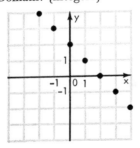

Graph of $\{(x, y) \,|\, x + y = 2\}$
Domain: {real numbers}

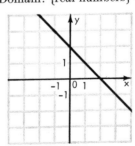

Fig. 2   Fig. 3

FUNCTIONS

There is an important difference between the following two relations:

$$A = \{(-2, 2), (-1, 1), (0, 0), (1, 1), (2, 2)\}$$

$$B = \{(0, 0), (1, 1), (1, -1), (2, 2), (2, -2)\}$$

In relation A, observe that every member of the domain $\{-2, -1, 0, 1, 2\}$ is paired with one and only one member of the range $\{0, 1, 2\}$. For example, the member of the domain, -1, is paired with a unique member of the range, 1.

In relation B, however, some members of the domain $\{0, 1, 2\}$ are paired with two members of the range $\{-2, -1, 0, 1, 2\}$. For example, one member of the domain, 2, is paired with two members of the range, 2 and -2. A relation such as set A is called a *function*. A relation such as set B is not a function, in accordance with the following definition:

A *function* is a relation (a set of ordered pairs) in which every member of the domain is paired with one and only one member of the range.

VERTICAL LINE TEST FOR A FUNCTION

If a relation is graphed, we can discover whether or not the given relation is a function. In a function, to every member of the domain there corresponds one and only one member of the range. Hence, a relation is a function if, when a vertical line is drawn through each point of its graph, we find that to the abscissa of each point there corresponds one and only one ordinate. Note that the graph of relation A (Fig. 4) confirms that this relation is a function. However, the graph of relation B (Fig. 5) shows that relation B is not a function.

Relation A Relation B

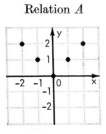

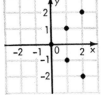

Fig. 4   Fig. 5

MAPPING TEST FOR A FUNCTION

The mapping diagram at the right (Fig. 6) pictures a pairing that defines the function:

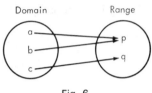

$$f = \{(a, p), (b, p), (c, q)\}$$

Observe that each member of the domain is mapped into one and only one member of the range.

Fig. 6

THE INVERSE OF A RELATION

Let us begin with the relation $A = \{(1, 4), (2, 6), (3, 8)\}$. By interchanging the two members of every ordered pair in relation A, we obtain relation $B = \{(4, 1), (6, 2), (8, 3)\}$. Relation B is called the *inverse* of relation A in accordance with the following definition:

The ***inverse of a relation*** is the relation that is formed when the members of each ordered pair of the given relation are interchanged.

From this definition, it can be seen that the domain of the original relation is the range of the inverse relation, and the range of the original relation is the domain of the inverse relation. For example, in relations A and B, which are inverse relations, the domain of relation A, $\{1, 2, 3\}$, is the range of relation B and the range of relation A, $\{4, 6, 8\}$, is the domain of relation B.

The inverse of a relation must always be a relation since interchanging the members of an ordered pair results in an ordered pair. For example, the inverse of $R = \{(1, 2), (3, 4), (3, 5)\}$ is the relation $S = \{(2, 1), (4, 3), (5, 3)\}$.

The inverse of a function need not be a function. For example, the inverse of the function $F = \{(1, 2), (3, 4), (5, 6)\}$ is the function $G = \{(2, 1), (4, 3), (6, 5)\}$. However, the inverse of the function $H = \{(1, 2), (3, 2), (5, 4)\}$ is $K = \{(2, 1), (2, 3), (4, 5)\}$, which is a relation that is not a function since both 1 and 3 in the range correspond to 2 in the domain.

When the inverse of a function is also a function, it is called the ***inverse function.*** Hence, in the previous paragraph, function G is the inverse function of function F.

The inverse of a function F may be indicated by the symbol F^{-1}, which is read "the inverse of F" or "F inverse." For example, if $F = \{(1, 2), (3, 4), (5, 6)\}$ then $F^{-1} = \{(2, 1), (4, 3), (6, 5)\}$.

Let us find the inverse of the function defined by $y = 3x - 1$, with the domain and range being the set of real numbers.

How To Proceed	*Solution*
1. In the equation, interchange x and y.	1. $\quad\quad y = 3x - 1$ $\quad\quad x = 3y - 1$
2. Solve for y in terms of x.	2. $\quad x + 1 = 3y$ $\quad\dfrac{x+1}{3} = y$

Therefore, the function defined by $y = \dfrac{x+1}{3}$ is the inverse function of the given function and it also has as its domain and range the set of real numbers.

There are cases where a given function does not have an inverse function. However, by restricting the domain of a function, it is often possible to find an inverse function. Such is the case in the function defined by $y = x^2$ whose domain is the set of real numbers and whose range is the set of non-negative real numbers. When we interchange x and y, we obtain $x = y^2$ or $y = \pm\sqrt{x}$, which does not define a function because with every positive number x there are associated *two* real values of y. For example, when $x = 4$, $y = 2$ and when $x = 4$, $y = -2$. However, if we limit the domain of x to the set of non-negative real numbers, we can confine the range of the inverse relation to the same set of numbers. Thus, when the function defined by $y = x^2$ has the set of non-negative numbers as its domain and range, then the inverse of this function is a function which may be defined by $x = y^2$, with its domain and range also being the set of non-negative real numbers.

~~~~~~~~~~ *MODEL PROBLEMS* ~~~~~~~~~~

1. If $A = \{(1, 3), (2, 5), (4, 9), (x, 6)\}$ is to be a function, list the integers which x may *not* represent.

Solution: If A is to be a function, no first component of its ordered pairs may have more than one second component. Therefore, x may not be the numbers 1, 2, 4 because these numbers are already first components of ordered pairs in A.

Answer: 1, 2, 4

2. If x and y are real numbers and the domain of the relation $\{(x, y) \mid y = 2x + 1\}$ is $\{x \mid 0 \le x \le 5\}$, find the range of the relation.

Solution: The relation is defined for all members of the domain.
When $x = 0$, $2x + 1 = 2(0) + 1 = 1 = y$
When $x = 5$, $2x + 1 = 2(5) + 1 = 11 = y$
Since the given relation is linear, when $0 \le x \le 5$ then $1 \le y \le 11$.
Hence, the range is the set of real numbers between and including 1 and 11.

Answer: $\{y \mid 1 \le y \le 11\}$

3. If x and y are real numbers, determine the restriction that must be placed on the domain of the function defined by $y = \dfrac{1}{x-3}$.

Solution: The domain is the set of all real numbers for which the equation has meaning. When $x = 3$, $y = \dfrac{1}{3-3} = \dfrac{1}{0}$, which is meaningless. Hence, x cannot be equal to 3.

Answer: $x \neq 3$

Exercises

In 1–4, (*a*) give the domain of the relation, (*b*) give the range of the relation, and (*c*) state whether or not the relation is a function.

1. $\{(1, 3), (3, 7), (5, 11), (7, 15)\}$

2. $\{(3, 4), (4, 3), (3, -4), (4, -3)\}$

3. $\{(2, 5), (4, 6), (-2, 5), (3, 4)\}$

4. $\{(0, 1), (0, 3), (0, -1), (0, -2)\}$

In 5–8, state whether or not the relation pictured by the mapping is a function. If it is not a function, tell why.

5.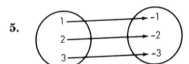

6.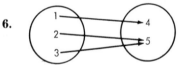

7.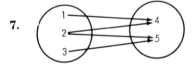

8.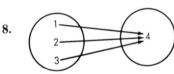

In 9–12, write the set of all ordered pairs pictured by the mapping shown.

9.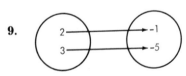

10.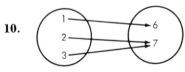

11.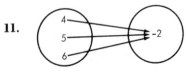

12.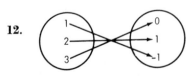

In 13–18, graph the relation. From the graph, determine whether or not the relation is a function.

13. $\{(x, y) \mid y = x\}$

14. $\{(x, y) \mid y = 2x - 3\}$

15. $\{(x, y) \mid y > 2x\}$

16. $\{(x, y) \mid y \leq 2x\}$

17. $\{(x, y) \mid x > 4\}$

18. $\{(x, y) \mid y = 4\}$

In 19–22, x and y are members of the set of real numbers. In each exercise:

a. Graph the relation described by the rule.

b. State whether the relation is a function.

c. State the range of the relation.

19. $\{(x, y) \mid y = 3x - 4\}$ when the domain is $\{x \mid -3 \leq x \leq 4\}$.

20. $\{(x, y) \mid y = 3\}$ when the domain of x is $\{x \mid x \geq 0\}$.

21. $\{(x, y) \mid y > x\}$ when the domain of x is $\{x \mid x \geq 5\}$.

22. $\{(x, y) \mid y < x + 4\}$ when the domain of x is $\{x \mid 0 \leq x \leq 2\}$.

In 23–31, each figure is the graph of a relation. The first and second members of each ordered pair of the relation are members of the set of real numbers. In each exercise:

a. State the domain of the relation.

b. State the range of the relation.

c. Determine whether or not the relation is a function by using the vertical line test.

23.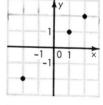

24.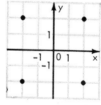

25.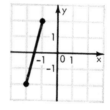

26.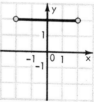

27.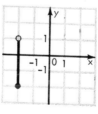

28.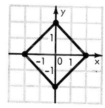

29.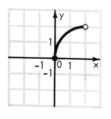

30.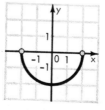

31.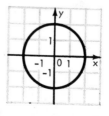

In 32–35:
a. Write the inverse of the relation.
b. State whether or not the inverse of the relation is a function.
c. Give the domain and range of the original relation.
d. Give the domain and range of the inverse of the original relation.
32. $\{(2, 5), (3, 8), (4, 11), (5, 14)\}$
33. $\{(1, 9), (-2, 3), (4, 9), (5, 7)\}$
34. $\{(-2, 5), (-4, 1), (-3, 7), (-5, 1)\}$
35. $\{(5, -3), (6, -2), (5, -8), (2, -7)\}$

In 36 and 37, list the integers that x may *not* represent if the given relation is to be a function.
36. $\{(3, 8), (x, 4), (1, 0), (0, -4)\}$
37. $\{(4, -1), (5, -1), (x, -2), (3, -2)\}$

In 38 and 39, list the integers that x may *not* be in order that the inverse of the given relation be a function.
38. $\{(1, 3), (2, 6), (3, 9), (4, x)\}$
39. $\{(3, 2), (3, -1), (5, x), (5, 3)\}$

In 40 and 41, write the set that is F^{-1} if the given set F is:
40. $\{(5, 2), (6, -1), (8, 0), (12, 9)\}$ **41.** $\{(0, 1), (5, 6), (9, -2), (8, 3)\}$

In 42 and 43, the replacement set is $\{3, 4, 5, 6, 7, 8\}$.
a. Determine whether or not the relation is a function.
b. Determine whether or not the inverse of the relation is a function.
42. $\{(x, y) \mid y = 2x\}$ **43.** $\{(x, y) \mid y > 2x\}$

44. State the range of the relation $\{(x, y) \mid x = 4\}$ and state whether or not the relation is a function.

In 45–47, write in the form of $y = mx + b$ the equation that defines the inverse of the function defined by the given equation.
45. $x = 5y - 2$ **46.** $y = 3x + 5$ **47.** $y = 6x$

In 48–51, if x and y are real numbers, determine the restriction, if any, that must be placed on the domain of the function.
48. $\{(x, y) \mid y = x - 5\}$ **49.** $\left\{(x, y) \mid y = \dfrac{1}{x - 5}\right\}$ **50.** $\{(x, y) \mid xy = 8\}$
51. $\{(x, y) \mid y = 4x\}$ when x represents the side of a square and y represents the perimeter of the square.

52. If F is a function in which no two ordered pairs have the same second member, will F^{-1} also be a function? Use an example to illustrate your answer. Explain your answer generally.

12. Understanding the Function Notation

We have learned that a letter such as f may be used to represent a function. When x represents an element of the domain of definition of a function f, we shall designate the corresponding element of the range which the function pairs with x—that is, assigns to x—as $f(x)$, read "f of x" or "f at x." Be careful to note that $f(x)$ does *not* mean "f times x." The number $f(x)$ is called the **value of f at x**.

This function notation can be used to describe the pairings of the numbers which are the members of the ordered pairs of a function. For example, the function f which is described by the word statement "with each real number x, pair the real number $x + 2$" can be written:

$$f(x) = x + 2 \text{ for each real number } x, \text{ or } f = \{(x, y) | y = x + 2\}$$

Then, $f(1)$ means the number which the function f pairs with 1. To find $f(1)$, we find the number that $x + 2$ represents when x is replaced by 1. Thus, if $f(x) = x + 2$, then $f(1) = 1 + 2 = 3$; that is, f assigns to 1 the number 3. Likewise:

To find $f(0)$, we replace x by 0 and obtain $f(0) = 0 + 2$ or $f(0) = 2$.
To find $f(-3)$, we replace x by -3 and obtain $f(-3) = -3 + 2$ or $f(-3) = -1$.
To find $f(x^2)$, we replace x by x^2 and obtain $f(x^2) = x^2 + 2$.

Both $\{(x, y) | y = x + 2\}$ and $\{(x, f(x)) | f(x) = x + 2\}$ represent the same function. Since both y and $f(x)$ represent the number which the function assigns to x, we may write $y = f(x)$.

There are times when it is advantageous to use the function notation. If we begin with $y = x + 2$ and replace x with 1, then $y = 1 + 2$, or $y = 3$. However, if we begin with $f(x) = x + 2$ and replace x with 1, then $f(1) = 1 + 2$, or $f(1) = 3$. Compare the two results $y = 3$ and $f(1) = 3$. In $f(1) = 3$, we know that x was replaced with 1; but in $y = 3$, we have no way of knowing what the replacement was.

~~~~~~~~~~ *MODEL PROBLEMS* ~~~~~~~~~~

1. If the function f is defined by $f(x) = 2x + 5$ for each real number x, find:
  a. $f(-4)$ *b.* $f(|-2|)$ *c.* $f(3b)$ *d.* $f(x + 2)$

  Solution: It is given that $f(x) = 2x + 5$. In each part of the question, x is a
    placeholder to be replaced by the expression within parentheses.
  a. $f(-4) = 2(-4) + 5 = -8 + 5 = -3$ $f(-4) = -3$ *Ans.*
  b. Since $|-2| = 2, f(|-2|) = 2(2) + 5 = 9$ $f(|-2|) = 9$ *Ans.*
  c. $f(3b) = 2(3b) + 5 = 6b + 5$ $f(3b) = 6b + 5$ *Ans.*
  d. $f(x + 2) = 2(x + 2) + 5 = 2x + 9$ $f(x + 2) = 2x + 9$ *Ans.*

2. If f is the function defined by $f(x) = \dfrac{5x - 6}{2}$ for each real number x, find the solution set for $f(x) > 2x$.

Solution: To find the solution set of $f(x) > 2x$, we must find the number(s) that can replace x in the open phrase $\dfrac{5x - 6}{2}$ and give a result that is greater than twice that number x. That is, we must find the solution set of the open sentence $\dfrac{5x - 6}{2} > 2x$.

$$\frac{5x - 6}{2} > 2x$$

$$5x - 6 > 4x$$
$$5x - 4x > 6$$
$$x > 6 \qquad \textit{Answer: } \{x \mid x > 6\}$$

〜〜〜〜〜〜〜〜〜〜〜〜〜〜〜〜〜〜〜〜〜〜〜〜〜〜〜

Exercises

In 1–6, the domain of the variable is the set of real numbers. For the function defined, compute the value of the function at $-2,\ -1,\ 0,\ 1,\ 2,\ |-3|,\ \tfrac{1}{2},\ \tfrac{2}{3}$.

1. $f(x) = 6x$ **2.** $g(y) = 4y - 7$

3. $h(a) = -a + 3$ **4.** $g(x) = x^2 - 3$

5. $h(s) = -s^2 + 2$ **6.** $h(a) = a^3 - a^2 - a$

7. For f defined by $f(x) = x^2 - 3x + 5$, for each real number x, find:

    a. $f(6)$ *b.* $f(\tfrac{2}{3})$ *c.* $f(0)$ *d.* $f(|-3|)$

    e. $3[f(2)]$ *f.* $f(2a)$ *g.* $f(c + 4)$ *h.* $f(3b - 1)$

8. If f is the function defined by $\dfrac{3x - 1}{4}$ for each real number x, find the solution set of each of the following sentences:

    a. $f(x) = 2$ *b.* $f(x) = 0$ *c.* $f(x) = -7$

    d. $f(x) = x$ *e.* $f(x) = 2x + 6$ *f.* $f(x) = \tfrac{1}{2}x + 3$

    g. $f(x) \geq 2$ *h.* $f(x) < \tfrac{1}{2}x + 9$ *i.* $f(x) \geq \tfrac{1}{2}x - \tfrac{7}{2}$

In 9 and 10, find the range of f if:

9. $f(x) = 2x - 4$ and the domain of x is $-3 < x < 3$.

10. $f(x) = x^2 + 3x - 2$ and the domain of x is $-4 < x < 2$.

In 11–13, find the value(s) of x for which $f(x)$ is meaningless or undefined.

11. $f(x) = \dfrac{3}{x + 6}$ **12.** $f(x) = \dfrac{5}{3x - 2}$ **13.** $f(x) = \dfrac{1}{x} + \dfrac{1}{x - 1}$

CHAPTER VI

SYSTEMS OF LINEAR OPEN SENTENCES IN TWO OR MORE VARIABLES

1. The Algebra of Sets

We have performed operations on numbers. Now we will perform operations on sets.

UNION OF SETS

The **union** of two sets, A and B, is the set containing the elements present in both set A and set B.

The union of set A and set B is represented by the symbol $A \cup B$, read "A union B" or "A cup B." Thus, if $A = \{1, 2, 3, 4, 5\}$ and $B = \{3, 4, 5, 6, 7\}$, then $A \cup B = \{1, 2, 3, 4, 5, 6, 7\}$. The shaded region of the Venn diagram (Fig. 1) pictures $A \cup B$.

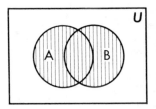

$A \cup B$ is shaded.

Fig. 1

If $A = \{$natural numbers between 10 and 20$\}$ and $B = \{$natural numbers between 15 and 25$\}$, then $A \cup B = \{$natural numbers between 10 and 25$\}$.

Superior College has only two teams, a baseball team and a basketball team. Hence, if $A = \{$baseball players in Superior College$\}$ and $B = \{$basketball players in Superior College$\}$, then $A \cup B = \{$athletes who play for Superior College$\}$.

Notice in each illustration that every element of $A \cup B$ is a member of at least one of the two given sets A and B.

When two open sentences are joined by the word *or*, the result is called a **disjunction** of two open sentences. For example, $x = 2$ or $x = -2$ is a disjunction of two open sentences. When we solve the disjunction $x = 2$ or $x = -2$, we are trying to find the set of numbers that belong to the solution set of at least one of the sentences. Therefore, the solution set of the disjunction is the union of the solution set of $x = 2$ and the solution set of $x = -2$.

We have learned that the solution set of $|x| = 2$ is $\{x \mid x = 2$ or $x = -2\}$. The sentence $x = 2$ or $x = -2$ is a disjunction. Therefore, the solution set of $|x| = 2$

is the union of the solution set of $x = 2$ and $x = -2$. Thus:

$$\{x:|x| = 2\} = \{x \,|\, x = 2\} \cup \{x \,|\, x = -2\}$$
$$= \{2\} \cup \{-2\}$$
$$= \{2, -2\}$$

The graph of the solution set $\{2, -2\}$ is

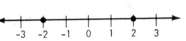

INTERSECTION OF SETS

The **intersection** of two sets, A and B, is the set containing those elements of set A that are also elements of set B.

The intersection of set A and set B is represented by the symbol $A \cap B$, read "A intersection B" or "A cap B." Thus, if $A = \{1, 2, 3, 4, 5\}$ and $B = \{2, 4, 6, 8, 10\}$, then $A \cap B = \{2, 4\}$. The shaded region of the Venn diagram (Fig. 2) pictures $A \cap B$.

$A \cap B$ is shaded.

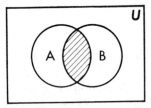

Fig. 2

If $A = \{$students in a school who study French$\}$ and $B = \{$students in the school who study German$\}$, then $A \cap B = \{$students in the school who study both French and German$\}$.

If $A = \{x \,|\, 2 < x\}$ and $B = \{x \,|\, x < 5\}$ then $A \cap B = \{x \,|\, 2 < x < 5\}$.

When two open sentences are joined by the word *and*, the result is called a **conjunction** of two open sentences. For example, $-2 < x - 1$ *and* $x - 1 < 2$ is a conjunction of two open sentences. When we solve the conjunction $-2 < x - 1$ and $x - 1 < 2$, we are trying to find the set of numbers that belong to the solution sets of both sentences. Therefore, the solution set of the conjunction is the intersection of the solution set of $-2 < x - 1$ and the solution set of $x - 1 < 2$.

We have learned that the solution of $|x - 1| < 2$ is $\{x \,|\, -2 < x - 1 < 2\}$. The sentence $-2 < x - 1 < 2$ is a conjunction which may be written

$$-2 < x - 1 \text{ and } x - 1 < 2$$

Therefore, the solution set of $|x - 1| < 2$ is the intersection of the solution set of $-2 < x - 1$ and the solution set of $x - 1 < 2$. Thus:

$$\{x:|x - 1| < 2\} = \{x \,|\, -2 < x - 1\} \cap \{x \,|\, x - 1 < 2\}$$
$$= \{x \,|\, -1 < x\} \cap \{x \,|\, x < 3\}$$
$$= \{x \,|\, -1 < x < 3\}$$

The graph of the solution set $\{x \,|\, -1 < x < 3\}$ is the "overlap" of the graphs of $\{x \,|\, -1 < x\}$ and $\{x \,|\, x < 3\}$ as shown:

graph of $\{x \mid -1 < x\}$

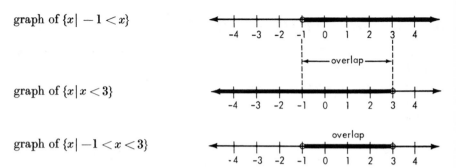

graph of $\{x \mid x < 3\}$

graph of $\{x \mid -1 < x < 3\}$

When two sets have no members in common they are called **disjoint sets.**
The intersection of two disjoint sets is, therefore, the empty set. Thus, if
$A = \{1, 3, 5\}$ and $B = \{2, 4, 6\}$, then A and B are disjoint sets. Hence, $A \cap B = \varnothing$. Therefore, if A and B are disjoint sets, the set $A \cap B$ may be pictured as
shown in Fig. 3 or Fig. 4.

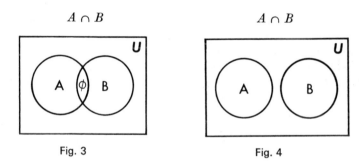

Fig. 3   Fig. 4

THE COMPLEMENT OF A SET

If A is a subset of a given universal set U,
the **complement** of set A with respect to set U is a
set whose elements are those elements of U that
are not in A. The complement of set A is represented by A'. Thus, if $U = \{1, 2, 3, 4, 5, 6, 7, 8, 9\}$ and
$A = \{2, 4, 6, 8\}$, then $A' = \{1, 3, 5, 7, 9\}$. The shaded region in the Venn diagram (Fig. 5) contains the
elements of A'.

A' is shaded.

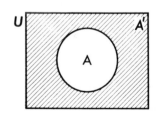

Fig. 5

If $U = \{$natural numbers$\}$ and $A = \{$natural
numbers divisible by 5$\}$, then $A' = \{$natural numbers not divisible by 5$\}$.

If $U = \{$animals$\}$ and $A = \{$lions$\}$, then $A' = \{$animals that are not lions$\}$.

~~~~~~~~~~~~~~~ *MODEL PROBLEMS* ~~~~~~~~~~~~~~~

1. If $U = \{1, 2, 3, 4, \ldots, 15\}$ and A, B, and C are sets whose elements are those numbers shown in the Venn diagram (Fig. 6), write the following sets:

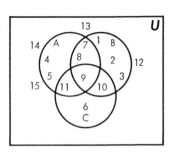

Fig. 6

     a. A, B, and C *b.* $A \cap B$
     c. $B \cup C$ *d.* $(B \cup C)'$
     e. $(A \cap B) \cap C$ *f.* $A \cup (B \cup C)$

Solution:
   a. $A = \{4, 5, 7, 8, 9, 11\}$ $B = \{1, 2, 3, 7, 8, 9, 10\}$ $C = \{6, 9, 10, 11\}$
   b. $A \cap B = \{7, 8, 9\}$
   c. $B \cup C = \{1, 2, 3, 6, 7, 8, 9, 10, 11\}$
   d. $(B \cup C)'$ means the complement of $B \cup C$.
      Since $B \cup C = \{1, 2, 3, 6, 7, 8, 9, 10, 11\}$, $(B \cup C)' = \{4, 5, 12, 13, 14, 15\}$.
   e. $(A \cap B) \cap C$ means the intersection of the set $A \cap B$ and the set C.
      Since $A \cap B = \{7, 8, 9\}$ and $C = \{6, 9, 10, 11\}$, then $(A \cap B) \cap C = \{9\}$.
   f. $A \cup (B \cup C)$ means the union of set A and the set $B \cup C$.
      Since $A = \{4, 5, 7, 8, 9, 11\}$ and $B \cup C = \{1, 2, 3, 6, 7, 8, 9, 10, 11\}$,
      $A \cup (B \cup C) = \{1, 2, 3, 4, 5, 6, 7, 8, 9, 10, 11\}$.

2. A, B, and C are sets which are subsets of universal set U. If A, B, and C have non-empty intersections, use a Venn diagram to illustrate that $(A \cap B) \cap C = A \cap (B \cap C)$.

Solution:

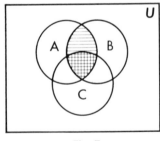

Fig. 7

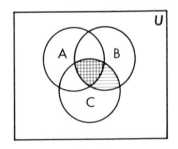

Fig. 8

Figs. 7 and 8 are Venn diagrams that picture sets A, B, and C. In Fig. 7, the horizontal hatched region pictures $A \cap B$ and the crosshatched region pictures $(A \cap B) \cap C$. In Fig. 8, the horizontal hatched region pictures

$B \cap C$ and the crosshatched region pictures $A \cap (B \cap C)$. Observe that the crosshatched region in Fig. 7 is exactly the same as the crosshatched region in Fig. 8. Therefore, $(A \cap B) \cap C = A \cap (B \cap C)$.

Exercises

In 1–13, using the roster notation, write the set that is indicated when $U = \{1, 2, 3, 4, \ldots, 12\}$, $A = \{1, 5, 7, 9\}$, $B = \{4, 5, 6, 7, 8\}$, and $C = \{3, 4, 11, 12\}$.

1. $A \cap B$ **2.** $B \cap C$ **3.** $A \cap C$ **4.** $A \cup B$ **5.** $B \cup C$
6. $A \cap (B \cap C)$ **7.** $(A \cup B) \cup C$ **8.** $(A \cap B) \cup C$ **9.** $A \cup (B \cap C)$
10. A' **11.** B' **12.** $(A \cap B)'$ **13.** $(A \cup C)'$

In 14–24, $U = \{$natural numbers less than 20$\}$, $A = \{$odd natural numbers less than 20 that are divisible by 3$\}$, $B = \{$odd natural numbers less than 20 that are divisible by 5$\}$, and $C = \{$even natural numbers less than 20 that are divisible by 5$\}$. Use the roster notation to designate the indicated set.

14. A **15.** B **16.** C **17.** $A \cap B$ **18.** $B \cap C$ **19.** $A \cap (B \cap C)$
20. $(A \cup B) \cup C$ **21.** A' **22.** B' **23.** $(A \cup B)'$ **24.** $(A \cap C)'$

25. Find the number of elements in A' when:
    a. the universal set has 20 elements and A has 5 elements.
    b. the universal set has y elements and A has x elements.
26. If $U = \{$triangles$\}$, $A = \{$isosceles triangles$\}$, $B = \{$right triangles$\}$, $C = \{$scalene triangles$\}$, picture with a Venn diagram:
    a. $A \cap B$ *b.* $A \cap C$ *c.* $A \cup B$ *d.* $A \cup C$
27. Draw a Venn diagram to show $A \cap B$ if:
    a. A and B are sets which have only some elements in common.
    b. A and B are sets which have no elements in common.
    c. Set B is a proper subset of set A.
28. Draw a Venn diagram to show $A \cup B$ if:
    a. A and B are sets which have only some elements in common.
    b. A and B are sets which have no elements in common.
    c. Set B is a proper subset of set A.

In 29–34, U is the universal set, and R, S, and T are proper subsets of U, each of which has some but not all of its elements in common with each of the other two sets. In a Venn diagram like the one shown at the right, shade the region that represents the indicated set.

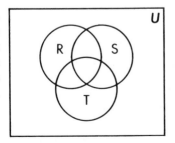

29. $(R \cap S) \cap T$ **30.** $(R \cup S) \cap T$
31. $R \cup (S \cup T)$ **32.** $(R \cap S) \cup T$
33. $(R \cap S) \cup (S \cap T)$ **34.** $(R \cap S) \cap (S \cap T)$

35. If universal set U is the set of all natural numbers, $A = \{2, 4, 6, 8, 10, 12, 15, 18\}$, $B = \{3, 6, 9, 12, 15, 18, 24\}$, and $C = \{5, 10, 15, 20\}$, draw a Venn diagram showing the relation of U, A, B, and C. Write the elements of sets A, B, and C in the proper regions in the diagram.

36. In a college, the languages which the romance language department teaches are French, Spanish, and Italian. There are 85 students who study French, 60 who study Spanish, and 25 who study Italian. Among those students, there are 18 who study both French and Spanish, 10 who study both French and Italian, 8 who study both Spanish and Italian, and 5 who study all three languages, French, Spanish, and 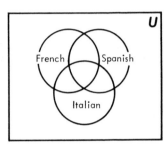 Italian. Use a Venn diagram like the one shown to help you find the number of students in the romance language department.

37. A is a subset of the universal set U, and $\varnothing$ is the empty set. Represent each of the following sets in a simpler way. Venn diagrams may help you discover the answers.
    a. $A \cap A$ *b.* $A \cup A$ *c.* $A \cap \varnothing$ *d.* $A \cup \varnothing$ *e.* $(A')'$

In 38–42, write for the given expression a simpler expression which does not contain parentheses.
38. $B \cup (A \cap B)$ **39.** $A \cap (A \cup B)$ **40.** $(A \cap B) \cap (A \cup B)$
41. $A \cup (A' \cap B)$ **42.** $A \cap (A' \cup B)$

43. If set A is equal to set B, then what must be true of the set $A \cup B$ and the set $A \cap B$?

In 44–48, A, B, and C are subsets of universal set U. Make a Venn diagram to illustrate that the statement is true.
44. $(A \cup B) \cup C = A \cup (B \cup C)$
45. $(A \cap B)' = A' \cup B'$
46. $(A \cup B)' = A' \cap B'$
47. $A \cap (B \cup C) = (A \cap B) \cup (A \cap C)$
48. $A \cup (B \cap C) = (A \cup B) \cap (A \cup C)$

In 49–54, state whether the word *or* should replace the question mark or the word *and* should replace the question mark to make the statement true.
49. $|x| = 4$ is equivalent to $x = -4$? $x = 4$.
50. $|y| > 2$ is equivalent to $-2 > y$? $y > 2$.
51. $|t| \leq 6$ is equivalent to $-6 \leq t$? $t \leq 6$.
52. $|x - 3| = 5$ is equivalent to $x - 3 = -5$? $x - 3 = 5$.

53. $|r-4| < 8$ is equivalent to $-8 < r-4$? $r-4 < 8$.
54. $|s+2| \geq 3$ is equivalent to $-3 \geq s+2$? $s+2 \geq 3$.

In 55–60, write a conjunction or a disjunction of open sentences which are equivalent to the given open sentence.

55. $|m| = 7$ **56.** $|t| > 1$ **57.** $|x| \leq 9$
58. $|x-4| = 2$ **59.** $|2y-1| < 5$ **60.** $|8-2x| \geq 10$

In 61–63, find and graph the solution set of the open sentence.

61. $|x-5| = 8$ **62.** $|x+2| \leq 6$ **63.** $|3y-5| > 2$

2. Graphic Solution of a System of Linear Equations in Two Variables

We see in a coordinate plane (Fig. 1) the line L_1, which is the graph of the infinite number of ordered pairs in the solution set of the equation $y - x = 3$. In the same coordinate plane with the same set of axes, we see the line L_2, which is the graph of the infinite number of ordered pairs in the solution set of the equation $2x + y = 6$. The one point that these straight lines have in common is their point of intersection $P(1, 4)$. Hence, the ordered pair $(1, 4)$ which is associated with P is the common solution of the pair of equations $y - x = 3$ and $2x + y = 6$. Thus, the solution set of this pair is $\{(1, 4)\}$.

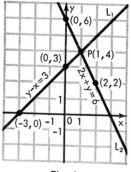

Fig. 1

If we represent the solution set of $y - x = 3$ by $A = \{(x, y) | y - x = 3\}$, and if we represent the solution set of $2x + y = 6$ by $B = \{(x, y) | 2x + y = 6\}$, then the set of ordered pairs common to A and B, that is, $A \cap B = \{(1, 4)\}$.

A pair of equations like $y - x = 3$ and $2x + y = 6$ is called a ***system of linear equations in two variables,*** or a ***set of simultaneous linear equations.***

A system of equations is really a conjunction of open sentences. Thus, the system $y - x = 3$ and $2x + y = 6$ is the conjunction

$$y - x = 3 \text{ and } 2x + y = 6$$

The solution of this conjunction is the set of all ordered pairs of numbers that satisfy *both* equations of the system. Each of these ordered pairs is called a ***solution*** of the system. The set of all solutions of the system is called the ***solution set*** of the system. Hence, the solution set of the system $y - x = 3$ and $2x + y = 6$ is $\{(1, 4)\}$.

Procedure. To solve a pair of linear equations graphically:
1. Graph each equation, using the same set of axes.
2. Find the common solution, which is the ordered number pair associated with the point of intersection of the two graphs.
3. Check the resulting solution by verifying that the ordered pair satisfies both given equations.

KEEP IN MIND

The solution set of a system of equations is the intersection of the solution sets of the individual equations.

MODEL PROBLEM

Solve the system graphically and check: $2x + y = 6$
$$y - x = 3$$

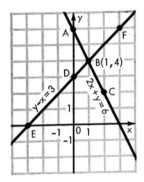

Solution:
1. Graph each equation of the system.

Graph $2x + y = 6$, or $y = -2x + 6$.	Graph $y - x = 3$, or $y = x + 3$.
(x, y)	(x, y)
$A(0, 6)$	$D(0, 3)$
$B(1, 4)$	$E(-3, 0)$
$C(2, 2)$	$F(3, 6)$

2. Find the common solution.
   The common solution is $(1, 4)$, the coordinates of B, the point of intersection.
3. *Check:* Substitute 1 for x and 4 for y in each given equation.

$2x + y = 6$	$y - x = 3$
$2(1) + 4 \stackrel{?}{=} 6$	$4 - 1 \stackrel{?}{=} 3$
$6 = 6$ (true)	$3 = 3$ (true)

Answer: The common solution is $(1, 4)$. The solution set is $\{(1, 4)\}$.

CONSISTENT, DEPENDENT, AND INCONSISTENT SYSTEMS OF EQUATIONS

When the graphs of two linear equations are drawn in a coordinate plane, they may be related to each other in only one of the following three ways:

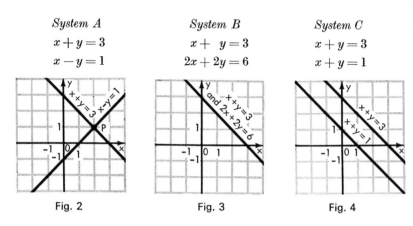

System A	System B	System C
$x + y = 3$	$x + y = 3$	$x + y = 3$
$x - y = 1$	$2x + 2y = 6$	$x + y = 1$

Fig. 2   Fig. 3   Fig. 4

In system A (Fig. 2), the graphs are lines that intersect in one and only one point. Since such lines have only one point of intersection, the solution set of such a system has one and only one ordered pair. A system of linear equations is a **consistent system** if one and only one ordered pair satisfies both of its equations. In a consistent system, if m_1 and m_2 are the slopes of the graphs of the equations, then $m_1 \neq m_2$.

In system B (Fig. 3), the graphs are lines that coincide. Since such lines have an infinite number of points in common, the solution set of such a system has an infinite number of ordered pairs. A system of linear equations is a **dependent system** if every ordered pair that satisfies one equation also satisfies the other equation. In a dependent system, if m_1 and m_2 are the slopes of the graphs of the equations, $m_1 = m_2$.

In system C (Fig. 4), the graphs are lines that are parallel. Since such lines have no points in common, the solution set of such a system has no ordered pairs; that is, it is the empty set $\varnothing$. A system of linear equations is an **inconsistent system** if no ordered pair satisfies both of its equations. In an inconsistent system, if m_1 and m_2 are the slopes of the graphs of the equations, $m_1 = m_2$.

PROPERTIES OF THE LINEAR SYSTEM
$$y = m_1 x + b_1 \text{ AND } y = m_2 x + b_2$$

Name of System	Relation Between Slopes	Relation Between Graphs	Number of Ordered Pairs of the Solution Set
Consistent	$m_1 \neq m_2$	intersecting	one
Dependent	$m_1 = m_2, b_1 = b_2$	coincident	infinite
Inconsistent	$m_1 = m_2, b_1 \neq b_2$	parallel	none

Exercises

In 1–12, solve the system of equations graphically. Check.

1. $x + y = 6$
$x - y = 2$

2. $x + 2y = 15$
$y = 2x$

3. $x + 4y = 7$
$x = 2y + 1$

4. $y - x = -2$
$x - 2y = 4$

5. $5x + 2y = -5$
$y - x = 1$

6. $3x - 4y = 6$
$y = 2x + 1$

7. $y = \frac{1}{3}x - 3$
$2x - y = 8$

8. $3x - y = 6$
$\frac{1}{3}y - x = 2$

9. $2x + 4y = 12$
$y = 3 - \frac{1}{2}x$

10. $x + y + 2 = 0$
$x = y - 8$

11. $y + 2x + 6 = 0$
$y = 2x$

12. $5x + 3y + 9 = 0$
$3x - 4y - 12 = 0$

In 13–20: (a) Determine whether the equations of the system are consistent, inconsistent, or dependent. (b) State whether the graphs of the equations of the system intersect, are parallel, or coincide. (c) State the number of ordered pairs that the solution set of the system contains.

13. $2x + y = 5$
$2x + y = 8$

14. $3x + y = 9$
$2x - y = 4$

15. $3x + y = 5$
$2y = 10 - 6x$

16. $4x - 3y = 7$
$8x - 6y = 7$

17. $x + y = 12$
$x - y = 2$

18. $y = x$
$3y - 3x = 4$

19. $2x + 3y = 8$
$3x + 2y = 10$

20. $2x = 5y + 4$
$4x - 10y = 8$

21. Write a system of two linear equations in two variables whose solution set contains (a) no members, (b) only one member, and (c) an infinite number of members.

3. Algebraic Solution of a System of Linear Equations in Two Variables Using Addition or Subtraction

Equivalent systems of equations are systems that have the same solution set. For example, the two systems shown below are equivalent systems because they have the same solution set, $\{(10, 3)\}$.

System S_1		*System* S_2
$x + 3y = 19$		$x = 10$
$x - 3y = 1$		$y = 3$

To solve a system of linear equations, such as S_1, whose solution set is not obvious, we make use of the properties of equality to transform the system into an equivalent system of equations, such as S_2, whose solution set is obvious.

~~~~~~~~~~~~~~ *MODEL PROBLEMS* ~~~~~~~~~~~~~~

1. Solve the system of equations and check: $x + 3y = 19$
$$x - 3y = 1$$

How To Proceed

Solution

1. The coefficients of the variable y have the same absolute value in both equations. Therefore, adding the members of equation (B) to the corresponding members of equation (A) will eliminate the variable y and will result in an equation which involves only the one variable x.

(A) $x + 3y = 19$
(B) $x - 3y = 1$
$$\overline{\qquad\qquad}$$
$$2x = 20$$

2. Solve the resulting equation for the variable x.
3. Replace x by its value 10 in any equation involving both variables, for example, equation (A).
4. Solve the resulting equation for the variable y.

$$x = 10$$
(A) $x + 3y = 19$
$$10 + 3y = 19$$
$$3y = 9$$
$$y = 3$$

5. *Check:* Substitute 10 for x and 3 for y in each given equation.

$$x + 3y = 19 \qquad\qquad x - 3y = 1$$
$$10 + 3(3) \overset{?}{=} 19 \qquad\qquad 10 - 3(3) \overset{?}{=} 1$$
$$19 = 19 \text{ (true)} \qquad\qquad 1 = 1 \text{ (true)}$$

Answer: Since $x = 10$ and $y = 3$, the solution is (10, 3), or the solution set is {(10, 3)}.

2. Solve the system of equations and check: $3r = 4s + 17$
$$2r = -3s$$

How To Proceed

Solution

1. Transform each of the given equations (A) and (B) into equivalent equations (C) and (D) in which the terms containing the variables appear on one side and the constant appears on the other side.

(A) $3r = 4s + 17$
(B) $2r = -3s$

(C) $3r - 4s = 17$
(D) $2r + 3s = 0$

2. To eliminate r, multiply both members of equation (C) by 2 and multiply both members of equation (D) by 3 so that in the resulting equivalent equations (E) and (F) the absolute values of the coefficients of r are equal.

(E) $6r - 8s = 34$
(F) $6r + 9s = 0$
$$\overline{\qquad\qquad}$$

3. Subtract the members of equation (F) from the corresponding members of equation (E) to eliminate the variable r.

$$-17s = 34$$

4. Solve the resulting equation for the variable s.

$$s = -2$$

5. Replace s by its value -2 in any equation containing both variables, for example equation (A).

(A) $\quad 3r = 4s + 17$
$\quad\quad 3r = 4(-2) + 17$

6. Solve the resulting equation for the remaining variable, r.

$$3r = 9$$
$$r = 3$$

7. *Check:* Substitute -2 for s and 3 for r in both given equations to verify that the resulting sentences are true. This is left to the student.

Answer: Since $r = 3$ and $s = -2$, the solution is $(3, -2)$, or the solution set is $\{(3, -2)\}$.

Exercises

In 1–21, solve the system of equations by eliminating one of the variables, using the methods of addition or subtraction. Check.

1. $x + y = 9$
$x - y = 3$

2. $x + 2y = 8$
$x - 2y = 4$

3. $y + 3x = 8$
$y - 3x = 2$

4. $m + 2n = 14$
$3n + m = 18$

5. $2a + 3b = 12$
$5a + 3b = 14$

6. $3x + 2y = 9$
$x + y = 3$

7. $3a - b = 3$
$a + 3b = 11$

8. $2c - d = -1$
$c + 3d = 17$

9. $4x + 5y = -8$
$3y - 4x = -8$

10. $2x + y = -2$
$x + 3y = 9$

11. $3r + 7s = -4$
$2r + 5s = -3$

12. $4y - 6x = 15$
$6y - 4x = 10$

13. $6x + 10y = 7$
$15x - 4y = 3$

14. $m = 11 + n$
$3m = 3 - 2n$

15. $x = 2(8 + y)$
$3y = 2(1 + 2x)$

16. $5a = 4b$
$\frac{1}{2}a + 2b = 12$

17. $.04x + .05y = 44$
$x + y = 1000$

18. $.02x = .03y + 1$
$x + y = 800$

19. $\dfrac{3x + 8}{5} = \dfrac{3y - 1}{2}$

$\dfrac{x + y}{2} = 3 + \dfrac{x - y}{2}$

20. $\dfrac{a}{3} + \dfrac{a + b}{6} = 3$

$\dfrac{b}{3} - \dfrac{a - b}{2} = 6$

21. $\dfrac{x + y}{6} - \dfrac{x - y}{4} = 3$

$\dfrac{x + y}{4} + \dfrac{x - y}{2} = 8$

In 22–30, consider x and y as the variables of the system of equations. Solve the system by eliminating one of these variables, using the methods of addition or subtraction. Check. (*Note.* In 28–30, the equations of the system are not linear equations.)

22. $x + y = 7a$
$x - y = 3a$

23. $3x + 2y = 14b$
$4x - y = 15b$

24. $x + y = a$
$x - y = b$

25. $5x - 2y = c$
$3x - 2y = d$

26. $x + 2y = 4m$
$3x - y = 5m$

27. $2x + 3y = 13b$
$3x + 2y = 12b$

28. $\dfrac{1}{x} + \dfrac{1}{y} = 7$ **29.** $\dfrac{4}{x} + \dfrac{9}{y} = -1$ **30.** $\dfrac{1}{x} + \dfrac{1}{y} = 5a$

$\dfrac{1}{x} - \dfrac{1}{y} = 1$ $\dfrac{6}{x} - \dfrac{12}{y} = 7$ $\dfrac{2}{x} + \dfrac{3}{y} = 13a$

In 31–37, consider the trigonometric functions of an angle as the variables of the system of equations. Solve the system, using addition or subtraction. Check. (For example, in exercise 34, consider sin y and cos y as the variables of the system.)

31. $2 \sin x + 3 \cos y = 2$ **32.** $2 \tan x + \tan y = 8$ **33.** $\tan x + 2 \sin y = 3$

     $4 \sin x - 3 \cos y = 1$ $\tan x - \tan y = 1$ $3 \tan x - 4 \sin y = 4$

34. $\sin y + \cos y = 3a$ **35.** $6 \sin A + \cot B = 2a + 2$

     $\sin y - \cos y = a$ $3 \sin A + \cot B = 2a + 1$

36. $2 \cos x + \tan y = 3a$ **37.** $4 \tan B + 3 \sin A = c$

     $- \cos x + 2 \tan y = 3b$ $2 \tan B - 6 \sin A = d$

4. Algebraic Solution of a System of Linear Equations in Two Variables Using Substitution

A second method, called the *substitution method*, can be used to solve a system of equations algebraically. This method depends upon transforming one of the equations of the system into an equivalent equation that contains only one variable.

〰〰〰〰〰〰〰 *MODEL PROBLEM* 〰〰〰〰〰〰〰

Solve the system by using the substitution method, and check.

$$2x - 5y = 3$$
$$3y + x = 7$$

How To Proceed	*Solution*
1. Transform one of the equations into an equivalent equation in which one of the variables can be expressed in terms of the other.	1. (A) $2x - 5y = 3$ (B) $3y + x = 7$ In equation (B), solve for x in terms of y. (C) $\quad x = 7 - 3y$
2. In the other equation, substitute the resulting expression for the first variable, thus eliminating the first variable.	2. In equation (A), substitute $7 - 3y$ for x. $2(7 - 3y) - 5y = 3$

3. Solve the resulting equation for the second variable.

3. Solve for y.
$$14 - 6y - 5y = 3$$
$$-11y = -11$$
$$y = 1$$

4. Substitute the value of the variable obtained in step 3 in any equation involving both variables and solve the resulting equation for the remaining variable.

4. Substitue 1 for y in equation (C).
$$x = 7 - 3y$$
$$x = 7 - 3(1)$$
$$x = 7 - 3$$
$$x = 4$$

5. *Check:* Substitute 4 for x and 1 for y in each of the given equations to verify that the resulting sentences are true. This is left to the student.

Answer: Since $x = 4$ and $y = 1$, the solution is $(4, 1)$, or the solution set is $\{(4, 1)\}$.

Exercises

In 1–12, solve the system of equations by eliminating one of the variables, using the substitution method. Check.

1. $y = 3x$
   $x + y = 8$

2. $x = 4y$
   $3x + 8y = 5$

3. $x = -2y$
   $4x + 2y = 6$

4. $y = 3x$
   $x - y = 2$

5. $x = 2y + 1$
   $x + y = -2$

6. $a - b = 3$
   $2a - 3b = 1$

7. $y = 3x - 1$
   $9x + 2y = 3$

8. $2x - y = 1$
   $y - x = 2$

9. $5c + d + 2 = 0$
   $c + 2d = 5$

10. $4x + y = 0$
   $8x + \frac{1}{4}y = 7$

11. $2x = 3y$
   $4x - 5y = 2$

12. $2x + 3y = 9$
   $4x - 5y = 7$

In 13–16, consider x and y as the variables of the system of equations. Solve the system of equations, using the method of substitution. Check.

13. $x + y = m$
   $x = y + n$

14. $6x - 4y = 2a$
   $x = y - a$

15. $3x = y + a$
   $5x = 3y + 7a$

16. $5x - 3y = -2d$
   $2x + 5y = 24d$

In 17–19, consider the trigonometric functions of an angle as the variables of the system of equations. Solve the system, using the method of substitution. Check. (For example, in exercise 17, consider $\sin x$ and $\cos y$ as variables.)

17. $\sin x + \cos y = 1$
   $\sin x = 2 \cos y$

18. $\cos x = \frac{1}{2} \sin y$
   $4 \cos x + \sin y = 2$

19. $\tan x - 2 \cos y = -r$
   $\tan x = 2r - \cos y$

5. Solving Verbal Problems by Using Two Variables

Now we will learn how to solve verbal problems by translating the given relationships into a system of two equations involving two variables. Frequently, a problem can be solved more readily by using two variables than by using one variable.

Procedure. To solve verbal problems by using a system of two equations involving two variables:
1. **Use different variables to represent the different unknown quantities in the problem.**
2. **Translate the given relationships in the problem into a system of equations.**
3. **Solve the system of equations to determine the answer(s) to the problem.**
4. **Check the answer(s) in the original problem.**

NUMBER PROBLEMS

~~~~~~~~~ *MODEL PROBLEM* ~~~~~~~~~

The sum of two numbers is 56. Twice the smaller number exceeds one-half the larger number by 22. Find the numbers.

How To Proceed	*Solution*
1. Represent the two different unknown quantities.	1. Let $x =$ smaller number. Let $y =$ larger number.
2. Translate the given relationships in the problem into a system of equations.	2. *The sum of the two numbers is* 56. (A) $x + y = 56$ *Twice the smaller number is* 22 *more than one-half of the larger number.* (B) $2x = \frac{1}{2}y + 22$
3. Solve the system of equations: In (B), M$_2$. Then transpose. Copy equation (A). Eliminate the y-term by addition.	3. $\quad 4x = y + 44$ $\quad 4x - y = 44$ $\quad \underline{x + y = 56}$ $\quad 5x \quad\;\; = 100$ $\quad x \quad\;\;\; = 20$
Substitute 20 for x in equation (A).	$\quad x + y = 56$ $\quad 20 + y = 56$ $\quad y = 36$

Answer: The smaller number is 20; the larger number is 36.

~~~~~~

Exercises

In 1–5, solve the problem by using a system of two equations involving two variables.

1. The sum of two numbers is 50. If twice the larger is subtracted from 4 times the smaller, the result is 8. Find the numbers.

2. If 3 times the smaller of two numbers is increased by the larger, the result is 63. If 5 times the smaller is subtracted from twice the larger, the result is 16. Find the numbers.

3. The sum of two numbers is 90. If 20 is added to 3 times the smaller number, the result exceeds twice the larger number by 50. Find the numbers.

4. Twice the smaller of two numbers is one-half of the larger number. The larger is 10 more than 3 times the smaller. Find the numbers.

5. The sum of $\frac{1}{3}$ of the smaller of two numbers and $\frac{2}{5}$ of the larger is 34. Also, $\frac{1}{2}$ of the smaller number is equal to $\frac{1}{4}$ of the larger. Find the numbers.

COIN PROBLEMS

~~~~~~~~~~~~~~ *MODEL PROBLEM* ~~~~~~~~~~~~~~

A collection of coins consisting of nickels and quarters has a value of $4.50. The number of quarters is 4 less than twice the number of nickels. Find the number of coins of each kind in the collection.

Let $n =$ the number of nickels.
Let $q =$ the number of quarters.

	(of coins) Number	$(\cent)$ $\times$ Value of each	$(\cent)$ $=$ Total value
Nickel	n	5	$5n$
Quarter	q	25	$25q$

The total value of the coins is 450 cents.

$$5n + 25q = 450$$

The number of quarters is 4 less than twice the number of nickels.

$$q = 2n - 4$$

(A) $5n + 25q = 450$

(B) $q = 2n - 4$

(C) $-2n + q = -4$

In (C), M_{25}. Then subtract (A).

$$-50n + 25q = -100$$
$$5n + 25q = 450$$
$$\overline{}$$
$$-55n = -550$$
$$n = 10$$

(B) $q = 2n - 4$
$$q = 2(10) - 4$$
$$q = 16$$

Check in the given problem:

Is the total value $4.50?
Value of 16 quarters = $4.00
Value of 10 nickels =   .50

Total value   = $4.50 (true)

Is 16, the number of quarters, 4 less
    than twice the number of nickels?
$16 \overset{?}{=} 2(10) - 4$
$16 = 16$ (true)

Answer: There are 10 nickels and 16 quarters.

~~~~~~

Exercises

In 1–5, solve the problem by using a system of two equations involving two variables.

1. Harry has a collection of coins consisting of dimes and quarters whose value is $17.60. The number of quarters exceeds twice the number of dimes by 8. Find the number of coins of each kind in the collection.

2. Mrs. Carey cashed a $600 check in her bank. She received $5 bills and $10 bills. The number of $10 bills was 10 less than 3 times the number of $5 bills. How many bills of each type did Mrs. Carey receive?

3. Ray has $7.60 in quarters and dimes. In all, he has 40 coins. How many coins of each kind does he have?

4. A class contributed $11.40 in dimes and quarters to a welfare fund. In all, there were 60 coins. How many coins of each kind were contributed?

5. In a collection box, there are dimes and quarters whose total value is $28. If there were as many quarters as there are dimes, and as many dimes as there are quarters, the total value would be $36.40. How many coins of each kind are in the collection box?

MIXTURE PROBLEMS

〜〜〜〜〜〜〜〜〜 *MODEL PROBLEM* 〜〜〜〜〜〜〜〜〜

A dealer has some candy worth $.50 per pound and some worth $.75 per pound. How many pounds of each kind should he use to make a mixture of 90 pounds that he can sell for $.60 per pound?

Solution:
Let $x =$ the number of pounds of $.75 candy to be used.
Let $y =$ the number of pounds of $.50 candy to be used.

	(lb.) Number	(¢) × Price per pound	(¢) = Total value
$.75 candy	x	75	$75x$
$.50 candy	y	50	$50y$
Mixture	90	60	90(60)

The total number of pounds of candy is 90.

$$x + y = 90$$

The total value of the $.75 candy and the $.50 candy is 90(60)¢.

$$75x + 50y = 90(60)$$

(A)	$75x + 50y = 90(60)$	*Check* in the given problem:
(B)	$x + y = 90$	

In (B), M$_{50}$: $50x + 50y = 4500$
Subtract (A): $75x + 50y = 5400$

$$-25x \quad\quad = -900$$
$$x = 36$$

(B) $x + y = 90$
$36 + y = 90$
$y = 54$

Check in the given problem:

Is the total number of pounds 90?
$36 + 54 = 90$ (true)
Is $90 \times $.60$ or $54.00 the total value?

Value of 36 lb. at $.75 per lb. $= 27.00
Value of 54 lb. at $.50 per lb. $= 27.00

Total value $= 54.00

Value of 90 lb. at $.60 per lb. $= 54.00
The values are the same.

Answer: He should use 36 pounds of the $.75 and 54 pounds of the $.50 candy.

Exercises

In 1–6, solve the problem by using two variables.

1. A dealer wishes to obtain 80 pounds of mixed cookies to sell for $1.00 per pound. If he mixes cookies worth $1.20 per pound with cookies worth $.70 per pound, find the number of pounds of each kind he should use.

2. A dealer mixed coffee worth 85 cents per pound with coffee worth 55 cents per pound. How many pounds of each kind did he use to make a mixture of 120 pounds to sell at 75 cents per pound?

3. How many pounds of seed worth $1.05 per pound must be mixed with 60 pounds of seed worth $.90 per pound in order to produce a mixture to sell for $1.00 per pound?

4. One bar of tin alloy is 25% pure tin and another bar is 10% pure tin. How many pounds of each alloy must be used to make 75 pounds of a new alloy which is 20% pure tin?

5. A chemist has a solution which is 18% pure salt and a second solution which is 45% pure salt. How many ounces of each solution should he use to make 24 ounces of a solution which is 36% pure salt?

6. A dairyman has milk which contains 4% butterfat and cream which contains 40% butterfat. How many gallons of each should he use in order to produce 36 gallons of a mixture which contains 20% butterfat?

INVESTMENT PROBLEMS

~~~~~~~~~~~ *MODEL PROBLEM* ~~~~~~~~~~~

Mr. Curran invested a sum of money in 4% bonds and $3000 more than this amount in 6% bonds. His annual income from the 6% bonds exceeded the annual income from the 4% bonds by $240. Find the amount he invested in each type of bond.

Solution:

Let x = the number of dollars invested in the 4% bonds.
Let y = the number of dollars invested in the 6% bonds.

	($) Principal	Annual rate × of interest	($) = Annual income
4% bonds	x	.04	$.04x$
6% bonds	y	.06	$.06y$

The 6% investment is $3000 more than the 4% investment.

$$y = x + 3000$$

The annual income from the 6% bonds is $240 more than the annual income from the 4% bonds.

$$.06y = .04x + 240$$

(A) $y = x + 3000$
(B) $.06y = .04x + 240$

In (B), M_{100}: $6y = 4x + 24,000$
Substitute $x + 3000$ for y.
$$6(x + 3000) = 4x + 24,000$$
$$6x + 18,000 = 4x + 24,000$$
$$2x = 6000$$
$$x = 3000$$

(A) $y = x + 3000$
        $y = 3000 + 3000$
        $y = 6000$

Check in the given problem:

Is the amount invested in 6% bonds $3000 more than the amount invested in 4% bonds?

$6000 = 3000 + 3000$ (true)

Does the annual income from the 6% bonds exceed the annual income from the 4% bonds by $240?

4% of $3000 = $120.00
6% of $6000 = $360.00
$360 exceeds $120 by $240 (true)

Answer: The amount invested in 4% bonds was $3000; the amount invested in 6% bonds was $6000.

~~~~~~

Exercises

In 1–5, solve the problems by using two variables.

1. Mrs. Brand invested $7000, part at 8% and the rest at 5%. Her total annual income from these investments was $500. Find the amount she invested at each rate.

2. Mr. Trask invested a certain sum of money in bonds yielding $4\frac{1}{2}\%$ a year and twice as much in bonds yielding 7% a year. If his total annual income from these investments was $1850, how much did he invest in each type of bond?

3. Mr. Orsini invested $36,000, part at 5% and the rest at 7%. If his annual incomes from both investments were equal, find the amount he invested at each rate.

4. Mr. Dunn invested $35,000, part at 8% and the rest at 5%. His annual income from the 8% investment was $450 less than his annual income from the 5% investment. Find the amount he invested at each rate.

5. Mr. Walsh invested $16,000 at 7%. How much additional money must he invest at 4% so that his total annual income will be 5% of his entire investment?

BUSINESS PROBLEMS

~~~~~~~~~~~~~~~~~~ *MODEL PROBLEM* ~~~~~~~~~~~~~~~~~~

The owner of a men's clothing store bought 12 shirts and 6 hats for $75. A week later, at the same prices, he bought 9 shirts and 4 hats for $53. Find the price of a shirt and the price of a hat.

Solution:

Let s = the cost of a shirt in dollars. Let h = the cost of a hat in dollars.

$$12 \text{ shirts and 6 hats cost } \$75. \quad \text{(A) } 12s + 6h = 75$$

$$9 \text{ shirts and 4 hats cost } \$53. \quad \text{(B) } 9s + 4h = 53$$

1. In order to eliminate h, in (A), M_2; in (B), M_3.
$$24s + 12h = 150$$
$$27s + 12h = 159$$

2. Subtract.
$$-3s \quad\quad = -9$$
$$s = 3$$

3. In (A), substitute 3 for s.
$$\text{(A) } 12s + 6h = 75$$
$$36 + 6h = 75$$
$$6h = 39$$
$$h = 6\tfrac{1}{2}$$

Answer: A shirt costs $3; a hat costs $6.50.

~~~~~~

Exercises

In 1–5, solve the problem by using two variables.

1. Mrs. Bond bought 3 cans of corn and 5 cans of tomatoes for $1.82. The following week, she bought 2 cans of corn and 3 cans of tomatoes for $1.11, paying the same prices. Find the cost of a can of corn and the cost of a can of tomatoes.

2. A baseball manager bought 4 bats and 9 balls for $33.75. On another day, he bought 3 bats and 1 dozen balls at the same prices and paid $34.50. How much did he pay for each bat and for each ball?

3. Eight roses and 9 carnations cost $3.35. At the same prices, one dozen roses and 5 carnations cost $3.75. Find the cost of a rose and the cost of a carnation.

4. One day 4 plumbers and 5 helpers earned $350. At the same rate of pay, another group of 5 plumbers and 6 helpers earned $430. How much does a plumber and how much does a helper earn each day?

• **5.** The cost of sending a telegram of 17 words from one city to another is $1.25. The cost of sending a telegram of 24 words between the same two cities is $1.60. The charge in each case is based upon a fixed charge for the first 10 words and an extra charge for each additional word beyond 10. Find the charge for the first 10 words and the charge for each extra word beyond 10.

PROBLEMS INVOLVING FRACTIONS

〰〰〰〰〰〰〰 *MODEL PROBLEM* 〰〰〰〰〰〰〰

If 1 is added to the numerator of a fraction and 3 is added to the denominator of the fraction, the value of the resulting fraction is $\frac{3}{5}$. If the numerator of the original fraction is decreased by 3, and the denominator of the original fraction is doubled, the value of the resulting fraction is $\frac{1}{7}$. Find the original fraction.

Solution:
Let $n =$ the numerator of the fraction.
Let $d =$ the denominator of the fraction.

(A) $\dfrac{n+1}{d+3} = \dfrac{3}{5}$

(B) $\dfrac{n-3}{2d} = \dfrac{1}{7}$

In (A), $M_{5(d+3)}$: $5(n+1) = 3(d+3)$
$5n + 5 = 3d + 9$

(C) $5n - 3d = 4$
In (B), M_{14d}: $7(n-3) = 2d$
(D) $7n - 21 = 2d$
(E) $7n - 2d = 21$

In (C), M_2: $10n - 6d = 8$
In (E), M_3: $21n - 6d = 63$
$-11n \qquad = -55$
$n = 5$

(D) $7n - 21 = 2d$
Let $n = 5$: $7(5) - 21 = 2d$
$14 = 2d$
$7 = d$

Check in the given problem:
If 1 is added to the numerator of the original fraction and 3 is added to the denominator of the original fraction, is the value of the resulting fraction $\frac{3}{5}$?

$\dfrac{5+1}{7+3} = \dfrac{6}{10} = \dfrac{3}{5}$ (true)

If the numerator of the original fraction is decreased by 3 and the denominator of the original fraction is doubled, is the value of the resulting fraction $\frac{1}{7}$?

$\dfrac{5-3}{2(7)} = \dfrac{2}{14} = \dfrac{1}{7}$ (true)

Answer: The original fraction is $\frac{5}{7}$.

Exercises

In 1–5, solve the problem by using two variables.

1. If 1 is added to both the numerator and the denominator of a certain fraction, the value of the fraction becomes $\frac{1}{3}$. If 1 is added to the denominator of the original fraction, the value of the fraction becomes $\frac{1}{4}$. Find the original fraction.

2. The sum of the numerator and the denominator of a fraction is 20. If the numerator is increased by 3 and the denominator is decreased by 2, the value of the resulting fraction is $\frac{3}{4}$. Find the original fraction.

3. The denominator of a fraction exceeds its numerator by 6. If 24 is added to the numerator of the fraction and the denominator of the fraction is doubled, the value of the resulting fraction is 1. Find the original fraction.

4. If 3 is added to the numerator of a fraction and 2 is subtracted from the denominator of the fraction, the value of the resulting fraction is $\frac{3}{4}$. If 1 is added to the numerator of the reciprocal of the given fraction, the value of the resulting fraction is $\frac{5}{2}$. Find the original fraction.

5. The numerator and denominator of a fraction are in the ratio 3 : 2. If 3 is subtracted from the denominator of the reciprocal of the fraction, the ratio of the numerator of the resulting fraction to its denominator is 8 : 11. Find the original fraction.

DIGIT PROBLEMS

Preparing to Solve Digit Problems

In our decimal number system, every integer may be written by using only the ten symbols 0, 1, 2, 3, 4, 5, 6, 7, 8, 9, which are called **digits**.

When we write an integer, each place is given a value ten times the value of the place immediately at its right. For example, $685 = 6(100) + 8(10) + 5(1)$. Likewise, $79 = 7(10) + 9(1)$. In the number 79, we call 7 the *tens digit* and 9 the *units digit*. The value of the tens digit 7 is $7(10)$, or 70; the value of the units digit 9 is $9(1)$, or 9.

If we wish to represent a two-digit number whose tens digit is represented by t and whose units digit is represented by u, we write $t(10) + u(1)$, or $10t + u$. Notice that we may *not* represent the two-digit number by tu because "tu" means "t times u."

If we reverse the digits of the number 79, we obtain a new number, 97. Observe that $97 = 9(10) + 7(1)$. That is, the new number 97 can be represented by adding 10 times 9, the units digit of the original number 79, and 1 times 7, the tens digit of the original number 79. Likewise, if t represents the tens digit of a two-digit number, and u represents the units digit of the number, when the digits are reversed, the new number that is formed is represented by $10u + t$.

KEEP IN MIND

If t represents the tens digit and u represents the units digit of a two-digit number:

$10t + u$ represents the original number.

$10u + t$ represents the original number with its digits reversed.

$t + u$ represents the sum of the digits of the original number.

Exercises

In 1–5, give the value of each digit in the number.

1. 47   **2.** 372   **3.** 5604   **4.** 706   **5.** 34027

In 6–8, represent the number which is described.

6. The number whose tens digit is 5 and whose units digit is 2.

7. The number whose units digit is 9 and whose tens digit is 5.

8. The number obtained by reversing the digits of 47.

Solving Digit Problems

$\sim\!\sim\!\sim\!\sim\!\sim\!\sim\!\sim\!\sim\!\sim\!\sim$ *MODEL PROBLEM* $\sim\!\sim\!\sim\!\sim\!\sim\!\sim\!\sim\!\sim\!\sim\!\sim$

The sum of the digits of a two-digit number is 12. If the digits are reversed, the resulting number exceeds twice the original number by 15. Find the original number.

Solution:

Let $t =$ the tens digit of the number.

And $u =$ the units digit of the number.

Then $10t + u =$ the original number.

And $10u + t =$ the original number with the digits reversed.

The sum of the digits is 12.

(A) $t + u = 12$

The number with the digits reversed is 15 more than twice the original number.

(B) $10u + t = 2(10t + u) + 15$

Simplify (B): $10u + t = 20t + 2u + 15$

$$-19t + 8u = 15$$

In (A), M_8: $8t + 8u = 96$

$$\overline{-27t = -81}$$

$$t = 3$$

(A) $t + u = 12$

In (A), let $t = 3$: $3 + u = 12$

$$u = 9$$

$$10t + u = 10(3) + 9 = 39$$

Check in the given problem:
Is the sum of the digits 12?
$3 + 9 = 12$ (true)

Does the number with the digits reversed, 93, exceed twice the original number, 39, by 15?
93 exceeds 2×39, or 78, by 15. (true)

Answer: The number is 39.

Exercises

1. The units digit of a two-digit number is 1 more than twice the tens digit. The sum of the digits is 10. Find the number.

2. The tens digit of a two-digit number is 1 less than 5 times the units digit. The sum of the digits is 11. Find the number.

3. The units digit of a two-digit number is 3 more than its tens digit. The sum of the digits is $\frac{1}{4}$ of the number. Find the number.

4. The units digit of a two-digit number is one more than twice the tens digit. If the digits are reversed, the resulting number is 27 more than the original number. Find the number.

5. The units digit of a two-digit number is 1 less than 5 times the tens digit. If the digits are reversed, the new number exceeds 3 times the original number by 5. Find the number.

6. The sum of the digits of a two-digit number is 12. If the digits are reversed, a new number is formed which is 12 less than twice the original number. Find the number.

7. The tens digit of a two-digit number exceeds the units digit by 2. If the digits are reversed, the resulting number is 4 times the sum of the digits. Find the original number.

8. The sum of the digits of a two-digit number is 13. If the digits are reversed, the new number is 27 less than the original number. Find the number.

9. The units digit of a two-digit number is one less than twice the tens digit. If the digits are reversed, the new number exceeds the original number by 27. Find the original number.

10. The sum of the digits of a two-digit number is 10. If 18 is added to the number, the sum is the number obtained by reversing the digits of the original number. Find the number.

11. The sum of the digits of a two-digit number is 9. The number is 7 times the sum of the digits. Find the number.

12. A two-digit number is 7 times the sum of the digits. The original number exceeds by 18 the number obtained by reversing the digits. Find the number.

13. The units digit of a two-digit number is 5 less than the tens digit. If the digits are reversed, a new number is formed which is $\frac{3}{8}$ of the original number. What is the original number?

14. The sum of the digits of a two-digit number is 12. If the digits are reversed, the new number exceeds $\frac{1}{3}$ of the original number by 20. Find the number.

15. A two-digit number is 9 more than the number obtained by reversing the digits. The number is also 6 more than 5 times the sum of the digits. Find the number.

16. The sum of the digits of a two-digit number is 6. If the number is divided by the sum of the digits, the quotient is 7. Find the number.

17. If a two-digit number is divided by the sum of the digits, the quotient is 4 and the remainder is 15. If the digits are reversed, the resulting number exceeds the original number by 18. Find the original number.

18. When a certain two-digit number is divided by the sum of its digits, the quotient is 4. If the digits are reversed, the resulting number is 18 more than the original number. Find the original number.

19. When a two-digit number is divided by the sum of the digits, the quotient is 5. The original number subtracted from the number obtained by reversing the digits gives a result of 9. Find the original number.

20. A two-digit number is equal to 3 times the sum of its digits. If the number obtained by reversing the digits is divided by the original number, the quotient is 2 and the remainder is 18. Find the original number.

21. In a two-digit number, the ratio of the tens digit to the units digit is $2:3$. If the digits are reversed, the resulting number exceeds the original number by 18. Find the original number.

MOTION PROBLEMS INVOLVING WATER CURRENTS AND AIR CURRENTS

~~~~~~~~~~~~~~~ *MODEL PROBLEM* ~~~~~~~~~~~~~~~

A motorboat can travel 24 miles downstream in 2 hours. It requires 3 hours to make the return trip. Find the rate of the boat in still water and the rate of the stream.

Solution:

Let r = rate of the boat in still water in mph.

And c = rate of the stream in mph.

	(mph) Rate ×	(hr.) Time =	(mi.) Distance
Downstream	$r+c$	2	$2(r+c)$
Upstream	$r-c$	3	$3(r-c)$

The distance downstream is 24 miles.

(A) $2(r+c)=24$

The distance upstream is 24 miles.

(B) $3(r-c)=24$

In (A), D_2: $r+c=12$
In (B), D_3: $r-c=8$
$$2r\ \ \ \ =20$$
$$r=10$$

$$r+c=12$$
Let $r=10$: $10+c=12$
$$c=2$$

Check in the given problem:
Can the boat travel 24 miles downstream in 2 hours?
Rate downstream $=10+2=12$ mph.
Distance downstream $=2(12)=24$ miles. (true)

Can the boat make the return trip in 3 hours?
Rate upstream $=10-2=8$ mph.
Distance upstream $=3(8)=24$ miles. (true)

Answer: The rate of the boat in still water is 10 mph; the rate of the stream is 2 mph.

Exercises

In 1–5, solve the problem by using two variables.

1. If a boat is rowed down a river a distance of 16 miles in 2 hours and it is rowed upstream the same distance in 8 hours, find the rate of rowing in still water and the rate of the stream.
2. A man rows 18 miles downstream in 2 hours. He finds that it takes 6 hours to row back. Find the rate of rowing in still water and the rate of the stream.
3. It takes a motorboat 50 minutes to travel upstream a distance of 10 miles, and 30 minutes to travel the same distance downstream. Find the rate of the boat in still water and the rate of the current.
4. A plane left an airport and flew with the wind for 3 hours, covering 1200 miles. It then returned over the same route to the airport against the wind in 4 hours. Find the rate of the plane in still air and the speed of the wind.

5. A motorboat which is driven at full speed (at its maximum speed in still water) upstream moves at the rate of 14 mph. When the boat is driven at half speed downstream, it moves at 10 mph. Find the boat's maximum speed in still water and the rate of the current.

6. Algebraic Solution of a System of Three First-Degree Equations in Three Variables

An equation such as $2x + 3y + 2z = 2$ is an example of a first-degree equation in three variables. Since the values $x = 2, y = -1, z = \frac{1}{2}$ satisfy this equation, the ordered triple $(2, -1, \frac{1}{2})$ is a solution of the equation. Note that $2(2) + 3(-1) + 2(\frac{1}{2}) = 2$ is a true sentence.

In space, the graph of the equation $2x + 3y + 2z = 2$ is a plane. In this course, we will not study the graphs of equations in space. However, we will learn how to solve a system of three first-degree equations in three variables algebraically. We will do this by making use of the properties of equality to transform the given system into an equivalent system whose solution is quite obvious.

MODEL PROBLEM

Solve the system of equations and check.

$$3x + y + 2z = 6$$
$$x + y + 4z = 3$$
$$2x + 3y + 2z = 2$$

How To Proceed

1. Eliminate one variable using any combination of the given equations. Thus, to eliminate z from equations (A) and (B), in equation (A) multiply by 2; then from the result subtract the members of equation (B).

2. Eliminate the same variable using a different combination of the given equations. Thus to eliminate z from equations (A) and (C), subtract the members of (C) from the members of (A).

Solution

(A) $3x + y + 2z = 6$
(B) $x + y + 4z = 3$
(C) $2x + 3y + 2z = 2$

In (A), M_2: $6x + 2y + 4z = 12$
Subtract (B): $\underline{x + y + 4z = 3}$
(D) $5x + y = 9$

(A) $3x + y + 2z = 6$
Subtract (C): $\underline{2x + 3y + 2z = 2}$
(E) $x - 2y = 4$

Systems of Linear Open Sentences in Two or More Varia

3. Solve the resulting equations (D) and (E) in two variables, x and y, to find the values of those variables.

In (D), M_2: $10x + 2y =$
(E) $\quad x - 2y = \quad$
$$\overline{11x \qquad = 22}$$
$$x = 2$$

In (D), let $x = 2$.
$$5(2) + y = 9$$
$$10 + y = 9$$
$$y = -1$$

4. Substitute the values of the variables found in step 3 in any convenient equation involving the third variable. Thus, in equation (A), replace x by 2 and y by -1 to find the value of z.

(A) $\quad 3x + y + 2z = 6$
$$3(2) - 1 + 2z = 6$$
$$2z = 1$$
$$z = \tfrac{1}{2}$$

Check: Substitute 2 for x, -1 for y, and $\tfrac{1}{2}$ for z in all the given equations to verify that the resulting sentences are true. This is left to the student.

Answer: Since $x = 2$, $y = -1$, and $z = \tfrac{1}{2}$, the solution is $(2, -1, \tfrac{1}{2})$, or the solution set is $\{(2, -1, \tfrac{1}{2})\}$.

Note. A variable may be eliminated by using a combination of all three equations. Thus, z may be eliminated by using the combination $(A) + (C) - (B)$, and x may be eliminated by using the combination $(B) + (C) - (A)$.

Exercises

In 1–15, solve the system of equations and check. (*Note.* In 13–15, the equations of the system are not first-degree equations.)

1. $x + 3y + 2z = 13$
$x - 2y + 3z = 6$
$2x + 2y - z = 3$

2. $a + 3b + 2c = 6$
$3a - 6b - 2c = 9$
$2a - 3b - 4c = 9$

3. $r + 3s + t = 3$
$r + 6s - t = 2$
$4r + 9s - 2t = 1$

4. $3x - 2y - 3z = -1$
$6x + y + 2z = 7$
$9x + 3y + 4z = 9$

5. $x - 2y + 20z = 1$
$3x + y - 4z = 2$
$2x + y - 8z = 3$

6. $x + 2y - z = 5$
$2x + z = -1$
$3x - 4y = 2z + 7$

7. $2x + y + 3z = -2$
$5x = 5 - 2y$
$2y + 3z = -13$

8. $3x + 2y = 5$
$4x = 3z + 7$
$6y - 6z = -5$

9. $3a + 2c = 2$
$4b + c = 6$
$2a + 3b = 10$

10. $2x + 3y = 2$
$8x - 4z = 3$
$3y - 8z = -1$

11. $2x + y = 43$
$x + 3z = 47$
$y - z = 14$

12. $4x + y = 5b$
$3x + 2z = 0$
$2y - 3z = 3b$

13. $\dfrac{2}{x}+\dfrac{1}{y}-\dfrac{1}{z}=4$

$\dfrac{3}{x}-\dfrac{1}{y}+\dfrac{2}{z}=15$

$\dfrac{1}{x}-\dfrac{3}{y}+\dfrac{4}{z}=13$

14. $\dfrac{1}{x}-\dfrac{2}{y}-\dfrac{2}{z}=1$

$\dfrac{3}{x}+\dfrac{4}{y}+\dfrac{6}{z}=-9$

$\dfrac{1}{x}+\dfrac{2}{y}+\dfrac{2}{z}=-5$

15. $\dfrac{2}{x}+\dfrac{3}{y}=2$

$\dfrac{1}{x}-\dfrac{1}{z}=\dfrac{3}{10}$

$\dfrac{12}{y}-\dfrac{5}{z}=3$

In 16–18, solve the problem using three variables.

16. The perimeter of a triangle is 24 in. The sum of the lengths of the first two sides of the triangle exceeds the length of its third side by 4 in. Twice the length of the first side increased by the length of the second side is equal to twice the length of the third side. Find the lengths of the sides of the triangle.

17. Harry has a bank in which there are nickels, dimes, and quarters. In all, there are 34 coins, whose value is $3.00. The number of nickels is 6 more than the number of dimes and the number of quarters put together. Find the number of coins of each kind that are in the bank.

18. The sum of the digits of a three-digit number is 14. The units digit is equal to the sum of the hundreds digit and the tens digit. The number with the digits reversed exceeds the original number by 297. Find the original number.

7. Graphing the Solution Set of a System of Linear Inequalities in Two Variables

The solution set of a system of linear inequalities consists of all ordered pairs which are common solutions of all the inequalities of the system. Therefore, the solution set of the system is the intersection of the solution sets of all the inequalities of the system.

Procedure. To graph the solution set of a system of inequalities:
1. For each inequality, graph the related plane divider and shade the region which is the graph of the solution set of the inequality.
2. Determine the graph of the solution set of the given system by finding the region which is common to (is the intersection of) the graphs of the inequalities that were made in step 1.

~~~~~~~~~~~~~ *MODEL PROBLEMS* ~~~~~~~~~~~~~

1. Graph the solution set of the system in the coordinate plane:

$$x + y \geq 4$$
$$y \leq 2x - 5$$

Solution:

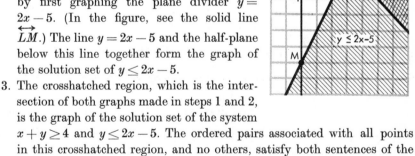

1. Transform the inequality $x + y \geq 4$ into the equivalent inequality $y \geq -x + 4$. Graph the inequality $y \geq -x + 4$ by first graphing the plane divider $y = -x + 4$. (In the figure, see the solid line $\overleftrightarrow{RS}$.) The line $y = -x + 4$ and the half-plane above this line are the graph of the solution set of $x + y \geq 4$.
2. Using the same set of axes, graph $y \leq 2x - 5$ by first graphing the plane divider $y = 2x - 5$. (In the figure, see the solid line $\overleftrightarrow{LM}$.) The line $y = 2x - 5$ and the half-plane below this line together form the graph of the solution set of $y \leq 2x - 5$.
3. The crosshatched region, which is the intersection of both graphs made in steps 1 and 2, is the graph of the solution set of the system $x + y \geq 4$ and $y \leq 2x - 5$. The ordered pairs associated with all points in this crosshatched region, and no others, satisfy both sentences of the system. For example, the point $(5, 1)$ lies in this region. Its coordinates satisfy both sentences of the system because $5 + 1 \geq 4$ is true, and $1 \leq 2(5) - 5$ is also true. The solution set of this system may be written as $\{(x, y) \mid x + y \geq 4\} \cap \{(x, y) \mid y \leq 2x - 5\}$.

2. Graph the solution set of the system in the coordinate plane:

$$3 \leq x \leq 5$$
$$|y| \geq 3$$

Solution:

1. The compound sentence $3 \leq x \leq 5$ is equivalent to $3 \leq x$ and $x \leq 5$, or $x \geq 3$ and $x \leq 5$ since $3 \leq x$ may be written as $x \geq 3$. Draw the graph of $x = 3$, which is $\overleftrightarrow{AC}$, and the graph of $x = 5$, which is $\overleftrightarrow{BD}$. The graph of $3 \leq x \leq 5$ is the rectangular region which is between $\overleftrightarrow{AC}$ and $\overleftrightarrow{BD}$ and includes these lines, the region hatched with horizontal lines.

2. The inequality $|y| \geq 3$ is equivalent to $y \geq 3$ or $y \leq -3$. Draw the graph of $y \geq 3$ and draw the graph of $y \leq -3$. The graph of $|y| \geq 3$ is those regions above the line $y = 3$, $\overleftrightarrow{AB}$, and below the line $y = -3$, $\overleftrightarrow{CD}$, which are hatched with vertical lines.

3. The graph of the solution set of the given system consists of all points in the open region that is crosshatched together with the points on the boundary lines of these regions. An example of such a point is $(4, 6)$ because $3 \leq 4 \leq 5$ is a true sentence, and $|6| \geq 3$ is also a true sentence. The solution set may be written as follows:

$$\{(x, y) \mid 3 \leq x \leq 5\} \cap \{(x, y) : |y| \geq 3\}$$

Exercises

In 1–18, graph the solution set of the system in a coordinate plane. Check one representative point in the given system.

1. $y \geq 2x$
$y \geq x + 4$

2. $y \geq 3x - 1$
$y < 3 - x$

3. $x + y > 4$
$x - y < 6$

4. $2x + 3y < 6$
$y \geq 2$

5. $x - y = 0$
$x \geq 3$

6. $2x - y - 2 > 0$
$x + y - 2 \leq 0$

7. $1 < x < 4$

8. $-1 \leq y \leq 3$

9. $-2 < x \leq 3$

10. $x < y < x + 3$

11. $x - 3 \leq y \leq x + 2$

12. $3 < y - x < 6$

13. $x + 2y \geq 4$
$|x| \geq 2$

14. $|x| \geq 1$
$|y| \leq 3$

15. $-2 < x < 3$
$y > 2x$

16. $-3 < x < 2$
$|y| \geq 2$

17. $x \leq 2$
$y \geq 2$
$x + y \geq 2$

18. $y \geq x$
$x + y - 3 \geq 0$
$x - 4 \leq 0$

CHAPTER VII

REVIEWING AND EXTENDING THE TRIGONOMETRY OF THE RIGHT TRIANGLE

1. Defining the Six Trigonometric Functions

In the figure, triangle ABC is a right triangle in which C is the right angle. $\overline{AB}$, the side opposite $\angle C$, is the **hypotenuse** of the right triangle; the length of $\overline{AB}$ is represented by c. The other two sides of $\triangle ABC$, $\overline{BC}$ and $\overline{AC}$, are called the **legs** of the triangle. We call $\overline{BC}$ the leg opposite $\angle A$; the length of $\overline{BC}$ is represented by a. We call $\overline{AC}$ the leg opposite $\angle B$; the length of $\overline{AC}$ is represented by b. We may also call $\overline{AC}$ the leg adjacent to (next to) $\angle A$. We may also call $\overline{BC}$ the leg adjacent to (next to) $\angle B$.

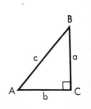

Now we will define six ratios, each of which involves two sides of the right triangle. These ratios are called **trigonometric ratios.**

For either acute angle in a right triangle:

$$\text{sine (sin) of the angle} = \frac{\text{length of leg opposite the angle}}{\text{length of hypotenuse}}$$

$$\text{cosine (cos) of the angle} = \frac{\text{length of leg adjacent to the angle}}{\text{length of hypotenuse}}$$

$$\text{tangent (tan) of the angle} = \frac{\text{length of leg opposite the angle}}{\text{length of leg adjacent to the angle}}$$

$$\text{cotangent (cot) of the angle} = \frac{\text{length of leg adjacent to the angle}}{\text{length of leg opposite the angle}}$$

$$\text{secant (sec) of the angle} = \frac{\text{length of hypotenuse}}{\text{length of leg adjacent to the angle}}$$

$$\text{cosecant (csc) of the angle} = \frac{\text{length of hypotenuse}}{\text{length of leg opposite the angle}}$$

Note. Next to the name of each ratio, we find in parentheses the abbreviation for that name.

Using these definitions, we can represent the trigonometric ratios involving acute angles A and B in right triangle ABC as follows:

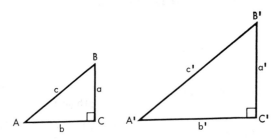

$$\sin A = \frac{a}{c} \qquad\qquad \sin B = \frac{b}{c}$$

$$\cos A = \frac{b}{c} \qquad\qquad \cos B = \frac{a}{c}$$

$$\tan A = \frac{a}{b} \qquad\qquad \tan B = \frac{b}{a}$$

$$\cot A = \frac{b}{a} \qquad\qquad \cot B = \frac{a}{b}$$

$$\sec A = \frac{c}{b} \qquad\qquad \sec B = \frac{c}{a}$$

$$\csc A = \frac{c}{a} \qquad\qquad \csc B = \frac{c}{b}$$

It might appear that each of these trigonometric ratios, for example $\sin A$, depends upon the size of the right triangle that contains $\angle A$. However, this is not the case. In the following figure, consider the two right triangles ABC and $A'B'C'$.

The lengths of the corresponding sides are different; however, $\angle A \cong \angle A'$. It follows that right triangle ABC is similar to right triangle $A'B'C'$ because they agree in two angles. Therefore, the lengths of the corresponding sides of these triangles are in proportion, giving $\dfrac{a}{c} = \dfrac{a'}{c'}$ or $\sin A = \sin A'$.

This proves that the number which is the value of $\sin A$ does not depend on the size of the right triangle which contains $\angle A$; it depends only on the measure of $\angle A$. The same reasoning is true for the five other trigonometric ratios.

Thus, with each acute angle there is associated one and only one number called the *sine*. Therefore, we have here an example of a function in which the first coordinate of every ordered pair is the measure of an acute angle and the second coordinate is the sine of that acute angle; that is, the set of ordered pairs $(A, \sin A)$ is a function. If the measure of $\angle A$ in degrees is represented by A, the domain of the function is the set of numbers between 0 and 90, $0 < A < 90$, and the range is the set of positive real numbers less than 1, $0 < \sin A < 1$. ($\sin A = \dfrac{a}{c}$ must be less than 1 because in a right triangle the hypotenuse is always greater than either leg.) Similarly, the remaining five trigonometric ratios are functions having the same domain $0 < A < 90$. These six functions—sine, cosine, tangent, cotangent, secant, and cosecant—are called **trigonometric functions.**

In future statements, the symbols $m\angle A = 50$ and $A = 50°$ will both mean "the measure of $\angle A$ is 50°."

~~~~~~~~~~~~~~~~~ **MODEL PROBLEMS** ~~~~~~~~~~~~~~~~~

1. In right triangle ABC, $a = 4$, $b = 3$, $c = 5$. Find all trigonometric functions of angle A and angle B.

Solution:

$$\sin A = \frac{a}{c} = \frac{4}{5} \qquad \sin B = \frac{b}{c} = \frac{3}{5}$$

$$\cos A = \frac{b}{c} = \frac{3}{5} \qquad \cos B = \frac{a}{c} = \frac{4}{5}$$

$$\tan A = \frac{a}{b} = \frac{4}{3} \qquad \tan B = \frac{b}{a} = \frac{3}{4}$$

$$\cot A = \frac{b}{a} = \frac{3}{4} \qquad \cot B = \frac{a}{b} = \frac{4}{3}$$

$$\sec A = \frac{c}{b} = \frac{5}{3} \qquad \sec B = \frac{c}{a} = \frac{5}{4}$$

$$\csc A = \frac{c}{a} = \frac{5}{4} \qquad \csc B = \frac{c}{b} = \frac{5}{3}$$

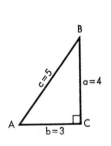

2. In right triangle RST, $\angle T = 90°$, $r = 1$, and $s = 2$. Find all trigonometric functions of $\angle R$.

Solution: In order to find all the functions of $\angle R$, it is first necessary to find the length of the hypotenuse, t.

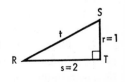

$$t^2 = r^2 + s^2$$

$$t^2 = 1 + 4$$ $\sin R = \dfrac{r}{t} = \dfrac{1}{\sqrt{5}} \cdot \dfrac{\sqrt{5}}{\sqrt{5}} = \dfrac{\sqrt{5}}{5}$ $\cot R = \dfrac{s}{r} = \dfrac{2}{1} = 2$

$$t^2 = 5$$

$$t = \sqrt{5}$$ $\cos R = \dfrac{s}{t} = \dfrac{2}{\sqrt{5}} \cdot \dfrac{\sqrt{5}}{\sqrt{5}} = \dfrac{2\sqrt{5}}{5}$ $\sec R = \dfrac{t}{s} = \dfrac{\sqrt{5}}{2}$

$\tan R = \dfrac{r}{s} = \dfrac{1}{2}$ $\csc R = \dfrac{t}{r} = \dfrac{\sqrt{5}}{1} = \sqrt{5}$

Exercises

In 1–6, find all trigonometric functions of the acute angles in the right triangles:

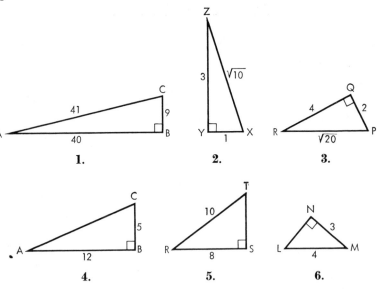

1.   2.   3.

4.   5.   6.

7. In right triangle RST, $m \angle T = 90$, $RS = 50$, and $ST = 30$. Find all the trigonometric functions of $\angle R$.

8. The three sides of a right triangle are 8, 15, 17. Find the trigonometric functions of the smaller acute angle.

9. In a right triangle, the hypotenuse is 4 and the shorter leg is 2. Find the trigonometric functions of the larger acute angle.

10. In right triangle RST, $m \angle T = 90$, $\tan S = \frac{5}{12}$, and $s = 10$. Find r.

11. In right triangle DEF, $m \angle F = 90$, $\cos D = \frac{15}{17}$, and $f = 68$. Find e.

12. In triangle ABC, $m \angle C = 90$. If $\sec A = \frac{6}{5}$ and $c = 30$, find b.

13. In triangle ABC, $m \angle C = 90$, $c = 51$, and $\sin B = \frac{8}{17}$. Find b.

2. Understanding Reciprocal Relations Among the Trigonometric Functions

We know that if the product of two numbers is 1, one of the numbers is the reciprocal of the other number. For example, since $\left(\dfrac{a}{c}\right)\left(\dfrac{c}{a}\right)=1$, then $\dfrac{a}{c}$ is the reciprocal of $\dfrac{c}{a}$, and $\dfrac{c}{a}$ is the reciprocal of $\dfrac{a}{c}$.

The trigonometric functions of A in right triangle ABC are arranged so that those functions which are reciprocals of each other are on the same line.

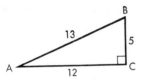

$$\sin A = \tfrac{5}{13} \qquad \csc A = \tfrac{13}{5}$$
$$\cos A = \tfrac{12}{13} \qquad \sec A = \tfrac{13}{12}$$
$$\tan A = \tfrac{5}{12} \qquad \cot A = \tfrac{12}{5}$$

In general, the six trigonometric functions of acute angle A are related reciprocally:

Since $\sin A = \dfrac{a}{c}$ and $\csc A = \dfrac{c}{a}$, then $\sin A$ and $\csc A$ are reciprocals of each other.

Since $\cos A = \dfrac{b}{c}$ and $\sec A = \dfrac{c}{b}$, $\cos A$ and $\sec A$ are reciprocals of each other.

Since $\tan A = \dfrac{a}{b}$ and $\cot A = \dfrac{b}{a}$, $\tan A$ and $\cot A$ are reciprocals of each other.

These reciprocal relationships may be expressed as follows:

$$\sin A = \frac{1}{\csc A} \qquad \csc A = \frac{1}{\sin A} \qquad \sin A \cdot \csc A = 1$$

$$\cos A = \frac{1}{\sec A} \qquad \sec A = \frac{1}{\cos A} \qquad \cos A \cdot \sec A = 1$$

$$\tan A = \frac{1}{\cot A} \qquad \cot A = \frac{1}{\tan A} \qquad \tan A \cdot \cot A = 1$$

Similar relationships may be expressed for the reciprocal functions of acute angle B.

~~~~~~~~~~~~ *MODEL PROBLEMS* ~~~~~~~~~~~~

1. If $\tan A = \frac{12}{5}$, find $\cot A$.

Solution: $\cot A$ is the reciprocal of $\tan A$.

$$\cot A = \frac{1}{\tan A} = \frac{1}{\frac{12}{5}} \text{ or}$$

$$\cot A = \frac{5}{12} \quad Ans.$$

2. If $\sin B = \frac{4}{7}$, name the trigonometric function of angle B which is equal to $\frac{7}{4}$.

Solution: Since $\frac{7}{4}$ is the reciprocal of $\frac{4}{7}$, the required function of angle B must be the reciprocal of $\sin B$, or $\csc B$. *Ans.*

~~~~~~

Exercises

In 1–6, find the value of the indicated function.

1. $\sin A = \frac{3}{5}$; $\csc A = ?$ **2.** $\tan B = \frac{2}{3}$; $\cot B = ?$

3. $\cos A = \frac{1}{4}$; $\sec A = ?$ **4.** $\sec A = \frac{13}{5}$; $\cos A = ?$

5. $\tan B = .3$; $\cot B = ?$ **6.** $\sec C = 1.6$; $\cos C = ?$

In 7–9, state the proper acute angle, or the proper trigonometric function, that can replace the question mark and make the resulting statement true.

7. $\sin 30° = \dfrac{1}{\csc (?)}$ **8.** $\cos 47° = \dfrac{1}{(?) \, 47°}$ **9.** $\tan 85° = \dfrac{1}{(?) \, 85°}$

In 10–15, without the use of tables, find the product.

10. $\sin 30° \cdot \csc 30°$ **11.** $\cos 45° \cdot \sec 45°$ **12.** $\tan 60° \cdot \cot 60°$

13. $\frac{1}{2} \sec 50° \cdot \cos 50°$ **14.** $10 \cot 22° \cdot \tan 22°$ **15.** $m \cdot \cos 74° \cdot \sec 74°$

In 16 and 17, state a trigonometric function of an acute angle which can replace the question mark and make the resulting statement true.

16. $\sin 45° \cdot (?) = 1$ **17.** $\tan 52° \cdot (?) = 1$

18. Express $\sec 45°$ in terms of $\cos 45°$.

19. Express $\csc 60°$ in terms of $\sin 60°$.

20. Express $\tan 35°$ in terms of $\cot 35°$.

21. If $\cos A \cdot \sec A = 1$, solve for $\sec A$ in terms of $\cos A$.

22. If $\tan A \cdot \cot A = 1$, express $\cot A$ in terms of $\tan A$.

3. Relating the Trigonometric Functions of Complementary Angles: Cofunctions

By prefixing *co-* to the sine, tangent, and secant, we obtain their respective cofunctions; namely, *co*sine, *co*tangent, and *co*secant. The pairs of cofunctions are (1) sine and cosine, (2) tangent and cotangent, and (3) secant and cosecant.

The relationships among the cofunctions may be seen by arranging the 12 functions of the acute angles of any right triangle as follows:

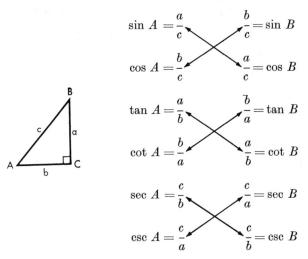

$$\sin A = \frac{a}{c} \qquad \frac{b}{c} = \sin B$$

$$\cos A = \frac{b}{c} \qquad \frac{a}{c} = \cos B$$

$$\tan A = \frac{a}{b} \qquad \frac{b}{a} = \tan B$$

$$\cot A = \frac{b}{a} \qquad \frac{a}{b} = \cot B$$

$$\sec A = \frac{c}{b} \qquad \frac{c}{a} = \sec B$$

$$\csc A = \frac{c}{a} \qquad \frac{c}{b} = \csc B$$

Notice that the arrows are used to join equal functions. These relationships lead to the following principle:

Principle 1. Any trigonometric function of an acute angle is equal to the cofunction of its complementary angle.

$$\text{Thus, if } A + B = 90°,$$
$$\sin A = \cos B \text{ and } \cos A = \sin B$$
$$\tan A = \cot B \text{ and } \cot A = \tan B$$
$$\sec A = \csc B \text{ and } \csc A = \sec B$$

If B is replaced by $(90° - A)$, we obtain
$$\sin A = \cos (90° - A) \text{ and } \cos A = \sin (90° - A)$$
$$\tan A = \cot (90° - A) \text{ and } \cot A = \tan (90° - A)$$
$$\sec A = \csc (90° - A) \text{ and } \csc A = \sec (90° - A)$$

Originally, " cofunction " was called " complement's function." The first use of " cosine A " was as " complement's sine A," which meant "the sine of the complement of A." Later " complement's sine A " was changed to " co-sine A " and finally to the modern form " cosine A."

On page 259, we shall see how the use of the cofunction rules makes possible the reduction of trigonometric tables to half-size.

Principle 2. If a function of one acute angle is equal to its cofunction of another acute angle, then these angles are complementary.

Thus, if $2A$ and $7A$ are acute angles and $\sin 2A = \cos 7A$, then $2A + 7A = 90°$.

MODEL PROBLEMS

1. Express $\sin 75°$ as a function of an acute angle less than $45°$.

   Solution: The complement of $75° = 90° - 75° = 15°$.
   Since a function of an acute angle is equal to the cofunction of its complementary acute angle, we get $\sin 75° = \cos 15°$. *Ans.*

2. If A and $(A + 30°)$ are acute angles and $\tan A = \cot (A + 30°)$, find the degree measure of angle A.

   Solution: If a function of an acute angle is equal to the cofunction of another acute angle, the two angles are complementary.
   Since $\tan A = \cot (A + 30°)$, $A + (A + 30) = 90$
   $$2A + 30 = 90$$
   $$2A = 60$$
   $$A = 30, m \angle A = 30 \quad Ans.$$

Exercises

In 1–9, find the degree measure of the missing acute angles.

1. $\sin 18° = \cos (?)$ **2.** $\tan 73° = \cot (?)$ **3.** $\sec 40° = \csc (?)$
4. $\cos 36° = \sin (?)$ **5.** $\csc 80° = \sec (?)$ **6.** $\cot 24° = \tan (?)$
7. $\tan 25° 30' = \cot (?)$ **8.** $\cos 64° 40' = \sin (?)$ **9.** $\sec 85° 15' = \csc (?)$

In 10–14, name the missing function.

10. $\tan 40° = \underline{\quad}50°$ **11.** $\sec 25° = \underline{\quad}65°$ **12.** $\csc 52° = \underline{\quad}38°$
13. $\sec 34° 30' = \underline{\quad}55° 30'$ **14.** $\cos 81° 32' = \underline{\quad}8° 28'$

In 15–24, express the given function of the acute angle as a function of its complementary angle.

15. $\sin 37°$ **16.** $\tan 84°$ **17.** $\cos 12°$ **18.** $\sec 65°$ **19.** $\cot 59°$
20. $\csc 73°$ **21.** $\sin 18° 20'$ **22.** $\cot 55° 35'$ **23.** $\tan x°$ **24.** $\csc y°$

In 25–32, express the given function of the acute angle as a function of an angle whose measure is less than $45°$.

25. $\sin 50°$ **26.** $\cos 68°$ **27.** $\csc 48°$ **28.** $\tan 85°$
29. $\sin 59° 30'$ **30.** $\csc 68° 50'$ **31.** $\cos 64° 27'$ **32.** $\sec 80° 44'$

In 33–36, find the number of degrees in acute angle B. All angles in this group are acute angles.

33. $\sin B = \cos B$ **34.** $\sec 4B = \csc 5B$

35. $\tan \frac{1}{2}B = \cot \frac{3}{2}B$ **36.** $\cot (3B + 20°) = \tan (2B - 30°)$

37. Express $\tan 75°$ as a function of $15°$.

38. Find the number of degrees in the acute angle A if $\cos A = \sin 23°$.

39. If $\cos A = \sin B$, then (1) $A = 90° - B$ (2) $A = 90° + B$ (3) $A = 180° - B$

40. A, B, and C are the angles of any triangle, is the expression $\sin \frac{1}{2}A = \cos \frac{1}{2}(B + C)$ true? (Answer *yes* or *no*.) Why?

41. Find the degree measure of acute angle x if $\sin 3x = \cos 54°$.

42. In triangle ABC, if $\sin A = x$ and if $\cos B = x$, then the angle $(A + B)$ is (1) acute   (2) right   (3) obtuse

4. Understanding the Changes in the Trigonometric Functions of Acute Angles

Mathematicians have computed the values of the trigonometric functions of positive acute angles as decimals correct to four decimal places. These have been listed in tables.

The principle—*the function of any acute angle equals the cofunction of its complementary angle*—makes it possible to reduce trigonometric tables to half-size. One value may be used for sin 1° and cos 89°, for tan 2° and cot 88°, or for any cofunctions when the angles are complementary. Therefore, tables such as the one on the following page may be constructed with the cofunctions on the top and bottom of the table and the complementary angles on the left and right sides of the table. Notice how this is done in the following shortened diagram of the table. The values of the functions have been omitted for the sake of simplicity.

	sin	cos	tan	cot	sec	csc	
1°							89°
2°							88°
44°							46°
45°							45°
	cos	sin	cot	tan	csc	sec	

To use the following table, *follow the arrows.* Functions at the top of the table must be used with the degrees to the left, while functions at the bottom are to be used only with the degrees to the right.

Notice that the *total of the number of degrees to the left and to the right in any horizontal row is* 90°, making the angles involved complementary.

The *functions at the top and bottom of any vertical column are cofunctions.*

TABLE OF FUNCTIONS OF ACUTE ANGLES

	sin	cos	tan	cot	sec	csc	
1°	.0175	.9998	.0175	57.2900	1.0002	57.2987	89°
2°	.0349	.9994	.0349	28.6363	1.0006	28.6537	88°
3°	.0523	.9986	.0524	19.0811	1.0014	19.1073	87°
4°	.0698	.9976	.0699	14.3007	1.0024	14.3356	86°
5°	.0872	.9962	.0875	11.4301	1.0038	11.4737	85°
6°	.1045	.9945	.1051	9.5144	1.0055	9.5668	84°
7°	.1219	.9925	.1228	8.1443	1.0075	8.2055	83°
8°	.1392	.9903	.1405	7.1154	1.0098	7.1853	82°
9°	.1564	.9877	.1584	6.3138	1.0125	6.3925	81°
10°	.1736	.9848	.1763	5.6713	1.0154	5.7588	80°
11°	.1908	.9816	.1944	5.1446	1.0187	5.2408	79°
12°	.2079	.9781	.2126	4.7046	1.0223	4.8097	78°
13°	.2250	.9744	.2309	4.3315	1.0263	4.4454	77°
14°	.2419	.9703	.2493	4.0108	1.0306	4.1336	76°
15°	.2588	.9659	.2679	3.7321	1.0353	3.8637	75°
16°	.2756	.9613	.2867	3.4874	1.0403	3.6280	74°
17°	.2924	.9563	.3057	3.2709	1.0457	3.4203	73°
18°	.3090	.9511	.3249	3.0777	1.0515	3.2361	72°
19°	.3256	.9455	.3443	2.9042	1.0576	3.0716	71°
20°	.3420	.9397	.3640	2.7475	1.0642	2.9238	70°
21°	.3584	.9336	.3839	2.6051	1.0711	2.7904	69°
22°	.3746	.9272	.4040	2.4751	1.0785	2.6695	68°
23°	.3907	.9205	.4245	2.3559	1.0864	2.5593	67°
24°	.4067	.9135	.4452	2.2460	1.0946	2.4586	66°
25°	.4226	.9063	.4663	2.1445	1.1034	2.3662	65°
26°	.4384	.8988	.4877	2.0503	1.1126	2.2812	64°
27°	.4540	.8910	.5095	1.9626	1.1223	2.2027	63°
28°	.4695	.8829	.5317	1.8807	1.1326	2.1301	62°
29°	.4848	.8746	.5543	1.8040	1.1434	2.0627	61°
30°	.5000	.8660	.5774	1.7321	1.1547	2.0000	60°
31°	.5150	.8572	.6009	1.6643	1.1666	1.9416	59°
32°	.5299	.8480	.6249	1.6003	1.1792	1.8871	58°
33°	.5446	.8387	.6494	1.5399	1.1924	1.8361	57°
34°	.5592	.8290	.6745	1.4826	1.2062	1.7883	56°
35°	.5736	.8192	.7002	1.4281	1.2208	1.7434	55°
36°	.5878	.8090	.7265	1.3764	1.2361	1.7013	54°
37°	.6018	.7986	.7536	1.3270	1.2521	1.6616	53°
38°	.6157	.7880	.7813	1.2799	1.2690	1.6243	52°
39°	.6293	.7771	.8098	1.2349	1.2868	1.5890	51°
40°	.6428	.7660	.8391	1.1918	1.3054	1.5557	50°
41°	.6561	.7547	.8693	1.1504	1.3250	1.5243	49°
42°	.6691	.7431	.9004	1.1106	1.3456	1.4945	48°
43°	.6820	.7314	.9325	1.0724	1.3673	1.4663	47°
44°	.6947	.7193	.9657	1.0355	1.3902	1.4396	46°
45°	.7071	.7071	1.0000	1.0000	1.4142	1.4142	45°
	cos	sin	cot	tan	csc	sec	

Reference to the table will show that .5736 represents both sin 35° and cos 55°. Similarly, any other numerical value in the body of the table represents both the function of an angle and the cofunction of its complementary angle.

CHANGES IN THE SAME SENSE AND IN THE OPPOSITE SENSE

Two varying quantities are said to *change in the same sense* if when one quantity increases, the other increases; and also, if when one quantity decreases, the other decreases.

Principle 1. An acute angle and the sine of the angle change in the same sense. This also is true for an acute angle and its tangent, and for an acute angle and its secant.

Two varying quantities are said to *change in the opposite sense* if when one quantity increases, the other decreases; and also, if when one quantity decreases, the other increases.

Principle 2. An acute angle and the cosine of the angle change in the opposite sense. This is also true for an acute angle and its cotangent, and for an acute angle and its cosecant.

KEEP IN MIND

As an acute angle changes:
1. The functions that change in the same sense are its sine, tangent, and secant.
2. The functions that change in the opposite sense are its functions whose names begin with *co*, that is, its cosine, cotangent, and cosecant.

Exercises

In 1–4, give the function value as a four-place decimal. Use the table on page 260.

1. sin 20°   **2.** tan 8°   **3.** sin 49°   **4.** sec 61°

In 5–10, state the change in the function values as angle A increases from 0° to 90°.

5. sin A **6.** cos A **7.** tan A **8.** cot A **9.** sec A **10.** csc A

In 11–16, state the change in the function values as angle A decreases from 90° to 0°.

11. sin A **12.** cos A **13.** tan A **14.** cot A **15.** sec A **16.** csc A

17. Which functions of angle B increase as B increases from $0°$ to $90°$?

18. Which functions of angle D decrease as D increases from $0°$ to $90°$?

19. As angle A changes from $0°$ to $90°$, what number is sin A approaching?

20. Explain why sin A is less than 1 if A is an acute angle.

21. Explain why cos A is less than 1 if A is an acute angle.

22. Explain why tan A is less than 1 when A is less than $45°$.

23. Explain why tan A is greater than 1 when A is greater than $45°$.

24. Explain why sin A is less than tan A when A is an acute angle.

25. Which of the following numbers cannot be the value of cos A?

$$\tfrac{3}{5}, \tfrac{5}{3}, .9, \sqrt{2}, \tfrac{1}{2}\sqrt{2}$$

26. Which of the following numbers can be the value of sec A?

$$6, \tfrac{1}{6}, \tfrac{3}{4}, \tfrac{4}{3}, \sqrt{2}, .25, 2.5$$

27. If acute angle B is twice acute angle A, then sin B is always twice sin A. (Answer *true* or *false*.)

28. As x increases from $0°$ to $90°$, the function sin x + cos x (1) increases and then decreases (2) decreases and then increases (3) remains the same

5. Finding the Measure of an Angle, Correct to the Nearest Degree, When a Function Value Is Given

If we know a function value of a positive acute angle, we can find the measure of the angle, correct to the nearest degree, by using the table on page 260. See how this is done in the model problem.

MODEL PROBLEM

If sin A = .2182, find the degree measure of positive acute angle A, correct to the nearest degree.

Solution:

In the Table of Functions of Acute Angles on page 260, if we search in the sine column for the value .2182, we find that it is not there. However, we find that the two closest values in the table between which .2182 lies are .2079, which is sin $12°$, and .2250, which is sin $13°$. As shown in the table, the difference between sin A and sin $12°$ is .0103 and the difference

Angle	Sine	Difference
13°	.2250	
		.0068
A	.2182	
		.0103
12°	.2079	

between sin 13° and sin A is .0068. Since .0068 is less than .0103, sin A is closer to sin 13° than it is to sin 12°. Therefore, we say that angle A is closer to 13° than it is to 12°.

Answer: $m \angle A = 13$, correct to the nearest degree.

~~~~~~

Exercises

In 1–12, use the table on page 260 to find the degree measure of positive acute angle A if:

1. sin $A = .4226$ **2.** cos $A = .9511$ **3.** tan $A = .7536$

4. cot $A = 1.4281$ **5.** sec $A = 1.0038$ **6.** csc $A = 4.1336$

7. sin $A = .7431$ **8.** cos $A = .3090$ **9.** tan $A = 2.9042$

10. cot $A = .5317$ **11.** sec $A = 6.3925$ **12.** csc $A = 1.2521$

In 13–24, use the table on page 260 to find the degree measure of positive acute angle A to the nearest degree if:

13. sin $A = .6025$ **14.** cos $A = .0775$ **15.** tan $A = .4668$

16. cot $A = 7.1280$ **17.** sec $A = 1.0550$ **18.** csc $A = 1.4812$

19. sin $A = .9416$ **20.** cos $A = .1123$ **21.** tan $A = 8.2557$

22. cot $A = .4372$ **23.** sec $A = 1.6824$ **24.** csc $A = 1.0110$

6. Fundamental Trigonometric Identities: Reciprocal, Quotient, and Pythagorean Relations

We have learned that an equation which becomes a true statement for all values of the variable over the domain of the variable (that is, the values for which the functions are defined) is called an *identity*. Examples of identities are $2x + 3x = 5x$ and $\dfrac{1 - x^2}{1 - x} = 1 + x, (x \neq 1)$.

Identities which involve trigonometric functions are called **trigonometric identities.** Examples of trigonometric identities are $2 \sin x + 3 \sin x = 5 \sin x$ and $\dfrac{1 - \sin^2 x}{1 - \sin x} = 1 + \sin x$, (sin $x \neq 1$). The symbol $\sin^2 x$, read "sine-squared x" or "sine-square of x" means (sin x) $\cdot$ (sin x) or (sin x)^2. Likewise, $\cos^2 x$ means (cos x) $\cdot$ (cos x) or (cos x)^2.

In contrast, a **conditional equation** is an equation which becomes a true statement for at least one but not for every value of the variable over the domain of the variable. Examples of algebraic conditional equations are $3x + x = 2$ and $\dfrac{1 - x^2}{1 - x} = 1, (x \neq 1)$. Examples of conditional trigonometric equations

264   Algebra Two and Trigonometry

are $3 \sin x + \sin x = 2$ and $\dfrac{1 - \sin^2 x}{1 - \sin x} = 1$, $(\sin x \neq 1)$. Later, we will learn how

to find the solution sets of conditional trigonometric equations.

We will now show that the following equations are true for all values of the angle involved for which the functions are defined. These trigonometric identities are so important that they are referred to as the *fundamental trigonometric identities.* By means of them, we can solve many trigonometric problems and derive many other relationships.

To establish these fundamental identities, we consider $\angle A$ as an acute angle in right triangle ABC.

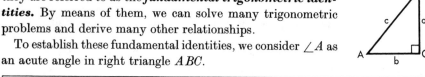

Reciprocal Identities		
$\sin A = \dfrac{1}{\csc A}$	$\csc A = \dfrac{1}{\sin A}$	$\sin A \cdot \csc A = 1$
$\cos A = \dfrac{1}{\sec A}$	$\sec A = \dfrac{1}{\cos A}$	$\cos A \cdot \sec A = 1$
$\tan A = \dfrac{1}{\cot A}$	$\cot A = \dfrac{1}{\tan A}$	$\tan A \cdot \cot A = 1$

Quotient Identities	Pythagorean Identities
$\tan A = \dfrac{\sin A}{\cos A}$	$\sin^2 A + \cos^2 A = 1$
$\cot A = \dfrac{\cos A}{\sin A}$	$\tan^2 A + 1 = \sec^2 A$
	$\cot^2 A + 1 = \csc^2 A$

PROOF OF RECIPROCAL IDENTITIES

The proofs of these identities have already been shown on page 255.

PROOF OF QUOTIENT IDENTITIES

Prove: $\tan A = \dfrac{\sin A}{\cos A}$

By definition, $\sin A = \dfrac{a}{c}$, $\cos A = \dfrac{b}{c}$, and $\tan A = \dfrac{a}{b}$.

Hence, $\dfrac{\sin A}{\cos A} = \dfrac{a}{c} \div \dfrac{b}{c} = \dfrac{a}{c} \cdot \dfrac{c}{b} = \dfrac{a}{b}$.   Therefore, $\dfrac{\sin A}{\cos A} = \tan A$.

Prove: $\cot A = \dfrac{\cos A}{\sin A}$

By definition, $\cos A = \dfrac{b}{c}$, $\sin A = \dfrac{a}{c}$, and $\cot A = \dfrac{b}{a}$.

Hence, $\dfrac{\cos A}{\sin A} = \dfrac{b}{c} \div \dfrac{a}{c} = \dfrac{b}{c} \cdot \dfrac{c}{a} = \dfrac{b}{a}$.   Therefore, $\dfrac{\cos A}{\sin A} = \cot A$.

PROOF OF PYTHAGOREAN IDENTITIES

Prove:

(a) $\sin^2 A + \cos^2 A = 1$ (b) $\tan^2 A + 1 = \sec^2 A$ (c) $\cot^2 A + 1 = \csc^2 A$

Proof

In rt. $\triangle ABC$,

$$a^2 + b^2 = c^2$$

$D_{c^2}: \dfrac{a^2}{c^2} + \dfrac{b^2}{c^2} = \dfrac{c^2}{c^2}$

$\left(\dfrac{a}{c}\right)^2 + \left(\dfrac{b}{c}\right)^2 = 1$

$\dfrac{a}{c} = \sin A, \dfrac{b}{c} = \cos A$

Hence,

$$\sin^2 A + \cos^2 A = 1$$

Proof

In rt. $\triangle ABC$,

$$a^2 + b^2 = c^2$$

$D_{b^2}: \dfrac{a^2}{b^2} + \dfrac{b^2}{b^2} = \dfrac{c^2}{b^2}$

$\left(\dfrac{a}{b}\right)^2 + 1 = \left(\dfrac{c}{b}\right)^2$

$\dfrac{a}{b} = \tan A, \dfrac{c}{b} = \sec A$

Hence,

$$\tan^2 A + 1 = \sec^2 A$$

Proof

In rt. $\triangle ABC$,

$$a^2 + b^2 = c^2$$

$D_{a^2}: \dfrac{a^2}{a^2} + \dfrac{b^2}{a^2} = \dfrac{c^2}{a^2}$

$1 + \left(\dfrac{b}{a}\right)^2 = \left(\dfrac{c}{a}\right)^2$

$\dfrac{b}{a} = \cot A, \dfrac{c}{a} = \csc A$

Hence,

$$1 + \cot^2 A = \csc^2 A$$

$$\text{or } \cot^2 A + 1 = \csc^2 A$$

Exercises

In 1 and 2, show that the equation is true if $\angle A$ is an angle in right triangle ABC in which $C = 90°$, $a = 3$, $b = 4$, and $c = 5$.

1. $\sin^2 A + \cos^2 A = 1$ **2.** $\tan A = \dfrac{\sin A}{\cos A}$

In 3–6, show that the equation is true if $\angle A$ is an angle in right triangle ABC in which $C = 90°$, $a = 5$, $b = 12$, and $c = 13$.

3. $\sin A = \tan A \cos A$ **4.** $\sin A \cdot \csc A = 1$

5. $\cot^2 A + 1 = \csc^2 A$ **6.** $\cos A \cdot \sec A = 1$

In 7 and 8, verify the identity when $\angle A$ is an angle in right triangle ABC in which $C = 90°$, $a = 1$, $b = 1$, and $c = \sqrt{2}$.

7. $\sin A = \dfrac{\cos A}{\cot A}$ **8.** $\cos A = \dfrac{\sin A}{\tan A}$

In 9 and 10, verify the identity when $\angle A$ is an angle in right triangle ABC in which $C = 90°$, $a = 1$, $b = \sqrt{3}$, and $c = 2$.

9. $\cot A = \cos A \csc A$ **10.** $\tan A \cdot \cos A \cdot \csc A = 1$

7. Trigonometric Functions of 30°, 45°, and 60°

The values of the trigonometric functions of most angles are irrational numbers whose decimal approximations have been computed by mathematicians and have been listed in tables. However, the values of the trigonometric functions of 30°, 45°, and 60°, values that we will make use of often, can be determined without the use of tables by applying geometric principles that should be familiar to us.

TRIGONOMETRIC FUNCTIONS OF 45°

In isosceles right triangle ABC, with $C = 90°$, let $a = 1$ unit and $b = 1$ unit. Then acute angles A and B have equal measures, each being 45°. Since $c^2 = a^2 + b^2$, $c^2 = 1 + 1 = 2$, or $c = \sqrt{2}$ units. The functions of a 45° angle can now be expressed by applying their definitions in the 45°, 45°, 90° triangle.

$\sin 45° = \dfrac{1}{\sqrt{2}} = \tfrac{1}{2}\sqrt{2}$ $\csc 45° = \dfrac{\sqrt{2}}{1} = \sqrt{2}$

$\cos 45° = \dfrac{1}{\sqrt{2}} = \tfrac{1}{2}\sqrt{2}$ $\sec 45° = \dfrac{\sqrt{2}}{1} = \sqrt{2}$

$\tan 45° = \dfrac{1}{1} = 1$ $\cot 45° = \dfrac{1}{1} = 1$

TRIGONOMETRIC FUNCTIONS OF 30° AND 60°

In right triangle ABC, $m \angle C = 90$, $m \angle A = 30$, and $m \angle B = 60$. Since in a 30°, 60°, 90° triangle, the side opposite the 30° angle is equal to one-half the hypotenuse, $a = \frac{1}{2}c$. If we let $c = 2$ units, then $a = 1$ unit. Since $b^2 = c^2 - a^2$, $b^2 = 4 - 1 = 3$, or $b = \sqrt{3}$ units. The trigonometric functions of a 30° angle and a 60° angle can now be expressed through the use of the 30°, 60°, 90° triangle.

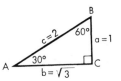

$$\sin 30° = \frac{1}{2} = \cos 60° \qquad\qquad \csc 30° = \frac{2}{1} = 2 = \sec 60°$$

$$\cos 30° = \frac{\sqrt{3}}{2} = \sin 60° \qquad\qquad \sec 30° = \frac{2}{\sqrt{3}} = \frac{2\sqrt{3}}{3} = \csc 60°$$

$$\tan 30° = \frac{1}{\sqrt{3}} = \frac{\sqrt{3}}{3} = \cot 60° \qquad\qquad \cot 30° = \frac{\sqrt{3}}{1} = \sqrt{3} = \tan 60°$$

Summary of Values for Trigonometric Functions of 30°, 45°, and 60°

	30°	45°	60°
sin	$\frac{1}{2}$	$\frac{1}{2}\sqrt{2}$	$\frac{1}{2}\sqrt{3}$
cos	$\frac{1}{2}\sqrt{3}$	$\frac{1}{2}\sqrt{2}$	$\frac{1}{2}$
tan	$\frac{1}{3}\sqrt{3}$	1	$\sqrt{3}$
cot	$\sqrt{3}$	1	$\frac{1}{3}\sqrt{3}$
sec	$\frac{2}{3}\sqrt{3}$	$\sqrt{2}$	2
csc	2	$\sqrt{2}$	$\frac{2}{3}\sqrt{3}$

~~~~~~~~~~ *MODEL PROBLEMS* ~~~~~~~~~~

1. Show that the numerical value of $\sin^2 x + \cos^2 x$ is 1 when $x = 30°$.

Solution: When $x = 30°$, $\sin x = \frac{1}{2}$ and $\cos x = \frac{1}{2}\sqrt{3}$.

$$\sin^2 x + \cos^2 x = (\tfrac{1}{2})^2 + (\tfrac{1}{2}\sqrt{3})^2$$
$$\sin^2 x + \cos^2 x = \tfrac{1}{4} + \tfrac{3}{4}$$
$$\sin^2 x + \cos^2 x = 1 \quad Ans.$$

2. Find acute angle x when $2 \cos x - \sqrt{2} = 0$.

Solution: $2 \cos x - \sqrt{2} = 0$

$2 \cos x = \sqrt{2}$ Adding $\sqrt{2}$ to both sides.

$\cos x = \frac{1}{2}\sqrt{2}$ Dividing both sides by 2.

Hence, x must be the angle whose cosine is $\frac{1}{2}\sqrt{2}$. Therefore,

$$x = 45° \quad Ans.$$

3. Find acute angle x when $4 \cos^2 x = 1$.

Solution: $4 \cos^2 x = 1$

$\cos^2 x = \frac{1}{4}$ Dividing both sides by 4.

$\cos x = \pm\frac{1}{2}$ Taking the square root of both sides.

Hence, x, being an acute angle, must be the angle whose cosine is $\frac{1}{2}$. Thus,

$$x = 60° \quad Ans.$$

Exercises

In 1–10, find the numerical value of the expression. (Leave each answer in radical form.)

1. $\sec 60° + \tan 45°$

2. $\tan 60° - \sec 30°$

3. $\sin 30° \sec 30°$

4. $2 \cos 30° + 3 \csc 60°$

5. $(\tan 45° + \sec 60°) \cot 60°$

6. $(\csc 30° - \tan 60°)^2$

7. $\dfrac{\cot 45°}{\tan 45°}$

8. $\dfrac{\cos 45°}{\cos 60°}$

9. $\dfrac{\sqrt{3} \tan 30°}{\sec 60°}$

10. $\dfrac{10 \sin 60°}{\sin 30°}$

11. If $x = 45°$, find the value of $\sec^2 x - \tan^2 x$.

12. If $x = 30°$, show that $2 \sin x - 1 = 0$.

13. If $x = 30°$, show that $6 \sin^2 x + 7 \sin x = 5$.

14. If $x = 30°$, show that $\cos 2x = 2 \cos^2 x - 1$.

In 15–20, find the degree measure of acute angle x.

15. $\cos x = \frac{1}{2}$

16. $\sin x = \frac{1}{2}\sqrt{2}$

17. $\tan x = \sqrt{3}$

18. $\cos x = \frac{1}{2}\sqrt{3}$

19. $2 \sin x - 1 = 0$

20. $\tan x - 1 = 0$

8. Finding All the Trigonometric Functions of an Acute Angle When the Value of One of Them Is Given

~~~~~~~~~~~~~ *MODEL PROBLEM* ~~~~~~~~~~~~~

If $\cos P = \frac{3}{4}$, find all other functions of acute angle P.

Solution: Since $\cos P = \frac{3}{4}$ and $\cos P = \dfrac{\text{adjacent leg}}{\text{hypotenuse}}$, we may place acute angle P in a right triangle PQR in which q (the leg adjacent to $\angle P$) $= 3$ and whose hypotenuse $r = 4$. We now can find p.

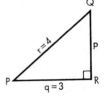

$$p^2 + q^2 = r^2$$

$$p^2 + 3^2 = 4^2$$

$$p^2 = 7$$

$$p = \sqrt{7}$$

Hence, $\sin P = \dfrac{\sqrt{7}}{4}$

$\cos P = \dfrac{3}{4}$

$\tan P = \dfrac{\sqrt{7}}{3}$

$\csc P = \dfrac{4}{\sqrt{7}} \cdot \dfrac{\sqrt{7}}{\sqrt{7}} = \dfrac{4\sqrt{7}}{7}$

$\sec P = \dfrac{4}{3}$

$\cot P = \dfrac{3}{\sqrt{7}} \cdot \dfrac{\sqrt{7}}{\sqrt{7}} = \dfrac{3\sqrt{7}}{7}$

Exercises

In 1–9, find the values of all the other functions of the given acute angle.

1. $\sin A = \frac{3}{5}$ **2.** $\tan P = \frac{5}{12}$ **3.** $\csc B = \frac{17}{8}$

4. $\cos A = \frac{2}{3}$ **5.** $\cot R = 2$ **6.** $\sec M = 3$

7. $\sin A = .8$ **8.** $\cot B = \sqrt{3}$ **9.** $\cos C = \frac{1}{2}\sqrt{2}$

10. If $\angle A$ is a positive acute angle and $\sec A = \frac{17}{8}$, find $\tan A$.

In 11–16, $\angle A$ and $\angle B$ are positive acute angles and $\sin A = \frac{3}{5}$ and $\tan B = \frac{5}{12}$. Find the value of the expression.

11. $\cos A + \cot B$ **12.** $\csc B - \sin A$ **13.** $\tan A + \sec B$

14. $\sin A \cdot \cos B$ **15.** $\sin B \cdot \cos A$ **16.** $1 - \tan A \cdot \tan B$

9. Finding a Trigonometric Function of an Acute Angle Measured in Degrees and Minutes

On pages 760–764, the table "Values of Trigonometric Functions" gives the values of the trigonometric functions of angles whose measures are from $0°$ to $90°$ in intervals of 10 minutes, $10'$. Remember that $1° = 60'$. These tables are used in the same way as the table on page 260. Thus, sin 25° 30′ = .4305.

To find a trigonometric function of a positive acute angle whose measure is not a multiple of 10′, we may use a method of approximation, called *linear interpolation.* We shall learn later that the graphs of trigonometric functions approximate a straight line within small intervals such as 10-minute intervals. The process of interpolation which we use is based on the following principles:

Principle 1. As an acute angle changes, the functions that change in the same sense are its sine, tangent, and secant. On the other hand, as an acute angle changes, the functions that change in the opposite sense are its cofunctions, that is, its cosine, cotangent, and cosecant.

Principle 2. For small changes of 10′ or less in an angle, the differences of corresponding values for the angle and its functions are approximately in proportion.

In taking differences, the computation is greatly simplified if the common units of minutes for the angle and ten-thousandths for the functions of the angle are not written in the ratios of the corresponding differences. In the process of finding the ratio of two quantities which have a common unit, the unit may be eliminated.

〰〰〰〰〰 **MODEL PROBLEMS** 〰〰〰〰〰

1. Find sin 25° 36′.

Solution:

1. Since 25° 36′ lies between 25° 30′ and 25° 40′, sin 25° 36′ lies between sin 25° 30′ and sin 25° 40′. Arrange these values in the following tabular form. Place the larger decimal at the top of the table to make subtraction more convenient. Let $x =$ the difference between sin 25° 30′ and sin 25° 36′. Then .4305 + $x =$ sin 25° 36′.

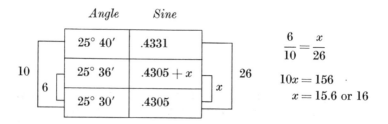

$$\frac{6}{10} = \frac{x}{26}$$
$$10x = 156$$
$$x = 15.6 \text{ or } 16$$

2. Find the corresponding differences as shown in the table.

3. Write and then solve the proportion involving these corresponding differences. Omit minutes and decimals in writing the proportion.

4. Since x is 16, correct to the nearest integer,

$$\sin 25° \ 36' = .4305 + .0016 \text{ or } .4321$$

5. *Check* to see that $\sin 25° \ 36'$ is larger than $\sin 25° \ 30'$ and smaller than $\sin 25° \ 40$. Make sure that the angle and its sine value change in the same sense.

Answer: $\sin 25° \ 36' = .4321$

2. Find $\cot 58° \ 53'$.
Solution:
1. Since $58° \ 53'$ lies between $58° \ 50'$ and $59°$ or $58° \ 60'$, $\cot 58° \ 53'$ lies between $\cot 58° \ 50'$ and $\cot 58° \ 60'$. Arrange these values in the following tabular form. Place the larger angle at the bottom of the table to simplify the subtracting of cotangent values. Let $x =$ the difference between $\cot 58° \ 60'$ and $\cot 58° \ 53'$. Then $.6009 + x = \cot 58° \ 53'$.

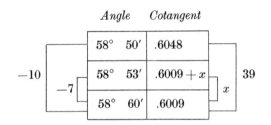

$$\frac{-7}{-10} = \frac{x}{39}$$

$$\frac{7}{10} = \frac{x}{39}$$

$$10x = 273$$

$$x = 27.3 \text{ or } 27$$

2. Find the corresponding differences as shown in the table.
3. Write and then solve the proportion involving these corresponding differences.
4. Since $x = 27$, correct to the nearest integer,

$$\cot 58° \ 53' = .6009 + .0027 = .6036$$

5. *Check* to see that $\cot 58° \ 53'$ is larger than $\cot 58° \ 60'$ and smaller than $\cot 58° \ 50'$. Make sure that the angle and its cotangent value change in the opposite sense.

Answer: $\cot 58° \ 53' = .6036$

Exercises

In 1–24, give the function value as a four-place decimal.
1. $\sin 35° \ 20'$ **2.** $\tan 56° \ 10'$ **3.** $\cos 18° \ 50'$ **4.** $\cot 64° \ 40'$
5. $\sin 33° \ 18'$ **6.** $\sin 39° \ 16'$ **7.** $\sin 48° \ 12'$ **8.** $\tan 18° \ 25'$

9. tan 31° 24′	**10.** tan 66° 36′	**11.** cos 22° 14′	**12.** cos 75° 34′
13. cos 50° 43′	**14.** cot 33° 24′	**15.** cot 41° 38′	**16.** cot 52° 16′
17. sin 65° 03′	**18.** cos 71° 08′	**19.** tan 85° 05′	**20.** cot 57° 06′
21. sin 26° 54′	**22.** cos 18° 57′	**23.** tan 68° 52′	**24.** cot 53° 56′

10. Finding the Measure of an Angle, Correct to the Nearest Minute, When a Function Value Is Given

In this unit, use the table "Values of Trigonometric Functions" appearing on pages 760–764.

~~~~~~~~~~ *MODEL PROBLEMS* ~~~~~~~~~~

1. Find, correct to the nearest minute, the degree measure of the positive acute angle whose tangent is 1.1880.

Solution:

1. In the tangent table, the value 1.1880 lies between 1.1847, which is tan 49° 50′, and 1.1918, which is tan 50° or tan 49° 60′. Arrange these values in tabular form. Place the larger decimal at the top of the table to make subtraction more convenient. Let x = the difference between 49° 50′ and angle A whose tangent is 1.1880. Then 49° $(50 + x)'$ = the measure of angle A.

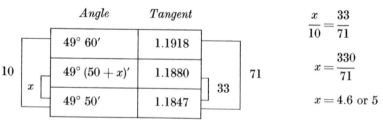

2. Find the corresponding differences as shown in the table.
3. Write and then solve the proportion involving these corresponding differences.
4. Since $x = 5$, $A = 49° 50′ + 5′$ or 49° 55′.
5. *Check* to see that the angle and its tangent value change in the same sense.

Answer: $A = 49° 55′$

2. If cos A = .8665, find the degree measure of positive acute angle A, correct to the nearest minute.

Solution:

1. In the cosine table, the value .8665 lies between .8660, which is cos 30° 00′ or cos 29° 60′, and .8675, which is cos 29° 50′. Arrange these values in the following tabular form. Place the larger decimal at the top of the table to make subtraction of the cosines more convenient. Let $x =$ the difference between 29° 60′ and the angle whose cosine is .8665. Then $29°(60 - x)' =$ the measure of angle A.

Angle	Cosine
29° 50′	.8675
29°(60 − x)′	.8665
29° 60′	.8660

−10 | | 15 | −x | | 5

$$\frac{-x}{-10} = \frac{5}{15}$$

$$x = \frac{-50}{-15}$$

$$x = 3.3 \text{ or } 3$$

2. Find the corresponding differences indicated in the table.
3. Write and then solve the proportion involving these corresponding differences.
4. Since $x = 3$, $A = 29°60' - 3'$ or $29° 57'$.
5. *Check* to see that the angle and the cofunction change in the opposite sense; that is, the angle decreases as the cosine increases.

Answer: $A = 29° 57'$

~~~~~~

Exercises

In 1–18, find, correct to the nearest minute, the degree measure of positive acute angle A which has the given function value.

1. sine is .6517   **2.** cosine is .7642   **3.** tangent is 2.3559
4. sine is .4625   **5.** sine is .5266   **6.** sine is .9618
7. tangent is .6432   **8.** tangent is .7893   **9.** tangent is 1.4400
10. cosine is .8330   **11.** cosine is .8613   **12.** cosine is .4623
13. cotangent is 1.6890   **14.** cotangent is .8465   **15.** cotangent is .4325
16. sine is .3240   **17.** cosine is .6675   **18.** tangent is 1.8000

In 19–33, find, correct to the nearest minute, the degree measure of positive acute angle A if:

19. $\sin A = .0987$ **20.** $\cos A = .5616$ **21.** $\cot A = .3640$
22. $\sin A = .5628$ **23.** $\sin A = .8930$ **24.** $\sin A = .9184$
25. $\tan A = .4322$ **26.** $\tan A = .9467$ **27.** $\tan A = 1.2758$
28. $\cos A = .9830$ **29.** $\cos A = .9318$ **30.** $\cos A = .6278$
31. $\cos A = .2864$ **32.** $\cot A = 1.6340$ **33.** $\cot A = .6278$

11. Using Trigonometric Functions in Right Triangles

To solve a right triangle means to use the given sides and angles to find the remaining unknown sides and angles.

Procedure. To solve right triangles by trigonometry:
1. **Make a careful diagram of the right triangle with the given parts.**
2. **Indicate the given measurements on the triangle.**
3. **Estimate the lines and angles to be found.**
4. **Find the remaining parts as follows:**

If One Acute Angle and One Side Are Given:	*If Two Sides Are Given:*
a. Compute the remaining angle by finding the complement of the given angle.	*a.* Select a trigonometric function equal to a ratio of the two given sides and write the equation expressing this relationship.
b. Select the trigonometric function which relates the given angle and the given side to the side to be found and write the equation expressing this relationship.	*b.* Express the ratio of the two given sides as a four-place decimal.
c. Find the second side by solving the equation and compare the answer to your previously found estimate.	*c.* Compute the angle by solving the equation.
d. Find the remaining side in the same way, using steps *b* and *c.*	*d.* Find the remaining acute angle by computing the complement of the first angle.
	e. Find the third side by using the two given sides in the Pythagorean relationship, $a^2 + b^2 = c^2$.

ANGLE OF ELEVATION AND ANGLE OF DEPRESSION

If a person, using a telescope or some similar instrument, wishes to sight the top of the telephone pole above him (see the figure at the right), he must elevate (raise) the instrument from a horizontal position. $\overleftrightarrow{OT}$, the line joining the eye of the observer, O, to the top of the pole, T, is called the **line of sight.** The angle determined by the horizontal line $(\overleftrightarrow{OA})$ and the line of sight $(\overleftrightarrow{OT})$, $\angle AOT$, is called the **angle of elevation** of the top of the pole, T, from point O. (The horizontal line and the line of sight must be in the same vertical plane.)

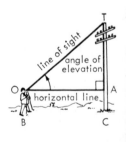

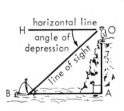

If a person, using a telescope or some similar instrument, wishes to sight the boat below him (see the figure at the left), he must depress (press down) the instrument from a horizontal position. $\overleftrightarrow{OB}$, the line joining the eye of the observer, O, and the boat, B, is called the **line of sight.** The angle determined by the horizontal line ($\overleftrightarrow{OH}$) and the line of sight ($\overleftrightarrow{OB}$), $\angle HOB$, is called the **angle of depression** of the boat, B, from point O. (The horizontal line and the line of sight must be in the same vertical plane.)

In the preceding figure if we measure the angle of elevation of O from B, $\angle OBA$, and also measure the angle of depression of B from O, $\angle HOB$, we discover that both angles contain the same number of degrees. We therefore say that the measure of the angle of elevation of O from B is equal to the measure of the angle of depression of B from O.

~~~~~~~~~ MODEL PROBLEMS ~~~~~~~~~

1. In right triangle ABC, $C = 90°$, $c = 25.0$, $A = 40°$; find B to the nearest degree; find a and b to the nearest tenth.

Given: $A = 40°$ *Find:* (1) B to the nearest degree
$C = 90°$ (2) a and b to the nearest
$c = 25.0$ tenth

Solution: $B = 90° - A = 90° - 40° = 50°$

$$\sin A = \frac{a}{c}$$

$$\sin 40° = \frac{a}{25}$$

$$.6428 = \frac{a}{25}$$

$$a = 25\,(.6428)$$
$$a = 16.07$$
Hence, $a = 16.1$ to the nearest tenth.

$$\cos A = \frac{b}{c}$$

$$\cos 40° = \frac{b}{25}$$

$$b = 25\cos 40°$$
$$b = 25\,(.7660)$$
$$b = 19.15$$
Hence, $b = 19.2$ to the nearest tenth.

Answer: $B = 50°$, $a = 16.1$, $b = 19.2$

2. From the top of a lighthouse 180 feet above sea level, the angle of depression of a boat at sea measures $38°$. Find, to the nearest foot, the distance from the boat to the foot of the lighthouse.

Given: $\angle LAB = 90°$ *Find:* The distance BA
       $\angle HLB = 38°$ to the nearest foot.
Distance $AL = 180$ ft.

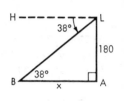

Solution: Since $\angle HLB$ is outside the triangle, find its congruent angle, $\angle LBA$, which is inside the triangle. Hence, $\angle LBA = 38°$.

Let $x =$ the number of feet in distance BA.

Method 1	*Method* 2
$\tan B = \dfrac{LA}{BA}$	$\cot B = \dfrac{BA}{LA}$
$\tan 38° = \dfrac{180}{x}$	$\cot 38° = \dfrac{x}{180}$
$.7813 = \dfrac{180}{x}$	$x = 180 \cot 38°$
$.7813x = 180$	$x = 180\,(1.2799)$
$x = \dfrac{180}{.7813} \approx 230.4$	$x \approx 230.4$
Hence, $x = 230$, to the nearest unit.	Hence, $x = 230$, to the nearest unit.

Answer: The distance is 230 feet.

3. An approach to the overpass above a highway is 400 ft. long. The overpass is 30 ft. above the ground. Find, to the nearest degree, the angle at which the approach is inclined to the horizontal.

Given: $\angle BCA = 90°$, $BC = 30$ ft., $AB = 400$ ft.
Find: $\angle BAC$ or x to the nearest degree

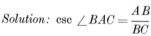

Solution: $\csc \angle BAC = \dfrac{AB}{BC}$

$$\csc x = \frac{400}{30}$$

$$\csc x = 13.3333$$
$$x = 4°$$

Answer: $4°$

Express $\dfrac{400}{30}$ as the decimal 13.3333.

In the table on page 260, note that $\csc 4° = 14.3356$ and $\csc 5° = 11.4737$. Since 13.3333 is closer to 14.3356 than it is to 11.4737, x is closer to $4°$.

Exercises

In 1–8, find the sides, to the nearest integer, and the angles, to the nearest degree.

In the right triangle ABC, $\angle C = 90°$:

1. If $A = 35°$, $c = 20$, find a.
2. If $A = 40°$, $b = 36$, find a.
3. If $A = 42°$, $a = 35$, find c.
4. If $a = 20$, $c = 40$, find A.
5. If $a = 12$, $b = 5$, find A.
6. If $A = 28°$, $c = 30$, find B, a, b.
7. If $A = 39°$, $a = 27$, find B, b, c.
8. If $a = 15$, $b = 20$, find c, A, B.

9. In right triangle ABC, $\angle C = 90°$, $a = 6$, $c = 10$. Find $\angle A$, to the nearest degree.

10. In right triangle DEF, angle $E = 90°$, $f = 666$, $e = 999$. Find $\angle F$, to the nearest ten minutes.

In 11–13, $\angle C$ is the right angle in right triangle ABC. Name a function which may be used:

11. to find a when A and c are given.
12. to find c when B and b are given.
13. to find A when a and b are given.

14. A captive balloon, fastened by a cable 1000 feet long, was blown by a wind so that the cable made an angle of 58° with the ground. Find, to the nearest foot, the height of the balloon.

15. A road is inclined at an angle of 10° with the horizontal. Find, to the nearest foot, the distance which must be driven on this road in order to be elevated 15 feet above the horizontal.

16. A plane takes off from a field and rises at an angle of 11° with the horizontal. Find, to the nearest foot, the height of the plane after it has traveled a horizontal distance of 1000 feet.

17. A lighthouse built at sea level is 170 feet high. From its top, the angle of depression of a buoy measures 25°. Find, to the nearest foot, the distance from the buoy to the foot of the lighthouse.

18. A ladder 30 feet long leans against a building and makes an angle of 72° with the ground. Find, to the nearest foot, how high on the building the ladder reaches.

19. At a point 30 feet from the base of a tree, the angle of elevation of its top measures 53°. Find, to the nearest foot, the height of the tree.

20. An artillery spotter in a plane at an altitude of 1000 feet observes the angle of depression of an enemy tank to measure 28°. How far, to the nearest foot, is the enemy tank from the point on the ground directly below the spotter?

21. A 20-foot ladder, AB, leans against a house that stands on level ground. The ladder, at A, makes an angle of 65° with the ground. How high, to the nearest foot, is B above the ground?

22. In triangle ABC, $C = 90°$, $c = 110$, $A = 42°$. Find b, to the nearest tenth.

23. In $\triangle ABC$, $C = 90°$, $c = 10$, $A = 22°\ 30'$. Find b, correct to the nearest integer.

24. The lengths of two sides of a parallelogram are 6 inches and 10 inches and the angle between them measures $41°\ 50'$. What is the length of the altitude on the longer side? (Express your answer to the nearest inch.)

25. One leg of a trapezoid is 10 and makes an angle of $53°\ 10'$ with the longer base. Find the altitude of the trapezoid. (Express your answer to the nearest integer.)

26. A plane takes off from a field and rises uniformly at an angle of $7°\ 30'$ with the horizontal ground. Find, to the nearest 10 feet, the height of the plane after it has traveled over a horizontal distance of 1850 feet.

27. Find, to the nearest foot, the height of a church spire that casts a shadow of 60 feet when the angle of elevation of the sun measures $63°\ 40'$.

28. A lighthouse built at sea level is 160 feet high. From its top, the angle of depression of a buoy in the ocean measures $22°\ 50'$. Find, to the nearest 10 feet, the distance from the buoy to the foot of the lighthouse.

29. In right triangle ABC, if $a = 13$, $b = 20$, and $C = 90°$, find the measure of angle A, to the nearest degree.

30. Find, to the nearest degree, the measure of the angle of elevation of the sun when a tree 40 feet high casts a shadow 30 feet long.

31. A road rises 24 feet in a horizontal distance of 300 feet. Find, to the nearest degree, the measure of the angle that the road makes with the horizontal.

32. If a road rises 328 feet in a horizontal distance of 4000 feet, find, to the nearest ten minutes, the measure of the angle that the road makes with the horizontal.

33. Find, to the nearest degree, the measure of the smaller acute angle of the right triangle whose legs are 20 inches and 25 inches.

34. If the vertex angle of an isosceles triangle measures $64°$ and each leg measures 10 inches, find, to the nearest tenth of an inch, the length of the altitude to the base.

35. In an isosceles triangle the vertex angle measures $50°$ and the length of the base is 30 inches. The length of the altitude drawn upon the base, to the nearest integer, is _____ inches.

36. The base of a rectangle measures 8 feet and the altitude measures 5 feet. Find, to the nearest degree, the measure of the angle that the diagonal makes with the base.

37. In a circle of radius 50 inches, a chord subtends an angle of $37°\ 40'$ at the center. Find the distance of the chord from the center of the circle. (Express your answer to the nearest inch.)

38. Find, to the nearest hundredth of an inch, the length of a chord which subtends an angle of $144°$ at the center of a circle of radius 10 inches.

39. In a circle of radius 10 inches, a chord subtends a central angle of 48°. Find the length of the chord, to the nearest inch.

40. In an isosceles triangle, each of the congruent sides measures 220 and the base measures 275. Find, to the nearest minute, the measure of each of the congruent angles of the triangle.

12. Navigation Involving Bearings and Courses

The direction in which one point lies from another or the course which a moving object follows may be indicated in two ways.

Method 1. Indicating a Bearing or a Course by Using a Rotation from a North-South Line

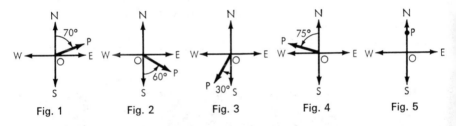

| Fig. 1 | Fig. 2 | Fig. 3 | Fig. 4 | Fig. 5 |

The bearing of a point P from an observation point O is expressed in terms of the acute angle which the ray from O to P forms with the north-south line through O. To indicate the bearing, we write to the left of the measure of the angle, N or S, depending on whether P is in a northerly or southerly direction from O; and we write to the right of the meaure of the angle, E or W, depending on whether P is in an easterly or westerly direction from O.

In Fig. 1, the bearing of P from O is N 70° E.
In Fig. 2, the bearing of P from O is S 60° E.
In Fig. 3, the bearing of P from O is S 30° W.
In Fig. 4, the bearing of P from O is N 75° W.

The course sailed by a boat or flown by a plane is indicated in the same way. If point P is directly north of point O (Fig. 5), we say that "P lies due north of O."

Method 2. Indicating a Bearing or a Course by Using a Clockwise Rotation from Due North

The course that a ship follows when sailing from point O to point P may be expressed in terms of the angle formed by a ray whose direction is due north from O and the ray from O to P, the angle being measured in a clockwise direc-

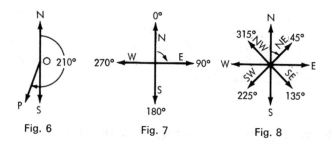

Fig. 6   Fig. 7   Fig. 8

tion. Fig. 6 illustrates a course of 210°. We also say that the bearing of P from O is 210°. Bearing angles and course angles range from 0° to 360°.

As shown in Fig. 7, a plane or ship traveling due north is on a course of 0°; going due east, its course is 90°; going due south, its course is 180°; going due west, its course is 270°. In Fig. 8, we see that when a ship follows a 45° course, it is sailing north-east; a 135° course means sailing south-east; a 225° course means sailing south-west; a 315° course means sailing north-west.

MODEL PROBLEM

A is 200 miles N 30° W of B. C is due south of A and due west of B. Find, to the nearest ten miles, the distance from A to C.

Solution: Let $x =$ the number of miles in distance AC.

$$\sin 60° = \frac{x}{200}$$

$$x = (200)\ .8660$$
$$x = 173.2$$

Hence, $x = 170$, rounded to tens.

Answer: The distance AC is 170 miles.

Exercises

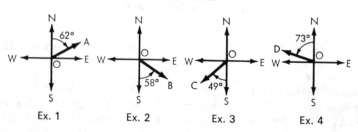

Ex. 1   Ex. 2   Ex. 3   Ex. 4

1. Write the bearing and course of A from O in two ways.
2. Write the bearing and course of B from O in two ways.
3. Write the bearing and course of C from O in two ways.
4. Write the bearing and course of D from O in two ways.

5. Make a diagram indicating the direction taken by a ship S from a point of departure O:
   a. if its bearing from O is N 42° E.
   b. if its bearing from O is S 13° W.
   c. if it sails from O on a course of 320°.
   d. if it sails from O on a course of 240°.

6. Make a diagram showing the direction taken by a plane P from its base B:
   a. if its bearing from B is S 59° E.
   b. if its bearing from B is N 28° W.
   c. if it flies from B on a course of 76°.
   d. if it flies from B on a course of 115°.

7. A plane flew from a base O on a course of 63° until it arrived at an airport R. It then flew the same distance on a different course to an airport T, which was due east of base O.
   a. Make a diagram to illustrate the facts in the problem.
   b. Find the course of the plane as it flew from the airport at R to the airport at T.

8. A ship at point S is due south of lighthouse H. The ship then sails 50 miles along a course N 30° E to a point P, which is due east of F. Find HP.

9. The bearing of point B from point A is N 65° 30′ W. If B is 580 feet from A, how far west, to the nearest foot, is B from A?

10. A ship starts from a shore which runs north and south and sails NNE (N 22° 30′ E). After sailing 150 miles, how far is the ship from the shore? (Express your answer to the nearest mile.)

13. Solving More Difficult Problems Involving Two Right Triangles

~~~~~~~~~~~~~~ *MODEL PROBLEM* ~~~~~~~~~~~~~~

An observer on the top of a cliff 2000 feet above sea level observes two ships due west of the foot of the cliff. The angles of depression of the ships measure 48° and 35°. Find, to the nearest foot, the distance between the ships.

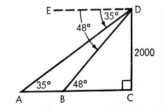

Given: $\angle EDB = 48°$, $\angle EDA = 35°$, distance $DC = 2000$ ft.
Find: The distance between the ships, AB, to the nearest foot.
Solution:

In right triangle CAD, $\cot 35° = \dfrac{AC}{2000}$. Hence, $AC = 2000 \cot 35°$.

In right triangle CBD, $\cot 48° = \dfrac{BC}{2000}$. Hence, $BC = 2000 \cot 48°$.

$AB = AC - BC$
$AB = 2000 \cot 35° - 2000 \cot 48° = 2000 (\cot 35° - \cot 48°)$
$AB = 2000 (1.4281 - .9004) = 2000 (.5277)$
$AB = 1055.4$

Hence, the distance $AB = 1055$ feet, to the nearest foot.

Answer: 1055 ft.

Exercises

1. A man observes the angle of elevation of the top of a vertical tower to measure 25°. He walks a distance of 250 feet toward the tower and in line with the foot of the tower and then observes the angle of elevation of the top of the tower to measure 50°. Find, to the nearest foot, the height of the tower.

2. A man on the top of a cliff 1000 feet above sea level observes two ships due west of the foot of the cliff. The angles of depression of the two ships measure 56° and 32°. Find, to the nearest foot, the distance between the ships.

3. $\overline{AB}$ is a flagpole which stands on top of a cliff $\overline{BC}$. At point P, 310 feet from the foot of the cliff, the angle of elevation of B measures 21° and the angle of elevation of A measures 25°. Find, to the nearest foot, the length of the flagpole $\overline{AB}$.

4. A vertical tree is growing at the bank of a river. The angle of elevation of the top of the tree from a point directly across on the other bank measures 36°. From a second point 100 feet from the first and in line with the first point and the foot of the tree, the angle of elevation of the top of the tree measures 20°. Find, to the nearest foot, the width of the river.

CHAPTER VIII

FUNDAMENTAL OPERATIONS APPLIED TO RELATED ALGEBRAIC AND TRIGONOMETRIC EXPRESSIONS

Algebraic expressions involve variables represented by letters such as x and y. Trigonometric expressions involve trigonometric functions of angles such as $\sin x$ and $\cos y$. In this chapter, each exercise has a part a, which deals with algebraic expressions and a part b, which deals with related trigonometric expressions. We will show how the skills used to perform operations on algebraic expressions can be used to perform the same operations on related trigonometric expressions. Exactly the same principles used to answer part a are used to answer part b. In all exercises, you are to assume that the required operations are to be performed only when the expressions and functions are defined. For example, you are to assume in the case of $\dfrac{4s^2 - 6s}{2sc}$ that $s \neq 0$ and $c \neq 0$, since a fraction is not defined when the denominator is zero.

1. Adding and Subtracting Related Algebraic and Trigonometric Expressions

~~~~~~~~~~ MODEL PROBLEMS ~~~~~~~~~~

1. Add:

   $a.$ $s^2 + 2s - 5$ and
     $2s^2 - 7s - 10$

   $b.$ $\sin^2 x + 2\sin x - 5$ and
     $2\sin^2 x - 7\sin x - 10$

Solution:

$a.$ $s^2 + 2s - 5$
     $2s^2 - 7s - 10$
     $\overline{3s^2 - 5s - 15}$ *Ans.*

$b.$ $\sin^2 x + 2\sin x - 5$
     $2\sin^2 x - 7\sin x - 10$
     $\overline{3\sin^2 x - 5\sin x - 15}$ *Ans.*

284   **Algebra Two and Trigonometry**

2. *a.* From $5s - 2c + 6t$ subtract $2s - 3c - 3t$

b. From $5\sin y - 2\cos y + 6\tan y$ subtract $2\sin y - 3\cos y - 3\tan y$

Solution:

a.
$$5s - 2c + 6t$$
$$2s - 3c - 3t$$
$$\overline{3s + \ c + 9t} \ Ans.$$

b.
$$5\sin y - 2\cos y + 6\tan y$$
$$2\sin y - 3\cos y - 3\tan y$$
$$\overline{3\sin y + \ \cos y + 9\tan y} \ Ans.$$

Exercises

In 1 and 2, add the expressions.

1. *a.* $3s - 2t$ / $2s + 8t$

b. $3\sin A - 2\tan A$ / $2\sin A + 8\tan A$

2. *a.* $7c^2 + 3cs - s^2$ / $-2c^2 - cs - 8s^2$

b. $7\cos^2 D + 3\cos D \sin D - \sin^2 D$ / $-2\cos^2 D - \cos D \sin D - 8\sin^2 D$

3. Find the sum of:

a. $s^3 - 3t^3$ and $-5s^3 + 7t^3$ *b.* $\sin^3 x - 3\tan^3 x$ and $-5\sin^3 x + 7\tan^3 x$

In 4 and 5, subtract the lower expression from the upper expression.

4. *a.* $12s + 2c$ / $5s - 3c$

b. $12\sec d + 2\csc d$ / $5\sec d - 3\csc d$

5. *a.* $2s^2 + 3sc - 2c^2$ / $-5s^2 + 5sc + c^2$

b. $2\sin^2 x + 3\sin x \cos x - 2\cos^2 x$ / $-5\sin^2 x + 5\sin x \cos x + \cos^2 x$

6. *a.* Subtract $8t + c$ from $10t - 8c$

b. Subtract $8\tan A + \cot B$ from $10\tan A - 8\cot B$

7. Combine:

a. $3s - (2s - 8c)$ *b.* $3\sin R - (2\sin R - 8\cos R)$

In 8 and 9, simplify the expression by collecting like terms.

8. *a.* $3t - 5 + 2t - t - 8$ *b.* $3\tan S - 5 + 2\tan S - \tan S - 8$

9. *a.* $5c^2s - 3cs^2 + cs^2$ *b.* $5\cos^2 y \sin y - 3\cos y \sin^2 y + \cos y \sin^2 y$

In 10 and 11, evaluate.

10. *a.* $s^2 - 3s$, when $s = .5$ *b.* $\sin^2 \theta - 3\sin \theta$, when $\sin \theta = .5$

11. *a.* $4c^2 - 1$, when $c = .7$ *b.* $4\cos^2 x - 1$, when $\cos x = .7$

2. Multiplying and Dividing Related Algebraic and Trigonometric Expressions

~~~~~~~~~~~~ *MODEL PROBLEM* ~~~~~~~~~~~~

Multiply:

   a. $3c^2 + c$ by $5c^3$

                                        b. $3 \cot^2 A + \cot A$ by $5 \cot^3 A$

Solution:

   a. $5c^3(3c^2 + c)$

      $15c^5 + 5c^4$ *Ans.*

                              b. $5 \cot^3 A(3 \cot^2 A + \cot A)$

                                    $15 \cot^5 A + 5 \cot^4 A$ *Ans.*

~~~~~~

Exercises

   In 1–8, multiply.

1. *a.* $5s$ by $3c$ *b.* $5 \sin x$ by $3 \cos x$

2. *a.* $2t^3$ by $-3t^2$ *b.* $2 \tan^3 \theta$ by $-3 \tan^2 \theta$

3. *a.* $-2c^2s$ by $-cs^2$ *b.* $-2 \csc^2 z \sec z$ by $-\csc z \sec^2 z$

4. *a.* $3t^2 - 3$ by $2t$ *b.* $3 \tan^2 A - 3$ by $2 \tan A$

5. *a.* $-5t^2 - 3t - 7$ by -2 *b.* $-5 \tan^2 d - 3 \tan d - 7$ by -2

6. *a.* $8c - 7$ by $8c + 7$ *b.* $8 \cos A - 7$ by $8 \cos A + 7$

7. *a.* $s - 5$ by $2s - 11$ *b.* $\sin A - 5$ by $2 \sin A - 11$

8. *a.* $(2t^2 - 3t + 1)(3t - 1)$ *b.* $(2 \tan^2 B - 3 \tan B + 1)$ by $(3 \tan B - 1)$

   In 9–11, find an expression in simple form that does not contain parentheses, and which is equivalent to the given expression.

9. *a.* $10c - (c - 2)$ *b.* $10 \cos y - (\cos y - 2)$

10. *a.* $5(t + 2) - 3(6 - t)$ *b.* $5(\tan x + 2) - 3(6 - \tan x)$

11. *a.* $4t^2 - 2(t + 1)(t + 4)$ *b.* $4 \tan^2 x - 2(\tan x + 1)(\tan x + 4)$

   In 12–17, divide.

12. *a.* t^5 by t^2 *b.* $\tan^5 \theta$ by $\tan^2 \theta$

13. *a.* $12s - 8c$ by 4 *b.* $12 \sec \theta - 8 \cot \theta$ by 4

14. *a.* $5c^2 + 10c - 25$ by -5 *b.* $5 \cot^2 \theta + 10 \cot \theta - 25$ by -5

15. *a.* $s^2 - 3s + 2$ by $s - 2$ *b.* $\sec^2 x - 3 \sec x + 2$ by $\sec x - 2$

16. *a.* $t^2 - 9$ by $t + 3$ *b.* $\tan^2 B - 9$ by $\tan B + 3$

17. *a.* $c^2 - 4c + 12$ by $c + 5$ *b.* $\cos^2 R - 4 \cos R + 12$ by $\cos R + 5$

3. Using Factoring To Reduce Related Algebraic and Trigonometric Fractions

As we stated earlier, when the numerator and denominator of a fraction are each divided by a common factor, the value of the fraction does not change.

Procedure. To reduce a fraction, algebraic or trigonometric:
1. **Factor both its numerator and its denominator completely.**
2. **Divide both the numerator and the denominator by all common factors.**

~~~~~~~ *MODEL PROBLEMS* ~~~~~~~

1. Reduce each fraction to its lowest terms.

   $a.\ \dfrac{4s^2 - 6s}{2sc}$
           $b.\ \dfrac{4\sin^2 x - 6\sin x}{2\sin x \cos x}$

Solution:

$a.\ \dfrac{4s^2 - 6s}{2sc} = \dfrac{\overset{1}{\cancel{2s}}(2s - 3)}{\underset{1}{\cancel{2s}}c}$
      $b.\ \dfrac{4\sin^2 x - 6\sin x}{2\sin x \cos x} = \dfrac{\overset{1}{\cancel{2\sin x}}(2\sin x - 3)}{\underset{1}{\cancel{2\sin x}}\cos x}$

$\qquad\qquad = \dfrac{2s - 3}{c}\ Ans.$
            $= \dfrac{2\sin x - 3}{\cos x}\ Ans.$

2. Reduce each fraction to its lowest terms.

   $a.\ \dfrac{c^2 - s^2}{s - c}$
           $b.\ \dfrac{\cos^2 x - \sin^2 x}{\sin x - \cos x}$

Solution:

$a.\ \dfrac{c^2 - s^2}{s - c}$
        $b.\ \dfrac{\cos^2 x - \sin^2 x}{\sin x - \cos x}$

$\qquad = \dfrac{\overset{-1}{\cancel{(c - s)}}(c + s)}{\underset{1}{\cancel{(s - c)}}}$
      $= \dfrac{\overset{-1}{\cancel{(\cos x - \sin x)}}(\cos x + \sin x)}{\underset{1}{\cancel{(\sin x - \cos x)}}}$

$\qquad = -(c + s)\ Ans.$
         $= -(\cos x + \sin x)\ Ans.$

Exercises

In 1–12, factor the related algebraic and trigonometric expressions.

1. *a.* $2c^2 + c$ *b.* $2\cos^2 x + \cos x$

2. *a.* $s^2 + s^2 t^2$ *b.* $\sin^2 x + \sin^2 x \tan^2 x$

3. *a.* $c^2 - s^2$ *b.* $\cos^2 x - \sin^2 x$

4. *a.* $s^2 - 1$ *b.* $\sec^2 x - 1$

5. *a.* $4t^2 - 9$ *b.* $4\tan^2 x - 9$

6. *a.* $c^4 - s^4$ *b.* $\cos^4 x - \sin^4 x$

7. *a.* $t^2 - 8t + 12$ *b.* $\tan^2 x - 8\tan x + 12$

8. *a.* $2s^2 + 3s + 1$ *b.* $2\sin^2 x + 3\sin x + 1$

9. *a.* $3c^2 - 11c + 10$ *b.* $3\cos^2 x - 11\cos x + 10$

10. *a.* $4s^2 - 13s + 3$ *b.* $4\sin^2 x - 13\sin x + 3$

11. *a.* $9s^2 + 12s + 4$ *b.* $9\sin^2 x + 12\sin x + 4$

12. *a.* $12c^2 - 4c - 1$ *b.* $12\cos^2 x - 4\cos x - 1$

In 13–15, write the related algebraic and trigonometric expressions as the indicated product of three factors.

13. *a.* $2t^2 - 18$ *b.* $2\tan^2 x - 18$

14. *a.* $c^3 - c$ *b.* $\cos^3 x - \cos x$

15. *a.* $3s^3 - s^2 - 2s$ *b.* $3\sin^3 x - \sin^2 x - 2\sin x$

In 16–24, reduce each fraction to its lowest terms.

16. *a.* $\dfrac{s^2}{2sc}$ *b.* $\dfrac{\sin^2 x}{2\sin x \cos x}$

17. *a.* $\dfrac{4c^2 - 12c}{10c}$ *b.* $\dfrac{4\cos^2 x - 12\cos x}{10\cos x}$

18. *a.* $\dfrac{s^2}{5s^2 - s}$ *b.* $\dfrac{\sin^2 x}{5\sin^2 x - \sin x}$

19. *a.* $\dfrac{1 - c^2}{1 - c}$ *b.* $\dfrac{1 - \cos^2 x}{1 - \cos x}$

20. *a.* $\dfrac{2 - 2c^2}{1 - c^2}$ *b.* $\dfrac{2 - 2\cos^2 x}{1 - \cos^2 x}$

21. *a.* $\dfrac{c^4 - s^4}{c^2 - s^2}$ *b.* $\dfrac{\cos^4 x - \sin^4 x}{\cos^2 x - \sin^2 x}$

22. *a.* $-\dfrac{1 - c}{3c - 3}$ *b.* $-\dfrac{1 - \cos x}{3\cos x - 3}$

23. *a.* $\dfrac{s^2 - t^2}{t - s}$ *b.* $\dfrac{\sec^2 x - \tan^2 x}{\tan x - \sec x}$

24. *a.* $\dfrac{t^2-36}{72-24t+2t^2}$ *b.* $\dfrac{\tan^2 B-36}{72-24\tan B+2\tan^2 B}$

4. Multiplying Related Algebraic and Trigonometric Fractions

∿∿∿∿∿∿∿∿∿∿ ***MODEL PROBLEM*** *∿∿∿∿∿∿∿∿∿*

Multiply the fractions and express the product in reduced form.

a. $\dfrac{1+s}{s}\cdot\dfrac{s^2}{1-s^2}$ *b.* $\dfrac{1+\sin A}{\sin A}\cdot\dfrac{\sin^2 A}{1-\sin^2 A}$

Solution:

a. $\dfrac{1+s}{s}\cdot\dfrac{s^2}{1-s^2}$

$$=\dfrac{\overset{1}{\cancel{(1+s)}}}{\underset{1}{\cancel{s}}}\cdot\dfrac{\overset{s}{\cancel{s^2}}}{\underset{1}{(\cancel{1+s})(1-s)}}$$

$$=\dfrac{s}{1-s}\ Ans.$$

b. $\dfrac{1+\sin A}{\sin A}\cdot\dfrac{\sin^2 A}{1-\sin^2 A}$

$$=\dfrac{\overset{1}{\cancel{(1+\sin A)}}}{\underset{1}{\cancel{\sin A}}}\cdot\dfrac{\overset{\sin A}{\cancel{\sin^2 A}}}{\underset{1}{(\cancel{1+\sin A})(1-\sin A)}}$$

$$=\dfrac{\sin A}{1-\sin A}\ Ans.$$

Exercises

In 1–4, multiply the fractions and express the product in reduced form.

1. *a.* $\dfrac{c}{s}\cdot\dfrac{s^2}{c^2}$ *b.* $\dfrac{\cos D}{\sin D}\cdot\dfrac{\sin^2 D}{\cos^2 D}$

2. *a.* $\dfrac{c^2-s^2}{2sc}\cdot\dfrac{3s^3}{c+s}$ *b.* $\dfrac{\cos^2 x-\sin^2 x}{2\sin x\cos x}\cdot\dfrac{3\sin^3 x}{\cos x+\sin x}$

3. *a.* $\dfrac{1+c}{2}\cdot\dfrac{1-c}{1-c^2}$ *b.* $\dfrac{1+\cos x}{2}\cdot\dfrac{1-\cos x}{1-\cos^2 x}$

4. *a.* $\dfrac{t+2}{c}\cdot\dfrac{6-3t}{c}\cdot\dfrac{c^2}{t^2-4}$ *b.* $\dfrac{\tan B+2}{\cos B}\cdot\dfrac{6-3\tan B}{\cos B}\cdot\dfrac{\cos^2 B}{\tan^2 B-4}$

5. Dividing Related Algebraic and Trigonometric Fractions

Recall the following procedure, which we have learned:

Procedure. To divide fractions:
1. Find the reciprocal of the divisor.
2. Multiply the dividend by the reciprocal of the divisor.

MODEL PROBLEM

Divide.

a. $\dfrac{9}{1-c^2} \div \dfrac{15s}{1-c^4}$

b. $\dfrac{9}{1-\cos^2 P} \div \dfrac{15 \sin P}{1-\cos^4 P}$

Solution:

a. $\dfrac{9}{1-c^2} \div \dfrac{15s}{1-c^4}$

$= \dfrac{\overset{3}{\cancel{9}}}{\underset{1}{(\cancel{1-c^2})}} \cdot \dfrac{(\cancel{1-c^2})\,(1+c^2)}{\underset{5}{\cancel{15s}}}$

$= \dfrac{3(1+c^2)}{5s} \ Ans.$

b. $\dfrac{9}{1-\cos^2 P} \div \dfrac{15 \sin P}{1-\cos^4 P}$

$= \dfrac{\overset{3}{\cancel{9}}}{\underset{1}{(\cancel{1-\cos^2 P})}} \cdot \dfrac{(\cancel{1-\cos^2 P})\,(1+\cos^2 P)}{\underset{5}{\cancel{15} \sin P}}$

$= \dfrac{3(1+\cos^2 P)}{5 \sin P} \ Ans.$

Exercises

In 1–5, divide.

1. *a.* $\dfrac{3s}{5} \div \dfrac{9s^2}{15}$

b. $\dfrac{3 \sin \theta}{5} \div \dfrac{9 \sin^2 \theta}{15}$

2. *a.* $\dfrac{1}{2sc} \div \dfrac{s}{c}$

b. $\dfrac{1}{2 \sin x \cos x} \div \dfrac{\sin x}{\cos x}$

3. *a.* $\dfrac{2t}{1-t^2} \div \dfrac{10t^2}{1-t}$

b. $\dfrac{2 \tan A}{1-\tan^2 A} \div \dfrac{10 \tan^2 A}{1-\tan A}$

4. *a.* $\dfrac{5t^2-20}{3} \div \dfrac{t-2}{6t}$

b. $\dfrac{5 \tan^2 B - 20}{3} \div \dfrac{\tan B - 2}{6 \tan B}$

5. *a.* $\dfrac{s^2 + 5s + 6}{s^2 - 4} \div \dfrac{3s + 9}{(s - 2)^2}$ *b.* $\dfrac{\sin^2 x + 5 \sin x + 6}{\sin^2 x - 4} \div \dfrac{3 \sin x + 9}{(\sin x - 2)^2}$

6. Adding or Subtracting Related Algebraic and Trigonometric Fractions Having the Same Denominator

Recall the following procedure, which we have learned:

Procedure. To add (or subtract) fractions that have the same denominator:
1. Write a fraction whose numerator is the sum (or difference) of the numerators and whose denominator is the common denominator of the given fractions.
2. Reduce the resulting fraction to its lowest terms.

MODEL PROBLEM

Subtract the fractions as indicated. Reduce answers to lowest terms.

a. $\dfrac{3t}{t^2 - 4} - \dfrac{-2 - 2t}{4 - t^2}$ *b.* $\dfrac{3 \tan A}{\tan^2 A - 4} - \dfrac{-2 - 2 \tan A}{4 - \tan^2 A}$

Solution:

a. $\dfrac{3t}{t^2 - 4} - \dfrac{-2 - 2t}{4 - t^2}$

$= \dfrac{3t}{t^2 - 4} - \dfrac{2 + 2t}{t^2 - 4}$

$= \dfrac{3t - 2 - 2t}{t^2 - 4}$

$= \dfrac{\overset{1}{\cancel{(t - 2)}}}{\cancel{(t - 2)}\,(t + 2)}$

$= \dfrac{1}{t + 2}$ *Ans.*

b. $\dfrac{3 \tan A}{\tan^2 A - 4} - \dfrac{-2 - 2 \tan A}{4 - \tan^2 A}$

$= \dfrac{3 \tan A}{\tan^2 A - 4} - \dfrac{2 + 2 \tan A}{\tan^2 A - 4}$

$= \dfrac{3 \tan A - 2 - 2 \tan A}{\tan^2 A - 4}$

$= \dfrac{\overset{1}{\cancel{(\tan A - 2)}}}{\cancel{(\tan A - 2)}\,(\tan A + 2)}$

$= \dfrac{1}{\tan A + 2}$ *Ans.*

Exercises

In 1–4, add or subtract (combine) the fractions as indicated. Reduce answers to lowest terms.

1. *a.* $\dfrac{9}{8t} + \dfrac{3}{8t} - \dfrac{2}{8t}$

b. $\dfrac{9}{8 \tan x} + \dfrac{3}{8 \tan x} - \dfrac{2}{8 \tan x}$

2. *a.* $\dfrac{c}{c+1} + \dfrac{1}{c+1}$

b. $\dfrac{\csc x}{\csc x + 1} + \dfrac{1}{\csc x + 1}$

3. *a.* $\dfrac{3}{s-4} + \dfrac{1}{4-s}$

b. $\dfrac{3}{\sin y - 4} + \dfrac{1}{4 - \sin y}$

4. *a.* $\dfrac{s}{s^2 - 1} + \dfrac{1}{1 - s^2}$

b. $\dfrac{\sin A}{\sin^2 A - 1} + \dfrac{1}{1 - \sin^2 A}$

7. Adding and Subtracting Related Algebraic and Trigonometric Fractions Having Different Denominators

Recall the following procedure, which we have learned:

Procedure. To add (or subtract) fractions that have different denominators:
1. Factor each denominator completely in order to find the lowest common denominator, L.C.D.
2. Transform each fraction to an equivalent fraction by multiplying its numerator and denominator by the quotient that is obtained when the L.C.D. is divided by the denominator of the fraction.
3. Write a fraction whose numerator is the sum (or difference) of the numerators of the new fractions and whose denominator is the L.C.D.
4. Reduce the resulting fraction to its lowest terms.

~~~~~~~~~ *MODEL PROBLEMS* ~~~~~~~~~

In 1 and 2, add the fractions as indicated. Reduce answers to lowest terms.

1. *a.* $\dfrac{s}{c} + \dfrac{c}{s}$

b. $\dfrac{\sin x}{\cos x} + \dfrac{\cos x}{\sin x}$

Solution:

a. $\dfrac{s}{c} + \dfrac{c}{s}$

    L.C.D. $= sc$

$= \dfrac{s}{c} \cdot \dfrac{s}{s} + \dfrac{c}{s} \cdot \dfrac{c}{c}$

$= \dfrac{s^2}{sc} + \dfrac{c^2}{sc}$

$= \dfrac{s^2 + c^2}{sc}$ *Ans.*

b. $\dfrac{\sin x}{\cos x} + \dfrac{\cos x}{\sin x}$

    L.C.D. $= \sin x \cos x$

$= \dfrac{\sin x}{\cos x} \cdot \dfrac{\sin x}{\sin x} + \dfrac{\cos x}{\sin x} \cdot \dfrac{\cos x}{\cos x}$

$= \dfrac{\sin^2 x}{\sin x \cos x} + \dfrac{\cos^2 x}{\sin x \cos x}$

$= \dfrac{\sin^2 x + \cos^2 x}{\sin x \cos x}$ or $\dfrac{1}{\sin x \cos x}$ *Ans.*

2. a. $\dfrac{s}{1+c} + \dfrac{c}{s}$ b. $\dfrac{\sin x}{1 + \cos x} + \dfrac{\cos x}{\sin x}$

Solution:

a. $\dfrac{s}{1+c} + \dfrac{c}{s}$

    L.C.D. $= s(1+c)$

$= \dfrac{s^2}{s(1+c)} + \dfrac{c(1+c)}{s(1+c)}$

$= \dfrac{s^2 + c^2 + c}{s(1+c)}$ *Ans.*

b. $\dfrac{\sin x}{1 + \cos x} + \dfrac{\cos x}{\sin x}$

    L.C.D. $= \sin x(1 + \cos x)$

$= \dfrac{\sin^2 x}{\sin x(1 + \cos x)} + \dfrac{\cos x(1 + \cos x)}{\sin x(1 + \cos x)}$

$= \dfrac{\sin^2 x + \cos^2 x + \cos x}{\sin x(1 + \cos x)}$ or

$$\dfrac{\overset{1}{\cancel{(1 + \cos x)}}}{\sin x \underset{1}{\cancel{(1 + \cos x)}}} \quad [\sin^2 x + \cos^2 x = 1]$$

$= \dfrac{1}{\sin x}$ or $\csc x$ *Ans.*

Exercises

In 1–8, add or subtract (combine) the fractions as indicated. Reduce answers to lowest terms.

1. *a.* $\dfrac{c}{s} - \dfrac{s}{c}$

     b. $\dfrac{\cos x}{\sin x} - \dfrac{\sin x}{\cos x}$

2. *a.* $\dfrac{c^2}{s} + s$

     b. $\dfrac{\cos^2 x}{\sin x} + \sin x$

3. *a.* $t + \dfrac{1}{t}$

     b. $\tan x + \dfrac{1}{\tan x}$

4. *a.* $\dfrac{1}{c^2} + 1$

     b. $\dfrac{1}{\cos^2 x} + 1$

5. *a.* $\dfrac{t-2}{3} + \dfrac{t+1}{6}$

     b. $\dfrac{\tan \theta - 2}{3} + \dfrac{\tan \theta + 1}{6}$

6. *a.* $\dfrac{c-4}{4c} - \dfrac{2c-3}{3c}$

     b. $\dfrac{\cot A - 4}{4 \cot A} - \dfrac{2 \cot A - 3}{3 \cot A}$

7. *a.* $\dfrac{5}{s^2 - 4} + \dfrac{3}{s - 2}$

     b. $\dfrac{5}{\sec^2 B - 4} + \dfrac{3}{\sec B - 2}$

8. *a.* $\dfrac{1}{c^2 - 4} - \dfrac{4}{2 - c}$

     b. $\dfrac{1}{\csc^2 y - 4} - \dfrac{4}{2 - \csc y}$

9. Find the sum of:

     a. $\dfrac{4}{t-1}$ and $\dfrac{3}{1-t}$

     b. $\dfrac{4}{\tan \theta - 1}$ and $\dfrac{3}{1 - \tan \theta}$

8. Simplifying Related Algebraic and Trigonometric Complex Fractions

Recall the following procedures, which we have learned:

Procedure. To simplify complex fractions (Method 1):
1. Combine the terms in the numerator into a single fraction.
2. Combine the terms in the denominator into a single fraction.
3. Divide the numerator by the denominator.

Procedure. To simplify complex fractions (Method 2):

1. Find the lowest common denominator of all the fractions that appear in the numerator and denominator of the complex fraction.
2. Multiply the numerator and denominator of the complex fraction by this lowest common denominator.
3. Simplify and reduce the resulting simple fraction to its lowest terms.

~~~~~~~~~~~~~~~ *MODEL PROBLEM* ~~~~~~~~~~~~~~~

Simplify the complex fraction.

a. $\dfrac{\dfrac{1}{c}}{\dfrac{c}{s}+\dfrac{s}{c}}$

b. $\dfrac{\dfrac{1}{\cos x}}{\dfrac{\cos x}{\sin x}+\dfrac{\sin x}{\cos x}}$

Solution:

Method 1

a. $\dfrac{\dfrac{1}{c}}{\dfrac{c}{s}+\dfrac{s}{c}} = \dfrac{1}{c} \div \left(\dfrac{c}{s}+\dfrac{s}{c}\right)$

$= \dfrac{1}{c} \div \dfrac{c^2+s^2}{cs}$

$= \dfrac{1}{\cancel{c}} \cdot \dfrac{\cancel{c}\, s}{(c^2+s^2)}$

$= \dfrac{s}{c^2+s^2}$ *Ans.*

Method 1

b. $\dfrac{\dfrac{1}{\cos x}}{\dfrac{\cos x}{\sin x}+\dfrac{\sin x}{\cos x}} = \dfrac{1}{\cos x} \div \left(\dfrac{\cos x}{\sin x}+\dfrac{\sin x}{\cos x}\right)$

$= \dfrac{1}{\cos x} \div \dfrac{\cos^2 x + \sin^2 x}{\sin x \cos x}$

$= \dfrac{1}{\cancel{\cos x}} \cdot \dfrac{\sin x\, \cancel{\cos x}}{(\cos^2 x + \sin^2 x)}$

$= \dfrac{\sin x}{\cos^2 x + \sin^2 x}$

$= \dfrac{\sin x}{1} \text{ or } \sin x \ \ Ans.$

Method 2

a. $\dfrac{\dfrac{1}{c}}{\dfrac{c}{s}+\dfrac{s}{c}} = \dfrac{sc\left(\dfrac{1}{c}\right)}{sc\left(\dfrac{c}{s}+\dfrac{s}{c}\right)}$

$= \dfrac{s}{c^2+s^2}$ *Ans.*

Method 2

b. $\dfrac{\dfrac{1}{\cos x}}{\dfrac{\cos x}{\sin x}+\dfrac{\sin x}{\cos x}} = \dfrac{\sin x \cos x\left(\dfrac{1}{\cos x}\right)}{\sin x \cos x\left(\dfrac{\cos x}{\sin x}+\dfrac{\sin x}{\cos x}\right)}$

$= \dfrac{\sin x}{\cos^2 x + \sin^2 x}$

$= \dfrac{\sin x}{1}$ or $\sin x$ *Ans.*

Exercises

In 1–5, simplify each of the complex fractions.

1. a. $\dfrac{1+\dfrac{s}{c}}{1-\dfrac{s}{c}}$ b. $\dfrac{1+\dfrac{\sin A}{\cos A}}{1-\dfrac{\sin A}{\cos A}}$

2. a. $\dfrac{\dfrac{1}{t}-t}{2}$ b. $\dfrac{\dfrac{1}{\tan x}-\tan x}{2}$

3. a. $\dfrac{2-\dfrac{1}{c^2}}{\dfrac{1}{c^2}}$ b. $\dfrac{2-\dfrac{1}{\cos^2 P}}{\dfrac{1}{\cos^2 P}}$

4. a. $\dfrac{1-\dfrac{s^2}{c^2}}{1+\dfrac{s^2}{c^2}}$ b. $\dfrac{1-\dfrac{\sin^2 s}{\cos^2 s}}{1+\dfrac{\sin^2 s}{\cos^2 s}}$

5. a. $\dfrac{\dfrac{1}{c}-\dfrac{1}{s}}{\dfrac{1}{c}+\dfrac{1}{s}}$ b. $\dfrac{\dfrac{1}{\cos\theta}-\dfrac{1}{\sin\theta}}{\dfrac{1}{\cos\theta}+\dfrac{1}{\sin\theta}}$

CHAPTER IX

REAL NUMBERS AND RADICALS

1. Understanding More About Real Numbers

We have learned that:

A **rational number** is a real number that can be expressed in the form $\frac{a}{b}$ where a and b are integers and $b \neq 0$. Recall that any rational number may be represented by one and only one point on a number line. Examples of rational numbers are:

$$\tfrac{2}{3} \qquad 5 \qquad 0 \qquad -\tfrac{5}{7} \qquad -2 \qquad \sin 30° \qquad \tan 45°$$

An **irrational number** is a real number than cannot be expressed in the form $\frac{a}{b}$ where a and b are integers and $b \neq 0$. It can be proved that any irrational number may be represented by one and only one point on a number line. Examples of irrational numbers are:

$$\frac{\sqrt{3}}{2} \qquad \frac{1}{\sqrt{2}} \qquad \sqrt{17} \qquad \sqrt[3]{4} \qquad \sin 60°$$

Also, the number π is an irrational number.

The set of real numbers may be considered to be the union of the set of rational numbers and the set of irrational numbers.

Hence, a real number is either a rational number or an irrational number.

A *perfect square* is the square of a rational number. For example, 36 is a perfect square since $6^2 = 36$. Also, $\frac{36}{49}$ is a perfect square since $(\frac{6}{7})^2 = \frac{36}{49}$.

EXPRESSING RATIONAL NUMBERS AS DECIMALS

To express a rational number as a decimal, we simply perform the indicated division. For example,

$$\frac{1}{2} = 2\overline{\smash)1.00000}^{\,.50000} \qquad \frac{3}{4} = 4\overline{\smash)3.00000}^{\,.75000} \qquad \frac{1}{16} = 16\overline{\smash)1.00000}^{\,.06250}$$

In each of these examples, the division terminates. Decimals which result from such divisions (for example, .5, .75, and .0625) are called ***terminating decimals.***

However, not all rational numbers can be expressed as terminating decimals. For example,

$$\frac{1}{3} = 3\overline{\smash)1.0000}^{\,.3333\ldots} \qquad \frac{2}{11} = 11\overline{\smash)2.0000}^{\,.1818\ldots} \qquad \frac{1}{6} = 6\overline{\smash)1.0000}^{\,.1666\ldots}$$

Decimals that keep repeating endlessly, such as .3333..., .1818..., and .1666..., are known as ***non-terminating repeating decimals.***

A non-terminating repeating decimal may be written in an abbreviated form by placing a bar (‾) over the group of digits that is to be continually repeated. For example,

$$.3333\ldots = .\overline{3} \qquad .1818\ldots = .\overline{18} \qquad .1666\ldots = .1\overline{6}$$

The previous examples, which we have studied, illustrate the truth of the following statement, which we will assume:

Every rational number can be expressed as either a terminating decimal or a non-terminating repeating decimal.

Note. Every terminating decimal can be treated as a repeating decimal. For example, $.35 = .34999\ldots = .34\overline{9}$ and $.7 = .6999\ldots = .6\overline{9}$.

EXPRESSING DECIMALS AS RATIONAL NUMBERS IN THE FORM $\frac{a}{b}$ WHERE a AND b ARE INTEGERS

We have learned how to express a terminating decimal in the form $\frac{a}{b}$ where a and b are integers. For example,

$$.7 = \frac{7}{10} \qquad .49 = \frac{49}{100} \qquad .672 = \frac{672}{1000} \qquad .0513 = \frac{513}{10,000}$$

Study the following model problems to learn how to express a non-terminating repeating decimal in the form $\frac{a}{b}$ where a and b are integers.

~~~~~~~~~~~ *MODEL PROBLEMS* ~~~~~~~~~~~

1. Change .727272... to the form $\frac{a}{b}$ where a and b are integers.

Solution:

$$\text{Let } N = \quad .727272...$$
$$\text{Then } 100N = 72.727272...$$
$$\text{Subtract: } N = \quad .727272...$$
$$\overline{\text{Hence, } 99N = 72}$$
$$N = \frac{72}{99} \text{ or } \frac{8}{11}$$

Answer: .727272... $= \frac{8}{11}$

2. Change .45555... to the form $\frac{a}{b}$ where a and b are integers.

Solution:

$$\text{Let } N = \quad .45555...$$
$$\text{Then } 10N = 4.55555...$$
$$\text{Subtract: } N = .45555...$$
$$\overline{\text{Hence, } 9N = 4.1}$$
$$N = \frac{4.1}{9} \text{ or } \frac{41}{90}$$

Answer: .45555... $= \frac{41}{90}$

Check: To verify the answer, divide the numerator by the denominator. See whether the quotient is the given decimal.

~~~~~~

The previous examples illustrate the truth of the following statement, which we will assume:

Every terminating and non-terminating repeating decimal can be expressed as a rational number in the form $\frac{a}{b}$ where a and b are integers.

EXPRESSING IRRATIONAL NUMBERS AS DECIMALS

There are decimals which are non-terminating and non-repeating. Examples of such decimals are .04004000400004... and —.27227222722227....

Since these non-terminating decimals are non-repeating, they cannot represent rational numbers. Hence, such decimals are irrational numbers.

It can be proved that $\sqrt{3}$ is a non-terminating and non-repeating decimal. Hence, $\sqrt{3}$ is an irrational number. The approximate value of $\sqrt{3}$ to six decimal places is 1.732051. Approximations of irrational numbers are rational numbers.

In general, if n is positive and not a perfect square, $\sqrt{n}$ is an irrational number.

PRINCIPLES OF OPERATIONS ON REAL NUMBERS

When we perform operations on real numbers, we will make use of the following principles, whose truth we will assume without proof:

Principle 1. The sum or difference of an irrational number and a rational number is an irrational number.

Thus, $3 + \sqrt{2}$, $\sqrt{5} - 3$, and $\sin 45° + \frac{2}{3}$ are irrational numbers.

Principle 2. The product of an irrational number and a nonzero rational number is an irrational number.

Thus, $5\sqrt{3}$ and 15π are irrational numbers.

Principle 3. The quotient obtained by dividing a nonzero rational number by an irrational number is an irrational number.

Thus, $\dfrac{3}{\sqrt{2}}$ and $\dfrac{10}{\tan 30°}$ are irrational numbers.

Principle 4. The quotient obtained by dividing an irrational number by a nonzero rational number is an irrational number.

Thus, $\dfrac{\sqrt{10}}{3}$, $\dfrac{\tan 60°}{5}$, and $\dfrac{\pi}{20}$ are irrational numbers.

Principle 5. If zero is multiplied by any real number, the product is zero.

Thus, $0\sqrt{15} = 0$. Also, $0(7 - \sqrt{8}) = 0$.

Principle 6. If zero is divided by any nonzero real number, the quotient is zero.

Thus, $\dfrac{0}{\sqrt{20}} = 0$. Also, $\dfrac{0}{5 + \sqrt{2}} = 0$.

Principle 7. Division of a real number by zero is impossible.

Thus, $\sqrt{17} \div 0$ is impossible. $\dfrac{\sqrt{17}}{0}$ is meaningless.

Exercises

In 2–12, complete the table as illustrated in exercise 1. (A number may be in more than one category.)

	Real Number	Positive Integer	Negative Integer	Rational Number	Irrational Number
1.	5	yes	no	yes	no
2.	$\sqrt{5}$				
3.	-3.5				
4.	$3\sqrt{5}$				
5.	$-7-\sqrt{25}$				
6.	$\dfrac{2}{\sqrt{3}}$				
7.	$4+\sqrt{2}$				
8.	$-\cos 30°$				
9.	$-3+2\tan 45°$				
10.	$.171717\ldots$				
11.	$.171171117\ldots$				
12.	$0(-5\sqrt{10})$				

In 13–24, change the decimal to the form $\dfrac{a}{b}$ where a and b are integers.

13. $.333\ldots$ **14.** $.777\ldots$ **15.** $.272727\ldots$
16. $.3666\ldots$ **17.** $.13555\ldots$ **18.** $.0454545\ldots$
19. $1.888\ldots$ **20.** $25.222\ldots$ **21.** $3.0141414\ldots$
22. $.125125125\ldots$ **23.** $125.125125\ldots$ **24.** $10.123123123\ldots$

25. Which of the following is undefined or meaningless?

a. $0(-\sqrt{5})$ b. $0(2-\sqrt{8})$ c. $\dfrac{2\sqrt{5}+\sqrt{3}}{0}$ d. $\dfrac{2+\sqrt{9}}{0}$ e. $2+\dfrac{\sqrt{9}}{0}$

2. Understanding Roots and Radicals

Now we will learn how to work with real numbers such as $\sqrt{3}$ and $\sqrt[3]{9}$ which have a **radical sign**, $\sqrt{\ }$. These numbers occur frequently in the solutions of equations of the second degree or higher, and in the solutions to problems using the theorem of Pythagoras.

A **square root** of a number is one of its two equal factors.

Thus, since $5 \times 5 = 25$, then 5 is a square root of 25. Also, since $(-5)(-5) = 25$, then -5 is also a square root of 25. Hence, 25 has two square roots, which may be written ± 5. In fact, *every positive number has two square roots*. For example, .49 has two square roots, $\pm.7$, and $\frac{16}{25}$ has two square roots, $\pm(\frac{4}{5})$.

The **principal square root** of a positive number a, symbolized $\sqrt{a}$, is its positive square root. Hence,

$$\sqrt{25} = 5 \qquad \sqrt{.49} = .7 \qquad \sqrt{\frac{16}{25}} = \frac{4}{5}$$

Since the square root of a number is one of its two equal factors, it follows that $\sqrt{a}\sqrt{a} = a$. Thus, $\sqrt{5}\sqrt{5} = 5$, $\sqrt{\frac{2}{3}}\sqrt{\frac{2}{3}} = \frac{2}{3}$, and $\sqrt{3.47}\sqrt{3.47} = 3.47$.

In general, if $a > 0$, there is a number $b > 0$ such that $b^2 = a$. The number b is called the principal square root of a and is symbolized $\sqrt{a}$. Hence, $(\sqrt{a})^2 = a$.

To indicate that the negative square root of a positive number a is to be found, we place a minus sign in front of the radical. Hence, $-\sqrt{a}$ is the negative square root of a. For example,

$$-\sqrt{25} = -5 \qquad -\sqrt{.49} = -.7 \qquad -\sqrt{\tfrac{16}{25}} = -\tfrac{4}{5}$$

Observe that if $b^2 = 25$, then $b = \pm\sqrt{25}$ and in general, if $b^2 = a$, then $b = \pm\sqrt{a}$.

A **cube root** of a number is one of its three equal factors. For example, since $2 \times 2 \times 2 = 8$, then 2 is a cube root of 8.

Every nonzero real number has three cube roots, one of which is a real number called the **principal cube root** of the number. (The other two roots, to be discussed later, are members of the set of *complex numbers*.)

The **principal cube root** of a real number a, symbolized $\sqrt[3]{a}$, is the cube root of a which is a real number. Hence,

$$\sqrt[3]{27} = 3 \qquad \sqrt[3]{-27} = -3 \qquad \sqrt[3]{\frac{8}{27}} = \frac{2}{3} \qquad \sqrt[3]{-\frac{8}{27}} = -\frac{2}{3} \qquad \sqrt[3]{0} = 0$$

In general, if a is a real number, there is a real number b such that $b^3 = a$. The number b is called the principal cube root of a and is symbolized $\sqrt[3]{a}$. Hence, $(\sqrt[3]{a})^3 = a$.

In general, the nth root of a number is one of its n equal factors, where n is a natural number. The principal nth root of a real number a is symbolized by $\sqrt[n]{a}$. The number, n, which indicates the root to be taken is called the **index;** the number a is called the **radicand;** and the entire symbol, $\sqrt[n]{a}$, is called a **radical.**

For example, in the case of the radical $\sqrt[3]{64}$, the index is 3 and the radicand is 64. When no index is written, as in the case of $\sqrt{25}$, the index is understood to be 2, and the radical is a square root.

MEANINGS OF THE SYMBOL $\sqrt[n]{a}$, CALLED THE PRINCIPAL nTH ROOT OF a

1. If n is an odd positive integer, then $\sqrt[n]{a}$ means the one real number b such that $b^n = a$. If a is positive, then b is positive; if a is negative, then b is negative; if a is zero, then b is zero. For example:

$$\sqrt[3]{64} = 4, \text{ since } (4)^3 = 64$$

$$\sqrt[5]{-1} = -1, \text{ since } (-1)^5 = -1$$

$$\sqrt[7]{0} = 0, \text{ since } (0)^7 = 0$$

2. If n is an even positive integer and a is a non-negative number, then $\sqrt[n]{a}$ means the real non-negative number b such that $b^n = a$. If a is positive, then b is positive; if a is zero, then b is zero. For example:

$$\sqrt{81} = 9, \text{ since } (9)^2 = 81$$

$$\sqrt{0} = 0, \text{ since } 0^2 = 0.$$

$$\sqrt[4]{16} = 2, \text{ since } (2)^4 = 16$$

$$\sqrt[6]{0} = 0, \text{ since } (0)^6 = 0$$

3. If n is an even positive integer and a is a negative number, then $\sqrt[n]{a}$ is not defined in the set of real numbers. For example, $\sqrt{-25}$ is not defined in the set of real numbers because there is no real number whose square is -25. In a later chapter, we will learn to define $\sqrt{-25}$ in the set of *complex numbers*.

⁓⁓⁓⁓⁓⁓⁓⁓ *MODEL PROBLEMS* ⁓⁓⁓⁓⁓⁓⁓⁓

1. Find the value of   *a.* $(\sqrt{11})^2$ *b.* $(\sqrt[3]{17})^3$ *c.* $(\sqrt[5]{2})^5$

Solution:

a. Since $(\sqrt{a})^2 = a$, then $(\sqrt{11})^2 = 11$.   11 *Ans.*

b. Since $(\sqrt[3]{a})^3 = a$, then $(\sqrt[3]{17})^3 = 17$.   17 *Ans.*

c. Since $(\sqrt[5]{a})^5 = a$, then $(\sqrt[5]{2})^5 = 2$.   2 *Ans.*

2. Solve for x: $x^2 = 36$

Solution: If $x^2 = a$, then $x = \pm\sqrt{a}$ when a is a positive number.

$x^2 = 36$	*Check:* $x^2 = 36$	$x^2 = 36$
$x = \pm\sqrt{36}$	$(+6)^2 \overset{?}{=} 36$	$(-6)^2 \overset{?}{=} 36$
$x = \pm 6$	$36 = 36$ (true)	$36 = 36$ (true)

Answer: $x = +6$ or $x = -6$; solution set is $\{+6, -6\}$.

Exercises

In 2–10, complete the table as illustrated in exercise 1.

	Radical	Index	Radicand	Principal Root
1.	$\sqrt[3]{8}$	3	8	2
2.	$\sqrt[5]{32}$	5	?	?
3.	$\sqrt{144}$	2	?	?
4.	?	2	49	?
5.	?	2	?	12
6.	?	?	125	5
7.	?	3	1000	?
8.	$\sqrt{\frac{100}{81}}$	?	?	?
9.	?	4	?	10
10.	?	3	a^3	?

In 11–26, find the indicated root. (The variables represent positive numbers.)

11. $\sqrt{36}$ **12.** $\sqrt{144}$ **13.** $-\sqrt{16}$ **14.** $-\sqrt{81}$

15. $\sqrt{4x^2}$ **16.** $\sqrt{9y^6}$ **17.** $-\sqrt{49c^2}$ **18.** $-\sqrt{25x^4}$

19. $\sqrt[3]{64}$ **20.** $-\sqrt[3]{64}$ **21.** $\sqrt[3]{-64}$ **22.** $-\sqrt[3]{-64}$

23. $\sqrt{\frac{81}{25}}$ **24.** $-\sqrt{\frac{x^2}{64}}$ **25.** $\sqrt[3]{-\frac{1}{125}}$ **26.** $-\sqrt[3]{\frac{x^6}{8}}$

In 27–39, find the value of the expression.

27. $\sqrt{(7)^2}$ **28.** $\sqrt{(\frac{1}{3})^2}$ **29.** $\sqrt{(.3)^2}$ **30.** $\sqrt[3]{(2)^3}$

31. $\sqrt[3]{(-\frac{3}{4})^3}$ **32.** $(\sqrt{8})^2$ **33.** $(\sqrt{13})^2$ **34.** $(\sqrt[3]{27})^3$

35. $(\sqrt[3]{2})^3$ **36.** $(\sqrt{35})(\sqrt{35})$ **37.** $\sqrt{81} - \sqrt{49}$

38. $(\sqrt{15})^2 + (\sqrt{8})(\sqrt{8})$ **39.** $\sqrt[3]{(-7)^3} + (\sqrt[3]{15})^3$

In 40–47, solve for the variable.

40. $x^2 = 9$ **41.** $y^2 = 100$ **42.** $m^2 = \frac{9}{25}$ **43.** $c^2 = .64$

44. $a^2 - 4 = 0$ **45.** $x^2 - 49 = 0$ **46.** $3x^2 = 75$ **47.** $2y^2 - 72 = 0$

3. Square Roots and Cube Roots That Are Irrational Numbers

Recall that $\sqrt{36}$ is a rational number because $\sqrt{36} = \frac{6}{1}$. Also, $\sqrt{0}$, or 0, is a rational number.

In general:

1. If n is a non-negative integer that is a perfect square, then $\sqrt{n}$ is a rational number.
2. If n is a non-negative integer that is not a perfect square, then $\sqrt{n}$ is an irrational number.

Hence, $\sqrt{25}$ and $\sqrt{144}$ are rational numbers because 25 and 144 are perfect squares. However, $\sqrt{3}$ and $\sqrt{19}$ are irrational numbers because 3 and 19 are not perfect squares.

Similarly, $\sqrt[3]{8}$ and $\sqrt[3]{125}$ are rational numbers because 8 and 125 are perfect cubes. However, $\sqrt[3]{4}$ and $\sqrt[3]{25}$ are irrational numbers because 4 and 25 are not perfect cubes.

We know that $\sqrt{2}$ is a number which is between 1 and 2 because $(1)^2 = 1$ and $(2)^2 = 4$. It can be proved that $\sqrt{2}$ cannot be expressed in the form $\frac{a}{b}$ where a and b are integers. Therefore, $\sqrt{2}$ is an irrational number.

In general:

If the square root of an integer is between two consecutive integers, then the root is an irrational number.

Thus, $\sqrt{50}$ is an irrational number because $\sqrt{50}$ lies between 7 and 8, since $(7)^2 = 49$ and $(8)^2 = 64$. Also, $\sqrt[3]{32}$ is an irrational number because $\sqrt[3]{32}$ lies between 3 and 4 since $(3)^3 = 27$ and $(4)^3 = 64$.

Exercises

In 1–10, state whether the radical is a rational or an irrational number.

1. $\sqrt{11}$ 2. $\sqrt{81}$ 3. $-\sqrt{125}$ 4. $\sqrt{169}$ 5. $-\sqrt{400}$
6. $\sqrt[3]{1}$ 7. $\sqrt[3]{36}$ 8. $\sqrt[3]{-64}$ 9. $-\sqrt[3]{8}$ 10. $-\sqrt[3]{100}$

In 11–20, name two consecutive integers between which the given number lies.

11. $\sqrt{5}$ 12. $\sqrt{12}$ 13. $\sqrt{37}$ 14. $-\sqrt{20}$ 15. $-\sqrt{95}$
16. $\sqrt[3]{2}$ 17. $\sqrt[3]{16}$ 18. $\sqrt[3]{70}$ 19. $-\sqrt[3]{25}$ 20. $-\sqrt[3]{75}$

21. Which is an *irrational* number? (1) $\sqrt[3]{27}$ (2) $\sqrt{90}$ (3) $\sqrt[3]{125}$ (4) $-\sqrt{4}$

4. Finding Squares and Square Roots by Using a Table

~~~~~~~~~~ *MODEL PROBLEM* ~~~~~~~~~~

Find the square root of 47, correct to the nearest tenth.

Solution: In the table on page 757, in the column headed **No.,** find 47. On the horizontal line containing 47, move over to the column headed **Square Root,** to find 6.856. Therefore, the square root of 47, correct to the nearest tenth, is 6.9.

Answer: $\sqrt{47} \approx 6.9$

Note. The symbol $\approx$ means "is approximately equal to."

Exercises

In 1–12, use the table on page 757 to find the square of the given number.
1. 18 **2.** 23 **3.** 27 **4.** 34 **5.** 38 **6.** 105
7. 81 **8.** 86 **9.** 89 **10.** 92 **11.** 94 **12.** 148

In 13–24, use the table on page 757 to find, correct to the nearest tenth, the principal square root of the given number.
13. 8 **14.** 12 **15.** 17 **16.** 19 **17.** 24 **18.** 107
19. 75 **20.** 83 **21.** 87 **22.** 91 **23.** 93 **24.** 142

In 25–34, use the table on page 757 to find the principal square root of the given number.
25. 1,156 **26.** 7,056 **27.** 4,356 **28.** 9,216 **29.** 1,024
30. 529 **31.** 961 **32.** 7,921 **33.** 8,464 **34.** 5,329

5. Computing the Square Root of a Number

There are several methods, in addition to consulting a table, that can be used to obtain the square root of a number to as many decimal places as may be desired. We will now illustrate one of these methods using a compact arrangement to show the computation.

COMPUTING THE SQUARE ROOT OF A PERFECT SQUARE

~~~~~~~~~~~~~ *MODEL PROBLEM* ~~~~~~~~~~~~~

Compute the positive square root of 1764.

How To Proceed	*Solution*

1. Starting at the decimal point and moving to the left, group the digits of the number in pairs of two digits. Place a decimal point directly above the decimal point in the number.

$$\sqrt{\overline{17}\ \overline{64}.}$$

2. Below the first group at the left, write the largest perfect square which is not more than that group. Write the square root of the perfect square above the first group.

$$\begin{array}{r} 4\quad\ . \\ \sqrt{\overline{17}\ \overline{64}.} \\ 16\quad\quad \end{array}$$

3. Subtract the perfect square from the first group and bring down and annex the next group to the remainder.

$$\begin{array}{r} 4\quad\ . \\ \sqrt{\overline{17}\ \overline{64}.} \\ 16\quad\quad \\ \hline 1\ 64\quad \end{array}$$

4. Form a trial divisor by doubling (multiplying by 2) the part of the root already found in step 3 and annexing a 0.
Thus, $4 \times 2 = 8$. Trial divisor is 80.

$$\begin{array}{r} 4\quad\ . \\ \sqrt{\overline{17}\ \overline{64}.} \\ 16\quad\quad \\ \hline 80\ \overline{|\ 1\ 64} \end{array}$$

5. Divide the remainder found in step 3 by the trial divisor found in step 4. Annex the quotient to the part of the root already found; also, add it to the trial divisor to form the complete divisor.
Thus, $164 \div 80 = 2 +$. Complete divisor is $80 + 2 = 82$.

$$\begin{array}{r} 4\quad 2. \\ \sqrt{\overline{17}\ \overline{64}.} \\ 16\quad\quad \\ \hline 82\ \overline{|\ 1\ 64} \end{array}$$

6. Multiply the complete divisor by the last digit which was placed in the root ($2 \times 82 = 164$). Then subtract the product from the remainder found in step 3. The remainder is 0. The required root is 42.

$$\begin{array}{r} 4\quad 2. \\ \sqrt{\overline{17}\ \overline{64}.} \\ 16\quad\quad \\ \hline 82\ \overline{|\ 1\ 64} \\ 1\ 64 \end{array}$$

Check: Since $(42)^2 = 1764$, then $\sqrt{1764} = 42$.

Answer: $\sqrt{1764} = 42$

Note. When necessary, the procedure given in steps 4, 5, 6 is repeated until the remainder is 0.

COMPUTING THE APPROXIMATE SQUARE ROOT OF A NUMBER

~~~~~~~~~~~~~~ *MODEL PROBLEM* ~~~~~~~~~~~~~~

Find $\sqrt{42}$, correct to the *nearest tenth*.

Solution:

1. In order to approximate $\sqrt{42}$, correct to the nearest tenth, we carry the work to two decimal places and then round off the result to the nearest tenth.

2. Since we wish to carry the result to two decimal places, we annex to 42 (at the right of the decimal point) two groups, each containing two zeros. Since $42 = 42.0000$, then $\sqrt{42} = \sqrt{42.0000}$.

3. Perform the computation and round off the answer to the nearest tenth. Since $6.48 \approx 6.5$, the required root is 6.5.

```
          6. 4  8
      _____
    √ 42.00 00
      36
  124 | 6 00
      | 4 96
      |_____
 1288 | 1 04 00
      | 1 03 04
      |_____
           96
```

Answer: $\sqrt{42} = 6.5$, to the nearest tenth

~~~~~~

Exercises

In 1–20, find the square root of the number.

1. 324	**2.** 2,035	**3.** 1,296	**4.** 4,225	**5.** 784
6. 5,184	**7.** 90.25	**8.** 9,801	**9.** 289	**10.** 11,025
11. 15,376	**12.** 56.25	**13.** 441	**14.** 161.29	**15.** 1.1025
16. 16,900	**17.** 9.61	**18.** 17,689	**19.** 161,604	**20.** 667,489

In 21–40, find, to the nearest tenth, the square root of the number.

21. 12	**22.** 19	**23.** 37	**24.** 58	**25.** 60
26. 75	**27.** 79	**28.** 150	**29.** 200	**30.** 416
31. 84	**32.** 90	**33.** 18.25	**34.** 73.61	**35.** 205.78
36. 95	**37.** 108	**38.** 8.5	**39.** 61.7	**40.** 4.052

6. Simplifying a Radical Whose Radicand Is a Product

Since $\sqrt{4 \cdot 25} = \sqrt{100} = 10$ and $\sqrt{4} \cdot \sqrt{25} = 2 \cdot 5 = 10$, then $\sqrt{4 \cdot 25} = \sqrt{4} \cdot \sqrt{25}$. This example illustrates the following property of radicals:

Property. The square root of a product of non-negative numbers is equal to the product of the square roots of the numbers.

In general, if a and b are non-negative numbers and n is a natural number, it can be proved that

$$\sqrt[n]{a \cdot b} = \sqrt[n]{a} \cdot \sqrt[n]{b}$$

Hence, $\sqrt{a \cdot b} = \sqrt{a} \cdot \sqrt{b}$. Also, $\sqrt[3]{a \cdot b} = \sqrt[3]{a} \cdot \sqrt[3]{b}$.

These rules permit us to transform a radical into an equivalent radical, as is illustrated in the following example:

$$\sqrt{12} = \sqrt{4 \cdot 3} = \sqrt{4}\sqrt{3} = 2\sqrt{3}$$

Observe that we expressed 12 as a product of 4, the largest perfect square factor of 12, and 3. Then we expressed $\sqrt{4}$ as 2. Also,

$$\sqrt[3]{24} = \sqrt[3]{8 \cdot 3} = \sqrt[3]{8}\sqrt[3]{3} = 2\sqrt[3]{3}$$

Observe that we expressed 24 as the product of 8, the largest perfect cube factor of 24, and 3. Then we expressed $\sqrt[3]{8}$ as 2.

When we expressed $\sqrt{12}$ as $2\sqrt{3}$, we simplified $\sqrt{12}$. When we expressed $\sqrt[3]{24}$ as $2\sqrt[3]{3}$, we simplified $\sqrt[3]{24}$.

A radical is considered to be in the **simplest form** when:

1. The radicand does not have a factor whose indicated root may be taken exactly. Thus, $\sqrt{80}$ and $\sqrt[3]{24}$ are *not* in simplest form. However, $4\sqrt{5}$ and $2\sqrt[3]{3}$ are in simplest form.

2. The radicand is not a fraction. Thus $\sqrt{\dfrac{5}{9}}$ is not in simplest form. Later we will learn how to transform $\sqrt{\dfrac{5}{9}}$ to $\frac{1}{3}\sqrt{5}$, which is in simplest form.

Note. In radicals whose index is an even number, if the radicand involves variables, assume that these variables represent positive numbers only.

~~~~~~~~~~ *MODEL PROBLEMS* ~~~~~~~~~~

In 1–6, simplify the radical.

1. $\sqrt{80}$ **2.** $\sqrt[3]{48}$ **3.** $3\sqrt{75}$ **4.** $\frac{1}{2}\sqrt{48}$ **5.** $-4\sqrt[3]{54}$ **6.** $\sqrt{8c^3 d^6}$

Solution:

	1. $\sqrt{80}$	**2.** $\sqrt[3]{48}$
How To Proceed	*Solution*	*Solution*
1. Factor the radicand, using the largest perfect power as one of the factors.	1. $\sqrt{80} = \sqrt{16 \cdot 5}$ (16 is the largest perfect square factor of 80.)	1. $\sqrt[3]{48} = \sqrt[3]{8 \cdot 6}$ (8 is the largest perfect cube factor of 48.)

2. Express the root of the product as the product of the roots of the factors, using the same index.

2. $\sqrt{80} = \sqrt{16} \cdot \sqrt{5}$

2. $\sqrt[3]{48} = \sqrt[3]{8} \cdot \sqrt[3]{6}$

3. Simplify the radical having the perfect power.

3. $\sqrt{80} = 4\sqrt{5}$ *Ans.*

3. $\sqrt[3]{48} = 2\sqrt[3]{6}$ *Ans.*

3. $3\sqrt{75} = 3\sqrt{25 \cdot 3} = 3\sqrt{25} \cdot \sqrt{3} = 3 \cdot 5\sqrt{3} = 15\sqrt{3}$ *Ans.*

4. $\frac{1}{2}\sqrt{48} = \frac{1}{2}\sqrt{16 \cdot 3} = \frac{1}{2}\sqrt{16} \cdot \sqrt{3} = \frac{1}{2} \cdot 4\sqrt{3} = 2\sqrt{3}$ *Ans.*

5. $-4\sqrt[3]{54} = -4\sqrt[3]{27 \cdot 2} = -4\sqrt[3]{27} \cdot \sqrt[3]{2} = -4 \cdot 3\sqrt[3]{2} = -12\sqrt[3]{2}$ *Ans.*

6. $\sqrt{8c^3d^6} = \sqrt{4c^2d^6 \cdot 2c} = \sqrt{4c^2d^6} \cdot \sqrt{2c} = 2cd^3\sqrt{2c}$ *Ans.*

Exercises

In 1–40, simplify the radical.

1. $\sqrt{45}$ **2.** $\sqrt{40}$ **3.** $-\sqrt{28}$ **4.** $\sqrt{98}$

5. $\sqrt{108}$ **6.** $-\sqrt{200}$ **7.** $\sqrt{162}$ **8.** $\sqrt{300}$

9. $-\sqrt{500}$ **10.** $\sqrt[3]{24}$ **11.** $\sqrt[3]{250}$ **12.** $-\sqrt[3]{40}$

13. $5\sqrt{8}$ **14.** $4\sqrt{28}$ **15.** $-7\sqrt{20}$ **16.** $3\sqrt{80}$

17. $2\sqrt{45}$ **18.** $-4\sqrt{98}$ **19.** $\frac{1}{3}\sqrt{27}$ **20.** $\frac{1}{2}\sqrt{48}$

21. $-\frac{1}{3}\sqrt{50}$ **22.** $\frac{3}{4}\sqrt{80}$ **23.** $\frac{3}{8}\sqrt{80}$ **24.** $-\frac{4}{5}\sqrt{150}$

25. $\sqrt{x^3}$ **26.** $\sqrt{x^2y}$ **27.** $5\sqrt{rs^4}$ **28.** $\sqrt{r^2s^3}$

29. $\sqrt{5x^3y}$ **30.** $3\sqrt{3x^2y^5}$ **31.** $\sqrt{25y}$ **32.** $\sqrt{4r^2s^2}$

33. $5\sqrt{9x^5y^3}$ **34.** $\sqrt{40s^2}$ **35.** $\sqrt{12r^4s^3}$ **36.** $6\sqrt{8x^3y^5}$

37. $\sqrt[3]{54}$ **38.** $3\sqrt[3]{5x^3}$ **39.** $\sqrt[3]{16y^7}$ **40.** $-\sqrt[3]{8y^4}$

In 41–44, use the table on page 757 to approximate the expression to the nearest tenth.

41. $\sqrt{300}$ **42.** $-\frac{2}{5}\sqrt{175}$ **43.** $-4 + \sqrt{200}$ **44.** $-5 - \sqrt{500}$

45. *a.* Does $\sqrt{36+64} = \sqrt{36} + \sqrt{64}$?

    b. Is finding a square root always distributive over addition?

    c. When does $\sqrt{x+y} = \sqrt{x} + \sqrt{y}$?

    d. Does $\sqrt{100-64} = \sqrt{100} - \sqrt{64}$?

    e. Is finding a square root always distributive over subtraction?

    f. When does $\sqrt{x-y} = \sqrt{x} - \sqrt{y}$?

46. *a.* Use the properties of the set of real numbers to prove that $\sqrt{a \cdot b} = \sqrt{a} \cdot \sqrt{b}$ where a and b are non-negative. (*Hint:* Show $(\sqrt{a} \cdot \sqrt{b})^2 = ab$.)

    b. Is finding a square root of the product of two non-negative numbers always distributive over multiplication?

47. *a.* Use the properties of the set of real numbers to prove that $\sqrt[n]{a \cdot b} = \sqrt[n]{a} \cdot \sqrt[n]{b}$ where a and b are non-negative.

    b. Is finding the *n*th root of the product of two non-negative numbers always distributive over multiplication?

7. Simplifying a Radical Whose Radicand Is a Fraction

Since $\sqrt{\dfrac{4}{25}} = \dfrac{2}{5}$ and $\dfrac{\sqrt{4}}{\sqrt{25}} = \dfrac{2}{5}$, then $\sqrt{\dfrac{4}{25}} = \dfrac{\sqrt{4}}{\sqrt{25}}$. This example illustrates the following property of radicals:

Property. The square root of a quotient of non-negative numbers is equal to the quotient of the square roots of the numbers.

In general, if a and b are non-negative numbers, $b \neq 0$, and n is a positive integer, it can be proved that

$$\sqrt[n]{\frac{a}{b}} = \frac{\sqrt[n]{a}}{\sqrt[n]{b}}$$

Hence, $\sqrt{\dfrac{a}{b}} = \dfrac{\sqrt{a}}{\sqrt{b}}$ and $\sqrt[3]{\dfrac{a}{b}} = \dfrac{\sqrt[3]{a}}{\sqrt[3]{b}}$. Thus, $\sqrt{\dfrac{4}{9}} = \dfrac{\sqrt{4}}{\sqrt{9}} = \dfrac{2}{3}$ and $\sqrt[3]{\dfrac{125}{27}} = \dfrac{\sqrt[3]{125}}{\sqrt[3]{27}} = \dfrac{5}{3}$.

〜〜〜〜〜〜 *MODEL PROBLEMS* 〜〜〜〜〜〜

In 1–6, simplify the radical

1. $\sqrt{\dfrac{2}{3}}$ **2.** $\sqrt[3]{\dfrac{1}{2}}$ **3.** $\sqrt{\dfrac{7}{12}}$ **4.** $4\sqrt[3]{\dfrac{1}{4}}$

Solution:

1. $\sqrt{\dfrac{2}{3}}$ 2. $\sqrt[3]{\dfrac{1}{2}}$

How To Proceed	*Solution*	*Solution*
1. Transform the radicand into an equivalent fraction whose denominator is the least perfect power.	1. $\sqrt{\dfrac{2}{3}} = \sqrt{\dfrac{2}{3} \cdot \dfrac{3}{3}}$ $= \sqrt{\dfrac{6}{9}}$	1. $\sqrt[3]{\dfrac{1}{2}} = \sqrt[3]{\dfrac{1}{2} \cdot \dfrac{4}{4}}$ $= \sqrt[3]{\dfrac{4}{8}}$
2. Express the root of the quotient as the quotient of the root of the numerator divided by the root of the denominator, using the same index.	2. $= \dfrac{\sqrt{6}}{\sqrt{9}}$	2. $= \dfrac{\sqrt[3]{4}}{\sqrt[3]{8}}$
3. Find the root of the denominator.	3. $= \dfrac{\sqrt{6}}{3}$ *Ans.*	3. $= \dfrac{\sqrt[3]{4}}{2}$ *Ans.*

3. $\sqrt{\dfrac{7}{12}} = \sqrt{\dfrac{7}{12} \cdot \dfrac{3}{3}} = \sqrt{\dfrac{21}{36}} = \dfrac{\sqrt{21}}{\sqrt{36}} = \dfrac{\sqrt{21}}{6}$ or $\tfrac{1}{6}\sqrt{21}$ *Ans.*

4. $4\sqrt[3]{\dfrac{1}{4}} = 4\sqrt[3]{\dfrac{1}{4} \cdot \dfrac{2}{2}} = 4\sqrt[3]{\dfrac{2}{8}} = 4\dfrac{\sqrt[3]{2}}{\sqrt[3]{8}} = 4\dfrac{\sqrt[3]{2}}{2} = 2\sqrt[3]{2}$ *Ans.*

Exercises

In 1–24, simplify the radical.

1. $\sqrt{\dfrac{3}{4}}$ **2.** $8\sqrt{\dfrac{7}{16}}$ **3.** $\sqrt{\dfrac{12}{25}}$ **4.** $2\sqrt{\dfrac{75}{64}}$

5. $\sqrt{\dfrac{1}{2}}$ **6.** $\sqrt{\dfrac{1}{3}}$ **7.** $10\sqrt{\dfrac{1}{5}}$ **8.** $3\sqrt{\dfrac{1}{6}}$

9. $\sqrt{\dfrac{2}{3}}$ **10.** $5\sqrt{\dfrac{3}{5}}$ **11.** $6\sqrt{\dfrac{11}{2}}$ **12.** $\sqrt{\dfrac{8}{7}}$

13. $8\sqrt{\dfrac{9}{2}}$ **14.** $9\sqrt{\dfrac{4}{3}}$ **15.** $\sqrt{\dfrac{7}{18}}$ **16.** $\sqrt{\dfrac{9}{32}}$

17. $5\sqrt{\dfrac{49}{20}}$ **18.** $\sqrt[3]{\dfrac{1}{2}}$ **19.** $\sqrt[3]{\dfrac{4}{9}}$ **20.** $9\sqrt[3]{\dfrac{8}{3}}$

21. $\sqrt{\dfrac{a}{b^2}}$ **22.** $\sqrt{\dfrac{x^2}{y}}$ **23.** $\sqrt{\dfrac{s}{6}}$ **24.** $\sqrt{\dfrac{2s}{g}}$

In 25–28, find the value of the radical, correct to the nearest tenth.

25. $\sqrt{\frac{5}{4}}$ **26.** $\sqrt{\frac{1}{3}}$ **27.** $20\sqrt{\frac{1}{5}}$ **28.** $6\sqrt{\frac{9}{2}}$

8. Adding or Subtracting Radicals That Have the Same Index

ADDING OR SUBTRACTING LIKE RADICALS

Like radicals are radicals that have the *same index* and the *same radicand*. Thus, $5\sqrt{3}$ and $2\sqrt{3}$ are like radicals, as are $8\sqrt[3]{5}$ and $3\sqrt[3]{5}$. However, $3\sqrt{18}$ and $5\sqrt{2}$ are not like radicals; also, $5\sqrt{3}$ and $2\sqrt[3]{3}$ are not like radicals.

To add or subtract like radicals, use the distributive property as follows:

$$5\sqrt{3} + 2\sqrt{3} = (5+2)\sqrt{3} = 7\sqrt{3}$$
$$8\sqrt[3]{5} - 3\sqrt[3]{5} = (8-3)\sqrt[3]{5} = 5\sqrt[3]{5}$$

Procedure. To add (or subtract) like radicals:
1. Add (or subtract) the coefficients of the radicals.
2. Multiply the sum (or difference) obtained by the common radical.

ADDING OR SUBTRACTING UNLIKE RADICALS

The sum of the unlike radicals $\sqrt{7}$ and $\sqrt{2}$ is indicated as $\sqrt{7} + \sqrt{2}$; the difference is indicated as $\sqrt{7} - \sqrt{2}$. Neither of these can be represented as a single term.

However, when it is possible to transform the unlike radicals into equivalent radicals all of which are like radicals, the resulting like radicals can be added or subtracted. For example,

$$\sqrt{12} + \sqrt{27} = \sqrt{4 \cdot 3} + \sqrt{9 \cdot 3}$$
$$= \sqrt{4}\sqrt{3} + \sqrt{9}\sqrt{3}$$
$$= 2\sqrt{3} + 3\sqrt{3} = (2+3)\sqrt{3} = 5\sqrt{3}$$

〰〰〰〰〰〰〰 *MODEL PROBLEMS* 〰〰〰〰〰〰〰

In 1 and 2, combine the radicals.

         1. $5\sqrt{18} - \sqrt{72}$ **2.** $\sqrt{\frac{1}{3}} + \sqrt{75} - \sqrt{2}$

How To Proceed	Solution	Solution
1. Simplify each radical.	1. $5\sqrt{18} - \sqrt{72}$ $= 5\sqrt{9} \cdot \sqrt{2} -$ $\quad \sqrt{36} \cdot \sqrt{2}$ $= 15\sqrt{2} - 6\sqrt{2}$	1. $\sqrt{\frac{1}{3}} + \sqrt{75} - \sqrt{2}$ $= \sqrt{\frac{1}{3} \cdot \frac{3}{3}} + \sqrt{25} \cdot \sqrt{3} - \sqrt{2}$ $= \dfrac{\sqrt{3}}{3} + 5\sqrt{3} - \sqrt{2}$
2. Combine like radicals by using the distributive property.	2. $= (15 - 6)\sqrt{2}$ $= 9\sqrt{2}$ *Ans.*	2. $= (\frac{1}{3} + 5)\sqrt{3} - \sqrt{2}$ $= 5\frac{1}{3}\sqrt{3} - \sqrt{2}$ *Ans.*

Exercises

In 1–19, combine the radicals.

1. $5\sqrt{2} + 6\sqrt{2}$ **2.** $4\sqrt{3} - 4\sqrt{3}$ **3.** $\sqrt{45} + \sqrt{20}$

4. $\sqrt{27} + \sqrt{12}$ **5.** $\sqrt{50} - \sqrt{8}$ **6.** $\sqrt{45} - \sqrt{80}$

7. $7\sqrt{28} - 4\sqrt{63}$ **8.** $3\sqrt[3]{16} + 5\sqrt[3]{54}$ **9.** $\frac{1}{2}\sqrt{20} + \sqrt{45}$

10. $4\sqrt{18} - \frac{3}{4}\sqrt{32}$ **11.** $\sqrt{32} + \sqrt{\frac{1}{2}}$ **12.** $9\sqrt{\frac{1}{3}} - 4\sqrt{\frac{1}{12}}$

13. $\sqrt{16x} + \sqrt{25x}$ **14.** $4\sqrt{49c} - \frac{1}{2}\sqrt{4c}$ **15.** $9\sqrt{c^3} - c\sqrt{4c}$

16. $\sqrt{32} - 5\sqrt{8} + 2\sqrt{50}$ **17.** $\sqrt{27x^2} + 2\sqrt{75x^2} - 2x\sqrt{12}$

18. $5\sqrt{6} - 4\sqrt{\frac{3}{2}} + 9\sqrt{\frac{2}{3}}$ **19.** $\sqrt[3]{24} + 5\sqrt[3]{3} - 6\sqrt[3]{\frac{1}{9}}$

SUMS INVOLVING IRRATIONAL NUMBERS

The number $5 + \sqrt{5}$, which represents the sum of the rational number 5 and the irrational number $\sqrt{5}$, is an irrational number. This example illustrates the following statement, whose truth we will assume:

The sum of a rational number and an irrational number is an irrational number. (See principle 1 on page 299.)

The sum $4\sqrt{3} + 2\sqrt{3} = 6\sqrt{3}$ is an irrational number, whereas the sum $(4 + \sqrt{3}) + (2 - \sqrt{3}) = 6$ is a rational number.

Therefore, we say:

The sum of two irrational numbers may be either rational or irrational.

Exercises

In 1–4, state whether the sum is a rational number or an irrational number.

1. $(5 + \sqrt{2}) + (\sqrt{4} + \sqrt{9})$

2. $(\sqrt{7} + 2\sqrt{3}) + (\sqrt{7} - 2\sqrt{3})$

3. $(6 + 2\sqrt{8}) + (-2 - 2\sqrt{8})$

4. $(9 + 2\pi) + (25 + 8\pi)$

9. Multiplying Radicals That Have the Same Index

MULTIPLYING MONOMIALS CONTAINING RADICALS

We have learned that $\sqrt[n]{a \cdot b} = \sqrt[n]{a} \cdot \sqrt[n]{b}$, when a and b are non-negative and n is a positive integer. By using the symmetric property of equality, we can interchange the members of the equation and obtain the following rule:

In general, if a and b are non-negative numbers and n is a positive integer,

$$\sqrt[n]{a} \cdot \sqrt[n]{b} = \sqrt[n]{a \cdot b}$$

Therefore, we say:

The product of two radicals with the same index is equivalent to the root of the product of their radicands, using the same index.

For example, $\sqrt{5} \cdot \sqrt{7} = \sqrt{35}$ and $\sqrt[3]{2} \cdot \sqrt[3]{5} = \sqrt[3]{10}$. To multiply $7\sqrt{3}$ by $5\sqrt{2}$, we use the commutative and associative properties of multiplication as follows:

$$(7\sqrt{3})(5\sqrt{2}) = (7)(5)(\sqrt{3})(\sqrt{2}) = (5 \cdot 7)(\sqrt{3 \cdot 2}) = 35\sqrt{6}$$

~~~~~~~~~~ *MODEL PROBLEMS* ~~~~~~~~~~

1. Multiply: $10\sqrt{2} \cdot \frac{1}{2}\sqrt{10}$

How To Proceed	*Solution*
1. Multiply the coefficients; multiply the radicands.	1. $10\sqrt{2} \cdot \frac{1}{2}\sqrt{10}$ $= (10 \cdot \frac{1}{2})(\sqrt{2} \cdot \sqrt{10})$ $= 5\sqrt{20}$
2. Simplify the resulting radical.	2. $= 5\sqrt{4 \cdot 5}$ $= 5\sqrt{4} \cdot \sqrt{5}$ $= 10\sqrt{5}$ *Ans.*

In 2–4, multiply the radicals.

2. $(3\sqrt{2})^2$ **3.** $\frac{2}{3}\sqrt[3]{9} \cdot 6\sqrt[3]{6}$ **4.** $\sqrt{8x^3} \cdot \sqrt{3x^2y}$

Solution:

2. $(3\sqrt{2})^2 = 3\sqrt{2} \cdot 3\sqrt{2} = (3 \cdot 3)\sqrt{2} \cdot \sqrt{2} = 9(2) = 18$ *Ans.*

3. $\frac{2}{3}\sqrt[3]{9} \cdot 6\sqrt[3]{6} = (\frac{2}{3} \cdot 6)\sqrt[3]{9} \cdot \sqrt[3]{6} = 4\sqrt[3]{54} = 4\sqrt[3]{27} \cdot \sqrt[3]{2} = 4 \cdot 3\sqrt[3]{2} =$
$$12\sqrt[3]{2} \quad Ans.$$

4. $\sqrt{8x^3}\sqrt{3x^2y} = \sqrt{24x^5y} = \sqrt{4x^4 \cdot 6xy} = \sqrt{4x^4}\sqrt{6xy} = 2x^2\sqrt{6xy}$ *Ans.*

MULTIPLYING POLYNOMIALS CONTAINING RADICALS

To find the product $\sqrt{2}(\sqrt{5} + \sqrt{7})$, we use the distributive property as follows:

$$\sqrt{2}(\sqrt{5} + \sqrt{7}) = \sqrt{2}\sqrt{5} + \sqrt{2}\sqrt{7} = \sqrt{10} + \sqrt{14}$$

To find the product $(3 + \sqrt{5})(4 - \sqrt{5})$, we use the distributive property of multiplication and arrange the solution in the same way that was previously used in finding the product of two binomials.

$$
\begin{array}{r}
3 + \sqrt{5} \\
4 - \sqrt{5} \\
\hline
12 + 4\sqrt{5} \\
-3\sqrt{5} - 5 \\
\hline
12 + \sqrt{5} - 5 = 7 + \sqrt{5}
\end{array}
$$

⌇⌇⌇⌇⌇ *MODEL PROBLEMS* ⌇⌇⌇⌇⌇

1. Multiply: $3\sqrt{3}(4\sqrt{6} - 3\sqrt{24})$

Solution:

$3\sqrt{3}(4\sqrt{6} - 3\sqrt{24})$
$= (3\sqrt{3})(4\sqrt{6}) - (3\sqrt{3})(3\sqrt{24})$
$= 12\sqrt{18} - 9\sqrt{72}$
$= 12\sqrt{9}\sqrt{2} - 9\sqrt{36}\sqrt{2}$
$= 36\sqrt{2} - 54\sqrt{2}$
$= -18\sqrt{2}$ *Ans.*

2. Multiply: $(5 + 2\sqrt{3})(2 - 3\sqrt{3})$

Solution:

$$
\begin{array}{r}
5 + 2\sqrt{3} \\
2 - 3\sqrt{3} \\
\hline
10 + 4\sqrt{3} \\
-15\sqrt{3} - 6\sqrt{9} \\
\hline
10 - 11\sqrt{3} - 18 \\
= -8 - 11\sqrt{3} \quad Ans.
\end{array}
$$

Exercises

In 1–36, multiply or raise to the power as indicated. Then simplify the result.

1. $\sqrt{8} \cdot \sqrt{2}$

2. $2\sqrt{50} \cdot 3\sqrt{2}$

3. $\sqrt{6} \cdot \sqrt{3}$

4. $\sqrt{40} \cdot \sqrt{5}$

5. $2\sqrt{6} \cdot \sqrt{2}$

6. $4\sqrt{18} \cdot 5\sqrt{3}$

7. $\frac{3}{5}\sqrt{24} \cdot 10\sqrt{3}$

8. $\frac{1}{2}\sqrt{12} \cdot 10\sqrt{2}$

9. $4\sqrt{\frac{1}{2}} \cdot 8\sqrt{18}$

10. $4\sqrt{\frac{1}{3}} \cdot 2\sqrt{96}$

11. $\sqrt{x} \cdot \sqrt{x^3}$

12. $\sqrt{3b}\sqrt{12b^4}$

13. $\sqrt{4x} \cdot \sqrt{xy}$

14. $\sqrt{4c^3d}\sqrt{6cd^2}$

15. $(\sqrt{5})^2$

16. $(\sqrt{x})^2$

17. $(5\sqrt{3})^2$

18. $(\frac{1}{2}\sqrt{3})^2$

19. $\sqrt[3]{2} \cdot \sqrt[3]{4}$

20. $(\sqrt[3]{5})^3$

21. $5\sqrt[3]{4} \cdot 2\sqrt[3]{2}$

22. $\sqrt[3]{4x^2} \cdot \sqrt[3]{6x^4}$

23. $(\sqrt{3x})^2$

24. $(5\sqrt{3y})^2$

25. $(\sqrt{x+1})^2$

26. $(\sqrt{3x-4})^2$

27. $2(\sqrt{5x-3})^2$

28. $\sqrt{2}(5\sqrt{2} + 3\sqrt{8} - 4\sqrt{32})$

29. $2\sqrt{3}(4\sqrt{5} - 3\sqrt{20} - \sqrt{45})$

30. $(4 + \sqrt{2})(3 + \sqrt{2})$

31. $(5 + \sqrt{7})^2$

32. $(2 + \sqrt{5})(8 - \sqrt{5})$

33. $(4 + \sqrt{3})(4 - \sqrt{3})$

34. $(5 + 6\sqrt{3})(5 - 6\sqrt{3})$

35. $(4\sqrt{3} + \sqrt{5})(4\sqrt{3} - \sqrt{5})$

36. $(\sqrt{x} + \sqrt{y})(\sqrt{x} + \sqrt{y})$

37. If $x = 3 + \sqrt{2}$, the value of x^2 is

   (1) 11   (2) $11 + 6\sqrt{2}$ (3) $9 + \sqrt{2}$ (4) 5

38. If $x = 3 - \sqrt{2}$, find the value of $x^2 - 6x + 7$.

PRODUCTS INVOLVING IRRATIONAL NUMBERS

The number $5\sqrt{3}$, which represents the product of the rational number 5 and the irrational number $\sqrt{3}$, is an irrational number.

This example illustrates the following statement, whose truth we will assume:

The product of a nonzero rational number and an irrational number is an irrational number. (See principle 2, page 299.)

The product $(\sqrt{8})(\sqrt{2}) = 4$ is a rational number; the product $(\sqrt{5})(\sqrt{2}) = \sqrt{10}$ is an irrational number.

Therefore, we say:

The product of two irrational numbers may be either rational or irrational.

Exercises

In 1–4, state whether the product is a rational number or an irrational number.

1. $(\sqrt{9} - \sqrt{1})(2 + \sqrt{3})$

2. $(7 + \sqrt{5})(3 - \sqrt{5})$

3. $(3\sqrt{7} + 2\sqrt{7})(\sqrt{7})$

4. $(\sqrt{4} + \sqrt{16})\pi$

10. Dividing Radicals That Have the Same Index

We already know that

$$\sqrt[n]{\frac{a}{b}} = \frac{\sqrt[n]{a}}{\sqrt[n]{b}}$$

when a is non-negative, b is positive, and n is a positive integer. By using the symmetric property of equality, we can interchange the members of the equation and obtain the following rule:

In general if a is non-negative, b is positive, and n is a positive integer:

$$\frac{\sqrt[n]{a}}{\sqrt[n]{b}} = \sqrt[n]{\frac{a}{b}}$$

Therefore, we say:

The quotient of two radicals with the same index is equivalent to the root of the quotient of their radicands, using the same index.

For example, $\dfrac{\sqrt{36}}{\sqrt{4}} = \sqrt{\dfrac{36}{4}} = \sqrt{9} = 3$ and $\dfrac{\sqrt[3]{64}}{\sqrt[3]{8}} = \sqrt[3]{\dfrac{64}{8}} = \sqrt[3]{8} = 2.$

To divide $8\sqrt{15}$ by $2\sqrt{3}$, we use the property of fractions, $\dfrac{ac}{bd} = \dfrac{a}{b} \cdot \dfrac{c}{d}.$ See how the division is performed:

$$\frac{8\sqrt{15}}{2\sqrt{3}} = \frac{8}{2} \cdot \frac{\sqrt{15}}{\sqrt{3}}$$

$$= \frac{8}{2} \sqrt{\frac{15}{3}}$$

$$= 4\sqrt{5}$$

〰〰〰〰〰〰〰 *MODEL PROBLEMS* 〰〰〰〰〰〰〰

1. Divide: $50\sqrt{24} \div 5\sqrt{2}$ **2.** Divide: $8\sqrt[3]{20c^4} \div 2\sqrt[3]{5c}$

How To Proceed	*Solution*	*Solution*
1. Divide the coefficients; divide the radicands.	1. $50\sqrt{24} \div 5\sqrt{2}$ $= \left(\dfrac{50}{5}\right)\left(\dfrac{\sqrt{24}}{\sqrt{2}}\right)$ $= 10\sqrt{12}$	1. $8\sqrt[3]{20c^4} \div 2\sqrt[3]{5c}$ $= \left(\dfrac{8}{2}\right)\left(\dfrac{\sqrt[3]{20c^4}}{\sqrt[3]{5c}}\right)$ $= 4\sqrt[3]{4c^3}$
2. Simplify the resulting radical.	2. $= 10\sqrt{4 \cdot 3}$ $= 10\sqrt{4} \cdot \sqrt{3}$ $= 20\sqrt{3}$ *Ans.*	2. $= 4\sqrt[3]{c^3 \cdot 4}$ $= 4\sqrt[3]{c^3} \cdot \sqrt[3]{4}$ $= 4c\sqrt[3]{4}$ *Ans.*

〰〰〰〰〰〰〰〰〰〰〰〰〰〰〰〰〰〰〰〰〰〰〰〰〰〰

Exercises

In 1–17, divide. Then simplify the quotient.

1. $\sqrt{50} \div \sqrt{2}$ **2.** $6\sqrt{45} \div 3\sqrt{5}$ **3.** $\sqrt{24} \div \sqrt{3}$

4. $8\sqrt{60} \div 4\sqrt{5}$ **5.** $10\sqrt{3} \div 5\sqrt{3}$ **6.** $4\sqrt{7} \div 8\sqrt{7}$

7. $\dfrac{15\sqrt{150}}{5\sqrt{2}}$ **8.** $\dfrac{6\sqrt{27}}{12\sqrt{3}}$ **9.** $\dfrac{2\sqrt{24}}{4\sqrt{3}}$ **10.** $\dfrac{18\sqrt{72}}{6\sqrt{6}}$

11. $\dfrac{\sqrt[3]{16}}{\sqrt[3]{2}}$ **12.** $\dfrac{4\sqrt[3]{15}}{2\sqrt[3]{3}}$ **13.** $\dfrac{\sqrt{12d^5}}{\sqrt{3d}}$ **14.** $\dfrac{\sqrt{75x^3y}}{\sqrt{3xy}}$

15. $\dfrac{\sqrt{32} + \sqrt{50}}{\sqrt{2}}$ **16.** $\dfrac{\sqrt{15} - \sqrt{180}}{\sqrt{3}}$ **17.** $\dfrac{10\sqrt{72} + 15\sqrt{18}}{\sqrt{3}}$

In 18–21, simplify the expression. Then approximate the result to the nearest tenth.

18. $\dfrac{\sqrt{27} + \sqrt{15}}{\sqrt{3}}$ **19.** $\dfrac{9 + \sqrt{18}}{3}$ **20.** $\dfrac{4 - \sqrt{8}}{2}$ **21.** $\dfrac{-5 - \sqrt{50}}{5}$

QUOTIENTS INVOLVING IRRATIONAL NUMBERS

The number $\dfrac{\sqrt{3}}{5}$, which represents the quotient of the irrational number $\sqrt{3}$

and the rational number 5, is an irrational number. Also, the number $\dfrac{5}{\sqrt{3}}$,

which represents the quotient of the rational number 5 and the irrational number $\sqrt{3}$, is an irrational number.

These examples illustrate the following statement, whose truth we will assume:

A quotient involving a nonzero rational number and an irrational number is an irrational number. (See principle 3, page 299.)

The quotient $(\sqrt{8}) \div (\sqrt{2}) = \sqrt{4} = 2$ is a rational number, whereas the quotient $(\sqrt{15}) \div (\sqrt{5}) = \sqrt{3}$ is an irrational number.

Therefore, we say:

The quotient of two irrational numbers may be either rational or irrational.

Exercises

In 1–4, state whether the quotient is a rational number or an irrational number.

1. $\sqrt{32} \div \sqrt{8}$ **2.** $6 \div \sqrt[3]{7}$ **3.** $(\sqrt{2} + 8) \div 2$ **4.** $\sqrt{48} \div \sqrt{2}$

11. Rationalizing an Irrational Monomial Radical Denominator

To find the approximate value of $\dfrac{1}{\sqrt{3}}$, we can use 1.732 as the approximate

value of $\sqrt{3}$ and then divide 1 by 1.732. The result obtained by this inconvenient

computation is $\dfrac{1}{\sqrt{3}} \approx .577$.

To simplify the computation, we *rationalize the denominator* of the fraction

$\dfrac{1}{\sqrt{3}}$. That is, we transform the fraction $\dfrac{1}{\sqrt{3}}$, which has an irrational denomina-

tor, into an equivalent fraction which has a rational denominator. We multiply

$\dfrac{1}{\sqrt{3}}$ by 1 in the form of $\dfrac{\sqrt{3}}{\sqrt{3}}$ and obtain:

$$\frac{1}{\sqrt{3}} = \frac{1}{\sqrt{3}} \cdot \frac{\sqrt{3}}{\sqrt{3}} = \frac{\sqrt{3}}{3} \approx \frac{1.732}{3} \approx .577$$

~~~~~~~~~~ *MODEL PROBLEMS* ~~~~~~~~~~

In 1 and 2, rationalize the denominator. **1.** $\dfrac{15}{\sqrt{20}}$ **2.** $\dfrac{5\sqrt[3]{3}}{7\sqrt[3]{2}}$

How To Proceed | *Solution* | *Solution*

1. Multiply the given fraction by 1 represented as a fraction whose numerator and denominator are both the least radical needed to make the denominator of the resulting fraction a rational number.

1. $\dfrac{15}{\sqrt{20}}$

$= \dfrac{15}{\sqrt{20}} \cdot \dfrac{\sqrt{5}}{\sqrt{5}}$

(Use $\sqrt{5}$ rather than $\sqrt{20}$.)

$= \dfrac{15\sqrt{5}}{\sqrt{100}}$

1. $\dfrac{5\sqrt[3]{3}}{7\sqrt[3]{2}}$

$= \dfrac{5\sqrt[3]{3}}{7\sqrt[3]{2}} \cdot \dfrac{\sqrt[3]{4}}{\sqrt[3]{4}}$

$= \dfrac{5\sqrt[3]{12}}{7\sqrt[3]{8}}$

2. Simplify the resulting fraction.

2. $= \dfrac{15\sqrt{5}}{10}$

$= \dfrac{3\sqrt{5}}{2}$ *Ans.*

2. $= \dfrac{5\sqrt[3]{12}}{7 \cdot 2}$

$= \dfrac{5\sqrt[3]{12}}{14}$ *Ans.*

~~~~~~~~~~~~~~~~~~~~

Exercises

In 1–25, rationalize the denominator.

1. $\dfrac{5}{\sqrt{2}}$ **2.** $\dfrac{7}{\sqrt{3}}$ **3.** $\dfrac{3}{\sqrt{5}}$ **4.** $\dfrac{2}{\sqrt{7}}$ **5.** $\dfrac{9}{\sqrt{11}}$

6. $\dfrac{4}{\sqrt{2}}$ **7.** $\dfrac{15}{\sqrt{5}}$ **8.** $\dfrac{14}{\sqrt{7}}$ **9.** $\dfrac{12}{\sqrt{6}}$ **10.** $\dfrac{12}{\sqrt{18}}$

11. $\dfrac{4}{\sqrt{12}}$ **12.** $\dfrac{25}{\sqrt{50}}$ **13.** $\dfrac{15}{\sqrt{20}}$ **14.** $\dfrac{6}{2\sqrt{3}}$ **15.** $\dfrac{40}{2\sqrt{20}}$

16. $\dfrac{18}{4\sqrt{12}}$ **17.** $\dfrac{14}{3\sqrt{8}}$ **18.** $\dfrac{\sqrt{3}}{\sqrt{5}}$ **19.** $\dfrac{10\sqrt{2}}{\sqrt{5}}$ **20.** $\dfrac{6\sqrt{3}}{\sqrt{8}}$

21. $\dfrac{15\sqrt{2}}{\sqrt{12}}$ **22.** $\dfrac{6}{\sqrt[3]{4}}$ **23.** $\dfrac{10}{\sqrt[3]{25}}$ **24.** $\dfrac{8\sqrt[3]{4}}{\sqrt[3]{2}}$ **25.** $\dfrac{7\sqrt[3]{18}}{3\sqrt[3]{9}}$

In 26–30, transform the fraction into an equivalent fraction that does not have a radical in the denominator.

26. $\dfrac{1}{\sqrt{x}}$ **27.** $\dfrac{\sqrt{c}}{\sqrt{d}}$ **28.** $\dfrac{9}{\sqrt{3a}}$ **29.** $\dfrac{cd}{\sqrt{d}}$ **30.** $\dfrac{15x}{\sqrt{5x}}$

In 31–34, rationalize the denominator and simplify the resulting fraction.

31. $\dfrac{\sqrt{18}+\sqrt{8}}{\sqrt{2}}$ **32.** $\dfrac{\sqrt{5}-1}{\sqrt{5}}$ **33.** $\dfrac{2\sqrt{3}-8}{\sqrt{2}}$ **34.** $\dfrac{\sqrt{3}-\sqrt{6}}{\sqrt{3}}$

In 35–39, approximate the value of the fraction to the nearest tenth.

35. $\dfrac{15}{\sqrt{3}}$ **36.** $\dfrac{4}{\sqrt{8}}$ **37.** $\dfrac{6}{\sqrt{6}}$ **38.** $\dfrac{9}{\sqrt{2}}$ **39.** $\dfrac{\sqrt{3}-1}{\sqrt{3}}$

40. The fraction $\dfrac{\sqrt{3}+\sqrt{2}}{\sqrt{2}}$ is equivalent to (1) $\sqrt{3}$ (2) $\dfrac{\sqrt{3}+2}{2}$ (3) $\dfrac{\sqrt{6}+2}{2}$

12. Rationalizing a Binomial Radical Denominator

The expressions $2+\sqrt{3}$ and $2-\sqrt{3}$ are called ***conjugate binomial radicals.*** Either of the binomials is called the ***conjugate*** of the other. Additional examples of conjugate binomial radicals are:

$$\sqrt{2}+\sqrt{5} \text{ and } \sqrt{2}-\sqrt{5}$$

$$2\sqrt{7}+5\sqrt{11} \text{ and } 2\sqrt{7}-5\sqrt{11}$$

Observe that in each example one of the binomials is the indicated sum of two numbers and the other is the indicated difference of the same two numbers.

The product $(5+\sqrt{3})(5-\sqrt{3})=25-3$, or 22, is a rational number. Also, the product $(\sqrt{5}+\sqrt{3})(\sqrt{5}-\sqrt{3})=5-3$, or 2, is a rational number.

In general, when a and b are positive rational numbers, the following products are rational numbers:

$$(a + \sqrt{b})(a - \sqrt{b}) = a^2 - b$$

$$(\sqrt{a} + \sqrt{b})(\sqrt{a} - \sqrt{b}) = a - b$$

We say:

The product of two conjugate binomial radicals is a rational number.

We make use of this fact in rationalizing a binomial radical denominator.

~~~~~~~~ *MODEL PROBLEMS* ~~~~~~~~

In 1 and 2, express each fraction as an equivalent fraction with a rational denominator.

1. $\dfrac{9}{3 - \sqrt{3}}$ 2. $\dfrac{3 - 5\sqrt{2}}{5 + 2\sqrt{2}}$

How To Proceed	*Solution*	*Solution*
1. Multiply the given fraction by 1 represented as a fraction whose numerator and denominator are both the conjugate of the denominator of the original fraction.	1. $\dfrac{9}{3 - \sqrt{3}}$ $= \dfrac{9}{3 - \sqrt{3}} \cdot \dfrac{3 + \sqrt{3}}{3 + \sqrt{3}}$ $= \dfrac{9(3 + \sqrt{3})}{9 - 3}$	1. $\dfrac{3 - 5\sqrt{2}}{5 + 2\sqrt{2}}$ $= \dfrac{3 - 5\sqrt{2}}{5 + 2\sqrt{2}} \cdot \dfrac{5 - 2\sqrt{2}}{5 - 2\sqrt{2}}$ $= \dfrac{15 - 31\sqrt{2} + 20}{25 - 8}$
2. Simplify the resulting fraction.	2. $= \dfrac{\overset{3}{\cancel{9}}(3 + \sqrt{3})}{\underset{2}{\cancel{6}}}$ $= \dfrac{3(3 + \sqrt{3})}{2}$ *Ans.*	2. $= \dfrac{35 - 31\sqrt{2}}{17}$ *Ans.*

Exercises

In 1–12, rationalize the denominator of the fraction.

1. $\dfrac{9}{3 - \sqrt{2}}$

2. $\dfrac{12}{3 - \sqrt{5}}$

3. $\dfrac{18}{\sqrt{3} - 3}$

4. $\dfrac{12}{\sqrt{5} - 2}$

5. $\dfrac{22}{2\sqrt{3} + 1}$

6. $\dfrac{44}{2\sqrt{5} - 3}$

7. $\dfrac{\sqrt{2} + 4}{\sqrt{2} - 1}$

8. $\dfrac{6 + \sqrt{3}}{4 - \sqrt{3}}$

9. $\dfrac{2\sqrt{3} - 1}{2\sqrt{3} + 1}$

10. $\dfrac{4 - 5\sqrt{2}}{7 + 3\sqrt{2}}$

11. $\dfrac{\sqrt{5} - \sqrt{3}}{\sqrt{5} - \sqrt{3}}$

12. $\dfrac{2\sqrt{5} + 3\sqrt{2}}{3\sqrt{5} - \sqrt{2}}$

In 13–15, express the fraction as an equivalent fraction with a rational denominator.

13. $\dfrac{5}{3 + \sqrt{2}}$

14. $\dfrac{1}{\sqrt{7} - 2}$

15. $\dfrac{3}{\sqrt{6} + 2}$

16. The expression $\dfrac{2}{\sqrt{3} - 1}$ is equivalent to   (1) $\dfrac{2\sqrt{3} + 1}{2}$ (2) $\sqrt{3} + 1$

(3) $\dfrac{\sqrt{3} + 1}{2}$ (4) $\sqrt{3}$

17. The fraction $\dfrac{6 - \sqrt{2}}{1 + \sqrt{2}}$ is equivalent to   (1) $7\sqrt{2} - 8$ (2) $\dfrac{8 - 7\sqrt{2}}{3}$

(3) $4 - 7\sqrt{2}$ (4) $8 - 7\sqrt{2}$

13. Solving Radical or Irrational Equations

A **radical equation** or **irrational equation** in one variable is an equation which has the variable in a radicand. For example, $\sqrt{x} = 5$ and $\sqrt{4 \sin x - 1} = 1$ are radical equations.

To solve a radical equation in which the radical is the only term of one side of the equation, we square both members of the equation if the radical is a square root, cube both members if the radical is a cube root, etc., in order to transform the equation into one which does not contain radicals.

To illustrate, let us solve the radical equations $\sqrt{x+1} = 5$ and $\sqrt{x+1} = -5$.

Solution	*Solution*
$\sqrt{x+1} = 5$	$\sqrt{x+1} = -5$
$(\sqrt{x+1})^2 = (5)^2$	$(\sqrt{x+1})^2 = (-5)^2$
$x+1 = 25$	$x+1 = 25$
$x = 24$	$x = 24$

Check	*Check*
$\sqrt{x+1} = 5$	$\sqrt{x+1} = -5$
$\sqrt{24+1} \overset{?}{=} 5$	$\sqrt{24+1} \overset{?}{=} -5$
$\sqrt{25} \overset{?}{=} 5$	$\sqrt{25} \overset{?}{=} -5$
$5 = 5$ (true)	$5 = -5$ (not true)

Observe that $\{24\}$ is the solution set of both the original equation $\sqrt{x+1} = 5$ and the derived equation $x+1 = 25$. Therefore, these two equations are equivalent equations whose solution set is $\{24\}$.

Observe that $\{24\}$ is the solution set of the derived equation $x+1 = 25$, but $\{24\}$ is not the solution set of the original equation. The original equation $\sqrt{x+1} = -5$ and the derived equation $x+1 = 25$ are not equivalent equations. Therefore, 24 is an ***extraneous value*** and must be rejected.

We see that when we solve an equation by squaring or cubing both members, the "squared" or the "cubed" equation and the original equations may not be equivalent equations. We must be careful to check the roots of the "squared" or the "cubed" equation in the given equation to see that these roots also satisfy the given equation. If they do not, they are extraneous values and we reject them.

The following procedure applies to the solution of a radical equation having a single radical in which the variable appears in the radicand.

Procedure. To solve a radical equation containing only one radical:
1. Isolate the radical on one side of the equation by transposing the remaining terms to the other side.
2. If the radical is a square root, square both sides; if the radical is a cube root, cube both sides; etc.
3. Solve the resulting equation.
4. Check to determine if the roots of the resulting equation are roots of the original equation. If not, reject any such root as an extraneous value.

Special procedures for radical equations containing two radicals are indicated in model problems 6 and 7 that follow.

~~~~~~~~~~~ **MODEL PROBLEMS** ~~~~~~~~~~~

In 1 and 2, solve and check.

1. $\sqrt{2x+1} - 1 = 4$

Solution:

$\sqrt{2x+1} - 1 = 4$
$\sqrt{2x+1} = 5$ Isolating the radical.
$2x + 1 = 25$ Squaring both sides.
$2x = 24$
$x = 12$

Check:

$\sqrt{2x+1} - 1 = 4$
$5 - 1 \overset{?}{=} 4$
$4 = 4$ (true)

Answer: $x = 12$, or the solution set is $\{12\}$.

2. $\sqrt{2x+1} - 1 = -4$

Solution:

$\sqrt{2x+1} - 1 = -4$
$\sqrt{2x+1} = -3$
$2x + 1 = 9$
$2x = 8$
$x = 4$

Check:

$\sqrt{2x+1} - 1 = -4$
$3 - 1 \overset{?}{=} -4$
$2 = -4$ (not true)

Hence, 4 is an extraneous value and must be rejected.

Answer: The equation has no root, or the solution set is the empty set $\varnothing$.

3. Solve and check: $\sqrt{x^2+9} - x = 1$

Solution:

$$\sqrt{x^2+9} - x = 1$$
$$\sqrt{x^2+9} = x + 1$$
$$(\sqrt{x^2+9})^2 = (x+1)^2$$
$$x^2 + 9 = x^2 + 2x + 1$$
$$8 = 2x$$
$$4 = x$$

Check:

$$\sqrt{x^2+9} - 4 = 1$$
$$\sqrt{25} - 4 \overset{?}{=} 1$$
$$5 - 4 \overset{?}{=} 1$$
$$1 = 1 \text{ (true)}$$

Answer: $x = 4$, or the solution set is $\{4\}$.

In 4 and 5, find the value of the trigonometric function.

4. $\sqrt{1 - \sin x} = \tfrac{1}{2}$

Solution:

$$\sqrt{1 - \sin x} = \tfrac{1}{2}$$
$$(\sqrt{1 - \sin x})^2 = (\tfrac{1}{2})^2$$
$$1 - \sin x = \tfrac{1}{4}$$
$$\tfrac{3}{4} = \sin x$$

Answer: $\sin x = \tfrac{3}{4}$

5. $5 - \sqrt{2 \tan x + 5} = 2$

Solution:

$$5 - \sqrt{2 \tan x + 5} = 2$$
$$3 = \sqrt{2 \tan x + 5}$$
$$9 = 2 \tan x + 5$$
$$4 = 2 \tan x$$
$$2 = \tan x$$

Answer: $\tan x = 2$

(The checks are left to the student.)

In 6 and 7, solve and check: (Special Procedures)

6. $\sqrt{2x + 1} = \dfrac{15}{\sqrt{2x + 1}}$

Solution:

$$\sqrt{2x + 1} = \dfrac{15}{\sqrt{2x + 1}}$$

Multiply each side by $\sqrt{2x + 1}$.
$$2x + 1 = 15$$
$$x = 7 \quad Ans.$$

7. $\sqrt{3y - 1} = 2\sqrt{8 - 2y}$

Solution:

$$\sqrt{3y - 1} = 2\sqrt{8 - 2y}$$
Square both sides.
$$(\sqrt{3y - 1})^2 = (2\sqrt{8 - 2y})^2$$
$$3y - 1 = 4(8 - 2y)$$
$$3y - 1 = 32 - 8y$$
$$11y = 33$$
$$y = 3 \quad Ans.$$

(The checks are left to the student.)

Exercises

In 1–18, solve the equation and check.

1. $\sqrt{x} = 7$

2. $\sqrt[3]{a} = 2$

3. $\sqrt{5x} = 5$

4. $\sqrt[3]{2b} = 4$

5. $4\sqrt{x} = 8$

6. $5\sqrt{5a} = 20$

7. $\sqrt{x - 5} = 3$

8. $\sqrt[3]{3a - 1} = 2$

9. $\sqrt{x + 3} = 5$

10. $7 - 3\sqrt{x} = 1$

11. $\sqrt{5a - 1} - 3 = 0$

12. $4\sqrt{a + 7} - 5 = 11$

13. $\sqrt{x^2 + 3} = x + 1$

14. $\sqrt{x^2 + 27} - 3 = x$

15. $x = 4 + \sqrt{x^2 - 32}$

16. $\dfrac{3}{\sqrt{x-5}} = \sqrt{x-5}$

17. $\sqrt{5x + 6} = \sqrt{9x - 2}$

18. $\sqrt[3]{5x + 1} - \sqrt[3]{2x - 8} = 0$

19. Solve for A: $R = \sqrt{\dfrac{A}{\pi}}$.

20. Solve for x: $7 - \sqrt{2x + 1} = 4$.

21. What value of x satisfies the equation $\sqrt{x^2 - 7} = x - 1$?

22. What value of x satisfies the equation $\sqrt{x^2 - 2x + 4} = x$?

23. Solve the equation $\sqrt{x^2 + 27} = 2x$ for x.

24. In the equation $\sqrt{2x + 3} - x = 0$, x is equal to (1) 3 only (2) -1 only (3) 3 and -1 (4) -3 and 1

25. The equation $x + \sqrt{x^2 + 3} = 3x$ has (1) both $+1$ and -1 as its roots (2) $+1$ as its only root (3) -1 as its only root (4) neither $+1$ nor -1 as its roots

26. Which equation has both 3 and 6 as roots? (1) $\sqrt{x-2} = \dfrac{3}{x}$

(2) $\sqrt{x-2} = \dfrac{x}{3}$ (3) $\sqrt{x-2} = -x + 4$ (4) $\sqrt{x-2} = x - 4$

27. Solve the equation $\sqrt[3]{x - 2} = \frac{1}{2}$ for the value of x.

In 28–33, show that the solution set is the empty set $\varnothing$.

28. $\sqrt{2x + 1} = -3$

29. $2\sqrt{x - 1} = -4$

30. $\sqrt{3x - 2} + 1 = 0$

31. $3 + \sqrt{5 - x} = 2$

32. $2 - \sqrt{3x} = 5$

33. $3 - 2\sqrt{x^2 - 1} = 5$

In 34–39, find the value of the trigonometric function that appears in the equation.

34. $\sqrt{\sin x} = \frac{1}{2}$

35. $\sqrt{\tan x + 3} = 3$

36. $\sqrt{1 - \cos x} = \frac{1}{2}$

37. $3 - \sqrt{1 + 3\tan x} = 1$

38. $3 + \sqrt{10\sin x - 1} = 5$

39. $\sqrt{1 + \tan x} = \sqrt{2 - \tan x}$

In 40–43, find x to the nearest degree, if $0° < x < 90°$.

40. $\sqrt{\cos x} = \frac{1}{2}$

41. $\sqrt{1 + 4\sin x} = 2$

42. $\sqrt{1 - \sin x} = 2\sqrt{\sin x}$

43. $\sqrt[3]{1 - \cos x} = \frac{1}{2}$

CHAPTER X

TRIGONOMETRIC FUNCTIONS OF ANGLES OF ANY SIZE: GENERAL ANGLE

1. Generating an Angle of Any Size: Standard Position

Until this point, we have studied only the trigonometric functions of acute angles. Since many of the important applications of trigonometry occur in situations which involve angles other than acute angles, it becomes necessary for us to extend our understanding of angles and their trigonometric functions beyond the acute angle. We will now study trigonometric functions of any angle.

MEASURING AN ANGLE IN DEGREES

An angle of any size may be generated by a ray which rotates about a fixed point (the vertex of the angle) from an initial position (side) to a terminal position (side). The degree measure of the angle is the number of degrees of a rotation, a complete rotation or cycle being 360°. The degree measure of an angle is a real number.

Thus, a straight angle is generated by a ray rotating a half-rotation of 180°; a right angle is generated by a ray rotating a quarter-rotation of 90°.

In referring to a ray whose endpoint is O, and which passes through point A, we may write "ray $\overrightarrow{OA}$," or simply "$\overrightarrow{OA}$."

In Figs. 1 and 2, $\overrightarrow{OP}$, which is rotating about the vertex O, coincides initially with $\overrightarrow{OA}$ and terminates the rotation by coinciding with $\overrightarrow{OB}$. Ray $\overrightarrow{OA}$, from which the rotation begins, is termed the **initial side.** Ray $\overrightarrow{OB}$, at which the rotation ends, is called the **terminal side.** Since the ray may continue to rotate past its initial position for any number of cycles, angles whose measures are greater than 360° may be generated.

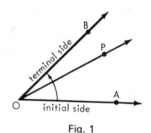

Fig. 1

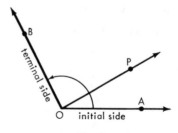

Fig. 2

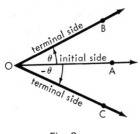

Fig. 3

Positive angles are those generated by a counter-clockwise or positive rotation. *Negative angles* are those generated by a clockwise or negative rotation. Positive angles are those whose measures are positive real numbers, whereas negative angles are those whose measures are negative real numbers.

Thus, in Fig. 3, if θ is the positive real number $30°$, then angle AOB is a positive angle whose measure is $30°$, and angle AOC is a negative angle whose measure is $-30°$. For the sake of brevity, we say $\angle AOB = 30°$ and $\angle AOC = -30°$.

Different angles may have the same initial and terminal sides. Such angles are called *coterminal angles.* In Fig. 4, the angles $(+140°)$ and $(-220°)$ are *coterminal.* Also, angles of $(-30°)$ and $(+330°)$ are coterminal.

Note, in the case of the two pairs of coterminal angles, that the sum of the absolute values of their measures is 360; that is, $140 + 220 = 360$ and $30 + 330 = 360$.

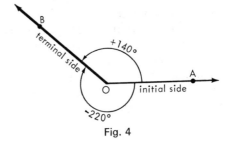

Fig. 4

Principle. For coterminal angles of less than one rotation, the sum of the absolute values of their degree measures is 360.

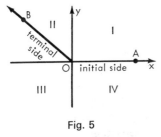

Fig. 5

The two perpendicular axes of a graph divide the plane into four quadrants. The quadrants are numbered I, II, III, and IV in a counterclockwise direction, as shown in Fig. 5.

The discussion of any angle is greatly simplified if the angle is placed in *standard position.* An angle is in standard position if its vertex is at the origin and its initial side coincides with the positive half of the x-axis.

The quadrant that an angle is in, or lies in, is the quadrant that contains its terminal side when the angle is placed in standard position. Thus, angle AOB, an angle of $+120°$ or $120°$, is in quadrant II; an angle of $210°$ is in quadrant III; an angle of $340°$ is in quadrant IV; an angle of $400°$ is in quadrant I.

An angle is a **quadrantal angle** if its terminal side coincides with one of the axes. Thus, $0°, 90°, 180°, 270°, 360°, 450°, 720°, -90°$, and $-720°$ are quadrantal angles.

Exercises

In 1–15, determine the quadrant in which the angle lies.

1. $118°$	**2.** $84°$	**3.** $250°$	**4.** $310°$	**5.** $97°$
6. $-110°$	**7.** $-50°$	**8.** $-330°$	**9.** $-250°$	**10.** $-92°$
11. $375°$	**12.** $560°$	**13.** $480°$	**14.** $700°$	**15.** $920°$

In 16–33, state whether or not the pair of angles is coterminal. For each pair, draw the angles in standard position, using curved arrows to indicate the direction of rotation.

16. $+300°$ and $-60°$	**17.** $+150°$ and $+210°$	**18.** $+250°$ and $-210°$
19. $+40°$ and $-320°$	**20.** $-200°$ and $-160°$	**21.** $-225°$ and $+135°$
22. $-315°$ and $+45°$	**23.** $-180°$ and $+280°$	**24.** $+475°$ and $-245°$
25. $0°$ and $720°$	**26.** $180°$ and $-180°$	**27.** $270°$ and $-270°$
28. $90°$ and $-270°$	**29.** $450°$ and $-90°$	**30.** $-90°$ and $270°$
31. $-180°$ and $540°$	**32.** $360°$ and $-360°$	**33.** $450°$ and $-450°$

2. Measuring an Angle in Radians

Thus far, the unit used in measuring an angle has been the degree. For our purposes, the degree has been a very convenient unit of measure. However, in higher mathematics, another unit of angle measure, the *radian*, is more useful.

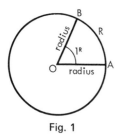

Fig. 1

To understand the radian measure of an angle, we draw a circle, Fig. 1, using the vertex of the angle as its center. If the length of arc AB equals the radius, R, then $\angle AOB$ is an angle of 1 radian, in accordance with the following definition:

A **radian** is the measure of an angle, which, if its vertex is placed at the center of a circle, the angle intercepts an arc equal in length to the radius of the circle. Think of radian as the contraction of "radius-angle."

The symbol "1^{R}" indicates "1 radian." In the same way that "$\angle A = x°$" means "the measure in degrees of angle A is x," so "$\angle A = x^{R}$" means "the measure in radians of angle A is x." The statement "$\angle A = x^{R}$" may be written simply as "$\angle A = x$."

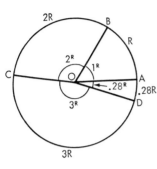

Fig. 2

In Fig. 2, $\angle BOC$, which intercepts an arc equal to twice the radius, equals 2 radians; that is, $\angle BOC = 2^R = 2$. Also, $\angle COD$, which intercepts an arc equal to three times the radius, equals 3 radians; that is, $\angle COD = 3^R = 3$. Since the circumference is 2π times the radius, $C = 2\pi R$, it follows that the radius can be laid off on the circle exactly 2π or approximately 6.28 times. Hence, in a complete rotation of $360°$, there are 2π or approximately 6.28 radians. Note, in Fig. 2, that $\angle AOD \approx .28$ radians, or about $\frac{2}{7}$ of a radian.

Since one complete rotation of $360°$ is equivalent to 2π radians, one-half a rotation equals $180°$ or π radians. The following table indicates other similar relationships:

Part of Rotation	Measure in Degrees	Measure in Radians	Part of Rotation	Measure in Degrees	Measure in Radians
$\frac{1}{4}$	$90°$	$\frac{\pi}{2}$	$\frac{1}{3}$	$120°$	$\frac{2\pi}{3}$
$\frac{3}{4}$	$270°$	$\frac{3\pi}{2}$	$\frac{2}{3}$	$240°$	$\frac{4\pi}{3}$
$\frac{1}{8}$	$45°$	$\frac{\pi}{4}$	$\frac{1}{6}$	$60°$	$\frac{\pi}{3}$
$\frac{3}{8}$	$135°$	$\frac{3\pi}{4}$	$\frac{5}{6}$	$300°$	$\frac{5\pi}{3}$
$\frac{1}{16}$	$22\frac{1}{2}°$	$\frac{\pi}{8}$	$\frac{1}{12}$	$30°$	$\frac{\pi}{6}$

Since 2π radians $= 360°$, then

$$\pi \text{ radians} = \mathbf{180°} \quad (A)$$

If we divide both sides of equation (A) by π, we have

$$1 \text{ radian} = \frac{180°}{\pi} \approx \mathbf{57.296°} \approx \mathbf{57° \ 17' \ 45''}$$

If we divide both sides of equation (A) by 180, we have

$$1 \text{ degree} = \frac{\pi}{180} \text{ radians} \approx .0175 \text{ radians}$$

When an angle is measured in radians, it is customary to omit the word *radians*. For example, "$\angle A = \frac{\pi}{3}$" means that $\angle A = \frac{\pi}{3}$ radians.

CONVERTING FROM RADIANS TO DEGREES

Since an angle of 1 radian $= \dfrac{180°}{\pi}$, an angle of 2 radians would equal $2 \times \dfrac{180°}{\pi}$, and an angle of n radians would contain $n \times \dfrac{180°}{\pi}$. Therefore, we have the following principle:

Principle 1. To convert the radian measure of an angle to its degree measure, multiply the number of radians by $\dfrac{180°}{\pi}$.

CONVERTING FROM DEGREES TO RADIANS

Since an angle of 1 degree $= \dfrac{\pi}{180}$ radians, an angle of $10° = 10 \times \dfrac{\pi}{180}$ radians, and an angle of $m°$ would contain $m \times \dfrac{\pi}{180}$ radians. Therefore, we have the following principle:

Principle 2. To convert the degree measure of an angle to radian measure, multiply the number of degrees by $\dfrac{\pi}{180}$.

RELATING RADIANS AND DEGREES IN A PROPORTION

Since π radians is equivalent to 180°, it can be shown that the ratio of the number of degrees in an angle to 180 is equal to the ratio of the number of radians in the angle to π. Thus, we have:

Principle 3. For any angle measured in both degrees and radians,

$$\frac{\text{number of degrees}}{180} = \frac{\text{number of radians}}{\pi}$$

~~~~~~~~~~~ *MODEL PROBLEMS* ~~~~~~~~~~~

1. Express $45°$ in radian measure.

Solution:

Method 1	*Method 2*
Multiply the number of degrees by $\frac{\pi}{180}$.	$\dfrac{\text{no. of degrees}}{180} = \dfrac{\text{no. of radians}}{\pi}$
	Let $x =$ number of radians.

Method 1

$$\overset{1}{\cancel{45}} \times \frac{\pi}{\underset{4}{\cancel{180}}} = \frac{\pi}{4} \text{ radians} \qquad Ans. \frac{\pi}{4}$$

Method 2

$$\frac{\overset{1}{\cancel{45}}}{\underset{4}{\cancel{180}}} = \frac{x}{\pi}$$

$$4x = \pi$$

$$x = \frac{\pi}{4} \quad Ans.$$

2. Express $\frac{5}{6}\pi$ radians in degrees.

Solution:

Method 1	*Method 2*
Multiply the number of radians by $\frac{180°}{\pi}$.	$\dfrac{\text{no. of degrees}}{180} = \dfrac{\text{no. of radians}}{\pi}$
	Let $x =$ number of degrees.

Method 1

$$\frac{5}{\underset{1}{\cancel{6}}}\cancel{\pi} \times \frac{\overset{30°}{\cancel{180°}}}{\underset{1}{\cancel{\pi}}} = 150°$$

Answer: $150°$

Method 2

$$\frac{x}{180} = \frac{\overset{5}{\cancel{6}}\cancel{\pi}}{\underset{1}{\cancel{\pi}}}$$

$$x = \frac{5}{6} \times 180 = 150° \quad Ans.$$

3. Find the value of $\tan \frac{\pi}{4}$ radians.

Solution:

$$\text{Since } \frac{\pi}{4} \text{ radians} = \frac{\overset{1}{\cancel{\pi}}}{\underset{1}{\cancel{4}}} \times \frac{\overset{45°}{\cancel{180°}}}{\underset{1}{\cancel{\pi}}} = 45°, \tan \frac{\pi}{4} = \tan 45° = 1. \quad Ans.$$

Exercises

In 1–25, express in terms of π the number of radians in the angle.

1. 30° **2.** 60° **3.** 75° **4.** 90° **5.** 120°
6. 135° **7.** 150° **8.** 180° **9.** 270° **10.** 105°
11. 140° **12.** 240° **13.** 225° **14.** 250° **15.** 200°
16. 17° **17.** 162° **18.** 324° **19.** 22.5° **20.** 67.5°
21. 5° 30′ **22.** 12° 15′ **23.** 32° 45′ **24.** 3° 36′ **25.** 1° 48′

26. Find, to the nearest tenth, the number of radians in 22° 30′.

In 27–38, convert the measure to degrees.

27. $\frac{\pi}{2}$ radians **28.** $\frac{\pi}{3}$ radians **29.** $\frac{\pi}{6}$ radians **30.** $\frac{\pi}{9}$ radians

31. $\frac{\pi}{10}$ radians **32.** $\frac{2}{3}\pi$ radians **33.** $\frac{4\pi}{3}$ radians **34.** $\frac{2\pi}{9}$ radians

35. $\frac{3}{2}\pi$ radians **36.** $\frac{17}{9}\pi$ radians **37.** $\frac{9\pi}{5}$ radians **38.** $\frac{17}{10}\pi$ radians

In 39–42, find the number of degrees in the angle, to the nearest degree.
39. 3 radians **40.** 6 radians **41.** 1.2 radians **42.** 2.2 radians

In 43–52, find the value of the trigonometric function. Express the answer as a radical or a rational number.

43. $\sin \frac{\pi}{4}$ **44.** $\cot \frac{\pi}{4}$ **45.** $\tan \frac{\pi}{6}$ **46.** $\tan \frac{\pi}{3}$ **47.** $\cos \frac{\pi}{4}$

48. $\sin \frac{\pi}{6}$ **49.** $2 \sin \frac{\pi}{6}$ **50.** $3 \tan \frac{\pi}{4}$ **51.** $\frac{1}{2} \sin \frac{\pi}{4}$ **52.** $\frac{1}{3} \cos \frac{\pi}{3}$

In 53–55, express in radians the positive acute angle x which satisfies the equation.
53. $\sin x = \cos x$ **54.** $\tan x = \cot 2x$ **55.** $\sin (x + 30) = \cos 3x$

56. If $\cos \dfrac{\pi}{3} = x - 1$, then   (1) $x = \dfrac{1}{2}$ (2) $x = \dfrac{3}{2}$ (3) $x = \dfrac{\pi}{3} + 1$ (4) x has more

than one value

57. The number of degrees in a half-radian is (1) between 20 and 25 (2) between 25 and 30 (3) between 30 and 35

3. Relating Radians to Arc-Length and Radius

In circle O having a radius of 6 inches, a central angle of 2 radians, such as $\angle AOB$, intercepts an arc whose length is 2·6, or 12 inches. On a larger circle, whose radius is 10 inches, the same angle will intercept an arc of 2·10, or 20 inches.

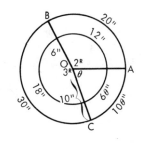

In a circle having a radius of 6 inches, a central angle of 3 radians, such as $\angle BOC$, intercepts an arc whose length is 3·6 or 18 inches. On a larger circle, whose radius is 10 inches, the same angle will intercept an arc of 3·10, or 30 inches.

More generally, a central angle of θ radians on a circle of radius 6 inches cuts off an arc-length of 6·θ inches, while on a larger circle of radius 10 inches, the arc-length cut off will be 10·θ inches.

Finally, it may be seen that in a circle having a radius of R linear units, a central angle of θ radians intercepts an arc-length equal to θ·R units.

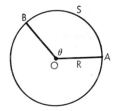

Principle. If θ represents the number of radians in a central angle, R the length of the radius of the circle, and S the length of the intercepted arc, then

$$S = \theta R$$

~~~~~~~~~~~ *MODEL PROBLEMS* ~~~~~~~~~~~

1. The length of a pendulum is 18 inches. Find the distance through which the tip of the pendulum travels when the pendulum turns through an arc of 1.5 radians.

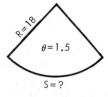

Solution:

$\qquad S = \theta R \qquad\qquad \theta = 1.5, \ R = 18$

$\qquad S = 1.5 \times 18$

$\qquad S = 27 \qquad\qquad$ *Ans.* 27 in.

2. An angle of $1\frac{1}{3}$ radians at the center of a circle subtends an arc of 28 inches. Find the length of the radius in inches.

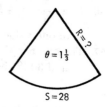

Solution:

$$S = \theta R \qquad\qquad S = 28, \ \theta = 1\frac{1}{3}$$
$$28 = 1\frac{1}{3}R \qquad\qquad \text{Divide by } 1\frac{1}{3}$$
$$21 = R \qquad\qquad \textit{Ans. } 21 \text{ in.}$$

Exercises

In circle O, a central angle θ intercepts an arc of S. The sides of the angle are r, the radius of circle O. In 1–7, find the missing values in the following table:

	Radius r	Central angle θ	Intercepted arc S
1.	10 in.	5 radians	?
2.	12 ft.	$2\frac{1}{2}$ radians	?
3.	6 yd.	?	9 yd.
4.	?	$\frac{1}{2}$ radian	20 in.
5.	?	$3\frac{1}{4}$ radians	26 ft.
6.	12 mi.	?	40 mi.
7.	r ft.	θ radians	?

8. A circle has a radius of 4 inches. Find the number of inches in the length of the arc intercepted by a central angle of 2 radians.

9. In a circle whose radius is 4 inches, find in inches the length of the arc intercepted by a central angle of $2\frac{1}{2}$ radians.

10. In a circle whose radius is 2 inches, find in inches the length of the arc intercepted by a central angle of 1.25 radians.

11. A circular arc of 30 feet subtends an angle of four radians at the center of its circle. Find the radius of the circle in feet.

12. The sides of a central angle of $1\frac{1}{2}$ radians intercept an arc whose length is 6 inches. Find, in inches, the radius of the circle.

13. A central angle of 2.5 radians intercepts an arc of 15 inches. Find the number of inches in the radius of the circle.

14. An arc of a circle is 24 inches long. If this arc subtends a central angle of 1.5 radians, then the length of the radius of this circle in inches is   (1) 36   (2) 16   (3) 3.6   (4) 1.6

15. A central angle in a circle whose radius is 4 inches intercepts an arc of 8 inches. How many radians are there in the angle?

16. Find the number of radians in a central angle whose sides intercept an arc on a circle equal in length to the diameter of the circle.

17. Find the number of radians in a central angle which intercepts an arc whose length is 3.2 times the radius of the circle.

In 18–20, the radius of a wheel is 30 inches. Find the number of radians through which a point on the circumference turns when the wheel moves a distance of:

18. 20 feet   **19.** $2\frac{1}{2}$ feet   **20.** 100 inches

21. In a circle whose radius is r, a central angle of n radians intercepts a minor arc whose length is s. Which one of the following is true?

(1) $s = \dfrac{n}{r}$ (2) $s = \dfrac{r}{n}$ (3) $n = \dfrac{s}{r}$ (4) $n = \dfrac{r}{s}$

4. Finding the Distance From a Point to the Origin

The theorem of Pythagoras enables us to express the distance from a point to the origin in terms of the coordinates of the point. The distance, r, is the measure of the **radius vector** of the point.

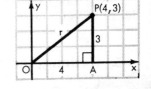

To find the distance from point $P(4,3)$ to the origin, draw $\overline{PA}$ perpendicular to the x-axis. Since $OA = 4$ and $AP = 3$, then $r^2 = 4^2 + 3^2 = 25$. Hence, $r = \sqrt{25} = 5$. Only the positive square root of 25 is taken, since the distance from a point to the origin is considered positive no matter in what quadrant the point may lie.

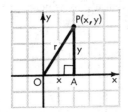

In general, to find the distance, r, from $P(x,y)$ to the origin, apply the formula $r = \sqrt{x^2 + y^2}$, obtained by drawing $\overline{PA}$ perpendicular to the x-axis and applying the theorem of Pythagoras, as follows:

$$r^2 = x^2 + y^2$$
$$r = \sqrt{x^2 + y^2}$$

~~~~~ MODEL PROBLEM ~~~~~

Find the distance from the origin to $P(-4, 2)$

Solution:

$$r = \sqrt{x^2 + y^2}$$

Substitute -4 for x and 2 for y. $r = \sqrt{(-4)^2 + 2^2}$

$$= \sqrt{16 + 4}$$

$$= \sqrt{20} = \sqrt{4}\,\sqrt{5} = 2\sqrt{5} \quad Ans.$$

Exercises

In 1–15, find the distance from the point to the origin.

1. $(6, 8)$ **2.** $(5, 12)$ **3.** $(4, 5)$ **4.** $(\sqrt{3}, 1)$

5. $(8, -15)$ **6.** $(-3, 4)$ **7.** $(-1, 8)$ **8.** $(2, -2\sqrt{3})$

9. $\left(\dfrac{3}{4}, 1\right)$ **10.** $\left(2, -\dfrac{3}{2}\right)$ **11.** $\left(\dfrac{-\sqrt{2}}{2}, \dfrac{\sqrt{2}}{2}\right)$

12. $(\sqrt{2}, 0)$ **13.** $(0, -\sqrt{5})$ **14.** $(\sqrt{3}, -1)$ **15.** $(0, -\sqrt{3})$

In 16–18, find the distance between the pair of points.

16. $(0, 0)$ and $(8, 6)$ **17.** $(0, 0)$ and $(-12, -5)$ **18.** $(0, 0)$ and $(-\sqrt{2}, \sqrt{2})$

5. Defining the Trigonometric Functions of Any Angle

Up to the present, the six trigonometric functions were defined for acute angles. Now that we have seen that angles may be of any size, it becomes necessary to revise our definitions of the trigonometric functions so that they will apply to an angle of any magnitude. However, the new definitions which we make must agree (that is, must be consistent with) the definitions which were made for acute angles.

Angle in Quadrant I

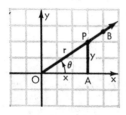

Angle in Quadrant II

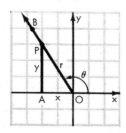

Angle in Quadrant III   *Angle in Quadrant IV*

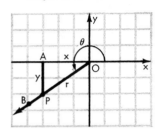   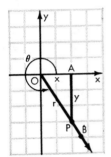

Let θ be the measure of an angle whose terminal side is $\overrightarrow{OB}$. As shown in the four diagrams, the angle may be in any of the four quadrants. Select any point P on the terminal line. We now define the trigonometric functions of any angle in terms of x, the abscissa of P; y, the ordinate of P; and r, the distance from the origin to P.

$$\sin \theta = \frac{\text{ordinate}}{\text{distance}} = \frac{y}{r} \qquad \csc \theta = \frac{\text{distance}}{\text{ordinate}} = \frac{r}{y}$$

$$\cos \theta = \frac{\text{abscissa}}{\text{distance}} = \frac{x}{r} \qquad \sec \theta = \frac{\text{distance}}{\text{abscissa}} = \frac{r}{x}$$

$$\tan \theta = \frac{\text{ordinate}}{\text{abscissa}} = \frac{y}{x} \qquad \cot \theta = \frac{\text{abscissa}}{\text{ordinate}} = \frac{x}{y}$$

Notice that these definitions are consistent with (that is, in complete agreement with) the definitions previously made for the functions of acute angles or angles which when placed in standard position are in quadrant I. The following words have been substituted:

> *ordinate* instead of *opposite leg*
> *abscissa* instead of *adjacent leg*
> *distance* instead of *hypotenuse*

When we find the values of the trigonometric functions of an angle, it does not matter which point of the terminal line is selected as P. This is true because the ratios which define any particular function will be equal for all positions of P on the terminal line.

Since the terminal lines for the angles 60°, 420°, and −300° are all in the same position in quadrant I, any function of the 60° angle is equal to the same-named function of 420° and −300°. Thus,

$$\sin 60° = \sin 420° = \sin (-300°)$$
$$\cos 60° = \cos 420° = \cos (-300°) \text{ etc.}$$

Principle. If angles which are in standard position have the same terminal side, their same-named functions are equal.

6. Signs of the Trigonometric Functions in Each of the Quadrants

Because the definitions of the trigonometric functions of an angle are in terms of x, y, and r (as shown in the previous section), the algebraic signs of these functions can now be readily determined.

KEEP IN MIND

The distance, r, is always positive.

Since $\sin \theta = \dfrac{y}{r}$ and $\csc \theta = \dfrac{r}{y}$, and r is positive, these functions will be positive when y is positive, that is, in quadrants I and II. These functions will be negative when y is negative, that is, in quadrants III and IV.

Since $\cos \theta = \dfrac{x}{r}$ and $\sec \theta = \dfrac{r}{x}$, and r is positive, these functions will be positive when x is positive, that is, in quadrants I and IV. These functions will be negative when x is negative, that is, in quadrants II and III.

Since $\tan \theta = \dfrac{y}{x}$ and $\cot \theta = \dfrac{x}{y}$, these functions will be positive when x and y have the same sign, that is, in quadrant I where both x and y are positive, and in quadrant III where both x and y are negative. These functions will be negative when x and y have different signs, that is, in quadrant II where x is negative and y is positive, and in quadrant IV where x is positive and y is negative.

Note how the reciprocal functions are paired with regard to sign. This agrees exactly with the fact that numbers that are reciprocals of each other must have the same sign; for example, $\frac{3}{4}$ and $\frac{4}{3}$, or $-\frac{2}{3}$ and $-\frac{3}{2}$.

KEEP IN MIND

A function and its reciprocal function must have the same sign. Both must be positive or both must be negative.

SUMMARY 1

Pairs of Reciprocal Functions	Quadrant Containing Terminal Side			
	I	II	III	IV
sine and cosecant	+	+	−	−
cosine and secant	+	−	−	+
tangent and cotangent	+	−	+	−

SUMMARY 2

$$\text{II} \qquad \text{I}$$

Only $\begin{cases} \sin \\ \csc \end{cases} (+)$ All $(+)$

Only $\begin{cases} \tan \\ \cot \end{cases} (+)$ Only $\begin{cases} \cos \\ \sec \end{cases} (+)$

$$\text{III} \qquad \text{IV}$$

How to remember: " s " is the first letter of sine and second.

" t " is the first letter of tangent and third.

" c " is the first letter of cosine and cuatro, Spanish for fourth.

~~~~~~~~~~ *MODEL PROBLEM* ~~~~~~~~~~

In which quadrant must an angle lie if its tangent is positive and its cosine is negative?

Solution:

If the tangent of an angle is positive, the angle lies in quadrant I or III.

If the cosine of an angle is negative, the angle lies in quadrant II or III.

Therefore, quadrant III is the quadrant in which the tangent of the angle is positive and its cosine is negative.

Answer: III

The model problem may be restated in another form as follows: "If tan A is positive and cos A is negative, in which quadrant does angle A lie?"

The solution of the model problem shows that angle A lies in quadrant III. In the restatement of the model problem, "tan A" means "tangent of an angle A" rather than "tangent of an angle whose measure is A."

In trigonometric expressions such as tan A or sin x, the context of a problem may be used to determine whether the letters A and x refer to the angle or to the measure of the angle.

Exercises

In 1–6, state the quadrants in which an angle may lie if its:
1. tangent is positive
2. sine is positive
3. cosine is positive
4. cotangent is negative
5. cosecant is negative
6. secant is positive

In 7–12, state the quadrant in which an angle lies if its
7. sine is positive and its tangent is negative
8. sine is negative and its cosine is negative
9. cosecant is positive and its secant is negative
10. secant is positive and its sine is negative
11. cosine and tangent are both positive
12. sine and tangent are both negative

13. If tan θ is negative and cos θ is positive, then θ lies in the (1) second quadrant (2) third quadrant (3) fourth quadrant
14. If sin θ is negative and tan θ is positive, then θ is an angle in the (1) first quadrant (2) second quadrant (3) third quadrant (4) fourth quadrant
15. The functions that are positive for angles in the fourth quadrant are (1) sine and cosine (2) cosine and tangent (3) tangent and cotangent (4) cosine and secant

7. Finding All Remaining Trigonometric Functions of Any Angle When One Function Is Known

If the value of one of the trigonometric functions of an angle is given, and the quadrant containing the terminal side can be found, then the values of all the remaining functions of the angle can be determined.

In future statements, for the sake of brevity, we shall use "trigonometric function of an angle," or simply, "function of an angle" to mean "value of the trigonometric function of an angle."

~~~~~~~~~~~~~~~ *MODEL PROBLEM* ~~~~~~~~~~~~~~

If $\tan A = \frac{4}{3}$ and $\sin A$ is negative, find all remaining functions of $\angle A$.

Solution: Since $\tan A$ is positive, the terminal side of A is either in quadrant I or quadrant III. Since $\sin A$ is negative, the terminal side of angle A is either in quadrant III or in quadrant IV. Therefore, angle A must terminate in quadrant III.

Since $\tan A = \frac{y}{x}$ and $\tan A = \frac{4}{3}$, the ratio $\frac{y}{x} = \frac{4}{3}$. In quadrant III, y is negative and x is negative. Therefore, let $y = -4$ and $x = -3$.

Check: $\dfrac{y}{x} = \dfrac{-4}{-3} = \dfrac{4}{3}$

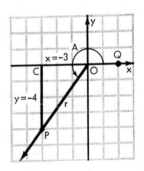

On a graph, locate point P, whose abscissa is -3 and whose ordinate is -4. Draw $\overrightarrow{OP}$. Angle QOP is angle A, whose functions are to be found.

In order to find the remaining functions of angle A, we must find PO, the distance to P from the origin.

$$OP \text{ or } r = \sqrt{(-3)^2 + (-4)^2},\ r = \sqrt{9+16},\ r = \sqrt{25},\ r = 5$$

Answer:

$\sin A = \dfrac{y}{r} = \dfrac{-4}{5} = -\dfrac{4}{5}$ $\csc A = \dfrac{r}{y} = \dfrac{5}{-4} = -\dfrac{5}{4}$

$\cos A = \dfrac{x}{r} = \dfrac{-3}{5} = -\dfrac{3}{5}$ $\sec A = \dfrac{r}{x} = \dfrac{5}{-3} = -\dfrac{5}{3}$

$\tan A = \dfrac{y}{x} = \dfrac{-4}{-3} = \dfrac{4}{3}$ $\cot A = \dfrac{x}{y} = \dfrac{-3}{-4} = \dfrac{3}{4}$

~~~~~~

Exercises

In 1–6, draw the angle and find the remaining functions.

1. $\sin A = \frac{3}{5}$, angle A is in quadrant I
2. $\sin A = \frac{3}{5}$, angle A is in quadrant II

3. $\cos A = \frac{5}{13}$, angle A is in quadrant IV
4. $\tan B = \frac{8}{6}$, angle B is in quadrant III
5. $\tan B = -\frac{6}{8}$, $\cos B$ is positive

6. $\sin C = \dfrac{1}{\sqrt{2}}$, $\cos C$ is negative

7. If $\tan x = \frac{1}{3}$ and $\sin x$ is negative, find $\cos x$.
8. If $\cos x = \frac{4}{5}$ and x is in the fourth quadrant, find $\cot x$.
9. If $\tan A = \frac{4}{3}$ and A is in the third quadrant, what is the value of $\cos A$?
10. If $\cos A = -\frac{4}{5}$ and $\sin A$ is positive, find $\tan A$.
11. If $\sin A = -\frac{4}{5}$ and $\tan A$ is positive, find $\cos A$.
12. If A is an angle in the second quadrant and if $\cos A = -\frac{4}{5}$, find the value of $\sin A$.

13. If $\sin x = \dfrac{5}{\sqrt{34}}$ and $\cos x$ is negative, find $\tan x$.

14. If $\cos x = -\dfrac{\sqrt{2}}{2}$ and $\cot x = -1$, what is the smallest positive measure of x?

8. Representing the Trigonometric Functions of an Angle As Line Segments

Many trigonometric ideas and principles are more readily visualized and better understood when each of the six functions of an angle is represented by a line segment. Through the use of line segments, we can (1) see at a glance whether a function of an angle in any quadrant is positive or negative, (2) understand the way in which any function of an angle changes as the angle changes, (3) represent all the functions of an angle in terms of any one function, and (4) graph trigonometric functions.

To obtain line segments which will represent all the functions of an angle, the ratios by means of which the functions are defined must have a denominator of 1. To do this, we use a circle which has a radius of 1 unit. A circle whose radius is 1 is a *unit circle*. Hence, in Fig. 1, the radii of the unit circle equal 1; that is, $OA = 1$ and $OP = 1$.

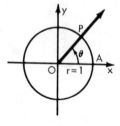

Fig. 1

USING LINE SEGMENTS IN A UNIT CIRCLE TO REPRESENT THE TRIGONOMETRIC FUNCTIONS OF AN ANGLE IN EACH OF THE FOUR QUADRANTS

Note, in Figs. 2 to 5, that the angle θ has been placed in standard position in the unit circle. Tangents to the unit circle have been drawn at the points where the unit circle intersects the positive halves of the x-axis and the y-axis. The terminal side of θ has been extended where necessary in order to meet these tangents.

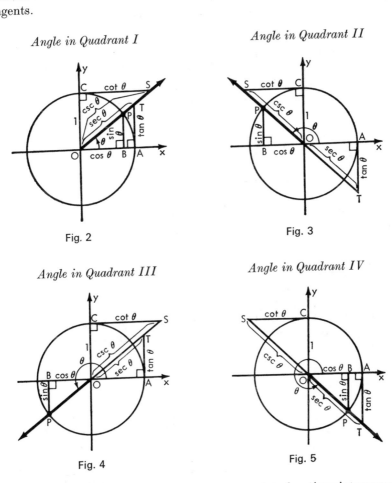

Angle in Quadrant I

Fig. 2

Angle in Quadrant II

Fig. 3

Angle in Quadrant III

Fig. 4

Angle in Quadrant IV

Fig. 5

In each of the quadrants, each of the trigonometric functions is represented by a line segment, as shown in Figs. 2 to 5. In a unit circle, the *absolute value* of a trigonometric function is the length of the line segment which represents the function. Note in the next paragraph how each function of an angle is expressed as a ratio in which the length of the line segment appears as the numerator of a fraction whose denominator is 1.

The functions of an angle in any quadrant can be expressed as ratios with denominators of 1, as follows:

$$\text{In } \triangle OPB, \ \sin \theta = \frac{BP}{OP} = \frac{BP}{1} = BP$$

$$\cos \theta = \frac{OB}{OP} = \frac{OB}{1} = OB$$

$$\text{In } \triangle OAT, \ \tan \theta = \frac{AT}{OA} = \frac{AT}{1} = AT$$

$$\sec \theta = \frac{OT}{OA} = \frac{OT}{1} = OT$$

$$\text{In } \triangle OCS, \ \cot \theta = \cot \angle CSO = \frac{CS}{OC} = \frac{CS}{1} = CS$$

$$\csc \theta = \csc \angle CSO = \frac{OS}{OC} = \frac{OS}{1} = OS$$

Thus, it follows that line segments may be used to represent each of the six functions of an angle in any quadrant of a unit circle.

ISOLATING THE THREE RIGHT TRIANGLES IN EACH QUADRANT OF THE UNIT CIRCLE

Examine Figs. 2 to 5 on the preceding page. In each quadrant, note how the six trigonometric functions are paired in three right triangles, as follows:

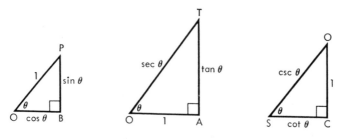

From these unit right triangles, we can see that for an angle in any quadrant, the Pythagorean and quotient relationships are true.

In triangle OBP, $\sin^2 \theta + \cos^2 \theta = 1$.
In triangle OAT, $1 + \tan^2 \theta = \sec^2 \theta$.
In triangle OCS, $1 + \cot^2 \theta = \csc^2 \theta$.

Note in unit right $\triangle OPB$ above that:

$$\tan \theta = \frac{\sin \theta}{\cos \theta} \qquad\qquad \cot \theta = \frac{\cos \theta}{\sin \theta}$$

REPRESENTING EACH OF THE TRIGONOMETRIC FUNCTIONS IN EACH OF THE QUADRANTS

We have seen why the length of a line segment representing a trigonometric function is the absolute value of the trigonometric function. Now, we will see how the same line segment can be used to determine the sign of the function represented by the line segment. As you study each of the following six diagrams, keep this summary in mind:

Summary of the Signs of the Trigonometric Functions in All Quadrants

In quadrant I, all the functions are positive.
In quadrant II, only the sine and cosecant are positive.
In quadrant III, only the tangent and cotangent are positive.
In quadrant IV, only the cosine and secant are positive.

Representing the Sine of an Angle in Each Quadrant

In each of the following circles whose radius is 1, $\sin \theta = BP$.

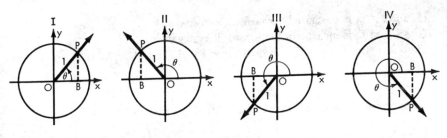

If $\sin \theta$, BP, is measured upward, it is positive.
If $\sin \theta$, BP, is measured downward, it is negative.
Therefore, $\sin \theta$ is positive in quadrants I and II and negative in quadrants III and IV.

Representing the Cosine of an Angle in Each Quadrant

In each of the following circles whose radius is 1, $\cos \theta = OB$.

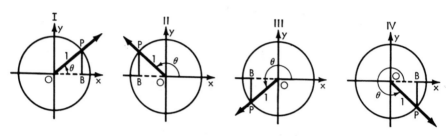

If $\cos \theta$, OB, is measured to the right, it is positive.
If $\cos \theta$, OB, is measured to the left, it is negative.
Therefore, $\cos \theta$ is positive in quadrants I and IV and negative in quadrants II and III.

Representing the Tangent of an Angle in Each Quadrant

In each of the following circles whose radius is 1, $\tan \theta = AT$.

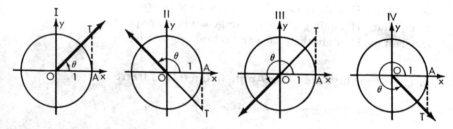

If $\tan \theta$, AT, is measured upward, it is positive.
If $\tan \theta$, AT, is measured downward, it is negative.
Therefore, $\tan \theta$ is positive in quadrants I and III and negative in quadrants II and IV.

Representing the Cotangent of an Angle in Each Quadrant

In each of the circles at the top of the facing page, whose radius is 1, $\cot \theta = CS$.

If $\cot \theta$, CS, is measured to the right, it is positive.
If $\cot \theta$, CS, is measured to the left, it is negative.
Therefore, $\cot \theta$ is positive in quadrants I and III and negative in quadrants II and IV.

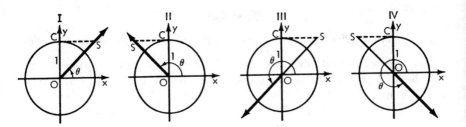

Representing the Secant of an Angle in Each Quadrant

In each of the following circles whose radius is 1, sec $\theta = OT$.

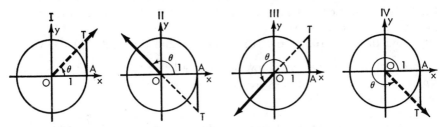

If sec θ, OT, is measured in the direction of the terminal line, it is positive.

If sec θ, OT, is measured on the terminal line produced in its opposite direction, it is negative.

Therefore, sec θ is positive in quadrants I and IV and negative in quadrants II and III.

Representing the Cosecant of an Angle in Each Quadrant

In each of the following circles whose radius is 1, csc $\theta = OS$.

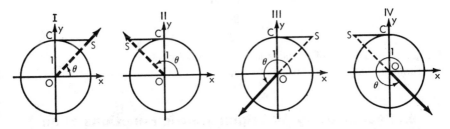

If csc θ, OS, is measured in the direction of the terminal line, it is positive.

If csc θ, OS, is measured on the terminal line produced in its opposite direction, it is negative.

Therefore, csc θ is positive in quadrants I and II and negative in quadrants III and IV.

Exercises

In each of the following exercises, consider θ to be an angle in standard position.

In 1–4, in a unit circle, draw and clearly letter the line segments whose lengths may be used to represent the six trigonometric functions of angle θ when θ lies in quadrant:

1. I   **2.** II   **3.** III   **4.** IV

In 5–8, in a unit circle, draw and clearly letter the line segments whose lengths may be used to represent sin θ and cos θ when θ lies in quadrant:

5. I   **6.** II   **7.** III   **8.** IV

In 9–12, in a unit circle, draw and clearly letter the line segments whose lengths may be used to represent tan θ and sec θ when θ is an angle whose measure in degrees is between:

9. 0 and 45   **10.** 90 and 135   **11.** 180 and 225   **12.** 270 and 315

In 13–16, in a unit circle, draw and clearly letter the line segments whose lengths may be used to represent cot θ and csc θ when θ is an angle whose measure in radians is between:

13. $\dfrac{\pi}{4}$ and $\dfrac{\pi}{2}$ **14.** $\dfrac{3\pi}{4}$ and π **15.** $\dfrac{5\pi}{4}$ and $\dfrac{3\pi}{2}$ **16.** $\dfrac{7\pi}{4}$ and 2π

In 17–22, in each of the four quadrants of a unit circle, draw and clearly letter the line segment whose length may be used to represent the given function of θ. Indicate next to each segment whether the function is positive or negative.

17. sin θ   **18.** cos θ   **19.** tan θ
20. cot θ   **21.** sec θ   **22.** csc θ

In 23–26, in a unit circle, draw the line segments whose lengths may be used to represent sin θ, cos θ, and tan θ if:

23. θ is greater than 90° and less than 135°.

24. θ is greater than π and less than $\dfrac{3\pi}{2}$.

25. the terminal side of θ passes through the point (.6, .8).

26. the terminal side of θ passes through the point (−.6, −.8).

9. Representing All Trigonometric Functions of an Angle in Terms of Any One Function

By applying the theorem of Pythagoras, it is possible to express any function of an angle in terms of any of the remaining five functions.

~~~~~~~~~~~~~~~ *MODEL PROBLEMS* ~~~~~~~~~~~~~~~

1. If angle A is acute,
a. express BC in terms of $\cos A$.
b. express all the other functions of A in terms of $\cos A$.

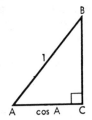

Solution: Since we wish to express all functions of angle A in terms of $\cos A$, we will first represent the sides of right triangle ABC in terms of $\cos A$.

Because $\cos A = \dfrac{\cos A}{1} = \dfrac{AC}{AB}$, let $AC = \cos A$ and $AB = 1$.

a. $(BC)^2 + (AC)^2 = (AB)^2$
$(BC)^2 + \cos^2 A = 1$
$(BC)^2 = 1 - \cos^2 A$
$BC = +\sqrt{1 - \cos^2 A}$ *Ans.* (Since A is acute, we take only the positive square root.)

b. Answer: $\sin A = \dfrac{BC}{AB} = \dfrac{\sqrt{1 - \cos^2 A}}{1} = \sqrt{1 - \cos^2 A}$

$\cos A = \dfrac{AC}{AB} = \dfrac{\cos A}{1} = \cos A$

$\tan A = \dfrac{BC}{AC} = \dfrac{\sqrt{1 - \cos^2 A}}{\cos A}$

$\cot A = \dfrac{AC}{BC} = \dfrac{\cos A}{\sqrt{1 - \cos^2 A}}$

$\sec A = \dfrac{AB}{AC} = \dfrac{1}{\cos A}$

$\csc A = \dfrac{AB}{BC} = \dfrac{1}{\sqrt{1 - \cos^2 A}}$

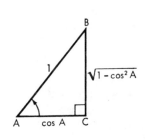

2. Express, in terms of $\tan A$, the remaining five functions of angle A.

Solution: Since we wish to express all functions of angle A in terms of $\tan A$, we will first represent the sides of right triangle ABC in terms of $\tan A$.

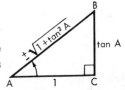

Because $\tan A = \dfrac{\tan A}{1} = \dfrac{BC}{AC}$, let $BC = \tan A$ and $AC = 1$.

Since $(AB)^2 = 1 + \tan^2 A$, $AB = \pm\sqrt{1 + \tan^2 A}$. Since A may be any angle, both positive and negative square roots are used.

Answer: $\sin A = \dfrac{BC}{AB} = \dfrac{\tan A}{\pm\sqrt{1 + \tan^2 A}}$ $\csc A = \dfrac{AB}{BC} = \dfrac{\pm\sqrt{1 + \tan^2 A}}{\tan A}$

$\cos A = \dfrac{AC}{AB} = \dfrac{1}{\pm\sqrt{1 + \tan^2 A}}$ $\sec A = \dfrac{AB}{AC} = \dfrac{\pm\sqrt{1 + \tan^2 A}}{1}$

$\tan A = \dfrac{BC}{AC} = \dfrac{\tan A}{1} = \tan A$ $\cot A = \dfrac{AC}{BC} = \dfrac{1}{\tan A}$

Exercises

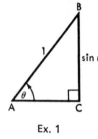

Ex. 1

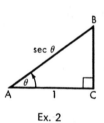

Ex. 2

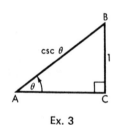

Ex. 3

1. *a.* Express AC in terms of $\sin\theta$.

   b. Express all the other functions of θ in terms of $\sin\theta$.

2. *a.* Express BC in terms of $\sec\theta$.

   b. Express all the other functions of θ in terms of $\sec\theta$.

3. *a.* Express AC in terms of $\csc\theta$.

   b. Express all the other functions of θ in terms of $\csc\theta$.

In 4–6, express the remaining five functions of angle θ in terms of:

4. $\sin\theta$ **5.** $\cos\theta$ **6.** $\cot\theta$

7. Express $\cos A$ in terms of $\tan A$ if A is an angle in the first quadrant.

8. Express $\cot x$ in terms of $\sin x$ when x is a positive acute angle.

9. If x is a positive acute angle and $\cos x = a$, express $\cot x$ in terms of a.

10. If A is a positive acute angle and $\sec A = r$, express $\tan A$ in terms of r.

11. Express $\tan^2 B$ in terms of $\sec B$.

12. $\tan^2 A$ expressed in terms of $\sin A$ is $\tan^2 A =$ _____ .

13. Express $\cot^2 x$ in terms of $\sin x$.

14. If A is an angle in quadrant II, express $\sin A$ in terms of $\cos A$.

15. If x is a positive obtuse angle, express $\tan x$ in terms of $\sin x$.

16. If A is an angle in quadrant III, express $\cos A$ in terms of $\tan A$.

17. If A is an angle in quadrant IV, express $\sec A$ in terms of $\cot A$.

10. Trigonometric Functions of $0°$, $90°$, $180°$, $270°$, and $360°$: Quadrantal Angles

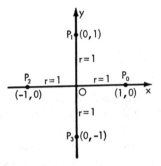

On the graph, points P_0, P_1, P_2, and P_3 have been taken on the terminal sides of the quadrantal angles $0°$ or $360°$, $90°$, $180°$, and $270°$. Since all these points are located a unit distance from the origin, $r = 1$. The table below indicates their respective abscissas and ordinates. Verify these.

	If		Then	
	$\theta =$	$r =$	$x =$	$y =$
P_0	$0°$ or 0 $360°$ or 2π	1	1	0
P_1	$90°$ or $\dfrac{\pi}{2}$	1	0	1
P_2	$180°$ or π	1	-1	0
P_3	$270°$ or $\dfrac{3\pi}{2}$	1	0	-1

By using the definitions for the functions of angles in standard position, the following values of functions of $0°$ and $90°$ are obtained:

Since $\sin \theta = \dfrac{y}{r}$, then $\sin 0° = \dfrac{0}{1} = 0$ and $\sin 90° = \dfrac{1}{1} = 1$.

Since $\cos \theta = \dfrac{x}{r}$, then $\cos 0° = \dfrac{1}{1} = 1$ and $\cos 90° = \dfrac{0}{1} = 0$.

Since $\tan \theta = \dfrac{y}{x}$, then $\tan 0° = \dfrac{0}{1} = 0$ and $\tan 90° = \dfrac{1}{0}$ (undefined).

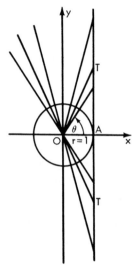

Recall that in a unit circle, $AT = \tan \theta$. The use of a line segment to represent the tangent function will enable us to understand further the meaning that should be given to the tangent of an angle that is very close to 90°.

In the diagram at the right, note that as θ increases in quadrant I, AT or $\tan \theta$ increases. Also, with values of θ very close to 90°, we see that AT increases without limit. Thus, if $\theta = 89° 57'$, which is 3′ less than 90°, $\tan 89° 57'$ exceeds 1000. If the difference between θ and 90° is made small enough, then $\tan \theta$ can be made to exceed 1,000,000, and so on.

When θ is in quadrant II and 3′ larger than 90°, then $\tan 90° 3'$ has an absolute value greater than 1000, although $\tan 90° 3'$ is negative. The closer θ is to 90°, the greater the absolute values of $\tan \theta$ become, and these absolute values can be increased without limit.

The fact that "$\tan \theta$ becomes infinite as θ approaches 90°" is usually written in the following symbolic form: $\tan 90° = \infty$. The meaning to be attached to this statement is that "$\tan \theta$ assumes values that change beyond all limits as θ approaches 90°."

Also, keep in mind that the statement "$\tan 90° = \infty$" is not an equation in the usual sense, and that "∞" is not a number.

Similarly, $\tan 270° = \infty$ because, when θ is very close to 270°, the same situation takes place. That is, $\tan \theta$ assumes values that change beyond all limits as θ approaches 270°. The closer θ is to 270°, the greater the absolute values of $\tan \theta$ become, and these absolute values can be increased without limit.

When the absolute values of a quantity become larger and larger, the reciprocals of these values become smaller and smaller, approaching zero as the quantity becomes infinitely large. Since $\tan 90° = \infty$ and $\tan 270° = \infty$, $\cot 90° = 0$ and $\cot 270° = 0$.

When the absolute values of a quantity become smaller and smaller, the reciprocals of these absolute values become larger and larger, and become infinitely large as the quantity approaches zero. Since $\tan 0° = 0$ and $\tan 180° = 0$, $\cot 0° = \infty$ and $\cot 180° = \infty$. In like manner, since $\sin 0° = 0$ and $\sin 180° = 0$, $\csc 0° = \infty$ and $\csc 180° = \infty$. Also, since $\cos 90° = 0$ and $\cos 270° = 0$, $\sec 90° = \infty$ and $\sec 270° = \infty$.

SUMMARY OF THE VALUES OF THE TRIGONOMETRIC FUNCTIONS OF THE QUADRANTAL ANGLES

The following table summarizes the values of the trigonometric functions of the angles of 0°, 90°, 180°, 270°, and 360°. It must be borne in mind that each of the " ∞ " values must be understood in the light of the previous explanation. The function of a quadrantal angle is *undefined* where a " ∞ " value is shown in the table. The previous explanation will help you understand why the symbol for infinity is used for functions that are undefined.

TABLE OF VALUES OF FUNCTIONS OF QUADRANTAL ANGLES

	0° or 360° 0 or 2π	90° or $\dfrac{\pi}{2}$	180° or π	270° or $\dfrac{3\pi}{2}$
sin	0	1	0	−1
cos	1	0	−1	0
tan	0	∞	0	∞
cot	∞	0	∞	0
sec	1	∞	−1	∞
csc	∞	1	∞	−1

Exercises

In 1–4, show that the expression equals 0.

1. $\sin 0° + \cos 90°$

2. $\sec 0° + \cos 180°$

3. $3 \sin 180° + 5 \tan 0°$

4. $\sin \dfrac{\pi}{2} - \csc \dfrac{\pi}{2}$

In 5–8, show that the expression equals 2.

5. $\sec 0° + \csc 90°$

6. $2 \sin 90° - 3 \tan 360°$

7. $\cos 90° + \cot 270° + 2 \sec 360°$

8. $2 \cos 0 - \sin \dfrac{\pi}{2} - \csc \dfrac{3\pi}{2}$

In 9–14, find the value of the expression.

9. $\sin 270° - \sin 90°$

10. $\sin 90° \cos 180°$

11. $\sin 270° + \cos 360°$

12. $2 \sin \dfrac{\pi}{6} + \cos 2\pi$

13. $\tan \dfrac{\pi}{3} + \sin \dfrac{\pi}{2}$

14. $\sin \dfrac{k}{2} + \sin k$ if $k = \dfrac{\pi}{2}$

In 15–19, answer *yes* or *no*.

15. Does $\sin 90° = 2 \sin 45°$?   **16.** Does $\sin 180° = 2 \sin 90°$?

17. Does $\sin 90° + \sin 180° = \sin 270°$?   **18.** Does $\sin^2 90° + \cos^2 90° = 1$?

19. Does $\tan^2 45° + 1 = \sec^2 45°$?

11. Reducing Trigonometric Functions of an Angle in Any Quadrant

METHOD 1: USING THE SAME-NAMED FUNCTION WHEN RELATING THE ANGLE TO 180° OR 360°

Although the table of values of trigonometric functions on page 260 contains only the functions of acute angles, this same table can be used to find the functions of any angle. In order to do this, we will discover how to express a function of any positive angle greater than 90° as a function of a related acute angle which is called the *reference angle*. In Method 1, the angle to be reduced is expressed in a form involving 180° or 360°, the forms being $(180° - \theta)$, $(180° + \theta)$, $(360° - \theta)$, and $(360° + \theta)$. The angle θ in each of the forms is an acute angle whose functions can be found in the table. For this reason, the acute angle θ is called the *reference angle*.

In the following diagrams, $\overrightarrow{OP}$ is rotated from its initial position along the positive half of the x-axis to terminal positions $\overrightarrow{OP_1}$ in quadrant I, Fig. 1; $\overrightarrow{OP_2}$ in quadrant II, Fig. 2; $\overrightarrow{OP_3}$ in quadrant III, Fig. 3; and $\overrightarrow{OP_4}$ in quadrant IV, Fig. 4. Note in each diagram that θ, an acute angle, is formed by the terminal side and the x-axis. Note also that the angles in standard position are θ in Fig. 1, $(180° - \theta)$ in Fig. 2, $(180° + \theta)$ in Fig. 3, and $(360° - \theta)$ in Fig. 4.

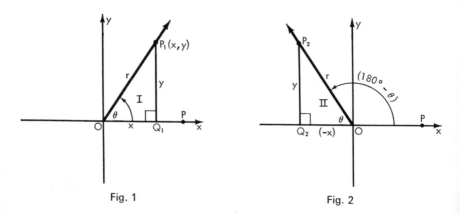

Fig. 1   Fig. 2

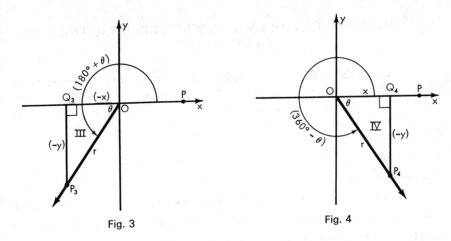

Fig. 3   Fig. 4

DETERMINING THE ABSOLUTE VALUES OF FUNCTIONS OF ANGLES GREATER THAN 90°

In the preceding diagrams, points P_1, P_2, P_3, and P_4 are each at a distance r from the origin. Hence, $OP_1 = OP_2 = OP_3 = OP_4$. If $\overline{P_1Q_1}$, $\overline{P_2Q_2}$, $\overline{P_3Q_3}$, and $\overline{P_4Q_4}$ are drawn perpendicular to the x-axis, the triangles I, II, III, and IV that are formed are congruent since they agree in two angles and a corresponding side. Hence, the following are true statements:

1. $P_1Q_1 = P_2Q_2 = P_3Q_3 = P_4Q_4$. Therefore, the ordinates of P_1, P_2, P_3, and P_4 have the same absolute value. Note that the ordinates of P_3 and P_4 are negative.

2. $OQ_1 = OQ_2 = OQ_3 = OQ_4$. Therefore, the abscissas of P_1, P_2, P_3, and P_4 have the same absolute value. Note that the abscissas of P_2 and P_3 are negative.

3. The absolute values of the same-named functions of the angles θ, $(180° - \theta)$, $(180° + \theta)$, and $(360° - \theta)$ are the same. For example,

$$|\sin \theta| = |\sin(180° - \theta)| = |\sin(180° + \theta)| = |\sin(360° - \theta)|$$

Therefore, the sine of the acute angle whose value is in the table can be referred to as the absolute value of the sine of the related angle in quadrants II, III, or IV.

Thus, $\sin\ 30° = |\sin(180° - 30°)| = |\sin(180° + 30°)| = |\sin(360° - 30°)|$; that is, $\sin 30° = |\sin 150°|$; $\sin 30° = |\sin 210°|$; and $\sin 30° = |\sin 330°|$.

METHOD 2: USING THE COFUNCTION WHEN RELATING THE ANGLE TO 90° OR 270°

In Method 2, the angle to be reduced is expressed in a form involving 90° or 270°, the forms being $(90° - \theta)$, $(90° + \theta)$, $(270° - \theta)$, and $(270° + \theta)$. The angle θ in each of the forms is an acute angle whose functions can be found in the table. For this reason, the acute angle θ is the reference angle for any of the forms involving 90° or 270°.

In the following diagrams, ray $\overrightarrow{OP}$ is rotated from its initial position along the positive half of the x-axis to terminal positions $\overrightarrow{OP_1}$ in quadrant I, Fig. 5; and $\overrightarrow{OP_2}$ in quadrant II, Fig. 6. Note in Fig. 6 that an acute angle whose measure is θ is formed by the terminal position $\overrightarrow{OP_2}$ and the y-axis and that the angle in standard position between $\overrightarrow{OP_2}$ and the x-axis is $(90° + \theta)$.

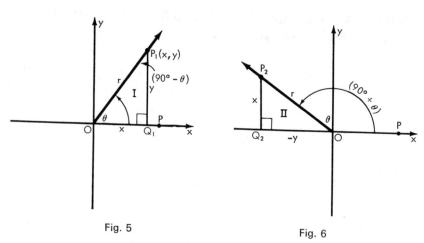

Fig. 5

Fig. 6

RELATING THE FUNCTIONS OF (90° + θ) TO FUNCTIONS OF θ

In Figs. 5 and 6, points P_1 and P_2 are at a distance r from the origin. Hence $OP_2 = OP_1$. $\overline{P_2Q_2}$ is drawn perpendicular to the x-axis, forming $\triangle$II (Fig. 6). Since the measures of alternate interior angles of parallel lines are equal, angle $OP_2Q_2 \cong \theta$. Hence, $\triangle$I $\cong \triangle$II since they agree in two angles and a corresponding side. Since the lengths of corresponding sides of congruent triangles are equal, $P_2Q_2 = OQ_1$ and $OQ_2 = P_1Q_1$. Hence, the coordinates of P_2 are $(-y, x)$.

The following relations are obtained by applying the definitions of the functions of any angle:

$$\sin(90° + \theta) = \frac{x}{r} \qquad \tan(90° + \theta) = -\frac{x}{y} \qquad \sec(90° + \theta) = -\frac{r}{y}$$

$$\cos(90° + \theta) = -\frac{y}{r} \qquad \cot(90° + \theta) = -\frac{y}{x} \qquad \csc(90° + \theta) = \frac{r}{x}$$

Substituting $\sin \theta$ for $\frac{y}{r}$, $\cos \theta$ for $\frac{x}{r}$, $\tan \theta$ for $\frac{y}{x}$, $\cot \theta$ for $\frac{x}{y}$, $\sec \theta$ for $\frac{r}{x}$, and

$\csc \theta$ for $\frac{r}{y}$, all obtainable from $\triangle$I in Fig. 5, we obtain the following:

$$\sin(90° + \theta) = \cos \theta \qquad \tan(90° + \theta) = -\cot \theta \qquad \sec(90° + \theta) = -\csc \theta$$
$$\cos(90° + \theta) = -\sin \theta \qquad \cot(90° + \theta) = -\tan \theta \qquad \csc(90° + \theta) = \sec \theta$$

In general, ***the function of an obtuse angle in the form of $(90° + \theta)$ has the same absolute value as the cofunction of acute angle θ.***

It can be shown in a proof similar to the one used above that the general rule for the function of an obtuse angle can be extended to cover any angle in the form $(270° - \theta)$ and $(270° + \theta)$.

The sign to be prefixed before the function of the acute angle is positive or negative according to whether the value of the function of the given angle is positive or negative. Recall that the value of a function of a given angle is positive or negative according to the quadrant in which the given angle lies. Refer to the table of signs of the functions of any angle on page 341.

The following sets of rules show how a function of an angle in any quadrant can be expressed in terms of either the same-named function or the *cofunction* of an acute angle.

KEEP IN MIND

If θ is an acute angle, any function of an angle expressed in the form $(180° - \theta)$, $(180° + \theta)$, $(360° - \theta)$, or $(360° + \theta)$ is equal to the same-named function of θ prefixed by a plus or a minus sign. The prefixed plus or minus sign is determined by the quadrant in which the given angle lies and the function of the given angle.

If θ is an acute angle, any function of an angle expressed in the form $(90° - \theta)$, $(90° + \theta)$, $(270° - \theta)$, or $(270° + \theta)$ is equal to the cofunction of the acute angle θ prefixed by a plus or a minus sign. The prefixed sign is determined by the quadrant in which the given angle lies and the function of the given angle.

Quadrant I

If θ is an acute angle, an angle in quadrant I can be represented as $(360° + \theta)$ or as $(90° - \theta)$.

Thus, $390° = (360° + 30°)$ $30° = (90° - 60°)$
$435° = (360° + 75°)$ $75° = (90° - 15°)$

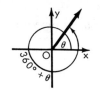

REDUCTION FORMULAS FOR ANGLES IN QUADRANT I

Using Same Function	*Using Cofunction*
$\sin(360° + \theta) = \sin\theta$	$\sin(90° - \theta) = \cos\theta$
$\cos(360° + \theta) = \cos\theta$	$\cos(90° - \theta) = \sin\theta$
$\tan(360° + \theta) = \tan\theta$	$\tan(90° - \theta) = \cot\theta$
$\cot(360° + \theta) = \cot\theta$	$\cot(90° - \theta) = \tan\theta$
$\sec(360° + \theta) = \sec\theta$	$\sec(90° - \theta) = \csc\theta$
$\csc(360° + \theta) = \csc\theta$	$\csc(90° - \theta) = \sec\theta$

Thus, $\sin 390° = \sin 30°$ Thus, $\cos 30° = \sin 60°$
$\tan 435° = \tan 75°$ $\cot 75° = \tan 15°$

Quadrant II

If θ is an acute angle, an angle in quadrant II can be represented as $(180° - \theta)$ or as $(90° + \theta)$.

Thus, $120° = (180° - 60°)$ $120° = (90° + 30°)$
$175° = (180° - 5°)$ $175° = (90° + 85°)$

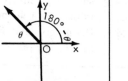

REDUCTION FORMULAS FOR ANGLES
IN QUADRANT II

Using Same Function	Using Cofunction
$\sin(180° - \theta) = \sin\theta$	$\sin(90° + \theta) = \cos\theta$
$\cos(180° - \theta) = -\cos\theta$	$\cos(90° + \theta) = -\sin\theta$
$\tan(180° - \theta) = -\tan\theta$	$\tan(90° + \theta) = -\cot\theta$
$\cot(180° - \theta) = -\cot\theta$	$\cot(90° + \theta) = -\tan\theta$
$\sec(180° - \theta) = -\sec\theta$	$\sec(90° + \theta) = -\csc\theta$
$\csc(180° - \theta) = \csc\theta$	$\csc(90° + \theta) = \sec\theta$

Thus, $\sin 120° = \sin 60°$ Thus, $\cos 120° = -\sin 30°$
$\tan 175° = -\tan 5°$ $\cot 175° = -\tan 85°$

Quadrant III

If θ is an acute angle, an angle in quadrant III can be represented as $(180° + \theta)$ or as $(270° - \theta)$.

Thus, $220° = (180° + 40°)$ $220° = (270° - 50°)$
$255° = (180° + 75°)$ $255° = (270° - 15°)$

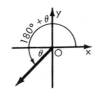 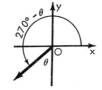

REDUCTION FORMULAS FOR ANGLES
IN QUADRANT III

Using Same Function	Using Cofunction
$\sin(180° + \theta) = -\sin\theta$	$\sin(270° - \theta) = -\cos\theta$
$\cos(180° + \theta) = -\cos\theta$	$\cos(270° - \theta) = -\sin\theta$
$\tan(180° + \theta) = \tan\theta$	$\tan(270° - \theta) = \cot\theta$
$\cot(180° + \theta) = \cot\theta$	$\cot(270° - \theta) = \tan\theta$
$\sec(180° + \theta) = -\sec\theta$	$\sec(270° - \theta) = -\csc\theta$
$\csc(180° + \theta) = -\csc\theta$	$\csc(270° - \theta) = -\sec\theta$

Thus, $\sin 220° = -\sin 40°$ Thus, $\cos 220° = -\sin 50°$
$\tan 225° = \tan 75°$ $\cot 255° = \tan 15°$

Quadrant IV

If θ is an acute angle, an angle in quadrant IV can be represented as $(360° - \theta)$ or as $(270° + \theta)$.

Thus, $305° = (360° - 55°)$ $305° = (270° + 35°)$
      $345° = (360° - 15°)$ $345° = (270° + 75°)$

REDUCTION FORMULAS FOR ANGLES IN QUADRANT IV

Using Same Function	*Using Cofunction*
$\sin (360° - \theta) = -\sin \theta$	$\sin (270° + \theta) = -\cos \theta$
$\cos (360° - \theta) = \cos \theta$	$\cos (270° + \theta) = \sin \theta$
$\tan (360° - \theta) = -\tan \theta$	$\tan (270° + \theta) = -\cot \theta$
$\cot (360° - \theta) = -\cot \theta$	$\cot (270° + \theta) = -\tan \theta$
$\sec (360° - \theta) = \sec \theta$	$\sec (270° + \theta) = \csc \theta$
$\csc (360° - \theta) = -\csc \theta$	$\csc (270° + \theta) = -\sec \theta$

Thus, $\sin 305° = -\sin 55°$ Thus, $\cos 305° = \sin 35°$
      $\tan 345° = -\tan 15°$ $\cot 345° = -\cot 75°$

~~~~~~~ *MODEL PROBLEMS* ~~~~~~~

In 1 and 2, (*a*) express the given function as a function of a positive acute angle and (*b*) find the value of the given function.

1. sin 167°   **2.** cos 220°

Solution:

1. Draw a diagram, including the given angle in standard position, the number of the quadrant in which the given angle lies, and the reference angle made with the *x*-axis.

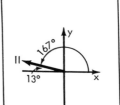

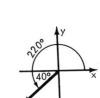

2. In the table on page 260, find the value of the same-named function of the reference angle.

$\sin 13° = .2250$	$\cos 40° = .7660$

3. Prefix the proper sign before the tabular value, depending on the quadrant and function of the original angle.

$\sin 167° = +.2250$	$\cos 220° = -.7660$

Answer:

(a) $+\sin 13°$	(a) $-\cos 40°$
(b) $+.2250$	(b) $-.7660$

3. Express $\tan 300°$ as a function of a positive acute angle less than $45°$ and give its value in radical form.

Solution:

$$\tan 300° = \tan (360° - 60°)$$
$$\tan 300° = -\tan 60°$$
$$\tan 300° = -\cot 30° = -\sqrt{3} \quad Ans.$$

4. Find the value of $\cos \frac{7}{6}\pi$ in radical form.

Solution: Express $\frac{7}{6}\pi$ radians in degrees.

$$\frac{7}{6}\pi \text{ radians} = \frac{7}{6}\pi \times \frac{\overset{30°}{\cancel{180°}}}{\cancel{\pi}} = 210°$$

Therefore, $\cos \frac{7}{6}\pi = \cos 210° = \cos(180° + 30°)$

$$\cos \frac{7}{6}\pi = -\cos 30° = -\frac{\sqrt{3}}{2} \quad Ans.$$

5. Express each of the following as a function of a positive acute angle less than $45°$: *a.* $\sin 95°$ *b.* $\cos \dfrac{17\pi}{12}$ *c.* $\cot 280°$

Solution:

a. $\sin 95° = \sin (90° + 5°) = \cos 5° \quad Ans.$

b. $\cos \dfrac{17\pi}{12} = \cos 255° = \cos (270° - 15°) = -\sin 15° \quad Ans.$

c. $\cot 280° = \cot (270° + 10°) = -\tan 10° \quad$ Ans.

Exercises

In 1–24, express the given function as a function of a positive acute angle.
1. tan 140°
2. sin 234°
3. cos 290°
4. sin 297°
5. sec 310°
6. cot 254°
7. cos 157°
8. csc 235°
9. cot 241°
10. sec 164°
11. sin 135° 30′
12. cos 213° 45′
13. tan 312° 50′
14. sin 430°
15. cos 555°
16. tan 470°
17. $\cos \frac{2}{3}\pi$
18. $\sin \frac{3}{4}\pi$
19. $\tan \frac{4}{3}\pi$
20. $\sin \frac{2}{3}\pi$
21. $\cos \frac{7}{6}\pi$
22. $\tan \frac{5}{4}\pi$
23. $\sin \frac{7}{4}\pi$
24. $\cos \frac{5}{3}\pi$

In 25–36, express the given function as a function of a positive acute angle less than 45°.
25. cot 190°
26. sin 118°
27. csc 100° 30′
28. tan 250°
29. cos 140°
30. cos 440°
31. sin 289°
32. cot 113°
33. $\sin \frac{2}{3}\pi$
34. tan 275°
35. sec 265°
36. $\cos \frac{4}{3}\pi$

In 37–42, give the value of the function in radical form.
37. tan 150°
38. sin 225°
39. sec 330°
40. tan 240°
41. cos 315°
42. cot 300°

In 43–50, give the value of the function.
43. sin 163°
44. sin 210°
45. cos 342°
46. tan 215°
47. cos 128° 40′
48. sin 220° 30′
49. cot 158° 20′
50. sin 115° 25′

In 51–62, express the given function as the cofunction of a positive acute angle, using a form combining the acute angle and either 90° or 270°.
51. sin 160°
52. tan 255°
53. cos 290°
54. cot 224°
55. sec 197°
56. csc 308°
57. sin 157° 20′
58. sec 219° 35′
59. csc 317° 22′
60. $\sin \frac{5\pi}{9}$
61. $\cos \frac{4\pi}{3}$
62. $\tan \frac{11\pi}{6}$

In 63–68, using the relationships between the functions of the angles $(90° - \theta)$, $(90° + \theta)$, $(270° - \theta)$, $(270° + \theta)$ and the functions of the angle θ, find the value of the function in radical form.
63. sin 120°
64. cos 210°
65. tan 210°
66. cot 330°
67. sec 135°
68. csc 225°

69. Is sin 60° equal to, greater than, or less than sin 120°?
70. tan 316° 20′ is equal to (1) −1.0477 (2) −0.9545 (3) 0.9545 (4) 1.0477
71. Find the value of tan 225° − sin 150°.
72. Express tan(180° − A) as a trigonometric function of angle A.
73. If sin A = x, express sin(360° − A) in terms of x.
74. Express cos(90° + A) as a trigonometric function of angle A.
75. Express sin(270° + A) as a trigonometric function of angle A.

76. If $\sin A = s$, express $\cos(90° + A)$ in terms of s.

77. If $\cot A = c$, express $\tan(270° - A)$ in terms of c.

12. Finding the Trigonometric Functions of a Negative Angle

Our discussions involving the reduction of the functions of any angle were restricted to the functions of positive angles, those angles that are generated by a ray rotating from its initial position in a counterclockwise direction. Now we will learn how to find the functions of negative angles, those angles that are formed by rotating a ray from an initial position in a clockwise direction.

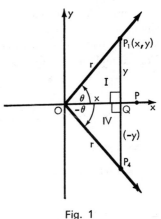

In Fig. 1, $\overrightarrow{OP}$ is rotated counterclockwise from its initial position along the positive half of the x-axis to terminal position $\overrightarrow{OP_1}$ in quadrant I. $\overrightarrow{OP}$ is also rotated clockwise from its initial position to terminal position $\overrightarrow{OP_4}$ in quadrant IV. The measures of the angles formed are θ and $-\theta$ respectively. Points P_1 and P_4 are each at a distance r from the origin. Hence, $OP_1 = OP_4$. Perpendiculars drawn from P_1 and from P_4 to the x-axis will meet at point Q. Since $\triangle$I and $\triangle$IV agree in two angles and a corresponding side, they are congruent. Hence, the ordinates QP_1 and QP_4 have the same absolute value. Note that ordinate QP_4 is negative.

Fig. 1

Applying the definitions of the functions of any angle:

$$\sin(-\theta) = \frac{-y}{r} \text{ and } \sin\theta = \frac{y}{r}. \text{ Hence, } \sin(-\theta) = -\sin\theta.$$

$$\cos(-\theta) = \frac{x}{r} \quad \text{and } \cos\theta = \frac{x}{r}. \text{ Hence, } \cos(-\theta) = \cos\theta.$$

$$\tan(-\theta) = \frac{-y}{x} \text{ and } \tan\theta = \frac{y}{x}. \text{ Hence, } \tan(-\theta) = -\tan\theta.$$

$$\cot(-\theta) = \frac{x}{-y} \text{ and } \cot\theta = \frac{x}{y}. \text{ Hence, } \cot(-\theta) = -\cot\theta.$$

$$\sec(-\theta) = \frac{r}{x} \quad \text{and } \sec\theta = \frac{r}{x}. \text{ Hence, } \sec(-\theta) = \sec\theta.$$

$$\csc(-\theta) = \frac{r}{-y} \text{ and } \csc\theta = \frac{r}{y}. \text{ Hence, } \csc(-\theta) = -\csc\theta.$$

Following are the rules for expressing a function of angle $(-\theta)$ as the same-named function of angle θ (refer to Fig. 2):

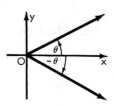

$$\sin(-\theta) = -\sin\theta \qquad \csc(-\theta) = -\csc\theta$$
$$\cos(-\theta) = +\cos\theta \qquad \sec(-\theta) = +\sec\theta$$
$$\tan(-\theta) = -\tan\theta \qquad \cot(-\theta) = -\cot\theta$$

Note. Use $(+)$ on the right only with the cosine and secant, the only functions whose values in quadrant IV are positive.

Fig. 2

In our previous discussion, the rules that we developed were true when θ was the measure of an acute angle; that is, $0° < \theta < 90°$. However, the rules can be shown to be true for all values that θ may have. (See the proofs on page 732.) For example, $\cos(-\theta) = \cos\theta$ when $\theta = 200°$; that is, $\cos(-200°) = \cos 200°$. Also, $\sin(-\theta) = -\sin\theta$ when $\theta = 527°$; that is, $\sin(-527°) = -\sin 527°$.

MODEL PROBLEMS

1. Express $\cos(-240°)$ as a function of a positive acute angle.

Solution: Since $\cos(-\theta) = +\cos\theta$, $\cos(-240°) = \cos 240°$.
$$\cos 240° = \cos(180° + 60°) = -\cos 60°. \quad Ans.$$

2. Find the value of $\sin(-135°)$.

Solution: Since $\sin(-\theta) = -\sin\theta$, $\sin(-135°) = -\sin 135°$.
$$\sin(135°) = \sin(180° - 45°) = \sin 45°.$$
Therefore, $-\sin 135° = -\sin 45° = -\frac{1}{2}\sqrt{2}. \quad Ans.$

Exercises

1. For all values of A, (1) $\sin(-A) = -\sin A$ (2) $\sin(-A) = \sin A$
(3) $\sin(-A) = \cos A$ (4) $\sin(-A) = -\cos A$

2. For all values of A, (1) $\dfrac{\cos(-A)}{\sin A} = -\tan A$ (2) $\dfrac{\cos(-A)}{\sin A} = \tan A$

(3) $\dfrac{\cos(-A)}{\sin A} = \cot A$ (4) $\dfrac{\cos(-A)}{\sin A} = -\cot A$

3. $\cos(-x)$ equals (1) $-\cos x$ (2) $\cos x$ (3) $-\sin x$

4. For all values of A, $\cot A$ is equal to (1) $\dfrac{1}{\tan(-A)}$ (2) $\dfrac{\cos(-A)}{\sin A}$

(3) $\dfrac{\cos A}{\sin(-A)}$

In 5–13, express the function as a function of a positive acute angle.

5. $\sin(-80°)$ **6.** $\cos(-140°)$ **7.** $\cot(-215°)$
8. $\cos(-327°)$ **9.** $\sec(-20°\ 30')$ **10.** $\csc(-105°\ 25')$

11. $\sin\left(-\dfrac{\pi}{3}\right)$ **12.** $\cos\left(-\dfrac{5}{6}\pi\right)$ **13.** $\tan\left(-\dfrac{9}{5}\pi\right)$

In 14–16, express the function as a function of a positive acute angle less than 45°.

14. $\tan(-195°)$ **15.** $\sin(-80°)$ **16.** $\sin(-230°)$

In 17–19, express the function in radical form.

17. $\sin(-225°)$ **18.** $\tan\left(-\dfrac{\pi}{6}\right)$ **19.** $\cos\left(-\dfrac{3}{4}\pi\right)$

In 20–31, give the value of the function.

20. $\sin(-72°)$ **21.** $\cos(-40°)$ **22.** $\tan(-45°)$
23. $\tan(-135°)$ **24.** $\sin(-210°)$ **25.** $\cos(-300°)$
26. $\sin(-84°)$ **27.** $\cos(-124°)$ **28.** $\tan\left(-\frac{9}{10}\pi\right)$
29. $\tan(-240°\ 20')$ **30.** $\cos(-117°\ 50')$ **31.** $\sin(-247°\ 23')$

32. Which of the following is equal to $\sin 40°$?   (1) $\sin 220°$ (2) $\sin 130°$
(3) $\cos(-50°)$

33. The expression $\dfrac{\sin(90° + x)}{\sin(-x)}$ can be reduced to (1) -1 (2) $-\cot x$ (3) $\cot x$

34. Show that $\dfrac{\cos(90° - A)\cos(-A)}{\tan(180° + A)}$ is equivalent to $\cos^2 A$.

13. Inverses of Trigonometric Functions

Recall that $\cos 60° = \frac{1}{2}$. Hence, we may say that "60° is an angle whose cosine is $\frac{1}{2}$." This statement may be written in either of two ways:

$$60° = \text{arc cos } \tfrac{1}{2} \quad \text{or} \quad 60° = \cos^{-1} \tfrac{1}{2}$$

Keep in mind that the symbol " $^{-1}$ " is a convenient way of stating "the angle whose." Do not confuse this use with the use of the same symbol as a negative exponent.

Similarly, $\theta = \text{arc tan } 1$ or $\theta = \tan^{-1} 1$ means "θ is an angle whose tangent is 1." In general, if $\sin \theta = y$, then "θ is an angle whose sine is y," which may be written as $\theta = \text{arc sin } y$ or as $\theta = \sin^{-1} y$. The expression arc sin y or $\sin^{-1} y$ is called the *inverse of a trigonometric function.*

Direct Notation	Inverse Notation
$\cos \theta = \frac{1}{2}$	$\theta = \text{arc cos } \frac{1}{2}$ or $\cos^{-1} \frac{1}{2}$
$\tan \theta = 1$	$\theta = \text{arc tan } 1$ or $\tan^{-1} 1$
$\sin \theta = y$	$\theta = \text{arc sin } y$ or $\sin^{-1} y$

PRINCIPAL VALUE OF AN INVERSE OF A TRIGONOMETRIC FUNCTION: SYMBOLIZING PRINCIPAL VALUE

If $\theta = \text{arc tan } 1$, θ is an angle whose tangent is 1. Hence, in this case, θ may be $45°$, $225°$, $405°$, $-135°$, $-315°$, and many other degree measures. Of these values, $45°$ is called the *principal value* of θ. "The principal value of arc tan 1 is $45°$" is written "Arc tan $1 = 45°$." The *capitalizing of the first letter of "arc"* indicates that $45°$ is the principal value. We may also write "$\text{Tan}^{-1} 1 = 45°$." By *capitalizing the first letter of the function that is involved*, in this case, the tangent function, we indicate that $45°$ is the principal value.

If $x = \cos^{-1}(-\frac{1}{2})$, then x is the measure of an angle whose cosine is $-\frac{1}{2}$ and x may be $120°$, $-120°$, $240°$, $-240°$, $480°$, and many other degree measures. Of these values, $120°$ is called the principal value of x and is symbolized either as Arc cos $(-\frac{1}{2}) = 120°$ or $\text{Cos}^{-1}(-\frac{1}{2}) = 120°$. Note that to symbolize the principal value, we capitalize the first letter of "arc" or the first letter of the trigonometric function that is involved.

In the previous two examples, the principal values of an angle were determined in accordance with the following rules:

Rule 1. The principal value of an inverse of a trigonometric function is the angle whose measure has the smallest absolute value, with the exception of Arc cotangent of a negative number.

Thus, Arc tan $1 = 45°$, Arc sin $\frac{1}{2} = 30°$, Arc tan $(-1) = -45°$, and also $\text{Sin}^{-1}(-\frac{1}{2}) = -30°$ illustrate the selection of the principal value in accordance with Rule 1.

Rule 2. The principal value of an inverse of a trigonometric function is the positive value when there are two measures having the same smallest absolute value, one positive and the other negative.

Thus, if $x =$ Arc cos $(-\frac{1}{2})$, then $x = 120°$, not $-120°$. Also Arc sec $(-\sqrt{2}) = 135°$ and not $-135°$.

DETERMINING THE QUADRANT IN WHICH THE PRINCIPAL VALUE LIES WHEN IT IS NOT A QUADRANTAL ANGLE

From the two rules previously stated, we can derive the following three principles to enable us to determine the quadrant in which the principal value of an angle lies when the principal value is not a quadrantal angle:

Principle 1. The principal value of an inverse of any trigonometric function of a positive number is a positive angle in quadrant I.

Thus, the principal value of arc sin $\frac{1}{2}\sqrt{2}$ is $45°$; that is, Arc sin $\frac{1}{2}\sqrt{2} = 45°$. Also, Arc sec $2 = 60°$ and Cot$^{-1}\sqrt{3} = 30°$.

Principle 2. The principal value of arc sine, arc tangent, or arc cosecant of a negative number is a negative angle in quadrant IV.

Thus, the principal value of arc sin $(-\frac{1}{2}\sqrt{3}) = -60°$ and not $240°$, and the principal value of arc tan $(-1) = -45°$ and not $135°$. Also, Csc$^{-1}(-2) = -30°$ and not $210°$.

Principle 3. The principal value of arc cosine or arc secant of a negative number is a positive angle in quadrant II.

Thus, the principal value of arc cos $(-\frac{1}{2}\sqrt{3})$ is $150°$; that is, Arc cos $(-\frac{1}{2}\sqrt{3}) = 150°$. Also, Sec$^{-1}(-2) = 120°$.

Note. In the case of arc cotangent of a negative number, its principal value is a positive angle in quadrant II. For example, Arc cot $(-1) = 135°$ and not $(-45°)$. Thus, finding Arc cotangent of a negative number does not follow the rule that the principal value of an inverse of a trigonometric function is the angle whose measure has the smallest absolute value.

TRIGONOMETRIC RELATIONS AND FUNCTIONS

The solution set of $y = \sin x$ may consist of ordered pairs (x, y), where x is the degree measure of an angle. Since $y = \sin x$, then its solution set includes ordered pairs such as $(0°, 0)$, $(180°, 0)$, $(90°, 1)$, $(-270°, 1)$, $(-30°, -\frac{1}{2})$, and $(210°, -\frac{1}{2})$. Since each x uniquely determines sin x, then $y = \sin x$ defines a relation that is a function. It is for this reason that we refer to sin x as a "trigonometric function." Similarly, the other five functions of an angle, cos x, tan x, cot x, sec x, and csc x, are trigonometric functions.

Recall that the inverse of a relation is formed by interchanging the members of each ordered pair of the relation. Thus, we see that the inverse of the relation

$\{(1, 2), (3, 4), (5, 4)\}$ is $\{(2, 1), (4, 3), (4, 5)\}$. The first set is a function, whereas the second set is not. Note that the second set contains the ordered pairs $(4, 3)$ and $(4, 5)$ in which the first element 4 does not uniquely determine a second element since there are two second elements, 3 and 5.

If we interchange the coordinates in the set of ordered pairs which is the function defined by $y = \sin x$, we obtain the inverse of the function defined by $x = \sin y$. The equation $x = \sin y$, which defines the inverse of the function, is obtained from $y = \sin x$, the equation which defines the function, by simply interchanging x and y in $y = \sin x$. Instead of writing $x = \sin y$, we may write $y = \text{arc sin } x$ or $y = \sin^{-1} x$. Since $y = \sin^{-1} x$ defines the inverse of the function defined by $y = \sin x$, we may obtain the solution set of $y = \sin^{-1} x$ by simply interchanging the members of the ordered pairs of the solution set of $y = \sin x$. We thus obtain ordered pairs such as $(0, 0°)$, $(0, 180°)$, $(1, 90°)$, $(1, -270°)$, $(-\frac{1}{2}, -30°)$ and $(-\frac{1}{2}, 210°)$. Since each x does *not* uniquely determine y or $\sin^{-1} x$, then the set of ordered pairs defined by $y = \sin^{-1} x$ is a relation that is *not* a function. Hence, we cannot refer to $\sin^{-1} x$ as a function although $\sin^{-1} x$ is the inverse of a trigonometric function.

OBTAINING RELATIONS THAT ARE FUNCTIONS BY USING PRINCIPAL VALUES

Let us now consider the solution set of $y = \text{Sin}^{-1} x$ or $y = \text{Arc sin } x$, which consists of the ordered pairs (x, y) where y is the degree measure of the principal value of an angle. By restricting the value of y to a single principal value, it follows that, for any real number x $(-1 \leq x \leq 1)$, there can be one and only one principal value, y. Hence, in the solution set of $y = \text{Sin}^{-1} x$, the ordered pairs (x, y) are such that the first element x uniquely determines the second element y. Therefore, the solution set of $y = \text{Sin}^{-1} x$ is a relation that is a function, and we may refer to $\text{Sin}^{-1} x$ as an "inverse trigonometric function." Using the same kind of reasoning, we find that we may refer to $\text{Cos}^{-1} x$, $\text{Tan}^{-1} x$, $\text{Cot}^{-1} x$, $\text{Sec}^{-1} x$, and $\text{Csc}^{-1} x$ as "inverse trigonometric functions."

By common consent, mathematicians have agreed to restrict the set of principal values, or the range of the inverse trigonometric functions, by defining these ranges in terms of radian measures, as follows:

$$-\frac{\pi}{2} \leq \text{Arc sin } x \leq \frac{\pi}{2} \qquad 0 < \text{Arc cot } x < \pi$$

$$0 \leq \text{Arc cos } x \leq \pi \qquad 0 \leq \text{Arc sec } x \leq \pi$$

$$-\frac{\pi}{2} < \text{Arc tan } x < \frac{\pi}{2} \qquad -\frac{\pi}{2} \leq \text{Arc csc } x \leq \frac{\pi}{2}$$

Bear in mind that:

π radians $= 180°$

$\dfrac{\pi}{2}$ radians $= 90°$

If $y = $ Arc sin x, note that the range of this inverse trigonometric function is restricted to $-90° \leq$ Arc sin $x \leq 90°$. Hence, when y is not a quadrantal angle, it must lie in quadrants I and IV, which agrees with principles 1 and 2. Note also that when y is a quadrantal angle, y may be $-90°$, $0°$, or $90°$.

If $y = $ Arc cos x, note that the range of this inverse trigonometric function is restricted to $0° \leq$ Arc cos $x \leq 180°$. Hence, when y is not a quadrantal angle, it must lie in quadrants I and II, which agrees with principles 1 and 3. Note also that when y is a quadrantal angle, y may be $0°$, $90°$, or $180°$.

If $y = $ Arc tan x, note that the range of this inverse trigonometric function is restricted to $-90° <$ Arc tan $x < 90°$. Hence, when y is not a quadrantal angle, it must lie in quadrants I and IV, which agrees with principles 1 and 2. If y is a quadrantal angle, it may be $0°$ only. The range does not include $-90°$ or $90°$ since the tangent of either of these quadrantal angles cannot be defined.

$\sim\sim\sim\sim\sim\sim\sim\sim\sim\sim$ *MODEL PROBLEMS* $\sim\sim\sim\sim\sim\sim\sim\sim$

1. Find Arc tan $\sqrt{3}$.

Solution: Since the first letter of *Arc* is a capital letter, then "Arc tan $\sqrt{3}$" means "the principal value of arc tan $\sqrt{3}$." According to principle 1, the principal value is in quadrant I. In quadrant I, tan $60° = \sqrt{3}$.   *Ans.* $60°$

2. Find sin A if $A = \text{Cos}^{-1}\left(-\dfrac{5}{13}\right)$.

Solution: Since the first letter of *Cos* is a capital letter, then "$\text{Cos}^{-1}\left(-\dfrac{5}{13}\right)$" means "the principal value of $\cos^{-1}\left(-\dfrac{5}{13}\right)$." According to principle 3, the principal value is in quadrant II. In quadrant II, sin A is positive. Find sin A as follows:

Since $\cos A = \dfrac{\text{abscissa}}{\text{distance}} = \dfrac{x}{r} = \dfrac{-5}{13}$, let $x = -5, r = 13$.

$y^2 = r^2 - x^2 = (13)^2 - (-5)^2 = 169 - 25 = 144, \ y = 12$

Therefore, sin $A = \dfrac{y}{r} = \dfrac{12}{13}$.   *Ans.* $\dfrac{12}{13}$

3. Find $\tan\left(\text{Arc } \cos \dfrac{2}{\sqrt 5}\right)$.

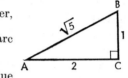

Solution: Since the first letter of *Arc* is a capital letter, then "Arc $\cos \dfrac{2}{\sqrt 5}$" means "the principal value of arc $\cos \dfrac{2}{\sqrt 5}$." According to principle 1, the principal value of the inverse function is in quadrant I, an acute angle. The acute angle is represented by x in $\triangle ABC$, as shown.

Hence, $\tan\left(\text{Arc } \cos \dfrac{2}{\sqrt 5}\right) = \tan x = \dfrac{1}{2}$.   *Ans.* $\dfrac{1}{2}$

4. Find $\text{Arc } \sin\left(\cos \dfrac{2\pi}{3}\right)$.

Solution: Since $\dfrac{2\pi}{3} = 120°$, then $\cos \dfrac{2\pi}{3} = -\tfrac{1}{2}$. Hence, $\text{Arc } \sin\left(\cos \dfrac{2\pi}{3}\right) =$ Arc $\sin\left(-\tfrac{1}{2}\right)$. Since the first letter of *Arc* is a capital letter, then "Arc $\sin\left(-\tfrac{1}{2}\right)$" means "the principal value of arc $\sin\left(-\tfrac{1}{2}\right)$." According to principle 2, the principal value of an angle whose sine is negative is in quadrant IV.

Hence, $\text{Arc } \sin\left(-\tfrac{1}{2}\right) = -30°$.   *Ans.* $-30°$ or $-\dfrac{\pi}{6}$

Exercises

In 1–4, find the principal value of A.

1. $A = \text{arc } \sin \dfrac{\sqrt 3}{2}$

2. $A = \cos^{-1} \dfrac{\sqrt 2}{2}$

3. $A = \text{arc } \tan 1$

4. $A = \tan^{-1}(0.8391)$

In 5 and 6, find A.

5. $A = \text{Arc } \sec \tfrac{2}{3}\sqrt 3$

6. $A = \text{Arc } \csc 2$

In 7–10, find the principal value of A.

7. $A = \text{arc } \sin\left(-\dfrac{\sqrt 2}{2}\right)$

8. $A = \text{arc } \tan (-1)$

9. $A = \text{arc csc } (-\sqrt{2})$

10. $A = \text{arc sin } (-0.2588)$

In 11 and 12, find A.

11. $A = \text{Arc cos } (-\frac{1}{2}\sqrt{2})$

12. $A = \text{Arc sec } (-2)$

In 13–16, express A as an inverse trigonometric function.

13. $3 \cot A = 2$

14. $5 + \tan A = 3$

15. $4 + 3 \sin A = 5$

16. $3 - 4 \sin A = 6 \sin A$

In 17 and 18, express A as the principal value of an inverse trigonometric function.

17. $4 \sin A + 2 = 3$

18. $\tan A - 2 \tan A = 3$

19. The principal value of $\cos^{-1} \frac{1}{2}$ is   (1) 30°   (2) 60°   (3) −60°

20. $\text{Sin}^{-1} (-\frac{1}{2})$ is   (1) 30°   (2) −30°   (3) 210°

21. The smallest positive angle whose cosine is   −0.8718 is (1) 119° 20′
  (2) 150° 40′   (3) 209° 20′   (4) 240° 40′

In 22–27, find A, to the nearest minute.

22. $A = \text{Arc sin } .2660$

23. $A = \text{Arc cos } .3975$

24. $A = \text{Tan}^{-1} .6065$

25. $A = \text{Arc sin } .8771$

26. $A = \text{Arc cos } .9381$

27. $A = \text{Cot}^{-1} 0.7$

28. If $A = \text{Cos}^{-1} \frac{3}{5}$, find $\tan A$.

In 29–34, find $\sin A$.

29. $A = \text{Arc tan } 1$

30. $A = \text{Arc cot } \frac{5}{12}$

31. $A = \text{Arc tan } 1.1918$

32. $A = \text{Arc cos } \frac{12}{13}$

33. $A = \text{Arc cos } (-\frac{3}{5})$

34. $A = \text{Arc cos } (-0.8290)$

In 35–43, find:

35. $\tan (\text{Arc cos } \frac{5}{13})$

36. $\sin (\text{Arc tan } 1)$

37. $\cos (\text{Sin}^{-1} \frac{7}{25})$

38. $\sin (\text{Arc csc } 2)$

39. $\sec (\text{Arc cos } \frac{1}{3})$

40. $\cos (\text{Tan}^{-1} \frac{5}{12})$

41. $\cot \left(\text{Arc sin } \frac{\sqrt{2}}{2} \right)$

42. $\tan \left(\text{Cos}^{-1} \frac{\sqrt{3}}{2} \right)$

43. $\tan \left(\text{Arc sin } \frac{\sqrt{2}}{2} \right)$

44. secant $(\text{Arc sin } \frac{1}{2})$ is equal to   (1) 2   (2) $\frac{2}{3}\sqrt{3}$ (3) 30°

45. If $x = \text{Arc cos } \frac{8}{17}$, find $\tan x$.

46. If $x = \text{Arc sin } \frac{8}{17}$, find $\cot x$.

47. Find A, an angle between 90° and 180°, if $A = \text{arc cos } (-\frac{1}{2}\sqrt{2})$.

48. If $A = \text{Arc tan } \dfrac{2}{\sqrt{41}}$, find $\sin A$.

49. Find the value of $(A + B)$ if $A = \text{Sin}^{-1} \frac{1}{2}$ and $B = \text{Sin}^{-1} \frac{1}{2}\sqrt{3}$.

50. Prove that $\cos^2 (\text{Cot}^{-1} m) = \dfrac{m^2}{m^2 + 1}$.

In 51–56, find:

51. Arc sin $\left(\sin \dfrac{\pi}{4}\right)$ **52.** Arc sin $\left(\cos \dfrac{\pi}{3}\right)$ **53.** Arc tan $\left(\sin \dfrac{\pi}{2}\right)$

54. Arc sin $\left[\cos\left(-\dfrac{\pi}{6}\right)\right]$ **55.** Arc tan $\left(\sin \dfrac{\pi}{3}\right)$ **56.** Arc tan $\left[\sin\left(-\dfrac{5\pi}{6}\right)\right]$

In 57 and 58, evaluate.

57. $\sin\left[\operatorname{Sin}^{-1}(-1) + \operatorname{Cos}^{-1}(-1)\right]$

58. $\tan\left[\operatorname{Tan}^{-1} 1 + 4\operatorname{Sin}^{-1}\tfrac{1}{2} - \operatorname{Cos}^{-1}\left(-\tfrac{1}{2}\right)\right]$

In 59–62, find each.

59. $\tan\left(2\text{ Arc sin }\tfrac{1}{2}\right)$ **60.** $\csc\left(2\text{ Arc tan }\sqrt{3}\right)$

61. $2\sin\left(3\text{ Arc cos }\dfrac{\sqrt{2}}{2}\right)$ **62.** $4\sec\left[\tfrac{1}{2}\text{ Arc cos }\left(-\tfrac{1}{2}\right)\right]$

63. The absolute value of sin (arc cos x) equals (1) $\sqrt{1+x^2}$ (2) $\sqrt{1-x^2}$
(3) $1+x$ (4) $1-x$

14. Expressing Rectangular Coordinates in Trigonometric Form

The rectangular coordinates, (x, y), of any point $P(x, y)$ may be expressed in trigonometric form. Let O be the center of a circle the length of whose radius $\overline{OP}$ is represented by r. If θ, the angle formed by $\overline{OP}$ and the positive side of the x-axis is in standard position, then, using right triangle OPA as shown:

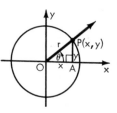

$x = r\cos\theta$, since $\cos\theta = \dfrac{x}{r}$ $r = \sqrt{x^2+y^2}$, since $x^2 + y^2 = r^2$ and r is positive

$y = r\sin\theta$, since $\sin\theta = \dfrac{y}{r}$ $\theta = \text{arc tan }\dfrac{y}{x}$, since $\tan\theta = \dfrac{y}{x}$

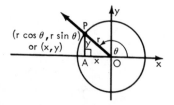

Hence, for any point $P(x, y)$ on a circle with radius r and center at the origin, the coordinates of P may be expressed in a new form $(r\cos\theta, r\sin\theta)$. As shown, P is in quadrant II. However, P may be in any other quadrant.

~~~~~~~~~~~~~~~ *MODEL PROBLEMS* ~~~~~~~~~~~~~~~

1. As shown, $OP = 8$ and $\theta = 300°$. Find x and y, the rectangular coordinates of P.

Solution:

(1) $x = r \cos \theta$
   $x = 8 \cos 300°$
   $x = 8(\frac{1}{2})$
   $x = 4$

(2) $y = r \sin \theta$
   $y = r \sin 300°$
   $y = 8(-\frac{1}{2}\sqrt{3})$
   $y = -4\sqrt{3}$

Answer: $(4, -4\sqrt{3})$

2. Express the coordinates of $P(-5\sqrt{3}, 5)$ in trigonometric form.

Solution:

(1) $r^2 = x^2 + y^2$

   $r^2 = (-5\sqrt{3})^2 + 5^2$

   $r^2 = 75 + 25$

   $r = 10$

(2) $\tan \theta = \dfrac{y}{x}$

   $\tan \theta = \dfrac{5}{-5\sqrt{3}}$

   $\tan \theta = -\dfrac{1}{\sqrt{3}} = -\frac{1}{3}\sqrt{3}$

Since θ is in quadrant II, $\theta = 150°$.
Since $x = r \cos \theta$, $x = 10 \cos 150°$.
Since $y = r \sin \theta$, $y = 10 \sin 150°$.

Answer: $(10 \cos 150°, 10 \sin 150°)$

3. Find the length of the line segment which joins

   $P\left(4 \cos \dfrac{5\pi}{6},\ 4 \sin \dfrac{5\pi}{6}\right)$ and $P'(0, -8)$.

Solution:

$\dfrac{5\pi}{6} = 150°$

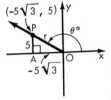
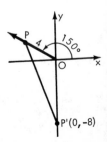

$$(PP')^2 = (x_2 - x_1)^2 + (y_2 - y_1)^2$$
$$(PP')^2 = (4 \cos 150° - 0)^2 + (4 \sin 150° + 8)^2$$
$$(PP')^2 = 16 \cos^2 150° + 16 \sin^2 150° + 64 \sin 150° + 64$$
$$(PP')^2 = 16(\cos^2 150° + \sin^2 150°) + 64 \sin 150° + 64$$
$$(PP')^2 = 16(1) + 64(+\tfrac{1}{2}) + 64$$
$$(PP')^2 = 16 + 32 + 64 = 112$$
$$PP' = \sqrt{112} = 4\sqrt{7} \quad Ans.$$

Exercises

In 1–6, plot the point.

1. $(4 \cos 30°, 4 \sin 30°)$

2. $(8 \cos 45°, 8 \sin 45°)$

3. $(3 \cos 120°, 3 \sin 120°)$

4. $(\cos 270°, \sin 270°)$

5. $\left(10 \cos \dfrac{\pi}{3}, 10 \sin \dfrac{\pi}{3}\right)$

6. $[12 \cos (-\pi), 12 \sin (-\pi)]$

7. Show that $x = r \cos \theta$ and $y = r \sin \theta$ satisfy the equation $x^2 + y^2 = r^2$.

8. If for point P, $r = 10$ and $\theta = 120°$, the rectangular coordinates of P can be expressed in trigonometric form as $(10 \cos 120°, 10 \sin 120°)$. Determine x and y, the rectangular coordinates of P.

In 9–14, determine x and y, the rectangular coordinates of P, if these coordinates expressed in trigonometric form are:

9. $(6 \cos 90°, 6 \sin 90°)$

10. $(25 \cos 180°, 25 \sin 180°)$

11. $(32 \cos 30°, 32 \sin 30°)$

12. $\left(14 \cos \dfrac{2\pi}{3}, 14 \sin \dfrac{2\pi}{3}\right)$

13. $(10 \cos 25°, 10 \sin 25°)$

14. $[10 \cos (-25°), 10 \sin (-25°)]$

In 15–24, find x and y, the rectangular coordinates of P, if $OP = r$ and angle θ is in standard position.

15. $r = 4$, $\theta = 30°$

16. $r = 6$, $\theta = \dfrac{\pi}{4}$

17. $r = 12$, $\theta = 135°$

18. $r = 20$, $\theta = \dfrac{2\pi}{3}$

19. $r = 17$, $\theta = 270°$

20. $r = 14$, $\theta = \dfrac{7\pi}{8}$

21. $r = 5$, $\theta = -30°$

22. $r = 2$, $\theta = -\dfrac{5\pi}{6}$

23. $r = 9$, $\theta = 720°$

24. $r = 11$, $\theta = 5\pi$

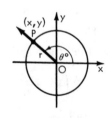

In 25–39, express, in trigonometric form, the pair of rectangular coordinates of a point P.

25. $(3\sqrt{2}, 3\sqrt{2})$ **26.** $(2, 2\sqrt{3})$ **27.** $(3\sqrt{3}, 3)$
28. $(13, 0)$ **29.** $(0, 5)$ **30.** $(-7, 0)$
31. $(3, 3)$ **32.** $(-3, 3)$ **33.** $(3, -3)$
34. $(0, -5)$ **35.** $(-4, 4\sqrt{3})$ **36.** $(-5\sqrt{2}, 5\sqrt{2})$
37. $(-8\sqrt{3}, -8)$ **38.** $(3, 4)$ **39.** $(-5, 12)$

In 40–49, express the coordinates of P in terms of r when θ, which is in standard position, equals:

40. $45°$ **41.** $150°$ **42.** $210°$ **43.** $-60°$ **44.** $-180°$

45. $\dfrac{\pi}{2}$ **46.** $\dfrac{\pi}{3}$ **47.** $\dfrac{3\pi}{4}$ **48.** $-\dfrac{\pi}{6}$ **49.** $-\dfrac{3\pi}{2}$

In 50–54, find the length of the line segment that joins the points P and P' whose rectangular coordinates are:

50. $P(0, 5)$, $P'(3, 9)$ **51.** $P(4, 0)$, $P'(9, 12)$
52. $P(0, 2)$, $P'(4 \cos 30°, 4 \sin 30°)$ **53.** $P(6 \cos 45°, 6 \sin 45°)$, $P'(3\sqrt{2}, 0)$
54. $P(8 \cos 0°, 8 \sin 0°)$, $P'(6 \cos 90°, 6 \sin 90°)$

In 55–57, find, to the nearest integer, the length of the line segment PP' which joins point $P(10 \cos 30°, 10 \sin 30°)$ and point P' whose coordinates are:

55. $P'(0, 0)$ **56.** $P'(5\sqrt{3}, 0)$ **57.** $P'(0, 5)$

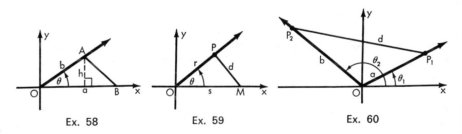

Ex. 58   Ex. 59   Ex. 60

58. Using $(b \cos \theta, b \sin \theta)$ for the coordinates of A, show that the area of $\triangle OAB = \tfrac{1}{2}ab \sin \theta$.

59. Using $(r \cos \theta, r \sin \theta)$ for the coordinates of P and $(s, 0)$ for the coordinates of M, show that
$$d^2 = r^2 + s^2 - 2rs \cos \theta$$

60. Using $(a \cos \theta_1, a \sin \theta_1)$ for the coordinates of P_1 and $(b \cos \theta_2, b \sin \theta_2)$ for the coordinates of P_2, show that $(P_1 P_2)^2$ may be expressed as
$$d^2 = a^2 + b^2 - 2ab(\cos \theta_1 \cos \theta_2 + \sin \theta_1 \sin \theta_2)$$

CHAPTER XI

THE SYSTEM OF COMPLEX NUMBERS

1. Pure Imaginary Numbers

EXTENDING THE NUMBER SYSTEM TO INCLUDE THE SET OF PURE IMAGINARY NUMBERS

To solve the equation $x^2 = -1$, or an equivalent equation such as $x^2 + 1 = 0$, we must have a number whose square is -1. There can be no such number in the system of real numbers since the square of a real number must be positive or zero and cannot be negative. Hence, it becomes desirable to extend the number system so that the equation $x^2 = -1$ and in general $x^2 = a$, when a is negative, will have a solution.

On several previous occasions, we extended the number system because it proved inadequate to solve a given equation or perform a given operation.

1. *The set of counting numbers, or natural numbers*, is adequate to solve $x - 2 = 4$, $x - 4 = 2$, and $x + 2 = 4$; but not $x + 4 = 4$. Hence, we extended the number system by inventing the set of whole numbers, which includes 0. In the set of whole numbers, the root of $x + 4 = 4$ is 0.

2. *The set of whole numbers* is adequate to solve $x + 4 = 4$, but not $x + 4 = 2$. Hence, we extended the number system by inventing the set of integers, which includes negative numbers. In the set of integers, the root of $x + 4 = 2$ is -2.

3. *The set of integers* is adequate to solve $x + 4 = 2$, $\dfrac{x}{2} = 4$, and $2x = 4$; but not $4x = 2$. Hence, we extended the number system by inventing the set of rational numbers, which includes numbers that are the quotient of two integers, except 0 as a divisor. In the set of rational numbers, the root of $4x = 2$ is $\frac{1}{2}$.

4. *The set of rational numbers* is adequate to solve $4x = 2$, $x^2 = 4$, and $x^2 = \frac{1}{4}$; but not $x^2 = 2$. Hence, we extended the number system to include the set of irrational numbers, which includes real numbers that are not rational. In the set of irrational numbers, the roots of $x^2 = 2$ are $\sqrt{2}$ and $-\sqrt{2}$. With the creation of the set of irrational numbers, the system of real numbers becomes complete.

5. *The system of real numbers, which includes the set of irrational numbers*, is adequate to solve $x^2 = 2$, $x^2 = \frac{1}{2}$, $x^2 = 16$, and, in general, $x^2 = a$, where a is a non-negative real number. However, the set of real numbers is not adequate to

solve $x^2 = -1$, $x^2 = -2$, $x^2 = -\frac{1}{4}$, and, in general, $x^2 = a$, where a is a negative real number. The roots of $x^2 = -1$ are $+\sqrt{-1}$ and $-\sqrt{-1}$, which cannot be real numbers, because the square of a real number cannot be a negative number. These numbers, $\sqrt{-1}$ and $-\sqrt{-1}$, are numbers belonging to the set of *pure imaginary numbers*. Hence, mathematicians invented the system of complex numbers, which includes the set of pure imaginary numbers.

6. *The system of complex numbers, which includes the set of pure imaginary numbers*, is adequate to solve equations such as $x^2 = -1$, $x^2 = -2$, $x^2 = -6$, $x^2 = -\frac{1}{4}$, and, in general, $x^2 = a$, where a is a negative number.

PURE IMAGINARY NUMBERS

We will understand what complex numbers are if we consider first complex numbers such as $\sqrt{-9}$ and $\sqrt{-20}$, which are called pure imaginary numbers, according to the following definition:

A *pure imaginary number* is a number that can be expressed as the product of a real number and $\sqrt{-1}$. If b is a real number, then $b\sqrt{-1}$ is a pure imaginary number.

For example, $\sqrt{-9} = \sqrt{9}\sqrt{-1} = 3\sqrt{-1}$.
Also, $\sqrt{-20} = \sqrt{20}\sqrt{-1} = \sqrt{4}\sqrt{5}\sqrt{-1} = 2\sqrt{5}\sqrt{-1}$.

IMAGINARY UNIT i OR $\sqrt{-1}$

Since $\sqrt{-1}$ is a factor of every pure imaginary number, the symbol i is used to represent $\sqrt{-1}$. The imaginary number i is called the *imaginary unit.*

Hence, $\sqrt{-9} = 3\sqrt{-1} = 3i$ and $\sqrt{-20} = 2\sqrt{5}\sqrt{-1} = 2i\sqrt{5}$.
In general, if b is a real number,

$$\sqrt{-b^2} = \sqrt{b^2}\sqrt{-1} = bi$$

Since pure imaginary numbers are not real numbers, they cannot be graphed using the real number line. Later, we shall show that there is another type of graph chart that can be used to graph pure imaginary numbers or any complex number.

POWERS OF i

Since $i = \sqrt{-1}$, then $i^2 = -1$. Since $i^3 = i^2 \cdot i$, then $i^3 = -1 \cdot i$ or $-i$.
Since $i^4 = i^2 \cdot i^2$, then $i^4 = (-1)(-1) = 1$.

Since $i^5 = i^4 \cdot i$, then $i^5 = 1 \cdot i$ or i.

Continuing in this way to obtain successive powers of i, we find that the first four powers of i are all different, as the following display shows; but, thereafter, there is a repetition in cycles of four:

$$i^1 = i \qquad\qquad i^5 = i \qquad\qquad i^9 = i$$
$$i^2 = -1 \qquad\qquad i^6 = -1 \qquad\qquad i^{10} = -1$$
$$i^3 = -i \qquad\qquad i^7 = -i \qquad\qquad i^{11} = -i$$
$$i^4 = 1 \qquad\qquad i^8 = 1 \qquad\qquad i^{12} = 1$$

In general, if n is a natural number, then

$$\boldsymbol{i^{4n} = 1} \qquad \boldsymbol{i^{4n+1} = i} \qquad \boldsymbol{i^{4n+2} = -1} \qquad \boldsymbol{i^{4n+3} = -i}$$

Thus,

$$\boldsymbol{i^{20} = i^{4(5)} = 1; \; i^{25} = i^{4(6)+1} = i; \; i^{102} = i^{4(25)+2} = -1; \; i^{403} = i^{4(100)+3} = -i.}$$

PROPERTIES OF *i*

Property 1. $i \cdot i = i^2 = -1$. $i^2 = -1$ because $\sqrt{-1}\sqrt{-1} = (\sqrt{-1})^2 = -1$. This property can be used to obtain higher powers of i such as i^4, i^6, etc.

Caution. When multiplying $\sqrt{-1}$ and $\sqrt{-1}$, do not apply the rule $\sqrt{a}\sqrt{b} = \sqrt{ab}$ since this rule applies to situations where a and b are not both negative; that is, $a \geq 0$ or $b \geq 0$. Keep in mind that $\sqrt{-1}\sqrt{-1} \neq \sqrt{1}$ or 1.

Property 2. $0i = 0 \cdot i = 0$. This property is the multiplicative property of zero.

Property 3. $i + 0 = i$. Here, 0 or $0i$ is the additive identity.

Property 4. $i + (-i) = 0$. Hence, i and $-i$ are additive inverses.

Property 5. $1i = 1 \cdot i = i$. Here, 1 is the multiplicative identity. It follows that $\dfrac{i}{i} = 1$.

Property 6. $i(-i) = 1$. Hence, i and $-i$ are multiplicative inverses, or reciprocals of each other. Proof: $i(-i) = -i^2 = -(-1) = 1$.

In the following model problems dealing with imaginary numbers, problems 1 and 2 involve addition and subtraction; problems 3–5 involve multiplication and division.

~~~~~~~~~~~~~~ *MODEL PROBLEMS* ~~~~~~~~~~~~~~

In 1 and 2, simplify in terms of i and combine.

1. $\sqrt{-49} - 2\sqrt{-4}$ **2.** $3\sqrt{-2} + \sqrt{-8}$

How To Proceed	*Solution*	*Solution*
1. Express each number in terms of i.	$\sqrt{49}\sqrt{-1} - 2\sqrt{4}\sqrt{-1}$	$3\sqrt{2}\sqrt{-1} + \sqrt{4}\sqrt{2}\sqrt{-1}$
2. Factor the highest common factor.	$7i - 4i$ $i(7-4)$	$3i\sqrt{2} + 2i\sqrt{2}$ $i\sqrt{2}(3+2)$
3. Perform the indicated operations.	$3i$ *Ans.*	$5i\sqrt{2}$ *Ans.*

In 3–5, simplify in terms of i and perform the indicated operation.

3. $\sqrt{-2} \cdot \sqrt{-8}$ **4.** $\dfrac{\sqrt{-20}}{\sqrt{-5}}$ **5.** $\dfrac{-\sqrt{-48}}{\sqrt{-6}}$

How To Proceed	*Solution*	*Solution*	*Solution*
1. Express each number in terms of i.	$i\sqrt{2} \cdot i\sqrt{8}$	$\dfrac{i\sqrt{20}}{i\sqrt{5}}$	$\dfrac{-i\sqrt{48}}{i\sqrt{6}}$
2. Perform the indicated operations, simplifying powers of i as needed.	$i^2\sqrt{16}$ $(-1)4$	$\dfrac{\sqrt{4}\sqrt{5}}{\sqrt{5}}$	$-\sqrt{8}$ $-\sqrt{4}\sqrt{2}$
	-4 *Ans.*	2 *Ans.*	$-2\sqrt{2}$ *Ans.*

The preceding model problems illustrate the following rules:
Rule 1. The product of two pure imaginary numbers is a real number.
Rule 2. The quotient of two pure imaginary numbers is a real number.

Exercises

In 1–32, express in terms of the unit i.

1. $\sqrt{-25}$ **2.** $\sqrt{-16}$ **3.** $\sqrt{-64}$ **4.** $\sqrt{-100}$

5. $8\sqrt{-4}$ **6.** $3\sqrt{-49}$ **7.** $2\sqrt{-36}$ **8.** $5\sqrt{-81}$

9. $\frac{1}{2}\sqrt{-16}$ **10.** $\frac{3}{4}\sqrt{-64}$ **11.** $\frac{2}{3}\sqrt{-81}$ **12.** $\frac{5}{6}\sqrt{-144}$

13. $\sqrt{-\frac{1}{9}}$ **14.** $\sqrt{-\frac{4}{25}}$ **15.** $8\sqrt{-\frac{9}{16}}$ **16.** $10\sqrt{-\frac{49}{25}}$

17. $\sqrt{-5}$ **18.** $\sqrt{-13}$ **19.** $2\sqrt{-7}$ **20.** $6\sqrt{-15}$

21. $\sqrt{-8}$ **22.** $\sqrt{-12}$ **23.** $-\sqrt{-75}$ **24.** $-\sqrt{-32}$

25. $4\sqrt{-12}$ **26.** $\frac{1}{3}\sqrt{-63}$ **27.** $-\frac{1}{2}\sqrt{-48}$ **28.** $-\frac{2}{5}\sqrt{-50}$

29. $\sqrt{-\frac{1}{2}}$ **30.** $\sqrt{-\frac{1}{7}}$ **31.** $-6\sqrt{-\frac{1}{3}}$ **32.** $-10\sqrt{-\frac{1}{5}}$

In 33–39, indicate whether the power of i is equal to 1, i, -1, or $-i$.

33. i^9 **34.** i^{40} **35.** i^{11} **36.** i^{102} **37.** i^{22} **38.** i^{100} **39.** i^{401}

In 40–42, express as a single term the sum of:

40. $5\sqrt{-1}$ and $2i$ **41.** $2\sqrt{-9}$ and $5i$ **42.** $\sqrt{-16}$ and $-i$

In 43–52, simplify in terms of i and combine.

43. $\sqrt{-16}+\sqrt{-49}$ **44.** $\sqrt{-25}-\sqrt{-144}$

45. $5\sqrt{-36}+2\sqrt{-81}$ **46.** $8\sqrt{-100}-4\sqrt{-64}$

47. $4\sqrt{-1}-\sqrt{-4}$ **48.** $10\sqrt{-\frac{1}{25}}+3\sqrt{-9}$

49. $\frac{3}{4}\sqrt{-64}-\frac{2}{3}\sqrt{-81}$ **50.** $20\sqrt{-\frac{1}{100}}-12\sqrt{-\frac{1}{36}}$

51. $\sqrt{-72}+\sqrt{-32}$ **52.** $5\sqrt{-27}-3\sqrt{-12}$

In 53–56, explain the error and state the correct answer.

53. A student replaced $\sqrt{-36}$ by $6\sqrt{i}$.

54. A student found the product of $\sqrt{-4}$ and $\sqrt{-9}$ to be 6.

55. A student said that $\sqrt{-49}-\sqrt{-9}=-4i$.

56. A student found the quotient of $\dfrac{-\sqrt{64}}{\sqrt{-4}}$ to be 4.

In 57–60, state the greatest positive integral value of x for which the radical is imaginary.

57. $\sqrt{x-8}$ **58.** $\sqrt{x^2-8}$ **59.** $\sqrt{2x-8}$ **60.** $\sqrt{2x^2-8}$

In 61–64, state the least positive integral value of x for which the radical is imaginary.

61. $\sqrt{8-x}$ **62.** $\sqrt{8-x^2}$ **63.** $\sqrt{8-2x}$ **64.** $\sqrt{8-2x^2}$

65. State the domain of x if $\sqrt{16-x^2}$ is a real number.

66. State the domain of x if $\sqrt{x^2-25}$ is imaginary.

In 67–70, simplify in terms of i and multiply.

67. $\sqrt{-1}\cdot\sqrt{-4}$ **68.** $\sqrt{-3}\cdot\sqrt{-12}$

69. $\sqrt{-4}\cdot\sqrt{-9}\cdot\sqrt{-100}$ **70.** $(2\sqrt{-8})(5\sqrt{-18})$

In 71–75, simplify in terms of i and divide.

71. $\dfrac{\sqrt{-18}}{\sqrt{-2}}$ **72.** $\dfrac{\sqrt{-3}}{\sqrt{-75}}$ **73.** $\dfrac{8\sqrt{-1}}{2\sqrt{-4}}$ **74.** $\dfrac{-\sqrt{-25}}{-\sqrt{5}}$ **75.** $\dfrac{\sqrt{-5}}{-\sqrt{25}}$

In 76–78, if x is a real number, simplify the expression in terms of i.

76. $\sqrt{-x^2} + \sqrt{-9x^2}$ **77.** $10\sqrt{-x^2} - \sqrt{-49x^2}$ **78.** $x\sqrt{-25} + \sqrt{-100x^2}$

In 79–82, state the roots of the equation in terms of i.

79. $x^2 + 4 = 0$ **80.** $2x^2 + 4 = 0$ **81.** $\dfrac{x^2}{2} + 4 = 0$ **82.** $18 + 3x^2 = x^2$

In 83–86, show that if a and b are positive real numbers, $a \neq b$, then:

83. $\sqrt{-a^2} + \sqrt{-b^2}$ is a pure imaginary number.

84. $\sqrt{-a^2} - \sqrt{-b^2}$ is a pure imaginary number.

85. $(\sqrt{-a})(\sqrt{-b})$ is a real negative number.

86. $\dfrac{\sqrt{-a}}{\sqrt{-b}}$ is a real positive number.

2. Complex Numbers

Numbers such as $2 + 3i$, $\frac{1}{2} - i\sqrt{3}$, and $\sqrt{2} + \frac{1}{4}i$ are *complex numbers*. Note that each of these numbers is the sum of a real number and a pure imaginary number. By definition, a **complex number** is a number that may be expressed in the form of $a + bi$ where a and b are real numbers and $i = \sqrt{-1}$.

The set of real numbers and the set of imaginary numbers are subsets of the system of complex numbers, for the following reasons:

1. A real number is expressible as a complex number, $a + bi$, if $b = 0$. Thus, the real numbers -6 and $3\sqrt{2}$ are expressible as the complex numbers $-6 + 0i$ and $3\sqrt{2} + 0i$.
2. An imaginary number is expressible as a complex number, $a + bi$, if $b \neq 0$. If $a = 0$, then the imaginary number $a + bi$ becomes $0 + bi$, or bi, which is a pure imaginary number. Thus, $2 + 3i$, $\frac{1}{2} - i\sqrt{3}$, and $2 + \frac{1}{4}i$ are imaginary numbers, whereas $0 + 3i$, or $3i$, and $0 + \frac{1}{4}i$, or $\frac{1}{4}i$, are pure imaginary numbers.

The following chart shows how the set of complex numbers includes the sets of real numbers, imaginary numbers, and pure imaginary numbers:

Complex numbers, $a + bi$

Real numbers, $a + 0i$ $(b = 0)$

Imaginary numbers, $a + bi$ $(b \neq 0)$
(called pure imaginary numbers if $a = 0$ and $b \neq 0$)

HISTORICAL NOTE

The terms *real* and *imaginary* were first used to refer to number systems in 1637 by the French mathematician and philosopher René Descartes. The term *imaginary* indicates the fact that when the imaginary numbers were first discovered, they were considered to be curiosities of no real significance. It was Karl Friedrich Gauss, one of the greatest mathematicians of all time, who demonstrated their importance in the development of mathematical theory. In 1832, Gauss used the term *complex number*. In modern times, Charles Steinmetz, an American engineer, through his use of complex numbers in the analysis of electrical problems, proved beyond all doubt the enormous practicality of the complex number system in the physical world.

PROPERTIES OF THE SYSTEM OF COMPLEX NUMBERS

We have assumed that the set of complex numbers has two special properties, namely, that the set has a special element i and that every complex number can be written in the form of $a + bi$.

Thus, $\sqrt{-81} = 9i$, which can be written as $0 + 9i$.

In addition to the two special properties, *the set of complex numbers has all the properties of the set of real numbers*. Among these properties are the commutative, associative, and distributive properties, which the following illustrate:

1. $i(2i) = (2i)i$ Commutative property of multiplication
$\quad = 2(i \cdot i)$ Associative property of multiplication
$\quad = 2i^2 = 2(-1) = -2$ Properties of the special element i

2. $5i + 17 + 3i = 17 + 5i + 3i$ Commutative property of addition
$\quad = 17 + (5 + 3)i$ Distributive property
$\quad = 17 + 8i$ Expressing the complex number in the form $a + bi$

Note in the two illustrations that the special complex element i can be treated in exactly the same way as any real number. Keep in mind that i has its own special property which is $i \cdot i = i^2 = -1$.

IDENTITY AND INVERSE ELEMENTS IN THE SYSTEM OF COMPLEX NUMBERS

The *additive identity element* in the set of complex numbers is $0i$ or 0. The *multiplicative identity element* is $1 + 0i$, or 1.

Thus, $(a + bi) + 0 = a + bi$. Also, $1(a + bi) = a + bi$. In each case, a and b are real numbers.

Each complex number has one and only one additive inverse. The additive inverse of the general complex number $a + bi$ is $-(a + bi)$, which can be proved equal to $-a - bi$.

Thus, the additive inverse of $5 - 3i$ is $-(5 - 3i)$, or $-5 + 3i$.

Each complex number except $0i$ has one and only one multiplicative inverse. The multiplicative inverse of the general complex number $a + bi$ is its reciprocal $\dfrac{1}{a + bi}$. Thus, the multiplicative inverse of $5i$ is $\dfrac{1}{5i}$. If the denominator is rationalized, we obtain $\dfrac{1}{5i} \cdot \dfrac{i}{i} = \dfrac{i}{5i^2} = \dfrac{i}{-5} = -\dfrac{i}{5}$, or $-\dfrac{1}{5}i$.

EQUALITY OF TWO COMPLEX NUMBERS

Two complex numbers are equal if and only if their real parts are equal and, also, their imaginary parts are equal.

Hence, if $a + bi$ and $c + di$ are equal complex numbers, $a + bi = c + di$ if and only if $a = c$ and $b = d$. For example, $\frac{1}{2} + xi = y + 7i$ if and only if $x = 7$ and $y = \frac{1}{2}$.

COMPLEX NUMBER CONJUGATES

Complex numbers such as $4 + 5i$ and $4 - 5i$ are *conjugates* of each other. If we assume that the familiar properties of real numbers are true for complex numbers, then we obtain the following sum, difference, and product of these conjugates:

Sum: $(4 + 5i) + (4 - 5i) = 4 + 4 = 8$
Difference: $(4 + 5i) - (4 - 5i) = 5i + 5i = 10i$
Product: $(4 + 5i)(4 - 5i) = 16 - 25i^2 = 16 - 25(-1) = 16 + 25 = 41$

The general forms of complex number conjugates are $a + bi$ and $a - bi$.

General Rules for the Sum, Difference, and Product of Any Two Complex Number Conjugates

Sum: $(a + bi) + (a - bi) = 2a$

Difference: $(a + bi) - (a - bi) = 2bi$

Product: $(a + bi)(a - bi) = a^2 - b^2i^2 = a^2 - b^2(-1) = a^2 + b^2$
     Hence, $(a + bi)(a - bi) = a^2 + b^2$.

─── *KEEP IN MIND* ───

If $a + bi$ and $a - bi$ are complex number conjugates, then:

1. Their sum, $2a$, is a real number.
2. Their difference, $2bi$, $b \neq 0$, is a pure imaginary number.
3. Their product, $a^2 + b^2$, is a positive real number unless both a and b are 0.

〜〜〜〜〜〜〜 *MODEL PROBLEMS* 〜〜〜〜〜〜〜

Express in the form $a + bi$ and combine.

$$(6 + \sqrt{-50}) - (4 - \sqrt{-18})$$

How To Proceed	*Solution*
1. Express in the form $a + bi$.	$(6 + 5i\sqrt{2}) - (4 - 3i\sqrt{2})$
2. Combine the complex numbers as real numbers are combined, and express the result in the form $a + bi$.	$(6 - 4) + (5i\sqrt{2} + 3i\sqrt{2})$
	$2 + 8i\sqrt{2}$ *Ans.*

〜〜〜〜〜〜〜〜〜〜〜〜〜〜〜〜〜〜〜〜〜〜〜〜〜

In general, the sum and the difference of complex numbers $(a + bi)$ and $(c + di)$ are:

$$\boldsymbol{(a + bi) + (c + di) = (a + c) + (b + d)i}$$

$$\boldsymbol{(a + bi) - (c + di) = (a - c) + (b - d)i}$$

Note. Since a, b, c, and d are real numbers, then $(a + c)$, $(a - c)$, $(b + d)$, and $(b - d)$ are real numbers. Therefore, the sum or the difference of two complex numbers is a complex number.

〜〜〜〜〜〜〜 *MODEL PROBLEMS* 〜〜〜〜〜〜〜

In 1 and 2, find the product.

1. $(6 + \sqrt{-49})(3 - \sqrt{-16})$ **2.** $(4 + \sqrt{-27})(1 - \sqrt{-12})$

How To Proceed	*Solution*	*Solution*
1. Express each complex number in the form $a + bi$.	$(6 + 7i)(3 - 4i)$	$(4 + 3i\sqrt{3})(1 - 2i\sqrt{3})$

2. Multiply the complex numbers as real numbers are multiplied, expressing the result in the form $a + bi$.

$$18 - 3i - 28i^2$$
$$18 - 3i + 28$$
$$46 - 3i \quad Ans.$$

$$4 - 5i\sqrt{3} - 18i^2$$
$$4 - 5i\sqrt{3} + 18$$
$$22 - 5i\sqrt{3} \quad Ans.$$

In general, the product of complex numbers $(a + bi)$ and $(c + di)$ is:

$$(a + bi)(c + di) = ac + adi + bci + bdi^2$$
$$= (ac - bd) + (ad + bc)i$$

Note. Since a, b, c, and d are real numbers, then $(ac - bd)$ and $(ad + bc)$ are real numbers. Therefore, the product of two complex numbers is a complex number.

Exercises

In 1–3, find the sum and the difference of the pair of conjugates.

1. $(1 + i)$ and $(1 - i)$ **2.** $(5 + 3i)$ and $(5 - 3i)$ **3.** $(4 + i\sqrt{3})$ and $(4 - i\sqrt{3})$

In 4–6, find the product of the pair of conjugates.

4. $(2 + 5i)$ and $(2 - 5i)$ **5.** $(12 - 7i)$ and $(12 + 7i)$

6. $(3 + 2i\sqrt{5})$ and $(3 - 2i\sqrt{5})$

In 7–12, find real numbers x and y for which the equation is true.

7. $x + 4i = -5 + yi$ **8.** $2.8 + xi = y - 3.5i$

9. $2(5 - i) = x + yi$ **10.** $x + 6i + 3 = 12 + yi$

11. $2(x + 2i) = 4(8 - yi)$ **12.** $(x + 3i) + 7i = 8 + 2(8 + yi)$

In 13–19, find the conjugate and the reciprocal of the complex number.

13. i **14.** $3i$ **15.** $-8i$ **16.** $\frac{1}{4}i$ **17.** $2 + i$

18. $5 - \sqrt{-25}$ **19.** $-3 + \sqrt{-2}$

In 20–25, express the fraction in the complex number form $a + bi$.

20. $\dfrac{5}{i}$ **21.** $\dfrac{1}{3i}$ **22.** $\dfrac{7}{4 - i}$ **23.** $\dfrac{1}{3 + 2i}$ **24.** $\dfrac{2i}{4 - i}$ **25.** $\dfrac{10 - i}{10 + i}$

In 26–50, find the complex number $a + bi$ equal to the expression.

26. $(3 + 5i) + (5 - 2i)$ **27.** $(4 - 7i) + (15 + 2i)$

28. $(7 + i\sqrt{2}) + (1 - 2i\sqrt{2})$ **29.** $(11 + \sqrt{-1}) + (-3 - \sqrt{-16})$

30. $(9 - \sqrt{-5}) + (-4 - \sqrt{-20})$ **31.** $(20 + \sqrt{-28}) + (4 - \sqrt{-7})$

32. $(5 + 2i) + (7 - 4i) + (15 - 8i)$

33. $3i + 8i - 4i - 2i + (6 - 7i) + (3 + 2i)$

34. $(15 + 3i) - (-10 + 4i)$ **35.** $(3 + 15i) - (-4 + 7i)$

36. $(2.5 + i) - (1.7 - 2i)$ **37.** $(9 - \sqrt{-100}) - \sqrt{-81}$

38. $2\sqrt{-25} - (2 - \sqrt{-36})$ **39.** $(4\sqrt{5} + \sqrt{-50}) - 3\sqrt{20}$

40. $6i(5i)$ **41.** $6(5 + i)(5 - i)$

42. $6i(10 - 2i)$ **43.** $(3 + i)(2 - i)$

44. $(1 + 3i)(1 - 4i)$ **45.** $10(1 + \sqrt{-4})(2 + \sqrt{-9})$

46. $(1 + i)^2$ **47.** $(2 - i)^2$

48. $(3 + 7i)^2$ **49.** $(2 + \sqrt{-49})^2$

50. $(1 + i)(1 - i)(1 - i^2)(1 + i^2)$

In 51–59, if v, w, x, and y are real numbers, write the expression in the form of $a + bi$.

51. $(v + wi) + (v - wi)$ **52.** $(x + yi) - (x - yi)$ **53.** $(v + xi)(v - xi)$

54. $(x + yi)^2$ **55.** $(v - wi)^2$ **56.** $(x + yi)^2 + (x - yi)^2$

57. $(x + yi)^2 - (x - yi)^2$ **58.** $(v + wi) + (x + yi)$ **59.** $(x - yi) - (x - wi)$

In 60–68, if a, b, c, and d are real numbers, prove the statement.

60. $(a + bi) + (0 + 0i) = a + bi$ **61.** $(c + di) + (-c - di) = 0$

62. The sum of any complex number $a + bi$ and its conjugate is a real number.

63. The difference between any complex number $a + bi$ and its conjugate is a pure imaginary number.

64. The product of any complex number $c + di$ and its conjugate is a real positive number, if either c or d does not equal 0.

65. The multiplicative inverse of bi is $-\dfrac{i}{b}$, or $-\dfrac{1}{b}i$.

66. The multiplicative inverse of $a + bi$ equals $\dfrac{a - bi}{a^2 + b^2}$, or $\dfrac{a}{a^2 + b^2} - \dfrac{b}{a^2 + b^2}i$.

(*Hint:* Multiply both numerator and denominator by $a - bi$.)

67. The conjugate of the sum of two complex numbers $(a + bi)$ and $(c + di)$ is the sum of the conjugates of the numbers.

68. The conjugate of the product of two complex numbers $(a + bi)$ and $(c + di)$ is the product of the conjugate of the two numbers.

69. By showing that $(a + bi) + (c + di) = (c + di) + (a + bi)$, prove that the set of complex numbers is commutative under addition.

70. By showing that $(a + bi)(c + di) = (c + di)(a + bi)$, prove that the set of complex numbers is commutative under multiplication.

3. Vectors and Complex Numbers

Some quantities, such as an age of 30 years, a bank balance of $500, a class having 35 pupils, and a speed of 50 miles per hour, have size or magnitude only. Note how a single real number is used to indicate this magnitude.

However, there are other quantities, such as a body displacement of 25 feet to the right, an upward lift of 100 pounds, a wind velocity of 15 miles per hour in a southerly direction, and a horizontal pressure of 10 pounds per square inch, that cannot be completely described by a single real number because such quantities have direction as well as magnitude. To describe quantities or entities having both magnitude and direction, we make use of *vectors*.

A *vector* is a directed line segment. That is, a vector has two aspects: *length* and *direction*. Note the two vectors in the following figure. One vector, indicated by −30, has a length of 30 units and its arrowhead points to the left. The other vector, indicated by +40, has a length of 40 units and its arrowhead points to the right. Vectors may be used to represent velocities, forces, accelerations, displacements, and any directional movements.

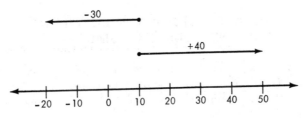

To describe a force completely, both its *magnitude* and the *direction* in which it is acting must be specified. For example, in the preceding figure, the vector pointing to the right may represent the force of a wind blowing due east at 40 mph for one hour; the vector pointing to the left may represent the movement of an automobile which has been displaced 30 miles to the west.

In the figure at the left is pictured a vector whose initial point is A and whose terminal point is B. In referring to this vector, we may write "vector $\overrightarrow{AB}$" or simply "$\overrightarrow{AB}$."

The arrowhead shows the direction of the vector. The number of units in the length of the vector is used to determine the magnitude of a distance or quantity. The magnitude of the distance or quantity depends on the scale involved.

Note. The notation $\overrightarrow{AB}$ also means "ray $\overrightarrow{AB}$." The student must determine from context whether $\overrightarrow{AB}$ means "ray $\overrightarrow{AB}$" or "vector $\overrightarrow{AB}$."

Thus, in the figure at the right, to represent the directed distance covered in one hour by a wind that is blowing due east with a speed of 30 mph, we start at point O and draw a line due east. If 1 unit represents 10 miles, we use 3 units to represent 30 miles. Vector $\overrightarrow{OA}$ would represent the directed distance covered in one hour by a wind blowing due east with a speed of 30 mph. Vector $\overrightarrow{OB}$ could be used to represent the directed distance covered in one hour by a wind blowing due north with a speed of 20 mph.

Scale:
1 unit = 10 miles

Exercises

In 1–4, using a scale in which one unit represents 10 miles, draw the vector that represents the directed distance covered in one hour by:
1. a wind blowing east at 75 mph.
2. a wind blowing south at 60 mph.
3. a wind blowing NW at 50 mph.
4. a wind blowing SE at 80 mph.

USING VECTORS AND POINTS IN A COMPLEX-NUMBER PLANE TO REPRESENT COMPLEX NUMBERS

We have found that complex numbers cannot be represented in the real-number plane. However, another type of plane called a *complex-number plane* can be used for the purpose. In this plane, a complex number may be represented by either a point or a vector.

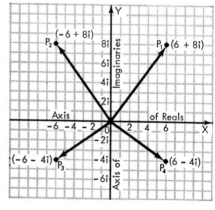

The complex-number plane, as shown in the figure, is created by using two axes at right angles to each other. The horizontal axis is called the *axis of reals* and the vertical axis, the *axis of imaginaries*, as shown. If the plane were a real-number plane, the point P_1 would represent the ordered pair $(6, 8)$. In the complex-number plane, the point P_1 represents the complex number $6 + 8i$. The vector $\overrightarrow{OP_1}$ also represents $6 + 8i$. Likewise, the point P_2, which would have represented $(-6, 8)$ if the plane were a real-number plane, represents the complex number $-6 + 8i$ in the complex-number plane. The vector $\overrightarrow{OP_2}$ also represents $-6 + 8i$. Vectors $\overrightarrow{OP_3}$ and $\overrightarrow{OP_4}$ represent $-6 - 4i$ and $6 - 4i$ respectively.

Note. To distinguish between the axes used in the real-number plane and those used in the complex-number plane, capital letters X and Y are used. Recall that the small letters x and y are used in the Cartesian plane. In the complex-number plane, the origin, O, represents $0 + 0i$; each point on the X-axis, $(a, 0)$, represents a real number expressible as $a + 0i$; and each point on the Y-axis, $(0, b)$, represents a pure imaginary expressible as $0 + bi$. In the complex-number plane, the point (a, b) is plotted in exactly the same way as it would have been in a real-number plane by laying off the real number a along the X-axis and the real number b along the Y-axis. When this is done, the complex number $a + bi$ is represented by the point (a, b) as well as the vector to this point from the origin.

Thus, if the point $(3, 4)$ is plotted in the complex-number plane, then the complex number $3 + 4i$ is represented by the point $(3, 4)$ as well as the vector to this point from the origin.

EQUIVALENT, FREE, AND CENTERED VECTORS

Vectors are **equivalent vectors** if and only if they have the same length and the same direction. Equivalent vectors do not necessarily start from the same point, nor must they be along the same line.

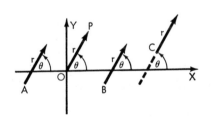

Consider the four vectors shown in the figure at the left. Each has the same magnitude r and makes the same direction-angle θ with the positive direction of the X-axis. These vectors are equivalent to each other, since they have equal magnitudes and equal direction-angles.

A **centered vector** starts from the origin; for example, vector $\overrightarrow{OP}$. A **free vector** starts from any point other than the origin. Thus, in the figure, the vectors starting from A, B, and C are free vectors. The centered vector $\overrightarrow{OP}$ may be used to represent all free equivalent vectors. It is the centered vector that is used to represent a complex number in a complex-number plane.

Using the figure at the right, let us study the centered vector $\overrightarrow{OP}$ having magnitude r and direction-angle θ. The coordinates x and y of point P now become the *rectangular components* of vector $\overrightarrow{OP}$. In a complex-number plane, the centered vector $\overrightarrow{OP}$ represents the complex number

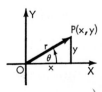

$x + yi$. If θ is the measure of the angle between $\overrightarrow{OP}$ and the X-axis, then the four variables x, y, r, and θ are related as follows:

$$x = r \cos \theta \qquad y = r \sin \theta \qquad x^2 + y^2 = r^2 \qquad \tan \theta = \frac{y}{x}$$

Keep in mind that r, by convention, is always positive.
Since $x = r \cos \theta$ and $y = r \sin \theta$, then:

$$x + yi = r \cos \theta + ri \sin \theta = r(\cos \theta + i \sin \theta)$$

NOTATION REPRESENTING THE MAGNITUDE AND DIRECTION-ANGLE OF A VECTOR

In electrical engineering, a vector having magnitude r and direction-angle θ (such as $\overrightarrow{OP}$ in the preceding figure) is denoted by $r\lfloor\theta$.

~~~~~~~~~~ *MODEL PROBLEMS* ~~~~~~~~~~

1. Find the x-component and y-component of the vector $10\lfloor 30°$ and state the complex number represented by the vector.

Solution: The vector $10\lfloor 30°$ lies in the first quadrant, as shown. Hence, both its x-component and y-component are positive.

$x = r \cos \theta$	$y = r \sin \theta$
$x = 10 \cos 30°$	$y = 10(\frac{1}{2})$
$x = 10\left(\dfrac{\sqrt{3}}{2}\right) = 5\sqrt{3}$	$y = 5$

Since $x = 5\sqrt{3}$ and $y = 5$, $\overrightarrow{OP}$ represents the complex number $5\sqrt{3} + 5i$.

Answer: $x = 5\sqrt{3}$ and $y = 5$; the complex number is $5\sqrt{3} + 5i$.

Note. The complex number represented by the vector may be found directly:
Since $x + yi = r(\cos \theta + i \sin \theta)$, then $x + yi = 10(\cos 30° + i \sin 30°)$
$$= 10(\tfrac{1}{2}\sqrt{3} + i \cdot \tfrac{1}{2}) = 5\sqrt{3} + 5i$$

2. To the nearest integer, find the x-component and y-component of the vector $30\lfloor 320°$ and state the complex number represented by the vector.

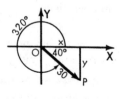

Solution: The vector $30\lfloor 320°$ lies in the fourth quadrant, as shown. Hence, its x-component is positive and its y-component is negative.

$$
\begin{array}{l|l}
x = r \cos \theta & y = r \sin \theta \\
x = 30 \cos 320° & y = 30 \sin 320° \\
x = 30 \cos 40° & y = 30(-\sin 40°) \\
x = 30(.7660) & y = 30(-.6428) \\
x = 22.98 & y = -19.284
\end{array}
$$

Note: $\cos 320° = \cos 40°$ and $\sin 320° = -\sin 40°$.

Answer: To the nearest integer, $x = 23$, and $y = -19$. In a complex-number plane, $\overrightarrow{OP}$ represents $23 - 19i$.

Exercises

In 1–16, find to the nearest integer the x-component and the y-component of the vector; state the complex number represented by the vector.

1. $16\underline{/30°}$ **2.** $20\underline{/45°}$ **3.** $24\underline{/57°}$ **4.** $8\underline{/75°}$

5. $13.5\underline{/90°}$ **6.** $25\underline{/180°}$ **7.** $7.2\underline{/270°}$ **8.** $65\underline{/720°}$

9. $12\underline{/120°}$ **10.** $40\underline{/135°}$ **11.** $40\underline{/230°}$ **12.** $40\underline{/345°}$

13. $20\underline{/35°}$ **14.** $15\underline{/105°}$ **15.** $50\underline{/200°}$ **16.** $30\underline{/310°}$

USING VECTORS TO COMBINE FORCES

Method 1. Vector Parallelogram

Let us consider a situation in which two forces of 10 lb. and 15 lb. are acting simultaneously on a body at an angle of 60° with each other. Note in the diagram that the two forces are represented by $\overrightarrow{OA}$ and $\overrightarrow{OB}$. By drawing $\overline{AC}\|\overline{OB}$ and $\overline{BC}\|\overline{OA}$, we form a parallelogram $OACB$. It can be established that $\overrightarrow{OC}$ represents a single force that combines the effects of the two separate 10-lb. and 15-lb. forces.

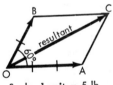

Scale: 1 unit = 5 lb.

The force represented by $\overrightarrow{OC}$, the vector diagonal of the parallelogram, is called the *resultant* of the forces represented by $\overrightarrow{OA}$ and $\overrightarrow{OB}$, the vector sides of the parallelogram. The given forces are called the *components* of the resultant force. The magnitude or size of the resultant force can be found by determining the number of units in the length of $\overrightarrow{OC}$ and multiplying by 5, since each unit in the diagram represents 5 pounds. The direction of the resultant can be obtained by measuring angle AOC or angle BOC.

Method 2.   Vector Triangle

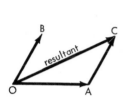

Two vectors, such as $\overrightarrow{OA}$ and $\overrightarrow{OB}$, may be combined in another way, by using a triangle. At A, the terminal point of $\overrightarrow{OA}$, $\overrightarrow{AC}$ is drawn, which has the same direction and the same magnitude as $\overrightarrow{OB}$. The resultant, $\overrightarrow{OC}$, is the vector from the initial point of $\overrightarrow{OA}$ to the terminal point of $\overrightarrow{AC}$. The two vectors $\overrightarrow{OB}$ and $\overrightarrow{AC}$, which have the same direction and the same magnitude, are termed *equivalent vectors*, or *equal vectors*, that is, $\overrightarrow{OB} = \overrightarrow{AC}$.

To understand the triangle method of vector addition, think of an automobile which cannot travel directly from O to C, but must detour through A. The displacement of the automobile from O to A followed by its displacement from A to C is equivalent to a displacement from O to C. In vector notation:

$$\overrightarrow{OA} + \overrightarrow{AC} = \overrightarrow{OC}$$

If $\overrightarrow{OB} = \overrightarrow{AC}$, then by substitution, $\overrightarrow{OA} + \overrightarrow{OB} = \overrightarrow{OC}$.

Remember that $\overrightarrow{OA} + \overrightarrow{AC} = \overrightarrow{OC}$ is a relation of vectors or *directed* line segments. It is *not* a relation of line segments. Hence, there is no violation of the principle that the sum of the lengths of two sides of a triangle is greater than the length of the third side.

Exercises

In 1–6, use a scale drawing to find (a) the magnitude of the resultant, correct to the nearest 10 pounds and (b) the angle between the resultant and larger force, correct to the nearest degree. (A trigonometric solution is not required. Use a ruler and protractor to obtain the answers.)

1. forces of 50 lb. and 120 lb. acting at right angles
2. forces of 150 lb. and 200 lb. acting at right angles
3. forces of 50 lb. and 40 lb. acting at an angle of 60°
4. forces of 70 lb. and 50 lb. acting at an angle of 45°
5. forces of 20 lb. and 40 lb. acting at an angle of 120°
6. forces of 40 lb. and 70 lb. acting at an angle of 160°

USING A GRAPH TO FIND THE HORIZONTAL AND VERTICAL COMPONENTS OF A GIVEN VECTOR

Any single given force may be thought of as being the resultant of the simultaneous action of two other forces, if the given force can be the diagonal of any parallelogram in which these other two forces are adjacent sides.

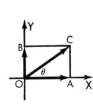

On a graph where the X-axis and Y-axis have been drawn, let $\overrightarrow{OC}$ be a vector which represents a force acting at an angle θ with the X-axis. Draw $\overline{CA} \perp \overrightarrow{OA}$, and draw $\overline{CB} \perp \overrightarrow{OB}$. Since $\overline{OC}$ is the diagonal of rectangle $OACB$, $\overrightarrow{OC}$ is the resultant of the components $\overrightarrow{OA}$ and $\overrightarrow{OB}$. When angle BOA is a right angle and $\overrightarrow{OA}$ is the *horizontal component*, or x-component, of $\overrightarrow{OC}$, then $\overrightarrow{OB}$ is the *vertical component*, or y-component, of $\overrightarrow{OC}$.

In a complex-number plane, if A represents $(a, 0)$, then $\overrightarrow{OA}$ represents $a + 0i$. If B represents $(0, b)$, then $\overrightarrow{OB}$ represents $0 + bi$. Since C represents (a, b), then $\overrightarrow{OC}$ represents the complex number $a + bi$. From this, we derive the following vector "addition":

$$\overrightarrow{OC} = \overrightarrow{OA} + \overrightarrow{OB}$$

Note also that the length or magnitude of vector $\overrightarrow{OC}$ is $\sqrt{a^2 + b^2}$.

THE COMPONENTS OF THE RESULTANT

In the complex-number plane shown at the right, $\overrightarrow{OA}$ represents the complex number $a + bi$ and $\overrightarrow{OB}$ represents the complex number $c + di$. By constructing a parallelogram $OBCA$, $\overrightarrow{OC}$ is the resultant of the vectors $\overrightarrow{OA}$ and $\overrightarrow{OB}$. We shall now show that the resultant, $\overrightarrow{OC}$, represents the complex number $(a + c) + (b + d)i$.

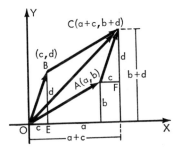

It is left to the student to show that right $\triangle OBE$ and right $\triangle ACF$ are congruent. Hence, the measure of the legs of $\triangle ACF$ are c and d as shown. Therefore, point C represents the ordered pair $(a + c, b + d)$ and $\overrightarrow{OC}$ represents the complex number $(a + c) + (b + d)i$. Recall that the sum of $a + bi$ and $c + di$ is $(a + c) + (b + d)i$. It follows that *the resultant* $\overrightarrow{OC}$ *is the sum of the vectors* $\overrightarrow{OA}$ *and* $\overrightarrow{OB}$. Note also that $a + c$, the horizontal component of the resultant, is the sum of the horizontal components of $\overrightarrow{OA}$ and $\overrightarrow{OB}$; and that $b + d$, the vertical component of the resultant, is the sum of the vertical components of $\overrightarrow{OA}$ and $\overrightarrow{OB}$.

The vector relationships shown to be true for quadrant I can also be shown to be true for any quadrant.

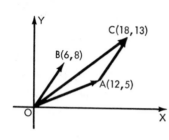

Thus, if the ordered pairs of vectors $\overrightarrow{OA}$ and $\overrightarrow{OB}$ are (12, 5) and (6, 8) as shown at the left, then the ordered pair represented by C is $(12 + 6, 5 + 8)$ or (18, 13) and $\overrightarrow{OC}$ represents $18 + 13i$.

Since the magnitude of a vector is its length, then the magnitudes of $\overrightarrow{OA}$, $\overrightarrow{OB}$, and $\overrightarrow{OC}$ are respectively:

$$OA = \sqrt{12^2 + 5^2} = 13 \qquad OB = \sqrt{6^2 + 8^2} = 10 \qquad OC = \sqrt{18^2 + 13^2} \approx 22.2$$

Observe that $OA + OB \neq OC$. However, $\overrightarrow{OA} + \overrightarrow{OB} = \overrightarrow{OC}$.

〰〰〰〰〰 *MODEL PROBLEMS* 〰〰〰〰〰

1. A force of 6 pounds and a force of 8 pounds are acting on a body at an angle of 90°.

    a. Find the magnitude of the resultant.

    b. Find the angle between the resultant and the 8-pound force, correct to the nearest degree.

Solution:

Let $\overrightarrow{OA}$ represent the 8-lb. force.

Let $\overrightarrow{OB}$, which is equal to $\overrightarrow{AC}$, represent the 6-lb. force.

Then $\overrightarrow{OC}$ represents the resultant force.

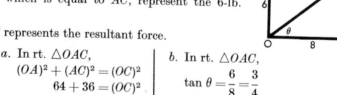

    a. In rt. $\triangle OAC$,
$$(OA)^2 + (AC)^2 = (OC)^2$$
$$64 + 36 = (OC)^2$$
$$100 = (OC)^2$$
$$10 = OC$$

Answer: The magnitude of the resultant is 10 pounds.

    b. In rt. $\triangle OAC$,
$$\tan \theta = \frac{6}{8} = \frac{3}{4}$$
$$\tan \theta = .7500$$
$$\theta \approx 37°$$

Answer: The resultant makes an angle of 37° with the 8-pound force.

2. Two forces of 12 lb. and 5 lb. act upon a body at an angle of 70°.

    a. Find the measure of the angle made by the resultant force with the 12-lb. force, correct to the nearest degree.

    b. Find the magnitude of the resultant force, correct to the nearest pound.

Solution:

a. $\overrightarrow{OC}$, the vector representing the resultant force, is the diagonal of the parallelogram formed as shown. Vector $\overrightarrow{OB}$ may be written as vector $5\underline{/70°}$.

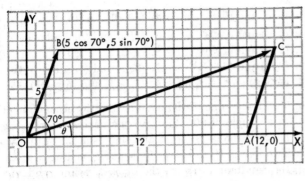

Hence, the coordinates of B are $(5 \cos 70°, 5 \sin 70°)$. The coordinates of point A are $(12, 0)$. By addition of components, the coordinates of point C are $(12 + 5 \cos 70°, 5 \sin 70°)$. θ, the angle of the resultant with the 12-lb. force, is found as follows:

$$\theta = \text{Arc tan } \frac{5 \sin 70°}{12 + 5 \cos 70°}$$

$$= \text{Arc tan } \frac{5(.9397)}{12 + 5(.3420)} = .3427$$

Hence, $\theta = 19°$, to the nearest degree.   *Ans.*

b. OC, the magnitude of the resultant, is found as follows:

$$OC = \sqrt{(12 + 5 \cos 70°)^2 + (5 \sin 70°)^2}$$
$$= \sqrt{144 + 120 \cos 70° + 25(\sin^2 70° + \cos^2 70°)}$$
$$= \sqrt{169 + 120 \cos 70°}$$

Hence, $OC = 14$, to the nearest pound.   *Ans.*

Exercises

In 1–15, the given number pairs are the coordinates of A and B respectively. If $\overrightarrow{OC} = \overrightarrow{OA} + \overrightarrow{OB}$:

a. find the x-component of $\overrightarrow{OC}$.

b. find the y-component of $\overrightarrow{OC}$.

c. find r, the magnitude of $\overrightarrow{OC}$. (Answer may be left in radical form.)

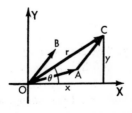

d. express θ, the direction-angle of $\overrightarrow{OC}$ in inverse trigonometric notation.

1. (6, 0) and (0, 8)   **2.** (12, 0) and (0, 5)   **3.** (12, 0) and (0, 9)

4. (4, 0) and (0, 4)   **5.** (2, 0) and (0, $2\sqrt{3}$)   **6.** ($\sqrt{2}$, 0) and (0, $\sqrt{2}$)

7. (2, 5) and (4, 3)   **8.** (1, 2) and (3, 1)   **9.** (2, 8) and (3, 4)

10. (2, 7) and (6, −1)   **11.** (3, 7) and (−8, 5)   **12.** (5, 14) and (−10, −2)

13. (−3, 4) and (−1, 0)   **14.** (4, −1) and (5, −11)   **15.** (−3, −6) and (5, 9)

16. Two forces, one of 100 pounds, and the other of 40 pounds, act upon a body at an angle of 90°. Find, to the nearest degree, the measure of the angle between the larger force and the resultant of the two forces.

17. Two forces, 10 and 12 pounds, act upon a body at an angle of 90°. Calculate the resultant force, to the nearest pound, and the measure of the angle between the resultant and the smaller force, to the nearest degree.

18. The resultant of two forces acting at right angles to each other is 50 pounds. If one of the forces is 40 pounds, find the other force, correct to the nearest pound. Find the measure of the angle that this force makes with the resultant, correct to the nearest degree.

19. A force of 80 pounds is acting at an angle of 55° with the horizontal. Find the magnitude of its horizontal and vertical components, correct to the nearest pound.

20. The resultant of two forces which are acting on a body at right angles is 40 pounds. If one force is three times the other, find the forces, correct to the nearest pound.

21. A force of 12 pounds is to be resolved into two forces, one of which is 5 pounds and makes an angle of 90° with the 12-pound force. Find the other force and the measure of the angle that it makes with the 12-pound force, correct to the nearest degree.

22. The vertical component of a given force is twice its horizontal component. Find, correct to the nearest degree, the measure of the angle between the force and its horizontal component.

CHAPTER XII

QUADRATIC EQUATIONS

1. Understanding Quadratic Equations in One Variable

STANDARD FORM OF A QUADRATIC EQUATION: $ax^2 + bx + c = 0$, $a \neq 0$

A *quadratic equation*, or a *second-degree equation* in x, is one that can be written in the *standard quadratic form*, $ax^2 + bx + c = 0$, in which a, b, and c are real numbers and $a \neq 0$.

Thus, $5x^2 + 7x + 6 = 0$ is in standard quadratic form; $a = 5$, $b = 7$, and $c = 6$.

TRANSFORMING A QUADRATIC EQUATION INTO STANDARD FORM

Note that if a quadratic equation is written in standard form, the expression $ax^2 + bx + c$ is "equated to 0." Hence, in order to transform a quadratic equation into standard form, it may be necessary to perform one or more of the following operations:

1. *Clear of fractions.* The equation $3x = \dfrac{8}{x} + 4$ is cleared of fractions by multiplying each side by x. By equating to 0, the result, $3x^2 = 8 + 4x$ is transformed into an equation in standard form, $3x^2 - 4x - 8 = 0$; $a = 3$, $b = -4$, and $c = -8$.

2. *Remove parentheses.* The parentheses in the equation $2(x^2 - 7) = 12x$ are removed by applying the distributive law. By equating to 0, the result, $2x^2 - 14 = 12x$, is transformed into an equation that is in standard form, $2x^2 - 12x - 14 = 0$; $a = 2$, $b = -12$, and $c = -14$.

3. *Remove radical signs.* The radical sign in the equation $x + 1 = \sqrt{3x + 7}$ is removed by squaring each side of the equation. By equating to 0, the result, $x^2 + 2x + 1 = 3x + 7$ is transformed into an equation in standard form, $x^2 - x - 6 = 0$; $a = 1$, $b = -1$, and $c = -6$.

4. *Collect like terms.* The like terms in the equation $x^2 + 2x + 1 = 3x + 3$ are

collected and combined by subtracting $3x + 3$ from each side. The result is $x^2 + 2x + 1 - 3x - 3 = 0$. By combining like terms, the result is transformed into an equation in standard form, $x^2 - x - 2 = 0$; $a = 1$, $b = -1$, and $c = -2$.

SETS OF NUMBERS INVOLVED IN QUADRATIC EQUATIONS

The real numbers a, b, and c in the standard quadratic form, $ax^2 + bx + c = 0$, could be either rational or irrational. However, *unless otherwise stated, a, b, and c are to be considered as rational numbers*.

KEEP IN MIND

In the standard quadratic form:
a is the coefficient of x^2, or the coefficient of the second-degree term.
b is the coefficient of x, or the coefficient of the first-degree term.
c is the constant term.

The roots of a quadratic equation need not be restricted to the set of real numbers but may be members of the set of complex numbers.

SOLVING A QUADRATIC EQUATION

A quadratic equation in one variable is solved when the replacements for the variable that satisfy the equation are found. The values of the variable that satisfy the equation are the roots of the equation and the elements of its solution set.

Thus, the equation $x^2 - x - 6 = 0$ is solved when its roots, 3 and -2, are found. The solution set of $x^2 - x - 6 = 0$ is $\{3, -2\}$.

CHECKING THE ROOTS OF A QUADRATIC EQUATION

The roots of a quadratic equation are checked by testing each of them in the *original* equation. There are two important reasons for this requirement:

1. A derived equation may be derived incorrectly.
2. A derived equation may be derived correctly, but its roots may not satisfy the original equation. Such roots, called ***extraneous values***, may occur when both sides of an equation are squared, cubed, or raised to a power to remove the radical sign.

Thus, when the radical sign in $x + 1 = \sqrt{3x + 7}$ is removed by squaring, the derived equation, $x^2 - x - 6 = 0$, has two roots, 3 and -2. However, the value -2 is a root of the derived equation $x^2 - x - 6 = 0$, but is not a root of the original equation $x + 1 = \sqrt{3x + 7}$. Hence, -2 is an extraneous value that does not satisfy the original equation.

The quadratic equation $x^2 = 25$ or $x^2 - 25 = 0$ has two unequal roots, 5 and -5. However, the quadratic equation $x^2 - 10x + 25 = 0$, or $(x - 5)^2 = 0$, has two equal roots, 5 and 5.

Rule. A quadratic equation has two roots which may be equal or unequal.

Equal roots are referred to as ***multiple roots.***

Exercises

In 1–12, transform the equation into standard quadratic form, $ax^2 + bx + c = 0$ with $a > 0$. Then state the values of a, b, and c in the resulting equation.

1. $3x = \dfrac{9}{x} + 26$ **2.** $2x + \dfrac{6}{x} = 13$ **3.** $5x - 8 = \dfrac{13}{x}$

4. $3(x^2 - 2) = 7x$ **5.** $x(6 - x) = 5$ **6.** $2(x - 3) = \dfrac{8}{x}$

7. $\sqrt{x^2 - 3x} = 2$ **8.** $\sqrt{8x + 9} = x + 2$ **9.** $x = \sqrt{2x^2 + 3x}$

10. $x^2 = 2x^2 + 7x$ **11.** $9x^2 - 4x^2 = 20$ **12.** $7x^2 + 4x = x^2 + 3x + 5$

In 13–20, by substituting the given values in parentheses, determine which of the values are roots of the given equation.

13. $x(x - 2) = 15$ (5 and -3) **14.** $x - \dfrac{10}{x} = -3$ (2 and 5)

15. $\sqrt{x^2 - 3x} = 2$ (4 and -1) **16.** $\sqrt{x^2 - 3x} = -2$ (4 and -1)

17. $\sqrt{x(5 - x)} = x - 2$ (4 and $\frac{1}{2}$) **18.** $9x^2 - 4x^2 = 20$ (2 and -2)

19. $3(x^2 - x) = 12 - 3x$ (2 and -2) **20.** $25(x - x^2) = 0$ (-1 and 0)

2. Solving Quadratic Equations by Factoring

Principle. The product of two real numbers is zero if and only if one of the factors is zero. That is, *for all real numbers a and b, $ab = 0$ if and only if $a = 0$ or $b = 0$.*

Thus, $(x - 4)(x + 5) = 0$ if and only if $x - 4 = 0$ or $x + 5 = 0$. Hence, $x = 4$ or $x = -5$. Also, $(x - 7)^2 = 0$, or $(x - 7)(x - 7) = 0$, if and only if $x - 7 = 0$, or $x = 7$. Hence, $(x - 7)^2 = 0$ has two equal roots, 7 and 7.

~~~~~~~~~~~~ *MODEL PROBLEMS* ~~~~~~~~~~~~

In 1 and 2, solve and check.

1. $x(x+4)=21$ **2.** $2x-1=\dfrac{10}{x}$

How To Proceed	*Solution*	*Solution*
1. Equate to 0.	$x^2+4x=21$	$2x^2-x=10$
	$x^2+4x-21=0$	$2x^2-x-10=0$
2. Factor ax^2+bx+c.	$(x-3)(x+7)=0$	$(2x-5)(x+2)=0$
3. Let each factor $=0$.	$x-3=0 \mid x+7=0$	$2x-5=0 \mid x+2=0$
4. Solve each resulting equation.	$x=3 \qquad x=-7$	$x=2\frac{1}{2} \qquad x=-2$
5. Check the roots in the original equation. (The check is left to the student.)	Check in the original equation, $x(x+4)=21$. $x=3$ or $x=-7$ *Ans.*	Check in the original equation, $2x-1=\dfrac{10}{x}$. $x=2\frac{1}{2}$ or $x=-2$ *Ans.*

3. Find the solution set of

$$2(x^2+1)=5x$$

Solution:
$$2(x^2+1)=5x$$
$$2x^2+2=5x$$
$$2x^2-5x+2=0$$
$$(2x-1)(x-2)=0$$
$$2x-1=0 \mid x-2=0$$
$$x=\tfrac{1}{2} \qquad x=2$$

Answer: $\{\tfrac{1}{2}, 2\}$

4. List the members of the following set:

$$\{x \mid x^2-2x=15\}$$

Solution:
$$x^2-2x=15$$
$$x^2-2x-15=0$$
$$(x-5)(x+3)=0$$
$$x-5=0 \mid x+3=0$$
$$x=5 \qquad x=-3$$

Answer: $\{5, -3\}$

5. Solve the equation $6\sin^2 x+1=5\sin x$ for $\sin x$.

Solution:

$$6\sin^2 x+1=5\sin x$$
$$6\sin^2 x-5\sin x+1=0$$
$$(3\sin x-1)(2\sin x-1)=0$$

$$3\sin x-1=0 \mid 2\sin x-1=0$$
$$\sin x=\tfrac{1}{3} \qquad \sin x=\tfrac{1}{2}$$

Answer: $\sin x=\tfrac{1}{3}$, $\sin x=\tfrac{1}{2}$

Exercises

In 1–27, solve and check the equation.

1. $x^2 - 5x + 4 = 0$ **2.** $y^2 + 10 = 7y$ **3.** $c^2 + 6c + 8 = 0$

4. $r^2 + 8r = -15$ **5.** $x^2 - x - 6 = 0$ **6.** $y^2 = y + 12$

7. $x^2 - 36 = 0$ **8.** $25y^2 = 16$ **9.** $d^2 + 7d = -10$

10. $8m = m^2 + 15$ **11.** $3x^2 - 8x + 4 = 0$ **12.** $5x^2 + 4 = 12x$

13. $9x - 10 = 2x^2$ **14.** $2x^2 + x = 15$ **15.** $x + 4 = 3x^2$

16. $\frac{1}{3}x^2 + \frac{4}{3}x + 1 = 0$ **17.** $\frac{9}{4}x = \frac{1}{2}x^2 + 1$ **18.** $1 = \frac{1}{2}x^2 - \frac{7}{6}x$

19. $x = \frac{24}{x-2}$ **20.** $\frac{c}{3} - 1 = \frac{6}{c}$ **21.** $\frac{2}{x-1} = \frac{x}{x+2}$

22. $\frac{4}{x-1} = \frac{5}{2x-2} + \frac{3x}{4}$ **23.** $\frac{200}{x} - 1 = \frac{200}{x+10}$ **24.** $\sqrt{2x^2 + x} = \sqrt{x^2 + 6}$

25. $4\sqrt{25 - x^2} = 3x$ **26.** $\sqrt{3x + 10} = x + 2$ **27.** $\sqrt{x^2 - 16} + 7 = 2x$

In 28–30, list the members of the set.

28. $\{x \mid x(x - 5) = 6\}$ **29.** $\{y \mid y^2 = 2(y + 4)\}$ **30.** $\left\{z \mid z - 5 = \frac{6}{z}\right\}$

31. If $(x - a)(x - b) = m$, then $(x - a) = m$ and $(x - b) = m$ when m is equal to either   (1) 1 or -1 (2) 1 or 0   (3) -1 or 0

In 32–39, solve for the trigonometric function.

32. $\tan x$: $\tan^2 x - 2 \tan x - 8 = 0$ **33.** $\cos x$: $2 \cos^2 x - \cos x = 0$

34. $\sin x$: $4 \sin^2 x - 1 = 0$ **35.** $\cot x$: $5 \cot^2 x + 2 = 11 \cot x$

36. $\cos x$: $10 \cos^2 x = 7 \cos x - 1$ **37.** $\tan x$: $\sqrt{\tan^2 x - 5} = 2$

38. $\tan x$: $\sqrt{2 \tan^2 x - 2} = \tan x - 1$ **39.** $\sin x$: $\sqrt{2 - \sin^2 x} - 1 = 2 \sin x$

3. Solving Quadratic Equations of the Form $ax^2 + bx = 0$

A quadratic equation lacking the constant term, c, is expressible in the form $ax^2 + bx = 0$. For example, $3x^2 + 5x = 0$ and $\frac{x^2}{3} - \frac{x}{2} = 0$ are quadratic equations lacking the constant term.

By factoring, $ax^2 + bx = 0$ becomes $x(ax + b) = 0$. Equating each factor to 0 yields $x = 0$ and $ax + b = 0$. Thus, $ax = -b$, and $x = -\frac{b}{a}$. The roots are 0 and $-\frac{b}{a}$.

Rule. A quadratic equation of the form $ax^2 + bx = 0$ has two roots, 0 and $-\frac{b}{a}$.

~~~~~~~~~~~~~~ *MODEL PROBLEMS* ~~~~~~~~~~~~~~

In 1 and 2, find the solution set by using the preceding rule.

1. $3(x^2 - x) = x^2$ **2.** $\dfrac{x^2}{3} + \dfrac{x}{9} = 0$

How To Proceed	*Solution*	*Solution*
1. Express in the form $ax^2 + bx = 0$.	$3x^2 - 3x = x^2$ $2x^2 - 3x = 0$	Multiply by 9. $3x^2 + x = 0$
2. Evaluate $-\dfrac{b}{a}$.	Since $a = 2$ and $b = -3$, $x = -\dfrac{-3}{2} = \dfrac{3}{2}$	Since $a = 3$ and $b = 1$, $x = -\frac{1}{3}$
3. State the roots, 0 and $-\dfrac{b}{a}$.	Roots are 0 and $\frac{3}{2}$. $\{0, \frac{3}{2}\}$ *Ans.*	Roots are 0 and $-\frac{1}{3}$. $\{0, -\frac{1}{3}\}$ *Ans.*

In 3 and 4, solve by factoring.

3. Solve for x and check:
$3x^2 = 9x$

Solution:

$$3x^2 = 9x$$
$$3x^2 - 9x = 0$$
$$3x(x - 3) = 0$$

$3x = 0 \mid x - 3 = 0$
$x = 0 \mid x = 3$

Check: $3x^2 = 9x$
If $x = 0$, $3(0)^2 \overset{?}{=} 9(0)$
$$0 = 0$$
If $x = 3$, $3(9) \overset{?}{=} 9(3)$
$$27 = 27$$

Answer: $x = 0$, $x = 3$

4. Solve for $\cos x$:
$2 \cos^2 x + 3 \cos x = 2 \cos x$

Solution:

$$2 \cos^2 x + 3 \cos x = 2 \cos x$$
$$2 \cos^2 x + 3 \cos x - 2 \cos x = 0$$
$$2 \cos^2 x + \cos x = 0$$
$$\cos x(2 \cos x + 1) = 0$$

$\cos x = 0 \mid 2 \cos x + 1 = 0$
$\cos x = -\frac{1}{2}$

Answer: $\cos x = 0$, $\cos x = -\frac{1}{2}$.

Exercises

In 1–8, solve for x.

1. $x^2 - 4x = 0$ **2.** $x^2 + 3x = 0$ **3.** $2x^2 - 5x = 0$ **4.** $3x^2 - 2x = 0$
5. $x^2 = 5x$ **6.** $x^2 = -x$ **7.** $4(x^2 - 2x) = x$ **8.** $3x = 5x(x - 2)$

In 9–11, find the solution set.

9. $\dfrac{x^2}{2} - 3x = 0$ **10.** $\dfrac{x^2}{3} + \dfrac{x}{2} = 0$ **11.** $x^2 = \frac{1}{3}x$

In 12–17, solve for x.

12. $x^2 - 4x = 3x^2$ **13.** $5x^2 + 2x = 3x^2 + 6x$ **14.** $rx^2 + sx = 0$

15. $cx^2 = dx$ **16.** $\frac{1}{2}x^2 - 5ax = 0$ **17.** $\frac{1}{2}mx^2 = \frac{1}{3}tx$

18. Solve for $\sin x$: $2 \sin^2 x - \sin x = 0$

19. Solve for $\cos x$: $4 \cos^2 x = \cos x$

20. Solve for $\tan x$: $3 \cot^2 x = \sqrt{3} \cot x$

21. Solve for $\tan x$: $3(\tan^2 x + 1) = 6 \tan x + 3$

22. Solve for $\sin x$: $5 + 2(\sin^2 x - 1) = \sin x + 3$

4. Solving Quadratic Equations of the Form $ax^2 = k$

A quadratic equation lacking the first-degree term, bx, is expressible in the form $ax^2 + c = 0$, or in the form $ax^2 = k$, where $k = -c$.

Dividing each side by a, $ax^2 = k$ becomes $x^2 = \dfrac{k}{a}$. Taking the square root of each side yields $x = \pm\sqrt{\dfrac{k}{a}}$. The roots are $\pm\sqrt{\dfrac{k}{a}}$.

Rule. A quadratic equation of the form $ax^2 = k$ has two roots, $\pm\sqrt{\dfrac{k}{a}}$.

~~~~~~~~~~ *MODEL PROBLEMS* ~~~~~~~~~~

In 1 and 2, solve the equation by using the preceding rule.

1. $4x^2 - 20 = 80$ **2.** $7x^2 = 4(x^2 + 6)$

How To Proceed	*Solution*	*Solution*
1. Express in the form $ax^2 = k$.	$4x^2 = 100$	$7x^2 = 4x^2 + 24$ $3x^2 = 24$
2. Evaluate $\dfrac{k}{a}$.	Since $a = 4$, and $k = 100$, $\dfrac{k}{a} = \dfrac{100}{4} = 25$	Since $a = 3$ and $k = 24$, $\dfrac{k}{a} = \dfrac{24}{3} = 8$

3. State the roots, $\pm\sqrt{\dfrac{k}{a}}$, in simplest radical form.

| Roots are $\pm\sqrt{25}$, or ±5. $\{5, -5\}$ *Ans.* | Roots are $\pm\sqrt{8}$, or $\pm2\sqrt{2}$. $\{2\sqrt{2}, -2\sqrt{2}\}$ *Ans.* |

In 3 and 4, solve the equation by taking the square root of each side. Do *not* use the preceding rule.

3. Solve: $5x^2 - 8 = 3x^2$

Solution:

$$5x^2 - 8 = 3x^2$$
$$5x^2 - 3x^2 = 8$$
$$2x^2 = 8$$
$$x^2 = 4$$
$$x = \pm2$$

Answer: $x = +2,\ x = -2$

4. Solve: $(2x - 3)^2 = 5$

Solution:

$$(2x - 3)^2 = 5$$
$$2x - 3 = \pm\sqrt{5}$$

$2x - 3 = \sqrt{5}$	$2x - 3 = -\sqrt{5}$
$2x = 3 + \sqrt{5}$	$2x = 3 - \sqrt{5}$
$x = \dfrac{3 + \sqrt{5}}{2}$	$x = \dfrac{3 - \sqrt{5}}{2}$

Answer: $x = \dfrac{3 + \sqrt{5}}{2},\ x = \dfrac{3 - \sqrt{5}}{2}$

Exercises

In 1–8, solve for x.

1. $x^2 = 25$ **2.** $x^2 = 8$ **3.** $4x^2 = 16$ **4.** $3x^2 = 21$
5. $(x + 4)^2 = 36$ **6.** $(2x - 1)^2 = 81$ **7.** $(x - 3)^2 = 3$ **8.** $(3x + 2)^2 = 2$

In 9–17, find the solution set of the equation.

9. $\dfrac{x^2}{3} = 12$ **10.** $5 = \dfrac{x^2}{4}$ **11.** $x + 7 = \dfrac{1}{x - 7}$

12. $\dfrac{x - 3}{2} = \dfrac{8}{x + 3}$ **13.** $\dfrac{5 + x}{7} = \dfrac{1}{5 - x}$ **14.** $\dfrac{x - 1}{x + 1} + \dfrac{x + 1}{x - 1} = 3$

15. $9x^2 = a^2$ **16.** $4x^2 - r^2 = 0$ **17.** $mx^2 - r = 0$

18. Solve for x: $x^2 + a^2 = c^2$
19. Solve for r: $A = \pi r^2$
20. Solve for r: $S = 4\pi r^2$

21. Solve for t: $S = \frac{1}{2}at^2$
22. Solve for $\tan x$: $\tan^2 x - 9 = 0$
23. Solve for $\cot x$: $4\cot^2 x - 12 = 0$
24. Solve for $\sin x$: $5\sin^2 x = \sin^2 x + 1$
25. Solve for $\cos x$: $3\cos^2 x = 5\cos^2 x - 1$
26. Solve for $\sin x$: $3\sin^2 x + \cos^2 x = 2$
27. Solve for $\sec x$: $1 + \tan^2 x = 2\sec^2 x - 9$
28. Solve for $\cot x$: $1 + \cot^2 x = 3\csc^2 x - 8$
29. Find the diagonal of a square whose side is 20.
30. Find the altitude of an equilateral triangle whose side is 10.

5. Solving Quadratic Equations by Completing the Square

Frequently, quadratic equations cannot be solved readily by factoring. If a quadratic equation has real coefficients, the method of *completing the square* can be used to find the roots, whether or not the method of factoring is applicable.

A **perfect square trinomial** is a trinomial which is the square of a binomial. Hence, a perfect square trinomial has two equal binomial factors.

Thus, the expression $x^2 + 10x + 25$ is a perfect square trinomial since $x^2 + 10x + 25 = (x + 5)^2$.

COMPLETING THE PERFECT SQUARE TRINOMIAL OR "COMPLETING THE SQUARE"

Suppose we are given $x^2 + 10x$, the first two terms of the perfect square trinomial $x^2 + 10x + 25$. To complete the perfect square trinomial, or simply to "complete the square," the last term, 25, must be obtained. This is done by squaring one-half of 10, the coefficient of x, in accordance with the following:

Rule. To obtain a perfect square trinomial, whose first two terms are $x^2 + px$, add $(\frac{1}{2}p)^2$, or $\frac{1}{4}p^2$, thus obtaining the perfect square trinomial, $x^2 + px + \frac{p^2}{4}$, or $\left(x + \frac{p}{2}\right)^2$.

Note that $\frac{1}{2}p$ is one-half the coefficient of x. The process of adding the term $\frac{1}{4}p^2$ is called "completing the square."

〜〜〜〜〜〜〜 *MODEL PROBLEMS* 〜〜〜〜〜〜〜

In 1 and 2, complete the square and express the resulting perfect square trinomial as the square of a binomial.

1. $6x + x^2$

2. $2x^2 - x^2 - \frac{3}{2}x$

How To Proceed	*Solution*	*Solution*
1. Express in the form $x^2 + px$.	$x^2 + 6x \ [p = 6]$	$x^2 - \frac{3}{2}x \ \left[p = -\frac{3}{2}\right]$
2. Evaluate $\left(\frac{p}{2}\right)^2$, or $\frac{p^2}{4}$.	Since $\frac{p}{2} = \frac{6}{2} = 3$, then $\frac{p^2}{4} = (3)^2 = 9$.	Since $\frac{p}{2} = \frac{1}{2}\left(-\frac{3}{2}\right) = -\frac{3}{4}$, then $\frac{p^2}{4} = \left(-\frac{3}{4}\right)^2 = \frac{9}{16}$.
3. Complete the square by adding $\frac{p^2}{4}$.	$x^2 + 6x + 9$	$x^2 - \frac{3}{2}x + \frac{9}{16}$
4. Express as $\left(x + \frac{p}{2}\right)^2$.	$(x + 3)^2$	$(x - \frac{3}{4})^2$

Procedure. To solve a quadratic equation by completing the square:
1. Transform the equation so that all terms containing the variable are on one side of the equation with the constant term on the other side.
2. If the coefficient of x^2 is not one, divide both members of the equation by the coefficient of x^2 to obtain an equation of the form $x^2 + px = q$, where q is a constant.
3. Square one-half the coefficient of x and add the result to both members of of the equation obtained in step 2.
4. Express the left member as the square of a binomial and simplify the right member.
5. Find the square root of both members. Write $\pm$ before the square root of the right member.
6. Let the square root of the left member equal the positive $(+)$ square root of the right member and solve the resulting equation.
7. Let the square root of the left member equal the negative $(-)$ square root of the right member and solve the resulting equation.

~~~~~~~~~ *MODEL PROBLEMS* ~~~~~~~~~

1. Solve by completing the square and check: $2x^2 - 3x - 2 = 0$

Solution:

$2x^2 - 3x - 2 = 0$

$2x^2 - 3x = 2$

$D_2 : x^2 - \frac{3}{2}x = 1$

$x^2 - \frac{3}{2}x + (-\frac{3}{4})^2 = 1 + (-\frac{3}{4})^2$

$x^2 - \frac{3}{2}x + \frac{9}{16} = 1 + \frac{9}{16}$

$(x - \frac{3}{4})^2 = \frac{25}{16}$

$R_2 : x - \frac{3}{4} = \pm\frac{5}{4}$

$x - \frac{3}{4} = +\frac{5}{4}$ | $x - \frac{3}{4} = -\frac{5}{4}$

$x = \frac{5}{4} + \frac{3}{4}$ | $x = -\frac{5}{4} + \frac{3}{4}$

$x = \frac{8}{4} = 2$ | $x = -\frac{2}{4} = -\frac{1}{2}$

Check: $2x^2 - 3x - 2 = 0$

If $x = 2$, $2(2)^2 - 3(2) - 2 \overset{?}{=} 0$

$8 - 6 - 2 \overset{?}{=} 0$

$0 = 0$

If $x = -\frac{1}{2}$, $2(-\frac{1}{2})^2 - 3(-\frac{1}{2}) - 2 \overset{?}{=} 0$

$2(\frac{1}{4}) + \frac{3}{2} - 2 \overset{?}{=} 0$

$\frac{1}{2} + \frac{3}{2} - 2 \overset{?}{=} 0$

$0 = 0$

Answer: $x = 2$, $x = -\frac{1}{2}$

Note. "R_2" means "Take the square root of each side of the equation."

2. By completing the square, solve for $\sin x$: $4\sin^2 x + 4\sin x = 3$

Solution:

1. $4\sin^2 x + 4\sin x = 3$
2. $D_4 : \sin^2 x + \sin x = \frac{3}{4}$
3. $\sin^2 x + \sin x + (\frac{1}{2})^2 = \frac{3}{4} + (\frac{1}{2})^2$
4. $\sin^2 x + \sin x + \frac{1}{4} = \frac{3}{4} + \frac{1}{4}$
5. $(\sin x + \frac{1}{2})^2 = 1$
6. $R_2 : \sin x + \frac{1}{2} = \pm 1$
7. $\sin x + \frac{1}{2} = 1$ | $\sin x + \frac{1}{2} = -1$
8. $\sin x = \frac{1}{2}$ | $\sin x = -\frac{3}{2}$ Reject

Answer: $\sin x = \frac{1}{2}$

Exercises

In 1–20, complete the square by replacing the question mark with a number and express the resulting trinomial as the square of a binomial.

1. $x^2 + 6x + (?)$ **2.** $d^2 - 4d + (?)$ **3.** $r^2 - 12r + (?)$ **4.** $y^2 + 16y + (?)$

5. $a^2 + 3a + (?)$ **6.** $x^2 + 5x + (?)$ **7.** $b^2 - b + (?)$ **8.** $m^2 - 7m + (?)$

9. $x^2 - \frac{1}{2}x + (?)$ **10.** $y^2 + \frac{1}{3}y + (?)$ **11.** $z^2 - \frac{2}{3}z + (?)$ **12.** $y^2 - \frac{4}{3}y + (?)$

13. $\cos^2 x + 2\cos x + (?)$ **14.** $\tan^2 x - 4\tan x + (?)$

15. $\sin^2 x - \sin x + (?)$ **16.** $\cot^2 x + 3\cot x + (?)$

17. $\sin^2 x + \frac{1}{2}\sin x + (?)$ **18.** $\cos^2 x - \frac{1}{3}\cos x + (?)$

19. $\tan^2 x + \frac{2}{3}\tan x + (?)$ **20.** $\sec^2 x + \frac{3}{5}\sec x + (?)$

In 21–35, solve the equation by completing the square. Write the solution set of the equation, expressing irrational roots in the simplest radical form.

21. $x^2 + 2x = 4$ **22.** $y^2 + 4y = 21$ **23.** $c^2 - 6c = 16$

24. $x^2 - 8x + 12 = 0$ **25.** $y^2 + 2y - 48 = 0$ **26.** $x^2 = 4x + 12$
27. $x^2 + 3x + 2 = 0$ **28.** $y^2 + 5y - 6 = 0$ **29.** $t^2 = 14 - 5t$
30. $3x^2 + 2x - 1 = 0$ **31.** $2c^2 - 3c - 2 = 0$ **32.** $5d^2 + 3d = 2$
33. $t^2 - 2t - 5 = 0$ **34.** $m^2 + 6m - 4 = 0$ **35.** $a^2 - 5a - 4 = 0$

In 36–38, using the method of completing the square, list the members of the set.

36. $\{y \mid y^2 = 6 - 5y\}$ **37.** $\{x \mid 2x^2 - 10x = 1\}$ **38.** $\{x \mid 3x(x - 1) = 1\}$

6. Solving Quadratic Equations by the Quadratic Formula

The following quadratic formula can be used to solve any quadratic equation expressed in standard quadratic form:

If a quadratic equation is of the form $ax^2 + bx + c = 0$, then

$$x = \frac{-b \pm \sqrt{b^2 - 4ac}}{2a}$$

Using r_1 and r_2 to represent the roots,

$$r_1 = \frac{-b + \sqrt{b^2 - 4ac}}{2a} \quad \text{and} \quad r_2 = \frac{-b - \sqrt{b^2 - 4ac}}{2a}$$

DERIVATION OF THE QUADRATIC FORMULA BY COMPLETING THE SQUARE

If $ax^2 + bx + c = 0$, the formula for the roots of this equation in terms of a, b, and c may be derived as follows:

1. $ax^2 + bx + c = 0$

2. $x^2 + \dfrac{b}{a}x + \dfrac{c}{a} = 0$ In equation 1, divide by a.

3. $x^2 + \dfrac{b}{a}x = -\dfrac{c}{a}$ In equation 2, subtract $\dfrac{c}{a}$ from each side.

To complete the square, take $\frac{1}{2}$ of the coefficient of x and square the result.

$$\frac{1}{2}\left(\frac{b}{a}\right) = \frac{b}{2a} \; ; \; \left(\frac{b}{2a}\right)^2 = \frac{b^2}{4a^2}$$

4. $x^2 + \dfrac{b}{a}x + \dfrac{b^2}{4a^2} = \dfrac{b^2}{4a^2} - \dfrac{c}{a}$ In equation 3, add $\dfrac{b^2}{4a^2}$ to each side.

5. $\left(x + \dfrac{b}{2a}\right)^2 = \dfrac{b^2 - 4ac}{4a^2}$ Combine the fractions.

6. $x + \dfrac{b}{2a} = \pm\dfrac{\sqrt{b^2 - 4ac}}{2a}$ In equation 5, take the square root of each side.

7. $x = -\dfrac{b}{2a} \pm \dfrac{\sqrt{b^2 - 4ac}}{2a}$ In equation 6, subtract $\dfrac{b}{2a}$ from each side.

8. $x = \dfrac{-b \pm \sqrt{b^2 - 4ac}}{2a}$ Combine the fractions.

MODEL PROBLEMS

1. Find the solution set of $2x^2 + 2 = 5x$.

How To Proceed	*Solution*
1. Equate to 0.	$2x^2 + 2 = 5x$ $2x^2 - 5x + 2 = 0$
2. Determine $a, b,$ and c by comparing with $ax^2 + bx + c = 0$.	$a = 2, b = -5, c = 2$
3. Substitute the values of $a, b,$ and c in the quadratic formula.	$x = \dfrac{-b \pm \sqrt{b^2 - 4ac}}{2a}$ $x = \dfrac{-(-5) \pm \sqrt{(-5)^2 - 4(2)(2)}}{2(2)}$
4. Compute the values of x by evaluating the result obtained in step 3.	$x = \dfrac{5 \pm \sqrt{25 - 16}}{4}$ $x = \dfrac{5 \pm \sqrt{9}}{4} = \dfrac{5 \pm 3}{4}$ $x = \dfrac{5+3}{4} \qquad x = \dfrac{5-3}{4}$ $x = \frac{8}{4} = 2 \qquad x = \frac{2}{4} = \frac{1}{2}$

Answer: $\{2, \frac{1}{2}\}$

2. Solve the equation $3x^2 - 3x = 2$ for values of x to the nearest tenth.

Solution:

Equate to 0: $3x^2 - 3x = 2$ becomes $3x^2 - 3x - 2 = 0$

Compare with $ax^2 + bx + c = 0$: $a = 3, b = -3, c = -2$

Quadratic formula is $x = \dfrac{-b \pm \sqrt{b^2 - 4ac}}{2a}$.

Substitute: $x = \dfrac{-(-3) \pm \sqrt{(-3)^2 - 4(3)(-2)}}{2(3)}$

$$x = \frac{3 \pm \sqrt{9 + 24}}{6}$$

$$x = \frac{3 \pm \sqrt{33}}{6} = \frac{3 \pm 5.74}{6}$$

$$x = \frac{3 + 5.74}{6}$$

$$x = \frac{8.74}{6} = 1.45+$$

$x = 1.5$, to the nearest tenth

$$x = \frac{3 - 5.74}{6}$$

$$x = \frac{-2.74}{6} = -.45+$$

$x = -.5$, to the nearest tenth

```
                5. 7  4
        √ 33.00 00
          25
   107 | 800
         749
  1144 | 5100
         4576
          524
```

Answer: 1.5 or $-.5$

Note. In finding the square root, carry it out to one decimal place more than the number of decimal places required in the answer.

Exercises

In 1–9, using the quadratic formula, find the solution set of the equation. Express irrational roots in simplest radical form.

1. $x^2 + 3x - 40 = 0$ **2.** $x^2 + 16 = 8x$ **3.** $3x^2 + 5x = -2$

4. $2(x^2 - 3) = x$ **5.** $c^2 - 10c + 15 = 0$ **6.** $2 + 4r = 5r^2$

7. $2x - \dfrac{4}{x} = 5$ **8.** $1 + \dfrac{2}{x^2} = \dfrac{7}{2x}$ **9.** $\dfrac{3}{x-2} - \dfrac{1}{x-1} = 2$

In 10–24, find, to the nearest tenth, the roots of the equation.

10. $x^2 - 3x - 3 = 0$ **11.** $y^2 + 4y - 2 = 0$ **12.** $2c^2 + 7c + 1 = 0$

13. $3d^2 = 5d + 4$ **14.** $3 = 2x^2 + 4x$ **15.** $2x^2 - 5x + 1 = 0$

16. $x^2 + 2x - 4 = 0$ **17.** $3x^2 - 2x - 6 = 0$ **18.** $2x^2 - 10x = 9$

19. $2x^2 - 8x + 1 = 0$ **20.** $2x^2 - 2x = 3$ **21.** $3x^2 + 5x - 1 = 0$

22. $x^2 - 20x - 10 = 0$ **23.** $x^2 + 9x - 12 = 0$ **24.** $x^2 + 4x - 16 = 0$

25. Given the equation $\tan^2 x - 3 \tan x + 1 = 0$. Find, to the nearest tenth, the values of $\tan x$ that satisfy this equation.

26. Given the equation $\sin^2 x + \sin x - 1 = 0$. Find, to the nearest tenth, the positive value of $\sin x$ that satisfies this equation.

27. Given the equation $2 \tan^2 A + 5 \tan A = 8$. Find, to the nearest tenth, the values of $\tan A$ that satisfy this equation.

28. Solve the equation $3 \sin^2 x - 2 = 3 \sin x$ for the negative value of $\sin x$, correct to the nearest hundredth.

7. Determining the Nature of the Roots of a Quadratic Equation

DISCRIMINANT OF A QUADRATIC EQUATION, $b^2 - 4ac$

We shall see that the value of $b^2 - 4ac$, the radicand, (that is, the expression under the radical sign) in the quadratic formula, can be used to determine the nature of the roots of any quadratic equation of the form $ax^2 + bx + c = 0$. Hence, $b^2 - 4ac$ is called the ***discriminant*** of the quadratic equation. If a, b, and c are rational numbers and $a \neq 0$, the discriminant reveals whether the roots are (1) real or imaginary, (2) equal or unequal, (3) rational or irrational, according to the following table:

USING THE DISCRIMINANT, $b^2 - 4ac$, TO DETERMINE THE NATURE OF THE ROOTS OF A QUADRATIC EQUATION WHEN $a, b,$ AND c ARE RATIONAL NUMBERS

Case	*Value of the Discriminant, $b^2 - 4ac$*	*Nature of the Roots*
(1)	zero or positive	real
	negative	imaginary
(2)	zero	equal
	nonzero	unequal
(3)	a perfect square	rational
	positive and not a perfect square	irrational

It can be seen from the table that the nature of the roots can be determined using one of the following rules, given a, b, and c are rational numbers, $a \neq 0$:

Rule 1. If $b^2 - 4ac$ is positive and not a perfect square, the roots are real, irrational, and unequal. This rule would apply if $b^2 - 4ac$ were 7.

Rule 2. If $b^2 - 4ac$ is a perfect square and not equal to 0, the roots are real, rational, and unequal. This rule would apply if $b^2 - 4ac$ were 9.

Rule 3. If $b^2 - 4ac = 0$, the roots are real, rational, and equal.

Rule 4. If $b^2 - 4ac$ is negative, the roots are imaginary. This rule would apply if $b^2 - 4ac$ were -4.

If the roots are imaginary, then these roots are conjugate complex numbers. (Recall that conjugate complex numbers are expressible in the form $a + bi$ and $a - bi$.) Conjugate complex numbers cannot be equal since equal complex numbers must have equal real parts and also equal imaginary parts. Furthermore, conjugate complex numbers can be neither rational nor irrational numbers since such numbers are real numbers.

～～～～～～ MODEL PROBLEMS ～～～～～～

In 1 and 2, state the nature of the roots of the equation.

1. $x^2 + 12 = 8x$ **2.** $4 = x(2 - x)$

How To Proceed	*Solution*	*Solution*
1. Equate to 0.	$x^2 - 8x + 12 = 0$	$4 = 2x - x^2$
		$x^2 - 2x + 4 = 0$
2. Determine values of a, b, and c.	$a = 1, b = -8, c = 12$	$a = 1, b = -2, c = 4$
3. Evaluate $b^2 - 4ac$.	$b^2 - 4ac$	$b^2 - 4ac$
	$(-8)^2 - 4(1)(12)$	$(-2)^2 - 4(1)(4)$
	$64 - 48 = 16$	$4 - 16 = -12$
4. State the nature of the roots.	Since $b^2 - 4ac$ is a positive perfect square, the roots are real, rational, and unequal.	Since $b^2 - 4ac$ is negative, the roots are imaginary. (The roots are conjugate complex numbers.)

3. Find the value of k for which the equation $x^2 - 6x + k = 0$ has equal roots.

Solution: From $x^2 - 6x + k = 0$, $a = 1$, $b = -6$, $c = k$.

If the equation has equal roots,
$$b^2 - 4ac = 0$$
$$(-6)^2 - 4(1)(k) = 0$$
$$36 - 4k = 0$$
$$36 = 4k$$
$$9 = k \quad \textit{Answer: } k = 9$$

Exercises

In each of the following exercises, assume that the coefficients of the quadratic equations are rational numbers, unless there is a statement to the contrary.

In 1–6, find the discriminant.

1. $x^2 - 5x + 6 = 0$ **2.** $c^2 + 2c - 10 = 0$ **3.** $r^2 = 7r + 5$
4. $8 = 2x^2 - 3x$ **5.** $4x^2 + 1 = 4x$ **6.** $2z^2 + 5 = 2z$

In 7–21, state the nature of the roots of a quadratic equation if its discriminant is:

7. 49	**8.** 0	**9.** 16	**10.** −4	**11.** 17
12. 100	**13.** −49	**14.** 23	**15.** −64	**16.** 121
17. 54	**18.** −13	**19.** 86	**20.** −25	**21.** 225

In 22–30, determine the nature of the roots of the equation without solving the equation.

22. $x^2 - 7x + 10 = 0$ **23.** $2x^2 - 5x - 4 = 0$ **24.** $y^2 + 3y + 4 = 0$
25. $3y^2 - 7y = 4$ **26.** $9c^2 = 6c$ **27.** $4d^2 = 3d - 5$
28. $5y^2 + 2 = 11y$ **29.** $2d - 10 = d^2$ **30.** $25x^2 + 4 = 0$

In 31–36, determine the values of k that will make the roots of the equation equal.

31. $y^2 - 10y + k = 0$ **32.** $ky^2 - 12y + 9 = 0$ **33** $x^2 - kx + 16 = 0$
34. $x^2 + 12x = k$ **35.** $y^2 + 2kx + 16 = 0$ **36.** $kx^2 - 12x + k + 5 = 0$

In 37–39, determine the values of k for which the roots of the equation will be imaginary.

37. $x^2 + 8x + k = 0$ **38.** $kx^2 - 10x + 5 = 0$ **39.** $2x^2 - 12x + 8 = k$

40. If the discriminant of a quadratic equation with real coefficients is 0, the roots of the equation are (1) real and equal (2) real and unequal (3) imaginary

41. The roots of the equation $2x^2 - 3x + 3 = 0$ are (1) real, equal, and rational (2) real, unequal, and irrational (3) real, unequal, and rational (4) imaginary

42. The roots of the equation $3x^2 + kx - 4 = 0$ are real, rational, and unequal if k is equal to (1) 1 (2) 2 (3) 0 (4) 6

43. The roots of the equation $ax^2 + bx + c = 0$ are real, rational, and unequal. What integer between 13 and 20 may be the value of the discriminant of the equation?

44. In the equation $\sin^2 x + \sin x + 1 = 0$, the values of $\sin x$ are (1) real and equal (2) imaginary (3) real and unequal

45. In the equation $6 \cos^2 x - 5 \cos x + 1 = 0$, the values of $\cos x$ are (1) imaginary (2) real and equal (3) real and rational

8. Expressing a Quadratic Equation in Terms of Its Roots: Sum and Product of the Roots

If 3 and 5 are the roots of a quadratic equation, then the equation in factored form is $(x - 3)(x - 5) = 0$. Multiplying the two binomials to remove parentheses, we obtain the quadratic equation in standard quadratic form, $x^2 - 8x + 15 = 0$.

In general, if r_1 and r_2 represent the roots of a quadratic equation, then the equation in factored form is $(x - r_1)(x - r_2) = 0$. Multiplying the two binomials to remove parentheses, as shown on the right, we obtain the quadratic equation in standard quadratic form:

$$
\begin{array}{r}
x - r_1 \\
x - r_2 \\
\hline
x^2 - r_1 x \\
- r_2 x + r_1 r_2 \\
\hline
x^2 - (r_1 + r_2)x + r_1 r_2
\end{array}
$$

$$(1) \quad x^2 - (r_1 + r_2)x + r_1 r_2 = 0$$

RELATING THE ROOTS OF A QUADRATIC EQUATION TO *a, b,* AND *c* OF THE STANDARD QUADRATIC FORM

If each side of the standard quadratic form, $ax^2 + bx + c = 0$, is divided by a, we obtain the equation

$$(2) \quad x^2 + \frac{b}{a} x + \frac{c}{a} = 0$$

Note in equations (1) and (2) that x^2 is the second-degree term of each. Hence, equating the coefficients of the first-degree term, we find that $-(r_1 + r_2) = \frac{b}{a}$. Therefore,

$$r_1 + r_2 = -\frac{b}{a}$$

Also, by equating the constant terms of (1) and (2), we find that

$$r_1 r_2 = \frac{c}{a}$$

Rules for the Sum and Product of the Roots of a Quadratic Equation

If a quadratic equation is in standard form, $ax^2 + bx + c = 0$, then:

Rule 1. The product of the roots, $r_1 r_2 = \frac{c}{a}$.

Rule 2. The sum of the roots, $r_1 + r_2 = -\frac{b}{a}$.

For alternate proofs of the rules for the sum and the product of the roots of a quadratic equation, refer to pages 742–743.

〰〰〰〰〰〰〰〰 *MODEL PROBLEMS* 〰〰〰〰〰〰〰

1. Find the sum and the product of the roots of $2x^2 - 8x + 3 = 0$.

Solution:

$a = 2, \ b = -8, \ c = 3$

$$r_1 + r_2 = \frac{-b}{a} = \frac{-(-8)}{2} = \frac{8}{2} = 4 \quad Ans. \qquad\qquad r_1 r_2 = \frac{c}{a} = \frac{3}{2} \text{ or } 1\tfrac{1}{2} \quad Ans.$$

2. If one root of the equation $x^2 - 4x + c = 0$ is 1, find the other root.

Solution: $\quad x^2 - 4x + c = 0 \qquad\qquad a = 1, \quad b = -4, \quad r_1 = 1$

$$r_1 + r_2 = 4$$
$$\underline{r_1 \qquad\ = 1} \qquad\qquad r_1 + r_2 = \frac{-b}{a} = 4$$

Therefore, $\qquad\qquad r_2 = 3 \quad Ans.$

〰〰〰〰〰〰〰〰〰〰〰〰〰〰〰〰〰〰〰〰〰〰〰〰〰

CHECKING THE ROOTS OF A QUADRATIC EQUATION BY USING THE SUM AND PRODUCT OF THE ROOTS

〰〰〰〰〰〰〰 *MODEL PROBLEM* 〰〰〰〰〰〰〰

Is $\{3 + \sqrt{2}, 3 - \sqrt{2}\}$ the solution set of $x^2 - 6x + 7 = 0$?

Solution: If the solution set is $\{3 + \sqrt{2}, 3 - \sqrt{2}\}$, then $r_1 = 3 + \sqrt{2}$ and $r_2 = 3 - \sqrt{2}$. Since the equation in standard form is $x^2 - 6x + 7 = 0$, then $a = 1, b = -6,$ and $c = 7$.

(*a*) Is the product, $r_1 r_2 = \dfrac{c}{a}$? $\qquad$ (*b*) Is the sum, $r_1 + r_2 = -\dfrac{b}{a}$?

$$(3 + \sqrt{2})(3 - \sqrt{2}) \overset{?}{=} \frac{7}{1} \qquad\qquad (3 + \sqrt{2}) + (3 - \sqrt{2}) \overset{?}{=} -\frac{-6}{1}$$

$$7 = 7 \qquad\qquad\qquad\qquad\qquad 6 = 6$$

Answer: $\{3 + \sqrt{2}, 3 - \sqrt{2}\}$ is the solution set of $x^2 - 6x + 7 = 0$.

〰〰〰〰〰〰〰〰〰〰〰〰〰〰〰〰〰〰〰〰〰〰〰〰〰

When checking roots that have been expressed to the nearest tenth or other decimal, the sum and the product method of checking can be used. The approximations obtained for the sum and the product of the roots will, if the roots are correct, closely approximate $-\dfrac{b}{a}$ and $\dfrac{c}{a}$, respectively.

Exercises

In 1–9, find the sum and the product of the roots of the equation.

1. $x^2 + 6x + 2 = 0$ **2.** $y^2 + 4y - 5 = 0$ **3.** $2c^2 + 4c - 7 = 0$

4. $3d^2 + 7d + 3 = 0$ **5.** $4x^2 - 3x = 9$ **6.** $2r^2 + 7 = 10r$

7. $2y^2 = 4y + 1$ **8.** $6 = 3y^2 + 7y$ **9.** $8y = 2 - y^2$

In 10–17, if the number in parentheses is one root of the equation, find the other root.

10. $x^2 - 5x + c = 0$ (2) **11.** $2y^2 + 4y + e = 0$ (-3)

12. $x^2 + dx + 6 = 0$ (2) **13.** $2c^2 + 9c + 4 = 0$ $(-\frac{1}{2})$

14. $r^2 + 4r + d = 0$ (1) **15.** $x^2 + cx - 5 = 0$ (1)

16. $3x^2 + ex - 4 = 0$ $(\frac{1}{3})$ **17.** $6x^2 + 1 = 5x$ $(\frac{1}{2})$

In 18–23, by using the rules for the sum and product of the roots of a quadratic equation, determine whether the statement is *true* or *false*.

18. The roots of $2x^2 - 5x + 2 = 0$ are $x = 2$ and $x = \frac{1}{2}$.

19. The roots of $4c^2 - 7c + 3 = 0$ are $c = -\frac{3}{4}$ and $c = -1$.

20. The roots of $6x^2 + 13x - 5 = 0$ are $x = \frac{1}{3}$ and $x = -2\frac{1}{2}$.

21. The roots of $x^2 - 4x + 2 = 0$ are $x = 2 + \sqrt{2}$ and $x = 2 - \sqrt{2}$.

22. The roots of $6 \sin^2 x - 5 \sin x + 1 = 0$ are $\sin x = \frac{1}{2}$ and $\sin x = \frac{1}{3}$.

23. The roots of $4 \cos^2 x - 5 \cos x + 1 = 0$ are $\cos x = \frac{1}{4}$ and $\cos x = 1$.

In 24–28, find the value of k in the equation $2x^2 - 3x + k = 0$ if one of the roots of the equation is the given number.

24. 5 **25.** -5 **26.** $\frac{1}{2}$ **27.** 2.1 **28.** $-1\frac{1}{4}$

29. If 2 is a root of $x^2 - 5x + n = 0$, find n.

30. Find c so that $\frac{1}{2}$ will be a root of $4x^2 + c = 4x$.

31. If $\frac{2}{3}$ is a root of $3x^2 - cx + 2 = 0$, find c.

32. Find k so that $-\frac{1}{5}$ will be a root of $5x^2 + kx = 4$.

33. Find the value of c so that one root of $x^2 - 3x + c = 0$ will be twice the other.

34. In the quadratic equation $x^2 - 5x + 2 = 0$, the sum of the roots exceeds the product of the roots by (1) -3 (2) 3 (3) 7

35. The sum of the roots of the equation $x^2 - px + p = 0$ is (1) always (2) sometimes (3) never equal to their product.

36. If the roots of the equation $x^2 + 4x + q = 0$ are equal, what is the value of q?

37. If 0 is one root of the equation $x^2 + px + q = 0$, what must be the value of q?

38. If the roots of the equation $x^2 + px + q = 0$ are numerically equal but opposite in sign, what is the value of p?

39. In the equation $\tan^2 x - 5 \tan x + c = 0$, one value of $\tan x$ is 3.5. Find the remaining value of $\tan x$.

9. Forming a Quadratic Equation Whose Roots Are Given

〜〜〜〜〜〜〜〜〜 *MODEL PROBLEMS* 〜〜〜〜〜〜〜〜〜

In 1 and 2, write a quadratic equation with integral coefficients whose solution set is the given set.

1. $\{2, -\frac{1}{2}\}$　　　　　　**2.** $\{3\sqrt{2}, -3\sqrt{2}\}$

Method 1:

How To Proceed	*Solution*	*Solution*
1. Substitute for r_1 and r_2 in the equation $(x - r_1)(x - r_2) = 0$.	Since $r_1 = 2$ and $r_2 = -\frac{1}{2}$, $(x - 2)(x + \frac{1}{2}) = 0$	Since $r_1 = 3\sqrt{2}$ and $r_2 = -3\sqrt{2}$, $(x - 3\sqrt{2})(x + 3\sqrt{2}) = 0$
2. Multiply the binomials.	$x^2 - \frac{3}{2}x - 1 = 0$	
3. Clear of fractions to obtain integral coefficients.	$2x^2 - 3x - 2 = 0$ *Ans.*	$x^2 - 18 = 0$ *Ans.*

Method 2:

How To Proceed	*Solution*	*Solution*
1. Find $(r_1 + r_2)$ and $r_1 r_2$.	Since $r_1 = 2$ and $r_2 = -\frac{1}{2}$, $r_1 + r_2 = \frac{3}{2}$ and $r_1 r_2 = -1$.	Since $r_1 = 3\sqrt{2}$ and $r_2 = -3\sqrt{2}$, $r_1 + r_2 = 0$ and $r_1 r_2 = -18$.
2. Substitute in the equation $x^2 - (r_1 + r_2)x + r_1 r_2 = 0$.	$x^2 - \frac{3}{2}x - 1 = 0$	$x^2 - 0x - 18 = 0$ $x^2 - 18 = 0$ *Ans.*
3. Clear of fractions to obtain integral coefficients.	$2x^2 - 3x - 2 = 0$ *Ans.*	

Exercises

In 1–19, form a quadratic equation, with integral coefficients, whose roots are:

1. $5, 2$ 2. $3, 7$ 3. $-1, -3$ 4. $-4, -5$

5. $5, -9$ 6. $-3, 7$ 7. $\frac{1}{2}, \frac{1}{5}$ 8. $\frac{2}{3}, 3$

9. $-\frac{1}{2}, \frac{3}{4}$ 10. $-\frac{3}{4}, -\frac{1}{3}$ 11. $2.5, 1.2$ 12. $-1.4, -.5$

13. $-1.5, .2$ 14. $.2, -.5$ 15. $\sqrt{2}, -\sqrt{2}$ 16. $\sqrt{5}, -\sqrt{5}$

17. $2 + \sqrt{5}, 2 - \sqrt{5}$ 18. $3 - \sqrt{7}, 3 + \sqrt{7}$ 19. $-2 + \sqrt{3}, -2 - \sqrt{3}$

In 20–31, write a quadratic equation, with integral coefficients, the sum and the product of whose roots are the given numbers.

20. 9 and 4 21. 7 and 1 22. -5 and -2 23. -2 and -4

24. -3 and -1 25. 1 and -3 26. -6 and 8 27. $\frac{1}{3}$ and $\frac{1}{9}$

28. $-\frac{5}{6}$ and $\frac{1}{6}$ 29. $-\frac{3}{4}$ and $\frac{3}{8}$ 30. $-\frac{5}{3}$ and -2 31. $-\frac{2}{5}$ and $\frac{1}{25}$

In 32–37, write a quadratic equation, with integral coefficients, whose roots are the given trigonometric function values.

32. $\tan x = 1, \tan x = 2$ 33. $\cot x = 3, \cot x = -1$

34. $\sin x = \frac{1}{2}, \sin x = 1$ 35. $\cos x = -\frac{1}{2}, \cos x = -\frac{1}{3}$

36. $\sin x = 0, \sin x = -1$ 37. $\cos x = -\frac{1}{4}, \cos x = 0$

10. Solving a Linear-Quadratic System of Equations Consisting of a First-Degree Equation and a Second-Degree Equation

We have learned how to solve a system of two linear equations in two variables. Now we will extend the ideas we have learned in a linear-linear system to a linear-quadratic system and also to a quadratic-quadratic system. In the linear-quadratic system, one of the equations is a first-degree equation, while the other is a second-degree equation. In the quadratic-quadratic system, both equations are second-degree equations. All equations to be treated involve two variables.

The following model problem shows how to solve a linear-quadratic system algebraically using the method of substitution:

〜〜〜〜〜〜〜 *MODEL PROBLEM* 〜〜〜〜〜〜〜

Solve and check: $\begin{cases} y + 3 = 2x \\ 3x^2 = 4 + xy \end{cases}$

How To Proceed

1. In the first-degree equation, solve for one variable in terms of the other.

2. In the second-degree equation, substitute the resulting expression to eliminate one variable.

3. Solve the resulting quadratic equation to obtain two values of the remaining variable.

4. Substitute each of the resulting two values in the equation found in (1) to obtain the corresponding values of the variable that had been eliminated.

5. Group the *two* common ordered number pairs as your answer.

6. Check in the original equations. (Check each of the ordered number pairs in each of the original equations, a total of four checks.)

Solution

Since $y + 3 = 2x$, then
$$y = 2x - 3$$

In $3x^2 = 4 + xy$, substitute $2x - 3$ for y to obtain $3x^2 = 4 + x(2x - 3)$.

$$3x^2 = 4 + 2x^2 - 3x$$
$$3x^2 - 2x^2 + 3x - 4 = 0$$
$$x^2 + 3x - 4 = 0$$
$$(x + 4)(x - 1) = 0$$

$x + 4 = 0$	$x - 1 = 0$
$x = -4$	$x = 1$

In $y = 2x - 3$, substitute -4 and 1 for x.

If $x = -4$,	If $x = 1$,
$y = 2(-4) - 3$	$y = 2(1) - 3$
$= -11$	$= -1$

Ans.

x	-4	1
y	-11	-1

or

x	y
-4	-11
1	-1

Check for $x = 1$ and $y = -1$:

$y + 3 = 2x$	$3x^2 = 4 + xy$
$(-1) + 3 \overset{?}{=} 2(1)$	$3(1)^2 \overset{?}{=} 4 + (1)(-1)$
$2 = 2$	$3 = 3$

Check for $x = -4$ and $y = -11$:

$y + 3 = 2x$	$3x^2 = 4 + xy$
$(-11) + 3 \overset{?}{=} 2(-4)$	$3(-4)^2 \overset{?}{=} 4 +$
$-8 = -8$	$(-4)(-11)$
	$48 = 48$

Exercises

In 1–30, solve the system of equations; group your answers and check one set.

1. $x^2 + y^2 = 18$
$x = y$

2. $4x^2 + y^2 = 40$
$2x = 3y$

3. $x^2 + y^2 = 41$
$x + y = 9$

4. $x^2 + 3y^2 = 7$
$x - y = 1$

5. $x^2 + y = 5$
$y = x + 5$

6. $x^2 + 3 = y$
$y = 5 - x$

7. $3x^2 + y^2 = 12$
$\quad$ $4x + y = 1$

8. $xy = 8$
$\quad$ $y = x + 2$

9. $x^2 - xy = 10$
$\quad$ $x + y = 8$

10. $y^2 = 2xy + 3$
$\quad$ $y = x - 2$

11. $x - 2y = 0$
$\quad$ $5xy - x^2 = 54$

12. $2x^2 - y^2 = 31$
$\quad$ $2x - y = 9$

13. $2x^2 - y^2 - 2 = 0$
$\quad$ $2x - y - 2 = 0$

14. $x^2 = 2y + 10$
$\quad$ $3x - y = 9$

15. $x^2 - 3y^2 = 13$
$\quad$ $1 + 2y = x$

16. $x^2 + y^2 = 10$
$\quad$ $2x - y = 5$

17. $x^2 - 3y = 7$
$\quad$ $2x - y = 4$

18. $x^2 = 2y + 6$
$\quad$ $5x - y = 15$

19. $x^2 - 3y^2 = 6$
$\quad$ $x + 2y = -1$

20. $2x^2 = 2 - y^2$
$\quad$ $2x - y = -2$

21. $x^2 + y^2 - 10y = 24$
$\quad$ $y = x - 2$

22. $x^2 - 2y = 11$
$\quad$ $x = y + 4$

23. $x^2 + y^2 = 25$
$\quad$ $y = 2x + 5$

24. $y^2 + 4x = 21$
$\quad$ $y - 2x + 3 = 0$

25. $3x^2 - xy = 3$
$\quad$ $6x - y = 10$

26. $y^2 + xy = 6$
$\quad$ $3y = x + 2$

27. $x^2 - xy - x = 18$
$\quad$ $x + y = -1$

28. $x^2 - xy + y^2 = 12$
$\quad$ $x - y = 2$

29. $x^2 - xy + y = 7$
$\quad$ $2y + x = 5$

30. $3xy + y^2 = 4$
$\quad$ $x + y = 3$

In 31–33, find the solution set of the system and show that, in the ordered pairs (x, y) of the solution set, x and y are not both real numbers.

31. $xy = 8$
$\quad$ $y = -x$

32. $y = x^2 - 5$
$\quad$ $y = -6$

33. $x^2 + y^2 = 4$
$\quad$ $2y = 5$

11. Solving a Quadratic-Quadratic System of Equations Consisting of Two Second-Degree Equations

Recall that in solving a system of linear equations, the methods of addition, subtraction, and substitution are used. These methods are also applied to the solution of many systems of second-degree equations. In the first model problem, the method of subtraction is used; in the second model problem, the method of substitution is applied.

~~~~~~~~~ *MODEL PROBLEMS* ~~~~~~~~~

1. Solve and check: $\begin{cases} 2x^2 + 3y^2 = 17 \\ x^2 + y^2 = 7 \end{cases}$

How To Proceed

1. For the given system, use the method of subtraction to eliminate one variable.

Solution

1. Since $x^2 + y^2 = 7$, then

$$3x^2 + 3y^2 = 21$$

Subtract: $\underline{2x^2 + 3y^2 = 17}$

$\qquad\qquad x^2 \qquad\quad = 4$

2. Solve the resulting equation to obtain two values of the remaining variable.

2. $x^2 = 4$. Thus, $x = \pm 2$.

3. Substitute each of the resulting values in a given equation to obtain corresponding values of the other variable.

3. In $x^2 + y^2 = 7$, substitute ± 2 for x. If $x = 2$, then $2^2 + y^2 = 7$. Transposing, $y^2 = 3$; $y = \pm\sqrt{3}$. If $x = -2$, then $(-2)^2 + y^2 = 7$. Transposing, $y^2 = 3$; $y = \pm\sqrt{3}$.

4. Group the *four* common ordered number pairs as your answer.

4.

x	2	2	-2	-2
y	$\sqrt{3}$	$-\sqrt{3}$	$\sqrt{3}$	$-\sqrt{3}$

or $\{(2, \sqrt{3}), (2, -\sqrt{3}), (-2, \sqrt{3}), (-2, -\sqrt{3})\}$ *Ans.*

5. Check in the original equations. (Check each of the common ordered number pairs in each of the original equations, a total of eight checks.)

5. The following check is for the first ordered pair, $(2, \sqrt{3})$. The check of the remaining pairs is left to the student.

$$2x^2 + 3y^2 = 17 \qquad\qquad x^2 + y^2 = 7$$
$$2(2^2) + 3(\sqrt{3})^2 \overset{?}{=} 17 \qquad 2^2 + (\sqrt{3})^2 \overset{?}{=} 7$$
$$8 + 9 \overset{?}{=} 17 \qquad\qquad 4 + 3 \overset{?}{=} 7$$
$$17 = 17 \qquad\qquad 7 = 7$$

2. Solve and check: $\begin{cases} x^2 - y^2 = 5 \\ xy = 6 \end{cases}$

Solution:

1. Since $xy = 6$, then $y = \dfrac{6}{x}$.

2. Substitute $\dfrac{6}{x}$ for y in $x^2 - y^2 = 5$ and solve.

$$x^2 - \left(\frac{6}{x}\right)^2 = 5$$

$$x^2 - \frac{36}{x^2} = 5$$

$\mathbf{M}_{x^2}:$ $\qquad x^4 - 36 = 5x^2$

Equate to 0: $\quad x^4 - 5x^2 - 36 = 0$

Factor: $(x^2 - 9)(x^2 + 4) = 0$

$x^2 - 9 = 0 \qquad | \qquad x^2 + 4 = 0$

$x^2 = 9 \qquad\qquad x^2 = -4$

$x = \pm 3 \qquad\qquad x = \pm\sqrt{-4} = \pm 2i$

3. In $xy = 6$, substitute 3, -3, $2i$, and $-2i$ for x to obtain corresponding values for y: If $x = 3$, then $y = 2$; if $x = -3$, then $y = -2$; if $x = 2i$, then $y = -3i$; if $x = -2i$, then $y = 3i$.

4.
x	3	-3	$2i$	$-2i$
y	2	-2	$-3i$	$3i$

or $\{(3, 2), (-3, -2), (2i, -3i), (-2i, 3i)\}$ *Ans.*

5. Check in the original equations. (The check of each of the four ordered number pairs in each of the original equations, a total of eight checks, is left to the student.)

Exercises

In 1–12, solve the system of equations; group your answers and check one set.

1. $x^2 + y^2 = 5$
   $x^2 - y^2 = 3$

2. $x^2 + y^2 = 8$
   $x^2 - y^2 = 2$

3. $x^2 + 2y^2 = 27$
   $x^2 - 2y^2 = 23$

4. $3x^2 + 2y^2 = 19$
   $3x^2 + y^2 = 17$

5. $4x^2 + 2y^2 = 19$
   $8x^2 + 3y^2 = 29$

6. $2x^2 + 3y^2 = 47$
   $3x^2 - 2y^2 = 38$

7. $x^2 + y^2 = 10$
   $xy = 3$

8. $x^2 + 2y^2 = 18$
   $xy = 6$

9. $x^2 + 5y^2 = 25$
   $x^2 + y^2 = 9$

10. $2x^2 + 3y^2 = 9$.
    $x^2 - y^2 = 2$

11. $x^2 + y^2 = 25$
    $3x^2 - 2y^2 = 30$

12. $2x^2 + 3y^2 = 23$
    $3x^2 - y^2 = 7$

In 13–16, solve the system of two equations in which one of the equations is $x^2 + y^2 = 25$ and the remaining equation is:

13. $x^2 - 4y = 4$ 14. $y^2 = 5x + 1$ 15. $xy = 12$ 16. $xy = -12$

12. Number Problems Involving Quadratic Equations

MODEL PROBLEM

Find three positive consecutive odd integers such that twice the square of the first is one less than the product of the second and the third.

Solution: Let $x =$ the first consecutive odd integer.
Then $x + 2 =$ the second consecutive odd integer,
and $x + 4 =$ the third consecutive odd integer.
Since twice the square of the first is one less than the product of the other two, then

$$2x^2 = (x+2)(x+4) - 1$$
$$2x^2 = x^2 + 6x + 8 - 1$$
$$x^2 - 6x - 7 = 0$$
$$(x-7)(x+1) = 0$$

$$x - 7 = 0 \quad | \quad x + 1 = 0$$
$$x = 7 \quad | \quad x = -1$$

The root -1 is rejected since the problem calls for positive integers. Since $x = 7$, then $x + 2 = 9$ and $x + 4 = 11$.

Answer: $7, 9, 11$

~~~~~~

Exercises

1. If 4 is subtracted from 9 times a certain number, the result is equal to 2 times the square of the number. Find the number.
2. The larger of two integers exceeds the smaller by 3. The sum of the squares of the two integers is 89. Find the integers.
3. Find three consecutive positive odd integers such that the square of the first exceeds 6 times the sum of the second and third by 9.
4. The sum of the reciprocals of two consecutive integers is $\frac{5}{6}$. Find the integers.
5. The sum of two positive integers is 10. The difference of their reciprocals is $\frac{3}{8}$. Find both positive integers.
6. Two positive integers are in the ratio 1 : 2. If their product is added to their sum, the result is 5. Find the integers.

13. Area Problems Involving Quadratic Equations

In this and succeeding sections, we will consider the solution of quadratic equations in verbal problems involving formulas and rules having relationships of the form $XY = Z$. In section 13, the formula of this type to be studied is the area formula, $LW = A$. In section 14, the motion formula, $D = RT$, is applied to the solution of verbal problems. Sections 15 and 16 involve the application of the cost formula, $NP = C$, to "business problems" and the work formula, $RT = W$, to problems where people work together.

Note that all of these formulas are relationships of the general form $XY = Z$. The number of such formulas in mathematics and science is a large one and only a few of these are listed in the following table:

TABLE OF FORMULAS AND RULES HAVING RELATIONSHIPS OF THE FORM $XY = Z$

Formula	Rule
$LW = A$	Length of a rectangle × Width of the rectangle = Area of the rectangle
$RT = D$	Rate of speed × Time of travel = Distance traveled
$NP = C$	Number of units × Price of each = Cost of the units
$RT = W$	Rate of work × Time of work = Work accomplished
$PR = I$	Principal × Rate of interest = Interest earned
$BR = P$	Base × Rate = Percentage
$SN = D$	Scale of map × Number of units in a map length = actual Distance
$FD = N$	Value of a Fraction × Denominator = Numerator
$PV = k$	Pressure of a confined gas × Volume of the gas = Constant (Boyle's Law)
$WD = M$	Weight × Distance from fulcrum = Moment of the weight

~~~~~~~~~~~~~~~ *MODEL PROBLEMS* ~~~~~~~~~~~~~~~

1. The perimeter of a rectangle is 16 inches and its area is 15 square inches. Find the dimensions of the rectangle.

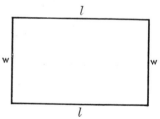

Solution: Let $l =$ length of the rectangle in inches.

$w =$ width of the rectangle in inches.

Then $2l + 2w =$ perimeter of the rectangle in inches.

$lw =$ area of the rectangle in square inches.

Since the area is 15 square inches, then $lw = 15$.
Since the perimeter is 16 inches, then $2l + 2w = 16$

$$D_2 : l + w = 8$$
$$w = 8 - l$$

In equation $lw = 15$, substitute $(8 - l)$ for w.

$$l(8 - l) = 15$$
Equate to 0: $8l - l^2 - 15 = 0$
$$l^2 - 8l + 15 = 0$$

Factor: $(l-5)(l-3)=0$

$$l-5=0 \quad | \quad l-3=0$$
$$l=5 \quad | \quad l=3$$
$$w=3 \quad | \quad w=5$$

Answer: The length is 5 inches and the width is 3 inches.
Or, the length is 3 inches and the width is 5 inches.

2. A rectangular lawn is 40 feet by 50 feet. How wide a uniform strip has been mowed around the edge if $\frac{3}{10}$ of the lawn has not yet been mowed?

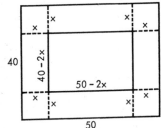

Solution: Let $x =$ width of the uniform strip in feet.

Then $50-2x =$ one side of rectangle not mowed in feet.

And $40-2x =$ other side of rectangle not mowed in feet.

Note that the inner rectangle is the area that has not yet been mowed. Since the area of the inner rectangle is $\frac{3}{10}$ of the area of the lawn,

$$(50-2x)(40-2x)=\tfrac{3}{10}(50 \times 40)$$
$$2000-180x+4x^2=600$$

Equate to 0: $4x^2-180x+1400=0$
$$x^2-45x+350=0$$

Factor: $(x-10)(x-35)=0$
$$x=10 \quad | \quad x=35 \quad \text{Impossible}$$

Answer: Strip is 10 feet wide.

~~~~~~

Exercises

In 1–4, find the dimensions of a rectangle whose width in inches is represented by w, whose length in inches is represented by $w+3$, and whose area in square inches is:

1. 10   **2.** 40   **3.** 70   **4.** 6.75

In 5–8, find the dimensions of a rectangle whose area is 72 square feet and whose perimeter in feet is:

5. 34   **6.** 36   **7.** 54   **8.** 76

In 9–12, find the dimensions of a rectangle whose perimeter in yards is 32 and whose area in square yards is:

9. 15   **10.** 63   **11.** 60   **12.** 63.75

13. The area of a rectangle is 600 square inches. Find the dimensions of the rectangle if they are in the ratio of 2 : 3.

14. A rectangular lot is 50 feet wide and 60 feet long. If both the width and the length are increased by the same amount, the area is increased by 1200 square feet. Find the amount by which both the width and the length are increased.

15. A rectangular lawn is 60 feet by 80 feet. How wide a uniform strip must be cut around the edge when mowing the grass in order that half of the grass be cut?

16. A picture 9 inches by 12 inches is surrounded by a frame of uniform width. If the area of the frame exceeds the area of the picture by 124 square inches, find the width of the frame.

In 17–20, the width of the rectangle is 2 inches more than the length. Find its length to the nearest tenth of an inch if the area in square inches is:

17. 5 **18.** 12 **19.** 20 **20.** 32

In 21–24, one side of a square is increased 2 feet and the adjacent side is decreased 3 feet. Find the side of the square in feet if the resulting rectangle has an area in square feet of:

21. 24 **22.** 66 **23.** 126 **24.** 29.75

25. A floor can be covered with 1728 small square tiles. If tiles 2 inches longer on each side are used, the floor can be covered with 432 tiles. Find the length of each side of the smaller tile.

26. The altitude of a triangle exceeds the base by 4 inches. If the area of the triangle is 30 square inches, find the base and altitude of the triangle.

27. A rectangular piece of cardboard is twice as long as it is wide. From each of its four corners a square piece 2 inches on a side is cut out. The flaps are then turned up to form an uncovered box.

   a. If the length of the shorter side of the original piece of cardboard is represented by x, express the volume V of the box in terms of x.
   b. If $V = 320$ cubic inches, find x.

14. Motion Problems Involving Quadratic Equations

~~~~~~~~~~~~~~ *MODEL PROBLEM* ~~~~~~~~~~~~~~

A train made a trip of 600 miles between two cities. If it had averaged 10 miles per hour more, it would have required 2 hours less to make the trip. Find the rate of speed of the train.

Method 1: Apply $D = RT$.

Solution: Let $r =$ rate of speed of the train in miles per hour (mph).

	(mph) Rate	×	(hr.) Time	=	(mi.) Distance
Slow trip	r		t		600
Fast trip	$(r+10)$		$(t-2)$		600

For each trip, the distance was 600 miles.

$$(r+10)(t-2) = 600$$
$$rt + 10t - 2r - 20 = 600$$
$$600 + 10t - 2r - 20 = 600 \quad (\text{since } rt = 600)$$
$$10t - 2r - 20 = 0$$

Since $rt = 600$, then $\dfrac{600}{r}$ may be substituted for t.

Equate to 0: $\quad 10\left(\dfrac{600}{r}\right) - 2r - 20 = 0$

$\text{M}_r: \quad 6000 - 2r^2 - 20r = 0$
$$2r^2 + 20r - 6000 = 0$$
$\text{D}_2: \quad r^2 + 10r - 3000 = 0$
Factor: $\quad (r-50)(r+60) = 0$

$r - 50 = 0 \quad | \quad r + 60 = 0$
$r = 50 \quad | \quad r = -60 \quad \text{Reject}$

Answer: The rate of speed of the train was 50 miles per hour.

Method 2: Apply $T = \dfrac{D}{R}$

Solution: If r and $r + 10$ represent the rates of the train in mph, the following is obtained:

Time for slow trip is 2 hours more than time for fast trip.

$$\text{M}_{r(r+10)}: \quad \frac{600}{r} = \frac{600}{r+10} + 2$$

Exercises

1. Two cars made the same trip of 200 miles. One traveled 15 miles an hour faster than the other and took 3 hours less to make the trip. Find the rate of each car.

2. A salesman made a trip of 90 miles to see a customer and returned home. On his return trip, he traveled 4 miles per hour faster than on his trip out and made it in 15 minutes less time. Find his rate each way.

3. Two men, A and B, traveled 96 miles and 100 miles respectively. A's average rate was 8 miles an hour less than B's, and A's trip took one-half hour more than B's. Find the average rate of each.

4. A woman makes a trip of 135 miles. By traveling 5 miles an hour faster, she can arrive 18 minutes earlier. Find both rates.

5. Two trains made the same run of 300 miles. One traveled 10 miles an hour faster than the other and used $1\frac{1}{2}$ hours less time. Find the rate at which each train traveled.

6. A train traveling at 8 miles an hour less than its usual rate arrives at its destination 5 hours late. The destination was 800 miles from the starting point. What was the usual rate of the train?

7. Sam drove 140 miles in $\frac{1}{2}$ hour less time than it took Tom to drive 176 miles. Sam's rate was 4 miles per hour less than Tom's rate. Find the rate of each.

8. On a 75-mile trip, Miss Jones' average rate for the first 15 miles was 10 miles per hour less than her average rate for the remainder of the trip. Her time for the entire trip was two hours. Find her average rate for the first 15 miles.

15. Business Problems Involving Quadratic Equations

⁓⁓⁓⁓⁓⁓⁓ *MODEL PROBLEM* ⁓⁓⁓⁓⁓⁓⁓

Some girls rented a cottage for $80. Just before they moved in, another girl joined them. This reduced by $4 the amount of rent each of the original group of girls had expected to pay. How many girls were in the original group?

Method 1: Apply $NS = T$.

Solution: Let n = number of girls in the original group.

And r = rent each girl was to pay in dollars.

	(of girls) Number $\times$	($) Share of rent $=$	($) Total rent
Original group	n	r	nr
New group	$(n+1)$	$(r-4)$	$(n+1)(r-4)$

Since the rent is $80, then $nr = 80$ and $(n + 1)(r - 4) = 80$.

$$(n + 1)(r - 4) = 80$$
$$nr + r - 4n - 4 = 80$$
$$80 + r - 4n - 4 = 80$$
$$r = 4n + 4$$

Substitute $4n + 4$ for r in the equation $nr = 80$.

$$n(4n + 4) = 80$$

Equate to 0: $4n^2 + 4n - 80 = 0$

$$n^2 + n - 20 = 0$$

Factor: $(n + 5)(n - 4) = 0$

$n + 5 = 0$	$n - 4 = 0$
$n = -5$	$n = 4$
Reject	

Answer: There were four girls in the original group.

Method 2: Apply $S = \dfrac{T}{N}$.

Solution: If n and $n + 1$ represent respectively the number of girls in the original group and in the new group, the following is obtained:

The new rent for each girl was $4 less than the old rent.

$$\text{M}_{n(n+1)}: \quad \frac{80}{n + 1} = \frac{80}{n} - 4$$

The remainder of the solution is the same as the previous solution.

Exercises

1. A group of boys agreed to buy a car for $900. Just before they paid for the car, 2 more boys joined the group. This reduced the amount that each boy had to pay by $75. How many boys were in the original group?

2. A man buys a certain number of shares of stock for $528. Had he bought the stock when each share was $2 less, he could have purchased 2 more shares for the same amount of money. How many shares did he buy?

3. A man worked a certain number of days to earn $300. If he had received $3 less per day, he would have had to work 5 days longer to earn the same amount. How many days did he work?

4. A dealer bought a number of birds for $440. After 5 birds had died, he sold the rest of the birds at a profit of $2 each, thereby making $60 on the whole transaction. How many birds did he buy?

5. At a certain school, the total receipts for a junior dance were \$75. If 5 more couples had attended the dance, the price per couple could have been reduced a half dollar without causing any change in the total receipts. What was the price per couple?

6. A workman received \$160 for a certain number of days' work. If he had received \$4 less per day, it would have taken him 2 days longer to earn the same amount. How many days did he work?

16. Work Problems Involving Quadratic Equations

~~~~~~~~~~~~~~ *MODEL PROBLEM* ~~~~~~~~~~~~~~

It takes Thomas 3 hours less time to paint a fence than it takes Larry. If the two boys work together, they can paint the fence in 2 hours. How many hours would each boy, working alone, need to paint the fence?

Solution: Let $x =$ number of hours Larry needs to do the job alone.

Then $x - 3 =$ number of hours Thomas needs to do the job alone.

	(part of job per hr.) Rate of work	$\times$ (hr.) Time of work $=$	(part of job) Work done
Larry	$\dfrac{1}{x}$	2	$\dfrac{2}{x}$
Thomas	$\dfrac{1}{x-3}$	2	$\dfrac{2}{x-3}$

If the job is finished, the sum of the fractional parts done by each boy must equal 1.

$$\text{Hence, } \frac{2}{x} + \frac{2}{x-3} = 1$$

Multiply each side by the L.C.D., which is $x(x-3)$.

$$2(x-3) + 2x = x(x-3)$$
$$2x - 6 + 2x = x^2 - 3x$$
Equate to 0: $x^2 - 7x + 6 = 0$

$$\text{Factor:} \quad (x-1)(x-6)=0$$
$$x=1 \quad | \quad x=6$$
$$\text{Reject} \quad |$$

Answer: Larry requires 6 hours; Thomas requires 3 hours.

Exercises

1. It takes Bill 6 hours longer than John to plow a certain field. Together they can plow it in 4 hours. How long would it take each man alone to plow the field?
2. A company contracted to make a certain number of planes. Its two factories can make the planes in 12 days. Working alone, one factory requires 7 days longer than the other. Find the time in which each factory alone can fulfill the contract.
3. Sally and Wilma working together can complete a job in $1\frac{1}{3}$ hours. If it takes Sally working alone 2 hours less time than Wilma to do the job, find the time required by each woman working alone.
4. It takes Tom three hours longer to do a certain job than it takes his brother Bill. They worked together for three hours; then Tom left and Bill finished the job in one hour. How many hours would it have taken Bill to do the job alone?

17. Right Triangle Problems Involving Quadratic Equations

~~~~~~~~~~~~ *MODEL PROBLEM* ~~~~~~~~~~~~

A and *B* start from the same point and travel along roads that are at right angles to each other. *A* travels 3 miles an hour faster than *B*. At the end of 2 hours, they are 30 miles apart. Find their rates.

Solution: Let $r =$ rate of *B* in mph.
Then $r + 3 =$ rate of *A* in mph.

	(mph) Rate	$\times$	(hr.) Time	$=$	(mi.) Distance
A	$r + 3$		2		$2r + 6$
B	r		2		$2r$

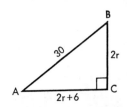

Apply the theorem of Pythagoras: $(\text{leg})^2 + (\text{leg})^2 = (\text{hypotenuse})^2$

$$(2r)^2 + (2r+6)^2 = (30)^2$$
$$4r^2 + 4r^2 + 24r + 36 = 900$$

Equate to 0: $\quad 8r^2 + 24r - 864 = 0$
$$r^2 + 3r - 108 = 0$$

Factor: $\quad (r-9)(r+12) = 0$

$r - 9 = 0$	$r + 12 = 0$
$r = 9$	$r = -12$
$r + 3 = 12$	Reject

Answer: A's rate is 12 mph; B's rate is 9 mph.

Exercises

1. One leg of a right triangle exceeds the other leg by 5 inches. The hypotenuse is 25 inches. Find the length of each leg of the triangle.
2. The hypotenuse of a right triangle is 2 inches longer than one leg and 4 inches longer than the other leg. Find the length of each side of the triangle.
3. The perimeter of a right triangle is 40 inches. If the hypotenuse is 17 inches, find the length of each leg.
4. Find the dimensions of a rectangle if its perimeter is 34 feet and its diagonal is 13 feet.
5. The hypotenuse of a right triangle exceeds the longer of the two legs by 2. If the perimeter of the triangle is 40, find the lengths of the three sides of the triangle.
6. Peter and William start from the point of intersection of two roads which are at right angles to each other. Peter travels along one road at the rate of 5 miles per hour and William travels along the other road at the rate of 12 miles per hour. In how many hours will they be 26 miles apart?
7. A ship sails due east from a certain point at a speed of 16 mph. Two hours later, a ship leaves the same point and sails due north at a speed of 20 mph. In how many hours after the first ship starts will the two ships be 100 miles apart?

In 8–10, A and B start from the same point and travel along straight roads that are at right angles to each other. Find their rates if:

8. A travels 7 miles per hour faster than B and, at the end of an hour, they are 13 miles apart.
9. A travels 7 miles an hour slower than B and, at the end of 2 hours, they are 34 miles apart.
10. The ratio of A's speed to B's speed is $3:4$ and, at the end of 5 hours, they are 125 miles apart.

CHAPTER XIII

GRAPHS OF QUADRATIC FUNCTIONS, RELATIONS, EQUATIONS, AND INEQUALITIES

1. The Parabola as a Graph

PARABOLAS OF THE FORM $y = ax^2 + bx + c$

A quadratic function is a function whose values are given by a quadratic polynomial of the form $ax^2 + bx + c$, where a, b, and c are real numbers, $a \neq 0$.

A quadratic function may be defined as:
1. the equation $y = ax^2 + bx + c$, $a \neq 0$
2. the set $\{(x, y) \mid y = ax^2 + bx + c, a \neq 0\}$
3. $f(x) = ax^2 + bx + c$, $a \neq 0$, using function notation

If, in the quadratic equation $y = ax^2 + bx + c$, a value is assigned to x, there is one and only one corresponding value of y. The set of ordered pairs (x, y) that satisfy $y = ax^2 + bx + c$ defines a function. If the ordered pairs of the solution set of $y = ax^2 + bx + c$ are graphed, the resulting points can be joined to form a curve called a *parabola*. This is illustrated in the graphing of the equation $y = x^2 - 4x + 3$, which follows.

In the discussions to follow, we will use the expression "***the parabola*** $y = ax^2 + bx + c$" as the simplified form of the expression "the parabola that is the graph of $y = ax^2 + bx + c$, where a, b, and c are real numbers, $a \neq 0$."

We begin by graphing the parabola $y = x^2 - 4x + 3$ for values of x from -1 to 5 inclusive. We will then consider several important features and properties of the parabola.

〜〜〜〜〜〜〜〜〜〜 *MODEL PROBLEM* 〜〜〜〜〜〜〜〜〜〜

Draw the graph of $y = x^2 - 4x + 3$ for values of x from -1 to 5 inclusive.

How To Proceed

1. Obtain a *table of ordered pairs* by substituting a set of consecutive integral values for x and finding the corresponding values of y.

2. Plot the points whose coordinates represent the ordered pairs (x, y) in the table. (Note each of the points in Fig. 1.)

3. Join the points with a smooth curve. The resulting curve, the graph of $y = x^2 - 4x + 3$, is a *parabola*.

Solution

TABLE OF ORDERED PAIRS

x	$x^2 - 4x + 3 = y$	
-1	$1 + \ 4 + 3$	8
0	$0 + \ 0 + 3$	3
1	$1 - \ 4 + 3$	0
2	$4 - \ 8 + 3$	-1
3	$9 - 12 + 3$	0
4	$16 - 16 + 3$	3
5	$25 - 20 + 3$	8

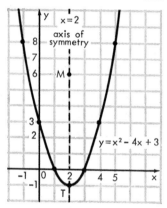

Fig. 1

A study of the table of values and the graph of $y = x^2 - 4x + 3$ in Fig. 1 leads to the following observations and conclusions:

1. As x increases from -1 to 2, y decreases from 8 to -1; then as x continues to increase from 2 to 5, y increases from -1 to 8.

2. The point $T(2, -1)$, where the values of y stop decreasing and begin to increase, is called the **turning point**, or **vertex**, of the parabola. Note that T is the lowest point of the graph. The point T is called the **minimum point** because y or its equivalent expression $x^2 - 4x + 3$ has its minimum or smallest value, -1, at T.

3. The **axis of symmetry** $(\overleftrightarrow{TM})$ of the parabola is the line $x = 2$. Note that the axis of symmetry passes through the turning point T and is parallel to the y-axis. If the parabola were folded over on the axis of symmetry, its left half would coincide with its right half.

MAXIMUM AND MINIMUM POINTS OF A PARABOLA $y = ax^2 + bx + c$

We shall now graph the parabola, $y = -x^2 + 4x - 3$ and consider several of its important features and properties. Note in the table of ordered pairs that the set of consecutive integral values substituted for x is the same as that used in the graphing of the parabola $y = x^2 - 4x + 3$.

TABLE OF ORDERED PAIRS

x	$-x^2 + 4x - 3 = y$	
-1	$-1 - 4 - 3$	-8
0	$-0 + 0 - 3$	-3
1	$-1 + 4 - 3$	0
2	$-4 + 8 - 3$	1
3	$-9 + 12 - 3$	0
4	$-16 + 16 - 3$	-3
5	$-25 + 20 - 3$	-8

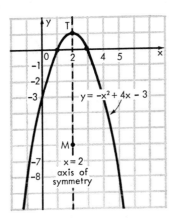

Fig. 2

Compare the expressions $x^2 - 4x + 3$ and $-x^2 + 4x - 3$ and note that either one is the negative of the other. Hence, for any assigned value of x, the resulting values of the expressions are negatives of each other. Verify this by examining the tables of ordered pairs that were used to graph $y = x^2 - 4x + 3$ and $y = -x^2 + 4x - 3$.

A study of the table of values and the graph of $y = -x^2 + 4x - 3$ in Fig. 2 leads to the following observations and conclusions:

1. As x increases from -1 to 2, y increases from -8 to 1; then as x continues to increase from 2 to 5, y decreases from 1 to -8.
2. The point $T(2, 1)$, where the values of y stop increasing and begin to decrease, is the *turning point*, or *vertex*, of the parabola. Note that T is the highest point of the graph. The point T is called the **maximum point** because y or its equivalent expression $-x^2 + 4x - 3$ has its maximum or greatest value, $+1$, at T.
3. The *axis of symmetry* $(\overleftrightarrow{TM})$ of the parabola is the line $x = 2$. Here again, the axis of symmetry through the turning point T and is parallel to the y-axis.

An examination of the two parabola graphs in Figs. 1 and 2 shows that:

The parabola $y = x^2 - 4x + 3$, in which the coefficient of x^2 is $+1$, has a *minimum turning point* and *opens upward*.

The parabola $y = -x^2 + 4x - 3$, in which the coefficient of x^2 is -1, has a *maximum turning point* and *opens downward*.

The two parabolas that we have considered in Figs. 1 and 2 illustrate the following:

Rule 1. If $y = ax^2 + bx + c$ and a is positive, $a > 0$, the graph of the equation is a parabola that *opens upward and has a minimum turning point* (Fig. 3).

Rule 2. If $y = ax^2 + bx + c$ and a is negative, $a < 0$, the graph of the equation is a parabola that *opens downward and has a maximum turning point* (Fig. 4).

Graph of $y = ax^2 + bx + c$
$a > 0$

Graph of $y = ax^2 + bx + c$
$a < 0$

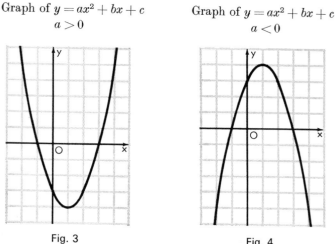

Fig. 3   Fig. 4

THE MEANING OF THE EXPRESSION "QUADRATIC FUNCTION $ax^2 + bx + c$"

Examine Figs. 3 and 4 again. Note that in the case of any parabola whose equation is of the form $y = ax^2 + bx + c$, for each value of x there is one and only one value of y. If the vertical test of a function is applied by drawing vertical lines crossing either parabola, the vertical lines cannot pass through more than one point. Hence, the set of all ordered pairs that satisfy $y = ax^2 + bx + c$ is a *relation that is a function*.

Keep in mind that the expression "*quadratic function $ax^2 + bx + c$*" is a simplified form of the expression "quadratic function that is the set of ordered pairs satisfying $y = ax^2 + bx + c$ where a, b, and c are real numbers, $a \neq 0$."

AXIS OF SYMMETRY OF A PARABOLA $y = ax^2 + bx + c$

Recall that the *axis of symmetry of a parabola* is the line over which one-half of the parabola may be folded so that both halves can be made to coincide. The equation of the axis of symmetry can be found by applying the following rule:

Rule. The equation $x = -\dfrac{b}{2a}$ is the equation of the axis of symmetry of the parabola $y = ax^2 + bx + c$.

See the proof of the rule on pages 744–745.

Thus, if $y = x^2 - 4x + 3$, $a = 1$ and $b = -4$. Using $x = -\dfrac{b}{2a}$ to find the equation of the axis of symmetry of the parabola $y = x^2 - 4x + 3$, then $x = -\dfrac{-4}{2}$, or $x = 2$. In the case of the parabola $y = -x^2 + 4x - 3$, the equation of the axis of symmetry is $x = -\dfrac{4}{-2}$ or $x = 2$. By examining Fig. 5, verify that the line $x = 2$ is the axis of symmetry of each of the parabolas.

Another kind of symmetry may be seen in Fig. 5. Note that either parabola may be obtained by revolving the other parabola 180° about the x-axis. For this reason, any point on one parabola is a "reflection" through the x-axis of a point on the other parabola. Hence, the x-axis is the axis of symmetry of the combined figure of both parabolas, in the sense that the x-axis is the line over which one parabola can be folded to make it coincide with the other. Think of the x-axis serving as a mirror through which a point on one parabola is reflected to a corresponding "image" point on the other parabola. Thus, the turning point of one parabola (2, 1) is the *mirror image* (or simply *image*) of the turning point of the other parabola (2, −1).

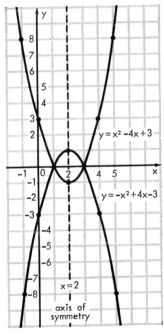

Fig. 5

In parabolas that have a vertical axis of symmetry, the equation of the axis of symmetry is useful in determining the x-values that should be chosen in a table of values needed to graph the parabola. We can now understand why the integral values from −1 to 5 were assigned to x in the graphing of both $y = x^2 - 4x + 3$ and $y = -x^2 + 4x - 3$. The middle value, 2, of the set $\{-1, 0, 1, 2, 3, 4, 5\}$ is the value of x obtainable from the equation of the axis of symmetry. Had more values been needed, the set of consecutive integers from -2 to 6 or from -3 to 7 could be used, keeping 2 as the middle value of the set.

If a problem requires the graphing of a parabola in the form $y = ax^2 + bx + c$, and no set of values is assigned to x, it is desirable to obtain the equation of the axis of symmetry. The value of x thus obtained should be made the middle value of a set consisting of a total of at least 7 consecutive integers.

FINDING THE COORDINATES OF THE TURNING POINT OF THE PARABOLA $y = ax^2 + bx + c$

The turning point of a parabola is one of the points of its axis of symmetry. Hence, the abscissa of the turning point of $y = ax^2 + bx + c$ is $x = -\dfrac{b}{2a}$. The ordinate of the turning point can be determined by substituting $-\dfrac{b}{2a}$ for x in the equation $y = ax^2 + bx + c$.

~~~~~~~~~~ *MODEL PROBLEMS* ~~~~~~~~~~

In 1 and 2, find the equation of the axis of symmetry and the coordinates of the turning point of the parabola.

1. $y = x^2 - 8x + 15$ **2.** $y = -3x^2 + 12x + 7$

How To Proceed	*Solution*	*Solution*
1. State the values of a and b.	$a = 1, b = -8$	$a = -3, b = 12$
2. Find the equation of the axis of symmetry, using $x = -\dfrac{b}{2a}$.	$x = -\dfrac{b}{2a}$ $= -\dfrac{-8}{2} = 4$	$x = -\dfrac{b}{2a}$ $= -\dfrac{12}{-6} = 2$
3. Find the y-coordinate of the turning point by substituting $-\dfrac{b}{2a}$ for x in the equation $y = ax^2 + bx + c$.	$y = x^2 - 8x + 15$ $= 4^2 - 8(4) + 15$ $= 16 - 32 + 15 = -1$ Axis of symmetry, $x = 4$; coordinates of turning point, $(4, -1)$. *Ans.*	$y = -3x^2 + 12x + 7$ $= -3(2^2) + 12(2) + 6$ $= -12 + 24 + 6 = 18$ Axis of symmetry, $x = 2$; coordinates of turning point, $(2, 18)$. *Ans.*

~~~~~~

PARABOLAS OF THE FORM $x = ay^2 + by + c$

The equation $x = ay^2 + by + c$ is obtained by interchanging x and y in the equation $y = ax^2 + bx + c$. When equations of the form $x = ay^2 + by + c$ are graphed, as in Figs. 6 and 7, the graphs are parabolas having an axis of symmetry parallel to the x-axis. The equation of the axis of symmetry of the parabolas of the form $x = ay^2 + by + c$, is $y = -\dfrac{b}{2a}$. The equation $y = -\dfrac{b}{2a}$ is obtained simply by substituting y for x in the equation $x = -\dfrac{b}{2a}$, which we found to be the axis of symmetry of the previous vertical parabolas.

Thus, using $y = -\dfrac{b}{2a}$, we can show that the line $y = 1$ is the axis of symmetry of both the parabola $x = y^2 - 2y$ (Fig. 6) and the parabola $x = -y^2 + 2y$ (Fig. 7).

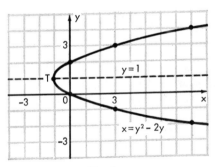

Fig. 6

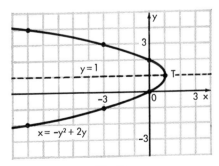

Fig. 7

THE RELATION $\{(x, y)\mid x = ay^2 + by + c\}$ IS NOT A FUNCTION

Note in Figs. 6 and 7 that the parabolas do not meet the vertical line test for a function, since vertical lines may pass through more than one point of each of these parabolas. In general, parabolas of the form $x = ay^2 + by + c$ do not meet the vertical line test of a function. Hence, the set of ordered pairs that satisfy $x = ay^2 + by + c$ is a *relation that is not a function.*

Figs. 6 and 7 illustrate the fact that parabolas of the form $x = ay^2 + by + c$ do not have a maximum or a minimum point. Instead, the turning point or vertex, T, may be a leftmost point, (Fig. 6) or a rightmost point, (Fig. 7).

Summary of the Properties of a Parabola $y = ax^2 + bx + c$

1. If a is positive, $a > 0$, the parabola opens upward and has a minimum turning point.
   If a is negative, $a < 0$, the parabola opens downward and has a maximum turning point.

2. The equation of the axis of symmetry is $x = -\dfrac{b}{2a}$.

   The x-coordinate of the turning point is also equal to $-\dfrac{b}{2a}$.

3. When $a > 0$: From left to right, the values of y decrease until the minimum point is reached; then the values of y increase.
   When $a < 0$: From left to right, the values of y increase until the maximum point is reached; then the values of y decrease.

4. The set of all ordered pairs that satisfy $y = ax^2 + bx + c$ is a relation that is a function.

Summary of the Properties of a Parabola $x = ay^2 + by + c$

1. If a is positive, $a > 0$, the parabola opens to the right and has a leftmost point.
   If a is negative, $a < 0$, the parabola opens to the left and has a rightmost point.

2. The equation of the axis of symmetry is $y = -\dfrac{b}{2a}$.

   The y-coordinate of the turning point is also equal to $-\dfrac{b}{2a}$.

3. The set of all ordered pairs that satisfy $x = ay^2 + by + c$ is a relation that is *not* a function.

Exercises

In 1–13, for the quadratic function: (a) draw a graph using the indicated values of x, (b) mark the turning point with the letter T and state whether it is a minimum or a maximum point, (c) state the coordinates of the turning point, and (d) draw the axis of symmetry and state its equation.

1. $y = x^2$ from $x = -5$ to $x = 5$ **2.** $y = 3x^2$ from $x = -2$ to $x = 2$

3. $y = -2x^2$ from $x = -2$ to $x = 2$ **4.** $y = x^2 - 9$ from $x = -4$ to $x = 4$

5. $y = -x^2 + 4$ from $x = -3$ to $x = 3$

6. $y = x^2 - 4x$ from $x = -2$ to $x = 6$

7. $y = x^2 - 6x + 8$ from $x = 0$ to $x = 6$

8. $y = x^2 - 4x + 3$ from $x = 0$ to $x = 4$

9. $y = -x^2 + 6x - 8$ from $x = 0$ to $x = 6$

10. $y = x^2 - 3x + 2$ from $x = -1$ to $x = 4$

11. $y = -x^2 + x + 2$ from $x = -2$ to $x = 3$

12. $y = 2x^2 - 5x + 2$ from $x = -1$ to $x = 4$

13. $y = -2x^2 + 7x - 3$ from $x = 0$ to $x = 4$

In 14–25, for the quadratic function: (a) prepare a table of values, (b) draw a graph, (c) mark the turning point with the letter T, (d) state the coordinates of the turning point, and (e) draw the axis of symmetry and state its equation.

14. $y = 2x^2$ **15.** $y = -3x^2$ **16.** $y = x^2 - 4$

17. $y = -x^2 + 9$ **18.** $y = x^2 - 6x$ **19.** $y = -x^2 + 4x$

20. $y = x^2 - 4x + 3$ **21.** $y = x^2 - x - 2$ **22.** $y = -x^2 + 3x + 2$

23. $x = 2y^2$ **24.** $x = -y^2$ **25.** $x = y^2 - 4y$

26. Which, if any, of the pairs of x and y values given in the table at the right are *not* roots of $x^2 - 3x = y$?

x	-1	2	3
y	4	2	0

27. The parabola whose equation is $y = ax^2$ passes through the point $(2, 3)$. Find the value of a.

28. The graph of the equation $y = x^2 + 3x + k$ passes through the point $(2, 0)$. Find k.

29. The graph of the equation $x^2 + bx + c = y$ (1) always   (2) sometimes   (3) never   passes through the origin.

In 30–35, give the equation of the axis of symmetry of the graph of the function.

30. $y = x^2 - 6x + 5$ **31.** $y = x^2 + 8x + 7$ **32.** $y = 3x^2 - 6x$

33. $y = x^2 - 16$ **34.** $y = -x^2 - 2x + 3$ **35.** $y = 2x^2 + 5x + 2$

In 36–41, find the turning point of the graph of the function.

36. $y = 4x^2$ **37.** $y = x^2 - 2x - 8$ **38.** $y = x^2 - 6x + 5$

39. $y = x^2 - 3x$ **40.** $y = -x^2 - x + 6$ **41.** $y = 2x^2 + 5x + 2$

2. Studying the Roles That *a*, *b*, and *c* Play in Changing Parabolas of the Form $y = ax^2 + bx + c$

Now we will study how changes in the values of a, b, and c in the equation $y = ax^2 + bx + c$ change parabolas having this form.

CHANGING THE WIDTH OF A PARABOLA BY CHANGING THE VALUE OF *a*

To simplify our discussion, we will study the effect of changing the value of a alone by considering the quadratic function defined by $y = ax^2$. If $y = ax^2$ and $a = 1$, we obtain $y = x^2$. The graph of $y = x^2$ is the parabola shown in Fig. 1.

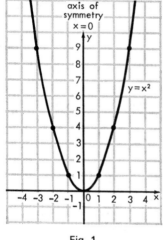

The parabola $y = x^2$ may be obtained by using the following table of ordered pairs and joining the points representing these ordered pairs by a smooth curve (Fig. 1).

TABLE OF
ORDERED PAIRS

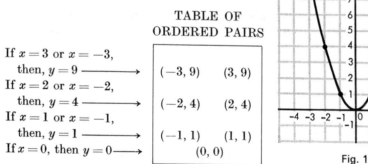

If $x = 3$ or $x = -3$,
   then, $y = 9$ ⟶ $(-3, 9)$ $(3, 9)$
If $x = 2$ or $x = -2$,
   then, $y = 4$ ⟶ $(-2, 4)$ $(2, 4)$
If $x = 1$ or $x = -1$,
   then, $y = 1$ ⟶ $(-1, 1)$ $(1, 1)$
If $x = 0$, then $y = 0$ ⟶ $(0, 0)$

Fig. 1

Note the following properties of the parabola $y = x^2$:
1. The origin, $(0, 0)$, is the vertex of the parabola and a minimum turning point.
2. The y-axis, $x = 0$, is the axis of symmetry of the parabola.
3. Since a is positive, the parabola faces upward.
4. Since $y = x^2$, then for all real values of x, the values of y must be non-negative. Hence, the parabola passes through the origin and is entirely within quadrants I and II; that is, the parabola is above the x-axis and tangent to it.

In Fig. 2, note the parabolas $y = x^2$, $y = 2x^2$, and $y = \frac{1}{2}x^2$, which face upward; also note the parabolas $y = -x^2, y = -2x^2$, and $y = -\frac{1}{2}x^2$, which face downward. Observe that all six parabolas have a turning point, or vertex, which is the origin. The origin serves as the minimum point for the parabolas that face upward and the maximum point for the parabolas that face downward. The y-axis is the axis of symmetry of each parabola. The x-axis is the axis of symmetry for the pair of parabolas $y = 2x^2$ and $y = -2x^2$, the pair $y = x^2$ and $y = -x^2$, and also the pair $y = \frac{1}{2}x^2$ and $y = -\frac{1}{2}x^2$. Note that in each of these pairs, the values of a are opposites, which means the absolute value of a is the same. In each of the pairs, the parabolas are congruent and, for this reason, have the same "width."

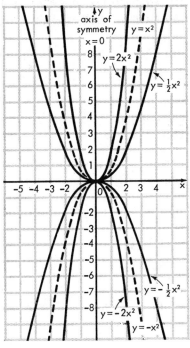

Fig. 2

Note in Fig. 2 that the narrowest pair of parabolas are those having the equations $y = 2x^2$ and $y = -2x^2$. Note further that when the absolute value of a is decreased, the parabolas widen. Thus, the parabolas $y = \frac{1}{2}x^2$ and $y = -\frac{1}{2}x^2$ are wider than the parabolas $y = x^2$ and $y = -x^2$; in turn, the parabolas $y = x^2$ and $y = -x^2$ are wider than the parabolas $y = 2x^2$ and $y = -2x^2$.

We may generalize the role played by a in the changing of the width of parabolas of the form $y = ax^2$ as follows:

Rule. In the quadratic function $y = ax^2$, increasing the absolute value of a, $|a|$, *narrows* the parabola; decreasing $|a|$ *widens* the parabola.

In a more general way, it may be shown that in the quadratic function $y = ax^2 + bx + c$, if the values of b and c are kept constant, increasing the absolute value of a, $|a|$, narrows the parabola; decreasing $|a|$ widens the parabola.

Thus, the parabola $y = 3x^2 + 4x - 5$ is narrower than the parabola $y = x^2 + 4x - 5$.

CHANGING THE VERTICAL POSITION OF A PARABOLA BY CHANGING THE VALUE OF c

In Fig. 3, note that the parabolas $y = \frac{1}{2}x^2 + 2$, $y = \frac{1}{2}x^2$, and $y = \frac{1}{2}x^2 - 2$ have the same axis of symmetry and are congruent. Note, however, that the parabolas differ in their y-intercept: The y-intercept is 2 in the case of $y = \frac{1}{2}x^2 + 2$; -2 in the case of $y = \frac{1}{2}x^2 - 2$; and 0 in the case of $y = \frac{1}{2}x^2$. Since the y-intercept of a graph is the ordinate of the point where the graph intersects the y-axis, $x = 0$. Hence, at this point, to find the y-intercept, simply substitute 0 for x. In the case of the general parabola, $y = ax^2 + bx + c$, if 0 is substituted for x, we see that $y = c$; that is, the y-intercept is c, the constant term.

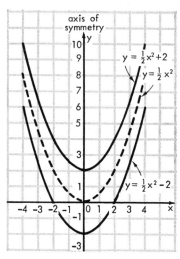

Fig. 3

Hence, increasing the constant term c results in an upward shift in the parabola; decreasing c results in a downward shift. Verify this in Fig. 3 by using transparent paper and making a trace of the parabola $y = \frac{1}{2}x^2$. Note that the trace can be made to coincide with each of the other parabolas, showing that the parabolas are congruent, having the same size and shape. By moving the trace vertically, we can obtain other parabolas such as $y = \frac{1}{2}x^2 + 4$, $y = \frac{1}{2}x^2 - 4$, $y = \frac{1}{2}x^2 + 4.5$, and $y = \frac{1}{2}x^2 - \frac{1}{4}$.

In general, if the equations of parabolas differ only in the constant term, as in the case of the parabola $y = ax^2 + bx + c$ and the parabola $y = ax^2 + bx + c'$, then:

1. The parabolas are congruent.

2. The parabolas have different y-intercepts: c in the case of $y = ax^2 + bx + c$, and c' in the case of $y = ax^2 + bx + c'$.

3. The parabolas have the same axis of symmetry. The reason that the axis of symmetry is the same for the parabolas is that a change in the value of c alone does not affect the equation of the axis of symmetry, $x = -\dfrac{b}{2a}$.

CHANGING THE AXIS OF SYMMETRY OF A PARABOLA

In Fig. 4, note that the parabolas $y = x^2 + 2x + 1$ and $y = x^2 - 2x + 1$ have the same y-intercept and are congruent. Note, however, that the parabolas differ in their axis of symmetry: The axis of symmetry is $x = 1$ in the case of $y = x^2 - 2x + 1$; it is $x = -1$ in the case of $y = x^2 + 2x + 1$. Note also in the two equations that the value of b has changed, while that of a is unchanged.

If a parabola is of the form $y = ax^2 + bx + c$, changing the value of b while keeping the value of a fixed will change the axis of symmetry. The reason is that the value of $-\dfrac{b}{2a}$ must change if there is a change in b and no change in a.

Fig. 4

Exercises

The parabolas shown in the figure at the right represent the graphs of $y = x^2$, $y = -x^2$, $y = \frac{1}{2}x^2$, and $y = -\frac{1}{2}x^2$. In 1–4, using the figure, state the equation represented by:

1. parabola a **2.** parabola b
3. parabola c **4.** parabola d

In 5–13, sketch the graphs of the given equations and explain how a change from one equation to another changes the graph represented by the equation.

5. $y = x^2$, $y = 2x^2$, $y = 3x^2$
6. $y = x^2$, $y = \frac{1}{2}x^2$, $y = \frac{1}{4}x^2$
7. $y = -x^2$, $y = -2x^2$, $y = -3x^2$
8. $y = -x^2$, $y = -\frac{1}{2}x^2$, $y = -\frac{1}{4}x^2$
9. $y = x^2$, $y = x^2 + 2$, $y = x^2 + 4$
10. $y = x^2$, $y = x^2 - 2$, $y = x^2 - 4$
11. $y = -x^2 - 3$, $y = -x^2$,
    $y = -x^2 + 3$

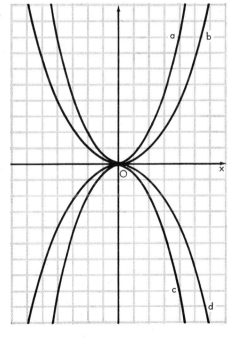

12. $y = x^2 + 2x$, $y = x^2 + 4x$, $y = x^2 - 2x$

13. $y = x^2 + 2x + 1$, $y = x^2 - 2x + 1$, $y = x^2 + 4x + 4$

14. By using the equation $x = -\dfrac{b}{2a}$, show that the axis of symmetry is the same for the parabolas $y = x^2 + 2x$, $y = 2x^2 + 4x$, and $y = -3x^2 - 6x$.

15. Graph $y = x^2$ and $y = 2x^2 - 3$ and show how changes in the coefficient of x^2 and the constant term affect the character of the graph.

16. Graph $y = x^2 + x + 3$ and $y = x^2 + x - 3$ and show how the change in the constant term affects the graph of $y = x^2 + x + 3$.

17. Graph $y = 2x^2 + 4x$ and $y = 2x^2 + 6x$ and show how the change in the coefficient of x affects the graph of $y = 2x^2 + 4x$.

18. Graph $y = 3x^2$ and $y = -3x^2$ and show how the change in the coefficient of x^2 affects the graph of $y = 3x^2$.

19. Graph $y = 3x^2$ and $y = \frac{1}{3}x^2$ and show how the change in the coefficient of x^2 affects the graph of $y = 3x^2$.

In 20–25, find the y-intercept and the equation of the axis of symmetry.

20. $y = x^2 + 9$ **21.** $y = x^2 + 6x + 9$ **22.** $y - 5 = x^2 + 6x + 9$

23. $y = (x - 3)^2$ **24.** $y - 5 = (x - 3)^2$ **25.** $y + 5 = (x - 3)^2$

26. If b and c are unchanged, what effect on the parabola $y = ax^2 + bx + c$ does the changing of the absolute value of a have?

27. If a and b are unchanged, what effect on the parabola $y = ax^2 + bx + c$ does the changing of c have?

28. If a is unchanged, what effect on the parabola $y = ax^2 + bx + c$ does the changing of b have?

29. Show that the coordinates of the vertex of the parabola $y = ax^2 + bx + c$ are

$$\left(-\frac{b}{2a},\ -\frac{b^2 - 4ac}{4a} \right) \quad \text{or} \quad \left(-\frac{b}{2a},\ c - \frac{b^2}{4a} \right).$$

30. Show that the coordinates of the vertex of the parabola $y - k = a(x - h)^2$ are (h, k).

3. Using Parabolas To Solve Quadratic Equations

The quadratic equation, $x^2 = 4x + 5$, can be solved graphically, as in the following model problem. This is done by applying the following rule:

Rule. If the parabola $y = ax^2 + bx + c$ intersects the x-axis, the x-intercepts are the real roots of the quadratic equation $ax^2 + bx + c = 0$.

This rule can be justified in the following manner:

If the parabola $y = ax^2 + bx + c$ intersects the x-axis at the points $(x_1, 0)$ and $(x_2, 0)$, then these points lie on both the parabola and the x-axis. Hence, the ordered pairs $(x_1, 0)$ and $(x_2, 0)$ satisfy the equations $y = ax^2 + bx + c$ and $y = 0$. If 0 is substituted for y, it follows that x_1 and x_2 are the real roots of $ax^2 + bx + c = 0$.

～～～～～～ *MODEL PROBLEM* ～～～～～～

Find the solution set of $x^2 = 4x + 5$ graphically.

How To Proceed	*Solution*
1. Transform the given equation into the form $ax^2 + bx + c = 0$.	$x^2 = 4x + 5$ $x^2 - 4x - 5 = 0$

2. Graph the parabola $y = ax^2 + bx + c$.
3. Determine the real roots of the given equation by finding the x-intercepts. That is, find the x-coordinates of the points where the parabola intersects the x-axis.

Note. The parabola $y = x^2 - 4x - 5$ intersects the x-axis at the points A and B. At these points, $y = 0$. Hence, the x-coordinates of A and B are the real roots of the equation $x^2 - 4x - 5 = 0$ and are also the real roots of the equation $x^2 = 4x + 5$. The x-coordinates of A and B are -1 and 5.

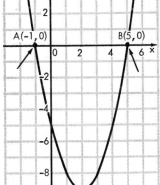

Answer: The solution set is $\{-1, 5\}$.

～～～～～～～～～～～～～～～～～～～～～～～～～～～

USING A PARABOLA $y = ax^2 + bx + c$ TO SOLVE QUADRATIC EQUATIONS OF THE FORM $ax^2 + bx + c = k$

Quadratic equations, such as $x^2 - 4x - 5 = 7$ and $x^2 - 4x - 5 = -5$, are of the form $ax^2 + bx + c = k$, where k is a constant. The real roots of such equations can be obtained graphically. In general, to solve graphically a quadratic equation of the form $ax^2 + bx + c = k$, use the following procedure:

Procedure:
1. **Graph the parabola $y = ax^2 + bx + c$.**
2. **On the same set of axes, graph the line $y = k$.**
3. **Determine the real roots of the given equation by finding the point(s) of intersection of the two graphs.**

Recall that $\{-1, 5\}$, the solution set of $x^2 - 4x - 5 = 0$, was found by noting points A and B, the intersection of the parabola $y = x^2 - 4x - 5 = 0$ and the x-axis, $y = 0$.

Using the figure at the right, let us now discover where the parabola $y = x^2 - 4x - 5$ intersects other lines of the form $y = k$, where k is a constant. Note that the parabola $y = x^2 - 4x - 5$ and the line $y = 7$ intersect at points C and D, whose x-coordinates are -2 and 6. It follows that $\{-2, 6\}$ is the solution set of $x^2 - 4x - 5 = 7$. Verify this by solving $x^2 - 4x - 5 = 7$ algebraically. Note further on the graph that 0 and 4, the roots of the equation $x^2 - 4x - 5 = -5$, are the x-coordinates of E and F, the points where the parabola $y = x^2 - 4x - 5$ intersects the line $y = -5$.

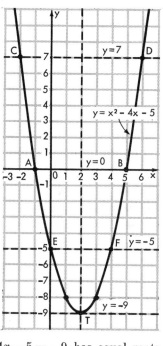

The parabola $y = x^2 - 4x - 5$ can be used to determine the values of k for which equations of the form $x^2 - 4x - 5 = k$ have no real roots. Note on the graph that when k is less than -9, the parabola does not intersect a line of the form $y = k$. Hence, equations such as $x^2 - 4x - 5 = -10$ and $x^2 - 4x - 5 = -20$ do not have real roots.

As you probably guessed, the equation $x^2 - 4x - 5 = -9$ has equal roots because the parabola is tangent to the line $y = -9$. Notice that -9 is the y-coordinate of the turning point of the parabola. The x-coordinate of the turning point, 2, is the value of each of the equal roots of $x^2 - 4x - 5 = -9$. Verify this algebraically.

Exercises

1. *a.* Draw the graph of $y = x^2 - 2x$ from $x = -3$ to $x = 5$ inclusive.
    b. From this graph, determine the roots of the following four equations:
        (1) $x^2 - 2x = 0$ (2) $x^2 - 2x = 3$ (3) $x^2 - 2x = 8$ (4) $x^2 - 2x = 5$

2. *a.* Draw the graph of $y = x^2 + 2x - 3$ from $x = -4$ to $x = 2$.

  b. From this graph, determine the roots of the following four equations:

  (1) $x^2 + 2x - 3 = 0$ (2) $x^2 + 2x - 3 = 5$
  (3) $x^2 + 2x - 3 = -4$ (4) $x^2 + 2x = 0$

In 3–8, solve the equation graphically.

3. $x^2 - 6x = 0$ **4.** $x^2 + 3x = 0$ **5.** $x^2 - 4 = 0$
6. $x^2 - 3x + 2 = 0$ **7.** $x^2 - x - 6 = 0$ **8.** $x^2 - 2x + 1 = 0$

9. *a.* Draw the graph of the equation $y = x^2 + 4x - 3$ from $x = -5$ to $x = 1$ inclusive.

  b. From the graph drawn in answer to *a*:

  1. Estimate, to the nearest tenth, the roots of the equation $x^2 + 4x - 3 = 0$.
  2. Write the equation of the axis of symmetry.
  3. Find a value of k for which the roots of the equation $x^2 + 4x - 3 = k$ are imaginary.

10. *a.* Draw the graph of $y = x^2 - 4x + 6$ from $x = -1$ to $x = 5$ inclusive.

  b. On the graph made in answer to *a*, indicate, by letters A and B, the points whose abscissas are the roots of the equation $x^2 - 4x + 6 = 8$.

  c. From the graph, determine the least value of k for which the roots of $x^2 - 4x + 6 = k$ are real.

11. *a.* Draw the graph of $y = x^2 - 2x - 4$ from $x = -2$ to $x = 4$ inclusive.

  b. From the graph, estimate, to the nearest tenth, the roots of $x^2 - 2x - 4 = 0$.

  c. On the same set of axes used in *a*, draw the graph $y = -8$.

  d. From the graphs made in answer to *a* and *c*, what conclusion can you draw about the roots of $x^2 - 2x - 4 = -8$?

In 12–17, solve the equation graphically; give the answers correct to the nearest tenth.

12. $x^2 + 2x - 5 = 0$ **13.** $x^2 - 4x + 1 = 0$ **14.** $x^2 - 2x - 2 = 0$
15. $x^2 - x - 3 = 0$ **16.** $x^2 + x - 1 = 0$ **17.** $x^2 - 3x + 1 = 0$

18. *a.* Draw the graph of the equation $y = -x^2 + 4x$, using all integral values of x from $x = -1$ to $x = 5$, inclusive.

  b. The value of K for which the roots of the equation $-x^2 + 4x = K$ are imaginary is   (1) $K = \pm 4$ (2) $K > 4$ (3) $K < 0$ (4) $0 < K < 4$

In 19–23, find the x-intercepts of the graph of the parabola defined by:

19. $y = x^2 - 6x + 8$ **20.** $y = x^2 - 5x$
21. $y = 16 - x^2$ **22.** $\{(x, y) \,|\, y = 2x^2 - 5x + 2\}$
23. $\{(x, y) \,|\, y = 3x^2\}$

4. Using Parabolas To Determine the Nature of the Roots of a Quadratic Equation

The nature of the roots of a quadratic equation of the form $ax^2 + bx + c = 0$ can be determined by an inspection of the position of parabola $y = ax^2 + bx + c$, relative to the x-axis. Note, in the figure, the positions of the three parabolas a, b, and c. Then examine the following table:

Parabola	Intersections with x-axis	Nature of Roots	Quadratic Equation
a: $y = x^2 - 4x - 5$	2	real, unequal	$x^2 - 4x - 5 = 0$
b: $y = x^2 - 4x + 4$	1	real, equal	$x^2 - 4x + 4 = 0$
c: $y = x^2 - 4x + 7$	0	not real	$x^2 - 4x + 7 = 0$

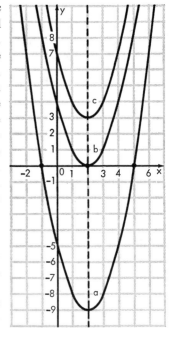

Recall that if the parabola $y = ax^2 + bx + c$ intersects the x-axis, the x-intercepts are the real roots of the quadratic equation $ax^2 + bx + c = 0$. Two intersections with the x-axis, as in the case of parabola a, mean that there are two roots, real and unequal. A single intersection, such as in the case of parabola b which is tangent to the x-axis, can only mean that the x-intercept is the value of each of the equal real roots. In the case of parabola c, there are no intersections with the x-axis. Hence, there are no real roots. Keep in mind that, in each case, the quadratic expression $ax^2 + bx + c$ is the same in both equations $y = ax^2 + bx + c$ and $ax^2 + bx + c = 0$.

Rule 1. If a parabola $y = ax^2 + bx + c$ intersects the x-axis in two points, then the quadratic equation $ax^2 + bx + c = 0$ has two real and unequal roots. Here, $b^2 - 4ac > 0$.

Rule 2. If a parabola $y = ax^2 + bx + c$ is tangent to the x-axis, then the quadratic equation $ax^2 + bx + c = 0$ has two real and equal roots. Here, $b^2 - 4ac = 0$.

Rule 3. If a parabola $y = ax^2 + bx + c$ does not intersect the x-axis, then the quadratic equation $ax^2 + bx + c = 0$ has no real roots. Here, $b^2 - 4ac < 0$.

COMPARING ALGEBRAIC AND GRAPHIC METHODS OF DETERMINING THE NATURE OF THE ROOTS

The three foregoing rules are used in the graphic methods of determining the nature of the roots of a quadratic equation. Recall that the algebraic method made use of the discriminant $b^2 - 4ac$. If $b^2 - 4ac > 0$, then the roots are real and unequal; if $b^2 - 4ac = 0$, then the roots are real and equal; if $b^2 - 4ac < 0$, then the roots are not real. The two methods are compared in the following table:

Parabola $y = ax^2 + bx + c$	*Discriminant* $b^2 - 4ac$	*Nature of Roots of* $ax^2 + bx + c = 0$
intersects x-axis (2 points)	positive	real and unequal
tangent to x-axis (1 point)	zero	real and equal
does not meet the x-axis	negative	not real

Exercises

In 1 and 2, indicate whether the discriminant of the equation $ax^2 + bx + c = 0$ is positive, zero, or negative if:

1. the parabola $y = ax^2 + bx + c$ is tangent to the x-axis.

2. the parabola $y = ax^2 + bx + c$ does not meet the x-axis.

In 3 and 4, indicate whether the roots of $ax^2 + bx + c = 0$ are real and unequal, real and equal, or not real if:

3. the parabola $y = ax^2 + bx + c$ intersects the x-axis in two points.

4. the parabola $y = ax^2 + bx + c$ is tangent to the x-axis.

In 5–10, without drawing the graph of the equation, determine the number of points that the graph of the equation and the x-axis have in common.

5. $y = x^2 - 2x - 3$ **6.** $y = x^2 - 2x + 3$ **7.** $y = x^2 - 2x + 1$

8. $y = x^2 + 2x + 1$ **9.** $y = x^2 + 2x$ **10.** $y = x^2 + 2x + 2$

In 11–15, indicate the number of points that the parabola $y = ax^2 + bx + c$ and the x-axis have in common if the roots of $ax^2 + bx + c = 0$ are:

11. 2 and -2 **12.** $2i$ and $-2i$

13. $3 + \sqrt{2}$ and $3 - \sqrt{2}$ **14.** $3 + \sqrt{-2}$ and $3 - \sqrt{-2}$

15. 12 and 12

5. Graphs of Second-Degree Equations: Conic Sections

When a second-degree equation is graphed, the resulting graph may be a *circle*, an *ellipse*, a *parabola*, or a *hyperbola*. Each of these curves is called a **conic section** since the curves may be obtained by cutting a right circular cone by a plane. In special cases, when a plane cuts a right circular cone, a *single point*, a *straight line*, or *two intersecting straight lines* may also be obtained. It can be shown that the graph of every second-degree equation in two variables must be either a conic section or one of the three special cases.

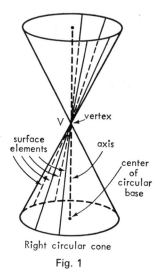

Right circular cone
Fig. 1

The right circular cone is the form of the familiar ice cream cone and also of many drinking cups. As shown in Fig. 1, the base is a circle. The *axis* of the cone is the line joining the vertex, V, to the center of the base. Any line joining the vertex to any point on the circle which is the base of the cone is an *element* of the cone. If the elements of the cone are extended, a second cone is obtained.

Figs. 2–8 illustrate the conic sections and also the special cases that result when a plane cuts one or both cones.

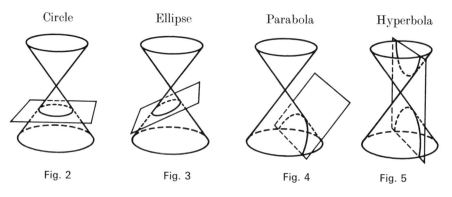

Circle	Ellipse	Parabola	Hyperbola
Fig. 2	Fig. 3	Fig. 4	Fig. 5

Fig. 2. A *circle* is formed when the cutting plane is parallel to the circular base of the cone.

Fig. 3. An *ellipse* is formed when the cutting plane cuts all the elements of the cone.

Point   Line   Double Line

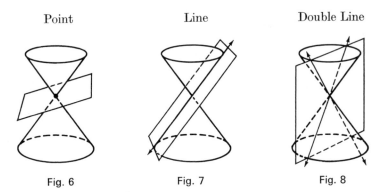

Fig. 6   Fig. 7   Fig. 8

Fig. 4. A *parabola* is formed when the cutting plane is parallel to one of the elements of the cone.

Fig. 5. A *hyperbola* is formed when the cutting plane is parallel to the axis of the cone and cuts both the cone and also its extension.

Figs. 6–8. By properly positioning the cutting plane, the special cases of intersections which are a *single point*, a *straight line*, or *two straight lines* are obtained. These three cases are considered as *limiting forms* of the conic sections.

In the discussions that follow, we will consider the graphs of second-degree equations associated with each of the conic sections.

SECOND-DEGREE EQUATIONS WHOSE GRAPH IS A POINT, A LINE, OR TWO LINES

A Point Graph

The solution set of $x^2 + y^2 = 0$ has one ordered pair, $(0, 0)$. Hence, the graph of this equation is a *point*. The point $(0, 0)$ is also the graph of $2x^2 + 3y^2 = 0$. The graph of $(x - 5)^2 + (y + 3)^2 = 0$ is the point $(5, -3)$.

A Single Straight-Line Graph

If the second-degree equation $(x - 5)^2 = 0$ is solved, then $x = 5$. The graph of $x = 5$ is a straight line parallel to the y-axis. The same line is the graph of equations equivalent to $(x - 5)^2 = 0$, such as $x^2 - 10x + 25 = 0$ and $x^2 = 10x - 25$. The line $y = -4$ is the graph of $(y + 4)^2 = 0$ or any of its equivalent transformations.

A Double Straight-Line Graph

If the second-degree equation $xy = 0$ is solved, then either $x = 0$ or $y = 0$. Hence, the graph of $xy = 0$ consists of the x-axis, which is the graph of $y = 0$ and the y-axis, which is the graph of $x = 0$. The lines $x = 5$ and $y = -2$ constitute the graph of the equation $(x - 5)(y + 2) = 0$ or any of its equivalent transformations.

Exercises

In 1–4, find the coordinates of the point that is the graph of the equation.

1. $x^2 + 2y^2 = 0$ **2.** $x^2 + (y - 3)^2 = 0$
3. $(x + 2)^2 + 3(y - 3)^2 = 0$ **4.** $(x - 1)^2 + y^2 = 0$

In 5–7, find the equation of the line that is the graph of the equation.

5. $(x - 3)^2 = 0$ **6.** $5(y + 3)^2 = 0$ **7.** $y^2 = 4(y - 1)$

In 8–16, state the equations of the two lines that form the graph of the equation.

8. $x(y - 2) = 0$ **9.** $(x - 3)(y + 2) = 0$ **10.** $(2x - 1)(4y + 1) = 0$
11. $(x - y)(x - 2y) = 0$ **12.** $x(x + 3y) = 0$ **13.** $x^2 = 5xy$
14. $xy = x + y - 1$ **15.** $2x^2 = 6xy - x^2$ **16.** $4x^2 - 9y^2 = 0$

6. The Circle as a Graph

THE CIRCLE WHOSE CENTER IS THE ORIGIN

The simplest second-degree equation whose graph is a circle is $x^2 + y^2 = r^2$, $r > 0$. This circle has its center at the origin and a radius r, as shown in the figure.

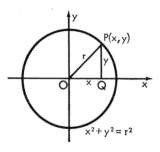

The equation $x^2 + y^2 = r^2$ is obtained by applying the theorem of Pythagoras in right triangle OPQ, where $P(x, y)$ is any point on the circle.

Thus, as shown in the following model problem, the graph of $x^2 + y^2 = 9$ is a circle whose center is the origin and whose radius is $\sqrt{9}$, or 3. To draw the circle using compasses, place the point of the compass at the origin and open the compass to 3 units. The following model problem shows how the circle can be graphed by means of a table of values:

~~~~~~~~ *MODEL PROBLEM* ~~~~~~~~~

Using a table of values, graph the equation $x^2 + y^2 = 9$.

How To Proceed	*Solution*
1. Solve the equation for y in terms of x.	$$y^2 = 9 - x^2$$ $$y = \pm\sqrt{9 - x^2}$$

2. Prepare a table of ordered pairs by assigning consecutive integral values for x and finding the corresponding values of y. (Use a table of square roots to obtain or to check values correct to the nearest tenth.)

3. Plot the points representing the ordered pairs in the table and join them with a smooth curve.

TABLE OF VALUES FOR
$$x^2 + y^2 = 9$$

x	0	± 1	± 2	± 3
y	± 3	± 2.8	± 2.2	0

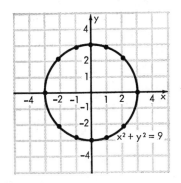

Note in the preceding graph of $x^2 + y^2 = 9$ that the x-coordinates of points on the circle are the values between -3 and 3 inclusive; that is, $-3 \le x \le 3$. These values constitute the domain of the relation. Similarly, the y-coordinates, whose values constitute the range of the relation, are restricted to $-3 \le y \le 3$.

The table of values for $x^2 + y^2 = 9$ shows ordered pairs that are real values of x and y. By using $y = \pm\sqrt{9 - x^2}$, the tabular values of y, to the nearest tenth, are obtained. If x equals 4, -4, or any value such that $|x| > 3$, the corresponding values of y would not be real but would be imaginary.

Note further that the circle graph does not pass the vertical line test of a function. Indeed, the equation $y = \pm\sqrt{9 - x^2}$ shows that each real value of x for $-3 < x < 3$ is not associated with a unique value of y. Hence, the relation, $\{(x, y) \,|\, x^2 + y^2 = 9\}$, is *not* a function.

The equation of a circle that has its center at the origin may be written as $ax^2 + by^2 = c$ where a, b, and c are all positive and $a = b$. If this equation is used, then $r = \sqrt{\dfrac{c}{a}}$.

Thus, the graph of $3x^2 + 3y^2 = 75$ is a circle whose center is at the origin. Since $c = 75$ and $a = 3$, then $\dfrac{c}{a} = 25$. Hence, the radius, $r = \sqrt{25} = 5$.

Exercises

In 1–6, state the center and radius of the graph of the equation.

1. $x^2 + y^2 = 121$ **2.** $x^2 + y^2 = 8$ **3.** $x^2 + y^2 = 75$

4. $x^2 = 400 - y^2$ **5.** $5x^2 + 5y^2 = 45$ **6.** $3x^2 + 3y^2 = 15$

In 7–15, draw the graph of the equation.

7. $x^2 + y^2 = 4$ **8.** $x^2 + y^2 = 49$ **9.** $x^2 + y^2 = 100$

10. $x^2 + y^2 = 12$ **11.** $x^2 + y^2 = 7$ **12.** $x^2 = 64 - y^2$

13. $y^2 = 15 - x^2$ **14.** $2x^2 + 2y^2 = 50$ **15.** $3x^2 + 3y^2 = 33$

In 16–21, write an equation of a circle whose center is at the origin and whose radius is:

16. 8 **17.** 13 **18.** $\frac{7}{2}$ **19.** $\frac{5}{3}$ **20.** $\sqrt{17}$ **21.** $\sqrt{20}$

In 22–26, write an equation of a circle whose center is at the origin and passes through the point:

22. (4, 3) **23.** (−5, 12) **24.** (6, −8) **25.** (0, −5) **26.** (1, 2)

27. Write an equation of a circle whose center is at the origin and whose radius is $\sqrt{3}$.

28. The locus of points whose distance from the origin is r is given by the equation (1) $x^2 + y^2 = r^2$ (2) $y = r$ (3) $x = r$

In 29–32, show, by transforming each equation into the form $x^2 + y^2 = r^2$, that the graph of the equation is a circle.

29. $x^2 = 25 - y^2$ **30.** $y^2 = (2 - x)(2 + x)$

31. $(x - 2)^2 = 10 - y^2 - 4x$ **32.** $9 + x(y - x) = y^2 + xy$

THE CIRCLE WHOSE CENTER IS THE POINT (h, k)

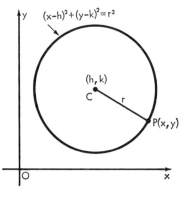

In the figure at the right, $P(x, y)$ is any point of a circle whose center is $C(h, k)$ and whose radius is r.

The general equation of a circle is obtained by applying the distance formula to the distance between the points C and P, as follows:

$$d = \sqrt{(x_2 - x_1)^2 + (y_2 - y_1)^2}$$

Hence, $r = \sqrt{(x - h)^2 + (y - k)^2}$

Squaring, $r^2 = (x - h)^2 + (y - k)^2$.

The equation $(x - h)^2 + (y - k)^2 = r^2$ is called the *standard form* of the equation of a circle. If the equation is expanded and simplified, we obtain the general form of the equation of a circle, as follows:

$$x^2 - 2hx + h^2 + y^2 - 2ky + k^2 - r^2 = 0$$
$$x^2 - 2hx + y^2 - 2ky + h^2 + k^2 - r^2 = 0$$
$$x^2 + y^2 - 2hx - 2ky + h^2 + k^2 - r^2 = 0$$

The last equation is in the *general form* of the equation of a circle, $x^2 + y^2 + Dx + Ey + F = 0$ where $D = -2h$, $E = -2k$, and $F = h^2 + k^2 - r^2$.

KEEP IN MIND

The equation of a circle with center (h, k) and radius $r > 0$ is

$$(x - h)^2 + (y - k)^2 = r^2$$

~~~~~~~~~~~~ *MODEL PROBLEMS* ~~~~~~~~~~~~

1. State the standard form and the general form of the equation of the circle whose center is $(-4, 3)$ and whose radius is 10.

   Solution: Substitute -4 for h, 3 for k, and 10 for r in the standard form of the equation.

   $$(x - h)^2 + (y - k)^2 = r^2$$
   $$(x + 4)^2 + (y - 3)^2 = 100 \quad \textit{Ans.} \text{ (equation in standard form)}$$

   Expand and simplify.
   $$x^2 + 8x + 16 + y^2 - 6y + 9 = 100$$
   $$x^2 + y^2 + 8x - 6y - 75 = 0 \qquad \textit{Ans.} \text{ (equation in general form)}$$

2. Find the coordinates of the center and the radius of a circle whose equation is $x^2 + y^2 + 10x - 4y - 7 = 0$.

   Solution:
   Express the given equation as $(x^2 + 10x + \,?) + (y^2 - 4y + \,?) = 7$
       Complete the squares: $(x^2 + 10x + 25) + (y^2 - 4y + 4) = 7 + 25 + 4$
   Express in standard form: $(x + 5)^2 + (y - 2)^2 = 36$
   Hence, the center of the circle is $(-5, 2)$ and the radius is 6.

   Answer: center is $(-5, 2)$; radius is 6.

Exercises

In 1–5, state the center and the radius of the circle whose equation is given.

1. $x^2 + (y-1)^2 = 25$ **2.** $(x-3)^2 + y^2 = 9$

3. $(x-4)^2 + (y-5)^2 = 100$ **4.** $(x-1)^2 + (y+3)^2 = 16$

5. $(x+3)^2 + (y+1)^2 = 49$

In 6–9, transform the equation into the standard form and state the center and the radius of the circle.

6. $x^2 + 4x + 4 + y^2 = 25$ **7.** $x^2 + y^2 + 10y + 25 = 100$

8. $x^2 + 2x + y^2 + 6y = 46$ **9.** $4x^2 + 8x + 4y^2 + 16y = 44$

In 10–15, draw the graph of the equation.

10. $(x-3)^2 + y^2 = 9$ **11.** $x^2 + (y+4)^2 = 16$

12. $(x-2)^2 + (y+2)^2 = 25$ **13.** $x^2 + y^2 + 4y = 12$

14. $x^2 + y^2 - 6x = 16$ **15.** $3x^2 + 3y^2 + 6x = 24$

7. The Ellipse as a Graph

THE ELLIPSE WHOSE CENTER IS THE ORIGIN: INTERCEPT FORM OF ITS EQUATION

The equation of an ellipse (Fig. 1) whose center is the origin, whose x-intercepts are 5 and −5, and whose y-intercepts are 3 and −3, is

$$\frac{x^2}{25} + \frac{y^2}{9} = 1$$

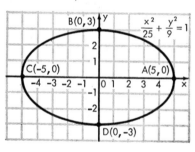

Fig. 1

If 0 is substituted for y, then $\dfrac{x^2}{25} = 1$.

Hence, $x^2 = 25$ and $x = \pm 5$, verifying that the x-intercepts are $+5$ and -5. If 0 is substituted for x, then $\dfrac{y^2}{9} = 1$. Hence, $y^2 = 9$ and $y = \pm 3$, verifying that the y-intercepts are 3 and -3. In Fig. 1, the length of the major axis, $CA = 10$. The length of the semimajor axis, $OA = 5$. The length of the minor axis, $BD = 6$. The length of the semiminor axis, $BO = 3$.

The equation $\dfrac{x^2}{25} + \dfrac{y^2}{9} = 1$ is the *intercept form* of the ellipse in Fig. 1.

In general, the intercept form of any ellipse whose center is the origin, whose x-intercepts are p and $-p$, and whose y-intercepts are q and $-q$, is

$$\frac{x^2}{p^2} + \frac{y^2}{q^2} = 1$$

Verify this by substituting 0 for y to obtain the x-intercepts, and by substituting 0 for x to obtain the y-intercepts.

THE ELLIPSE WHOSE CENTER IS THE ORIGIN: GENERAL FORM OF ITS EQUATION

The equation $\frac{x^2}{25} + \frac{y^2}{9} = 1$ is transformed into $9x^2 + 25y^2 = 225$ by multiplying each side by 225. The resulting equation, $9x^2 + 25y^2 = 225$, is an illustration of the *general form* of the equation of an ellipse whose center is the origin.

The general form of any ellipse whose center is the origin, and where a, b, and c are positive, is

$$ax^2 + by^2 = c$$

Thus, as shown in the following model problem, the graph of $4x^2 + 9y^2 = 36$ is an ellipse whose center is at the origin. Dividing each side by 36, we obtain $\frac{x^2}{9} + \frac{y^2}{4} = 1$, showing that the intercepts of the ellipse in the model problem are ± 3 for the x-intercepts and ± 2 for the y-intercepts.

The following model problem shows how the ellipse $4x^2 + 9y^2 = 36$ can be graphed by means of a table of values:

~~~~~~~~~~~ *MODEL PROBLEM* ~~~~~~~~~~~

Using a table of values, graph the equation $4x^2 + 9y^2 = 36$.

How To Proceed	*Solution*
1. Solve the equation for y in terms of x.	$9y^2 = 36 - 4x^2$
	$y^2 = \dfrac{36 - 4x^2}{9}$
	$y = \pm\tfrac{1}{3}\sqrt{36 - 4x^2}$

2. Prepare a table of ordered pairs by assigning consecutive integral values for x and finding the corresponding values of y. (Use a table of square roots to obtain or to check values correct to the nearest tenth.)

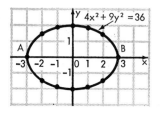

TABLE OF VALUES FOR
$4x^2 + 9y^2 = 36$

x	0	± 1	± 2	± 3
y	± 2	± 1.9	± 1.5	0

3. Plot the points representing the ordered pairs in the table and join them with a smooth curve.

In the preceding figure, note in the graph of $4x^2 + 9y^2 = 36$ that the x-coordinates of points on the ellipse include the values between -3 and 3 inclusive; that is, $-3 \le x \le 3$. Similarly, the y-coordinates are restricted to the range, $-2 \le y \le 2$. If $|x| > 3$, then the corresponding values of y are imaginary; if $|y| > 2$, then the corresponding values of x are imaginary. For example, if $x = \pm 4$, then $y = \pm \frac{2}{3}i\sqrt{7}$.

Note further that the graph of the ellipse does not pass the vertical line test of a function. Indeed, the equation $y = \pm \frac{2}{3}\sqrt{9 - x^2}$ shows that each real value of x for $-3 < x < 3$ is not associated with a unique value of y. Hence, the relation, $\{(x, y) \mid 4x^2 + 9y^2 = 36\}$ is not a function.

DRAWING AN ELLIPSE BY A MECHANICAL METHOD

An ellipse may be drawn by the following mechanical method:

Tack a piece of string at two points, F and F', on a sheet of paper. In Fig. 2, $FF' = 6$ units. Keeping FP and $F'P$ taut, pass a pencil along the string, drawing the ellipse in the process. P represents the changing point of contact as the pencil passes along the string. Be sure that the length of string is greater than the distance between F and F'.

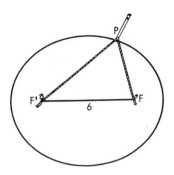

Fig. 2

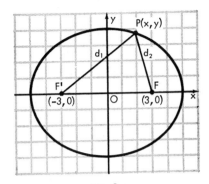

Fig. 3

The drawing of the ellipse is made in accordance with the following definition:

An **_ellipse_** is a set of points, the sum of whose distances from two fixed points is a constant distance greater than the distance between the fixed points.

Each of the points F and F' is a **_focus_** of the ellipse. Note in the resulting graph, Fig. 3, that the center of the ellipse is the midpoint of FF'. If the center is placed at the origin, then the coordinates of F and F' are $(3, 0)$ and $(-3, 0)$ respectively. The length of string, $d_1 + d_2$, is a constant, which may be shown to equal the length of the major axis.

THE CIRCLE IS A SPECIAL CASE OF AN ELLIPSE

Previously, we noted that the equation of a circle whose center is the origin may be written in the general form $ax^2 + by^2 = c$, where a, b, and c are all positive and $a = b$. The added condition, $a = b$, means that the circle is a special case of an ellipse. Note in the diagram of the circle and ellipse as conic sections, Fig. 4, that the ellipse is the section formed when the plane intersects all the elements of the cone. This is true for the circle with the added condition that the plane be parallel to the base of the cone.

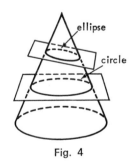

Fig. 4

Exercises

In 1–9, state the center, x-intercepts, and y-intercepts of the graph of the equation.

1. $x^2 + \dfrac{y^2}{4} = 1$ **2.** $\dfrac{x^2}{9} + y^2 = 1$ **3.** $\dfrac{x^2}{4} + \dfrac{y^2}{9} = 1$

4. $x^2 + 9y^2 = 36$ **5.** $25x^2 + y^2 = 25$ **6.** $25x^2 + 4y^2 = 100$

7. $x^2 = 1 - \dfrac{y^2}{49}$ **8.** $y^2 = 1 - \dfrac{x^2}{64}$ **9.** $y^2 = \dfrac{100 - x^2}{100}$

In 10–21, draw the graph of the equation.

10. $x^2 + 4y^2 = 36$ **11.** $4x^2 + y^2 = 36$ **12.** $x^2 + 9y^2 = 36$

13. $9x^2 + y^2 = 36$ **14.** $4x^2 + 25y^2 = 100$ **15.** $25x^2 + 4y^2 = 100$

16. $x^2 + 3y^2 = 12$ **17.** $3x^2 + y^2 = 12$ **18.** $4x^2 + 3y^2 = 48$

19. $x^2 + \dfrac{y^2}{4} = 1$ **20.** $\dfrac{x^2}{9} + y^2 = 1$ **21.** $\dfrac{x^2}{4} + \dfrac{y^2}{9} = 1$

In 22–27, by transforming the equation into the form $ax^2 + by^2 = c$, show that the graph of the equation is an ellipse whose center is the origin.

22. $2x^2 + 3y^2 - 10 = 0$ **23.** $2y^2 = 20 - 3x^2$

24. $10 - 4x^2 = 8y^2$ **25.** $\dfrac{x^2}{9} = 1 - \dfrac{y^2}{25}$

26. $\dfrac{x^2 - 16}{y} = -2y$ **27.** $2x(x + 5) = 10x + 8 - y^2$

8. The Hyperbola as a Graph

THE HYPERBOLA WHOSE CENTER IS THE ORIGIN: GENERAL FORM OF ITS EQUATION

In Fig. 1, the equation $x^2 - 4y^2 = 16$ is an example of the *general form* of the equation of a hyperbola whose center is the origin.

The general form of any hyperbola intersecting the x-axis whose center is the origin, and where a, b, and c are positive, is

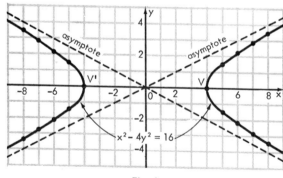

Fig. 1

$$ax^2 - by^2 = c$$

The graphing of the hyperbola is accomplished by following the same procedure as that used in the graphing of the ellipse. The first step is to solve the equation for y in terms of x. If $x^2 - 4y^2 = 16$, then $4y^2 = x^2 - 16$ and

$y = \pm\frac{1}{2}\sqrt{x^2 - 16}$. Note that when the absolute value of x is less than 4, the radicand, $x^2 - 16$, is negative and corresponding values of y are not real. Hence, in preparing a table of values for $x^2 - 4y^2 = 16$, avoid absolute values of x that are less than 4.

TABLE OF VALUES FOR $x^2 - 4y^2 = 16$

x	±4	±5	±6	±7	±8
y	±0	$\pm\frac{1}{2}\sqrt{9}$ or ±1.5	$\pm\frac{1}{2}\sqrt{20} \approx \pm2.2$	$\pm\frac{1}{2}\sqrt{33} \approx \pm2.9$	$\pm\frac{1}{2}\sqrt{48} \approx \pm3.5$

When the points representing the ordered pairs are plotted and joined with a smooth curve, the result is the hyperbola whose center is the origin, Fig. 1.

Note in Fig. 1 that the hyperbola is a discontinuous curve having two branches, unlike the other conic sections. The other conic sections—the circle, the ellipse, and the parabola—are continuous curves. Recall that the two branches of the hyperbola are obtained when a plane cuts a right circular cone and its extension.

TERMS USED WITH THE HYPERBOLA

The terms used with the hyperbola are illustrated in Fig. 1. The **vertices** of the hyperbola are $V(4, 0)$ and $V'(-4, 0)$. The **transverse axis** of the hyperbola is the line segment whose endpoints are the vertices of the hyperbola. The **conjugate axis** is a line segment that is the perpendicular bisector of the transverse axis. In Fig. 1, the transverse axis is a segment of the x-axis, whereas the conjugate axis is a segment of the y-axis. The **center** of the hyperbola, which is the origin in Fig. 1, is the point of intersection of the transverse and conjugate axes.

Note in Fig. 1 the two lines that are marked **asymptote.** These are the lines $y = \frac{1}{2}x$ and $y = -\frac{1}{2}x$. The asymptotes are the lines that the branches of the hyperbola approach as they recede farther and farther from the origin, that is, as the absolute value of x becomes greater and greater. As the absolute value of x becomes very large, a value of y for the hyperbola, found by using $\pm\frac{1}{2}\sqrt{x^2 - 16}$, is very close to a value of y for the asymptotes, found by using $\pm\frac{1}{2}\sqrt{x^2}$, or $\pm\frac{1}{2}x$.

Another way of obtaining the equations of the asymptotes, $y = \frac{1}{2}x$ and $y = -\frac{1}{2}x$, is to replace 16 with 0 in the equation $x^2 - 4y^2 = 16$ to obtain $x^2 - 4y^2 = 0$. When the resulting equation is solved for y, we obtain $y = \frac{1}{2}x$ and $y = -\frac{1}{2}x$.

Figs. 2 and 3 show hyperbolas that either intersect the x-axis or intersect the y-axis. In Fig. 2, the hyperbola $4x^2 - y^2 = 16$ intersects the x-axis; in Fig. 3, the hyperbola $4y^2 - x^2 = 16$ intersects the y-axis.

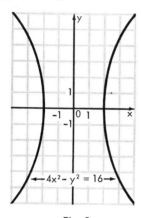

Fig. 2

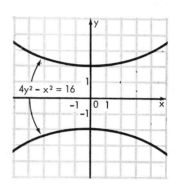

Fig. 3

TABLE OF ORDERED PAIRS FOR $xy = 4$

	Quadrant I					*Quadrant* III				
x	$\frac{1}{2}$	1	2	4	8	$-\frac{1}{2}$	-1	-2	-4	-8
y	8	4	2	1	$\frac{1}{2}$	-8	-4	-2	-1	$-\frac{1}{2}$

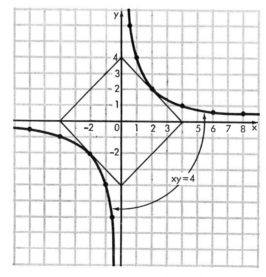

Fig. 4

Figs. 4 and 5 show hyperbolas that do not intersect either the x-axis or the y-axis. The x-axis and the y-axis are the asymptotes of each of the hyperbolas. The hyperbola $xy = 4$ (Fig. 4) has branches in quadrants I and III, while the hyperbola $xy = -4$ (Fig. 5) has branches in quadrants II and IV. It is left to the student to make a table of ordered pairs for $xy = -4$.

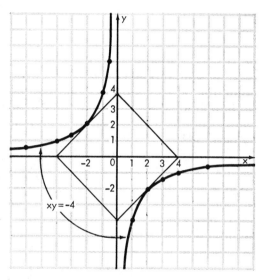

Fig. 5

Note in Figs. 4 and 5 that the x-axis and the y-axis are the extensions of the diagonals of a square or equilateral rectangle. Hence, the hyperbolas $xy = 4$ and $xy = -4$ are called ***equilateral hyperbolas***. The general equations of equilateral hyperbolas whose asymptotes are the x-axis and the y-axis are $xy = k$ and $xy = -k$, where k is positive.

Exercises

In 1–9, state the coordinates of the points where the hyperbola crosses the x-axis or the y-axis.

1. $x^2 - y^2 = 9$ **2.** $y^2 - x^2 = 25$ **3.** $x^2 - 4y^2 = 36$

4. $4y^2 - x^2 = 36$ **5.** $4x^2 - 25y^2 = 100$ **6.** $25y^2 - x^2 = 25$

7. $4y^2 - 9x^2 = 36$ **8.** $\dfrac{x^2}{25} - \dfrac{y^2}{36} = 1$ **9.** $\dfrac{y^2}{25} - \dfrac{x^2}{64} = 1$

In 10–13, state the quadrants of the branches of the hyperbola.

10. $xy = 12$ **11.** $xy = -12$ **12.** $xy + 10 = 15$ **13.** $xy + 10 = 6$

In 14–17, by transforming the equation into the form $ax^2 - by^2 = c$ or $xy = k$, show that the graph of the equation is a hyperbola.

14. $x^2 = 25 + y^2$ 　　　　　　　**15.** $2y^2 = 20 + x^2$

16. $\dfrac{16}{x} = \dfrac{y}{2}$ 　　　　　　**17.** $(x - y)(x + y) = 36$

In 18–23, draw the graph of the equation.

18. $xy = 6$ 　　　　**19.** $xy = -6$ 　　　　**20.** $x^2 - 4y^2 = 16$

21. $\dfrac{x^2}{25} - y^2 = 1$ 　　**22.** $y^2 - \dfrac{x^2}{25} = 1$ 　　**23.** $25x^2 - 4y^2 = 100$

SKETCHING AN ELLIPSE AND ITS RELATED HYPERBOLAS

Note in Fig. 6 that the sides of rectangle $ABCD$ are tangent to an inscribed ellipse. Also, sides $\overline{AD}$ and $\overline{BC}$ are tangent to the two branches of hyperbola 1, while sides $\overline{AB}$ and $\overline{CD}$ are tangent to the branches of hyperbola 2. The midpoints of the sides of the rectangle are the points of contact with the three curves.

In Fig. 6, the ellipse and its related hyperbolas are defined by equations that have many elements in common. Note these common elements and differences in the Table of Equations of an Ellipse and Its Related Hyperbolas (on the facing page).

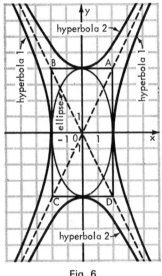

Fig. 6

Also, the same table lists the equations of the ellipse and its related hyperbolas, Fig. 6, in the second column. The last column sets forth the general equations for any set of an ellipse and its related hyperbolas that can be sketched or constructed in the same manner.

In the table, note the following differences in the equations:
1. The only difference between the general equations of the ellipse and hyperbola 1 is the change of sign between ax^2 and by^2, the terms in x and y.
2. The only difference between the general equations of the two hyperbolas is the interchanging of the terms containing x and y, the terms ax^2 and by^2.

TABLE OF EQUATIONS OF AN ELLIPSE
AND ITS RELATED HYPERBOLAS

Conic Section	*Equations of Curves in Fig. 6*	*General Equation Forms (a, b, c > 0)*
ellipse	$\dfrac{x^2}{4} + \dfrac{y^2}{16} = 1$ or $4x^2 + y^2 = 16$	$ax^2 + by^2 = c$
hyperbola 1 (crossing x-axis)	$\dfrac{x^2}{4} - \dfrac{y^2}{16} = 1$ or $4x^2 - y^2 = 16$	$ax^2 - by^2 = c$
hyperbola 2 (crossing y-axis)	$\dfrac{y^2}{16} - \dfrac{x^2}{4} = 1$ or $y^2 - 4x^2 = 16$	$by^2 - ax^2 = c$

GENERAL INTERCEPT FORMS OF AN ELLIPSE AND ITS RELATED HYPERBOLAS

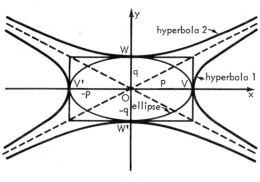

Fig. 7

If the x-intercepts are p and $-p$ and the y-intercepts are q and $-q$, as shown in Fig. 7, then the general equations of the ellipse and its related hyperbolas are:

ellipse: $\dfrac{x^2}{p^2} + \dfrac{y^2}{q^2} = 1$ hyperbola 1: $\dfrac{x^2}{p^2} - \dfrac{y^2}{q^2} = 1$ hyperbola 2: $\dfrac{y^2}{q^2} - \dfrac{x^2}{p^2} = 1$

Exercises

In 1–3, state the equations of the hyperbolas that are related to the ellipse whose equation is:

1. $x^2 + y^2 = 16$ **2.** $2x^2 + 5y^2 = 50$ **3.** $\dfrac{x^2}{9} + \dfrac{y^2}{49} = 1$

In the figure at the right, an ellipse and its related hyperbolas have been sketched. The lengths of the segments p and q are one-half the length of the axes of the ellipse. In 4–7, state the equations of the ellipse and its related hyperbolas if:

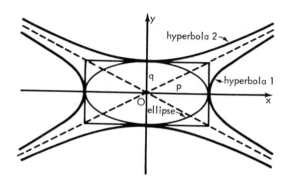

4. $p = 1$ and $q = 1$
5. $p = 6$ and $q = 5$
6. $p = 10$ and $q = 3$
7. $p = 1$ and $q = 9$

9. Identifying the Graphs of Second-Degree Equations

Following are the general second-degree equations of the parabola, circle, ellipse, and hyperbola:

Parabola

$\quad y = ax^2 + bx + c$, $a \neq 0$ (axis of symmetry is parallel to the y-axis)
$\quad x = ay^2 + by + c$, $a \neq 0$ (axis of symmetry is parallel to the x-axis)

Circle with center at the origin and radius r

$\quad x^2 + y^2 = r^2$, $r > 0$
$\quad ax^2 + by^2 = c$, where a, b, and c are all positive and $a = b$
$\quad$ *Note.* If $r = 0$ or $c = 0$, the graph is a point.

Ellipse with center at the origin

$\quad ax^2 + by^2 = c$, where a, b, and c are all positive

Hyperbola with center at the origin

    1. Hyperbola whose transverse axis is on the x-axis:
        $ax^2 - by^2 = c$, where a, b, and c are all positive
    2. Hyperbola whose transverse axis is on the y-axis:
        $ay^2 - bx^2 = c$, where a, b, and c are all positive
    3. Equilateral hyperbola whose asymptotes are the x-axis and the y-axis:
        $xy = k$, $k \neq 0$
            If k is positive, the branches are in quadrants I and III.
            If k is negative, the branches are in quadrants II and IV.

Note. The general equation of hyperbolas 1 and 2 (see Fig. 7) may be written as $ax^2 - by^2 = c$, where a and b are positive and $c \neq 0$. If $c = 0$, then the graph consists of two lines intersecting at the origin. (The two lines, $ax^2 - by^2 = 0$, are the asymptotes of the hyperbola $ax^2 - by^2 = c$.)

In the model problems and in the exercises that follow, answer "circle" if the curve is an ellipse that is a circle.

~~~~~~~~~~~ *MODEL PROBLEMS* ~~~~~~~~~~~

In each of the following, name the curve that is the graph of the equation:

Equation	Answer		Equation	Answer
1. $x^2 + y^2 = 16$	circle		**9.** $(x-3)^2 = 0$	line
2. $2x^2 + y^2 = 16$	ellipse		**10.** $4xy = 16$	hyperbola
3. $2x^2 - y^2 = 16$	hyperbola		**11.** $4xy = -16$	hyperbola
4. $2x^2 - y = 16$	parabola		**12.** $4xy = 0$	two lines
5. $2x - y^2 = 16$	parabola		**13.** $4x + y^2 = 25$	parabola
6. $2x - y^2 = 0$	parabola		**14.** $4y^2 + x^2 = 25$	ellipse
7. $x^2 - y^2 = 0$	two lines		**15.** $4y^2 - 9x^2 = 25$	hyperbola
8. $x^2 + y^2 = 0$	point			

~~~~~~

Exercises

In 1–15, name the curve that is the graph of the equation.

1. $y^2 = 5x$ **2.** $x^2 + y^2 = 7$ **3.** $x^2 - y^2 = 9$

4. $x^2 + y^2 - 17 = 0$ **5.** $x^2 - y^2 = 3$ **6.** $3x^2 + y^2 = 15$

7. $x^2 + 3x + 2 - y = 0$ **8.** $xy = 14$ **9.** $xy = -6$

10. $y^2 = 19 - x^2$ **11.** $2x + 3y - 6 = 0$ **12.** $y = x^2 - 5$

13. $y^2 = 20 - 2x^2$ **14.** $x = y^2 + 6y$ **15.** $y = 2x^2 + 6$

16. The graph of $2x^2 + 2y^2 = 50$ is (1) a parabola (2) a circle (3) a hyperbola

17. The graph of $x^2 + 4y^2 = 25$ is (1) an ellipse (2) a hyperbola (3) a parabola (4) a circle.

18. The graph of $8x^2 + 8y^2 = 32$ is (1) a parabola (2) a circle (3) a hyperbola

19. What is the name of the graph of $y = x^2$?

20. The graph of $3x^2 + 3y^2 = 10$ is (1) a circle (2) a parabola (3) a hyperbola

21. The graph of $ax^2 + ay^2 = c$ is always a circle. (Answer *true* or *false*.)

22. An equation of an ellipse may be (1) $3x^2 + y = 4$ (2) $3x^2 + y^2 = 4$ (3) $3x^2 - y^2 = 4$

23. The graph of the equation $y^2 = 6x$ is (1) a circle (2) an ellipse (3) a hyperbola (4) a parabola

24. Which equation has a circle as its graph? (1) $3x^2 = 5 + 3y^2$ (2) $3x^2 = 5 - 3y^2$ (3) $3x^2 = 5 - y^2$ (4) $3x^2 = 5 + y^2$

25. Which of the following is the equation of an ellipse? (1) $9x^2 = 4y^2 + 36$ (2) $xy = -8$ (3) $x^2 = 25 - 4y^2$ (4) $x^2 = y - 16x + 4$

26. Which of the following is the equation of a hyperbola? (1) $x^2 = 10 - y^2$ (2) $x = y^2 - 9$ (3) $xy = -6$ (4) $4x^2 + y^2 = 9$

27. The graph of the equation $x^2 - 1 = 2x + 2y$ is a (1) parabola (2) straight line (3) circle (4) hyperbola

In 28–36, state whether the graph of the equation is a point, a line, or a double line.

28. $x^2 + y^2 = 0$ **29.** $x^2 - y^2 = 0$ **30.** $xy = 0$

31. $x^2 = 4y^2$ **32.** $(x - 3)(x + 2) = 0$ **33.** $x(y - 5) = 0$

34. $(x + 2y)(x - 2y) = 0$ **35.** $(x - 5)^2 = 0$ **36.** $x^2 + 49 = 14x$

10. Solving a System of Two Equations Graphically

SOLVING A SYSTEM OF TWO EQUATIONS GRAPHICALLY: ONE A FIRST-DEGREE EQUATION AND THE OTHER A SECOND-DEGREE EQUATION

To solve a system of equations consisting of a first-degree equation and a second-degree equation graphically, both equations must be graphed using the same set of axes. The coordinates of the points of intersection of the two graphs, if any, are the ordered number pairs of real numbers of the solution set of the system.

Recall that the graph of a first-degree equation in two variables is a straight line. The graph of a second-degree equation in two variables is a conic section, a point, a line, or a double line. The number of ordered pairs of real numbers in the solution set of the system may be 0, 1, or 2 depending on the number of intersections of the graphs. If there are no intersections, then the solution set of the system has no ordered pairs of real numbers.

If the straight line is *tangent* to a conic section, there is one intersection. Hence, in the following cases, the solution set of the system has one ordered number pair:

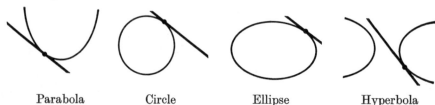

Parabola   Circle   Ellipse   Hyperbola

If the straight line intersects a conic section in two points, the solution set of the system has two ordered number pairs, as in the following cases:

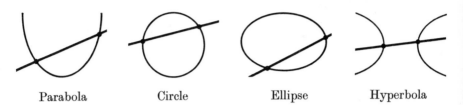

Parabola   Circle   Ellipse   Hyperbola

~~~~~~~~~~~~~~~ *MODEL PROBLEMS* ~~~~~~~~~~~~~~~

1. Solve graphically: $\begin{cases} y = 2x + 1 \\ y = x^2 - 4x + 9 \end{cases}$

How To Proceed	*Solution*
1. Graph the first equation.	The graph of $y = 2x + 1$ is a straight line.
2. Using the same set of axes, graph the second equation.	The graph of $y = x^2 - 4x + 9$ is a parabola.
3. Read the coordinates of the points of intersection of the two graphs.	The common solutions are: At A, $x = 2$, $y = 5$ At B, $x = 4$, $y = 9$

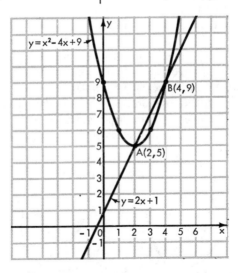

Answer: The solution set of the system is $\{(2, 5), (4, 9)\}$.

In 2–4, solve the system of equations algebraically; state whether the number of points of intersection will be 2, 1, or 0 if the graphs of the pair of equations in the system are plotted using the same set of axes.

2. $y = x^2 - 4x + 9$ **3.** $y = x^2 - 4x + 9$ **4.** $y = x^2 - 4x + 9$
  $y = 5$ $y = 2x$ $y = 4x - 7$

Solution:

2. If $y = 5$, then $5 = x^2 - 4x + 9$.
  Hence, $(x - 2)^2 = 0$ and $x = 2$.
  Ans. $\{(2, 5)\}$ 1 point

3. If $y = 2x$, then $2x = x^2 - 4x + 9$.
  Hence, $(x - 3)^2 = 0$ and $x = 3$.
  Ans. $\{(3, 6)\}$ 1 point

4. If $y = 4x - 7$, then $4x - 7 = x^2 - 4x + 9$.
  Hence, $(x - 4)^2 = 0$ and $x = 4$.
  Ans. $\{(4, 9)\}$ 1 point

It is left to the student to use the parabola in model problem 1 and show that each of the lines $y = 5$, $y = 2x$, and $y = 4x - 7$ is tangent to the parabola at a point whose coordinates are an ordered number pair of the solution set.

~~~~~~

SOLVING A SYSTEM OF TWO EQUATIONS GRAPHICALLY: BOTH SECOND-DEGREE EQUATIONS

If the graph of each of the second-degree equations is a conic section, there may be as many as 4 ordered pairs of real numbers in the solution set of the system. The following figures, showing the relative positions of a circle and a parabola, indicate when the solution set of the system has either 4, 3, 2, or 1 ordered pairs of real numbers. (If the circle and parabola do not meet, there is no ordered pair of real numbers in the system.)

4 pairs

3 pairs

2 pairs

1 pair

~~~~~~~~~~~~~~~ *MODEL PROBLEM* ~~~~~~~~~~~~~~~

Find the solution set of the system and express irrational roots to the nearest tenth:

$$x^2 + y^2 = 25$$
$$xy = 10$$

How To Proceed	*Solution*
1. Graph the first equation.	The graph of $x^2 + y^2 = 25$ is a circle with its center at the origin and a radius of 5.
2. Using the same set of axes, graph the second equation.	The graph of $xy = 10$ is an equilateral hyperbola with branches in quadrants I and III.
3. Read the coordinates of the points of intersection of the two graphs.	The common solutions to the nearest tenth are: At A, $x = 4.5$, $y = 2.2$ At B, $x = 2.2$, $y = 4.5$ At C, $x = -4.5$, $y = -2.2$ At D, $x = -2.2$, $y = -4.5$

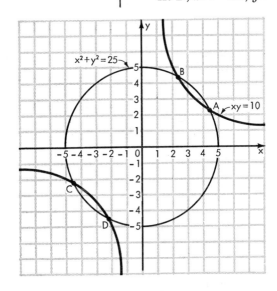

Answer: The solution set is $\{(4.5, 2.2), (2.2, 4.5), (-2.2, -4.5), (-4.5, -2.2)\}$.

~~~~~~

Note. In $\begin{cases} x^2 + y^2 = 1 \\ xy = 10 \end{cases}$ the graphs of the equations are a circle of radius 1 and the hyperbola of the previous model problem. These graphs do not intersect. When the graphs of the equations of a system do not intersect, the solutions of the system are not real numbers but complex numbers.

Exercises

In 1–9, solve the system of equations algebraically and state whether the number of points of intersection will be 2, 1, or 0 if the graphs of the pair of equations in the system are plotted using the same set of axes.

1. $x^2 + y^2 = 25$
   $y = x - 1$

2. $x^2 + y^2 = 16$
   $y = x$

3. $x^2 + y^2 = 9$
   $y = 3$

4. $x^2 + y^2 = 9$
   $x - 2y + 3 = 0$

5. $x^2 + y^2 = 36$
   $x + y = 10$

6. $y = x^2 + 7x - 10$
   $y = 4x$

7. $xy = 12$
   $x - y = 5$

8. $xy = 16$
   $x = y$

9. $x^2 - y^2 = 25$
   $x = 3$

10. *a.* Draw the graph of the equation $y = x^2 - 2x - 5$ from $x = -2$ to $x = 4$ inclusive.

   b. On the same set of axes used in answer to *a*, draw the graph of the equation $x + 2y = 2$.

   c. From the graphs made in answer to *a* and *b*, estimate, correct to the nearest tenth, the values of x and y common to the two equations.

11. *a.* Using the same set of axes, draw the graphs of the equations $xy = 12$ and $x - y = 1$.

   b. From the graphs made in answer to *a*, determine the values of x and y common to the two equations.

In 12–20, solve the system of equations graphically.

12. $y = x^2 + 4$
   $y = 4x + 1$

13. $y = x^2 + 3x$
   $y - 3x = 4$

14. $x^2 - 2x - 4 = y$
   $y + 4 = x$

15. $xy = 4$
   $x = y + 3$

16. $xy = 24$
   $x - 3y = 6$

17. $xy = 12$
   $3x + 4y = 24$

18. $x^2 + y^2 = 16$
   $x - y = 4$

19. $x^2 + y^2 = 25$
   $y = 2x + 5$

20. $x^2 + y^2 = 50$
   $2x = 15 - y$

21. The line $y = 2x - 4$ intersects a circle whose center is the origin at a point whose coordinates are represented by $(x, 8)$. Find the radius of the circle.

In 22–27, determine whether the number of points of intersection of the graphs of the pair of equations of the system is 4, 3, 2, 1, or 0.

22. $x^2 + y^2 = 25$
$xy = 10$

23. $x^2 + y^2 = 25$
$y^2 = x$

24. $y = x^2 - 3x$
$y = 2x^2$

25. $x^2 + y^2 = 9$
$x = y^2 + 5$

26. $x^2 - y^2 = 9$
$x^2 + y^2 = 9$

27. $x^2 + 4y^2 = 64$
$4y^2 - x^2 = 64$

28. *a.* Draw the graph of $y = x^2 - 4x$ from $x = -1$ to $x = 5$ inclusive.
   b. On the set of axes used in answer to *a*, draw the graph of $xy = 6$ from $x = 1$ to $x = 6$ inclusive.
   c. From the graphs, estimate, correct to the nearest tenth, a value of x and a value of y common to the two equations.

29. *a.* Draw the graph of the equation $x^2 + y^2 = 9$.
   b. On the axes used in answer to *a*, draw the graph of $x = y^2 - 5$.
   c. From the graphs, estimate the values of x and y common to the two equations.

11. Using the Parabola To Solve Problems Involving Maximum or Minimum

The graph of a parabola that opens downward can be used to solve a problem in which a maximum value is to be found at the turning point. Similarly, the graph of a parabola that opens upward can be used to solve a problem in which a minimum value is to be found.

~~~~~~~~~~ *MODEL PROBLEM* ~~~~~~~~~~

A man has 200 feet of wire fencing with which to enclose a vegetable garden. What are the dimensions and the area of the largest rectangular garden which he can fence off with this wire?

Solution:

Let x = length of the garden in feet.
Then $100 - x$ = width of the garden.
Then $x(100 - x)$ = area of the garden.
$A = x(100 - x)$ [A = area of garden]
$A = -x^2 + 100x$
Make a graph of $A = -x^2 + 100x$.

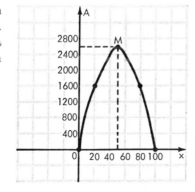

x	A
0	0
20	1600
40	2400
50	2500
60	2400
80	1600
100	0

From the graph, we observe that the garden will have a maximum area of 2500 square feet when the length of the rectangle is 50 feet. The width of the rectangle will be $100 - 50$, or 50 feet.

Answer: The length of the largest rectangle is 50 feet; the width is 50 feet; the area is 2500 square feet.

Exercises

1. Separate 40 into two parts such that their product will be a maximum. Find the maximum product.
2. Find two numbers whose sum is 10 and whose product is as large as possible.
3. The perimeter of a rectangle is 24 feet.
   a. If x represents the length of the rectangle, express the width in terms of x.
   b. If A represents the area of the rectangle, express A in terms of x.
   c. Make a graph of the formula obtained in answer to *b*.
   d. From the graph, determine the maximum value of A.
4. Find the maximum area of a rectangle whose perimeter is 80 feet.
5. *a.* Show that the largest rectangle whose perimeter is represented by P is a square.
   b. Find the area of the square.
6. A rectangular flower garden is to be enclosed on three sides by wire fencing and on the fourth side by the side of a building; 12 yards of wire fencing are to be used for this purpose.
   a. Express the area, A, in terms of the width w.
   b. Draw the graph of the equation written in answer to *a*.
   c. From the graph, determine the value of w that will give the greatest area.
7. Find the number which when added to its square gives the smallest possible sum.
8. Find two numbers such that their sum is 10 and the sum of their squares is a minimum.

12. Solving Quadratic Inequalities in One Variable Graphically and Algebraically

Do you know what number has a square less than 4? You probably know many such numbers, such as 1, $\frac{1}{2}$, or $\frac{1}{4}$.

A more difficult question is: "Do you know the set of all the numbers whose square is less than 4?" Either of the following answers is correct:

1. The set of all numbers whose absolute value is less than 2.
2. The set of all numbers greater than -2 and less than 2.

Thus, 0, $\frac{1}{2}$, $-\frac{1}{2}$, $\frac{1}{4}$, $-\frac{1}{4}$, and -1 are numbers whose square is less than 4.

Let us consider the graphic and algebraic methods that can be used to solve such problems. If we begin by letting x represent any number whose square is less than 4, then $x^2 < 4$. When 4 is subtracted from each side, then we obtain the equivalent inequality $x^2 - 4 < 0$. The inequality $x^2 - 4 < 0$ is in the standard form of a **quadratic inequality,** which is $ax^2 + bx + c \neq 0$ where $a \neq 0$. This standard form of a quadratic inequality may be written either as $ax^2 + bx + c < 0$ or as $ax^2 + bx + c > 0$, where $a \neq 0$.

The model problems that follow show how quadratic inequalities in one variable can be solved graphically by means of a parabola, and how such inequalities can be solved algebraically. If a quadratic inequality is factorable, it can be solved by applying the following rules:

Rule 1. If the product of two factors is positive, then the factors denote numbers that have the same sign; that is, either (1) both numbers are positive or (2) both numbers are negative.

Rule 2. If the product of two factors is negative, then the factors denote numbers that differ in sign; that is, either (1) the first number is positive and the second number is negative or (2) the first number is negative and the second number is positive.

The rules may be better understood if the numbers denoted by the factors are represented by a and b, as follows:

Rule 1. If $ab > 0$, then either (1) $a > 0$ and $b > 0$ or (2) $a < 0$ and $b < 0$.

Rule 2. If $ab < 0$, then either (1) $a > 0$ and $b < 0$ or (2) $a < 0$ and $b > 0$.

~~~~~~~~~~ *MODEL PROBLEMS* ~~~~~~~~~~

Graphic Solution of the Inequality $x^2 < 4$

1. Find the solution set of $x^2 < 4$ graphically

How To Proceed	*Solution*
1. Transform the given inequality into the standard form $ax^2 + bx + c < 0$.	Transform $x^2 < 4$ into $x^2 - 4 < 0$.

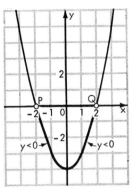

2. Graph the parabola $y = ax^2 + bx + c$.

Graph the parabola $y = x^2 - 4$.

3. If $y < 0$, then $ax^2 + bx + c < 0$ and the required solution set is the set of the x-coordinates of those points whose y-coordinate is negative.

Points on the parabola whose y-coordinate is *negative* are shown in heavy black. Their x-coordinates agree with those points in $\overline{PQ}$, not including points P and Q. Hence, $-2 < x < 2$.

The solution set is shown on the number line below.

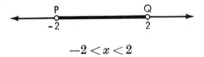

$$-2 < x < 2$$

Answer: The solution set is $\{x \mid -2 < x < 2\}$.

Note. If x has any real value between -2 and 2, then the absolute value of x is less than 2.

Using the Same Parabola To Solve the Inequality $x^2 > 4$

2. Find the solution set of $x^2 > 4$ graphically.

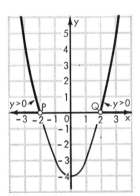

Solution: Suppose we wish to know which numbers have squares that are greater than 4. The same parabola, $y = x^2 - 4$, can be used to solve the inequality $x^2 > 4$ or $x^2 - 4 > 0$. However, we now look for the points on the parabola whose y-coordinate is *positive*, shown in heavy black. Their x-coordinates agree with the points on the x-axis to the left of P or to the right of Q, but not including P and Q. Hence, $x < -2$ or $x > 2$.

Answer: Numbers whose square exceeds 4 are those numbers that are less than -2 or greater than 2; or, numbers whose absolute value exceeds 2.

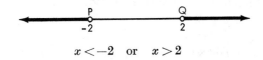

$$x < -2 \quad \text{or} \quad x > 2$$

Algebraic Solution of the Inequality $x^2 < 4$

3. Find the solution set of $x^2 < 4$ algebraically.

How To Proceed	*Solution*
1. Transform the given inequality into the form $ax^2 + bx + c < 0$.	Transform $x^2 < 4$ into $x^2 - 4 < 0$.
2. Factor $ax^2 + bx + c$.	$$x^2 - 4 < 0$$ $$(x + 2)(x - 2) < 0$$
3. Since the product of the two factors is negative, apply the following rule. *If the product of two factors is negative, then the factors denote numbers that differ in sign.*	Either (1) $x + 2 > 0$ and $x - 2 < 0$ or (2) $x + 2 < 0$ and $x - 2 > 0$.

	(1)	(2)
4. Solve each of the first-degree inequalities.	If $x + 2 > 0$, $x > -2$. If $x - 2 < 0$, $x < 2$.	If $x + 2 < 0$, $x < -2$. If $x - 2 > 0$, $x > 2$.
5. Obtain the required solution set by combining the results of step 4.	If $x > -2$ and $x < 2$, then $-2 < x < 2$.	Reject, since x cannot be less than -2 and also greater than 2.

Answer: The solution set is $\{x \mid -2 < x < 2\}$.

Algebraic Solution of the Inequality $x^2 > 4$

4. Find the solution set of $x^2 > 4$ algebraically.

How To Proceed	*Solution*
1. Transform the given inequality into the standard form $ax^2 + bx + c > 0$.	Transform $x^2 > 4$ into $x^2 - 4 > 0$.
2. Factor $ax^2 + bx + c$.	$$x^2 - 4 > 0$$ $$(x + 2)(x - 2) > 0$$

3. Since the product of the two factors is positive, apply the following rule: *If the product of two factors is positive, then the factors denote numbers that have the same sign.*

Either (1) $x + 2 > 0$ and $x - 2 > 0$
or (2) $x + 2 < 0$ and $x - 2 < 0$.

4. Solve each of the resulting first-degree inequalities.

(1)	(2)
If $x + 2 > 0$, $x > -2$.	If $x + 2 < 0$, $x < -2$.
If $x - 2 > 0$, $x > 2$.	If $x - 2 < 0$, $x < 2$.

5. Obtain the solution set by combining the results of step 4.

If $x > -2$ and $x > 2$, then $x > 2$.

If $x < -2$ and $x < 2$, then $x < -2$.

Answer: The solution set is $\{x \mid x > 2 \ \text{ or } \ x < -2\}$.

Solution of a Combination Equality and Inequality

5. The graph of the solution of the inequality $x^2 - 4x \geq 0$ is to be shown by a heavy line or lines on the real number axis. Which graph is correct?

(1)
(2)
(3)
(4)

Solution: It is given that $x^2 - 4x \geq 0$.
Since $x^2 - 4x$ is the product of x and $(x - 4)$, then $x(x - 4) \geq 0$.

$x(x - 4) \geq 0$ is a combination of the equality $x(x - 4) = 0$ and the inequality $x(x - 4) > 0$.

If $x(x - 4) = 0$, then $x = 0$ or $x = 4$.
If $x(x - 4) > 0$, then either x and $(x - 4)$ are both positive or x and $(x - 4)$ are both negative.

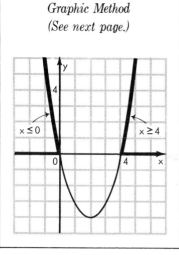

Graphic Method
(See next page.)

1. If both x and $(x - 4)$ are positive, then x must be greater than 4.
2. If both x and $(x - 4)$ are negative, then x must be less than 0.

Hence, the solution has the form $x \leq 0$ or $x \geq 4$.

Answer: The correct choice is (4).

Graphic Method

By graphing $y = x^2 - 4x$, as shown, it can be seen that $y \geq 0$ for values of x such that $x \leq 0$ or $x \geq 4$.

Exercises

1. Graph the parabola $y = x^2 - 1$. Using the parabola, find the solution set of (a) $x^2 - 1 < 0$ and (b) $x^2 > 1$.

2. Graph the parabola $y = x^2 - 4x$. Using the parabola, find the solution set of (a) $x^2 - 4x > 0$ and (b) $x^2 < 4x$.

3. Graph the parabola $f(x) = x^2 - 3x - 4$. Using the parabola, find the solution set of (a) $x^2 - 3x \leq 4$ and (b) $x^2 \geq 3x + 4$.

In 4–12, find graphically the solution set and use a number line to represent the solution set.

4. $x^2 - 5x > 0$ **5.** $x^2 < 5x$ **6.** $x^2 - 5x + 6 < 0$

7. $x^2 > 5x - 6$ **8.** $6 - 5x < x^2$ **9.** $2x^2 - 18 < 0$

10. $3x^2 \geq 12$ **11.** $3x^2 - 12x \geq 0$ **12.** $3x^2 \leq 12x$

In 13–27, find algebraically the solution set and use a number line to represent the solution set.

13. $(x - 3)(x + 3) < 0$ **14.** $(x - 3)(x + 3) > 0$ **15.** $(x - 3)(x - 5) < 0$

16. $(x + 3)(x - 4) > 0$ **17.** $x(x - 6) < 0$ **18.** $y(y + 6) > 0$

19. $x^2 < 25$ **20.** $y^2 - 49 > 0$ **21.** $y(2y - 5) < 0$

22. $5n^2 \geq 45$ **23.** $20 \geq 5n^2$ **24.** $x^2 - 8x + 12 \leq 0$

25. $x^2 - 11x \geq 12$ **26.** $2x^2 + 3x \leq 0$ **27.** $2x^2 + 5x + 3 \leq 0$

In 28–31, use the same graph of a parabola to find the solution sets in parts a, b, and c. Then represent each solution set on a number line.

	Part a	Part b	Part c
28.	$x^2 - 4x - 5 = 0$	$x^2 - 4x - 5 > 0$	$x^2 - 4x - 5 < 0$
29.	$x^2 - 25 = 0$	$x^2 - 25 > 0$	$x^2 - 25 < 0$
30.	$-x^2 - 2x + 3 = 0$	$-x^2 - 2x + 3 > 0$	$-x^2 - 2x + 3 < 0$
31.	$2x^2 - 5x + 2 = 0$	$2x^2 - 5x + 2 > 0$	$2x^2 - 5x + 2 < 0$

In 32–34, find the set of numbers such that in the case of any number in the set:

32. the square of the number is less than 64.

33. the square of the number exceeds 4 less than 5 times the number.

34. twice the square of the number exceeds 3 more than 5 times the number.

13. Systems of Inequalities

GRAPHS OF INEQUALITIES OF THE SECOND DEGREE

The graph of a second-degree equation in two variables divides the Cartesian plane into three sets of points. In Fig. 1, for example, the graph of $x^2 + y^2 = 16$ divides the plane into the following sets of points:

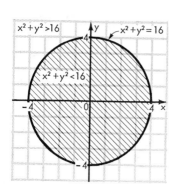

1. The set of the points of the circle, which consists of the graphs of the ordered pairs that satisfy the equation $x^2 + y^2 = 16$. Examples of such points are $(0, 4)$ and $(-4, 0)$.

Fig. 1

2. The set of points in the shaded interior region of the circle, which consists of the graphs of the ordered pairs that satisfy the inequality $x^2 + y^2 < 16$. Examples of such points are $(0, 2)$ and $(-3, 1)$.

3. The set of points in the nonshaded region outside the circle, which consists of the graphs of the ordered pairs that satisfy the inequality $x^2 + y^2 > 16$. Examples of such points are $(0, 6)$ and $(-5, 5)$.

In this case, the circle acts as a ***plane divider*** since it divides the Cartesian plane into two regions, the interior region within the circle and the region exterior to the circle.

In Fig. 2, the graph of $y = x^2$ divides the plane into three sets of points: (1) the set of points on the parabola $y = x^2$, (2) the set of points in the shaded interior region, which consists of the graphs of ordered pairs satisfying $y > x^2$, and (3) the set of points in the non-shaded exterior region, which consists of the graphs of ordered pairs satisfying $y < x^2$. In this case, the parabola is a plane divider.

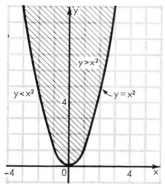

Fig. 2

GRAPHS OF SOLUTION SETS OF SYSTEMS OF INEQUALITIES OF THE SECOND DEGREE

Fig. 3 shows how the circle $x^2 + y^2 = 16$ and the parabola $y = x^2$ divide the Cartesian plane into four regions, A, B, C, and D. Since the points *on* the circle and *on* the parabola do not satisfy the inequalities, the curves are shown as dashed.

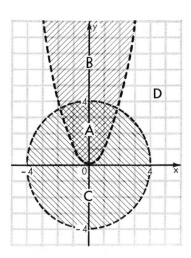

Fig. 3

$$Region\ A\ \begin{cases} x^2 + y^2 < 16 \\ y > x^2 \end{cases}$$

The points in crosshatched region A, such as $(1, 2)$ and $(0, 3)$ are both in the interior region of the circle and in the interior region of the parabola.

$$Region\ B\ \begin{cases} x^2 + y^2 > 16 \\ y > x^2 \end{cases}$$

The points in region B, such as $(1, 6)$ and $(-1, 7)$, are both in the exterior region of the circle and in the interior region of the parabola.

$$Region\ C\ \begin{cases} x^2 + y^2 < 16 \\ y < x^2 \end{cases}$$

The points in region C, such as $(1, -2)$ and $(-2, -1)$, are both in the interior region of the circle and in the exterior region of the parabola.

$$Region\ D\ \begin{cases} x^2 + y^2 > 16 \\ y < x^2 \end{cases}$$

The points in region D, such as $(5, 5)$ and $(5, -3)$, are both in the exterior region of the circle and in the exterior region of the parabola.

Procedure. To graph the solution set of a system of two inequalities:
1. **Graph each inequality, using the same set of coordinate axes.**
2. **The solution set of the system of inequalities is the region common to both graphs.**

~~~~~~~~~~~~~~~~~~~~~ *MODEL PROBLEM* ~~~~~~~~~~~~~~~~~~~~

Find graphically the solution set of $\begin{cases} y > x + 2 \\ \dfrac{x^2}{16} + \dfrac{y^2}{4} \leq 1 \end{cases}$

Solution:

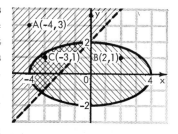

1. The graph of the inequality $y > x + 2$ is the shaded region above the line, $y = x + 2$. Since the points on the line do not satisfy the inequality, the line is shown as dashed. For example, the pair of coordinates of $A(-4, 3)$ satisfies $y > x + 2$.

2. The graph of the combination inequality and equation $\dfrac{x^2}{16} + \dfrac{y^2}{4} \leq 1$ is the union of the ellipse and its shaded interior region.

   Since the points on the ellipse satisfy the equation, the ellipse is shown as a solid line. For example, the pair of coordinates of $B(2, 1)$ satisfies $\dfrac{x^2}{16} + \dfrac{y^2}{4} \leq 1$.

3. The crosshatched region that is the intersection of both graphs made in steps 1 and 2 is the graph of the solution set of the given system. For example, the pair of coordinates of $C(-3, 1)$ satisfies both sentences of the system.

Answer: The crosshatched region is the graph of the required solution set.

~~~~~~

Exercises

In 1–15, find graphically the solution set of the system.

1. $x^2 + y^2 < 25$
    $x + y < 5$

2. $x^2 + y^2 \leq 25$
    $x - y > 5$

3. $x^2 + y^2 \leq 25$
    $y \geq 2x$

4. $y < x^2 - 4$
    $y < 2$

5. $y \leq x^2 - 4$
    $x > -1$

6. $y > x^2 - 4$
    $y > 2x - 1$

7. $xy > 8$
    $y > x$

8. $xy \geq 12$
    $y < x - 3$

9. $xy < -6$
    $x + 2y \leq 6$

10. $x^2 + 4y^2 < 16$
    $y - x < 3$

11. $4x^2 + 9y^2 \leq 36$
    $2x + 3y \leq 6$

12. $x^2 + y^2 < 16$
    $xy > 8$

13. $x^2 + y^2 > 9$
    $xy \geq 4$

14. $y < x^2 + 1$
    $x^2 - y^2 < 1$

15. $y \geq x^2 + 2$
    $xy \geq -4$

CHAPTER XIV

GENERALIZED TRIGONOMETRIC RELATIONSHIPS

In our study of trigonometric functions so far, the rules and formulas used have involved functions of a single angle for the most part, such as $\sin 30°$, $\cos(-60°)$, or $\tan \theta$. However, trigonometric functions of the sum or the difference of two angles, such as $\sin(90° - A)$, $\cos(180° + A)$, or $\tan(270° - A)$, have been found in simple right triangle relationships and in reduction formulas. If the scope of trigonometry is to be extended and used to solve important problems in science, engineering, astronomy, and navigation, then formulas must be applied involving trigonometric functions such as the following:

1. Functions of the sum of two angles in terms of functions of the angles, such as $\sin(A + B)$.

2. Functions of the difference of two angles in terms of functions of the angles, such as $\cos(x - y)$.

3. Functions of the double of an angle in terms of functions of the angle, such as $\tan 2x$.

4. Functions of one-half of an angle in terms of functions of the angle, such as $\tan \frac{1}{2}\theta$.

In addition, formulas will be developed that express, as the product of trigonometric functions, the sum and difference of the sines of two angles and the sum and difference of the cosines of two angles. In general, $\sin A + \sin B \neq \sin(A + B)$ and $\cos A - \cos B \neq \cos(A - B)$.

For example, $\sin 60° + \sin 30° \neq \sin(60° + 30°)$ since $\frac{1}{2}\sqrt{3} + \frac{1}{2} \neq 1$. Also, $\cos 60° - \cos 60° \neq \cos(60° - 60°)$ since $\frac{1}{2} - \frac{1}{2} \neq 1$.

In this chapter, we will study generalized trigonometric relationships of the types set forth above. The proofs of the generalized trigonometric relationships or formulas are included in Chapter 25.

1. Functions of the Sum of Two Angles: Sine, Cosine, and Tangent of the Sum of Two Angles

The following formulas express a function of the sum of two angles in terms of functions of the separate angles. See pages 733–734 for the derivations of these formulas.

$$\sin(x+y) = \sin x \cos y + \cos x \sin y$$

$$\cos(x+y) = \cos x \cos y - \sin x \sin y$$

$$\tan(x+y) = \frac{\tan x + \tan y}{1 - \tan x \tan y}$$

A formula cannot be defined for any value of a variable or variables that makes a denominator equal to zero. Hence, in the formula for $\tan(x+y)$, the denominator $1 - \tan x \tan y \neq 0$.

~~~~~~~~~ *MODEL PROBLEMS* ~~~~~~~~~

1. If $\sin x = \frac{3}{5}$, $\cos x = -\frac{4}{5}$, $\sin y = \frac{5}{13}$, and $\cos y = \frac{12}{13}$, find the value of $\sin(x+y)$.

Solution: Begin with $\sin(x+y) = \sin x \cos y + \cos x \sin y$.
Substitute the given values.

$$\sin(x+y) = \frac{3}{5}\left(\frac{12}{13}\right) + \left(-\frac{4}{5}\right)\frac{5}{13} = \frac{36}{65} - \frac{20}{65} = \frac{16}{65} \quad Ans.$$

2. If x and y are acute angles, $\tan x = \frac{2}{3}$ and $\sin y = \frac{3}{5}$, find the numerical value of $\tan(x+y)$.

Solution: Since $\sin y = \dfrac{\text{ordinate}}{\text{distance}} = \frac{3}{5}$, then

$$\tan y = \frac{\text{ordinate}}{\text{abscissa}} = \frac{3}{4}.$$

$$\tan(x+y) = \frac{\tan x + \tan y}{1 - \tan x \tan y}$$

$$\tan(x+y) = \frac{\frac{2}{3} + \frac{3}{4}}{1 - (\frac{2}{3})(\frac{3}{4})}$$

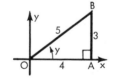

Method 1	*Method 2*

$$\tan(x+y) = \frac{\frac{17}{12}}{1-\frac{1}{2}} = \frac{\frac{17}{12}}{\frac{1}{2}} = \frac{17}{12} \div \frac{1}{2}$$

$$= \frac{17}{\underset{6}{\cancel{12}}} \times \frac{\cancel{2}}{1} = \frac{17}{6} \quad Ans.$$

$$\tan(x+y) = \frac{12(\frac{2}{3}+\frac{3}{4})}{12(1-\frac{1}{2})}$$

$$= \frac{8+9}{12-6} = \frac{17}{6} \quad Ans.$$

3. Express $(\cos 100° \cos 80°) - (\sin 100° \sin 80°)$ as a function of an angle between 0° and 90° inclusive and state the value of the result.

Solution: Begin with $\cos x \cos y - \sin x \sin y = \cos(x+y)$.
Let $x = 100°$ and $y = 80°$.

$$\cos 100° \cos 80° - \sin 100° \sin 80° = \cos(100° + 80°)$$
$$= \cos 180° = -\cos 0°$$
$$= -1$$

Answer: $-\cos 0°$, -1

4. Beginning with the formula for $\sin(x+y)$, prove that $\sin 2x = 2 \sin x \cos x$.

Solution: Begin with $\sin(x+y) = \sin x \cos y + \cos x \sin y$.
Let $y = x$; that is, y represents x.

$$\sin(x+x) = \sin x \cos x + \cos x \sin x$$
$$\sin 2x = 2 \sin x \cos x$$

Note. In like fashion, by substituting x for y, we can derive the formula for $\cos 2x$ from the formula for $\cos(x+y)$; also, we can derive the formula for $\tan 2x$ from the formula for $\tan(x+y)$.

5. Beginning with the formula for $\cos(x+y)$, prove that
$\cos(180° + A) = -\cos A$.

Solution: Begin with $\cos(x+y) = \cos x \cos y - \sin x \sin y$.
Let $x = 180°$ and $y = A$.

$$\cos(180° + A) = \cos 180° \cos A - \sin 180° \sin A$$

Substitute (-1) for $\cos 180°$ and 0 for $\sin 180°$.

$$\cos(180° + A) = (-1) \cos A - (0) \sin A$$
$$\cos(180° + A) = -\cos A$$

6. If $\tan y = a$, express $\tan(y + 45°)$ as a function of a.

Solution: Begin with $\tan(y + 45°) = \dfrac{\tan y + \tan 45°}{1 - \tan y \tan 45}$.

Let $a = \tan y$ and substitute 1 for $\tan 45°$.

$$\tan(y + 45°) = \frac{a + 1}{1 - (a)(1)} = \frac{a + 1}{1 - a} \quad Ans.$$

Exercises

In 1–3, complete the formula.

1. $\sin(A + B) = $ _____   **2.** $\cos(A + B) = $ _____   **3.** $\tan(A + B) = $ _____

In 4–7, transform the expression into a function of an angle between $0°$ and $90°$ inclusive, and state the value of the result.

4. $\sin 50° \cos 40° + \cos 50° \sin 40°$ **5.** $\cos 50° \cos 10° - \sin 50° \sin 10°$

6. $\dfrac{\tan 25° + \tan 20°}{1 - \tan 25° \tan 20°}$

7. $\sin 100° \cos(-70°) + \cos 100° \sin(-70°)$

8. Find the value of $\sin(A + B)$ if $\sin A = \frac{3}{5}$, $\sin B = \frac{4}{5}$, and A and B are acute angles.

9. If $\cos A = \frac{12}{13}$, $\sin B = \frac{12}{13}$, and A and B are positive acute angles, the value of $\cos(A + B)$ is _____.

10. If x and y are both acute angles such that $\tan x = \frac{1}{2}$ and $\tan y = \frac{1}{3}$, find the value of $\tan(x + y)$.

11. If $\tan x = \frac{1}{2}$ and $\tan y = \frac{3}{4}$, find $\tan(x + y)$.

12. If $\tan x = 2$ and $\tan y = \frac{1}{2}$, find $\tan(x + y)$.

13. Answer without the use of trigonometric tables. Angles x and y are acute, $\sin x = \frac{4}{5}$, and $\cos y = \frac{5}{13}$. Find the value of $\tan(x + y)$.

In 14–16, if $\cos A = \frac{3}{5}$ with angle A in quadrant I, and $\sin B = -\frac{12}{13}$ with angle B in quadrant III, find:

14. $\sin(A + B)$ **15.** $\cos(A + B)$ **16.** $\tan(A + B)$

In 17–19, express the given function in terms of functions of x.

17. $\sin(x + x)$, or $\sin 2x$ **18.** $\cos(x + x)$, or $\cos 2x$ **19.** $\tan(x + x)$, or $\tan 2x$

20. Does $\sin(60° + 30°) = \sin 60° + \sin 30°$? (Answer *yes* or *no*.)

21. Is the statement $\tan x + \tan y = \tan(x + y)$ true for all values of x and y?

In 22 and 23, use the formula for $\sin(x + y)$ to prove the statement.

22. $\sin(90° + \theta) = \cos \theta$ **23.** $\sin(180° + \theta) = -\sin \theta$

In 24 and 25, use the formula for $\cos(x + y)$ to prove the statement.

24. $\cos(90° + \theta) = -\sin \theta$ **25.** $\cos\left(\dfrac{3\pi}{2} + \theta\right) = \sin \theta$

In 26–28, express the given function in terms of functions of θ.

26. $\cos(30° + \theta)$ **27.** $\sin(60° + \theta)$ **28.** $\tan\left(\dfrac{5\pi}{4} + \theta\right)$

29. $\tan(45° + x)$ is equal to (1) $1 + \tan x$ (2) $\dfrac{1 - \tan x}{1 + \tan x}$ (3) $\dfrac{1 + \tan x}{1 - \tan x}$

30. Express $\tan(135° + \theta)$ in terms of $\tan \theta$.

2. Functions of the Difference of Two Angles: Sine, Cosine, and Tangent of the Difference of Two Angles

The following formulas express a function of the difference of two angles in terms of functions of the separate angles. See pages 731–735 for the derivation of these formulas.

$$\sin (x - y) = \sin x \cos y - \cos x \sin y$$

$$\cos (x - y) = \cos x \cos y + \sin x \sin y$$

$$\tan (x - y) = \frac{\tan x - \tan y}{1 + \tan x \tan y}$$

~~~~~~~~~~~ *MODEL PROBLEMS* ~~~~~~~~~~~

1. Express $\tan(225° - x)$ in terms of a if $\tan x = a$.

Solution: Begin with $\tan(x - y) = \dfrac{\tan x - \tan y}{1 + \tan x \tan y}$.

Let $x = 225°$ and $y = x$.

$$\tan(225° - x) = \frac{\tan 225° - \tan x}{1 + \tan 225° \tan x}$$

$$\boxed{\begin{aligned}\tan 225° &= \tan(180° + 45°)\\ &= \tan 45° = 1\end{aligned}}$$

Let $a = \tan x$, and substitute 1 for $\tan 225°$.

$$\tan(225° - x) = \frac{1 - a}{1 + a}, \quad a \neq -1 \quad Ans.$$

2. Beginning with the formula for $\cos(x - y)$, prove:

$$\cos(x + y) = \cos x \cos y - \sin x \sin y$$

Solution: This proof is on page 733.

3. Beginning with the formula for $\sin(x - y)$, prove:

$$\sin (270° - \theta) = -\cos \theta$$

Solution: Begin with $\sin(x - y) = \sin x \cos y - \cos x \sin y$.
Let $x = 270°$ and $y = \theta$.

$$\sin(270° - \theta) = \sin 270° \cos \theta - \cos 270° \sin \theta$$

Substitute -1 for $\sin 270°$ and 0 for $\cos 270°$.

$$\sin(270° - \theta) = (-1)(\cos \theta) - (0) \sin \theta$$
$$\sin(270° - \theta) = -\cos \theta$$

4. Express $\sin 140° \cos(-10°) - \cos 140° \sin (-10°)$ as a function of a positive acute angle and state the value of the result.

Solution: Begin with $\sin x \cos y - \cos x \sin y = \sin (x - y)$.
Let $x = 140°$ and $y = (-10°)$.

$$\sin 140° \cos(-10°) - \cos 140° \sin(-10°) = \sin[140° - (-10°)]$$
$$= \sin 150°$$
$$= \sin 30° = \tfrac{1}{2}$$

Answer: $\sin 30°$, $\tfrac{1}{2}$

Exercises

In 1–3, complete the formula.

1. $\sin(A - B) =$ ——   **2.** $\cos(A - B) =$ ——   **3.** $\tan(A - B) =$ ——

4. $\sin (x - y)$ equals (1) $\sin x \cos y + \cos x \sin y$ (2) $\sin x \cos y - \cos x \sin y$ (3) $\cos x \cos y - \sin x \sin y$.

5. Does $\cos(60° - 30°) = \cos 60° - \cos 30°$? (Answer *yes* or *no*.)

6. Is $\tan x - \tan y = \tan(x - y)$ true for all values of x and y?

In 7–10, transform the expression as a function of an angle between $0°$ and $90°$ inclusive and state the value of the result.

7. $\sin 125° \cos 95° - \cos 125° \sin 95°$ **8.** $\cos 85° \cos(-5°) + \sin 85° \sin(-5°)$

9. $\dfrac{\tan 140° - \tan 5°}{1 + \tan 140° \tan 5°}$ **10.** $\sin 40° \cos 85° - \cos 40° \sin 85°$

11. Beginning with the formula for $\sin(x-y)$, prove the formula for $\sin(x+y)$.

12. Beginning with the formula for $\tan(x+y)$, prove the formula for $\tan(x-y)$.

In 13 and 14, use the formula for $\sin(x-y)$ to prove the statement.

13. $\sin(360° - \theta) = -\sin\theta$ **14.** $\sin(270° - \theta) = -\cos\theta$

In 15–17 use the formula for $\cos(x-y)$ to prove the statement.

15. $\cos(90° - \theta) = \sin\theta$ **16.** $\cos(270° - \theta) = -\sin\theta$

17. $\cos(2\pi - \theta) = \cos\theta$

In 18–20, express the given function in terms of functions of θ.

18. $\sin(30° - \theta)$ **19.** $\cos(60° - \theta)$ **20.** $\tan\left(\dfrac{3\pi}{4} - \theta\right)$

21. Express $\sin(x - 30°)$ in terms of $\sin x$ and $\cos x$. (Answer may be left in radical form.)

22. $\sin(180° - x)$ equals   (1) $\sin x$ (2) $-\sin x$ (3) $-\cos x$

23. $\cos(180° - A)$ equals   (1) $\cos A$ (2) $-\cos A$ (3) $-\sin A$

24. If $\cos x = \frac{5}{13}$ and x is an angle in the first quadrant, find $\cos(180° - x)$.

25. In triangle ABC, if $\sin(A+B) = \frac{3}{5}$, what is the value of $\sin C$?

26. If $\tan A = -\frac{3}{7}$, find $\tan(\pi - A)$.

27. $\cot(180° - x)$ is equal to   (1) $\tan x$ (2) $-\tan x$ (3) $\cot x$ (4) $-\cot x$

28. Express $\cos(360° - x)$ in terms of $\cos x$.

29. Express $\tan(45° - x)$ in terms of $\tan x$.

30. Express $\tan(315° - A)$ in terms of $\tan A$.

31. Given $\tan A = r$ and $\tan B = s$. Express $\tan(A - B)$ as a function of r and s.

32. Angle x is acute, angle y is obtuse, $\cos x = \frac{15}{17}$, and $\sin y = \frac{3}{5}$. Find $\sin(x - y)$.

33. If $\sin A = \frac{4}{5}$, $\cos B = \frac{12}{13}$, and both A and B are positive acute angles, find the value of $\cos(A - B)$.

34. Given $\tan x = \frac{1}{2}$ and $\tan y = \frac{1}{3}$. Find the value of $\tan(x - y)$.

35. If x and y are acute angles and $\sin x = \dfrac{2}{\sqrt{13}}$ and $\sin y = \dfrac{4}{\sqrt{41}}$, find $\sin(x - y)$.

36. If A and B are positive acute angles and $\cos A = \dfrac{1}{\sqrt{5}}$ and $\sin B = \dfrac{2}{\sqrt{13}}$, find $\tan(A - B)$.

In 37–39, if $\sin A = \frac{12}{13}$ and A is in quadrant I, and $\cos B = -\frac{4}{5}$ and B is in quadrant III, find:

37. $\sin(B - A)$ **38.** $\cos(B - A)$ **39.** $\tan(B - A)$

In 40–42, beginning with $\sin(x - y) = \sin x \cos y - \cos x \sin y$, and without using tables, find in radical form the value of:

40. $\sin 150°$, letting $x = 180°$ and $y = 30°$.

41. $\sin 315°$, letting $x = 360°$ and $y = 45°$.

42. sin 15°, letting $x = 60°$ and $y = 45°$.

In 43 and 44, without the use of tables, find in radical form the value of:

43. cos 15°   **44.** $\tan \dfrac{\pi}{12}$

In 45–47, expand.

45. $\cos(3A - A)$ **46.** $\sin(5a - 2a)$ **47.** $\tan(4A - 2A)$

3. Functions of Double Angles:
Sine, Cosine, and Tangent of Twice an Angle

The following formulas express a function of double an angle in terms of functions of the angle. See pages 735–736 for derivations of these formulas.

Beginning with the formula for cos $2x$, we can prove that

$$\sin 2x = 2 \sin x \cos x$$

$$\cos 2x = \cos^2 x - \sin^2 x$$

$$\cos 2x = 1 - 2 \sin^2 x$$

$$\cos 2x = 2 \cos^2 x - 1$$

$$\tan 2x = \frac{2 \tan x}{1 - \tan^2 x}$$

⟿⟿⟿ *MODEL PROBLEMS* ⟿⟿⟿

1. If $\cos \theta = \dfrac{-3}{\sqrt{13}}$ and θ is in the second quadrant, find the value of sin 2θ.

Solution: Since $\cos \theta = \dfrac{-3}{\sqrt{13}} = \dfrac{\text{abscissa}}{\text{distance}}$, $x = -3$ and $r = \sqrt{13}$.

$(AP)^2 = (\sqrt{13})^2 - (-3)^2$

$(AP)^2 = 13 - 9 = 4$

Therefore, $AP = 2$.

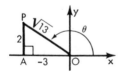

Since $\sin \theta = \dfrac{\text{ordinate}}{\text{distance}}$, then $\sin \theta = \dfrac{2}{\sqrt{13}}$.

Begin with $\sin 2\theta = 2 \sin \theta \cos \theta$.

Substitute: $\sin 2\theta = 2\left(\dfrac{2}{\sqrt{13}}\right)\left(\dfrac{-3}{\sqrt{13}}\right) = -\dfrac{12}{13}$ *Ans.*

2. The statement $2\sin \frac{7}{2}y \cos \frac{7}{2}y = \sin 7y$ is true for (1) no values of y (2) only certain values of y (3) all values of y

Solution: Since $7y$ is twice the angle $\frac{7}{2}y$, we can let $7y = 2A$ and $\frac{7}{2}y = A$ in the identity $\sin 2A = 2\sin A \cos A$ to obtain the new identity $\sin 7y = 2\sin \frac{7}{2}y \cos \frac{7}{2}y$. Since this is an identity, it is true for all values of y.

Answer: (3)

3. Simplify and evaluate $\dfrac{2\tan 22°\,30'}{1 - \tan^2 22°\,30'}$.

Solution: Since $\dfrac{2\tan x}{1 - \tan^2 x} = \tan 2x$,

$$\dfrac{2\tan 22°\,30'}{1 - \tan^2 22°\,30'} = \tan 2(22°\,30')$$

$$= \tan 45° = 1 \quad Ans.$$

4. If $A = \text{Arc cos } \frac{4}{5}$, find the value of $\tan 2A$.

Solution:

"Arc cos $\frac{4}{5}$" means the principal value of the angle whose cosine is $\frac{4}{5}$.

In a right triangle having sides of 3, 4, and 5, A is the acute angle opposite the leg of length 3. Hence, $\tan A = \frac{3}{4}$.

Begin with $\quad\quad\quad \tan 2A = \dfrac{2\tan A}{1 - \tan^2 A}$.

Substitute: $\tan 2A = \dfrac{2(\frac{3}{4})}{1 - (\frac{3}{4})^2} = \dfrac{\frac{3}{2}}{1 - \frac{9}{16}} = \dfrac{\frac{3}{2}}{\frac{7}{16}} = \frac{24}{7}$ *Ans.*

Exercises

In 1 and 2, complete the formula.

1. $\sin 2A =$ _____ **2.** $\tan 2A =$ _____

3. Express $\cos 2A$ in terms of $\sin A$ and $\cos A$.
4. Express $\cos 2A$ in terms of $\sin A$.
5. Express $\cos 2A$ in terms of $\cos A$.

6. Beginning with the formula $\cos(x + y)$, prove $\cos 2x = 2\cos^2 x - 1$.

7. Beginning with the formula $\tan(x + y)$, prove $\tan 2x = \dfrac{2\tan x}{1 - \tan^2 x}$.

8. If $\tan A = \frac{2}{5}$, find the value of $\tan 2A$.

9. If $\cos A = \dfrac{2}{\sqrt{5}}$, find the value of $\cos 2A$.

10. If $\sin A = \frac{3}{5}$ and A is in the second quadrant, find $\sin 2A$.

11. If $\sin x = a$ and $\cos x = b$, express $\sin 2x$ in terms of a and b.

12. If $\sin x = a$, express $\cos 2x$ in terms of a.

13. If $\cos x = a$, express $\cos 2x$ in terms of a.

14. If $\tan t = \sqrt{2}$, $\tan 2t$ equals (1) $\sqrt{2}$ (2) $2\sqrt{2} - 4$ (3) $2\sqrt{2}$ (4) $-2\sqrt{2}$

15. The statement $2\sin \frac{5}{2}x \cos \frac{5}{2}x = \sin 5x$ is true for (1) no values of x (2) only certain values of x (3) all values of x

16. $\cos 10B = \cos^2 5B - \sin^2 5B$ is an identity. (Answer *true* or *false*.)

17. Given $\cos y = \dfrac{-5}{13}$ and y is an angle in the second quadrant, find the value of $\sin 2y$.

18. *a.* If $\tan \theta = \frac{1}{2}$, find $\sin 2\theta$.   *b.* If $\tan x = \frac{2}{3}$, find $\sin 2x$.

19. If x is a positive acute angle and $\sin x = \dfrac{2}{\sqrt{13}}$, find $\sin 2x$.

20. If $\tan A = \frac{2}{3}$ then the value of $\tan 2A$ is (1) $\frac{12}{5}$ (2) $\frac{12}{13}$ (3) $\frac{6}{5}$ (4) $\frac{4}{3}$

21. If A is a positive acute angle and $\cos A = \frac{4}{5}$, what is the value of $\cos 2A$?

   (1) 1 (2) $\dfrac{7}{25}$ (3) $\dfrac{9}{25}$ (4) $\dfrac{24}{25}$

22. $\sin 2A = 2\sin A$ (1) for all values of A (2) when $A = 180°$ (3) when $A = 90°$

23. The expression $\sin^2 \theta - \cos^2 \theta$ is identically equal to the expression (1) $\cos(-2\theta)$ (2) $\cos 2\theta$ (3) $-\cos 2\theta$

24. The statement $1 + \cos 2x = 2\cos^2 x$ is true for (1) no values of x (2) certain values of x (3) all values of x

25. Express $\dfrac{2\cot x}{\csc^2 x}$ as a single function of $2x$.

26. If $A = \operatorname{Arc\,cos} \frac{1}{2}$, find the value of $\sin 2A$.

27. If $A = \tan^{-1} 1$, find the value of $\cos 2A$.

28. If $A = \operatorname{Arc\,sin} \frac{5}{13}$, find the value of $\tan 2A$.

In 29 and 30, derive the required formula by replacing y with $2x$.

29. Beginning with the formula for $\sin(x + y)$, derive the formula
   $\sin 3x = 3\sin x - 4\sin^3 x$.

30. Beginning with the formula for $\cos(x + y)$, derive the formula
$\cos 3x = 4 \cos^3 x - 3 \cos x$.

4. Functions of Half Angles:
Sine, Cosine, and Tangent of One-Half an Angle

The following formulas express a function of one-half an angle in terms of functions of the whole angle. See pages 736–737 for derivations of these formulas.

$$\sin \tfrac{1}{2}x = \pm \sqrt{\frac{1 - \cos x}{2}} \qquad \cos \tfrac{1}{2}x = \pm \sqrt{\frac{1 + \cos x}{2}} \qquad \tan \tfrac{1}{2}x = \pm \sqrt{\frac{1 - \cos x}{1 + \cos x}}$$

Note that each radical is preceded by $\pm$. Whether $+$ or $-$ is to be used depends on the quadrant in which the half-angle belongs.

Thus, if $x = 300°$, then $\tfrac{1}{2}x = 150°$. Hence, using the $\sin \tfrac{1}{2}x$ formula, place $+$ before the radical sign; using the $\cos \tfrac{1}{2}x$ formula or $\tan \tfrac{1}{2}x$ formula, use $-$ before the radical sign.

~~~~~~~~~~ *MODEL PROBLEMS* ~~~~~~~~~~

1. If $\cos x = \tfrac{4}{5}$ and x is an acute angle, find the value of $\tan \tfrac{1}{2}x$.
   Solution: Since x is an acute angle, then $\tfrac{1}{2}x$ is also an acute angle. Therefore, $\tan \tfrac{1}{2}x$ is positive.

Hence, $\tan \tfrac{1}{2}x = + \sqrt{\dfrac{1 - \cos x}{1 + \cos x}}.$

Substitute $\tfrac{4}{5}$ for $\cos x$.

$$\tan \tfrac{1}{2}x = \sqrt{\frac{1 - \tfrac{4}{5}}{1 + \tfrac{4}{5}}} = \sqrt{\frac{\tfrac{1}{5}}{\tfrac{9}{5}}} = \sqrt{\frac{1}{9}} = \frac{1}{3} \quad Ans.$$

2. If $\cos x = \dfrac{-14}{64}$ and x is in the third quadrant, find $\cos \tfrac{1}{2}x$.

   Solution: If $\cos x = \dfrac{-14}{64}$ and x is in the third quadrant, then the value of x is between $180°$ and $270°$. Then $\tfrac{1}{2}x$ is an angle whose value is between $90°$ and $135°$. Therefore, $\cos \tfrac{1}{2}x$ is negative.

Hence, $\cos \tfrac{1}{2}x = - \sqrt{\dfrac{1 + \cos x}{2}}.$

Substitute $\dfrac{-14}{64}$ for cos x.

$$\cos \tfrac{1}{2}x = -\sqrt{\frac{1+(-\frac{14}{64})}{2}} = -\sqrt{\frac{25}{64}} = -\frac{5}{8} \quad Ans.$$

3. If $\cos \theta = b$, express $\sin^2 \tfrac{1}{2}\theta$ in terms of b.

Solution: Begin with $\sin \tfrac{1}{2}\theta = \pm\sqrt{\dfrac{1-\cos \theta}{2}}$.

Square each side.

$$\sin^2 \tfrac{1}{2}\theta = \frac{1-\cos \theta}{2}$$

Substitute b for $\cos \theta$.

$$\sin^2 \tfrac{1}{2}\theta = \frac{1-b}{2} \quad Ans.$$

Exercises

In 1–3, complete the formula.

1. $\sin \tfrac{1}{2}A = $ _____   **2.** $\cos \tfrac{1}{2}A = $ _____   **3.** $\tan \tfrac{1}{2}A = $ _____

In 4–6, express the function in terms of $\cos x$.

4. $\sin^2 \tfrac{1}{2}x$ **5.** $\cos^2 \tfrac{1}{2}x$ **6.** $\tan^2 \tfrac{1}{2}x$

In 7–10, state the quadrant in which $\tfrac{1}{2}A$ lies if $A < 360°$ and A is in:

7. quadrant I   **8.** quadrant II   **9.** quadrant III   **10.** quadrant IV

In 11–13, simplify and evaluate the expression.

11. $\sqrt{\dfrac{1-\cos 60°}{2}}$ **12.** $-\sqrt{\dfrac{1+\cos 300°}{2}}$ **13.** $\sqrt{\dfrac{1+\cos(-60°)}{2}}$

14. Express $\sin 10°$ in terms of $\cos 20°$.

15. Express $\cos 35°$ in terms of $\cos 70°$.

16. Express $\tan 40°$ in terms of $\cos 80°$.

17. Beginning with a formula for $\cos 2\theta$, prove that $\cos \tfrac{1}{2}x = 1 - 2\sin^2 \tfrac{1}{4}x$.

18. If $\cos x = m$, express the positive value of $\sin \dfrac{x}{2}$ in terms of m.

19. If $\cos x = a$, express $\tan^2 \dfrac{x}{2}$ in terms of a.

20. If $\cos A = x$, then $\sin^2 \frac{1}{2}A$ is   (1) $\dfrac{1-x}{2}$ (2) $\dfrac{1+x}{2}$ (3) $\dfrac{1-x}{1+x}$

21. Given $\cos x = \frac{1}{9}$. Find the positive value of $\sin \frac{1}{2}x$.

22. Given $\cos y = \frac{7}{25}$ and y a positive angle in the first quadrant. Find $\cos \frac{1}{2}y$.

23. Find the value of $\tan \frac{1}{2}x$ if x is the acute angle whose cosine is $\frac{3}{5}$.

24. If $\cos x = \frac{1}{9}$ and x is a positive acute angle, find $\sin \frac{1}{2}x$.

25. If $\cos x = 0.8$, find the value of $\sin^2 \frac{1}{2}x$.

26. If A is a positive acute angle and $\cos A = \frac{7}{9}$, find the value of $\sin \frac{1}{2}A$.

27. Angle x is in quadrant IV. If $\tan x = \dfrac{-24}{7}$, find $\cos \frac{1}{2}x$.

28. If $\cos x = \frac{4}{5}$, find the positive value of $\tan \frac{1}{2}x$.

29. Given that A is a positive acute angle and that $\cos A = \frac{1}{4}$. Express, in radical form, the value of $\tan \frac{1}{2}A$.

30. If $\cos x = .02$, find, without the use of tables, the positive value of $\sin \frac{1}{2}x$.

31. If $\cos A = -\frac{7}{25}$, find, without the use of tables, the positive value of $\sin \frac{1}{2}A$.

In 32–34, if $\sin x = \dfrac{-5}{13}$ and x is in the fourth quadrant, find:

32. $\sin \frac{1}{2}x$ **33.** $\cos \frac{1}{2}x$ **34.** $\tan \frac{1}{2}x$

35. The statement $\sin \dfrac{\theta}{2} = \pm \sqrt{\dfrac{1 - \cos \theta}{2}}$ is (1) true for all values of θ (2) true for only certain values of θ (3) not true for any value of θ

36. $\cos^2 3A = \dfrac{1 + \cos 6A}{2}$ is an identity. (Answer *true* or *false*.)

5. Sums and Differences of Two Sines or Two Cosines

In the following formulas, sums and differences of the sines or cosines of two angles are transformed into equivalent expressions involving products. Such formulas are useful in:

1. logarithmic computation.
2. the simplification of trigonometric expressions.
3. the proving of identities.
4. the solution of trigonometric equations.

$\sin A + \sin B = 2 \sin \frac{1}{2}(A + B) \cos \frac{1}{2}(A - B)$ (See model problem 1.)

$\sin A - \sin B = 2 \cos \frac{1}{2}(A + B) \sin \frac{1}{2}(A - B)$

$\cos A + \cos B = 2 \cos \frac{1}{2}(A + B) \cos \frac{1}{2}(A - B)$

$\cos A - \cos B = -2 \sin \frac{1}{2}(A + B) \sin \frac{1}{2}(A - B)$

~~~~~~~~~~~~~ *MODEL PROBLEMS* ~~~~~~~~~~~~~

1. Beginning with the formulas for $\sin(x + y)$ and $\sin(x - y)$, derive

$\sin A + \sin B = 2 \sin \frac{1}{2}(A + B) \cos \frac{1}{2}(A - B)$.

Solution:

$$\sin(x + y) = \sin x \cos y + \cos x \sin y$$

$$\text{Add: } \underline{\sin(x - y) = \sin x \cos y - \cos x \sin y}$$

$$\sin(x + y) + \sin(x - y) = 2 \sin x \cos y \quad (1)$$

Let $A = x + y$ and $B = x - y$. Hence, $A + B = 2x$ and $A - B = 2y$. Thus, $\frac{1}{2}(A + B) = x$ and $\frac{1}{2}(A - B) = y$.

In equation (1), replace $(x + y)$ with A; replace $(x - y)$ with B; replace x with $\frac{1}{2}(A + B)$; replace y with $\frac{1}{2}(A - B)$:

$$\sin A + \sin B = 2 \sin \frac{1}{2}(A + B) \cos \frac{1}{2}(A - B)$$

2. Express $\cos 7x + \cos 3x$ as the product of two functions.

Solution: Begin with $\cos A + \cos B = 2 \cos \frac{1}{2}(A + B) \cos \frac{1}{2}(A - B)$.
Let $A = 7x$ and $B = 3x$.

$$\cos 7x + \cos 3x = 2 \cos \frac{1}{2}(7x + 3x) \cos \frac{1}{2}(7x - 3x)$$
$$= 2 \cos \frac{1}{2}(10x) \cos \frac{1}{2}(4x)$$
$$= 2 \cos 5x \cos 2x \quad Ans.$$

3. Express $\sin 140° - \sin 80°$ as a function of $70°$.

Solution: Begin with $\sin A - \sin B = 2 \cos \frac{1}{2}(A + B) \sin \frac{1}{2}(A - B)$.
Let $A = 140°$ and $B = 80°$.

$$\sin 140° - \sin 80° = 2 \cos \frac{1}{2}(140° + 80°) \sin \frac{1}{2}(140° - 80°)$$

$\cos 110° = \cos(180° - 70°)$	$= 2 \cos 110° \sin 30°$
$= -\cos 70°$	$= 2(-\cos 70°)(\frac{1}{2})$
	$= -\cos 70° \quad Ans.$

4. Express $\cos 8x - \cos 4x$ as a product.

Solution: Begin with $\cos A - \cos B = -2 \sin \frac{1}{2}(A + B) \sin \frac{1}{2}(A - B)$.
Let $A = 8x$ and $B = 4x$.

$$\cos 8x - \cos 4x = -2 \sin \frac{1}{2}(8x + 4x) \sin \frac{1}{2}(8x - 4x)$$
$$= -2 \sin 6x \sin 2x \quad Ans.$$

Exercises

In 1–6, transform the expression into a product of two functions and then state the result in the simplest radical form.

1. $\cos 75° + \cos 15°$ **2.** $\cos 195° - \cos 75°$ **3.** $\sin 165° + \sin 75°$

4. $\cos 225° + \cos 135°$ **5.** $\sin \dfrac{5\pi}{4} + \sin \dfrac{3\pi}{4}$ **6.** $\sin 75° - \sin(-15°)$

7. Beginning with the formulas for $\sin(x + y)$ and $\sin(x - y)$, prove:
$$\sin A - \sin B = 2 \sin \tfrac{1}{2}(A - B) \cos \tfrac{1}{2}(A + B)$$

8. Beginning with the formulas for $\cos(x + y)$ and $\cos(x - y)$, prove:
  a. $\cos A + \cos B = 2 \cos \tfrac{1}{2}(A + B) \cos \tfrac{1}{2}(A - B)$
  b. $\cos A - \cos B = -2 \sin \tfrac{1}{2}(A + B) \cos \tfrac{1}{2}(A - B)$

9. Express $\sin(x + y) + \sin(x - y)$ as a product of two functions.

10. Express $\cos(A + B) - \cos(A - B)$ as a product of two functions.

In 11–19, express the sum or difference as the product of two functions.

11. $\sin x + \sin y$ **12.** $\sin 80° - \sin 30°$ **13.** $\cos 40° + \cos 10°$
14. $\cos 70° - \cos 26°$ **15.** $\sin 3A + \sin A$ **16.** $\cos 9x - \cos 3x$
17. $\cos 10x + \cos 6x$ **18.** $\sin 7B - \sin 3B$ **19.** $\sin A - \sin 5A$

20. $\sin 3x + \sin x$ is equal to (1) $\sin 4x$ (2) $2 \sin 2x \cos x$ (3) $2 \sin x \cos 2x$
21. Express $\sin 130° + \sin 10°$ as a function of $70°$.
22. Express $\cos 70° - \cos 50°$ as a function of $10°$.
23. Express $\cos 110° - \cos 50°$ as a function of $80°$.
24. Express $\sin 80° - \sin 20°$ as a function of $50°$.
25. $\sin 40° + \sin 20°$ equals   (1) $\sin 60°$ (2) $\cos 20°$ (3) $\cos 10°$
26. $\sin 80° + \sin 10°$ equals   (1) $\sin 90°$ (2) $\sqrt{2} \sin 35°$ (3) $\sqrt{2} \cos 35°$
27. $\sin 65° - \sin 15°$ equals (1) $\sin 50°$ (2) $2 \sin 40° \cos 25°$ (3) $2 \cos 40° \sin 25°$
28. $\sin 32° + \sin 28°$ equals   (1) $\sqrt{3} \sin 2°$ (2) $\sqrt{3} \cos 2°$ (3) $\cos 2°$
29. $\cos 100° + \cos 20°$ equals   (1) $\cos 40°$ (2) $\sin 40°$ (3) $\sqrt{3} \cos 40°$
30. $\cos 70° - \cos 10°$ equals (1) $\cos 60°$ (2) $-\sin 40°$ (3) $\sin 40°$
31. Find the value of $\sin 150° - \sin 210°$.

32. Find the value of $\dfrac{\cos 50° + \cos 40°}{\sin 50° + \sin 40°}$.

33. Express $\sin \left(\dfrac{\pi}{2} + A\right) + \sin \left(\dfrac{\pi}{2} - A\right)$ as a function of A.

34. Show that the expression $\dfrac{\sin 3x + \sin x}{\cos 3x + \cos x}$ may be reduced to the form $\tan 2x$.

35. Show that $\dfrac{\sin 7x + \sin 5x}{\cos 7x - \cos 5x}$ may be reduced to $-\cot x$.

CHAPTER XV

EQUATIONS: IDENTITIES AND CONDITIONAL EQUATIONS

1. Kinds of Equations: Identities and Conditional Equations

You are already familiar with equations in one variable such as $4x + 2x = 6x$ and $4x + 2x = 12$. You are now ready to extend your understanding to equations involving trigonometric functions, that is, to **trigonometric equations** such as $4 \sin x + 2 \sin x = 6 \sin x$ and $4 \sin x + 2 \sin x = 12$.

There is an important difference between the first two equations. The equation $4x + 2x = 12$ is a true statement for only one value of x, namely, $x = 2$. This equation is called a *conditional equation* in accordance with the following definition:

A **conditional equation** is an equation that is a true statement for no replacement, one replacement, or more than one but not all replacements for the variable.

On the other hand, the equation $4x + 2x = 6x$ is a true statement for all values of x in the replacement set. This equation is called an *identity* in accordance with the following definition:

An **identity** is an equation that is a true statement for all values in the replacement set for which the equation is defined.

Unless otherwise stated, we will assume that the replacement set of the variable is the set of real numbers.

An identity cannot be defined for any value of a variable or variables which make a denominator in the identity equal to 0.

Thus, the equation $\dfrac{x^2 - 1}{x - 1} = x + 1$, $x \neq 1$, is an identity since the value of 1 for x has been excluded, a value that makes the denominator, $x - 1$, equal 0. Also, $\cos x = \dfrac{\sin x}{\tan x}$ is an identity if the values of x that make the denominator 0 or undefined are excluded. Such exclusions would include x-values of 0, 180°, and −180°, which make $\tan x = 0$; and x-values of 90°, 270°, and −90°, which make $\tan x$ undefined.

An equation cannot be an identity if it can be proved false for a single value of any of its variables. Any such value is called a ***counterexample.***

Thus, the equation $\sin x + \cos x = 1$ is a conditional equation, not an identity, since $30°$ is a counterexample. If x is replaced with $30°$, then $\sin 30° + \cos 30° = 1$ is a false statement because $\frac{1}{2} + \frac{1}{2}\sqrt{3} \neq 1$.

Exercises

In 1–6, determine whether the given equation is an identity or a conditional equation.

1. $2x + 4x = 6x$ **2.** $2x + 4x = 6$ **3.** $2x + 4 = 6x$

4. $x^2 + 4x = x(x + 4)$ **5.** $\dfrac{x^2 + 4x}{x} = x + 4$ **6.** $\dfrac{x^2 + 4x}{x + 4} = x$

In 7–17, determine whether the given equation is an identity or a conditional equation. If the given equation is an identity, state the law or principle that applies.

7. $a + b = b + a$ **8.** $a - b = b - a$ **9.** $a(b + c) = ab + ac$

10. $a + b - c = a - c + b$ **11.** $a + b - c = a - b + c$ **12.** $(a + b)^2 = a^2 + b^2$

13. $ab = ba$ **14.** $a^b = b^a$ **15.** $a(b - c) = ab - c$

16. $a + (-a) = 0$ **17.** $a + 0 = a$

In 18–26, show that the equation is *not* an identity by testing for the indicated value of x or y.

18. $\sin 2x = 2 \cos x$ (let $x = 45°$)   **19.** $\cos 2x = \cos^2 x$ (let $x = 60°$)

20. $\cos^2 x - \sin^2 x = \frac{1}{2}$ (let $x = 0°$)   **21.** $\dfrac{\sin 2x}{2} + \cos x = 1$ (let $x = 30°$)

22. $\tan 2x = 2 \tan x$ (let $x = 30°$)

23. $\cos(90° - x) = \cos x$ (let $x = 60°$)

24. $(x + y)^2 = x^2 + y^2$ (let $x = 1$ and $y = 2$)

25. $(a + x)^2 - (a - x)^2 = 2ax$ (let $x = a$ and $a \neq 0$)

26. $a^2 - (a - x)(a + x) = a^2$ (let $x = 0$ and $a \neq 0$)

27. The expression $a^2 - (a - x)(a + x) = x^2$ is an identity. (Answer *true* or *false*.)

2. Reviewing the Basic Identities

Recall the following eight fundamental identities, which were previously established for an acute angle. These identities are also true for an angle of any size. As in the case of any identity, we shall assume that all values for which the identity is not defined have been excluded, such as those that make a denominator of the identity equal to 0.

Reciprocal Identities	Quotient Identities	Pythagorean Identities
$\cot \theta = \dfrac{1}{\tan \theta}$ $\sec \theta = \dfrac{1}{\cos \theta}$ $\csc \theta = \dfrac{1}{\sin \theta}$	$\tan \theta = \dfrac{\sin \theta}{\cos \theta}$ $\cot \theta = \dfrac{\cos \theta}{\sin \theta}$	$\sin^2 \theta + \cos^2 \theta = 1$ $\tan^2 \theta + 1 = \sec^2 \theta$ $\cot^2 \theta + 1 = \csc^2 \theta$

MODEL PROBLEM

Express $\tan x(\csc x - \sin x)$ in terms of $\cos x$.

Solution: Since $\tan x = \dfrac{\sin x}{\cos x}$ and $\csc x = \dfrac{1}{\sin x}$,

$$\tan x(\csc x - \sin x) = \frac{\sin x}{\cos x}\left(\frac{1}{\sin x} - \sin x\right)$$

$$= \frac{1}{\cos x} - \frac{\sin^2 x}{\cos x}$$

$$= \frac{1 - \sin^2 x}{\cos x}$$

$$= \frac{\cos^2 x}{\cos x} = \cos x \quad Ans.$$

Exercises

In 1–6, write a function of the angle or the value 1 in the space provided so that the resulting equation will be an identity.

1. $1 - \sin^2 \theta = ($ $)^2$

2. $\sec^2 \theta - 1 = ($ $)^2$

3. $\sec^2 \theta - \tan^2 \theta = ($ $)$

4. $\csc^2 \theta - ($ $)^2 = 1$

5. $\pm\sqrt{\tan^2 \theta + 1} = ($ $)$

6. $\pm\sqrt{\csc^2 \theta - 1} = ($ $)$

In 7–12, write a function of the angle in the space provided so that the resulting equation will be an identity.

7. $\dfrac{1}{\cot \theta} = ($ $)$

8. $\dfrac{\sin \theta}{\tan \theta} = ($ $)$

9. $\sin \theta \cot \theta = (\quad)$ **10.** $\tan \theta \csc \theta = (\quad)$

11. $(\sin \theta)(\cot \theta)(\quad) = 1$ **12.** $(\tan \theta)(\csc \theta)(\quad) = 1$

In 13–24, transform the given expression in terms of the sine of the angle, the cosine of the angle, or both the sine and cosine of the angle. Express the results in simplest terms.

13. $\dfrac{\sin A}{\csc A}$ **14.** $\dfrac{\cos A}{\sec A}$

15. $\sec B \csc B$ **16.** $\tan^2 C + 1$

17. $\tan D + \cot D$ **18.** $\sec R + \csc R$

19. $\tan A(\cos A + \csc A)$ **20.** $\cot \theta(\sin \theta - \sec \theta)$

21. $(\sec C + 1)(\sec C - 1)$ **22.** $(1 - \cos G)(1 + \cos G)$

23. $\dfrac{\tan^2 A}{\tan^2 A + 1}$ **24.** $\dfrac{1 - \sin^2 \theta}{\cot^2 \theta}$

25. Prove that the expression $(\tan B + \cot B) \sin B \cos B$ equals 1.

3. Transforming an Identity To Obtain New Related Identities

An identity can be transformed into a new related identity through the substitution of an equivalent expression.

For example, if we begin with the identity $\sin 2x = 2 \sin x \cos x$ and let $x = 3A$, then we obtain the new related identity $\sin 6A = 2 \sin 3A \cos 3A$. If we begin with the identity $\cos \frac{1}{2}x = \pm\sqrt{\dfrac{1 + \cos x}{2}}$ and square both sides, we obtain the new related identity, $\cos^2 \frac{1}{2}x = \dfrac{1 + \cos x}{2}$. If both sides of the latter identity are multiplied by 2 and then 1 is subtracted from each side of the result, we obtain the new related identity $\cos x = 2 \cos^2 \frac{1}{2}x - 1$.

~~~~~~~~~~~~ *MODEL PROBLEMS* ~~~~~~~~~~~~

1. $\sin^2 5x + \cos^2 5x = 1$ is true for (1) no values of x (2) only certain values of x (3) all values of x

Solution: If we begin with the identity $\sin^2 \theta + \cos^2 \theta = 1$ and let $\theta = 5x$, we obtain the new related identity $\sin^2 5x + \cos^2 5x = 1$.

Answer: The correct choice is (3).

2. Beginning with $\cos 2x = \cos^2 x - \sin^2 x$, obtain the identity
$$\cos^2 x = \frac{1 + \cos 2x}{2}.$$

Solution: Begin with $\cos 2x = \cos^2 x - \sin^2 x$.
For $\sin^2 x$, substitute the equivalent expression $1 - \cos^2 x$.
$$\cos 2x = \cos^2 x - (1 - \cos^2 x)$$
Remove parentheses and combine terms.
$$\cos 2x = \cos^2 x - 1 + \cos^2 x$$
$$\cos 2x = 2 \cos^2 x - 1$$
$$A_1: \ 1 + \cos 2x = 2 \cos^2 x$$
$$D_2: \ \frac{1 + \cos 2x}{2} = \cos^2 x \quad Ans.$$

3. Beginning with $\sin^2 x + \cos^2 x = 1$, obtain the identity
$\sin^2 3y = (1 - \cos 3y)(1 + \cos 3y)$.

Solution: Begin with $\sin^2 x + \cos^2 x = 1$.
Subtract $\cos^2 x$ from each side and factor.
$$\sin^2 x = 1 - \cos^2 x$$
$$\sin^2 x = (1 - \cos x)(1 + \cos x)$$
$$\text{Let } x = 3y: \ \sin^2 3y = (1 - \cos 3y)(1 + \cos 3y) \quad Ans.$$

Exercises

In 1–3, beginning with $\sin 2A = 2 \sin A \cos A$, state the resulting identity obtained when the indicated substitution is made.

1. 6θ for A **2.** $\dfrac{\theta}{4}$ for A **3.** $(90° + x)$ for A

In 4 and 5, indicate the substitution required in the first identity to obtain the second identity.

4. $\cos 2A = 1 - 2 \sin^2 A$ to $\cos 8B = 1 - 2 \sin^2 4B$

5. $\sin 2\theta = 2 \sin \theta \cos \theta$ to $\sin x = 2 \sin \dfrac{x}{2} \cos \dfrac{x}{2}$

6. Which equation is an identity?   (1) $\sin 4x = 4 \sin x \cos x$ (2) $\cos 4x = \cos^4 x - \sin^4 x$ (3) $\sin^2 4x + \cos^2 4x = 1$ (4) $\sin^4 x + \cos^4 x = 1$

7. The expression $\sin(-A) + \cos(-A)$ is equivalent to (1) $\sin A + \cos A$ (2) $-\sin A - \cos A$ (3) $\sin A - \cos A$ (4) $-\sin A + \cos A$

8. Find the value of $\sin^2 70° + \cos^2 70°$.

9. What is the value of $\sin^2 3A + \cos^2 3A$?

10. The value of $\sin^2 2A + \cos^2 2A$ is (1) 1   (2) 2   (3) 4

11. $\sin^2 6\theta + \cos^2 6\theta = 1$ is true for (1) no value of θ (2) only certain values of θ (3) all values of θ

12. The value of $2\sin^2 x + 2\cos^2 x$ is (1) 1 (2) 2 (3) 4

13. $2\sin \frac{5}{2}x \cos \frac{5}{2}x = \sin 5x$ is true for (1) all values of x (2) only certain values of x (3) no values of x.

14. $\sin 5x = \sin 3x \cos 2x + \cos 3x \sin 2x$ is true for (1) no values of x (2) all values of x (3) only certain values of x

15. Which of the following equations is an identity? (1) $\sin^2 2A + \cos^2 2A = 1$ (2) $\sin^2 2A + \cos^2 2A = 2$ (3) $\sin^2 A - \cos^2 A = 1$ (4) $\sin A + \cos 2A = 1$

16. The expression $\cos 2x = 1 - 2\sin^2 x$ is (1) true for all values of x (2) true for only certain values of x (3) not true for any value of x

17. Beginning with $\cos 2\theta = \cos^2 \theta - \sin^2 \theta$, show how the following identities may be obtained in order:

$a.$ $\cos 2\theta = 2\cos^2 \theta - 1$ $\qquad$ $b.$ $1 + \cos 2\theta = 2\cos^2 \theta$

$c.$ $1 + \cos 2\theta = \dfrac{2}{\sec^2 \theta}$ $\qquad$ $d.$ $1 + \cos 2\theta = \dfrac{2}{1 + \tan^2 \theta}$

18. Beginning with $\tan \dfrac{A}{2} = \pm\sqrt{\dfrac{1 - \cos A}{1 + \cos A}}$ show how the following identities may be obtained in order:

$a.$ $\tan^2 \dfrac{A}{2} = \dfrac{1 - \cos A}{1 + \cos A}$ $\qquad$ $b.$ $\tan^2 \dfrac{A}{2} = \dfrac{(1 - \cos A)^2}{1 - \cos^2 A}$

$c.$ $\tan^2 \dfrac{A}{2} = \dfrac{(1 - \cos A)^2}{\sin^2 A}$ $\qquad$ $d.$ $\tan \dfrac{A}{2} = \dfrac{1 - \cos A}{\sin A}$

$e.$ $\tan \dfrac{A}{2} = \csc A - \cot A$

19. The expression $\dfrac{\tan \theta + \sec \theta}{1 + \sin \theta}$ is equivalent to (1) $\cos \theta$ (2) $\dfrac{1}{\cos \theta}$ (3) $\sin \theta$

20. Show that $\dfrac{\frac{1}{2}\sin^2 x}{\sin^2 \frac{1}{2}x} - 1$ is equivalent to $\cos x$.

21. The expression $(\sin x - \cos x)^2$ is equivalent to (1) 1 (2) $1 - \sin 2x$ (3) $-\cos 2x$ (4) $1 - \cos 2x$

4. Proving Trigonometric Identities

In the previous unit, we began with identities and transformed them into new related identities by making a valid substitution or by applying a valid operation. However, it does not follow that if an equation can be transformed into an identity, then the equation with which we began is an identity. For example, if we begin with a conditional equation, we can obtain an identity by simply multiplying each side by an expression equal to 0, or by 0 itself. If we begin with a conditional equation such as $x = -x$, in which two opposites are equated, and square both sides, the result is $x^2 = x^2$, which is an identity. However, the original equation, $x = -x$, is not an identity. "Multiplying each side of an equation by zero" and "squaring each side of an equation" are examples of operations that cannot be reversed. "Adding the same number to each side of an equation" is an example of a reversible operation. For example, $x = 3 - y$ becomes $x + y = 3$ if y is added to each side. In turn, the reverse is true since $x + y = 3$ can be transformed into an equivalent equation $x = 3 - y$.

In order to avoid the pitfalls of using a nonreversible operation when we are trying to prove that an equation is an identity, it is best to treat both members of the equation independently, using either of the following procedures:

Procedure. To prove an identity:
1. **Transform one of the members into an expression that is identical with the other.**

OR

2. **Transform both members *independently* into identical expressions.**

Procedure 1 is shown in model problems 1 and 2. In model problem 1, only the left member is transformed; in model problem 2, only the right member is transformed.

Procedure 2 is shown in model problems 3 and 4. Note in model problems 3 and 4 how the transformations made on each side are made independently.

USEFUL SUGGESTIONS FOR PROVING IDENTITIES

1. Avoid aimless transformations. Any transformation that is made in one of the members should lead in some way to the form of the other.
2. Start with the more complicated member of the identity and transform it into the form of the simpler member.
3. Where possible, express different functions in terms of the same function.
4. It is often useful to express all functions in terms of sines and cosines, or in tangents and secants.
5. As a rule, trigonometric functions of a double angle, a half angle, or the sums and differences of angles should be expressed in terms of functions of the single angle.
6. Simplify expressions by utilizing basic identities and combining like terms. For example, replace $1 - \cos^2 x$ by $\sin^2 x$.
7. Simplify fractions. For example, transform complex fractions into simple fractions or divide the terms of a fraction by the common factors.

~~~~~~~~~~~~~~~~~~ *MODEL PROBLEMS* ~~~~~~~~~~~~~~~~~~

1. *a.* Prove the identity: $\dfrac{1 - \sin x}{\cos^2 x} = \dfrac{1}{1 + \sin x}$

  b. State the values of the variable for which the identity is not valid.

Solution:

a.   Prove: $\dfrac{1 - \sin x}{\cos^2 x} = \dfrac{1}{1 + \sin x}$

   Substitute $1 - \sin^2 x$ for $\cos^2 x$: $\dfrac{1 - \sin x}{1 - \sin^2 x}$

       Factor: $\dfrac{\overset{1}{\cancel{(1 - \sin x)}}}{\cancel{(1 - \sin x)}(1 + \sin x)}$

    Reduce the fraction: $\dfrac{1}{1 + \sin x}$

The equation $\dfrac{1 - \sin x}{\cos^2 x} = \dfrac{1}{1 + \sin x}$ is an identity since one member has been transformed into an expression that is identical with the other.

  b. The identity is not valid if $\cos^2 x = 0$ or if $1 + \sin x = 0$. Hence, exclude values of x such as $90°$, $270°$, or $-90°$, which make $\cos x = 0$; also exclude an x-value of $270°$, which makes $\sin x = -1$.

2. Prove the identity: $\cos^2 A - \sin^2 A = \dfrac{1 - \tan^2 A}{1 + \tan^2 A}$

Solution:

Prove: $\cos^2 A - \sin^2 A = \dfrac{1 - \tan^2 A}{1 + \tan^2 A}$

     $\dfrac{1 - \dfrac{\sin^2 A}{\cos^2 A}}{1 + \dfrac{\sin^2 A}{\cos^2 A}}$ Substituting $\dfrac{\sin A}{\cos A}$ for $\tan A$.

     $\dfrac{\cos^2 A - \sin^2 A}{\cos^2 A + \sin^2 A}$ Simplifying the complex fraction.

     $\dfrac{\cos^2 A - \sin^2 A}{1}$ Substituting 1 for $\sin^2 A + \cos^2 A$.

     $\cos^2 A - \sin^2 A$

The equation $\cos^2 A - \sin^2 A = \dfrac{1 - \tan^2 A}{1 + \tan^2 A}$ is an identity since one member has been transformed into an expression that is identical with the other. Note that the original identity is defined for all real values of tan A. (Keep in mind that when the replacement set is not indicated, it is assumed to be the set of real numbers.)

3. Prove the identity: $\sec x \csc x = \tan x + \cot x$

Solution:

Prove: $\sec x \csc x = \tan x + \cot x$

$\dfrac{1}{\cos x} \cdot \dfrac{1}{\sin x}$	$\dfrac{\sin x}{\cos x} + \dfrac{\cos x}{\sin x}$
$\dfrac{1}{\cos x \sin x}$	$\dfrac{\sin x}{\cos x} \cdot \dfrac{\sin x}{\sin x} + \dfrac{\cos x}{\sin x} \cdot \dfrac{\cos x}{\cos x}$ Combining into a fraction using $\sin x \cos x$ as the L.C.D.
	$\dfrac{\sin^2 x}{\cos x \sin x} + \dfrac{\cos^2 x}{\cos x \sin x}$
	$\dfrac{\sin^2 x + \cos^2 x}{\cos x \sin x}$
	$\dfrac{1}{\cos x \sin x}$ Substituting 1 for $\sin^2 x + \cos^2 x$.

The equation $\sec x \csc x = \tan x + \cot x$ is an identity since the two members have been transformed into identical expressions independently.

4. Prove the identity: $\dfrac{1 + \cos 2A}{\sin 2A} = \cot A$

Solution:

Prove: $\dfrac{1 + \cos 2A}{\sin 2A} = \cot A$

Replace the functions of a double angle: $\dfrac{1 + (2\cos^2 A - 1)}{2 \sin A \cos A}$ $\bigg|$ $\dfrac{\cos A}{\sin A}$

$\dfrac{1 + 2 \cos^2 A - 1}{2 \sin A \cos A}$

Reduce the fraction: $\dfrac{2 \cos^2 A}{2 \sin A \cos A}$ $\bigg|$

$\dfrac{\cos A}{\sin A}$ $\bigg|$

The equation $\dfrac{1 + \cos 2A}{\sin 2A} = \cot A$ is an identity since the two members have been transformed into identical expressions independently. Note that the original identity is not defined for values of A that make $\sin 2A = 0$. Hence, $A \neq 0°,\ 90°,\ -90°$, etc.

〰〰〰〰〰〰〰〰〰〰〰〰〰〰〰〰〰〰〰〰〰〰〰〰〰〰〰〰〰〰〰

Exercises

Set A: Nonfractional Equations

In 1–14, prove that the equation is an identity.

1. $\tan x \csc x = \sec x$
2. $\cos x \csc x = \cot x$

3. $\cos^2 x = \csc x \sin x - \sin^2 x$
4. $\tan^2 x = \sec^2 x - \cos x \sec x$

5. $\tan^2 x + \sin^2 x + \cos^2 x = \sec^2 x$
6. $\cot^2 x = \csc^2 x - \sin^2 x - \cos^2 x$

7. $\tan^2 x = (\sec x - 1)(\sec x + 1)$
8. $\cos^4 x - \sin^4 x = \cos^2 x - \sin^2 x$

9. $(\sin \theta + \cos \theta)^2 = 1 + 2 \sin \theta \cos \theta$
10. $(\sin \theta - \cos \theta)^2 = 1 - 2 \sin \theta \cos \theta$

11. $\tan^2 A(1 + \cot^2 A) = \sec^2 A$
12. $(1 - \sin^2 \theta)(\sec^2 \theta - 1) = \sin^2 \theta$

13. $\sin^2 x + \sin^2 x \tan^2 x = \tan^2 x$
14. $(1 + \sec x)(1 - \cos x) = \cos x \tan^2 x$

Set B: Fractional Equations

In 15–35, prove that the equation is an identity.

15. $\tan x \cos x = \dfrac{1}{\csc x}$
16. $\sin x \cot x = \dfrac{1}{\sec x}$
17. $\sin \theta \sec \theta = \dfrac{1}{\cot \theta}$

18. $\cos x = \dfrac{\cot x}{\csc x}$
19. $\cot x = \dfrac{\csc x}{\sec x}$
20. $\dfrac{\sec x}{\tan x} = \dfrac{\cot x}{\cos x}$

21. $\dfrac{\sin x \csc x}{\tan x} = \cot x$
22. $\dfrac{\tan x}{\sec x} = \dfrac{\cos x}{\cot x}$
23. $\dfrac{\sin x \csc x}{\cos x} = \sec x$

24. $(\cos \theta)(\csc \theta) = \dfrac{1}{\tan \theta}$
25. $(1 - \cos x)(1 + \cos x) = \dfrac{1}{\csc^2 x}$

26. $\dfrac{(1 + \sin x)^2}{\cos^2 x} = \dfrac{1 + \sin x}{1 - \sin x}$
27. $\dfrac{1 - \cos A}{\sin A} = \csc A - \cot A$

28. $\dfrac{1 + \tan A}{\sin A} = \csc A + \sec A$
29. $\dfrac{1 + \sec x}{\csc x} = \sin x + \tan x$

30. $\dfrac{\sec A}{\cot A + \tan A} = \sin A$
31. $\dfrac{\sin x}{1 + \cos x} + \cot x = \csc x$

32. $\dfrac{\sec x + \csc x}{\tan x + \cot x} = \sin x + \cos x$
33. $\dfrac{\cot A}{\tan A} + \dfrac{\tan A}{\cot A} = \dfrac{\cot^4 A + 1}{\cot^2 A}$

34. $\dfrac{\cos\theta\,\sin^2\theta}{1+\cos\theta} = \cos\theta - \cos^2\theta$ **35.** $\dfrac{\sin\theta}{1+\cos\theta} + \dfrac{1+\cos\theta}{\sin\theta} = 2\cot\theta\sec\theta$

Set C: Generalized Trigonometric Relationships
(Double Angle, Half Angle, Sums and Differences of Angles, etc.)

In 36–59, prove that the equation is an identity.

36. $(\sin x - \cos x)^2 = 1 - \sin 2x$ **37.** $\tan A \sin 2A = 2\sin^2 A$

38. $\sin 2x = \dfrac{2\tan x}{1+\tan^2 x}$ **39.** $\cos 2A = \dfrac{2-\sec^2 A}{\sec^2 A}$

40. $\csc 2x = \dfrac{\sec x}{2\sin x}$ **41.** $\tan 2\theta = \dfrac{2\tan\theta}{\sec^2\theta - 2\tan^2\theta}$

42. $\dfrac{\cos x}{\sin x} + \dfrac{\sin x}{\cos x} = \dfrac{2}{\sin 2x}$ **43.** $\sec 2x = \dfrac{1+\tan^2 x}{1-\tan^2 x}$

44. $\dfrac{1-\cos 2x}{\sec^2 x - \tan^2 x} = 2\sin^2 x$ **45.** $\cot\theta - \dfrac{\cos 2\theta}{\sin\theta\cos\theta} = \tan\theta$

46. $\dfrac{\cos B + \sin B}{\cos B - \sin B} = \dfrac{\sin 2B + 1}{\cos 2B}$ **47.** $\dfrac{\cos 2x}{\sin x} + \dfrac{\sin 2x}{\cos x} = \csc x$

48. $\dfrac{\sin 2x}{\sin x} - \dfrac{\cos 2x}{\cos x} = \sec x$ **49.** $\dfrac{2\tan x - \sin 2x}{2\sin^2 x} = \tan x$

50. $\dfrac{\sin(x+y)}{\sin(x-y)} = \dfrac{\tan x + \tan y}{\tan x - \tan y}$ **51.** $\tan x = \dfrac{\sin(x-y)}{\cos x\cos y} + \tan y$

52. $\tan\left(\dfrac{\pi}{4} + x\right) = \dfrac{\cos x + \sin x}{\cos x - \sin x}$ **53.** $\tan(45° + A) = \dfrac{\cos A + \sin A}{\cos A - \sin A}$

54. $\tan(45° + x) = \dfrac{\cos 2x}{1 - \sin 2x}$ **55.** $\dfrac{\sin(x+y) + \sin(x-y)}{\sin x} = 2\cos y$

56. $\sin^2\dfrac{x}{2} = \dfrac{\sec x - 1}{2\sec x}$ **57.** $\tan\tfrac{1}{2}x = \dfrac{\sin x}{1+\cos x}$

58. $\cot\tfrac{1}{2}x = \csc x + \cot x$ **59.** $\sec^2\tfrac{1}{2}x = \dfrac{2(1-\cos x)}{\sin^2 x}$

5. Solving Trigonometric Equations of the First Degree

To solve a conditional trigonometric equation is to find the values of the variable (the measure of an angle) that satisfy the equation. These values are the real roots of the equation and are also members of the solution set of the equation. We shall refer to conditional trigonometric equations as simply "trigonometric equations."

Thus, if $2 \sin x = 1$, then $\sin x = \frac{1}{2}$ and x may have an unlimited number of values such as $30°$, $150°$, $390°$, $-330°$, and $-210°$. Hence, in the statement of the problem, restrictions are placed on the domain of the variable. For example: "Solve for x if x is a positive acute angle" or "Solve for x in the interval $0° < x < 360°$."

The simplest trigonometric equations are those of the first degree in which there is a single function of the angle and the highest power of this function is the first.

Thus, $2 \sin x - \sqrt{3} = 0$, $\tan x - 2.5 = 0$, and $\sin 2A = \frac{1}{2}$ are trigonometric equations of the first degree.

USEFUL SUGGESTIONS FOR SOLVING TRIGONOMETRIC EQUATIONS

1. Simplify the equation by clearing fractions, removing parentheses, collecting like terms, squaring both members of a radical equation involving square root, etc.
2. Express functions of double angles, half angles, and other generalized relationships as functions of single angles.
3. Express different functions of an angle in terms of a single function of the angle.
4. Be sure to solve the equation obtained in step 3 for *all* values of the angle in the required domain.
5. Check the results by substituting in the original equation.

~~~~~~~~~ *MODEL PROBLEMS* ~~~~~~~~~

1. In (*a*) solve for x. In (*b*) solve for the positive acute angle x.

(*a*) $2x - \sqrt{3} = 0$ (*b*) $2 \sin x - \sqrt{3} = 0$

Solution   *Solution*

(*a*) $2x - \sqrt{3} = 0$ (*b*) $2 \sin x - \sqrt{3} = 0$

$2x = \sqrt{3}$ $2 \sin x = \sqrt{3}$

Answer: $\quad x = \dfrac{\sqrt{3}}{2}$ $\sin x = \dfrac{\sqrt{3}}{2}$

Answer: $\quad x = 60°$

$$\begin{array}{ll} \textit{Check} \\ 2x - \sqrt{3} = 0 \\ 2\left(\dfrac{\sqrt{3}}{2}\right) - \sqrt{3} \overset{?}{=} 0 \\ \sqrt{3} - \sqrt{3} \overset{?}{=} 0 \\ 0 = 0 \end{array}$$

$$\begin{array}{ll} \textit{Check} \\ 2\sin x - \sqrt{3} = 0 \\ 2\sin 60^\circ - \sqrt{3} \overset{?}{=} 0 \\ 2\left(\dfrac{\sqrt{3}}{2}\right) - \sqrt{3} \overset{?}{=} 0 \\ \sqrt{3} - \sqrt{3} \overset{?}{=} 0 \\ 0 = 0 \end{array}$$

2. In (a) solve for s. In (b) solve for x in the interval $0 < x < \dfrac{\pi}{2}$.

(a) $\sqrt{4s + 7} = 3$ (b) $\sqrt{4\sin x + 7} = 3$

Solution

(a) $\sqrt{4s + 7} = 3$
Square both sides.
$$4s + 7 = 9$$
$$4s = 2$$

Answer: $s = \tfrac{1}{2}$

Solution

(b) $\sqrt{4\sin x + 7} = 3$
Square both sides.
$$4\sin x + 7 = 9$$
$$4\sin x = 2$$
$$\sin x = \tfrac{1}{2}$$

Answer: $x = 30^\circ$ or $\dfrac{\pi}{6}$

PART A: TRIGONOMETRIC EQUATIONS OF THE FIRST DEGREE TO BE SOLVED FOR A POSITIVE ACUTE ANGLE

Exercises

In 1–4, does $x = 30^\circ$ satisfy the equation? (Answer *yes* or *no*.)

1. $\sin x + \cos 2x = 1$ **2.** $\sin 2x + \cos x = 1$

3. $2\sin 2x - 4\sin x = 0$ **4.** $6\sin x + 2\cos 2x = 4$

In 5 and 6, is $x = \dfrac{\pi}{4}$ a root of the equation? (Answer *yes* or *no*.)

5. $3\tan x - 3 = 1$ **6.** $5\cot x + \dfrac{2}{\tan x} = 3$

In 7–14, solve for x in the interval $0° < x < 90°$.

7. $2 \sin x - 1 = 0$ **8.** $2 \cos x - \sqrt{3} = 0$

9. $3 \tan x - 1 = 2$ **10.** $2(\cot x - 2) + 2 = 0$

11. $3 \tan x - \sqrt{3} = 0$ **12.** $6 \cot x - \sqrt{3} = \sqrt{3}$

13. $\dfrac{1 + \sin x}{9} = \dfrac{\sin x}{3}$ **14.** $\dfrac{4 - \tan x}{\tan x} = 3$

In 15–20, using a trigonometric table of values, find, to the nearest degree, the positive acute angle x that satisfies the equation.

15. $5 \sin x + 2 = 3$ **16.** $4 \cos x - 1 = \cos x$

17. $2(\tan x - 1) = \tan x$ **18.** $6 - (2 - 3 \cot x) = 5 \cot x$

19. $\dfrac{1 + \sin x}{\sin x} = 5$ **20.** $\dfrac{3 \tan x - 2}{7} = \dfrac{1 + \tan x}{4}$

In 21–23, find the positive acute angle A which satisfies the equation.

21. $\sin 2A = 1$ (*Hint:* Since $\sin 90° = 1$, $2A = 90°$.)

22. $\sin \frac{1}{2}A = \frac{1}{2}$ **23.** $\cos(A + 30°) = \frac{1}{2}$

In 24–27, solve for the smallest positive value of x.

24. $\sqrt{4 \cos x + 2} - 2 = 0$ **25.** $\sqrt{2 \cos x + 2} = 2$

26. $\sqrt{3 \sin x + 1} = 2$ **27.** $\sqrt{3 \tan x + 1} - 1 = 1$

28. Solve the equation $2 - \sqrt{6 \cos x + 1} = 0$ for the smallest positive value of x.

PART B: TRIGONOMETRIC EQUATIONS OF THE FIRST DEGREE TO BE SOLVED FOR NON-NEGATIVE ANGLES LESS THAN 360° OR 2π; THAT IS, $0° \le x < 360°$ OR $0 \le x < 2\pi$

Procedure. To solve a trigonometric equation of the first degree for non-negative angles whose measures are less than 360° or 2π:

1. Solve the equation for the value of the trigonometric function.

2. Using the absolute value of the result found in step 1, determine the reference *acute angle* θ for the angles to be found.

3. Using the sign of the value found in step 1, determine the quadrants of the angles to be found; then observe the following rules to find the measure in degrees of the required angle: (In each of the following rules, acute angle θ is the reference angle for angle x. If the measure in radians is to be found, replace 180° by π and replace 360° by 2π.)

a. For values of $\sin x$ or $\csc x$:

If positive, x is in I and II. The required values of x are θ and $180° - \theta$.

If negative, x is in III and IV. The required values of x are $180° + \theta$ and $360° - \theta$.

b. For values of $\cos x$ or $\sec x$:

If positive, x is in I and IV. The required values of x are θ and $360° - \theta$.
If negative, x is in II and III. The required values of x are $180° - \theta$ and $180° + \theta$.

c. For values of $\tan x$ or $\cot x$:

If positive, x is in I and III. The required values of x are θ and $180° + \theta$.
If negative, x is in II and IV. The required values of x are $180° - \theta$ and $360° - \theta$.

Thus, if $\tan x = \sqrt{3}$, the reference angle $\theta = \text{Arc tan } \sqrt{3}$. Hence, $\theta = 60°$, or $\dfrac{\pi}{3}$. Since the value of $\tan x$ is positive, x is in I or III. Hence, the degree measures of x are $60°$ and $(180° + 60°)$, or $240°$; and the radian measures of x are $\dfrac{\pi}{3}$ and $\dfrac{4\pi}{3}$.

Also, if $\sin x = -\tfrac{1}{2}\sqrt{2}$, the reference angle $\theta = \text{Arc sin } \tfrac{1}{2}\sqrt{2} = 45°$, or $\dfrac{\pi}{4}$. Since the value of $\sin x$ is negative, x is in III or IV. Hence, the degree measures of x are $(180° + 45°)$, or $225°$, and $(360° - 45°)$, or $315°$; and the radian measures are $\dfrac{5\pi}{4}$ and $\dfrac{7\pi}{4}$.

4. Check the results by substituting in the original equation.

~~~~~~~~~~ *MODEL PROBLEMS* ~~~~~~~~~~

1. In (*a*) solve for x. In (*b*) solve for x in the interval $0° \leq x < 360°$.

$(a) \ \dfrac{2 + 3x}{x} = 5$ $(b) \ \dfrac{2 + 3 \tan x}{\tan x} = 5$

Solution *Solution*

$(a) \ \dfrac{2 + 3x}{x} = 5$ $(b) \ \dfrac{2 + 3 \tan x}{\tan x} = 5$

Multiply both sides by x. Multiply both sides by $\tan x$.

$2 + 3x = 5x$ $2 + 3 \tan x = 5 \tan x$
$2 = 2x$ $2 = 2 \tan x$
$1 = x$ $1 = \tan x$

Answer: $x = 1$ In quad. I: $x = 45°$
 In quad. III: $x = 180° + 45° = 225°$
 Answer: $x = 45°$ or $225°$

2. Find the solution set of the equation $\sin x = -\sqrt{3} \cos x$ in the interval $0 < x \leq 2\pi$.

Solution:

$$\sin x = -\sqrt{3} \cos x$$

Divide each side by $\cos x$.

$$\frac{\sin x}{\cos x} = -\sqrt{3}$$

$$\tan x = -\sqrt{3}$$

$\dfrac{\pi}{3}$ is the acute angle whose tangent is $\sqrt{3}$.

In quadrant II, $x = \pi - \dfrac{\pi}{3} = \dfrac{2\pi}{3}$.

In quadrant IV, $x = 2\pi - \dfrac{\pi}{3} = \dfrac{5\pi}{3}$.   *Answer:* $\left\{\dfrac{2\pi}{3}, \dfrac{5\pi}{3}\right\}$

Exercises

In 1–3, answer *yes* or *no*.

1. Is $45°$ a value which satisfies the equation $\sin 3x + \sin 2x - \sin x = 0$?

2. Is $225°$ a root of the equation $4 \tan x - 4 = 0$?

3. Is $\dfrac{2\pi}{3}$ a root of the equation $4 \cos x - 4 \cos 2x = 0$?

4. A root of the equation $2 \sin \theta + \sqrt{3} = 0$ is   (1) $120°$ (2) $240°$ (3) $150°$

5. A root of the equation $2 \cos \theta - \sqrt{3} = 0$ is   (1) $\dfrac{5\pi}{6}$ (2) $\dfrac{7\pi}{6}$ (3) $\dfrac{11\pi}{6}$

6. A root of the equation $2 \sin \theta - 3 = 0$ (1) is in quadrant I   (2) is in quadrant II   (3) does not exist

In 7–14, solve for x in the interval $0° \leq x < 360°$.

7. $\sin x = \dfrac{\sqrt{3}}{2}$ **8.** $\sin x = -\dfrac{\sqrt{3}}{2}$ **9.** $2 \tan x = 2\sqrt{3}$

10. $\cot x = -\sqrt{3}$ **11.** $-\tan x = 1$ **12.** $-3 \cot x = \sqrt{3}$

13. $4 \sin x + 3 = 1$ **14.** $3 \tan x + \sqrt{3} = 0$

In 15–22, find, to the nearest degree, the positive values of x less than $360°$ that satisfy the equation.

15. $\sin x = .25$ **16.** $3 \cos x = -1$ **17.** $4 \tan x = 1$ **18.** $\tan x = -4$
19. $5 \cot x = -1$ **20.** $10 \sin x = 7$ **21.** $20 \cos x = 1$ **22.** $8 \tan x = 1$

In 23–26, find the solution set of the equation in the interval $0 < x < 2\pi$.

23. $\cos x = \sqrt{3} \sin x$ **24.** $\sin x \sec x = 1$

25. $3 \sin x = \sqrt{3} \cos x$ **26.** $\cos x = \sin x$

In 27–38, find the smallest positive value of x that satisfies the equation.

27. $\sin 2x = -\frac{1}{2}$ (*Hint:* Since $\sin 210° = -\frac{1}{2}$, $2x = 210°$.)

28. $\sin 3x = -\frac{1}{2}$ **29.** $\sin \dfrac{x}{2} = \frac{1}{2}\sqrt{3}$ **30.** $\cot 5x = -1$

31. $\tan(x - 30°) = -1$ **32.** $\tan(2x - 50°) = -\sqrt{3}$

33. $\sin 3x = \cos 12°$ (*Hint:* Since $\cos 12° = \sin 78°$, $3x = 78°$.)

34. $\cos 2x = \sin 40°$ **35.** $\tan 4x = \cot 10°$ **36.** $\tan(x + 30°) = \cot 45°$

37. $\sin 3x = \cos(-12°)$ **38.** $\cos x = \sin(-20°)$

6. Solving Trigonometric Quadratic Equations of the Form $ax^2 + bx + c = 0$, $a \neq 0$

The trigonometric equation $4 \sin^2 A - 5 \sin A + 1 = 0$ is of the form $ax^2 + bx + c = 0$ when $x = \sin A$. The equation $\tan A + 3 = \cot A$ becomes $\tan A + 3 = \dfrac{1}{\tan A}$ if $\dfrac{1}{\tan A}$ replaces $\cot A$. By transforming $\tan A + 3 = \dfrac{1}{\tan A}$, we obtain $\tan^2 A + 3 \tan A - 1 = 0$, which is of the form $ax^2 + bx + c = 0$ when $x = \tan A$.

Solving a trigonometric equation expressible in quadratic form in terms of a trigonometric function is done in exactly the same way as solving an algebraic equation in quadratic form.

SOLVING TRIGONOMETRIC EQUATIONS OF THE FORM $ax^2 = k$

Equations such as $3 \tan^2 x = 12$ and $2 \sin^2 y = 1$ are examples of trigonometric quadratic equations of the form $ax^2 = k$.

Rule. A quadratic equation of the form $ax^2 = k$ has two roots, $\pm \sqrt{\dfrac{k}{a}}$.

Thus, in the equation $2 \sin^2 y = 1$, $a = 2$ and $k = 1$. Hence, $\sin y = \pm\sqrt{\frac{1}{2}} = \pm\frac{1}{2}\sqrt{2}$ and the values of y if $0 \leq y \leq 2\pi$ are $\dfrac{\pi}{4}, \dfrac{3\pi}{4}, \dfrac{5\pi}{4}$, and $\dfrac{7\pi}{4}$.

Model problems 1 and 2 indicate the complete procedure for finding the values of the function. However, the use of the rule is recommended as an additional method.

~~~~~~~~~~~~~~~~ *MODEL PROBLEMS* ~~~~~~~~~~~~~~~

1. In (a) solve for s.

In (b) find positive values of x less than $360°$ that satisfy the equation.

(a) $2s^2 + 3 = 4$ $\qquad\qquad\qquad$ (b) $2 \sin^2 x + 3 = 4$

Solution	*Solution*

(a) $2s^2 + 3 = 4$

$\qquad 2s^2 = 1$

$\qquad\ \ s^2 = \tfrac{1}{2}$

Take the square root of both sides.

$$s = \pm\sqrt{\tfrac{1}{2}}$$

Rationalize the denominator.

$$s = \pm\tfrac{1}{2}\sqrt{2} \quad Ans.$$

(b) $2 \sin^2 x + 3 = 4$

$\qquad 2 \sin^2 x = 1$

$\qquad\ \ \sin^2 x = \tfrac{1}{2}$

Take the square root of both sides.

$$\sin x = \pm\sqrt{\tfrac{1}{2}}$$

Rationalize the denominator.

$$\sin x = \pm\tfrac{1}{2}\sqrt{2}$$

Let $\sin x = \tfrac{1}{2}\sqrt{2}$.

In quad. I: $x = 45°$

In quad. II: $x = 135°$

Let $\sin x = -\tfrac{1}{2}\sqrt{2}$.

In quad. III: $x = 225°$

In quad. IV: $x = 315°$

$x = 45°, 135°, 225°,$ and $315°$ *Ans.*

2. Solve for x in the interval $0 \le x \le 2\pi$: $\tan 2x = \cot x$

Solution:

$$\tan 2x = \cot x$$

Substitute $\dfrac{2 \tan x}{1 - \tan^2 x}$ for $\tan 2x$: $\dfrac{2 \tan x}{1 - \tan^2 x} = \cot x$

Substitute $\dfrac{1}{\tan x}$ for $\cot x$: $\dfrac{2 \tan x}{1 - \tan^2 x} = \dfrac{1}{\tan x}$

Clear of fractions: $2 \tan^2 x = 1 - \tan^2 x$

$\qquad\qquad\qquad\qquad\qquad\qquad\ \ 3 \tan^2 x = 1$

$\qquad\qquad\qquad\qquad\qquad\qquad\ \ \ \tan^2 x = \tfrac{1}{3}$

Take the square root of both sides: $\tan x = \pm\sqrt{\tfrac{1}{3}}$

$\qquad\qquad\qquad\qquad\qquad\qquad\qquad\ \ \ \tan x = \pm\tfrac{1}{3}\sqrt{3}$

$$\text{Let } \tan x = +\tfrac{1}{3}\sqrt{3}.$$

In quad. I: $x = \dfrac{\pi}{6}$

In quad. III: $x = \dfrac{7\pi}{6}$

$$\text{Let } \tan x = -\tfrac{1}{3}\sqrt{3}.$$

In quad. II: $x = \dfrac{5\pi}{6}$

In quad. IV: $x = \dfrac{11\pi}{6}$

Answer: $x = \dfrac{\pi}{6}, \dfrac{5\pi}{6}, \dfrac{7\pi}{6}, \dfrac{11\pi}{6}$

Exercises

In 1–9, solve for x in the interval $0° < x < 90°$.

1. $\tan^2 x = 1$ **2.** $\tan^2 x = 3$ **3.** $4\sin^2 x = 1$

4. $3\tan^2 x = 1$ **5.** $4\sin^2 x = 2$ **6.** $4\sin^2 x = 3$

7. $2\cos^2 x = 1$ **8.** $4\cos^2 x = 3$ **9.** $8\cos^2 x = 2$

In 10–18, find the solution set of the equation in the interval $0° \leq x \leq 90°$. Express the members of the solution set to the nearest degree.

10. $\tan^2 x = 9$ **11.** $3\tan^2 x = 12$ **12.** $2\cot^2 x = 32$

13. $25\sin^2 x = 9$ **14.** $9\cos^2 x = 4$ **15.** $16\sin^2 x = 9$

16. $\tan x = \dfrac{1}{\tan x}$ **17.** $2\sin x = \dfrac{1}{\sin x}$ **18.** $\cot x = 3\tan x$

In 19–21, find, to the nearest degree, the positive acute angle x which satisfies the equation.

19. $\csc^2 x - 4 = 0$ **20.** $\sec^2 x - 2 = 0$ **21.** $2\sec^2 x - 8 = 10$

22. Find the positive acute angle that satisfies the equation $4\cos^2 x = 1$.

23. Find the positive acute angle that satisfies the equation $4\sin^2 x - 1 = 0$.

24. Find the positive acute angle that satisfies the equation $\tan^2 x - 3 = 0$.

25. What value of x between $0°$ and $90°$ satisfies the equation $4\sin^2 x - 3 = 0$?

26. Find the positive acute angle that satisfies the equation $2\sin^2 x - 1 = 0$.

27. Find the positive acute angle that satisfies the equation $3\tan^2 x - 1 = 0$.

28. Find the value of x between $180°$ and $270°$ that satisfies the equation $\tan^2 x - 1 = 0$.

29. Find the value of A between π and $\dfrac{3\pi}{2}$ that satisfies the equation $3\tan^2 A = 1$.

30. How many values of x are there between 0 and 2π that satisfy the equation $2\tan^2 x - 1 = 0$?

31. Find two values of x between π and 2π that satisfy the equation $4\cos^2 x = 3$.

32. If $2\cos^2 x = 1$, find two values of x between $90°$ and $270°$.

33. Find the positive value of $\sin x$ from the equation $\cos 2x = 2\sin^2 x$.

34. Solve for all values of x between $0°$ and $360°$: $2\sin^2 x - \cos 2x = 0$.

35. Solve $\tan 2x = \cot x$ for the smallest positive value of x.

36. Solve the following equation for all values of x between 0 and 2π: $\cot x \tan 2x = 3$.

SOLVING TRIGONOMETRIC EQUATIONS OF THE FORM
$ax^2 + bx = 0$

The trigonometric equations $2\sin^2 A - \sin A = 0$ and $4\tan^2 y + 5\tan y = 0$ are of the form $ax^2 + bx = 0$ when $x = \sin A$ in the first equation and $x = \tan y$ in the second.

Rule. An equation of the form $ax^2 + bx = 0$ has two roots, 0 and $-\dfrac{b}{a}$.

Thus, in $2\sin^2 A - \sin A = 0$, $a = 2$ and $b = -1$. Hence, $\sin A = 0$ or $\sin A = -\dfrac{-1}{2}$; that is, the roots are 0 and $\frac{1}{2}$. Therefore, for the interval $0 \le A < 2\pi$, the A-values are 0, $\dfrac{\pi}{6}$, $\dfrac{5\pi}{6}$, and π.

The model problem that follows indicates the complete procedure for finding the values of the functions. However, the use of the rule is suggested as an additional method.

〰〰〰〰〰〰〰 *MODEL PROBLEM* 〰〰〰〰〰〰〰

Solve for x in the interval $0° \le x < 360°$: $3 + 2(\cos^2 x - 1) = \cos x + 1$

Solution:
$$3 + 2(\cos^2 x - 1) = \cos x + 1$$
$$3 + 2\cos^2 x - 2 = \cos x + 1$$
$$2\cos^2 x + 1 = \cos x + 1$$
$$2\cos^2 x - \cos x = 0$$

Factor: $\cos x(2\cos x - 1) = 0$

$\cos x = 0$ | $2\cos x - 1 = 0$

$x = 90°$ and | $\cos x = \frac{1}{2}$

$x = 270°$ | In quad. I: $x = 60°$

                      | In quad. IV: $x = 300°$

Answer: $x = 60°, 90°, 270°, 300°$

〰〰〰〰〰〰〰〰〰〰〰〰〰〰〰〰〰〰〰〰〰〰〰〰

Exercises

In 1–8, solve for x in the interval $0° < x < 90°$.

1. $2 \cos^2 x - \cos x = 0$

2. $\cot^2 x - \cot x = 0$

3. $2 \cos^2 x - \sqrt{3} \cos x = 0$

4. $2 \cos^2 x - \sqrt{2} \cos x = 0$

5. $2 \sin^2 x = \sin x$

6. $3 \tan^2 x = \sqrt{3} \tan x$

7. $\sec^2 x - 2 \sec x = 0$

8. $\sec^2 x - \sqrt{2} \sec x = 0$

9. Find the value of x between 0 and $\dfrac{\pi}{2}$ that satisfies the equation $\tan^2 x - \tan x = 0$.

In 10–13, solve for x in the interval $0° \le x < 360°$, to the nearest degree.

10. $5 \sin^2 x = \sin x$

11. $3 \cos^2 x = \cos x$

12. $2 \tan^2 x = 6 \tan x$

13. $3(\cot^2 x + 1) = 6 \cot x + 3$

In 14–18, find, to the nearest degree, the smallest positive angle that satisfies the equation.

14. $\sin 2x - 2 \cos x = 0$ (*Hint:* Substitute $2 \sin x \cos x$ for $\sin 2x$ and solve by factoring the common factor $\cos x$.)

15. $\sin 2x = \sin x$

16. $3 \sin x \cos x = \cos x$

17. $\sin 2x - \frac{1}{2} \sin x = 0$

18. $\sin 2x = \dfrac{1}{\sec x}$

19. If $\sin^2 B - \sin B = 0$, find a value of B greater than $0°$ and less than $180°$ which satisfies this equation.

20. Find in degrees the value of x greater than $0°$ and less than $360°$ which satisfies the equation $\tan x - \tan x \cos x = 0$.

21. Find in degrees the value of x greater than $0°$ and less than $360°$ which satisfies the equation $2 \tan x + \sin x \tan x = 0$.

SOLVING TRIGONOMETRIC EQUATIONS OF THE FORM $ax^2 + bx + c = 0,\ a \neq 0,\ b \neq 0,\ c \neq 0$

The trigonometric equation $4 \cos^2 \theta - 4 \cos \theta + 1 = 0$ is of the form $ax^2 + bx + c = 0$ when $\cos \theta = x$.

Rule. To solve an algebraic or a trigonometric quadratic equation of the form $ax^2 + bx + c = 0$, if $ax^2 + bx + c$ is factorable, use factoring or use the quadratic formula. If $ax^2 + bx + c$ is not factorable, use the quadratic formula.

~~~~~~~~~~~~~ *MODEL PROBLEMS* ~~~~~~~~~~~~~

1. In (a) solve for c. In (b) solve for x in the interval $0° \leq x < 360°$.

(a) $2c^2 + c = 1$ (b) $2 \cos^2 x + \cos x = 1$

Solution   *Solution*

(a)
$$2c^2 + c = 1$$
$$2c^2 + c - 1 = 0$$
$$(2c - 1)(c + 1) = 0$$

$2c - 1 = 0 \quad | \quad c + 1 = 0$

$c = \frac{1}{2} \quad | \quad c = -1$

Answer: $c = \frac{1}{2}$ or -1

(b)
$$2 \cos^2 x + \cos x = 1$$
$$2 \cos^2 x + \cos x - 1 = 0$$
$$(2 \cos x - 1)(\cos x + 1) = 0$$

$2 \cos x - 1 = 0 \quad | \quad \cos x + 1 = 0$

$\cos x = \frac{1}{2} \quad\quad | \quad\quad \cos x = -1$

In quad. I: $x = 60°$ $\quad | \quad$ $x = 180°$

In quad. IV: $x = 300°$

Answer: $x = 60°, 180°, 300°$

2. Find, correct to the nearest minute, all positive values of A less than $360°$ which satisfy the equation $2 \cos 2A + 3 \cos A = -1$.

Solution:

$$2 \cos 2A + 3 \cos A = -1$$
$$2(2 \cos^2 A - 1) + 3 \cos A = -1$$
$$4 \cos^2 A - 2 + 3 \cos A = -1$$
$$4 \cos^2 A + 3 \cos A - 1 = 0$$
$$(\cos A + 1)(4 \cos A - 1) = 0$$

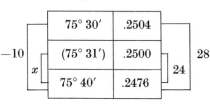

Angle	Cosine
75° 30′	.2504
(75° 31′)	.2500
75° 40′	.2476

$-10 \quad\quad\quad\quad\quad\quad\quad 28$

$x \quad\quad\quad\quad\quad\quad\quad\quad 24$

$\cos A + 1 = 0 \quad | \quad 4 \cos A - 1 = 0$

$\cos A = -1 \quad\quad | \quad\quad \cos A = \frac{1}{4}$

$A = 180° \quad\quad\quad | \quad\quad\quad = .2500$

$\dfrac{x}{-10} = \dfrac{24}{28}$

$x = -\dfrac{240}{28}$

$x \approx -9$

In quad. I: $A = 75° 31′$

$75° 40′ - 9′ = 75° 31′$

In quad. IV: $A = 360° - 75° 31′$
$\quad\quad\quad\quad\quad = 284° 29′$

Answer: $A = 75° 31′, 180°, 284° 29′$

3. Solve for θ, to the nearest degree, in the interval $0° \leq \theta < 180°$.
$$5 \tan \theta - 4 \cos \theta + \sec \theta = 0$$

Solution:

$$5 \tan \theta - 4 \cos \theta + \sec \theta = 0$$

$$\frac{5 \sin \theta}{\cos \theta} - 4 \cos \theta + \frac{1}{\cos \theta} = 0$$

Multiply each side by $\cos \theta$.

$$5 \sin \theta - 4 \cos^2 \theta + 1 = 0$$
$$5 \sin \theta - 4(1 - \sin^2 \theta) + 1 = 0$$
$$5 \sin \theta - 4 + 4 \sin^2 \theta + 1 = 0$$
$$4 \sin^2 \theta + 5 \sin \theta - 3 = 0$$

$$\sin \theta = \frac{-b \pm \sqrt{b^2 - 4ac}}{2a}$$

$a = 4,$
$b = 5,$
$c = -3$

```
         8. 5  4  4
  √73.00 00 00
    64
165 | 900
    | 825
  1704 | 7500
       | 6816
 17084 | 68400
       | 68336
            64
```

$$= \frac{-5 \pm \sqrt{25 + 48}}{8}$$

$$= \frac{-5 \pm \sqrt{73}}{8}$$

$\sin \theta = \dfrac{-5 + 8.544}{8}$	$\sin \theta = \dfrac{-5 - 8.544}{8}$
$= \dfrac{3.544}{8}$	$= \dfrac{-13.544}{8}$
$= .443$	$= -1.693$
In quad. I, $\theta = 26°$ to the nearest degree.	Reject, since there are no values of θ in the interval $0° \leq \theta < 180°$ for which $\sin \theta < 0$.
In quad. II, $\theta = 180° - 26° = 154°$ to the nearest degree.	

Answer: $\theta = 26°, 154°$

Exercises

1. Is $45°$ a root of the equation $\tan^2 x - 5 \cot x + 4 = 0$? (Answer *yes* or *no*.)

2. Is the equation $2 \sin^2 x + 5 \sin x = 3$ satisfied for $x = \dfrac{\pi}{6}$?

In 3–14, find, to the nearest degree, the positive acute angle or angles that satisfy the equation.

3. $\tan^2 x - 4 \tan x + 3 = 0$

4. $\tan^2 x - 2 \tan x = 3$

5. $6 \sin^2 x - 5 \sin x + 1 = 0$

6. $5 \sin^2 x + 1 = 6 \sin x$

7. $2 \cot^2 x - 7 \cot x - 4 = 0$

8. $3 \cos^2 x + 2 = 7 \cos x$

9. $2 \tan^2 x + \tan x = 3$

10. $3 \sin^2 x + 4 \sin x = 4$

11. $\sin A = 1 - 2 \sin^2 A$

12. $3 \sin^2 x = 2 - 5 \sin x$

13. $\sin^2 x = 1 - \sin x$

14. $7 \sin x = 4 + 2 \sin^2 x$

In 15–20, find, to the nearest degree, all angles greater than or equal to $0°$ but less than $360°$ that satisfy the equation.

15. $\sin^2 x - 3 \sin x + 2 = 0$

16. $2 \cos^2 x + 5 \cos x = 4$

17. $\tan^2 x = 14 + 5 \tan x$

18. $8 - 2 \tan^2 A = 5 \tan A$

19. $6 \tan B = 2 - 5 \tan^2 B$

20. $\cos^2 Q - 1 = 2 \cos Q$

In 21–28, find, to the nearest degree, the positive acute angle or angles that satisfy the equation.

21. $3 \cos^2 x - 5 \sin x - 1 = 0$

22. $3 \sin^2 A + 7 \cos A = 5$

23. $\sec^2 \theta - 3 \tan \theta + 1 = 0$

24. $2 \sec^2 \theta + 1 = 7 \tan \theta$

25. $1 - 3 \cos^2 x + 5 \sin x = 0$

26. $3 \cos^2 x + 7 \sin x - 5 = 0$

27. $3 \cos^2 x = 7 - 8 \sin x$

28. $4 \sin x = 1 + 3 \cos^2 x$

In 29–36, find all angles greater than or equal to $0°$ and less than $360°$ that satisfy the equation. (Express approximate values to the nearest degree.)

29. $6 \cos^2 x + 5 \sin x - 2 = 0$

30. $2 \sec^2 y + \tan y - 3 = 0$

31. $7 \cos^2 x - 4 \sin x = 4$

32. $5 \cos^2 A - \sin A = 1$

33. $11 \sin \theta = 11 - 7 \cos^2 \theta$

34. $\sin^2 y - 2 \cos y + \frac{1}{4} = 0$

35. $\cos^2 x = 2 \sin^2 x - \frac{1}{2} \sin x$

36. $5 \sec^2 x = 7 \tan x + 6$

In 37–42, find, to the nearest minute, all angles greater than $0°$ and less than $360°$ that satisfy the equation.

37. $4 \cos^2 x - 5 \sin x + 2 = 0$

38. $6 \sin^2 x + 5 \cos x = 7$

39. $5 \cos^2 x = 11 - 13 \sin x$

40. $8 \sin A = 5 \cos^2 A - 1$

41. $\sec^2 R - 2 \tan R = 3$

42. $\csc^2 D = 8 - 4 \cot D$

In 43–50, find, to the nearest degree, all positive angles less than $360°$ that satisfy the equation.

43. $2 \cos x + 3 = 2 \sec x$

44. $3 \sin x - \csc x = 2$

45. $2 \tan x - 1 = \cot x$

46. $2 \tan x = 3 - \cot x$

47. $7 \sin A + 1 = 6 \csc A$

48. $\tan A - 2 \cot A = 2$

49. $2(\tan x + 1) = \cot x$

50. $3(\sin x - 1) = 2 \csc x$

51. Solve the equation $\cos 2x - \sin x = 0$ for all values of x between 0 and 2π.

52. Solve the following equation for all positive values of A less than $360°$:
$\cos 2A + \sin A = 0$.

53. Find, to the nearest ten minutes, all positive angles less than $360°$ that satisfy the equation $2 \sin^2 \frac{1}{2}x = 3 \sin^2 x$.

In 54–59, find, to the nearest degree, all values of x greater than $0°$ and less than $360°$ that satisfy the equation.

54. $\sin^2 x + \sin x - 1 = 0$ **55.** $\cos^2 x + 2 \cos x = 1$

56. $\cos^2 x + 2 \sin x = 0$ **57.** $\sec^2 x = 2 + 2 \tan x$

58. $\tan x = \cos x$ **59.** $3(\sin x + 1) = 5 \csc x$

60. *a.* Find, to the nearest tenth, the roots of the equation $2x^2 - 7 = 3x$.

   b. If $x = \tan \theta$ in the equation $2x^2 - 7 = 3x$ and θ is in the interval $180° < \theta < 270°$, find θ to the nearest degree.

7. Using Inverse Functions To Express Solutions of Trigonometric Equations

The measures of the angles which represent the solutions of trigonometric equations may be expressed by using inverse trigonometric notation.

Thus, if $4 \cos x - 1 = 0$, then $\cos x = \frac{1}{4}$. Using inverse trigonometric notation: $x = \text{arc cos } \frac{1}{4}$ or $x = \cos^{-1} \frac{1}{4}$.

Recall that to indicate the principal value of arc cos $\frac{1}{4}$, we may write Arc cos $\frac{1}{4}$. The capitalizing of the first letter of arc indicates that only the principal value of arc cos $\frac{1}{4}$ is required. Similarly, the notation $\text{Cos}^{-1} \frac{1}{4}$ indicates only the principal value of $\cos^{-1} \frac{1}{4}$.

~~~~~~~~~~ *MODEL PROBLEMS* ~~~~~~~~~~

1. If $8 \tan A = 5$, express the principal value of A as an inverse trigonometric function.

Solution:
$$8 \tan A = 5$$
$$\tan A = \frac{5}{8}$$
$$\text{Therefore, } A = \text{Arc tan } \frac{5}{8} \quad Ans.$$

2. Solve the equation $8 \cos^2 x = 14 \cos x - 3$ for x. Express the principal value or values of x by using inverse trigonometric notation.

Solution:

$$8 \cos^2 x = 14 \cos x - 3$$
$$8 \cos^2 x - 14 \cos x + 3 = 0$$
$$(4 \cos x - 1)(2 \cos x - 3) = 0$$

$4 \cos x - 1 = 0$	$2 \cos x - 3 = 0$
$\cos x = \frac{1}{4}$	$\cos x = \frac{3}{2}$
$x = \text{Cos}^{-1} \frac{1}{4}$	Reject, since the cosine of an angle cannot be greater than 1.

Answer: $x = \text{Cos}^{-1} \frac{1}{4}$

Exercises

In 1–6, express the principal value of A using inverse trigonometric notation.

1. $5 \sin A = 4$ **2.** $9 \cot A = 3$ **3.** $3 \tan A = 2$

4. $10 \sin A - 3 = 0$ **5.** $5 \cos A - 1 = 0$ **6.** $4 \tan A - 10 = 0$

In 7–18, express the principal value of x using inverse trigonometric notation.

7. $\tan^2 x = 1$ **8.** $4 \sin^2 x = 1$

9. $4 \cos^2 x - 3 = 0$ **10.** $5 \sin^2 x - 6 \sin x + 1 = 0$

11. $2 \cos^2 x - 5 \cos x + 2 = 0$ **12.** $6 \tan^2 x - 5 \tan x = 6$

13. $\sec^2 x - \tan x = 7$ **14.** $9 \cos^2 x = 10 - 6 \sin x$

15. $4 \sin^2 x = 3 + 3 \cos x$ **16.** $\sin^2 x + 2 \cos x = 2$

17. $\sec^2 x - 2 \tan x = 0$ **18.** $\sec^2 x + \tan^2 x + \tan x - 2 = 0$

CHAPTER XVI

GRAPHS OF TRIGONOMETRIC FUNCTIONS

1. Graphs of the Basic Sine, Cosine, and Tangent Curves in Degrees and Radians

As we study the graphs of the sine and cosine functions, $y = \sin x$ and $y = \cos x$, we shall see that these graphs approximate the cross sections of ocean waves. An understanding of these functions and their graphs is valuable in studying the wave motions that occur in light, sound, electricity, and other scientific phenomena. Knowledge of the graphs of trigonometric functions helps in an understanding of periodic phenomena such as the oscillations of the pendulum, the vibrations of a violin string, and the tides.

The graph of any function in the Cartesian plane consists of a set of points that are the graphs of the ordered pairs of real numbers that are the members of the function. Thus, the graph of the trigonometric function $y = \sin x$ is the graph of the set of ordered pairs (x, y) such that $y = \sin x$. An example of such an ordered pair is $(30°, \frac{1}{2})$ in which $30°$ is the measure of an angle in degrees. In radian measure, the same ordered pair is expressed as $\left(\frac{\pi}{6}, \frac{1}{2}\right)$. By using radian measure, we may use the same scale for labeling both axes.

The procedure for making a graph of a trigonometric function is the same as that used in graphing an algebraic function.

Procedure. To make the graph of a trigonometric function:
1. Prepare a table of ordered pairs of real numbers in which values of the function being graphed, such as $\sin x$, are paired with selected values that are the measures of the angle x.
2. Plot the points that are the graphs of the ordered pairs in the table.
3. Join the plotted points with a smooth curve.

Examine the following tables for $y = \sin x$, Fig. 1; $y = \cos x$, Fig. 2; and $y = \tan x$, Fig. 4. Note that the values of x are those from $-360°$ to $360°$ in degrees and from -2π to 2π in radians, using intervals of 30° or $\dfrac{\pi}{6}$. Irrational values of sin x, cos x, and tan x are rounded off to the nearest hundredth. The table of trigonometric function values may be used to find these values.

GRAPH OF THE BASIC SINE CURVE

TABLE OF $y = \sin x$

$\left(\text{for 0 and positive values of } x \text{ at intervals of 30° or } \dfrac{\pi}{6} \text{ radians}\right)$

	0	$\dfrac{\pi}{6}$	$\dfrac{\pi}{3}$	$\dfrac{\pi}{2}$	$\dfrac{2\pi}{3}$	$\dfrac{5\pi}{6}$	π	$\dfrac{7\pi}{6}$	$\dfrac{4\pi}{3}$	$\dfrac{3\pi}{2}$	$\dfrac{5\pi}{3}$	$\dfrac{11\pi}{6}$	2π
x	0°	30°	60°	90°	120°	150°	180°	210°	240°	270°	300°	330°	360°
y	0	.5	.87	1	.87	.5	0	−.5	−.87	−1	−.87	−.5	0

TABLE OF $y = \sin x$

$\left(\text{for 0 and negative values of } x \text{ at intervals of 30° or } \dfrac{\pi}{6} \text{ radians}\right)$

	0	$-\dfrac{\pi}{6}$	$-\dfrac{\pi}{3}$	$-\dfrac{\pi}{2}$	$-\dfrac{2\pi}{3}$	$-\dfrac{5\pi}{6}$	$-\pi$	$-\dfrac{7\pi}{6}$	$-\dfrac{4\pi}{3}$	$-\dfrac{3\pi}{2}$	$-\dfrac{5\pi}{3}$	$-\dfrac{11\pi}{6}$	-2π
x	0°	−30°	−60°	−90°	−120°	−150°	−180°	−210°	−240°	−270°	−300°	−330°	−360°
y	0	−.5	−.87	−1	−.87	−.5	0	.5	.87	1	.87	.5	0

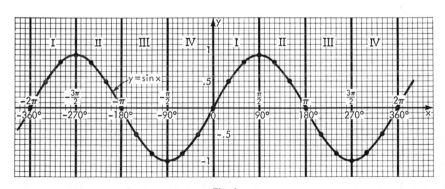

Fig. 1

Look at the graph of the sine function along the x-axis, Fig. 1. Note that the replacement set for x, that is, the domain of the function $y = \sin x$, is the set of real numbers. Also, from the graph we see that the ordinates, y, are such that $-1 \leq y \leq 1$. Hence, the range of the function $y = \sin x$ is the set of real numbers between -1 and 1, inclusive.

GRAPH OF THE BASIC COSINE CURVE

TABLE OF $y = \cos x$

$\left(\text{for 0 and positive values of } x \text{ at intervals of } 30° \text{ or } \dfrac{\pi}{6} \text{ radians}\right)$

x	0	$\dfrac{\pi}{6}$	$\dfrac{\pi}{3}$	$\dfrac{\pi}{2}$	$\dfrac{2\pi}{3}$	$\dfrac{5\pi}{6}$	π	$\dfrac{7\pi}{6}$	$\dfrac{4\pi}{3}$	$\dfrac{3\pi}{2}$	$\dfrac{5\pi}{3}$	$\dfrac{11\pi}{6}$	2π
	0°	30°	60°	90°	120°	150°	180°	210°	240°	270°	300°	330°	360°
y	1	.87	.5	0	−.5	−.87	−1	−.87	−.5	0	.5	.87	1

TABLE OF $y = \cos x$

$\left(\text{for 0 and negative values of } x \text{ at intervals of } 30° \text{ or } \dfrac{\pi}{6} \text{ radians}\right)$

x	0	$-\dfrac{\pi}{6}$	$-\dfrac{\pi}{3}$	$-\dfrac{\pi}{2}$	$-\dfrac{2\pi}{3}$	$-\dfrac{5\pi}{6}$	$-\pi$	$-\dfrac{7\pi}{6}$	$-\dfrac{4\pi}{3}$	$-\dfrac{3\pi}{2}$	$-\dfrac{5\pi}{3}$	$-\dfrac{11\pi}{6}$	-2π
	0°	−30°	−60°	−90°	−120°	−150°	−180°	−210°	−240°	−270°	−300°	−330°	−360°
y	1	.87	.5	0	−.5	−.87	−1	−.87	−.5	0	.5	.87	1

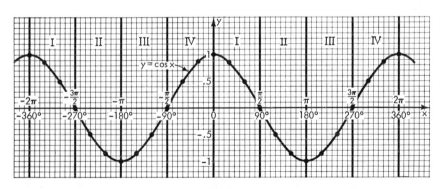

Fig. 2

Note on the graph of $y = \cos x$, Fig. 2, that the domain of $y = \cos x$ is the set of real numbers; also, the range of $y = \cos x$ is the set of real numbers between -1 and 1, inclusive.

You have probably noticed the fact that the basic sine and cosine curves are exactly the same in size and shape. Perhaps you have noticed, as in Fig. 3, that each cycle of the cosine curve is $90°$ or $\dfrac{\pi}{2}$ radians to the left of the closest cycle of the sine curve. In fact, it is said that the cosine curve "leads" the

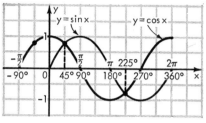

Fig. 3

sine curve by $90°$. The curves are also said to be $90°$ "out of phase" with each other. If the sine curve is slid $90°$ to the left, it will coincide with the cosine curve. This graphic idea illustrates the rule that $\cos x = \sin(x + 90°)$ or $\cos x = \sin\left(x + \dfrac{\pi}{2}\right)$.

GRAPH OF THE BASIC TANGENT CURVE

TABLE OF $y = \tan x$

$\left(\text{for } 0 \text{ and positive values of } x \text{ at intervals of } 30° \text{ or } \dfrac{\pi}{6} \text{ radians}\right)$

x	0	$\dfrac{\pi}{6}$	$\dfrac{\pi}{3}$	$\dfrac{\pi}{2}$	$\dfrac{2\pi}{3}$	$\dfrac{5\pi}{6}$	π	$\dfrac{7\pi}{6}$	$\dfrac{4\pi}{3}$	$\dfrac{3\pi}{2}$	$\dfrac{5\pi}{3}$	$\dfrac{11\pi}{6}$	2π
	0°	30°	60°	90°	120°	150°	180°	210°	240°	270°	300°	330°	360°
y	0	.58	1.73	*∞	−1.73	−.58	0	.58	1.73	*∞	−1.73	−.58	0

TABLE OF $y = \tan x$

$\left(\text{for } 0 \text{ and negative values of } x \text{ at intervals of } 30° \text{ or } \dfrac{\pi}{6} \text{ radians}\right)$

x	0	$-\dfrac{\pi}{6}$	$-\dfrac{\pi}{3}$	$-\dfrac{\pi}{2}$	$-\dfrac{2\pi}{3}$	$-\dfrac{5\pi}{6}$	$-\pi$	$-\dfrac{7\pi}{6}$	$-\dfrac{4\pi}{3}$	$-\dfrac{3\pi}{2}$	$-\dfrac{5\pi}{3}$	$-\dfrac{11\pi}{6}$	-2π
	0°	−30°	−60°	−90°	−120°	−150°	−180°	−210°	−240°	−270°	−300°	−330°	−360°
y	0	−.58	−1.73	*∞	1.73	.58	0	−.58	−1.73	*∞	1.73	.58	0

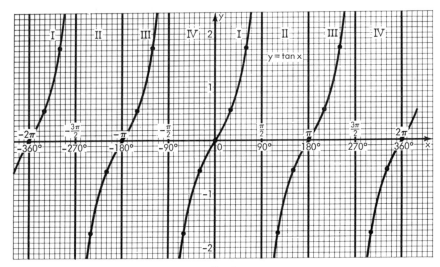

Fig. 4

The reason for each of the starred values (*∞) in the table for $y = \tan x$ is that the values of $\tan x$ at such quadrantal values of x as $\dfrac{\pi}{2}, \dfrac{3\pi}{2}, -\dfrac{\pi}{2}$, and $-\dfrac{3\pi}{2}$ are undefined. However, since the absolute values of x increase without limit very close to these quadrantal values, we will use the symbol " ∞ " to indicate the situation. For a more complete explanation, see page 354.

Because the tangent curve approaches lines such as $x = \dfrac{\pi}{2}$ and $x = -\dfrac{\pi}{2}$, these lines are called **asymptotes,** and the curve is said to be **asymptotic** to the lines.

GRAPHING $y = \sin x$, USING THE ORDINATES OF POINTS OF A UNIT CIRCLE

In Fig. 5, the circle is a unit circle of radius 1. Recall that in a unit circle, if x is the central angle, then the coordinates of a point P are $(\cos x, \sin x)$. Since the ordinate of P is $\sin x$, the sine curve, $y = \sin x$, can be graphed, as shown in Fig. 6, without using a table.

Study the curve in Fig. 6. Note that the unit circle at the left has been divided into arcs of 15°, or $\dfrac{\pi}{12}$, beginning at the point $(1, 0)$

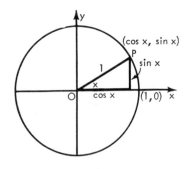

Fig. 5

and moving counterclockwise. At each of the points at these intervals of 15°, or $\frac{\pi}{12}$, the ordinates of the points have been drawn. In the graph of $y = \sin x$, you can see that the x-axis has been divided into equal intervals of 15°, or $\frac{\pi}{12}$. In order to graph $y = \sin x$, the ordinates of the successive points at 15° intervals have been "transcribed" from their initial position in the unit circle to the position indicated by the value of x along the x-axis. For example, consider the point on the unit circle at $\frac{\pi}{6}$ and the corresponding point on the sine curve whose x-coordinate is $\frac{\pi}{6}$. You can see that the ordinates of these points are equal in length. Similarly, the ordinate of any point on the unit circle at a 15° interval is equal in length to the ordinate of a corresponding point on the sine curve whose x-coordinate has the same interval value.

The final step in the graphing of $y = \sin x$ is the joining of the tops of the ordinates with a smooth curve.

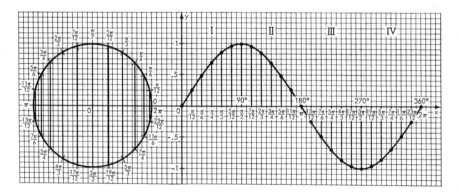

Fig. 6

The same unit circle as the one in Fig. 6 can be used to graph $y = \cos x$ without the use of a table. For this purpose, the abscissas of the successive points on the unit circle become the successive ordinates of the corresponding points on the cosine curve. In Fig. 5, note that it is the abscissa of a point on the unit circle that is $\cos x$, if x is a central angle. Since the equation of the cosine curve is $y = \cos x$, it is the abscissa of a point on the unit circle that must be "transcribed" to become the ordinate of the corresponding point on the cosine curve.

Exercises

1. Using the table of trigonometric function values, complete the table shown by entering the values of sin x, cos x, and tan x, correct to the nearest hundredth, after each indicated value of x. Also, enter radian measures of x. Use the completed table to answer the questions in 2–4. Keep in mind that 70° is the reference angle for 110°, 50° for 130°, 30° for 150°, etc.

x		sin x	cos x	tan x
degrees	radians			
0°	0	0	1	0
10°	$\dfrac{\pi}{18}$	.17	.98	.18
30°				
50°				
70°				
90°				
110°				
130°				
150°				
170°				
180°				

2. Graph $y = \sin x$ from $x = 0$ to $x = \pi$, or 180°, using the table prepared in exercise 1. On the graph, draw the ordinates that represent sin 20°, sin 40°, and sin 60°.

3. Graph $y = \cos x$ from $x = 0$ to $x = \pi$, or 180°, using the table prepared in exercise 1. On the graph, draw the ordinates that represent cos 80°, cos 100°, and cos 120°.

4. Graph $y = \tan x$ from $x = 0$ to $x = \pi$, or 180°, using the table prepared in exercise 1. On the graph, draw the ordinates that represent tan 140° and tan 160°.

5. Draw the graph of $y = \sin x$ from $x = -\pi$, to $x = \pi$, $-\pi \le x \le \pi$, at intervals of $\dfrac{\pi}{6}$ or 30°. On the graph, show that (a) sin ($-30°$) $= -\sin 30°$ and (b) sin 60° $= -\sin 60°$. Is it true that $\sin(-x) = -\sin x$ for all values of x?

6. Draw the graph of $y = \cos x$ from $x = -\pi$ to $x = \pi$, $-\pi \le x \le \pi$, at intervals of $\dfrac{\pi}{6}$ or 30°. On the graph, show that (a) $\cos(-45°) = \cos 45°$ and (b) $\cos(-120°) = \cos 120°$. Is it true that $\cos(-x) = \cos x$ for all values of x?

7. Draw the graph of $y = \tan x$ from $x = -\pi$ to $x = \pi$, $-\pi \leq x \leq \pi$, at intervals of $\dfrac{\pi}{6}$ or 30°. On the graph, show that (a) $\tan(-60°) = -\tan 60°$ and (b) $\tan(-150°) = -\tan 150°$. Is it true that $\tan(-x) = -\tan x$ for all values of x?

8. The graph of the function $y = \sin x$ passes through the point whose co-ordinates are (1) $\left(\dfrac{\pi}{2}, 0\right)$ (2) $\left(\dfrac{3\pi}{2}, -1\right)$ (3) $(2\pi, 1)$

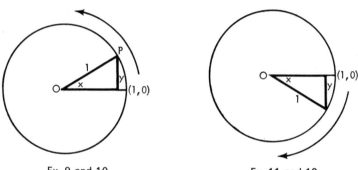

Ex. 9 and 10   Ex. 11 and 12

9. At intervals of 15°, or $\dfrac{\pi}{12}$, draw the graph of $y = \sin x$ in the interval $0 \leq x \leq 2\pi$ by using the ordinates of points on a unit circle. Divide the circle into the required intervals, beginning at $(1, 0)$, and move counter-clockwise around the circle. (Keep in mind that $y = \sin x = $ ordinate of P on a unit circle.)

10. At intervals of 15°, or $\dfrac{\pi}{12}$, draw the graph of $y = \cos x$ in the interval $0 \leq x \leq 2\pi$ by using the abscissas of points on a unit circle. (Keep in mind that $y = \cos x = $ abscissa of P on a unit circle.)

11. At intervals of 15°, or $\dfrac{\pi}{12}$, draw the graph of $y = \sin x$ in the interval $-2\pi \leq x \leq 0$ by using the ordinates of points on a unit circle. Divide the circle into the required intervals, beginning at $(1, 0)$, and move clockwise around the circle.

12. At intervals of 15°, or $\dfrac{\pi}{12}$, draw the graph of $y = \cos x$ in the interval $-2\pi \leq x \leq 0$ by using the abscissas of points on a unit circle.

13. At intervals of 15°, or $\dfrac{\pi}{12}$, draw the graph
of $y = \tan x$ in the interval $0 \le x \le 2\pi$ by
using the segments QP of points on the
tangent to the unit circle passing through
$Q(1, 0)$. Note that $y = \tan x = QP$. (For
second quadrant angles, point P will be
be found to be below Q since the tangent
values are negative for such angles.)

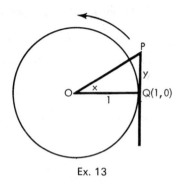

Ex. 13

2. Properties of the Basic Sine, Cosine, and Tangent Curves

PERIODICITY

From the graphs of $y = \sin x$ and $y = \cos x$, we see that $\sin x$ and $\cos x$ repeat
their values at intervals of 2π, or 360°. The graph of $\tan x$ does this at intervals
of π, or 180°.

A function that repeats its values at regular intervals is a ***periodic function.***
Hence, the sine, cosine, and tangent functions are periodic functions. The interval between successive repetitions is the ***period*** of the function.

Thus, the period for $\sin x$ or $\cos x$ is 2π, or 360°; the period for $\tan x$ is π, or
180°.

Since the period for $\sin x$ is 360°, then $\sin x = \sin(x + 360°) = \sin(x + 720°) =
\sin(x + 1080°) = \sin(x + 1440°) = \dots$ In general, $\sin x = \sin(x + n \cdot 360°)$,
where n is an integer. Likewise, $\cos x = \cos(x + n \cdot 360°)$, where n is an integer.
Refer to the table of values for $\sin x$ on page 529 and for $\cos x$ on page 530
and verify the fact that the set of values of y in the interval $0 \le x \le 2\pi$ is
repeated in the interval $-2\pi \le x \le 0$ in both cases.

Since the period for $\tan x$ is 180°, then $\tan x = \tan(x + n \cdot 180°)$, where n is
an integer. Refer to the table of values for $\tan x$ on page 531 and verify the fact
that the set of values of y in the interval $0 \le x \le \pi$ is repeated in the interval
$\pi \le x \le 2\pi$.

AMPLITUDE

Observe that the graphs of the periodic functions $y = \sin x$ and $y = \cos x$
oscillate above and below the x-axis, reaching a maximum ordinate of 1 above

the x-axis and falling to a minimum ordinate of -1 below the x-axis. When the graph of a periodic function oscillates above and below the x-axis, as in these functions, the maximum ordinate is the *amplitude* of the function. Hence, the amplitude of $y = \sin x$ is 1, and the amplitude of $y = \cos x$ is 1.

Although $y = \tan x$ is a periodic function, it does not have an amplitude, since the graph of $y = \tan x$ has neither a maximum nor a minimum value.

DOMAIN

Since the values of x constitute the first component of the ordered pairs of the functions $y = \sin x$ and $y = \cos x$, then the set of values of x from which each function is defined is the *domain* of each of these functions. Note on the graph of $y = \sin x$ and also on the graph of $y = \cos x$ that x may be any real number, positive, negative, or 0. Hence, the domain of both $y = \sin x$ and $y = \cos x$ is the set of real numbers, which can be indicated by $-\infty < x < \infty$.

In the case of $y = \tan x$, the domain is the set of real numbers except for such values as $x = 90°$, or $\dfrac{\pi}{2}$, and $x = 270°$, or $\dfrac{3\pi}{2}$, etc. In general, the values of x that must be excluded from the domain are odd multiples of $90°$, or $\dfrac{\pi}{2}$, which may be represented by $90° \cdot (2n + 1)$ or $\dfrac{\pi}{2}(2n + 1)$, where n is an integer.

RANGE

Since the values of y constitute the second component of the ordered pairs of the functions $y = \sin x$, $y = \cos x$, and $y = \tan x$, then the set of values of y is the *range* of each of these functions. Note in the graph of $y = \sin x$ or $y = \cos x$ that y may be any real number having an absolute value not greater than 1; that is, $-1 \le y \le 1$. Hence, the range of both $y = \sin x$ and $y = \cos x$ is limited to $-1 \le y \le 1$.

In the case of $y = \tan x$, y may be any real number; that is, the range of $y = \tan x$ is the set of real numbers, which can be indicated by $-\infty < x < \infty$.

INTERSECTIONS WITH THE x-AXIS, OR y = 0

Note that the three basic graphs, $y = \sin x$, $y = \cos x$, and $y = \tan x$, intersect the x-axis at $180°$ intervals (or intervals of π). To locate the points at which the sine curve and tangent curve intersect the x-axis, start at the origin and proceed at $180°$ intervals to the right and to the left. To locate the points at which the cosine curve intersects the x-axis, start at the intersection at $90°$ and proceed at $180°$ intervals to the right and to the left.

CONTINUITY AND DISCONTINUITY

In contrast to the graphs of $y = \sin x$ and $y = \cos x$, which are *continuous* curves, the graph of $y = \tan x$ is a *discontinuous* curve which breaks at odd multiples of $90°$, or $\dfrac{\pi}{2}$. In drawing the graph for $y = \tan x$, make certain that the branches come closer and closer to the lines $x = -270°$, $x = -90°$, $x = 90°$, $x = 270°$, and so forth, at $180°$ intervals, but do not intersect or touch them.

KEEP IN MIND

1. The period of both the basic sine curve and the basic cosine curve is $360°$, or 2π. The period for the basic tangent curve is $180°$, or π.
2. The amplitude of both the basic sine curve and the basic cosine curve is 1.
3. For all three basic curves, the intersections with the x-axis occur at intervals of $180°$, or π.
4. The sine and cosine curves are continuous. The tangent curve is discontinuous.

GRAPHING THE RECIPROCAL FUNCTIONS:
$y = \csc x$, $y = \sec x$, $y = \cot x$

The cosecant, the secant, and the cotangent functions are graphed in the same way as the sine, cosine, and tangent functions. In each case, we first prepare a table of ordered pairs, find the graphs of these ordered pairs, and then join the resulting set of points with a smooth curve. When this is done, the graphs are those in Fig. 1, Fig. 2, and Fig. 3.

Note in Fig. 1 that the graph of $y = \csc x$ is combined with the graph of $y = \sin x$; in Fig. 2, the graph of $y = \sec x$ is combined with that of $y = \cos x$; and in Fig. 3, the graph of $y = \cot x$ is combined with the graph of $y = \tan x$. In each case, the graph of a function is combined with the graph of the reciprocal function.

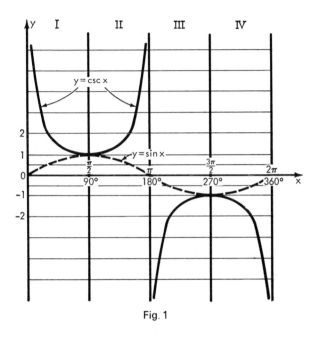

Fig. 1

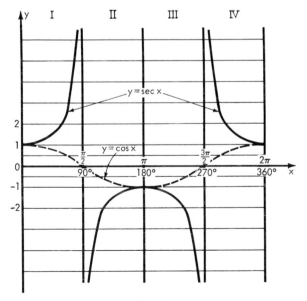

Fig. 2

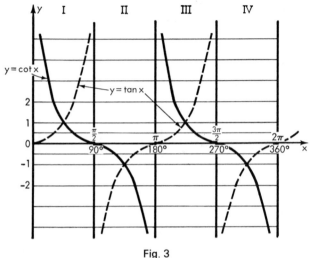

Fig. 3

The reason for combining the graph of a function with the graph of its reciprocal function (as is done in Figs. 1, 2, and 3) is that the behavior of a pair of reciprocal functions can be studied using the following principles that govern reciprocals in general:

Principle 1. A real number and its reciprocal change in the opposite sense.
Hence, if sin x increases, csc x decreases; if sin x decreases, csc x increases. The same is true for tan x and cot x, also for cos x and sec x.

Principle 2. A real number and its reciprocal have the same sign.
Hence, the pairs of reciprocal functions are positive together or negative together.

Principle 3. The reciprocal of 1 is 1; the reciprocal of -1 is -1.
Hence, whenever a function is 1, as is the case of sin 90°, the reciprocal function for the same angle, csc 90°, equals 1. Note that cos 180° and sec 180° $= -1$.

Principle 4. If a function approaches 0 in value, its reciprocal function approaches infinity, that is, it increases or decreases without limit. Conversely, whenever a function is said to approach infinity, its reciprocal function approaches 0.

SUMMARY OF CHANGES IN TRIGONOMETRIC FUNCTIONS

The following table summarizes the changes that take place in the values of the six trigonometric functions as angle x increases from 0° to 360° (0 to 2π).

	Value of Trigonometric Function in:			
	Quadrant I 0° to 90° or 0 to $\dfrac{\pi}{2}$	*Quadrant II* 90° to 180° or $\dfrac{\pi}{2}$ to π	*Quadrant III* 180° to 270° or π to $\dfrac{3\pi}{2}$	*Quadrant IV* 270° to 360° or $\dfrac{3\pi}{2}$ to 2π
$y = \sin x$ (Fig. 1, page 539)	increases from 0 to 1	decreases from 1 to 0	decreases from 0 to −1	increases from −1 to 0
$y = \cos x$ (Fig. 2, page 539)	decreases from 1 to 0	decreases from 0 to −1	increases from −1 to 0	increases from 0 to 1
$y = \tan x$ (Fig. 3, page 540)	← increases in every quadrant →			
	from 0 to ∞	from −∞ to 0	from 0 to ∞	from −∞ to 0
$y = \cot x$ (Fig. 3, page 540)	← decreases in every quadrant →			
	from ∞ to 0	from 0 to −∞	from ∞ to 0	from 0 to −∞
$y = \sec x$ (Fig. 2, page 539)	increases from 1 to ∞	increases from −∞ to −1	decreases from −1 to −∞	decreases from ∞ to 1
$y = \csc x$ (Fig. 1, page 539)	decreases from ∞ to 1	increases from 1 to ∞	increases from −∞ to −1	decreases from −1 to −∞

Exercises

In 1–4, as angle x increases, which functions of x increase in quadrant:

1. I   **2.** II   **3.** III   **4.** IV

In 5–8, as angle x increases, which functions of x decrease in quadrant:

5. I   **6.** II   **7.** III   **8.** IV

In 9–12, as x increases from 0° to 180°, which functions of x:

9. increase   **10.** decrease then increase

11. decrease   **12.** increase then decrease

In 13–16, as x increases from 90° to 270°, which functions of x:

13. increase

14. increase then decrease

15. decrease

16. decrease then increase

In 17–19, how does a function of x change if its reciprocal function:

17. increases from 0 to 1

18. decreases from ∞ to 1

19. decreases from 1 to 0

In 20–22, sketch the graphs of the two reciprocal functions in the interval $0 \le x \le 2\pi$, using the same set of axes.

20. $y = \sin x$ and $y = \csc x$

21. $y = \cos x$ and $y = \sec x$

22. $y = \tan x$ and $y = \cot x$

In answering 23–40, it is sufficient to use the following abbreviations:

  a for $y = \sin x$ b for $y = \cos x$ c for $y = \tan x$
  d for $y = \csc x$ e for $y = \sec x$ f for $y = \cot x$

In 23–40, state the trigonometric function or functions:

23. whose period is 360°.

24. whose period is 180°.

25. which intersect the x-axis.

26. which intersect the y-axis.

27. whose curves are continuous.

28. whose curves are discontinuous.

29. whose amplitude is 1.

30. which have no amplitude.

31. which intersect the x-axis at 180° intervals.

32. which do not intersect the x-axis.

33. whose domain is the set of all real numbers.

34. whose domain is the set of real numbers with even multiples of 90° excluded.

35. whose domain is the set of real numbers with odd multiples of 90° excluded.

36. whose range is the set of all real numbers.

37. whose range is the set of real numbers between 1 and −1 inclusive.

38. whose range is the set of real numbers *except* values between 1 and −1.

39. which have a maximum positive value and a minimum negative value.

40. whose graphs in the case of a related pair of reciprocal functions intersect at 90° intervals, using the same set of axes.

41. If both $\sin x$ and $\sec x$ increase, then x must be an angle in quadrant (1) I (2) II   (3) III

42. As x varies from π to 2π, which function of x other than $\cot x$ decreases throughout this interval?

43. In which quadrant do both the sine and the cosine of a positive angle increase as the angle increases?

44. As an angle increases from π to 2π, its cosine (1) increases throughout (2) decreases and then increases   (3) increases and then decreases

45. As an angle increases from 90° to 180°, its cosecant (1) decreases from 1 to −1 (2) increases from −∞ to −1   (3) increases from 1 to ∞

46. As a positive angle in the second quadrant increases, what function other than the secant and cosecant increases?

47. As angle A increases from $180°$ to $270°$, the value of $\cos A$ (1) decreases from 1 to 0   (2) increases from -1 to 0   (3) decreases from 0 to -1

48. As A increases from $180°$ to $270°$, $\tan A$ increases (1) from 0 to $+\infty$ (2) from $-\infty$ to $+\infty$ (3) from $-\infty$ to 0

49. As angle A increases from $180°$ to $270°$, does tangent A increase or decrease?

50. As A increases from $270°$ to $360°$, (1) $\sin A$ increases from 0 to 1   (2) $\cos A$ increases from 0 to 1   (3) $\tan A$ increases from $-\infty$ to $+\infty$

51. As a positive angle in the fourth quadrant increases, what function other than the sine and the tangent increases?

52. As x varies from 0 to π, $\csc x$ decreases and then increases. (Answer *true* or *false*.)

3. Amplitude, Frequency, and Period of Sine and Cosine Curves

AMPLITUDE OF SINE AND COSINE CURVES

The following figure shows the graphs of three sine curves, using the same set of axes: $y = \frac{1}{2} \sin x$, $y = \sin x$, and $y = 2 \sin x$.

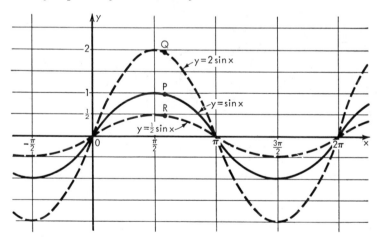

Note in the figure that the ordinate of a point Q, which is on the graph of $y = 2 \sin x$, is twice the ordinate of a point P, which is on the graph of $y = \sin x$, when Q and P have the same abscissa. Likewise, the ordinate of a point R, which is on the graph of $y = \frac{1}{2} \sin x$, is one-half the ordinate of a point P, which is on the graph of $y = \sin x$, when R and P have the same abscissa.

In general, for each x, the ordinate of a point on the graph of $y = a \sin x$, where a is positive, is a times the corresponding ordinate on the graph of $y =$

sin x. This being the case, the amplitude of $y = a \sin x$, where a is positive, is represented by a. Recall that the amplitude of $y = a \sin x$ is the maximum ordinate of the graph.

The same principles apply to the functions $y = a \cos x$ and $y = \cos x$. For each x, the ordinate of a point on the graph of $y = a \cos x$, where a is positive, is a times the corresponding ordinate on the graph of $y = \cos x$. The amplitude of $y = a \cos x$, where a is positive, is represented by a.

Keep in mind that the amplitude of the graph of $y = \sin x$ or $y = \cos x$ is not the same as the "width" of the curve. The width is the vertical distance between the tangents to the curve that are parallel to the x-axis and pass through highest and lowest points. The amplitude of $y = \sin x$ or $y = \cos x$ is 1, whereas the width of the curve is 2; the amplitude of $y = a \sin x$ or $y = a \cos x$ is a, whereas the width of each curve is $2a$.

FREQUENCY AND PERIOD OF SINE AND COSINE CURVES

The following figure shows the graphs of three cosine curves, using the same set of axes: $y = \cos \frac{1}{2}x$, $y = \cos x$, and $y = \cos 2x$.

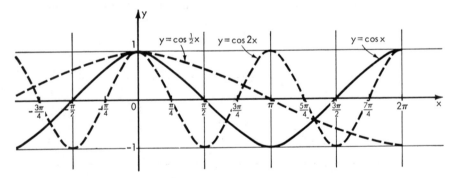

Note in the figure that the amplitude of each of the three cosine graphs is 1. Their difference lies in the *frequency* or the number of cycles within 360°, or 2π radians. Within 360°, the frequency of the graph of $y = \cos \frac{1}{2}x$ is $\frac{1}{2}$, that of $y = \cos x$ is 1, and that of $\cos 2x$ is 2.

In general, the frequency of the graph of $y = \cos bx$ (within 360°) is b, where b is positive. This general rule applies equally well to the frequency of sine curves since a sine curve is obtained by shifting or displacing a cosine curve 90° to the right. Such a shift does not change the frequency of the graph.

The number of degrees or the number of radians in a complete cycle is the *period* of a sine or cosine curve. The period is found by dividing 360° (or 2π) by b, the frequency.

Thus, if the frequency b is 2, the period $= \dfrac{360°}{b} = \dfrac{360°}{2} = 180°$. In radians, the period $=\dfrac{2\pi}{b}=\dfrac{2\pi}{2}=\pi.$ Also, the period of $y=\cos\frac{1}{2}x$ is $\dfrac{360°}{\frac{1}{2}}$, or $720°$. In

radians, the period of $y=\cos\frac{1}{2}x$ is $\dfrac{2\pi}{\frac{1}{2}}$, or $4\pi.$

RULES FOR AMPLITUDE, FREQUENCY, AND PERIOD

For $y=a\sin bx$ or $y=a\cos bx$, $a>0$, $b>0$:

Rule 1. The *amplitude* or maximum ordinate $=a$.
Rule 2. The *frequency* or the numbers of cycles within $360°$ or $2\pi=b$.
Rule 3. The *period* $=\dfrac{360°}{b}$ or $\dfrac{2\pi}{b}$.

The following table shows applications of these rules:

Equation $y=a\sin bx$ or $y=a\cos bx$ $(a>0, b>0)$	Amplitude (a) (maximum ordinate)	Frequency (b) (no. of cycles in $360°$ or 2π)	Period $\left(\dfrac{2\pi}{b}\right)$ (no. of degrees or radians for one cycle)
$y=\sin x$	1	1	$360°$ or 2π
$y=\cos x$	1	1	$360°$ or 2π
$y=2\sin x$	2	1	$360°$ or 2π
$y=3\cos x$	3	1	$360°$ or 2π
$y=\sin 2x$	1	2	$180°$ or π
$y=\cos 3x$	1	3	$120°$ or $\dfrac{2\pi}{3}$
$y=\sin\frac{1}{2}x$	1	$\frac{1}{2}$	$720°$ or 4π
$y=\cos\frac{1}{3}x$	1	$\frac{1}{3}$	$1080°$ or 6π
$y=3\sin 5x$	3	5	$72°$ or $\dfrac{2\pi}{5}$
$y=5\cos\frac{1}{4}x$	5	$\frac{1}{4}$	$1440°$ or 8π

Recall that a change in the equation from $y = 2x^2$ to $y = -2x^2$ led to a reflection of the graph of the parabola $y = 2x^2$ in the x-axis. Another reflection is shown in the figure at the right, which contains the graphs of $y = 2 \sin x$ and $y = -2 \sin x$. Note that the graph of $y = -2 \sin x$ is the reflection in the x-axis of the graph of $y = 2 \sin x$. In general, the graph

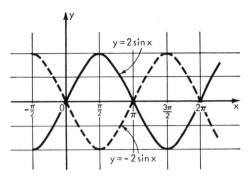

of $y = a \sin x$ is the reflection in the x-axis of the graph of $y = -a \sin x$. Similarly, the graph of $y = a \cos x$ is the reflection in the x-axis of the graph of $y = -a \cos x$.

Exercises

In 1–12, for the given curve, state the amplitude, the frequency, and the period in degrees and radians.

1. $y = \sin x$ **2.** $y = \cos x$ **3.** $y = \sin 4x$ **4.** $y = \cos 2x$

5. $y = 4 \sin x$ **6.** $y = 5 \cos x$ **7.** $y = 3 \sin 2x$ **8.** $y = 2 \cos 3x$

9. $y = 2 \sin \frac{1}{2}x$ **10.** $y = \frac{1}{2} \sin 3x$ **11.** $y = 3 \cos \frac{1}{3}x$ **12.** $y = 15 \sin 5x$

In 13–15, write the equation for a sine curve whose period is π and whose amplitude is:

13. 2   **14.** $\frac{1}{2}$ **15.** 6

In 16–18, write the equation for a cosine curve whose amplitude is 3 and whose period is:

16. $360°$ **17.** 4π **18.** $72°$

19. Which of the following curves have the same maximum value?
   (1) $y = 3 \cos 4x$ (2) $y = 4 \cos 4x$ (3) $y = 3 \cos 3x$

20. Which of the following curves have the same period? (1) $y = 2 \sin 3x$
   (2) $y = 3 \sin 2x$ (3) $y = 3 \sin 3x$

In 21 and 22, find the maximum value.

21. $1000 \sin \frac{1}{2}x$ **22.** $\frac{1}{2} \sin 1000x$

In 23 and 24, find the minimum value.

23. $40 \cos \frac{1}{3}x$ **24.** $\frac{1}{3} \cos 40x$

25. The maximum value of $2 \sin 3x$ is (1) 1   (2) 2   (3) 6

26. The maximum value of $3 \cos \frac{1}{2}x$ is (1) 1   (2) 2   (3) 3

27. What is the minimum positive value of $3 \sec 2x$?

28. The minimum value of 2 sin x is   (1) 0   (2) -1 (3) -2

29. The amplitude of $y = 3 \cos 4\theta$ is   (1) 12   (2) 3   (3) 4   (4) none of these

30. The period of $y = 3 \sin 2x$ is   (1) 90°   (2) 180°   (3) 360°   (3) 720°

31. The period of the curve $y = 2 \sin x$ is   (1) π (2) 2   (3) 2π (4) $\dfrac{\pi}{2}$

32. The period of the curve $y = 3 \cos 2x$ is   (1) $\dfrac{2\pi}{3}$ (2) π (3) 3   (4) 4π

33. A curve whose amplitude is $\frac{1}{2}$ and whose period is π is (1) $y = 2 \sin 2x$
(2) $y = \frac{1}{2} \sin 2x$ (3) $y = \frac{1}{2} \sin x$ (4) $y = 2 \sin \frac{1}{2}x$

4. Sketching Sine and Cosine Curves

Procedure. To sketch sine and cosine curves having the form $y = a \sin bx$ or $y = a \cos bx$:

1. Make sure that the graph contains the essential elements of any graph, including both axes, the origin, and the scale units along both axes.

2. Determine the period of the sine or cosine function involved, and plot the intersections of the curve with the x-axis and y-axis. Remember that the sine curves will cross the x-axis at the origin. Cosine curves will cross the y-axis at a maximum point on the curve.

3. Determine the amplitude from the equation and, using this value, plot the maximum or minimum points on the curve.

4. Follow the instructions in the problem concerning the interval through which the angle changes.

5. Carefully draw a smooth curve, approximating the general shape of all sine and cosine curves.

SKETCHING SINE CURVES OF THE FAMILY $y = a \sin bx$

The following model problems illustrate how to sketch sine curves. These curves are special cases of the more general equation $y = a \sin bx$.

~~~~~~~~~~~ *MODEL PROBLEMS* ~~~~~~~~~~~

In 1–5, state the amplitude and the period. Then sketch the sine curve.

1. $y = 2 \sin x$
amplitude $= 2$
period $= 360°$ or 2π

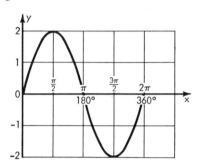

2. $y = \sin 2x$
amplitude $= 1$
period $= 180°$ or π

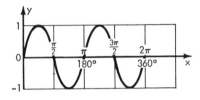

3. $y = \frac{1}{2} \sin x$
amplitude $= \frac{1}{2}$
period $= 360°$ or 2π

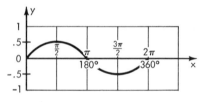

4. $y = 3 \sin 2x$
amplitude $= 3$
period $= 180°$ or π

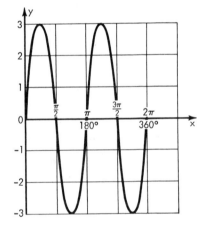

5. $y = \sin \frac{1}{2}x$
amplitude $= 1$
period $= 720°$ or 4π

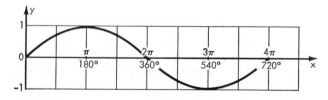

SKETCHING COSINE CURVES OF THE FAMILY $y = a \cos bx$

The following model problems illustrate how to sketch cosine curves. These curves are special cases of the more general equation $y = a \cos bx$.

~~~~~~~~~~~~ *MODEL PROBLEMS* ~~~~~~~~~~~~

In 6 and 7, state the amplitude and the period. Then sketch the cosine curve.

6. $y = 3 \cos x$
amplitude $= 3$
period $= 360°$ or 2π

7. $y = \cos 3x$
amplitude $= 1$

period $= 120°$ or $\dfrac{2\pi}{3}$

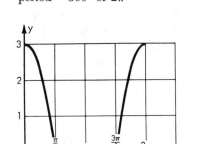

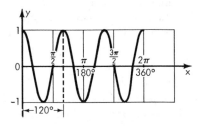

MAKING COMPOSITE SKETCHES OF TWO CURVES USING THE SAME SET OF AXES

The following model problems illustrate how to sketch two graphs of trigonometric curves on the same set of axes.

~~~~~~~~~~ *MODEL PROBLEMS* ~~~~~~~~~~

8. *a.* On the same set of axes, *sketch* the graphs of $y = 2 \cos \frac{1}{2}x$ and $y = \sin 2x$ as x varies from 0 to 2π radians. (Label *each* curve with its equation.)
   b. What is the amplitude of the curve $y = 2 \cos \frac{1}{2}x$?
   c. What is the period of the curve $y = \sin 2x$?

Solution:

a. To sketch sine and cosine curves, apply the following principle:

If the equation of a curve is of the form $y = a \sin bx$ or $y = a \cos bx$, then a is the maximum y-value and b is the number of cycles within 360°, or 2π radians.

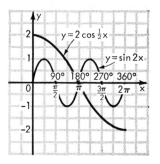

In $y = 2 \cos \frac{1}{2}x$, $a = 2$ and $b = \frac{1}{2}$. Since $a = 2$, the maximum y-value $= 2$ (at 0°).

Since $b = \frac{1}{2}$, there is a half-cycle within 360° or 2π radians.

In $y = 1 \sin 2x$, $a = 1$ and $b = 2$. Since $a = 1$, the maximum y-value $= 1$ (at 45° and 225°).

Since $b = 2$, there are two cycles within 360° or one complete cycle within 180° or π radians.

b. The amplitude of the curve $y = 2 \cos \frac{1}{2}x$ is the value of a, or 2.
Ans.   (b) 2

c. The period of the curve $y = \sin 2x$ is 180°, or π radians, since the period is the interval in which one complete cycle occurs.   *Ans. (c)* π or 180°

9. a. *Sketch* the graph of $y = \tan x$ as x varies from 0 to π radians.

   b. On the same set of axes used in answer to *a*, *sketch* the graph of $y = \cos 2x$ as x varies from 0 to π radians.

   c. State the number of values of x between 0 and π that satisfy the equation $\tan x = \cos 2x$.

Solution:

a. In sketching $y = \tan x$, keep in mind that the curve is discontinuous. From 0 to $\dfrac{\pi}{2}$, the values of $\tan x$ increase from 0 to very large values when x approaches 90°. At 45°, the value of $y = 1$. The next branch of $y = \tan x$ is from 90° to 180°, or from $\dfrac{\pi}{2}$ to π. Here again the values of $\tan x$ increase from very small values when x is very close to 90° to a value of 0 when $x = \pi$ or 180°.

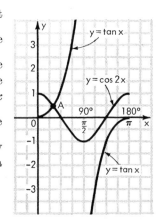

Note. Be sure that the graph of $y = \tan x$ does not touch the line $x = \dfrac{\pi}{2}$.

   b. If a curve is of the form $y = a \cos bx$, then a is the maximum y-value and b is the number of cycles within 360°, or 2π radians. For $y = \cos 2x$, $a = 1$ and $b = 2$. Since $a = 1$, the maximum value of y is 1 (at 0° and 180°). Since $b = 2$, there are two cycles within 360° or 2π radians and one complete cycle within 180° or π radians.

   c. The number of values between 0 and π that satisfy the equation $\tan x = \cos 2x$ is the number of points of intersection of the two curves. Note the one point of intersection at A.   *Ans. (c)* 1

Exercises

   In 1–4, state the equation of the curve. The curve is either a sine curve or a cosine curve, one of whose complete cycles is shown.

1.

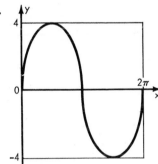

2.

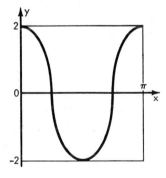

3.

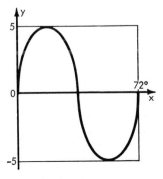

4.

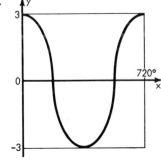

In 5–10, sketch a single cycle of the curve whose equation is given.

5. $y = \sin 10x$ **6.** $y = 10 \sin x$ **7.** $y = 2 \sin 3x$

8. $y = 3 \cos 2x$ **9.** $y = 4 \cos \frac{1}{2}x$ **10.** $\frac{1}{2} \cos 4x = y$

In 11–14, the curve at the right is a complete cycle of a sine curve. Find the maximum value, c; the minimum value, d; and the period, e, if the equation of the curve is:

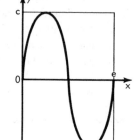

11. $y = 3 \sin x$ **12.** $y = 4 \sin 4x$

13. $y = 6 \sin 3x$ **14.** $y = 2 \sin \frac{1}{2}x$

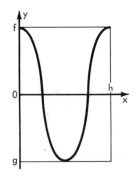

In 15–18, the curve at the left is a complete cycle of a cosine curve. Find the maximum value, f; the minimum value, g; and the period, h, if the equation of the curve is:

15. $y = 4 \cos x$ **16.** $y = \cos 10x$

17. $y = 8 \cos 2x$ **18.** $y = 2 \cos 8x$

In 19–22, let x vary from 0 to 2π radians.

19. Sketch on one set of axes the graphs of $\sin 2x$, $\sin x$, and $2 \sin x$.

20. Sketch on one set of axes the graphs of $\sin 2x$, $2 \sin x$, and $\sin \frac{1}{2}x$.

21. Sketch on one set of axes the graphs of $\cos x$, $\cos 3x$, and $3 \cos x$.

22. Sketch on one set of axes the graphs of $\sin x$, $\cos x$, and $\tan x$.

23. As angle x increases from $0°$ to $180°$, for what value of x do the graphs of $y = \sin x$ and $y = \cos x$ intersect?

24. For what value of x between 0 and π radians are the ordinates of the curves $y = \sin x$ and $y = \cos x$ equal?

25. For what value of x between $\dfrac{\pi}{2}$ and $\dfrac{3\pi}{2}$ does the graph of $y = \sin x$ cross the x-axis?

26. For how many values of x between $0°$ to $180°$ does the line $y = \frac{1}{2}$ intersect the curve $y = \sin x$?

27. As x varies from 0 to π radians, the graphs of $y = 2$ and $y = 2 \sin x$ when drawn on the same set of axes (1) intersect in distinct points   (2) are tangent   (3) have no points in common

28. As x varies from $0°$ to $270°$, the graphs of $y = \tan x$ and $y = \cos x$ intersect in (1) one point   (2) two points   (3) three points

29. When drawn on the same set of axes, the graphs of $y = \sin x$ and $y = \tan x$, for values of x from $0°$ to $360°$ inclusive, intersect (1) once   (2) three times   (3) five times

30. For values of x between 0 and π radians, the graphs of $y = 2 \sin x$ and $y = 1$ when drawn on the same axes (1) intersect in two points   (2) intersect in only one point   (3) do not intersect

31. *a.* Sketch the graph of $y = \cos x$ as x varies from $0°$ to $360°$.

  b. By means of the graph made in answer to *a*, show that there are always four values of x between $0°$ and $360°$ which satisfy the equation $\cos^2 x = k$ where k is a positive number less than 1.

32. *a.* On the same set of axes, sketch the graphs of $y = 2 \sin x$ and $y = \cos x$ from 0 to 2π radians inclusive.

  b. From the graphs made in *a*, determine the quadrants in which are found the angles that satisfy the equation $2 \sin x = \cos x$.

33. *a.* Using the same set of axes, sketch the graphs of $y = \cos x$ and $y = \tan x$ as x varies from 0 to 2π radians.

  b. Indicate on the graphs made in answer to *a* the point whose abscissas give solutions of the equation $\cos x = \tan x$.

34. *a.* Sketch the graph of $y = \sin x$ as x varies from $-\pi$ to $+\pi$ radians.

  b. On the graph drawn in answer to *a*, illustrate the fact that $\sin(-x)$ is equal to $-\sin x$ for values of x between $+\pi$ and $-\pi$ radians.

  c. Is the fact illustrated in answer to *b* true for all values of x?

35. *a.* Sketch the graph of $y = 2 \cos x$ from $x = 0°$ to $x = 360°$ inclusive.

  b. On the set of axes used in *a*, sketch the graph of $y = \sin 2x$ from $x = 0°$ to $x = 360°$ inclusive.

  c. What is the amplitude of the graph of $y = 2 \cos x$?

  d. What is the period of the graph of $y = \sin 2x$?

36. *a.* On the same set of axes, sketch the graphs of $y = \sin x$ and $y = \cos \frac{1}{2}x$ as x varies from 0 to 2π radians.

  b. From the graphs made in answer to part *a*, determine the quadrant in which $\sin x - \cos \frac{1}{2}x$ is always positive.

37. *a.* Sketch the graph of $y = \tan x$ as x varies from $0°$ to $180°$.

  b. On the set of axes used in answer to *a*, sketch the graph of $y = \cos 2x$ as x varies from $0°$ to $180°$.

  c. How many values of x between $0°$ and $180°$ satisfy the equation $\tan x = \cos 2x$?

38. *a.* Sketch and label the graph of $y = 2 \cos x$ as x varies from 0 to 2π radians.
  b. On the same set of axes used in part *a*, sketch and label the graph of $y = \tan x$ as x varies from 0 to 2π radians.
  c. Write the number of the expression that best completes the following statement: In the equation $y = \tan x - 2 \cos x$, when x is equal to $\dfrac{\pi}{2}$, the value of y is   (1) 1   (2) 2   (3) undefined   (4) -1

5. Solving Trigonometric Equations Graphically

In each of the following model problems, a graph of a trigonometric function is to be drawn, using a table of ordered number pairs. The table is prepared by using a stated domain for x and a given interval. The use of a table enables us to draw a trigonometric graph with much more accuracy than a sketch.

〜〜〜〜〜〜〜〜〜 *MODEL PROBLEMS* 〜〜〜〜〜〜〜〜〜

1. *a.* On the same set of axes, draw the graphs of $y = \cos x$ and $y = \tan x$ as x varies from 0° to 360° inclusive at intervals of 30°.
  b. With the aid of the graphs drawn in answer to *a*, find, correct to the nearest degree, the values of x for which $\cos x = \tan x$.

Solution:

TABLE OF $y = \cos x$

a.   (for 0 and positive values of x at intervals of 30°)

x	0°	30°	60°	90°	120°	150°	180°	210°	240°	270°	300°	330°	360°
y	1	.87	.5	0	$-.5$	$-.87$	-1	$-.87$	$-.5$	0	.5	.87	1

TABLE OF $y = \tan x$

(for 0 and positive values of x at intervals of 30°)

x	0°	30°	60°	90°	120°	150°	180°	210°	240°	270°	300°	330°	360°
y	0	.58	1.73	∞	-1.73	$-.58$	0	.58	1.73	∞	-1.73	$-.58$	0

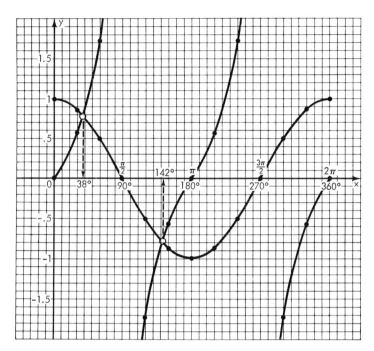

b. The values of x, correct to the nearest degree, for which $\cos x = \tan x$ are 38° and 142°.

2. *a.* Draw the graph of $y = \sin 2x$ as x varies from 0 to π radians at intervals of $\dfrac{\pi}{12}$ radians.

   b. On the set of axes used in answer to *a*, draw the graph of $y = .6$ and $y = -.6$.

   c. By means of capital letters, indicate on the graphs made in answer to *a* and *b* the points whose x-values satisfy the equation $\sin 2x = .6$ or the equation $\sin 2x = -.6$.

Solution:

a and *b.*   TABLE OF $y = \sin 2x$

$$\left(\text{for 0 and positive values of } x \text{ at intervals of } \frac{\pi}{12} \text{ radians}\right)$$

x	0	$\dfrac{\pi}{12}$	$\dfrac{\pi}{6}$	$\dfrac{\pi}{4}$	$\dfrac{\pi}{3}$	$\dfrac{5\pi}{12}$	$\dfrac{\pi}{2}$	$\dfrac{7\pi}{12}$	$\dfrac{2\pi}{3}$	$\dfrac{3\pi}{4}$	$\dfrac{5\pi}{6}$	$\dfrac{11\pi}{12}$	π
y	0	.5	.87	1	.87	.5	0	$-.5$	$-.87$	-1	$-.87$	$-.5$	0

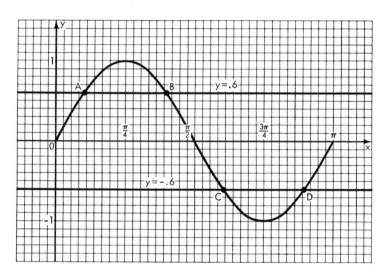

c. Points A and B satisfy $\sin 2x = .6$, and points C and D satisfy $\sin 2x = -.6$.

~~~~~~

Exercises

1. *a.* Draw the graph of the equation $y = \sin x$ as x varies from $0°$ to $90°$ at intervals of $15°$.

    b. Using the same set of axes as in *a*, plot the graph of the equation $y = .4$.

    c. With the aid of the graphs made in answer to *a* and *b*, find, correct to the nearest degree, a positive acute angle x which is an approximate solution of the equation $\sin x = .4$.

2. *a.* Draw the graph of the equation $y = \cos x$ as x varies from $0°$ to $180°$ at intervals of $30°$.

    b. Using the same set of axes as in *a*, plot the graph of the equations $y = .4$ and $y = -.4$.

    c. With the aid of the graphs made in answer to *a* and *b*, find, correct to the nearest degree, the positive values of x which are approximate solutions of the equation $\cos x = \pm.4$.

3. *a.* Draw the graph of the equation $y = \tan x$ as x varies from $0°$ to $90°$ at intervals of $15°$.

    b. Using the same set of axes as in *a*, plot the graph of the equation $y = 3$.

    c. With the aid of the graphs made in answer to *a* and *b*, find, correct to the nearest degree, a positive acute angle x which is an approximate solution of the equation $\tan x = 3$.

4. *a.* Draw the graphs of $y = 1$ and $y = -1$.

  b. On the same set of axes used in *a*, sketch the graph of $y = 2 \cos x$ as x varies from 0 to 2π.

  c. From the graphs made in answer to *a* and *b*, determine the number of values of x between 0 and 2π that satisfy the equations $2 \cos x = \pm 1$.

5. *a.* Draw the graph of the equation $y = \sin x$ as x varies from $0°$ to $180°$ inclusive in intervals of $15°$.

  b. Using the same set of axes as in *a*, draw the graph of $y = \cos x$ as x varies from $0°$ to $180°$ inclusive in intervals of $15°$.

  c. With the aid of the graphs drawn in answer to *a* and *b*, find a value of x common to both equations.

6. *a.* Draw the graph of $y = \sin 2x$ as x varies from $0°$ to $180°$ inclusive at intervals of $15°$.

  b. Using the same set of axes as in *a*, draw the graph of $y = \tan x$ as x varies from $0°$ to $180°$ inclusive at intervals of $30°$.

  c. With the aid of the graphs drawn in answer to *a* and *b*, find all the values of x between $0°$ and $180°$ for which $\sin 2x = \tan x$.

7. *a.* Draw the graph of $y = 2 \sin x$ for values of x from $0°$ to $180°$.

  b. On the same set of axes used in *a*, draw the graph of $y = \tan x$ for values of x from $0°$ to $180°$.

  c. From the graphs made in answer to *a* and *b*, estimate, to within approximately $10°$, the value of x between $0°$ and $180°$ that satisfies the equation $\tan x = 2 \sin x$.

8. *a.* On the same set of axes, draw the graphs of $y = \cos x$ and $y = \sin 2x$ as x varies from 0 to π radians inclusive at intervals of $\dfrac{\pi}{6}$ radians.

  b. Indicate on the graphs, by means of capital letters, the points whose abscissas give solutions of the equation $\cos x = \sin 2x$.

In 9–14, using the same set of axes: *a.* Draw the graphs of the equations as x varies from 0 to π at intervals of $\dfrac{\pi}{6}$. *b.* From the graphs made in *a*, state the number of values of x greater than 0 and less than π common to both equations.

9. $y = \sin 2x$ and $y = 2 \sin x$

10. $y = 2 \sin x$ and $y = \sin \frac{1}{2}x$

11. $y = 2 \cos x$ and $y = \cos 2x$

12. $y = \sin x$ and $y = \cos 2x$

13. $y = 2 \cos x$ and $y = \tan x$

14. $y = \frac{1}{2} \sin x$ and $y = \sin \frac{1}{2}x$

6. Graphs of the Inverses of Trigonometric Functions

RELATIONS AND THE INVERSES OF RELATIONS

Recall that a relation in x and y *is* a set of ordered pairs (x, y). For example, the relation $R = \{(x, y) \mid y = x^2\}$ includes ordered pairs such as $(2, 4)$, $(-2, 4)$, $(3, 9)$, $(-3, 9)$. As we have discovered, the graph of the relation R is a parabola that meets the vertical test of a function since no vertical line can intersect the graph in more than one point.

Every relation has associated with it an inverse relation that is formed by interchanging the components in each ordered pair of the relation.

Thus, the relation $R = \{(x, y) \mid y = x^2\}$ has associated with it an inverse relation R^{-1}, such that $R^{-1} = \{(x, y) \mid x = y^2\}$. Note, in Fig. 1, that the graph of R^{-1} is a parabola that does not meet the vertical test of a function.

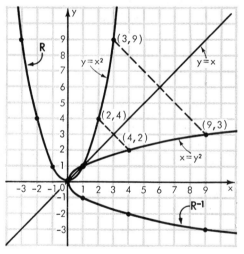

Fig. 1

The following table shows how the components of a few of the ordered pairs of R are interchanged to obtain the components of the related ordered pairs of R^{-1}:

Relations	Ordered Pairs
$R = \{(x, y) \mid y = x^2\}$	$(0, 0)$, $(1, 1)$, $(-1, 1)$, $(2, 4)$, $(-2, 4)$, $(3, 9)$, $(-3, 9)$
$R^{-1} = \{(x, y) \mid x = y^2\}$	$(0, 0)$, $(1, 1)$, $(1, -1)$, $(4, 2)$, $(4, -2)$, $(9, 3)$, $(9, -3)$

Note that the ordered pairs (0, 0) and (1, 1) are the only ordered pairs that the given relation and its inverse relation have in common. In these ordered pairs, the first and second components are equal; that is, $y = x$. Note in Fig. 1 that the points (0, 0) and (1, 1) lie on the line $y = x$ and that the graphs of the two parabolas have no other points in common. Note further, that the line $y = x$ is the perpendicular bisector of the segments whose endpoints are a point on the graph of the relation and the corresponding point on the graph of the inverse of the relation as in the case of the points (3, 9) and (9, 3); also, in the case of the points (2, 4) and (4, 2). We describe this situation by saying that the points (3, 9) and (9, 3) are symmetric with respect to the line $y = x$; the same is true of the points (2, 4) and (4, 2).

In general, the graphs of a relation R and its inverse relation R^{-1} are symmetric with respect to the line $y = x$; also, R and R^{-1} are reflections of each other in the line $y = x$.

TRIGONOMETRIC RELATIONS AND THE INVERSES OF TRIGONOMETRIC RELATIONS

The following table associates the three basic trigonometric functions and the inverses of these functions. Note in the second column how x and y are interchanged to obtain the inverses.

Trigonometric Functions	Interchange of x and y	Inverse Trigonometric Relations
$y = \sin x$	$x = \sin y$	$y = \text{arc sin } x$ or $\sin^{-1} x$
$y = \cos x$	$x = \cos y$	$y = \text{arc cos } x$ or $\cos^{-1} x$
$y = \tan x$	$x = \tan y$	$y = \text{arc tan } x$ or $\tan^{-1} x$

The graphs of the three inverse trigonometric relations are obtained by interchanging the values of x and y in the tables used earlier in this chapter to obtain the graphs of $y = \sin x$, $y = \cos x$, and $y = \tan x$. To obtain the tables of ordered pairs for the inverse trigonometric relations, simply interchange the values of x and y, thus making the domain of one the range of the other or the range of one the domain of the other. When the graphs of the inverse trigonometric relations are drawn, using the new ordered number pairs, the resulting graphs obtained are: $y = \text{arc sin } x$, Fig. 2; $y = \text{arc cos } x$, Fig. 3; $y = \text{arc tan } x$, Fig. 4.

A study of the graphs of the inverse trigonometric relations show us why they are called relations rather than functions. The reason is that the graphs do not

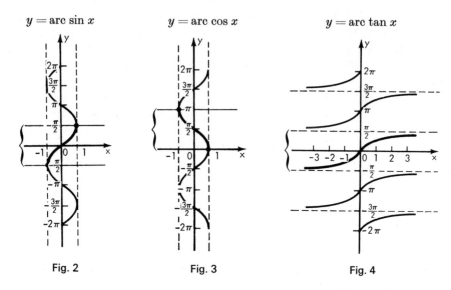

$y = \text{arc sin } x$ $y = \text{arc cos } x$ $y = \text{arc tan } x$

Fig. 2   Fig. 3   Fig. 4

meet the vertical line test of a function. Hence, in the case of each relation, mathematicians have agreed that a suitable restriction should be placed on the range of that relation, the set of y-values, in order that the resulting inverse relation should be a function.

The following table sets forth the restricted range of the inverse trigonometric functions. Keep in mind that principal values of inverse trigonometric functions are shown by capitalizing the first letter, thus: $Arc \sin x$ or $Sin^{-1} x$, $Arc \cos x$ or $Cos^{-1} x$, etc.

Restricted Range of the Inverse Trigonometric Functions		
$y = \text{Arc sin } x$	$y = \text{Arc cos } x$	$y = \text{Arc tan } x$
$-\dfrac{\pi}{2} \leq \text{Arc sin } x \leq \dfrac{\pi}{2}$	$0 \leq \text{Arc cos } x \leq \pi$	$-\dfrac{\pi}{2} < \text{Arc tan } x < \dfrac{\pi}{2}$
(See Fig. 2)	(See Fig. 3)	(See Fig. 4)

By restricting the ranges of the inverse trigonometric functions, we limit ourselves to a discussion of the "principal values" of the inverse functions. When inverse trigonometric functions were first discussed in Chapter 10, the principal values of these functions were so defined that the ranges of these values were exactly the same as the restricted ranges set forth in the above table.

Examine the graphs of the inverse trigonometric functions in Figs. 2, 3, and 4. Note that the restrictions on the ranges have been shown by a heavy line in each graph and also by a brace. Study these graphs carefully. They will help you understand the character of the inverse trigonometric functions and the restrictions on their ranges.

We stated earlier that the graph of a relation and its inverse relation are reflections of each other in the line $y = x$. Think of the line $y = x$ as an axis of symmetry such that if it is used as the folding line, the relation can be made to coincide with the inverse relation, or conversely. Note in Fig. 5 how the graph of $y = \sin x$ and the graph of $y = \arcsin x$ are reflections of each other in the line $y = x$; that is, they are symmetric with respect to the line $y = x$. In Fig. 5, the graph of $y = \arcsin x$ is drawn as a solid line, whereas that of $y = \sin x$ is dashed.

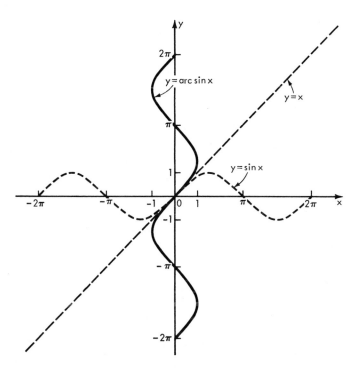

Fig. 5

Exercises

In 1–3, draw the graph of the inverse trigonometric relation and use a heavy line and brace to set forth the given restricted range.

1. $y = \text{arc cot } x,\ 0 < \text{Arc cot } x < \pi$

2. $y = \text{arc sec } x,\ 0 \le \text{Arc sec } x \le \pi,\ y \ne \dfrac{\pi}{2}$

3. $y = \text{arc csc } x,\ -\dfrac{\pi}{2} \le \text{Arc csc } x \le \dfrac{\pi}{2},\ y \ne 0$

In 4–9, draw the graph of the expression.

4. $y = \text{arc sin } 2x$ **5.** $y = 2 \text{ arc sin } 2x$ **6.** $y = 2 \text{ arc sin } 2x$

7. $y = \text{arc cos } \frac{1}{2}x$ **8.** $y = \frac{1}{2} \text{ arc cos } \frac{1}{2}x$ **9.** $y = \frac{1}{2} \text{ arc cos } \frac{1}{2}x$

CHAPTER XVII

SIMPLE APPLICATIONS OF THE FUNDAMENTAL LAWS OF OBLIQUE TRIANGLES

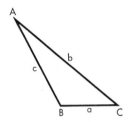

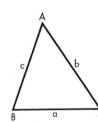

Oblique triangles, such as the ones in the figure at the left, are triangles that are not right triangles. In this chapter, we will study the following fundamental relations that exist among the sides and angles of oblique triangles: (1) the *law of sines*, (2) the *law of cosines*, and (3) the *law of tangents*.

1. Applying the Law of Sines

In any triangle,

1. $\dfrac{a}{\sin A} = \dfrac{b}{\sin B} = \dfrac{c}{\sin C}$

2. $\dfrac{a}{b} = \dfrac{\sin A}{\sin B}$

$\dfrac{a}{c} = \dfrac{\sin A}{\sin C}$

$\dfrac{b}{c} = \dfrac{\sin B}{\sin C}$

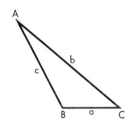

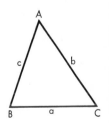

In the rules that follow, the term "side" means "length of a side."

Rule 1. In any triangle, the sides are proportional to the sines of the opposite angles. (See the equation in **1** above.)

Rule 2. In any triangle, the ratio of a side to the sine of the opposite angle is constant. (See the equation in **1** above.)

Rule 3. The ratio of any two sides of a triangle is equal to the ratio of the sines of the angles opposite these sides. (See the three equations in **2** above.)

Thus, if a side of a triangle is twice another side, then the sine of the angle opposite the greater side is twice the sine of the angle opposite the smaller side.

PROVING THE LAW OF SINES

See page 742 for the proof of the law of sines.

USING THE LAW OF SINES

1. The law of sines can be used in a problem involving two sides of a triangle and their opposite angles when three of these four parts are given or can be found. In such a case, the law of sines can be used to find the fourth part.
2. The law of sines is a powerful instrument that can be used in the proofs of additional theorems. See exercises 28–32 on page 567.

〰〰〰〰〰〰〰 *MODEL PROBLEMS* 〰〰〰〰〰〰〰

1. In triangle ABC, $a = 24$, $\sin A = \frac{2}{3}$, and $\sin B = \frac{1}{4}$. Find b.

Solution:

$$\frac{b}{\sin B} = \frac{a}{\sin A}$$

$a = 24$, $\sin A = \frac{2}{3}$, $\sin B = \frac{1}{4}$

$$\frac{b}{\frac{1}{4}} = \frac{24}{\frac{2}{3}}$$

$$\tfrac{2}{3}b = \tfrac{1}{4} \times 24$$

$$\tfrac{2}{3}b = 6$$

$$b = 9 \quad Ans.$$

2. In triangle RST, $r = 36$, $t = 18$, and $\sin R = \frac{2}{5}$. Find $\sin T$.

Solution:

$$\frac{r}{\sin R} = \frac{t}{\sin T}$$

$r = 36$, $t = 18$, $\sin R = \frac{2}{5}$

$$\frac{36}{\frac{2}{5}} = \frac{18}{\sin T}$$

$$36 \sin T = \tfrac{36}{5}$$

$$\sin T = \tfrac{1}{5} \quad Ans.$$

3. In triangle PQR, express q in terms of p, $\sin Q$, and $\sin P$.

Solution:

Using the law of sines,
$$\frac{q}{p} = \frac{\sin Q}{\sin P}$$
Multiply each side of the equation by p.
$$q = \frac{p \sin Q}{\sin P} \quad Ans.$$

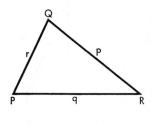

4. In triangle DEF, $\angle D = 135°$, $\angle E = 30°$. Find the value of the ratio $d : e$. (Answer may be left in radical form.)

Solution: The law of sines may be expressed as:
$$\frac{d}{e} = \frac{\sin D}{\sin E}$$
$$\angle D = 135°, \angle E = 30°$$
$$\frac{d}{e} = \frac{\sin 135°}{\sin 30°}$$
$$\sin 135° = \sin(180° - 45°)$$
$$= \sin 45°$$
$$\frac{d}{e} = \frac{\sin 45°}{\sin 30°}$$
$$= \frac{\frac{1}{2}\sqrt{2}}{\frac{1}{2}} = \sqrt{2} \quad Ans.$$

5. In triangle ABC, $a = 130$ ft., $\angle A = 39°$, $\angle B = 65°$. Find side b, correct to the nearest 10 feet.

Solution:
$$\frac{b}{\sin B} = \frac{a}{\sin A}$$
$$a = 130, \angle A = 39°, \angle B = 65°$$
$$\frac{b}{\sin 65°} = \frac{130}{\sin 39°}$$
$$b = \frac{130 \sin 65°}{\sin 39°}$$
$$= \frac{130(.9063)}{.6293} \approx 187$$
$$= 190 \text{ feet, to the nearest 10 feet} \quad Ans.$$

Exercises

1. In triangle KLM, use the law of sines to complete the following:

a. $\dfrac{k}{\sin K} = \dfrac{?}{?} = \dfrac{?}{?}$ b. $\dfrac{k}{m} = \dfrac{?}{?}$ c. $k : l : m = ? \; : \; ? \; : \; ?$

2. In triangle PQR, relate the sides p, q, and r to their opposite angles, using the law of sines.

3. In triangle ABC, express b in terms of a, $\sin A$, and $\sin B$.

4. In triangle DEF, express $\sin D$ in terms of d, f, and $\sin F$.

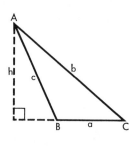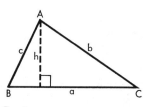

Ex. 5

5. In triangle ABC (see the figure), if h is the altitude to side a, obtain each of the following steps in order:

   a. $h = b \sin C$.

   b. If K is the area of triangle $\triangle ABC$, then $K = \frac{1}{2}ab \sin C$.

   c. By using altitudes to the other two sides, $K = \frac{1}{2}bc \sin A$ or $K = \frac{1}{2}ac \sin B$.

   d. Since $K = \frac{1}{2}bc \sin A = \frac{1}{2}ac \sin B = \frac{1}{2}ab \sin C$, then $\dfrac{a}{\sin A} = \dfrac{b}{\sin B} = \dfrac{c}{\sin C}$.

6. In triangle ABC, $\sin A = 0.3$, $\sin B = 0.5$, and $b = 20$. Find a.

7. In triangle ABC, $a = 10$, $\sin A = .30$, and $\sin C = .24$. Find c.

8. In triangle ABC, $a = 10$, $\sin A = \frac{2}{3}$, and $\sin B = \frac{3}{5}$. Find b.

9. In triangle ABC, if $a = 10$, $A = 45°$, and $\sin B = \frac{1}{2}$, then the length of side

   b is (1) 5   (2) $5\sqrt{2}$ (3) $\dfrac{10\sqrt{3}}{3}$ (4) $10\sqrt{2}$

10. In triangle ABC, if $A = 30°$, $B = 45°$, and $a = 10$, then $b = $ _____ . (Answer may be left in radical form.)

11. In triangle ABC, $b = 4$, $c = 6$, and $B = 30°$. Find $\sin C$.

12. In triangle ABC, $b = 3$, $c = 4$, and $C = 30°$. Find $\sin B$.

13. In triangle ABC, $\sin A = \frac{1}{4}$, $a = 6$, and $b = 20$. Find $\sin B$.

14. In triangle ABC, $a = 10$, $c = 12$, and $\sin C = .4$. Find $\sin A$.

15. In triangle ABC, $\sin A = .2$, $a = 1.5$, and $b = 6$. Find $\sin B$.

16. In triangle ABC, $A = 45°$ and $B = 30°$. Find $\dfrac{a}{b}$. (Answer may be left in radical form.)

17. In triangle ABC, $B = 60°$ and $C = 45°$. Find the value of the ratio of b to c. (Answer may be left in radical form.)

18. In triangle ABC, $\dfrac{a}{b} = \dfrac{\sqrt{2}}{2}$ and $A = 30°$. Find acute angle B.

In 19 and 20, find the value of a and b. (Answers may be left in radical form.)

19. 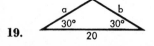   20.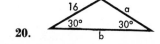

In 21 and 22, find the value of x and y, correct to the nearest foot.

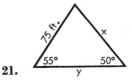

21.

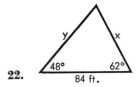

22.

In 23 and 24, in triangle ABC, $\angle A = 84°$ and $\angle B = 41°$. Find a, to the nearest foot, when b equals:

23. 25 feet.   **24.** 52 feet.

25. In triangle ABC, $AB = 81$ feet, $A = 61°$, and $C = 73°$. Find the length of AC, correct to the nearest foot.

26. In triangle ABC, $AB = 50$, $A = 71°$, and $C = 49°$. Find the length of the altitude on AB, correct to the nearest integer.

27. Two angles of a triangle are $25°$ and $70°$ and the longest side is 56 feet. Find the shortest side, correct to the nearest foot.

In 28–32, use the law of sines to prove the theorem.

28. If the measures of two angles of a triangle are equal, the lengths of the sides opposite these angles are equal.

29. If the lengths of two sides of a triangle are equal, the measures of the angles opposite these sides are equal.

30. An equiangular triangle is equilateral.

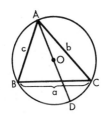

31. The ratio of the length of any side of a triangle to the sine of the opposite angle is equal to the length of the diameter of the circumscribed circle. (*Hint:* In the figure at the left, draw BD and prove that

$$AD = \frac{c}{\sin C} = \frac{b}{\sin B} = \frac{a}{\sin A}.)$$

32. If a line is drawn parallel to the side of a triangle, the other two sides are divided proportionately. In the figure, $DE \parallel BC$.

Prove: $\dfrac{AD}{AB} = \dfrac{AE}{AC}$.

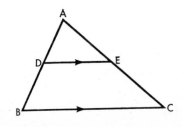

2. Applying the Law of Cosines

In any triangle,

1. $a^2 = b^2 + c^2 - 2bc \cos A$
$b^2 = a^2 + c^2 - 2ac \cos B$
$c^2 = a^2 + b^2 - 2ab \cos C$

2. $\cos A = \dfrac{b^2 + c^2 - a^2}{2bc}$

$\cos B = \dfrac{a^2 + c^2 - b^2}{2ac}$

$\cos C = \dfrac{a^2 + b^2 - c^2}{2ab}$

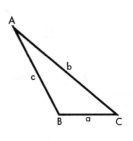
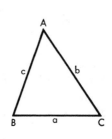

Note. Each of the equations in **2** above is derivable from an equation in **1** above by transformation. For example,

$$a^2 = b^2 + c^2 - 2bc \cos A$$
$$2bc \cos A = b^2 + c^2 - a^2$$
$$\cos A = \frac{b^2 + c^2 - a^2}{2bc}$$

Rule. In any triangle, the square of any side of the triangle equals the sum of the squares of the other two sides, minus twice the product of these other two sides and the cosine of their included angle.

PROVING THE LAW OF COSINES

See pages 730–731 for the proof of the law of cosines.

USING THE LAW OF COSINES

The law of cosines can be used in a problem involving the three sides of a triangle and one of the angles when three of these four parts are given or can be found. In such a case, the law of cosines can be used to find the fourth part.

~~~~~~~~~~~~~~~ *MODEL PROBLEMS* ~~~~~~~~~~~~~~~

1. In triangle ABC, $b = 5$, $c = 4$, and $\cos A = \frac{1}{8}$. Find a.

2. In triangle ABC, $a = 3$, $b = 4$, and $C = 120°$. Find c. (Answer may be left in radical form.)

Solution:

$a^2 = b^2 + c^2 - 2bc \cos A$

$b = 5, c = 4, \cos A = \frac{1}{8}$

$a^2 = (5)^2 + (4)^2 - 2(5)(4)(\frac{1}{8})$

$\quad = 25 + 16 - 5$

$\quad = 36$

$a = 6 \quad Ans.$

Solution:

$c^2 = a^2 + b^2 - 2ab \cos C$

$a = 3, b = 4, C = 120°$

$c^2 = (3)^2 + (4)^2 - 2(3)(4)(\cos 120°)$

$\cos 120° = \cos(180° - 60°)$

$\quad = -\cos 60°$

$\quad = -\frac{1}{2}$

$c^2 = 9 + 16 - 2(3)(4)(-\frac{1}{2})$

$\quad = 25 + 12$

$\quad = 37$

$c = \sqrt{37} \quad Ans.$

3. In triangle ABC, $a = 5$, $b = 7$, and $c = 6$. Find $\cos B$.

Solution:

$$a = 5, b = 7, c = 6$$

Method 1

$b^2 = a^2 + c^2 - 2ac \cos B$

$(7)^2 = (5)^2 + (6)^2 - 2(5)(6) \cos B$

$49 = 25 + 36 - 60 \cos B$

$60 \cos B = 12$

$\cos B = \dfrac{12}{60} = \dfrac{1}{5} \quad Ans.$

Method 2

$\cos B = \dfrac{a^2 + c^2 - b^2}{2ac}$

$\quad = \dfrac{(5)^2 + (6)^2 - (7)^2}{2(5)(6)}$

$\quad = \dfrac{25 + 36 - 49}{60}$

$\quad = \dfrac{12}{60} = \dfrac{1}{5} \quad Ans.$

4. In triangle ABC, the sides are 2, 4, and 5. Find, correct to the nearest degree, the smallest angle of the triangle.

Solution: Since we are to find the smallest angle, we must find the angle opposite the smallest side of the triangle.

$a^2 = b^2 + c^2 - 2bc \cos A$

$a = 2, b = 4, c = 5$

$(2)^2 = (4)^2 + (5)^2 - 2(4)(5) \cos A$

$4 = 16 + 25 - 40 \cos A$

$40 \cos A = 37$

$\cos A = \frac{37}{40} \approx .9250$

$A = 22°$, to the nearest degree $\quad Ans.$

Exercises

1. For triangle PQR (see the figure), state the form of the law of cosines beginning with:

   a. $p^2 =$ b. $q^2 =$ c. $r^2 =$

2. For triangle PQR (see the figure), state the form of the law of cosines beginning with:

   a. $\cos P =$ b. $\cos Q =$ c. $\cos R =$

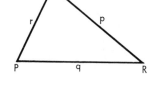

3. If a, b, and c are the sides of a triangle, express c^2 in terms of a and b if C equals:

   a. $45°$ b. $60°$ c. $135°$ d. $150°$

4. If a, b, and c are the sides of a triangle and $C = 90°$, show that $c^2 = a^2 + b^2$ is a special case of $c^2 = a^2 + b^2 - 2bc \cos C$.

5. If a, b, and c are the sides of a triangle and $c^2 = a^2 + b^2$, prove that triangle ABC is a right triangle, using the law of cosines. (This is the converse of the theorem of Pythagoras.)

6. If a, b, and c represent the sides of a triangle and if $\dfrac{a^2 + b^2 - c^2}{2ab}$ is equal to zero, the triangle is   (1) acute   (2) right   (3) obtuse

7. Beginning with the formula for the distance between two points,

$$d = \sqrt{(x_2 - x_1)^2 + (y_2 - y_1)^2}$$

obtain each of the following steps in order:

   a. $c = \sqrt{(b \cos \theta - a)^2 + (b \sin \theta)^2}$

   b. $c =$
   $\sqrt{b^2(\cos^2 \theta + \sin^2 \theta) + a^2 - 2ab \cos \theta}$

   c. $c^2 = a^2 + b^2 - 2ab \cos (360° - C)$

   d. $c^2 = a^2 + b^2 - 2ab \cos C$

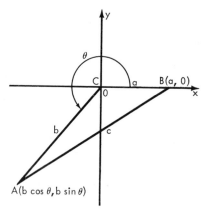

8. In triangle ABC, $a = 5$, $b = 6$, and $\cos C = \frac{1}{5}$. Find c.

9. In triangle ABC, $a = 5$, $b = 9$, and $\cos C = \frac{7}{15}$. Find c.

10. In triangle ABC, side $b = 10$, side $c = 12$, and $\cos A = -\frac{1}{3}$. Find side a.

11. In triangle ABC, $b = 4$, $c = 5$, and $\cos A = -\frac{1}{5}$. Find a.

12. In triangle ABC, $A = 60°$, $b = 5$, and $c = 8$. Find a.

13. Two sides of a triangle are 15 and 24 and the included angle measures $60°$. Find the third side.

14. Two adjacent sides of a parallelogram are 6 and 10 and the included angle measures $120°$. Find the length of the longer diagonal.

15. If in triangle ABC, $a = 8$, $b = 6$, and $c = 5$, find cos B.
16. In triangle ABC, $a = 5$, $b = 11$, and $c = 13$. Find cos B.
17. In triangle ABC, $a = 5$, $b = 10$, and $c = 12$. Find cos C.
18. In triangle ABC, $a = 8$, $b = 7$, and $c = 4$. Find cos A.
19. The sides of a triangle are 6, 4, and 3. Find the cosine of the smallest angle.
20. Find the cosine of the largest angle of the triangle whose sides are 4, 5, and 6.
21. In triangle ABC, $a = 5$, $b = 8$, and $c = 7$. Find C.
22. In triangle ABC, $a = 8$, $b = 13$, and $c = 15$. Find B.
23. If the sides of a triangle are $a = 7$, $b = 5$, $c = 3$, find angle A.
24. In triangle ABC, $a = \sqrt{3}$, $b = 1$, and $c = 2$. Find A.
25. If, in triangle ABC, $a = 3$, $b = 5$, and $c = 6$, the cosine of the largest angle is equal to (1) $-\frac{1}{15}$ (2) $-\frac{5}{6}$ (3) $\frac{1}{9}$
26. Find the perimeter of a triangle ABC if $b = 10$, $c = 16$, and $A = 60°$.

3. Applying the Law of Tangents

The law of tangents can be expressed as formulas or as a rule.
In any triangle,

1. $\dfrac{a-b}{a+b} = \dfrac{\tan \frac{1}{2}(A-B)}{\tan \frac{1}{2}(A+B)}$

$\dfrac{b-c}{b+c} = \dfrac{\tan \frac{1}{2}(B-C)}{\tan \frac{1}{2}(B+C)}$

$\dfrac{a-c}{a+c} = \dfrac{\tan \frac{1}{2}(A-C)}{\tan \frac{1}{2}(A+C)}$

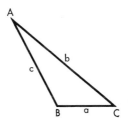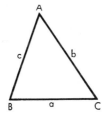

2. If $b > a$, use $\dfrac{b-a}{b+a} = \dfrac{\tan \frac{1}{2}(B-A)}{\tan \frac{1}{2}(B+A)}$

If $c > b$, use $\dfrac{c-b}{c+b} = \dfrac{\tan \frac{1}{2}(C-B)}{\tan \frac{1}{2}(C+B)}$

If $c > a$, use $\dfrac{c-a}{c+a} = \dfrac{\tan \frac{1}{2}(C-A)}{\tan \frac{1}{2}(C+A)}$

Note. The formulas in **2** above are equivalent forms of these in **1** above and are used to avoid negative numbers. Each of the formulas in **1** and **2** is meaningless if the sides involved are equal.

Rule. In any triangle, the ratio of the difference of any two sides of the triangle to their sum equals the ratio of the tangent of half the difference of the angles opposite these sides to the tangent of half the sum of these angles.

PROVING THE LAW OF TANGENTS

See exercise 13, page 574, for the proof of the law of tangents.

USING THE LAW OF TANGENTS

Where two sides of a triangle and their included angle are given or can be found, the law of tangents can be used to find the remaining two angles of the triangle; whereas the law of cosines can be used in such a case to find the third side.

~~~~~~~~~~~~ *MODEL PROBLEMS* ~~~~~~~~~~~~

1. In triangle DEF, $D = 105°$, $E = 15°$. Find the value of $(d - e):(d + e)$. (Answer may be left in radical form.)

Solution:

$$\frac{d - e}{d + e} = \frac{\tan \frac{1}{2}(D - E)}{\tan \frac{1}{2}(D + E)}$$

$$D = 105°, E = 15°$$

$$\frac{d - e}{d + e} = \frac{\tan \frac{1}{2}(105° - 15°)}{\tan \frac{1}{2}(105° + 15°)}$$

$$= \frac{\tan 45°}{\tan 60°} = \frac{1}{\sqrt{3}}$$

$$= \frac{1}{\sqrt{3}} \cdot \frac{\sqrt{3}}{\sqrt{3}} = \frac{\sqrt{3}}{3} \quad Ans.$$

2. If $c + b = 30$ and $c - b = 10$ and $\tan \frac{1}{2}(C + B) = 1$, find the value of $\tan \frac{1}{2}(C - B)$.

Solution:

$$\frac{\tan \frac{1}{2}(C - B)}{\tan \frac{1}{2}(C + B)} = \frac{c - b}{c + b}$$

$$c + b = 30, c - b = 10,$$
$$\tan \frac{1}{2}(C + B) = 1$$

$$\frac{\tan \frac{1}{2}(C - B)}{1} = \frac{10}{30}$$

$$\tan \frac{1}{2}(C - B) = \frac{1}{3} \quad Ans.$$

3. In triangle ABC, $a = 36$, $b = 18$, $C = 100°$.
   a. Find, to the nearest hundredth, $\tan \frac{1}{2}(A - B)$.
   b. Using the result obtained in part a, find A and B, to the nearest degree.

Solution:

a. Since the sum of the angles of a triangle equals 180°,

$$A + B + C = 180°$$
$$A + B = 180° - C$$
$$A + B = 180° - 100° = 80°$$

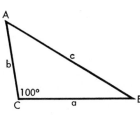

$$\frac{\tan \frac{1}{2}(A - B)}{\tan \frac{1}{2}(A + B)} = \frac{a - b}{a + b}$$

$a = 36, b = 18, A + B = 80°$

$$\frac{\tan \frac{1}{2}(A - B)}{\tan \frac{1}{2}(80°)} = \frac{36 - 18}{36 + 18}$$

$$\frac{\tan \frac{1}{2}(A - B)}{\tan 40°} = \frac{18}{54} = \frac{1}{3}$$

$$\tan \tfrac{1}{2}(A - B) = \tfrac{1}{3} \tan 40°$$
$$\approx \tfrac{1}{3}(.8391) \approx .2797$$
$$= .28, \text{ to the nearest hundredth}\quad Ans.$$

b. Since $\tan \frac{1}{2}(A - B) = .28$, then $\frac{1}{2}(A - B) = 16°$, to the nearest degree (by reference to the table).

If $C = 100°$, then $A + B = 80°$. Hence, $\frac{1}{2}(A + B) = 40°$.

Add:
$$\frac{1}{2}(A + B) = 40°$$
$$\underline{\frac{1}{2}(A - B) = 16°}$$
$$A \quad\quad = 56°$$

Subtract:
$$\frac{1}{2}(A + B) = 40°$$
$$\underline{\frac{1}{2}(A - B) = 16°}$$
$$B \quad = 24°$$

$A = 56°$ and $B = 24°$, to the nearest degree.   *Ans.*

Exercises

1. In triangle PQR (see the figure), use the law of tangents to complete each of the following:

a. $\dfrac{p - q}{p + q} = \dfrac{?}{?}$ *b.* $\dfrac{q - p}{q + p} = \dfrac{?}{?}$

2. In triangle FGH, use the law of tangents to complete each of the following:

a. $\dfrac{\tan \frac{1}{2}(H - G)}{\tan \frac{1}{2}(H + G)} = \dfrac{?}{?}$ *b.* $\dfrac{\tan \frac{1}{2}(F - H)}{\tan \frac{1}{2}(F + H)} = \dfrac{?}{?}$

3. In triangle ABC, $\frac{1}{2}(A + B) = 58°\ 10'$ and $\frac{1}{2}(A - B) = 16°\ 30'$. Find B.

4. In triangle ABC, $\frac{1}{2}(A + B) = c$ and $\frac{1}{2}(A - B) = d$. Find A and B in terms of c and d.

5. If A, B, and C are the angles of a triangle and $C = 100°$, find A and B to the nearest degree and check each result if:

$$a.\ \tfrac{1}{2}(A - B) = 20°\qquad b.\ \tan \tfrac{1}{2}(A - B) = .14$$

6. In triangle ABC, $A = 75°$ and $B = 15°$. Find the numerical value of the ratio $\dfrac{a + b}{a - b}$. (Answer may be left in radical form.)

7. In triangle ABC, $B = 105°$, and $C = 15°$. Find the value of $(b + c):(b - c)$. (Answer may be left in radical form.)

8. In triangle ABC, $a = 12$, $b = 8$, and $C = 90°$. Find the value of $\tan \frac{1}{2}(A - B)$.

9. In triangle ABC, $a = 5$, $c = 4$, and $B = 60°$. Find the value of $\tan \frac{1}{2}(A - C)$. (Answer may be left in radical form.)

10. In triangle ABC, $a = 15$, $b = 5$, and $A - B = 60°$. Find the value of $\tan \frac{1}{2}(A + B)$. (Answer may be left in radical form.)

11. In triangle ABC, $\tan \frac{1}{2}(A + B) = \frac{3}{4}$, $\tan \frac{1}{2}(A - B) = \frac{1}{2}$, and $a + b = 18$. Find $a - b$.

12. In triangle ABC, $a = 10$, $b = 6$, and $C = 58°$. Find, to the nearest hundredth, $\tan \frac{1}{2}(A - B)$.

13. Beginning with the law of sines, $\dfrac{a}{b} = \dfrac{\sin A}{\sin B}$, obtain the following steps in the proof of the law of tangents:

(1) $\dfrac{a - b}{b} = \dfrac{\sin A - \sin B}{\sin B}$ (*Hint:* In law of sines, S_1)

(2) $\dfrac{a + b}{b} = \dfrac{\sin A + \sin B}{\sin B}$ (*Hint:* In law of sines, A_1)

(3) $\dfrac{a - b}{a + b} = \dfrac{\sin A - \sin B}{\sin A + \sin B}$

(4) $\dfrac{a - b}{a + b} = \dfrac{2 \sin \frac{1}{2}(A - B) \cos \frac{1}{2}(A + B)}{2 \cos \frac{1}{2}(A - B) \sin \frac{1}{2}(A + B)} = \dfrac{\tan \frac{1}{2}(A - B)}{\tan \frac{1}{2}(A + B)}$

CHAPTER XVIII

EXPONENTS AND LOGARITHMS

1. Exponents That Are Positive Integers

Recall (page 54) the following relationship:

$$\text{BASE}^{\text{EXPONENT}} = \text{POWER}$$

Thus, the expression x^m involves (1) the *base*, which is x, (2) the *exponent*, which is m, and (3) the *power*, which is x^m.

EXPONENTS

By definition, $x^1 = x$; $x^2 = x \cdot x$; $x^3 = x \cdot x \cdot x$; $x^m = \underbrace{x \cdot x \cdot x \cdot \ldots \cdot x}_{m \text{ factors}}$, if m is a positive integer greater than 1.

Hence, if m is a positive integral exponent greater than 1, then m indicates the number of times the base is a factor. For example, $x^4 = x \cdot x \cdot x \cdot x$, $3^x = 3 \cdot 3 \cdot 3 \cdot \ldots \cdot 3$ (x factors), and $2^6 = 2 \cdot 2 \cdot 2 \cdot 2 \cdot 2 \cdot 2 = 64$.

Note, in 2^6, that 2 is the base, 6 is the exponent, and 2^6, or 64, is the power. We say that 2^6, or 64, is the 6th power of 2.

LAWS OF EXPONENTS FOR POSITIVE INTEGRAL EXPONENTS

The following six laws involving positive integral exponents can be derived by applying the definitions of exponent.

1. The Multiplication of Powers Law

$$x^m \cdot x^n = x^{m+n}$$

Rule. To multiply two powers having the same base, keep the base and *add* the exponents.

Thus, $x^3 \cdot x^2 = x^5$, $10^5 \cdot 10^4 = 10^9$, $(-3)^3(-3)(-3)^2 = (-3)^4(-3)^2 = (-3)^6$, and $2^x \cdot 2^y = 2^{x+y}$.

2. The Division of Powers Law

If $m > n,$ $\dfrac{x^m}{x^n} = x^{m-n},$ $x \neq 0$ $\qquad$ If $m < n,$ $\dfrac{x^m}{x^n} = \dfrac{1}{x^{n-m}},$ $x \neq 0$

Rule. To divide two powers having the same base, keep the base and *subtract* the exponents.

Thus, $\dfrac{x^5}{x^2} = x^3,$ $\dfrac{x^2}{x^5} = \dfrac{1}{x^3},$ $\dfrac{3^9}{3^5} = 3^4,$ and $\dfrac{3^5}{3^9} = \dfrac{1}{3^4}.$

3. The Power of a Power Law

$$(x^m)^n = x^{mn}$$

Rule. To find the power of a power, keep the base and *multiply* the exponents.
Thus, $(x^2)^3 = x^6,$ $[(\pi^2)^3]^4 = (\pi^6)^4 = \pi^{24},$ and $(5^a)^b = 5^{ab}.$

4. The Root of a Power Law

If m is a multiple of $n,$ $\sqrt[n]{x^m} = x^{\frac{m}{n}},$ $n \neq 0$

Rule. To find the root of a power, keep the base and *divide* the exponent by the index.

Thus, $\sqrt{x^6} = x^{\frac{6}{2}} = x^3,$ $\sqrt[3]{2^{12}} = 2^{\frac{12}{3}} = 2^4,$ and $\sqrt[a]{5^{4a}} = 5^{\frac{4a}{a}} = 5^4.$

5. The Power of a Product Law

$$(xy)^m = x^m y^m$$

Rule. To find the power of a product, make the exponent of the product the exponent of each of the separate factors and multiply the resulting powers. (This rule is part of the **extended law of distribution.** The power operation is distributive over multiplication.)
Thus, $(x^2 y^3)^2 = (x^2)^2 (y^3)^2 = x^4 y^6$ and $(2x^2)^5 = (2)^5 (x^2)^5 = 2^5 x^{10} = 32 x^{10}.$

6. The Power of a Quotient Law

$$\left(\frac{x}{y}\right)^m = \frac{x^m}{y^m}, \, y \neq 0$$

Rule. To find the power of a quotient, make the exponent of the quotient the exponent of both the dividend (numerator) and the divisor (denominator). Then divide the resulting powers. (This rule is part of the extended law of distribution. The power operation is distributive over division.)

Thus, $\left(\dfrac{a}{b}\right)^7 = \dfrac{a^7}{b^7}$, $\left(\dfrac{x^2}{y^3}\right)^2 = \dfrac{(x^2)^2}{(y^3)^2} = \dfrac{x^4}{y^6}$, and $\left(\dfrac{-3}{a}\right)^3 = \dfrac{(-3)^3}{a^3} = \dfrac{-27}{a^3}$.

Exercises

In 1–64, simplify. Use the set of positive integers as the domain of each literal exponent.

1. $x^5 \cdot x^7$
2. $y^3 \cdot y$
3. $r^4 \cdot r^6$
4. $t \cdot t^5$
5. $x^a \cdot x^b$
6. $a^{2b} \cdot a^{4b}$
7. $y^{2n} \cdot y^5$
8. $C^2 \cdot C^d$
9. $x^{a+2} \cdot x^{2a}$
10. $y^3 \cdot y^{2b-1}$
11. $y^{2c} \cdot y$
12. $z^{2x} \cdot z^{3y}$
13. $2^3 \cdot 2^2$
14. $5^4 \cdot 5^2$
15. $8^3 \cdot 8$
16. $10^4 \cdot 10^2$
17. $x^2 x^3 x^4$
18. $x^2 y^3 x^4 y$
19. $(\sin^2 x)(\sin^3 x)$
20. $(x+y)^3 (x+y)^4$
21. $y^8 \div y^3$
22. $y^2 \div y^8$
23. $A^5 \div A^2$
24. $A^2 \div A^5$
25. $a^{3n} \div a^n$
26. $c^{2n+2} \div c^2$
27. $x^{n+1} \div x^n$
28. $y^{3n+4} \div y^{n+1}$
29. $5^6 \div 5^2$
30. $2^5 \div 2$
31. $9^5 \div 9^7$
32. $10^4 \div 10^5$
33. $(y^3)^5$
34. $(a^2)^3$
35. $(b^4)^4$
36. $(C^2)^5$
37. $(-2)^3$
38. $(-4)^4$
39. $(-10)^2$
40. $(-3)^5$
41. $(ab)^4$
42. $(x^2 y)^7$
43. $(c^2 d^3)^5$
44. $(abc^2)^6$
45. $(-5a)^3$
46. $(-3y^3)^2$
47. $(2rs)^4$
48. $(-2x^2 y^3)^3$
49. $(\frac{1}{2}x)^4$
50. $(-\frac{2}{3}c^2)^3$
51. $(\frac{3}{4}c^2 d^3)^2$
52. $(-\frac{1}{2}xy^2)^4$
53. $(a^d)^2$
54. $(x^n y^r)^3$
55. $(r^2 s^3)^b$
56. $(c^r d^s)^t$
57. $\left(\dfrac{a}{b}\right)^c$
58. $\left(\dfrac{r^2 s^3}{t^3}\right)^a$
59. $\left(\dfrac{2x^2}{3y^3}\right)^3$
60. $\left(-\dfrac{3c}{d^3}\right)^4$
61. $\sqrt{x^8}$
62. $\sqrt[3]{y^9}$
63. $\sqrt[4]{r^4}$
64. $\sqrt[3]{a^3 b^6}$

65. Express 64 as a power of (*a*) 2, (*b*) 4, (*c*) 8.
66. Express x^{12} as a power of (*a*) x^2, (*b*) x^3, (*c*) x^4.
67. Express as a power of 10: (*a*) 100 (*b*) 1000 (*c*) 10,000.
68. Express as a power of 3: (*a*) 9 (*b*) 81 (*c*) 9^4 (*d*) $27^x \cdot 3^{2x}$.
69. Express as a power of 2: (*a*) 8 (*b*) 32 (*c*) 4^s (*d*) $4^x \cdot 8^x$.
70. Express as a power of 5: (*a*) 125 (*b*) 25^{4x} (*c*) $25^{4x} \div 5^x$ (*d*) $125^{2x} \cdot 5^x$.
71. The expression $(x^4)^2$ is equal to (1) x^{16} (2) x^8 (3) x^6

In 72–74, transform $a^2 + b^3$ into an equivalent expression in terms of x and y if:

72. $a = x^2, b = y^3$
73. $a = \dfrac{x}{3}, b = \dfrac{y}{2}$
74. $a = \sqrt{x}, b = \sqrt[3]{y}$

2. Exponents as Rational Numbers: Zero, Negative, and Fractional Exponents

Rational numbers, such as 0, $\frac{1}{2}$, $-\frac{1}{4}$, and 2.3456, may be used as exponents. To make this possible, new definitions are needed for powers having zero, negative, and fractional exponents. These definitions will not only provide meaning for powers having these new types of exponents, but will also preserve the laws, previously studied, that govern powers having the positive integral exponents.

DEFINITION OF A POWER HAVING A ZERO EXPONENT

By definition,

$$x^0 = 1, \qquad x \neq 0$$

We know that $\dfrac{x^5}{x^5} = 1$. By extending the division of powers law, $\dfrac{x^5}{x^5} = x^{5-5} = x^0$. Since $\dfrac{x^5}{x^5}$ equals both 1 and x^0, then x^0 must be defined as 1, provided $x \neq 0$.

Note that the new definition, $x^0 = 1$, $x \neq 0$, enables us to extend the division of powers law to cover the case involving division of powers that have equal exponents. That is,

$$\frac{x^m}{x^m} = x^{m-m} = x^0$$

This result agrees with the definition, $x^0 = 1$.

Rule. The zero power of any number, except 0, equals 1. Thus, $5^0 = 1$, $(-5)^0 = 1$, and $-5x^0 = -5$; $(5x)^0 = 1$ and $5x^0 = 5$; $(x+5)^0 = 1$ and $x + 5^0 = x + 1$.

DEFINITION OF A POWER HAVING A NEGATIVE EXPONENT

By definition,

$$x^{-n} = \frac{1}{x^n}, \qquad x \neq 0$$

We know that $\dfrac{x^5}{x^9} = \dfrac{1}{x^4}$. By extending the division of powers law, $\dfrac{x^5}{x^9} = x^{5-9} = x^{-4}$. Since $\dfrac{x^5}{x^9}$ equals both x^{-4} and $\dfrac{1}{x^4}$, then x^{-4} must be defined as

$\dfrac{1}{x^4}$, provided $x \neq 0$. This definition of x^{-4} conforms to the general definition of a negative exponent set forth above.

The definition of a power having a negative exponent may be stated in the following rule:

Rule. A power of any nonzero number having a negative exponent equals the reciprocal of the corresponding positive power of the same number.

Thus, $a^{-10} = \dfrac{1}{a^{10}}$, $2^{-5} = \dfrac{1}{2^5} = \dfrac{1}{32}$, $x^{-y} = \dfrac{1}{x^y}$, and $(x+2)^{-1} = \dfrac{1}{x+2}$.

Note in each of the illustrations that when the exponents of the same base are additive inverses of each other, the powers themselves are multiplicative inverses of each other.

DEFINITION OF A POWER HAVING A RATIONAL NUMBER AS AN EXPONENT

A power can have a rational number as an exponent. For $x^{\frac{1}{2}}$ to have a meaning consistent with the laws of exponents, it should be true that $(x^{\frac{1}{2}})^2 = x^{\frac{1}{2} \cdot 2} = x^1 = x$. Since $x^{\frac{1}{2}}$ denotes a number whose square is x, then $x^{\frac{1}{2}}$ must be defined as $\sqrt{x}$ rather than $-\sqrt{x}$ so that the inequality $x^0 < x^{\frac{1}{2}} < x^1$ is true for all values of x greater than 1. Similarly, $x^{\frac{1}{4}}$ must be defined as $\sqrt[4]{x}$.

By definition: $x^{\frac{1}{n}} = \sqrt[n]{x}$, $n \neq 0$.

Hence, $x^{\frac{1}{2}} = \sqrt{x}$, the principal square root of x; also, $x^{\frac{1}{3}} = \sqrt[3]{x}$, the principal cube root of x; and so on.

Applying the definition of $x^{\frac{1}{n}}$, then $\sqrt[n]{x^m} = (x^m)^{\frac{1}{n}} = x^{\frac{m}{n}}$; also, $(\sqrt[n]{x})^m = (x^{\frac{1}{n}})^m = x^{\frac{m}{n}}$.

By definition: $x^{\frac{m}{n}} = \sqrt[n]{x^m}$ or $x^{\frac{m}{n}} = (\sqrt[n]{x})^m$, $n \neq 0$.

Thus, $x^{\frac{2}{3}}$ is equivalent to either $\sqrt[3]{x^2}$ or $(\sqrt[3]{x})^2$. Hence, the value of $9^{\frac{3}{2}}$ may be shown to be 27 in the following ways:

(1) $(\sqrt{9})^3 = 3^3 = 27$, (2) $\sqrt{9^3} = \sqrt{729} = 27$, (3) $(3^2)^{\frac{3}{2}} = 3^3 = 27$.

Note. In extending powers to include all rational exponents, the root of a power law does not apply to cases *where n is even and x is negative.* The familiar laws of exponents do not hold in such cases.

Thus, if the root of a power law were to be applied to the evaluation of $(-8)^{\frac{2}{6}}$, we would obtain $(-8)^{\frac{2}{6}} = \sqrt[6]{(-8)^2} = \sqrt[6]{64} = 2$. This result would not be correct because $(-8)^{\frac{2}{6}} = (-8)^{\frac{1}{3}} = -2$ and not 2.

~~~~~~~~~~~~~~ *MODEL PROBLEMS* ~~~~~~~~~~~~~~

1. Find the value of
$$2(4^0) + 4^{\frac{1}{2}} - 4^{-\frac{1}{2}}.$$

Solution:

$$2(1) + \sqrt{4} - \frac{1}{\sqrt{4}}$$

$$2 + 2 - \tfrac{1}{2}$$

$3\tfrac{1}{2}$ *Ans.*

2. Find the value of
$$3x^0 + x^{\frac{2}{3}} \text{ when } x = 27.$$

Solution:

$$3(27^0) + 27^{\frac{2}{3}}$$
$$3(1) + (\sqrt[3]{27})^2$$
$$3 + 3^2$$
$$3 + 9 = 12 \quad Ans.$$

3. Find the value of
$$(x+2)^0 + (x+1)^{-\frac{3}{2}} \text{ if } x = 7.$$

Solution:

$$(7+2)^0 + (7+1)^{-\frac{3}{2}}$$

$$9^0 + 8^{-\frac{3}{2}}$$

$$1 + (2^3)^{-\frac{3}{2}}$$

$$[(2^3)^{-\frac{3}{2}} = 2^{3(-\frac{3}{2})} = 2^{-2}]$$

$$1 + 2^{-2}$$

$$1 + \frac{1}{2^2}$$

$$1 + \tfrac{1}{4} = 1\tfrac{1}{4} \quad Ans.$$

4. Find the value of
$$3x^0 - 54x^3 + 64^x \text{ if } x = -\tfrac{1}{3}.$$

Solution:

$$3\left(-\frac{1}{3}\right)^0 - 54\left(-\frac{1}{3}\right)^3 + 64^{-\frac{1}{3}}$$

$$3(1) - 54\left(-\frac{1}{27}\right) + \frac{1}{\sqrt[3]{64}}$$

$$3 + 2 + \tfrac{1}{4} = 5\tfrac{1}{4} \quad Ans.$$

5. Simplify the expression $\left(\dfrac{Z^6}{27}\right)^{\frac{1}{3}}$.

Solution:

$$\left(\frac{x}{y}\right)^m = \frac{x^m}{y^m} \quad \text{Apply the power of a quotient law.}$$

Hence, $\left(\dfrac{Z^6}{27}\right)^{\frac{1}{3}} = \dfrac{(Z^6)^{\frac{1}{3}}}{27^{\frac{1}{3}}}$ In the numerator, multiply exponents to obtain Z^2.
In the denominator, the cube root of 27 is 3.

$$= \frac{Z^2}{3} \quad Ans.$$

Exercises

In 1–16, use a radical sign to indicate the expression.

1. $5^{\frac{1}{2}}$ **2.** $7^{\frac{1}{3}}$ **3.** $c^{\frac{1}{4}}$ **4.** $(2b)^{\frac{1}{2}}$
5. $(-8)^{\frac{1}{3}}$ **6.** $(-32)^{\frac{1}{5}}$ **7.** $(-5a)^{\frac{1}{2}}$ **8.** $(-3bc)^{\frac{1}{3}}$
9. $x^{\frac{2}{3}}$ **10.** $y^{\frac{1}{4}}$ **11.** $(3a)^{\frac{2}{3}}$ **12.** $(4b)^{\frac{2}{3}}$
13. $(-x)^{\frac{2}{3}}$ **14.** $(2y)^{\frac{3}{2}}$ **15.** $(ab)^{\frac{1}{4}}$ **16.** $(-8b)^{\frac{1}{4}}$

In 17–24, use a fractional exponent to express the radical.

17. $\sqrt{7}$ **18.** $\sqrt[3]{8}$ **19.** $\sqrt[3]{x}$ **20.** $\sqrt[4]{2y}$
21. $\sqrt{x^3}$ **22.** $\sqrt[3]{a^4}$ **23.** $\sqrt[4]{x^2y^3}$ **24.** $\sqrt[5]{r^2s^3}$

In 25–40, transform the expression into an equivalent expression involving only positive exponents.

25. y^{-5} **26.** d^{-2} **27.** $3a^{-4}$ **28.** $5b^{-3}$
29. $a^{-2}b^3$ **30.** $5c^{-1}d^2$ **31.** $(8r)^{-2}$ **32.** $(3s)^{-4}$

33. $\dfrac{1}{a^{-3}}$ **34.** $\dfrac{1}{c^{-2}}$ **35.** $\dfrac{5}{x^{-1}}$ **36.** $\dfrac{3}{y^{-5}}$

37. $\dfrac{r^{-2}}{t^{-3}}$ **38.** $\dfrac{m^2}{n^{-3}}$ **39.** $\dfrac{a^{-4}b}{cd^{-3}}$ **40.** $\dfrac{5x^{-4}}{7y^3}$

In 41–44, transform the fraction into an equivalent expression without a denominator.

41. $\dfrac{x^2}{y^3}$ **42.** $\dfrac{5ab^3}{c^4}$ **43.** $\dfrac{c^2}{d^{-1}}$ **44.** $\dfrac{8rs^2}{mn^3}$

In 45–113, simplify, using the set of rational numbers as the domain of each literal exponent.

45. 5^0 **46.** c^0 **47.** $(5x)^0$ **48.** $(a+b)^0$
49. $4x^0$ **50.** $8c^0$ **51.** 2^0x **52.** 5^0y^a
53. $25^{\frac{1}{2}}$ **54.** $49^{\frac{1}{2}}$ **55.** $81^{\frac{1}{2}}$ **56.** $16^{\frac{1}{2}}$
57. $(8)^{\frac{1}{3}}$ **58.** $(-8)^{\frac{1}{3}}$ **59.** $(64)^{\frac{1}{3}}$ **60.** $(-27)^{\frac{1}{3}}$
61. $(16)^{\frac{1}{4}}$ **62.** $(a^8)^{\frac{1}{4}}$ **63.** $(32)^{\frac{1}{5}}$ **64.** $(y^{10})^{\frac{1}{5}}$

65. $\left(\dfrac{x^2}{25}\right)^{\frac{1}{2}}$ **66.** $\left(\dfrac{a^{3a}}{27}\right)^{\frac{1}{3}}$ **67.** $\left(\dfrac{x^{4c}}{y^8}\right)^{\frac{1}{4}}$ **68.** $\left(\dfrac{x^{3a}}{y^{6b}}\right)^{\frac{1}{3}}$

69. $(.64)^{\frac{1}{2}}$ **70.** $(.008)^{\frac{1}{3}}$ **71.** $(.04x^4)^{\frac{1}{2}}$ **72.** $(.125y^6)^{\frac{1}{3}}$
73. $(25)^{\frac{3}{2}}$ **74.** $(16)^{\frac{3}{4}}$ **75.** $(-8)^{\frac{2}{3}}$ **76.** $(-32)^{\frac{2}{5}}$
77. $(64)^{\frac{2}{3}}$ **78.** $(-27)^{\frac{2}{3}}$ **79.** $(625)^{\frac{3}{4}}$ **80.** $(-64)^{\frac{2}{3}}$
81. $(.16)^{\frac{3}{2}}$ **82.** $(.027)^{\frac{2}{3}}$ **83.** $(.0001)^{\frac{3}{4}}$ **84.** $(-.125)^{\frac{2}{3}}$
85. $4(16)^{\frac{1}{2}}$ **86.** $3(\tfrac{1}{8})^{\frac{2}{3}}$ **87.** $\tfrac{1}{2}(16)^{\frac{1}{2}}$ **88.** $\tfrac{1}{3}(81)^{\frac{1}{4}}$
89. $(5)^{-2}$ **90.** 10^{-5} **91.** $(-2)^{-3}$ **92.** $(-4)^{-1}$
93. $(100)^{-\frac{1}{2}}$ **94.** $(25)^{-\frac{1}{2}}$ **95.** $(27)^{-\frac{1}{3}}$ **96.** $(-8)^{-\frac{1}{3}}$

97. $(.04)^{-\frac{1}{2}}$ **98.** $(.027)^{-\frac{1}{3}}$ **99.** $(.81)^{-\frac{1}{2}}$ **100.** $(.0001)^{-\frac{1}{4}}$

101. $(49)^{-\frac{3}{2}}$ **102.** $(8)^{-\frac{4}{3}}$ **103.** $(-32)^{-\frac{2}{5}}$ **104.** $(-27)^{-\frac{2}{3}}$

105. $4^0 - 4^{\frac{1}{2}}$ **106.** $8^{\frac{2}{3}} + 8x^0$ **107.** $(64)^{\frac{2}{3}} \cdot 2^{-2}$

108. $16 \cdot 2^{-3}$ **109.** $64^{\frac{1}{2}} \cdot 4^{-\frac{3}{2}}$ **110.** $4^{-\frac{1}{2}} - 8^{-\frac{1}{3}}$

111. $4 \times (8)^{\frac{2}{3}}$ **112.** $(81)^{-\frac{1}{4}} \times 3$ **113.** $9^0 \times 64^{-1}$

114. Find the value of $2a^0 + 3a^{-\frac{1}{2}}$ when $a = 9$.

115. Find the value of $2x^{\frac{3}{2}} + x^{-1}$ when $x = 4$.

116. Find the value of $x^{\frac{3}{2}} - x^0$ when $x = 4$.

117. When $x = 4$, the value of $x^{\frac{3}{2}} + 2x^0$ is   (1) 8   (2) 9   (3) 10

118. Find the value of $(a + 1)^0 + (4a)^{-\frac{1}{2}}$ when $a = 1$.

119. The expression $x^{-1} + y^{-1}$ is equal to   (1) $(x + y)^{-2}$ (2) $\dfrac{1}{x} + \dfrac{1}{y}$ (3) $\dfrac{1}{x + y}$

3. Applying the Laws of Exponents to All Rational Exponents Including Zero, Negative, and Fractional Exponents

It can be shown that the six laws of exponents, which were used previously for only positive integral exponents, may be extended to apply to any exponent which is a rational number, including exponents that are zero, negative, or fractional. The proof of such extensions is beyond the scope of this book.

The division of powers law may now be stated as follows: For all rational values of m and n,

$$\frac{x^m}{x^n} = x^{m-n}, \; x \neq 0$$

The root of a power law becomes: For all rational values of m and n,

$$\sqrt[n]{x^m} = x^{\frac{m}{n}}, \qquad n \neq 0$$

Thus, $x^{-2} \cdot x^3 \cdot x^{\frac{1}{2}} = x^{-2+3+\frac{1}{2}} = x^{1\frac{1}{2}}$, $a^5 \div a^{-3} = a^{5-(-3)} = a^8$, and $(b^{\frac{2}{3}})^6 = b^{(\frac{2}{3} \cdot 6)} = b^4$.

Exercises

In 1–72, simplify. Use the set of rational numbers as the domain of each literal exponent.

1. $x^5 \cdot x^{-3}$ **2.** $a^{-1} \cdot a^4$ **3.** $b \cdot b^{-5}$ **4.** $s^{-4} \cdot s^{-2}$

5. $y^4 \cdot y^0$ **6.** $c^4 \cdot c^{-3}$ **7.** $r^3 s^2 \cdot r^{-2}$ **8.** $a^{-3} b^2 \cdot a^2 b^{-4}$

9. $a^2 \cdot a^{\frac{2}{3}}$ **10.** $b \cdot b^{\frac{1}{2}}$ **11.** $d^2 \cdot d^{2.5}$ **12.** $r^{-1} \cdot r^{.5}$

13. $x^{\frac{2}{3}} \cdot x^{\frac{1}{3}}$ **14.** $y^{\frac{1}{4}} \cdot y^{-\frac{1}{4}}$ **15.** $m^{\frac{3}{4}} \cdot m^{-\frac{1}{2}}$ **16.** $n^{-\frac{1}{4}} \cdot n^{-\frac{1}{4}}$

17. $3^{-2} \cdot 9$ **18.** $4^{\frac{1}{2}} \cdot 2^3$ **19.** $25 \cdot 5^{\frac{3}{2}}$ **20.** $16^{-1} \cdot 4^{-\frac{1}{2}}$

21. $x^3 \div x^5$ **22.** $y^2 \div y^{-3}$ **23.** $a^{-5} \div a$ **24.** $a^2 \div a^{-6}$

25. $x^{\frac{1}{2}} \div x^{\frac{1}{3}}$ **26.** $a^{-1} \div a^{\frac{1}{2}}$ **27.** $b^{-5} \div b^0$ **28.** $m^{\frac{3}{4}} \div m^{\frac{1}{4}}$

29. $r^{\frac{1}{3}} \div r^{-\frac{1}{3}}$ **30.** $s^{-\frac{1}{4}} \div s^{\frac{1}{4}}$ **31.** $c^{-\frac{3}{4}} \div c^{-\frac{1}{4}}$ **32.** $d^{-1} \div d$

33. $2^5 \div 2^7$ **34.** $8^{-\frac{2}{3}} \div 8^{-\frac{1}{3}}$ **35.** $9^{2\frac{1}{2}} \div 9^{-\frac{1}{2}}$ **36.** $5^{-\frac{3}{4}} \div 5^{\frac{1}{4}}$

37. $10^{-3} \div 10^2$ **38.** $10^4 \div 10^{-1}$ **39.** $10^{-2} \div 10^{-3}$ **40.** $100 \div 10^{-4}$

41. $(a^{\frac{1}{4}})^2$ **42.** $(b^{-3})^3$ **43.** $(c^{\frac{2}{3}})^{-2}$ **44.** $(d^{-4})^{-\frac{1}{2}}$

45. $(m^4)^{\frac{3}{4}}$ **46.** $(c^{-6})^{-\frac{1}{3}}$ **47.** $(c^8)^{-\frac{3}{4}}$ **48.** $(y^5)^{-\frac{2}{3}}$

49. $(x^2 y^{-3})^3$ **50.** $(x^{\frac{1}{2}} y)^{-4}$ **51.** $(a^{\frac{1}{2}} b^{-\frac{1}{3}})^6$ **52.** $(2c^{\frac{1}{2}} d^{\frac{1}{4}})^2$

53. $(10^2)^3$ **54.** $(10^{-1})^2$ **55.** $(10^{3 \cdot 6})^{\frac{1}{3}}$ **56.** $(10^4)^{-\frac{1}{2}}$

57. $3^x \cdot 3^y$ **58.** $2^{2a} \cdot 2^{-a}$ **59.** $5^{2x} \cdot 25$ **60.** $4^x \cdot 8^{-x}$

61. $7^{2x} \div 7^{3x}$ **62.** $4^2 \div 4^x$ **63.** $3^{2a} \div 3^{-a}$ **64.** $9^{-3x} \div 9^{-2x}$

65. $(2^{2a})^{\frac{1}{2}}$ **66.** $(9^{3x})^{\frac{1}{2}}$ **67.** $(3^c)^{-2}$ **68.** $(6^{4d})^{-\frac{3}{4}}$

69. $\sqrt{10^{-4}}$ **70.** $\sqrt[3]{x^3}$ **71.** $\sqrt{a^{\frac{1}{2}}}$ **72.** $\sqrt[4]{a^{\frac{1}{2}}}$

73. The value of $5^{\frac{2}{3}} \times 5^{\frac{1}{3}}$ is   (1) $5^{\frac{2}{3}}$ (2) 25   (3) 5

74. The expression $(a^2)^{-3}$ equals (1) a^{-6} (2) a^{-5} (3) a^{-1} (4) a^{-8}

75. Answer *true* or *false:* $(x^2)^{-\frac{2}{3}} = \sqrt[3]{x^{-4}}$.

76. If $3^y = x$, then 3^{y+1} equals (1) $x + 3$ (2) $3x$ (3) $x + 1$

4. Scientific Notation

In *scientific notation,* a number is expressed as the product of two factors: One factor is a number between 1 and 10, the other factor is an integral power of 10.

Thus, 630,000,000, the approximate number of seconds in 20 years, may be expressed in scientific notation as 6.3×10^8. Also, .00000000053, the approximate number of millimeters in the diameter of the orbit of an electron of a certain atom, may be expressed in scientific notation as 5.3×10^{-10}.

Scientific notation is used:

1. To provide a concise notation for very large and very small numbers, such as those shown above.
2. To simplify computations by applying the laws of exponents to numbers expressed in scientific notation.
3. To estimate or approximate the results of computation. Thus,

$$\frac{255,000}{.00125} = \frac{2.55 \times 10^5}{1.25 \times 10^{-3}} = \frac{2.55}{1.25} \times 10^8 \approx 2 \times 10^8 \approx 200,000,000$$

Procedure. To write numbers in scientific notation:

1. **Place an apostrophe (') immediately after the first nonzero digit of the given number.**
2. **Starting from the apostrophe, count the number of places to the decimal point in the given number.**
3. **Write the first factor of the number in scientific notation by placing a decimal point at the position of the apostrophe, the result being a number between 1 and 10.**
4. **Write the second factor of the number in scientific notation by using the number of places counted in step 2 as the exponent of the power of 10. If the count is to the right, the exponent is positive; if the count is to the left, the exponent is negative.**

In the following table, the arrow indicates the direction of counting.

$Number =$	$\begin{pmatrix} Number\ between \\ 1\ and\ 10 \end{pmatrix}$	$\times (Power\ of\ 10)$
$\overrightarrow{7'340.}$ =	7.34	$\times$ 10^3
$\overleftarrow{.0007'34}$ =	7.34	$\times$ 10^{-4}
$5'7$ =	5.7	$\times$ 10^0
$\overrightarrow{5'7000000.}$ =	5.7	$\times$ 10^7
$\overleftarrow{.5'7}$ =	5.7	$\times$ 10^{-1}

~~~~~~~~~~ *MODEL PROBLEMS* ~~~~~~~~~~

1. Write the number 4.86×10^{-3} in ordinary decimal notation.

Solution:

$$10^{-3} = \frac{1}{10^3} = \frac{1}{1000} \qquad \text{Hence, } 4.86 \times 10^{-3} = 4.86 \times \frac{1}{1000} = .00486. \ \textit{Ans.}$$

Note. To multiply a decimal by 10^{-3}, simply move the decimal point 3 places to the left. Think of -3 as "3 to the left."

2. If each of the following numbers is expressed in scientific notation as 3.28×10^n, what is the value of n in each case?   *a.* 328,000   *b.* 0.000328

Solution: In each case, to find n, place an apostrophe immediately after the first nonzero digit of the given number; then count from the apostrophe to the decimal.

a. In the case of 3'28,000, the count from the apostrophe to the decimal is five places to the right. Hence, $n = 5$. *Ans.*

b. In the case of 0.0003'28, the count from the apostrophe to the decimal is four places to the left. Hence, $n = -4$. *Ans.*

Exercises

In 1–10, complete the table.

	Number	$=$	$\left(\begin{array}{c}Number\ between\\ 1\ and\ 10\end{array}\right)$	$\times\ (10^n)$
1.	750	$=$	7.5	$\times\ 10^?$
2.	.075	$=$	7.5	$\times\ 10^?$
3.	?	$=$	7.5	$\times\ 10^6$
4.	?	$=$	7.5	$\times\ 10^{-6}$
5.	80000	$=$	?	$\times\ 10^4$
6.	.00008	$=$	?	$\times\ 10^{-5}$
7.	?	$=$	3.25	$\times\ 10^{10}$
8.	?	$=$	3.25	$\times\ 10^{-10}$
9.	32500000	$=$	?	$\times$?
10.	.000000325	$=$	?	$\times$?

In 11–16, express the number as a power of 10.

11. 1,000,000

12. .000001

13. $\dfrac{1}{1,000,000}$

14. 1,000,000,000

15. .000000001

16. $\dfrac{1}{1,000,000,000}$

In 17–25, write the number in scientific notation.

17. 83,000

18. 83,000,000

19. 83,000,000,000

20. .0075

21. .0000075

22. .00000000075

23. $\dfrac{9}{1000}$

24. $\dfrac{9}{1,000,000}$

25. $\dfrac{9}{1,000,000,000,000}$

In 26–31, write the number as an integer or in ordinary decimal notation.

26. 5.8×10^3 **27.** 5.8×10^{-3} **28.** 5.8×10^{-6}

29. 9.3×10^{12} **30.** 9.3×10^{-12} **31.** 9.356×10^{-12}

In 32–39, applying the laws of exponents, calculate the result and express the result in both scientific notation and as an integer or in ordinary decimal notation.

32. $(2.5 \times 10^2)(4 \times 10^3)$

33. $(1.5 \times 10^{-2})(1.5 \times 10^{-3})$

34. $\dfrac{5 \times 10^2}{2.5 \times 10^3}$

35. $\dfrac{7.5 \times 10^{-3}}{1.5 \times 10^3}$

36. $(2.5 \times 10^5)^2$

37. $\sqrt{1.44 \times 10^8}$

38. $\dfrac{(9.3 \times 10^6)(5 \times 10^{-4})}{1.25 \times 10^{-3}}$

39. $\dfrac{(4 \times 10^{-5})^3(0.8 \times 10^{-4})^2}{(6.25 \times 10^{-6})^{\frac{1}{2}}}$

In 40–45, find the value of n.

40. $4000 = 4 \times 10^n$

41. $4,000,000 = 4 \times 10^n$

42. $.000004 = 4 \times 10^n$

43. $54,000,000 = 5.4 \times 10^n$

44. $.00000054 = 5.4 \times 10^n$

45. $.00000000054 = 5.4 \times 10^n$

In 46–49, express the number in scientific notation.

46. The approximate distance between our solar system and its nearest known star, Alpha Centauri, is 25,000,000,000,000 miles.

47. The number of atoms in a gram of hydrogen is approximately 600,000,000,000,000,000,000,000.

48. A light year is the distance light travels in a year. A light year is approximately 5,900,000,000,000 miles.

49. The diameter of the smallest visible particle is .0002 inch.

In 50–54, express the number as an integer, or in ordinary decimal notation.

50. The earth's mass is 1.32×10^{25} lb.

51. The distance from the earth to the sun is 9.3×10^7 miles.

52. The age of the earth's crust is 5×10^9 years.

53. The velocity of light is 3×10^{10} cm. per sec.

54. The average density of matter in metagalactic space is 10^{-29} gm. per cu. cm.

5. The Exponential Function

POWERS HAVING IRRATIONAL NUMBERS AS EXPONENTS

Until now we have defined all numbers b^x where b is a positive real number and x is a rational number. For example, we have defined 2^2 as 4, 8^0 as 1,

10^{-1} as $\frac{1}{10}$, and $27^{\frac{2}{3}}$ as 9. Now we will consider the meaning of b^x when b is a positive real number and x is an *irrational number*. We begin by investigating the meaning of 2^x, the special case of b^x when $b = 2$.

The following table contains ordered pairs of numbers which satisfy the equation $y = 2^x$:

x	-3	-2	-1	0	1	2	3
$y = 2^x$	$\frac{1}{8}$	$\frac{1}{4}$	$\frac{1}{2}$	1	2	4	8

To draw the graph of $y = 2^x$, we plot the points whose ordered pairs are included in the above table and then join them with a smooth curve as shown in the figure. In order to draw the smooth curve, we assume that, for every real value of x, there corresponds a unique real value of y such that $y = 2^x$. Note that the curve intersects the y-axis at $P(0, 1)$, but does not intersect the x-axis. Since y is positive for any real value of x, the curve lies entirely above the x-axis. As we proceed from right to left, the values of x become smaller and smaller and the curve draws closer and closer to the x-axis but does not touch the x-axis. The x-axis is an asymptote of the graph of $y = 2^x$.

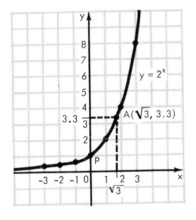

On the graph of $y = 2^x$, we can locate points whose x-coordinates are irrational numbers. For example, at point A, whose x-coordinate is $\sqrt{3}$, the y-coordinate is found to approximate 3.3. Hence, $2^{\sqrt{3}} \approx 3.3$.

Note that the curve meets the vertical line test, since no vertical line may intersect the curve in more than one point. Hence, the relation defined by $y = 2^x$ is a function. This function is called an *exponential function*.

Another method can be used to approximate the value of $2^{\sqrt{3}}$. First we approximate $\sqrt{3}$, the approximation being a rational number; then we use the result to approximate $2^{\sqrt{3}}$. For example, if we use 1.732 as an approximation of $\sqrt{3}$, then, using a method to be studied later in this chapter, we find that $2^{1.732} \approx 3.32$.

The definition of an exponent can be extended to include any irrational number as well as any rational number. Hence 2^x and, in general, b^x when $b > 0$ and $b \neq 1$, have meaning for all real numbers. With these definitions and meanings, the laws of exponents that we have used previously can be extended to include exponents that may be any real number, irrational as well as rational. The proof of such extensions is beyond the scope of this book.

DEFINITION OF THE EXPONENTIAL FUNCTION

When $y = 2^x$, to each real value of x there corresponds a unique real value of y. Hence, the equation $y = 2^x$ defines a function. We call this function an *exponential function* in accordance with the following general definition:

The function $\{(x, y) \mid y = b^x, b > 0, b \neq 1\}$ is an exponential function whose base is b. The domain of the exponential function, the set of values of x, is the set of real numbers; the range of the exponential function, the set of the corresponding values of y, is the set of positive numbers.

~~~~~~~~~~ *MODEL PROBLEMS* ~~~~~~~~~~

1. The graph of $(\frac{1}{2})^x = y$ lies only in (1) quadrant I   (2) quadrant II   (3) quadrants I and II   (4) quadrants I and IV

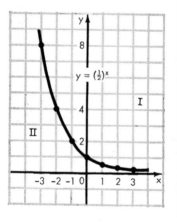

Solution: For any real values of x, positive, negative, or zero, $(\frac{1}{2})^x$ is always positive. Hence, y, which equals $(\frac{1}{2})^x$, is always positive for all real values of x. Since y is positive only in quadrants I and II, the graph of $y = (\frac{1}{2})^x$ lies only in these quadrants.

Answer: The correct choice is (3).

Note. The following table was used to sketch the graph of $y = (\frac{1}{2})^x$ for values of x from $x = -3$ to $x = 3$:

x	-3	-2	-1	0	1	2	3
y	8	4	2	1	$\frac{1}{2}$	$\frac{1}{4}$	$\frac{1}{8}$

Since $y = (\frac{1}{2})^x = (2^{-1})^x = 2^{-x}$, then the graph of $y = (\frac{1}{2})^x$ is also the graph of $y = 2^{-x}$.

2. The graphs of the functions defined by $y = 2^x$ and $y = 2^{-x}$ are (1) symmetric to each other with respect to the x-axis   (2) symmetric to each other with respect to the y-axis   (3) symmetric to each other with respect to the origin   (4) not symmetric to each other

Solution: From the graphs of $y = 2^x$ and $y = 2^{-x}$, note that the curves are symmetric with respect to the y-axis; that is, the y-axis serves as the folding line or axis of symmetry with respect to the two curves. If the entire graph is folded along the y-axis, either curve can be made to coincide with the other.

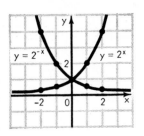

The following symmetry test can be applied to show that the curves are symmetric with respect to the y-axis:

In $y = 2^x$, if $-x$ replaces x, the other equation, $y = 2^{-x}$, is obtained.

Similarly, in $y = 2^{-x}$, if x replaces $-x$, then the other equation, $y = 2^x$, is obtained.

Such interchangeability of x and $-x$ indicates that the graphs of equations in x and y will be symmetric with respect to the y-axis.

Answer: The correct choice is (2).

~~~~~~

Exercises

1. *a.* Plot the graph of $y = 3^x$, using integral values of x from -3 to 3, inclusive.

   b. Using the graph made in answer to part *a*, find the approximate value of:

   1. $3^{\frac{1}{2}}$ 2. $3^{1\frac{1}{4}}$ 3. $3^{\sqrt{2}}$ 4. $3^{\sqrt{3}}$

2. *a.* Plot the graph of $\{(x, y) \,|\, y = 4^x\}$, using integral values of x from -3 to 3.

   b. Using the graph made in answer to part *a*, find the approximate value of:

   1. $4^{\frac{1}{2}}$ 2. $4^{1\frac{1}{3}}$ 3. $4^{\sqrt{2}}$ 4. $4^{\sqrt{5}}$

In 3–6, sketch the graph of the function.

3. $y = 2^{-x}$

4. $y = 3^{-x}$

5. $\{(x, y) \,|\, y = 5^x\}$

6. $\{(x, y) \,|\, y = 10^x\}$

In 7–10, use an appropriate graph to find an approximation of the number.

7. $3^{2\frac{1}{4}}$ **8.** $4^{1 \cdot 25}$ **9.** $5^{\sqrt{2}}$ **10.** $(\frac{1}{2})^{-\sqrt{2}}$

11. Name the point or points that the graphs of $y = 2^x$, $y = 3^x$, $y = (\frac{1}{2})^x$, and $y = (\frac{1}{3})^x$ have in common.

12. *a.* Sketch the graphs of $y = 3^x$ and $y = 3^{-x}$ and state how the graphs are related.

   b. Are the graphs of $y = 4^x$ and $y = (\frac{1}{4})^x$ related in the same way? If so, explain.

13. *a.* Is $\{(x, y) \,|\, y = a^x, a > 0, a \neq 1\}$ an exponential function?

   b. State the reason for the answer given in part *a*.

6. Solving Equations Containing Fractional and Negative Exponents

The definitions and laws of exponents can be used to solve equations in which the variable base has a fractional or a negative exponent.

Thus, to solve $x^{\frac{1}{4}} = 10$, raise both sides to the fourth power: $(x^{\frac{1}{4}})^4 = 10^4$. Apply the power of a power law to multiply exponents. The product of the exponents is $\frac{1}{4}(4)$, or 1: $x^1 = 10,000$, or $x = 10,000$.

Observe that we raised both sides of the equation to a power whose exponent is the reciprocal of the exponent of the variable so that the exponent of the variable in the resulting equation became 1.

~~~~~~~~~~~~ *MODEL PROBLEMS* ~~~~~~~~~~~~

In 1 and 2, solve for the positive value of x.

1. $x^{\frac{3}{2}} - 125 = 0$ **2.** $x^{-2} - 9 = 0$

How To Proceed	*Solution*	*Solution*
1. Transform the equation into the form $x^{\frac{m}{n}} = k$, where k is a constant.	$x^{\frac{3}{2}} = 125$	$x^{-2} = 9$
2. Raise both sides to the same power, using as an exponent $\dfrac{n}{m}$, the reciprocal of the exponent of the variable base x.	$(x^{\frac{3}{2}})^{\frac{2}{3}} = 125^{\frac{2}{3}}$ $x^1 = (5^3)^{\frac{2}{3}}$ $x = 5^2$ $= 25$ *Ans.*	$(x^{-2})^{-\frac{1}{2}} = 9^{-\frac{1}{2}}$ $x^1 = (3^2)^{-\frac{1}{2}}$ $x = 3^{-1}$ $= \frac{1}{3}$ *Ans.*
3. Check in the original equation.	$x^{\frac{3}{2}} - 125 = 0$ $25^{\frac{3}{2}} - 125 \overset{?}{=} 0$ $125 - 125 \overset{?}{=} 0$ $0 = 0$	$x^{-2} - 9 = 0$ $(\frac{1}{3})^{-2} - 9 \overset{?}{=} 0$ $\dfrac{1}{(\frac{1}{3})^2} - 9 \overset{?}{=} 0$ $9 - 9 \overset{?}{=} 0$ $0 = 0$

Exercises

In 1–18, solve the equation for the positive value of the variable and check.

1. $x^{\frac{1}{2}} = 10$ **2.** $x^{\frac{1}{4}} = 2$ **3.** $x^{\frac{1}{3}} = 3$

4. $x^{\frac{1}{2}} - 4 = 2$ **5.** $4x^{\frac{1}{2}} = 20$ **6.** $2x^{\frac{1}{2}} + 7 = 11$

7. $x^{-\frac{1}{2}} = 6$ **8.** $x^{-\frac{1}{4}} = 2$ **9.** $x^{-\frac{1}{2}} + 1 = 2$

10. $x^{\frac{2}{3}} = 25$ **11.** $x^{-\frac{2}{3}} = 16$ **12.** $x^{\frac{2}{3}} - 27 = 0$

13. $x^{\frac{3}{2}} = 27$ **14.** $y^{-2} = 49$ **15.** $y^{-3} - 8 = 0$

16. $y^{\frac{1}{3}} = 125$ **17.** $y^{\frac{1}{2}} = \frac{4}{9}$ **18.** $z^{\frac{5}{2}} - 12 = 20$

7. Solving Problems Involving Exponential Equations

An **exponential equation** is an equation in which the variable appears as an exponent or a part of an exponential expression. Examples of exponential equations are $2^x = 8$, $2^{x+1} = 8^{2x}$, and $5^x = 25^{x-2}$.

Exponential equations, such as the illustrations given above, are readily solvable when both sides of the equation are expressed as powers of the same base. Exponential equations in which both sides cannot be expressed as powers of the same base will be considered later in the chapter.

In an exponential equation, if both sides are expressed as powers of the same base, then the exponents of the powers are equal.

Thus, if $3^{2x} = 81$, then $3^{2x} = 3^4$. Hence, $2x = 4$ and $x = 2$.

Also, if $2^{4+y} = 4^y$, then $2^{4+y} = (2^2)^y$. Hence, $4 + y = 2y$ and $y = 4$.

~~~~~~~~~~ *MODEL PROBLEMS* ~~~~~~~~~~

1. Solve for t: $27^{6-t} = 9^{t-1}$

Solution:

To solve the given equation for t, express both sides as powers of the same base. Do this by substituting 3^3 for 27 and 3^2 for 9.

$$27^{6-t} = 9^{t-1}$$
$$(3^3)^{6-t} = (3^2)^{t-1}$$
$$3^{18-3t} = 3^{2t-2}$$

Since both sides now have the same base, equate the exponents.

$$18 - 3t = 2t - 2$$
$$20 = 5t$$
$$t = 4 \quad Ans.$$

2. In the equation $y = 3^x$, if the variable x is decreased by 3, then y is
(1) decreased by 3   (2) divided by 3   (3) decreased by 27   (4) divided by 27

Solution:

If x is decreased by 3, the expression 3^x becomes 3^{x-3}.

Since $3^{x-3} = 3^x \cdot 3^{-3} = \dfrac{3^x}{3^3} = \dfrac{3^x}{27}$ and $y = 3^x$, then $3^{x-3} = \dfrac{y}{27}$.

Hence, y is divided by 27.

Answer: The correct choice is (4).

Exercises

In 1–18, solve the equation and check.

1. $2^x = 64$

2. $2^{-x} = 32$

3. $2^{-x} = \frac{1}{16}$

4. $3^x = \frac{1}{27}$

5. $3^{x-1} = 81$

6. $3^x + 3 = 30$

7. $9 \cdot 3^x = \frac{1}{27}$

8. $4^x = 8^{x-1}$

9. $8^x = 4^{2x-2}$

10. $10^{3y} = 100^{y+2}$

11. $100^{x+1} = 1000^{x-1}$

12. $100^x = .0001$

13. $8^{2x-3} = 16^{x+2}$

14. $4^{2x} = (\frac{1}{16})^{x-1}$

15. $16^{3x} = 8^{x+4}$

16. $8^{x-3} = 16^{\frac{x}{2}}$

17. $25^{6-x} = 125^x$

18. $27^{t+3} = (\frac{1}{3})^{2-t}$

19. If, in the equation $y = 2^x$, the variable x is increased by 2, then the value of y is (1) divided by 2   (2) multiplied by 2   (3) squared   (4) multiplied by 4

20. If $7^{-x} = 10$, then 7^{2x} is equal to (1) $\dfrac{1}{100}$ (2) $\dfrac{1}{20}$ (3) 20   (4) 100

21. If $a^x = b$, then a^{x+3} is equal to (1) $3 + b$ (2) $a^3 b$ (3) b^3 (4) $3b$

In 22–25, if $a^x = b$, transform the expression into a power of a.

22. $a^2 b^2$

23. $\dfrac{a}{b}$

24. $\dfrac{b^2}{a^3}$

25. $(ab)^3$

In 26–28, find the solution set of the system of equations.

26. $2^x \cdot 2^y = 8$

$\dfrac{2^x}{2^y} = 32$

27. $3^x \cdot 3^y = 27$

$\dfrac{3^x}{27^y} = \dfrac{1}{3}$

28. $100^x \cdot 10^y = \frac{1}{10}$

$\dfrac{10^x}{10^{2y}} = 100$

8. Using Exponents To Simplify Calculations: Powers of 2

The numbers in the following table are powers of the same base, 2. Operations upon numbers that can be expressed as powers of the same base are simplified through the application of the laws of exponents. Laborious calculations involving the numbers are replaced by mental operations involving exponents.

TABLE OF POWERS OF 2

$2^1 = 2$	$2^{11} = 2048$	$2^{21} = 2,097,152$
$2^2 = 4$	$2^{12} = 4096$	$2^{22} = 4,194,304$
$2^3 = 8$	$2^{13} = 8192$	$2^{23} = 8,388,608$
$2^4 = 16$	$2^{14} = 16,384$	$2^{24} = 16,777,216$
$2^5 = 32$	$2^{15} = 32,768$	$2^{25} = 33,554,432$
$2^6 = 64$	$2^{16} = 65,536$	$2^{26} = 67,108,864$
$2^7 = 128$	$2^{17} = 131,072$	$2^{27} = 134,217,728$
$2^8 = 256$	$2^{18} = 262,144$	$2^{28} = 268,435,456$
$2^9 = 512$	$2^{19} = 524,288$	$2^{29} = 536,870,912$
$2^{10} = 1024$	$2^{20} = 1,048,576$	$2^{30} = 1,073,741,824$

∼∼∼∼∼∼∼ *MODEL PROBLEM* ∼∼∼∼∼∼∼

Using the table of powers of 2, evaluate $\dfrac{(131,072)^2 \sqrt[3]{262,144}}{\sqrt{268,435,456}}$.

How To Proceed	*Solution*
1. Express each number as a power of 2.	1. $\dfrac{(2^{17})^2 (2^{18})^{\frac{1}{3}}}{(2^{28})^{\frac{1}{2}}}$
2. Apply the laws of exponents.	2. $\dfrac{2^{34}(2^6)}{2^{14}}$
	$2^{34+6-14} = 2^{26}$
3. Write the number which equals the resulting power of 2.	3. $= 67,108,864$ *Ans.*

Exercises

In 1–21, evaluate, using the table of powers of 2.

1. 32×16 **2.** $4 \times 64 \times 1024$ **3.** $2 \times 8 \times 128 \times 256$

4. $4096 \div 32$ **5.** $524{,}288 \div 65{,}536$ **6.** $1{,}073{,}741{,}824 \div 64$

7. 512^2 **8.** 1024^3 **9.** 128^4

10. $\sqrt{1{,}048{,}576}$ **11.** $\sqrt[3]{2{,}097{,}152}$ **12.** $\sqrt[5]{33{,}554{,}432}$

13. $67{,}108{,}864^{\frac{1}{2}}$ **14.** $16{,}777{,}216^{\frac{1}{4}}$ **15.** $134{,}217{,}728^{\frac{1}{9}}$

16. $4096^{\frac{3}{2}}$ **17.** $4096^{\frac{3}{2}}$ **18.** $4096^{\frac{1}{2}}(4096^{\frac{1}{4}})$

19. $\dfrac{524{,}288}{16{,}384^{\frac{1}{2}}}$ **20.** $\dfrac{1024^2(131{,}072)}{134{,}217{,}728}$ **21.** $\dfrac{67{,}108{,}864^{\frac{1}{2}}}{16^3(256^{\frac{1}{4}})}$

In 22–27, solve for x, using the table of powers of 2.

22. $2^{x+1} = 512$ **23.** $2^{3x} = 262{,}144$ **24.** $2^{4x-3} = 2{,}097{,}152$

25. $4^x = 1{,}048{,}576$ **26.** $2^x(4^x)(8) = 512$ **27.** $16^{x+2} = 32{,}768$

9. Understanding Logarithms: Writing Equations in Exponential and Logarithmic Form

The previous unit showed how laborious calculations involving numbers can be replaced by mental operations involving exponents—if the numbers can be expressed as powers of the same base. You can understand that the table of powers of 2 can be used to simplify calculations only if the numbers involved are the few numbers listed in the table.

In the beginning of the 17th century, a Scotsman named John Napier designed a table of logarithms by means of which *all numbers* could be expressed as powers of the same base. This new tool not only enabled mathematicians to simplify calculations of an extensive and laborious kind, but also made it possible to solve problems that could not have been done before the invention of the table. An understanding of logarithms is indispensable in advanced mathematics, science, and technology.

In $3^4 = 81$, the exponent 4 is called the *logarithm* of 81 to the base 3. The statement "4 is the logarithm of 81 to the base 3" is written as "$4 = \log_3 81$." Read "$4 = \log_3 81$" as "4 is the log of 81 to the base 3."

In the equation $3^4 = 81$, the number 4 plays a dual role, because 4 is the exponent of the base 3; and, at the same time, 4 is the logarithm of the power 81. Keep in mind that the same number is both an exponent and a logarithm.

By definition, the **logarithm** of a number, to a given base, is the exponent that is used with the base to obtain the number.

If $b^e = n$, then $e = \log_b n$.

The equation $3^4 = 81$ is in **exponential form**. The equivalent equation, $\log_3 81 = 4$, is in **logarithmic form**. Note these two forms of equivalent equations in the following table:

Exponential Form	Logarithmic Form
$10^3 = 1000$	$\log_{10} 1000 = 3$
$16^{\frac{1}{2}} = 4$	$\log_{16} 4 = \frac{1}{2}$
$5^{-2} = \frac{1}{25}$	$\log_5 \frac{1}{25} = -2$
$3^4 = x$	$\log_3 x = 4$
$x^2 = 49$	$\log_x 49 = 2$

If no base is indicated when we find the logarithm of a number, the base is understood to be 10. Thus, $\log 1000 = 3$ means $\log_{10} 1000 = 3$. Logarithms which have 10 as their base are called **common logarithms**.

~~~~~~~~ MODEL PROBLEMS ~~~~~~~~

1. Express in logarithmic form $5^3 = 125$.   *Answer:* $\log_5 125 = 3$
2. Express in exponential form $\log_4 64 = 3$.   *Answer:* $4^3 = 64$
3. Express in exponential form $\log 100 = 2$.   *Answer:* $10^2 = 100$

4. Find the positive value of x: $\log_x 16 = 4$.
   Solution:
   $$\log_x 16 = 4$$
   Express in exponential form: $x^4 = 16$
   Find the fourth root of 16: $x = 2$ *Ans.*

Exercises

In 1–10, express in logarithmic form.

1. $2^5 = 32$ 2. $10^0 = 1$ 3. $3^5 = 243$ 4. $4^3 = 64$ 5. $36^{\frac{1}{2}} = 6$
6. $8^{\frac{1}{3}} = 2$ 7. $8^{\frac{2}{3}} = 4$ 8. $10^{-1} = \frac{1}{10}$ 9. $5^{-2} = \frac{1}{25}$ 10. $4^{-\frac{3}{2}} = \frac{1}{8}$

In 11–18, express in exponential form.

11. $\log_2 16 = 4$ **12.** $\log_9 81 = 2$ **13.** $\log 10 = 1$ **14.** $\log_3 1 = 0$

15. $\log_8 \frac{1}{8} = -1$ **16.** $\log .01 = -2$ **17.** $\log_9 3 = \frac{1}{2}$ **18.** $\log_8 2 = \frac{1}{3}$

In 19–27, solve for x.

19. $\log_x 81 = 2$ **20.** $\log_x 64 = 3$ **21.** $\log_2 x = 5$

22. $\log_x .1 = -1$ **23.** $\log_x .01 = -2$ **24.** $\log_7 49 = x$

25. $\log 100 = x$ **26.** $\log .001 = x$ **27.** $\log .1 = x$

In 28–30, evaluate.

28. $\log_3 27 + \log_2 16$ **29.** $5 \log 1 - 2 \log 10$ **30.** $\log_4 2 + \log_8 64$

In 31–33, express in exponential form.

31. $\log_a b = c$ **32.** $\log_c a = b$ **33.** $\log_b c = a$

In 34–36, express in logarithmic form.

34. $p^q = r$ **35.** $r^p = q$ **36.** $q^r = p$

10. The Logarithmic Function

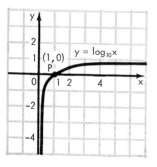

The inverse of the exponential function $y = 10^x$, obtained by interchanging x and y, is $x = 10^y$. When $x = 10^y$ is expressed in logarithmic form, we obtain the equation $y = \log_{10} x$.

The graph of $y = \log_{10} x$ is shown at the right. Note the following on the graph of $y = \log_{10} x$:

1. Since $x = 10^y$, if $y = 0$ then $x = 1$. Hence, the curve intersects the x-axis at $P(1, 0)$.

2. For any real values of y, positive, negative, or zero, 10^y must be positive; that is, the graph of $y = \log_{10} x$ is always to the right of the y-axis.

3. As we proceed from top to bottom, the values of y become smaller and smaller and the curve draws closer and closer to the y-axis but does not touch the y-axis. The y-axis is an asymptote to the graph of $y = \log_{10} x$.

4. Note that the curve meets the vertical line test since no vertical line may intersect the curve in more than one point. Hence, the relation defined by $y = \log_{10} x$ is a function. This function is called the *logarithmic function*.

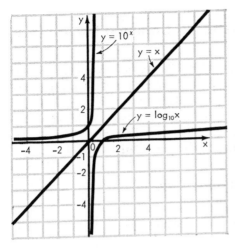

In the figure at the left, the graph of the logarithmic function defined by $y = \log_{10} x$ and also the graph of its inverse function, the exponential function defined by $y = 10^x$, have both been drawn. Note that the graph of the logarithmic function is symmetric to the graph of the exponential function with respect to the line $y = x$.

DEFINITION OF THE LOGARITHMIC FUNCTION

When $y = \log_{10} x$, to each real value of x there corresponds a unique real value of y. Hence, the equation $y = \log_{10} x$ defines a function. We call this function a *logarithmic function* in accordance with the following general definition:

The function $\{(x, y) \mid y = \log_b x, b > 0, b \neq 1\}$ is a logarithmic function whose base is b. The domain of the logarithmic function, the set of values of x, is the set of positive numbers. The range of the logarithmic function, the set of the corresponding values of y, is the set of real numbers.

Exercises

1. Sketch the graph of $y = \log_3 x$, using the following values of x: $\frac{1}{9}$, $\frac{1}{3}$, 1, 3, and 9.

2. Name the point or points that the graphs of $y = \log_2 x$, $y = \log_3 x$, and $y = \log_{10} x$ have in common.

3. To answer the following questions, refer to the preceding graphs of $y = \log_{10} x$.
   a. If $x > 1$, is the logarithm of x a positive or a negative number?
   b. If $x = 1$, what is the logarithm of x to any base?
   c. If $0 < x < 1$, is the logarithm of x a positive or a negative number?
   d. If $x < 0$, is the logarithm of x a real number?

11. Finding the Characteristics of Common Logarithms

Since 10 is the basis of the decimal system of numbers, computations with logarithms will be performed with *common logarithms*, logarithms whose base is 10. To evaluate a numerical expression using logarithmic rules, we obtain the common logarithm of numbers in the expression. Let us begin with the integral powers of 10, the ones contained in the following table, since these are the numbers whose common logarithms are most easily determined.

TABLE OF POWERS OF 10

$(10^e = N)$	$(\text{Log } N = e)$
Exponential Form	*Logarithmic Form*
$10^4 = 10{,}000$	$\log 10{,}000 = 4$
$10^3 = 1{,}000$	$\log 1000 = 3$
$10^2 = 100$	$\log 100 = 2$
$10^1 = 10$	$\log 10 = 1$
$10^0 = 1$	$\log 1 = 0$
$10^{-1} = .1$	$\log .1 = -1$
$10^{-2} = .01$	$\log .01 = -2$
$10^{-3} = .001$	$\log .001 = -3$
$10^{-4} = .0001$	$\log .0001 = -4$

Note in the table, illustrations of the following principles:

Principle 1. The common logarithm of a number is *positive* if the number is greater than 1; the common logarithm of a number is *negative* if the number is less than 1 and greater than 0. Also, the common logarithm of 1 is 0.

Thus, $\log 100 = +2$ and $\log .01$ is -2.

Principle 2. Numbers and logarithms vary in the same sense; that is, the greater a number, the greater the logarithm, whereas the smaller a number, the smaller the logarithm.

Thus, since $100 > 10$, then $\log 100 > \log 10$. Also, since $.01 < .1$, then $\log .01 < \log .1$.

Principle 3. If a number is multiplied by 10, its common logarithm is increased by 1, whereas if a number is divided by 10, its common logarithm is decreased by 1.

For example, $\log 100 = 2$, $\log (100 \cdot 10) = 2 + 1$, and $\log 1000 = 3$. Also, $\log 100 = 2$, $\log (100 \div 10) = 2 - 1$, and $\log 10 = 1$.

Note. The common logarithm of a negative number is not a real number. It can be shown that the common logarithm of a negative number is a complex number.

Whether a number is an integral power of 10, such as 100 or 1000, or is not an integral power of 10, such as 3.25 or 31.7, *the common logarithm of any number is expressible as a combination of two parts: an integral part called the* **character-** **istic** *and a decimal part called the* **mantissa.**

Thus, $\log 1000 = 3.0000$. Here, 3 is the characteristic and .0000 is the mantissa.

However, most numbers are not exact integral powers of 10. For example, $3.25 = 10^{0.5119}$. Hence, $\log 3.25 = 0.5119$, approximately. Here, 0 is the characteristic and .5119 is the mantissa. Let us now see what happens when 3.25 is multiplied or divided by an integral power of 10.

If 3.25 is multiplied by 100, then $3.25 \times 100 = 10^{0.5119} \times 10^2 = 10^{2.5119}$. Since $325 = 3.25 \times 100$, then $325 = 10^{2.5119}$ and $\log 325 = 2.5119$. Observe that both $\log 325$ and $\log 3.25$ have the same mantissa, which is .5119. However, the characteristic of $\log 325$ is 2 more than the characteristic of $\log 3.25$ due to the multiplication of 3.25 by 100.

If 3.25 is divided by 100, then $3.25 \div 100 = 10^{0.5119} \div 10^2 = 10^{.5119-2}$. Since $3.25 \div 100 = .0325$, then $\log .0325 = .5119 - 2$. Observe that both $\log 3.25$ and $\log .0325$ have the same mantissa, which is .5119. However, the characteristic of $\log .0325$ is 2 less than the characteristic of $\log 3.25$ due to the division of 3.25 by 100.

The following table shows the results obtained when 3.25 is multiplied or divided by 100, as above, and also when 3.25 is multiplied or divided by 10.

Logarithm	*Characteristic*	*Mantissa*
$\log (3.25 \times 100) = \log 325 = 2.5119$	2	.5119
$\log (3.25 \times\ \ 10) = \log 32.5 = 1.5119$	1	.5119
$\log 3.25 = 0.5119$	0	.5119
$\log(3.25 \div 10)\ \ = \log .325 = .5119 - 1$	-1	.5119
$\log(3.25 \div 100) = \log .0325 = .5119 - 2$	-2	.5119

Observe in the table that the effect of multiplying a number by an integral power of 10 is to change the characteristic of its logarithm, but that the mantissa remains unchanged. Note also that multiplying a number by an integral power of 10 changes the position of the decimal point in the number, but the significant digits of the number remain unchanged. For example, 3, 2, and 5, the significant digits of 3.25, are unchanged.

Note in the table that log 3.25 has a characteristic of 0. Numbers whose logarithms have a characteristic of 0 are numbers greater than 1 and less than 10 since log 1 = 0 and log 10 = 1. In the case of numbers between 1 and 10, such as 3.25, 5.61, and 9.97, their *decimal point is located immediately after the first significant digit and the decimal point is said to be in standard position.* Observe in the table that when the decimal point in a number is to the right of the standard position, the characteristic is positive and equal to this number of decimal places. For example, in 32.5, the decimal point is one place to the right of the standard position and the characteristic of log 32.5 is 1. When the decimal point is to the left of the standard position, the characteristic is negative and has an absolute value equal to this number of decimal places. For example, in .0325, the decimal point is two places to the left of the standard position and the characteristic of log .0325 is −2. Hence, in finding the characteristic of the common logarithm of a number, it is useful to place an apostrophe in the standard position of the decimal point and then count the number of decimal places which this decimal point is to the right or the left of the apostrophe. Note how this is done in the following procedure:

Procedure: To find the characteristics of common logarithms using the apostrophe method:

1. Place an apostrophe (') immediately to the right of the first significant digit. (Doing this places the apostrophe in the standard position of the decimal point.)

In determining which digits or figures in a number are significant, or not significant, observe the following rules:

(1) Any digit other than zero is significant.
(2) Any zero is significant if it is between two other digits which are not zeros.
(3) Any zero used only to place the decimal point is not significant.

Thus, 3.5 has two significant digits, 40.25 has four significant digits, .03 has one significant digit.

2. Starting from the apostrophe, count the number of places to the decimal point of the number. The number of places so counted is the absolute value of the characteristic of the logarithm.

3. If the position of the decimal point is to the right of the apostrophe, the characteristic is positive. If the position of the decimal point is to the left of the apostrophe, the characteristic is negative.

Thus, to find the characteristic of log 723.4, place an apostrophe between the 7 and the 2, as follows: log 7'23.4. Counting from the apostrophe to the decimal point shows that the decimal point is two places to the right of the apostrophe. Therefore, the characteristic of log 723.4 is +2.

Also, to find the characteristic of log .0001, place an apostrophe after 1 as follows: log .0001'. Counting from the apostrophe to the decimal point shows that the decimal point is four places to the left of the apostrophe. Therefore, the characteristic of log .0001 is −4. Check this in the table of powers of 10.

ALTERNATE METHOD FOR FINDING THE CHARACTERISTICS OF COMMON LOGARITHMS

The following rules are useful, especially at the start, to check the characteristics found by the apostrophe method:

Rule 1. If a number is greater than 1, the positive characteristic of its common logarithm is *one less* than the number of digits to the left of the decimal point.

Thus, in the number 723.4, since there are three digits to the left of the decimal point, then the characteristic of log 723.4 is 3–1 or **2**. Also, in the number 3.25, since there is but one digit to the left of the decimal point, the characteristic of log 3.25 is 1–1 or **0**.

Rule 2. If a number is positive and less than 1, the negative characteristic of its common logarithm has an absolute value that is *one more* than the number of zeros between the decimal point and the first significant digit.

Thus, in the number .000325, since there are three zeros between the decimal point and the first significant digit of the number .000325, then the characteristic of log .000325 is −4. Also, in the number .325, since there are no zeros between the decimal point and the first significant digit, then the characteristic of log .325 is 0 − 1 or −1.

THE CHARACTERISTIC IN SCIENTIFIC NOTATION

Study the following table and discover the important relationship that exists between the exponent of 10 when a number is written in scientific notation and the characteristic of the common logarithm of the number.

Number	Scientific Notation	Characteristic
31.7	3.17×10^1	1
325	3.25×10^2	2
10,000	$1. \quad \times 10^4$	4
.0302	3.02×10^{-2}	-2
.00001	$1. \quad \times 10^{-5}$	-5

Rule. The characteristic of the common logarithm of a number is equal to the exponent of 10 when the number is written in scientific notation.

MODEL PROBLEMS

1. Find the characteristic of log 543.2.

Solution:

(1) *Apostrophe Method:* Place an apostrophe immediately to the right of the first significant digit, obtaining 5'43.2. Count the number of decimal places from the apostrophe to the decimal point. The count to the right is 2. Hence, the characteristic is 2.

(2) *Alternate Method:* Since 543.2 is greater than 1, the characteristic of log 543.2 is one less than 3, the number of significant digits to the left of the decimal point: $3 - 1 = 2$.

(3) *Scientific Notation Method:* Since $543.2 = 5.432 \times 10^2$, the characteristic of log 543.2 is 2, the exponent of 10^2.

Answer: 2

2. The characteristic of the common logarithm of a number is -4. If the significant digits of the number are 302, find the number.

Solution:

(1) *Apostrophe Method:* Place an apostrophe immediately to the right of the first significant digit, obtaining 3'02. Since the characteristic is -4, place the decimal point four places to the left of the apostrophe, obtaining the number .000302. Notice that we annexed three zeros to the left of the first significant digit of 302.

(2) *Alternate Method:* Since the characteristic is -4, three zeros are needed between the decimal point and the first significant digit of 302. Hence, the number is .000302.

(3) *Scientific Notation Method:* Since the characteristic is −4, the number in scientific notation is 3.02×10^{-4}. Written in ordinary notation, this is .000302.

Answer: .000302

Note. In computation problems, the term "log of a number" means "common log of a number," unless otherwise indicated.

~~~~~~

Exercises

In 1–20, find the characteristic of the logarithm of the number.
1. 326   2. 73   3. 8294   4. 2   5. 350,000
6. 89,400   7. 5.26   8. 58.96   9. 728.2   10. 8.002
11. .826   12. .49   13. .6   14. .08   15. .0834
16. .3021   17. .0408   18. .00009   19. .00076   20. .00405

In 21–26, find the number of significant digits to the left of the decimal point in the number whose logarithm has the given characteristic.
21. 5   22. 0   23. 3   24. 2   25. 4   26. 1

In 27–32, find the number of zeros between the decimal point and the first significant digit in the number whose logarithm has the given characteristic.
27. −3   28. −1   29. −4   30. −2   31. −5   32. −6

In 33–38, if the significant digits of a number are 517, find the number when the characteristic of its logarithm is the given integer.
33. 2   34. 3   35. −1   36. −3   37. 4   38. 0

In 39–44, state the characteristic of the logarithm of a number between the two given numbers
39. 1 and 10   40. 1000 and 10,000   41. 1,000,000 and 10,000,000
42. .01 and .1   43. .0001 and .001   44. .000001 and .0000001

In 45–48, state the smallest and the largest integers whose logarithms have the given characteristic.
45. 0   46. 1   47. 2   48. 3

In 49–51, state the possible characteristics for log N when N has the indicated possible values.
49. $1 \leq N < 100$ 50. $10 \leq N < 10,000$ 51. $.0001 \leq N < .1$

In 52–55, find the value of x in the given equation.
52. $10^x = 100$ 53. $10^x = 10,000$ 54. $10^x = .1$ 55. $10^x = .001$

12. Finding the Logarithm of a Number Having Three or Fewer Than Three Significant Digits

In the previous unit, we learned how to find the characteristic of the common logarithm of a positive number, the characteristic being the integral part of the logarithm. There still remains the problem of finding the mantissa, which is the decimal part of the logarithm.

The mantissas of logarithms of numbers are found in the two-page table **Common Logarithms of Numbers** on pages 758 and 759. It is startling to realize that a short two-page table is all that is needed to find the mantissas of the common logarithms of all positive numbers! This is possible because of the following rule:

Rule. If positive numbers have the same significant digits, then their common logarithms have the same mantissa.

Thus, log 325, log 325,000, log .325, and log .0000325 have the same mantissa, .5119.

In the previous unit, we pointed out that changing the position of the decimal point of a number changes the characteristic of its logarithm, but that the mantissa remains unchanged. This is another way of expressing the rule stated above.

The following is a portion of the table, which we shall now use for ready reference:

COMMON LOGARITHMS OF NUMBERS*

N	0	1	2	3	4	5	6	7	8	9
30	4771	4786	4800	4814	4829	4843	4857	4871	4886	4900
31	4914	4928	4942	4955	4969	4983	4997	5011	5024	5038
32	5051	5065	5079	5092	5105	5119	5132	5145	5159	5172
33	5185	5198	5211	5224	5237	5250	5263	5276	5289	5302
34	5315	5328	5340	5353	5366	5378	5391	5403	5416	5428

* This table gives the mantissas of numbers with the decimal point omitted in each case.

*The matissas shown in the table are correct to **4 decimal places.*** The decimal point of each mantissa is omitted and must be supplied when needed. The decimal point of a mantissa belongs before the first digit. (See the note below the table.) Thus, the mantissas in the **30** row are .4771, .4786, .4800, .4814, etc.

Let us find log 325. We have learned that the characteristic is 2. To obtain the mantissa, find 32, the first two digits of 325, in the column headed **N** and then move across the row to the right of **32** until you reach the column under **5**, the third digit of 325. The entry to the right of **32** and under **5** is 5119. Hence, the required mantissa is .5119. We conclude that log 325 = 2.5119.

To find log 3170, find its mantissa, 5011, in the **31** row under the **7** column. Since the characteristic of log 3170 is 3, we conclude that log 3170 = 3.5011. Similarly, since the entry 5289 is in the **33** row under **8**, we conclude that log 3.38 = 0.5289. Verify that log 30200 = 4.4800.

COMBINING A NEGATIVE CHARACTERISTIC WITH A POSITIVE MANTISSA

Recall that if a number is between 0 and 1, the characteristic of its common logarithm is negative. For example, the characteristic of log .0325 is -2. The table of common logarithms shows that the mantissa of log .0325 is .5119, a positive number. If you write log .0325 = -2.5119, in effect you have made the mantissa .5119 negative since $-2.5119 = -2 + (-.5119)$.

A procedure to use when a negative characteristic is combined with a positive mantissa is to place the characteristic after the mantissa; thus, log .0325 = .5119 $-$ 2. Another procedure is to write -2 as "$8 - 10$," in which case we obtain log .0325 = 8.5119 $-$ 10. Similarly, a characteristic -1 can be written in the form 9. ---- -10, and a characteristic -3 can be written 7. ---- -10.

Caution. Never place a negative characteristic before the mantissa found in the table.

PROCEDURE FOR FINDING THE MANTISSA OF THE LOGARITHM OF A NUMBER HAVING ONE OR TWO SIGNIFICANT DIGITS

To find the mantissa of the logarithm of a one-digit or a two-digit number, we find the mantissa of the logarithm of a three-digit number that has the same significant digits. For example, to find the mantissa of log 3, find the mantissa of log 300, which is .4771; to find the mantissa of log 34, find the mantissa of log 340, which is .5315. Therefore, log 3 or log 3.00 = 0.4771. Also, log 34 or log 34.0 = 1.5315.

~~~~~~~~~ *MODEL PROBLEMS* ~~~~~~~~~

1. Find log 37.8

Solution:
The characteristic of log 37.8 is 1
The mantissa of log 37.8 is the same as the mantissa of log 378, which is
.5775
Therefore, log 37.8 = 1.5775   *Ans.*

2. Find log .9

Solution:
The characteristic of log .9 is −1, or 9. - - - - −10
The mantissa of log .9 is the same as the mantissa of log 900, which is .9542
Therefore, log .9 = 9.9542 − 10   *Ans.*

3. If $10^x = 5.41$, find x, correct to four decimal places.

Solution:
1. Transform $10^x = 5.41$ into the logarithmic form log 5.41 = x.
2. Locate 54, the first two digits of 5.41, in the column headed **N**.
3. In the same row, find the entry in the column headed **1**, the third digit of 5.41.
4. Since this entry is 7332, then log 5.41 = 0.7332.
5. Hence, $x = 0.7332$ *Ans.*

Exercises

In 1–15, using the table on page 758, find the logarithm of the given number.
1. 732   **2.** 546   **3.** 6.38   **4.** 400   **5.** 94
6. 8.7   **7.** 5   **8.** 4950   **9.** 72,600   **10.** .137
11. .00643   **12.** .0654   **13.** .2   **14.** .05   **15.** .0038

In 16–19, if the log 37.8 = 1.5775, state the log of the given number without
using tables.
16. 3780   **17.** .378   **18.** 3.78   **19.** .000378

In 20–23, if the log 900 = 2.9542, state the log of the given number without
using tables.
20. 90   **21.** 9   **22.** .009   **23.** .09

In 24–26, if log $N = 2.3456$, find the indicated logarithm.

24. log 100N **25.** log 10,000N **26.** log $\dfrac{N}{100}$

In 27–30, if $10^{0.4771} = 3$, find the value of the given powers of 10.
27. $10^{2.4771}$ **28.** $10^{4.4771}$ **29.** $10^{.4771-2}$ **30.** $10^{7.4771-10}$

13. Finding the Logarithm of a Four-Digit Number

Since the table of common logarithms in this book is limited to the finding of mantissas of logarithms of numbers having three or fewer significant digits, a method of approximation, called ***interpolation,*** is used to find the logarithm of a four-digit number. The method of interpolation, or more properly, *linear interpolation*, is based on the following principle:

Principle. For small changes in numbers, the differences of the numbers, and the corresponding differences of their logarithms, are approximately in proportion.

The process shown in the model problem will, with very few exceptions, provide mantissas correct to the fourth decimal place.

For a very small segment of the curve $y = \log x$, the curve approximates a straight line. Hence, as shown, with few exceptions, the error resulting from the use of linear interpolation is not large enough to affect the fourth decimal place of the mantissa.

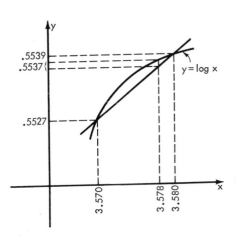

~~~~~~~~~~~~~~ *MODEL PROBLEM* ~~~~~~~~~~~~~~

Find log 357.8, using the table on page 758.

Solution:

1. The characteristic of log 357.8 is 2.
2. Since 357.8 lies between 357.0 and 358.0, the mantissa of log 357.8 lies between the mantissa of log 357.0 and the mantissa of log 358.0.
3. Arrange these numbers and their corresponding mantissas in the following tabular form. Under "number" in the table, place the significant digits of each number. The decimal point may be omitted, since it does not affect the mantissa.

	Number	Mantissa	
	3580	.5539	
	3578	.5527 + x	
	3570	.5527	

Proportion of Differences

$$\frac{8}{10} = \frac{x}{12}$$

$$10x = 96$$

$$x = 9.6 \approx 10$$

4. Find the corresponding differences as shown in the table.
5. Write and then solve the proportion of these corresponding differences for x. Omit the decimal points in writing the proportion.
6. Since x is 10, the mantissa of log 3578 = .5527 + .0010 = .5537.
7. Therefore, log 357.8 = 2.5537. *Ans.*

Exercises

In 1–19, find the logarithm of the given number.

1. 2073
2. 354.4
3. 703.2
4. 62.54
5. 34.72
6. 3.142
7. 2.718
8. 6.573
9. 0.8926
10. 0.5663
11. 0.4312
12. 0.2347
13. 0.5473
14. 0.03742
15. .04732
16. .03928
17. .002973
18. .0003174
19. .000001581

In 20–22, solve the given equation for x, correct to four decimal places.
20. $10^x = 75.24$
21. $10^x = 180.6$
22. $10^x = 5.632$

14. Finding a Number Whose Logarithm Is Given: Finding the Antilogarithm

In general, if $a = \log N$, then N is the antilogarithm of a. That is, N is the number whose logarithm is a.

Thus, if $2.5119 = \log 325$, then 325 is the antilogarithm of 2.5119.

The process of finding a number whose logarithm is given is called *finding the antilogarithm*. The first two model problems illustrate the procedure to use if the mantissa is in the table.

~~~~~~~~~~~~ *MODEL PROBLEMS* ~~~~~~~~~~~~

1. Find the antilogarithm of 2.5119.

Solution:

1. Use the given mantissa, .5119, to determine the significant digits of the antilogarithm. Locate the mantissa, .5119, in the table of common logarithms of numbers (page 758). Since .5119 is in the **32** row under **5**, then 325 are the significant digits of the antilogarithm.
2. Use the given characteristic, 2, to determine the position of the decimal point. Since the characteristic is 2, place the apostrophe after the first significant digit, 3'25, and count two places to the right of the apostrophe.

Answer: 325

Note: Refer to model problem 3 for the procedure to use if the mantissa is *not* in the table. In such a case, the process of linear interpolation must be employed.

2. Find the number whose logarithm is 8.4082 − 10.

Solution:

1. Use the given mantissa, .4082, to determine the significant digits of the antilogarithm. Locate the mantissa, .4082, in the table of common logarithms of numbers (page 758). Since .4082 is in the **25** row under **6**, then 256 are the significant digits of the antilogarithm.
2. Use the given characteristic 8 − 10, or −2, to determine the position of the decimal place. Since the characteristic is −2, place the apostrophe after the first significant digit, 2'56, and count two places to the left of the apostrophe, prefixing one zero before 256.

Answer: .0256

3. If log $n = 8.9367 - 10$, find n.

Solution:

1. Since the mantissa .9367 does not appear in the table of mantissas on page 759, we will have to interpolate.
2. In the table, the mantissa .9367 lies between the mantissas .9365 and .9370. Therefore, the number which corresponds to the mantissa .9367 will lie between the numbers which correspond to the mantissas .9365 and .9370.

3. Arrange these mantissas and their corresponding numbers in the following tabular form. Under "number" in the table, place the significant digits of each number.

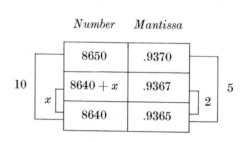

4. Find the corresponding differences as shown in the table.
5. Write and then solve the proportion of these corresponding differences for x. Omit the decimal points in writing the proportion.
6. If the difference, x, whose value is 4 is added to 8640, the result obtained is 8644. Therefore, the number we are trying to find has the significant digits 8644.
7. Since the characteristic is 8. ---- $- 10$, or -2, the number is .08644.

Answer: .08644

Note. The answer to model problem 3 would be the same if the instructions were worded, "Find the antilogarithm of 8.9367 $- 10$."

~~~~~~

Exercises

In 1–6, if the log $5.9 = 0.7709$, state the number whose log is:

1. 2.7709   **2.** 5.7709   **3.** 8.7709 $- 10$
4. 7.7709 $- 10$ **5.** .7709 $- 1$ **6.** 5.7709 $- 10$

In 7–21, find the number whose logarithm is:

7. 2.8162   **8.** 1.7767   **9.** 0.5391
10. 3.2900   **11.** 0.6532   **12.** 9.3962 $- 10$
13. 8.5276 $- 10$ **14.** 1.8612   **15.** 8.9579 $- 10$
16. 0.7303   **17.** 9.7820 $- 10$ **18.** 3.8558
19. 1.8043   **20.** 0.0248   **21.** 8.0765 $- 10$

In 22–24, find the antilogarithm of:

22. 2.4752   **23.** 3.4060   **24.** 9.7353 $- 10$

In 25–27, find n if log n equals:

25. 1.7718   **26.** 0.6732   **27.** 9.6791 − 10

28. Find, to the nearest tenth, the number whose logarithm is 2.6687.

29. Find, to the nearest hundredth, the antilogarithm of 1.7060.

30. Find, to the nearest thousandth, the antilogarithm of 0.7111.

31. Find the four-place decimal whose logarithm is 9.6060 − 10.

32. If $x = 10^{2.6609}$, find x.   **33.** If $n = 10^{1.9540}$, find n.

In 34–37, if the antilogarithm of 2.5977 is 396, state the antilogarithm of:

34. 0.5977   **35.** 4.5977   **36.** .5977 − 2   **37.** 7.5977 − 10

In 38–40, if $10^{0.6487} = 4.453$, find:

38. $10^{3.6487}$ **39.** $10^{.6487-3}$ **40.** $10^{8.6487-10}$

15. Finding Logarithms of Trigonometric Functions

To find the logarithm of a trigonometric function, it is not necessary to find the value of the function and then obtain the logarithm of this number. The table **Logarithms of Trigonometric Functions** on pages 765 to 769 can be used to find such values as log sin 18° in one step. This table is read in the same manner as the table **Values of Trigonometric Functions.** See the note at the top of the table, "Subtract 10 from each logarithm." Therefore, log sin 18° = 9.4900 − 10, log tan 18° = 9.5118 − 10, and log cot 18° = 10.4882 − 10 or 0.4882.

KEEP IN MIND

When using the table of logarithms of trigonometric functions, 10 must be subtracted from each logarithm in the table.

LOG SINE AND LOG COSINE VALUES IN THE TABLE

If $0° < x < 90°$, then both sin x and cos x must be positive and less than 1. Hence, log sin x and log cos x must have negative characteristics such as 9 − 10, 8 − 10, 7 − 10, etc.

LOG TANGENT AND LOG COTANGENT VALUES IN THE TABLE

If $0° < x < 90°$, then both tan x and cotangent x must be positive. For angles less than 45°, tan x is less than 1, whereas cot x is greater than 1. Hence, if

$0° < x < 45°$, log tan x has negative characteristics, whereas log cot x has positive characteristics. If $45° < x < 90°$, the reverse is true. Therefore, in this interval, the characteristics of log tan x are positive; those of log cot x are negative.

Interpolation is needed to find the logarithm of a trigonometric function that is not in the table **Logarithms of Trigonometric Functions.** Note in the model problems that the same procedure is used to find the logarithm of a trigonometric function as is used to find the value of the trigonometric function.

〰〰〰〰〰〰〰 *MODEL PROBLEMS* 〰〰〰〰〰〰〰

1. Find log tan 34° 28′.

Solution:

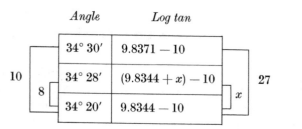

Proportion of Differences

$$\frac{8}{10} = \frac{x}{27}$$

$$10x = 216$$

$$x = 21.6 \approx 22$$

1. Since $x = 22$, correct to the nearest integer,
   log tan 34° 28′ = (9.8344 + .0022) − 10 = 9.8366 − 10.
2. Check to be sure that the answer found for the log tan 34° 28′ is larger than log tan 34° 20′ and smaller than log tan 34° 30′. This must be true since an angle and its log tangent change in the same sense, that is, increase or decrease together.

Answer: log tan 34° 28′ = 9.8366 − 10

2. Find log cos 51° 58′.

Solution:

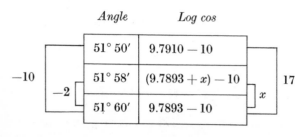

Proportion of Differences

$$\frac{-2}{-10} = \frac{x}{17}$$

$$\frac{2}{10} = \frac{x}{17}$$

$$10x = 34$$

$$x = 3.4 \approx 3$$

1. Since $x = 3$, correct to the nearest integer,
   log cos 51° 58' = $(9.7893 + .0003) - 10 = 9.7896 - 10$.
2. Check to be sure that the answer found for the log cos 51° 58' is larger than log cos 51° 60' and smaller than log cos 51° 50'. This must be true since an angle in the first quadrant and its log cosine change in the opposite sense; that is, as one increases, the other decreases.

Answer: log cos 51° 58' $= 9.7896 - 10$

Exercises

In 1–30, find:

1. log sin 26°	**2.** log cos 57°	**3.** log tan 68°
4. log sin 64° 20'	**5.** log cot 19° 40'	**6.** log sin 156° 50'
7. log sin 34° 16'	**8.** log sin 37° 24'	**9.** log sin 41° 24'
10. log sin 61° 23'	**11.** log sin 63° 48'	**12.** log sin 75° 8'
13. log tan 31° 12'	**14.** log tan 27° 13'	**15.** log tan 24° 36'
16. log tan 57° 33'	**17.** log tan 72° 17'	**18.** log tan 81° 4'
19. log cos 22° 34'	**20.** log cos 29° 46'	**21.** log cos 38° 22'
22. log cos 52° 38'	**23.** log cos 73° 22'	**24.** log cos 73° 54'
25. log cot 15° 12'	**26.** log cot 48° 19'	**27.** log cot 64° 7'
28. log sin 138° 46'	**29.** log sin 141° 24'	**30.** log sin 159° 38'

31. Log cot 25° 13' is equal to (1) 0.3270   (2) 0.3290   (3) 9.3270 − 10   (4) 9.3290 − 10

16. Finding an Angle When the Logarithm of One of Its Trigonometric Functions Is Given

If the logarithm of a trigonometric function of an angle is given, the angle can be found in the table on pages 765 to 769 if the number of minutes is a multiple of 10. If the logarithm is not in the table, interpolation must be used with the same procedure that was followed when the value of a trigonometric function was given and the angle was to be found (see page 272).

MODEL PROBLEM

If log cos $A = 9.7185 - 10$, find, correct to the nearest minute, the value of A if A is a positive acute angle.

Solution:

	Angle	Log cosine
	58° 20′	9.7201 − 10
	58° 30′ + x′	9.7185 − 10
	58° 30′	9.7181 − 10

−10 ⎰ x ⎱   ⎰ 4 ⎱ 20

Proportion of Differences

$$\frac{x}{-10} = \frac{4}{20}$$

$$20x = -40$$

$$x = -2$$

1. Since $x = -2$, $A = 58°$ 30′ $-2′$, or $58°$ 28′. Since an angle in the first quadrant and its cosine change in the opposite sense, then the angle and the logarithm of its cosine also change in the opposite sense. Hence, the angle must decrease as the log cosine increases.
2. Check to be sure that the angle and its log cosine change in the opposite sense.

Answer: 58° 28′

~~~~~~

Exercises

In 1–8, find the degree measure of positive acute angle A.

1. $\log \sin A = 9.4130 - 10$ **2.** $\log \sin A = 9.9656 - 10$

3. $\log \tan A = 9.3085 - 10$ **4.** $\log \tan A = 10.1282 - 10$

5. $\log \cos A = 9.8925 - 10$ **6.** $\log \cos A = 9.5199 - 10$

7. $\log \cot A = 10.6086 - 10$ **8.** $\log \cot A = 9.8070 - 10$

In 9–30, find, correct to the nearest minute, the degree measure of positive acute angle x

9. $\log \sin x = 9.3692 - 10$ **10.** $\log \sin x = 9.8355 - 10$

11. $\log \sin x = 9.8072 - 10$ **12.** $\log \sin x = 9.7265 - 10$

13. $\log \sin x = 9.8737 - 10$ **14.** $\log \sin x = 9.9586 - 10$

15. $\log \tan x = 9.6324 - 10$ **16.** $\log \tan x = 9.4631 - 10$

17. $\log \tan x = 9.8737 - 10$ **18.** $\log \tan x = 9.9016 - 10$

19. $\log \tan x = 10.3355 - 10$ **20.** $\log \tan x = 10.7560 - 10$

21. $\log \tan x = 0.2264$ **22.** $\log \tan x = .3457$

23. $\log \cos x = 9.8719 - 10$ **24.** $\log \cos x = 9.9020 - 10$

25. $\log \cos x = 9.5655 - 10$ **26.** $\log \cos x = 9.9605 - 10$

27. $\log \cot x = 9.4799 - 10$ **28.** $\log \cot x = 9.8080 - 10$

29. $4 \log \tan x = 1.0086$ **30.** $2 \log \sin x = 9.9145 - 10$

31. $\log \sin \theta = 0.8557$ (1) when $\theta = 31°$ 10′ (2) when $\theta = 58°$ 50′ (3) when $\theta = 44°$ 10′ (4) for no real value of θ

17. Laws of Logarithms: Using Logarithms To Find Products

Since logarithms are exponents, each of the following laws of logarithms follows from a corresponding law of exponents. In these laws, A and B are positive real numbers.

Name of Logarithmic Law	Statement of Law
logarithm of a product law	$\log (A \times B) = \log A + \log B$
logarithm of a quotient law	$\log \dfrac{A}{B} = \log A - \log B$
logarithm of a power law	$\log A^b = b \log A$
logarithm of a root law	$\log \sqrt[b]{A} = \log A^{\frac{1}{b}} = \dfrac{\log A}{b}$ or $\dfrac{1}{b} \log A$

Beginning with this unit, a separate unit will be devoted to each of the four logarithmic laws. In this unit, we consider the logarithm of a product law.

LOGARITHM OF A PRODUCT LAW

$$\log (A \times B) = \log A + \log B$$

EXTENSION OF THE LOGARITHM OF A PRODUCT LAW

$$\log (A \times B \times C \times D \ldots) = \log A + \log B + \log C + \log D + \ldots$$

Rule. The logarithm of a product is equal to the sum of the logarithms of its factors.

Thus, $\log \frac{1}{2}ab \sin C = \log .5 + \log a + \log b + \log \sin C$. Also, $\log \sin 2x = \log (2 \sin x \cos x) = \log 2 + \log \sin x + \log \cos x$.

Proving the Logarithm of a Product Law

See the proof on page 747.

616   **Algebra Two and Trigonometry**

〰〰〰〰〰〰〰 *MODEL PROBLEMS* 〰〰〰〰〰〰〰

1. Using logarithms, find the value of 32.5×14.

How To Proceed	*Solution*
1. Let the product equal N.	$N = 32.5 \times 14$
2. Apply the logarithm of a product law.	$\log N = \log 32.5 + \log 14$
3. Find the needed logarithms and do the operations indicated in step 2.	$\log 32.5 = 1.5119$ $+ \log 14 = 1.1461$ $\log N = \overline{2.6580}$
4. Find the antilogarithm of N.	$N = 455$ *Ans.*

2. $N = a \sin B$. Find N, to the nearest tenth, if $a = 58.8$ and $B = 23° 50'$.

Solution:

$$N = a \sin B$$
$$\text{Hence, } N = 58.8 \times \sin 23° 50'$$
$$\log N = \log 58.8 + \log \sin 23° 50'$$
$$\log 58.8 = \ \ 1.7694$$
$$+ \log \sin 23° 50' = \ \ 9.6065 - 10$$
$$\log N = \overline{11.3759} - 10 = 1.3759$$

$$N = 23.8, \text{ to nearest tenth}$$

Answer: 23.8

〰〰〰〰〰〰〰〰〰〰〰〰〰〰〰〰〰〰〰〰〰〰〰〰〰〰〰〰〰

Exercises

In 1–18, find the value of the product by using logarithms.

1. 15.6×5.84

2. 59×3.14

3. 550×1.41

4. 75.25×3.65

5. $65 \times .4245$

6. $.875 \times .9063$

7. $8.16 \times 1.72 \times 3.14$

8. $2.7 \times 5.6 \times .4384$

9. $162 \times 53.6 \times .2391$

10. $52 \times \cos 78°$

11. $9.4 \tan 68°$

12. $15 \times 74 \times \sin 80°$

13. $37.4 \cot 18° 20'$

14. $3.25 \cos 58° 10'$

15. $178 \sin 47° 50'$

16. $395.6 \tan 17° 28'$

17. $1.375 \cos 41° 47'$

18. $.875 \sin 54° 16'$

19. $C = 2\pi r$. Find C when $\pi = 3.14$, $r = 46.8$.

20. $A = ab \sin C$. Find A when $a = 6.25$, $b = 4.75$, $C = 38° 40'$.

21. $A = \frac{1}{2}ab \sin C$. Find A when $a = 14.6$, $b = 73.4$, $C = 115° 20'$.

22. If $\log x = 1.4814$, find $\log 10x$.

23. If $\log y = 8.3010 - 10$, find $\log 1000y$.

24. Find the value of log $100y - \log y$.

25. If log $b = x$, then log $100b$ equals (1) $100x$ (2) $2x$ (3) $x + 2$

26. If log 4.72 equals m, then log 472 equals (1) $100m$ (2) $2m$ (3) $m + 2$

27. Write as a single term the sum of log $1000 + \log \tan 45° + \log .1$.

28. If log $x = \log a + \log b$, express x in terms of a and b.

29. If log $y = \log r + \log s + \log t$, express y in terms of r, s, and t.

30. If log $n = a$, then log np equals (1) ap (2) $a + p$ (3) $a + \log p$

In 31–34, if log $2 = 0.3010$, log $3 = 0.4771$, and log $6 = 0.7782$, find the indicated logarithm without the use of tables.

31. log 12   **32.** log 18   **33.** log 36   **34.** log 3600

18. Using Logarithms To Find Quotients

LOGARITHM OF A QUOTIENT LAW

$$\log \frac{A}{B} = \log A - \log B$$

Rule. The logarithm of the quotient of two numbers is equal to the logarithm of the dividend minus the logarithm of the divisor. If the quotient is in fraction form, the logarithm of a fraction is equal to the logarithm of the numerator minus the logarithm of the denominator.

Thus, since $\tan x = \dfrac{\sin x}{\cos x}$, then log $\tan x = \log \sin x - \log \cos x$.

Proving the Logarithm of a Quotient Law

See proof on page 747.

Caution: When subtracting a greater logarithm from a smaller one, you can avoid difficulties in computation by writing the characteristic of the smaller logarithm in an equivalent form. This is done by adding 10 and subtracting 10, or adding 20 and subtracting 20, etc., from the logarithm of the smaller number.

For example, let us subtract the logarithm, 3.4567, from the logarithm, 1.2345; that is, we wish to find $(1.2345) - (3.4567)$. The characteristic 1 may be written as $11. \text{-----} - 10$; this avoids having a minus sign in front of the remainder. Add $(10 - 10)$ to 1.2345 to get $11.2345 - 10$. Then subtract:

$$\begin{array}{r} 11.2345 - 10 \\ -3.4567 \\ \hline 7.7778 - 10 \end{array}$$

~~~~~~~~~~~ *MODEL PROBLEMS* ~~~~~~~~~~~

1. Using logarithms, find the value of $690 \div 3.75$.

How To Proceed	*Solution*
1. Let the quotient equal N.	$N = 690 \div 3.75$
2. Apply the logarithm of a quotient law.	$\log N = \log 690 - \log 3.75$
3. Find the needed logarithms and do the operations indicated in step 2.	$\log 690 = 2.8388$ $-\log 3.75 = 0.5740$ $\log N = \overline{2.2648}$
4. Find the antilogarithm of N.	$N = 184$ *Ans.*

2. Find the value of $\dfrac{38.4 \times 6.78}{536 \times .471}$, correct to the nearest hundredth.

$$\text{Solution}: N = \frac{38.4 \times 6.78}{536 \times .471}$$

$$\log N = \log \text{ numerator} - \log \text{ denominator}$$
$$\log N = (\log 38.4 + \log 6.78) - (\log 536 + \log .471)$$

$$\log 38.4 = 1.5843 \qquad\qquad \log 536 = 2.7292$$
$$+\log 6.78 = 0.8312 \qquad\qquad +\log .471 = 9.6730 - 10$$
$$\log \text{ numerator} = \overline{2.4155} \qquad \log \text{ denominator} = \overline{12.4022 - 10}, \text{ or}$$
$$-\log \text{ denominator} = 2.4022 \longleftarrow \qquad\qquad\qquad 2.4022$$
$$\log N = \overline{0.0133}$$
$$N = 1.03 \quad Ans.$$

3. $N = \dfrac{a}{\tan B}$. Find N, to the nearest tenth, if $a = 12.8$ and $B = 17° \, 20'$.

$$\text{Solution}: N = \frac{a}{\tan B}$$

$$\text{Hence, } N = \frac{12.8}{\tan 17° \, 20'}$$

$$\log N = \log 12.8 - \log \tan 17° \, 20'$$
$$\log 12.8 = 1.1072 \qquad \text{Since a negative mantissa results if we}$$
$$\text{or } \log 12.8 = 11.1072 - 10 \qquad \text{subtract } 9.4943 - 10 \text{ from } 1.1072, \text{ we}$$
$$-\log \tan 17° \, 20' = 9.4943 - 10 \qquad \text{rewrite } \log 12.8 \text{ as } 11.1072 - 10.$$
$$\log N = \overline{1.6129}$$
$$N = 41.01 \quad Ans.$$

4. The expression $2 - \log a$ is equivalent to (1) $\log \dfrac{100}{a}$ (2) $\dfrac{2}{\log a}$ (3) $\log \dfrac{2}{a}$ (4) $\sqrt{\log a}$

Solution:

Since $2 = \log 100$, then the expression $2 - \log a$ is equivalent to the expression $\log 100 - \log a$.

If the logarithm of a quotient law is applied, then $\log 100 - \log a = \log \dfrac{100}{a}$.

Answer: The correct choice is (1).

Exercises

In 1–24, find the value, using logarithms.

1. $594 \div 237$

2. $9.63 \div 4.56$

3. $8.29 \div .974$

4. $.459 \div .84$

5. $756.8 \div 49.7$

6. $9.608 \div .746$

7. $\dfrac{.537}{.0469}$

8. $\dfrac{3.05}{.00008}$

9. $\dfrac{.06814}{.000053}$

10. $\dfrac{8.34 \times 74.8}{53.9}$

11. $\dfrac{46.35}{.82 \times 980}$

12. $\dfrac{.85 \times 1300}{160 \times .056}$

13. $\dfrac{\tan 40°}{85.3}$

14. $\dfrac{\sin 54°}{.441}$

15. $\dfrac{19.5}{\cos 41° 20'}$

16. $\dfrac{\sin 18°}{\sin 47°}$

17. $\dfrac{\sin 56° 40'}{524}$

18. $\dfrac{28.12}{\sin 27° 18'}$

19. $\dfrac{25 \sin 37°}{\sin 62°}$

20. $\dfrac{92.4 \sin 28° 50'}{\sin 49° 20'}$

21. $\dfrac{3260 \sin 48° 10'}{\sin 41° 25'}$

22. $\dfrac{75 \tan 56°}{92}$

23. $\dfrac{32.6 \tan 48° 30'}{78.6}$

24. $\dfrac{295.2 \tan 61° 54'}{425.8}$

25. $\log \left(\dfrac{\tan x}{2} \right)$ equals (1) $\log \tan x - 2$ (2) $\dfrac{\log \tan x}{2}$ (3) $\log \tan x - \log 2$

26. If $\log n = \log a - \log b$, express n in terms of a and b.

27. If $\log n = \log r + \log s - \log t$, express n in terms of r, s, and t.

In 28–31, if $\log \sin x = a$ and $\log \cos x = b$, express the logarithm of the function in terms of a or b, or a and b.

28. $\log \tan x$

29. $\log \cot x$

30. $\log \sec x$

31. $\log \csc x$

In 32–35, if log 2 = 0.3010, log 5 = 0.6990, and log 11 = 1.0414, find the indicated logarithm without the use of tables.

32. log 2.5   **33.** log 5.5   **34.** log 2.2   **35.** $\log \dfrac{50}{11}$

19. Using Logarithms To Find Powers

LOGARITHM OF A POWER LAW

$$\log A^b = b \log A$$

Rule. The logarithm of a power of any number is equal to the logarithm of the number multiplied by the exponent of the power.

Thus, if $A = 1.05^{20}$, then $\log A = 20 \log 1.05$.

Proving the Logarithm of a Power Law

See proof on page 748.

~~~~~~~~~~ *MODEL PROBLEMS* ~~~~~~~~~~

In 1 and 2, using logarithms, find the value of the power, correct to the nearest hundredth.

1. 1.02^{20} **2.** $\sin^2 58°$

How To Proceed	*Solution*	*Solution*
1. Let the power equal N.	$N = 1.02^{20}$	$N = \sin^2 58°$
2. Apply the logarithm of a power law.	$\log N = 20 \log 1.02$	$\log N = 2 \sin 58°$
3. Find the needed logarithm and do the operation indicated in step 2.	$\log 1.02 = 0.0086$ $\underline{\times 20}$ $\log N = \overline{0.1720}$	$\log \sin 58° = 9.9284 - 10$ $\underline{\times 2}$ $\log N = \overline{19.8568 - 20}$ $ = 9.8568 - 10$
4. Find the antilogarithm of N.	$N = 1.49 \quad Ans.$	$N = .72 \quad Ans.$

3. If $\log x = n$, then $\log \dfrac{x^3}{10}$ is (1) $3n - 1$ (2) $\dfrac{3n}{10}$ (3) $\dfrac{n^3}{10}$ (4) $3 \log n - 1$

Solution:

First express $\log \dfrac{x^3}{10}$ in terms of $\log x$.

$$\log \frac{x^3}{10} = \log x^3 - \log 10 \qquad \text{(logarithm of a quotient law)}$$
$$= 3 \log x - \log 10 \qquad \text{(logarithm of a power law)}$$

Substitute n for $\log x$ and 1 for $\log 10$.

$$\log \frac{x^3}{10} = 3n - 1$$

Answer: The correct choice is (1).

~~~~~~

Exercises

In 1–14, find the value using logarithms.

1. $(21)^2$ **2.** $(1.04)^{20}$ **3.** $(1.025)^{10}$ **4.** $(.896)^2$ **5.** $(.075)^3$

6. $3.14 \times (9.25)^2$ **7.** $16 \times (2.5)^2$ **8.** $4 \times 3.14 \times (6.5)^2$

9. $5000(1.02)^{10}$ **10.** $4000(1.06)^{15}$ **11.** $3500(1.015)^{20}$

12. $\cos^2 59°$ **13.** $\tan^2 24° \, 50'$ **14.** $\sin^2 37° \, 25'$

15. If $\log x = 0.5692$, find $\log x^2$ and $\log x^3$.

16. If $\log x^3 = 3.3624$, find $\log x$, $\log x^2$ and $\log x^4$.

17. If $\log x = 9.3010 - 10$, find $\log x^2$ and $\log 100x^3$.

18. If $\log x^2 = 0.8762$, then $\log 10x$ is (1) 4.3810   (2) 1.4381   (3) 1.7524

19. Express $\log \dfrac{a^2}{b}$ in terms of $\log a$ and $\log b$.

20. If $50 = 10^{1.6990}$, find $\log (50)^2$.

21. If $x = 10^{1.6990}$, find $\log x^2$.

In 22–24, if $\log a = 2.3000$ and $\log b = 1.7000$, find the value of the indicated logarithm without the use of tables.

22. $\log \dfrac{a}{b}$ **23.** $\log \dfrac{10a}{b^2}$ **24.** $\log \dfrac{a^3}{1000b}$

In 25–27, if $\log a = r$ and $\log b = s$, express the indicated logarithm in terms of r and s.

25. $\log \dfrac{a^3}{b^2}$ **26.** $\log \dfrac{a^2}{b^3}$ **27.** $\log \dfrac{10a}{b^2}$

28. If log $a = p$, express log $10a^2$ in terms of p.
29. If log $n = 4$ log $r -$ log s, express n in terms of r and s.
30. If log $n = $ log $4 + $ log $\pi + 2$ log r, express n in terms of π and r.
31. If log $s = $ log $g + 2$ log $t -$ log 2, express s in terms of g and t.
32. If log $n - 3$ log $x = $ log y, express n in terms of x and y.
33. The expression log $r + $ log r^2 is equal to (1) $\log(r + r^2)$ (2) 3 log r (3) r^3

In 34–36, find the value of the expression, using logarithms.
34. $125 \cos^3 42°$ **35.** $658 \tan^3 15°$ **36.** $97.3^2 \sin^3 20° 40'$

In 37–39, if log $y = a$, express the indicated logarithm in terms of a.

37. $\log \dfrac{y^2}{10}$ **38.** $\log \dfrac{100}{y^2}$ **39.** log $1000y^3$

40. If $T = 10x^2$, then log T equals (1) $1 + 2$ log x (2) $1 + 2x$ (3) $10 + 2$ log x
(4) 20 log x

20. Using Logarithms To Find Roots

LOGARITHM OF A ROOT LAW

$$\log \sqrt[b]{A} = \log A^{\frac{1}{b}} = \frac{1}{b} \log A = \frac{\log A}{b}$$

Rule. The logarithm of the root of a number is equal to the logarithm of the number divided by the index of the root.

Thus, if $A = \sqrt[3]{100}$, then $\log A = \dfrac{\log 100}{3} = \dfrac{2}{3}$.

Caution. When dividing a logarithm by a number, avoid obtaining a fractional characteristic in the quotient by writing the characteristic of the dividend in an equivalent form, as shown in the following illustration:

To divide a logarithm such as $9.3637 - 10$ by 3, write the characteristic $9 - 10$ as $29 - 30$:

$$\frac{9.3637 - 10}{3} = \frac{29.3637 - 30}{3} = 9.7879 - 10$$

Proving the Logarithm of a Root Law

See proof on page 748.

~~~~~~~~~ *MODEL PROBLEMS* ~~~~~~~~~

In 1 and 2, using logarithms, find the value of the root, correct to the nearest hundredth.

1. $\sqrt[3]{.358}$ **2.** $\sqrt{\sin 43°}$

How To Proceed	*Solution*	*Solution*
1. Let the root equal N.	$N = \sqrt[3]{.358}$	$N = \sqrt{\sin 43°}$
2. Apply the logarithm of a root law.	$\log N = \frac{1}{3} \log .358$	$\log N = \frac{1}{2} \log \sin 43°$
3. Find the needed logarithm and do the operation indicated in step 2.	$\log N = \frac{1}{3}(9.5539 - 10)$ In order to divide by 3 and obtain a characteristic which ends in -10, express the above characteristic 9. --- -10 as 29. --- -30. $\log N = \frac{1}{3}(29.5539 - 30)$ $\log N = 9.8513 - 10$	$\log N = \frac{1}{2}(9.8338 - 10)$ In order to divide by 2 and obtain a characteristic which ends in -10, express the above characteristic 9. --- -10 as 19. --- -20. $\log N = \frac{1}{2}(19.8338 - 10)$ $\log N = 9.9169 - 10$
4. Find the antilogarithm of N.	$N = .71$ *Ans.*	$N = .83$ *Ans.*

3. Express $\log \dfrac{a^2}{\sqrt[3]{b}}$ in terms of $\log a$ and $\log b$.

Solution:

$$\log \frac{a^2}{\sqrt[3]{b}} = \log \frac{a^2}{b^{\frac{1}{3}}} = \log a^2 - \log b^{\frac{1}{3}} \qquad \text{(logarithm of a quotient law)}$$

$$= 2 \log a - \frac{1}{3} \log b \qquad \text{(logarithm of a power law; logarithm of a root law)}$$

Answer: $2 \log a - \dfrac{1}{3} \log b$

~~~~~~

Exercises

In 1–12, find the value, using logarithms.

1. $\sqrt{625}$ **2.** $\sqrt[3]{59.3}$ **3.** $\sqrt{.144}$ **4.** $\sqrt[3]{.476}$

5. $\dfrac{\sqrt[3]{536}}{3.2}$ **6.** $\dfrac{\sqrt{1764}}{14.8}$ **7.** $\dfrac{137}{\sqrt[3]{.8964}}$ **8.** $\sqrt{\dfrac{9800}{76.3}}$

9. $\sqrt{\sin 37°}$ **10.** $\sqrt{\cos 58° 40'}$ **11.** $\sqrt[3]{\tan 38° 20'}$ **12.** $\sqrt[3]{\sin 51° 22'}$

13. If $\log x = 2.7186$, find (a) $\log \sqrt{x}$, (b) $\log \sqrt[3]{x}$.

14. If $\log x = 9.3012 - 10$, find (a) $\log \sqrt{x}$, (b) $\log \sqrt[3]{x}$.

15. If $\log \sqrt{x} = 0.1526$, find (a) $\log x$, (b) $\log x^2$.

16. If $50 = 10^{1.6990}$, find $\log \sqrt{50}$.

17. If $x = 10^{1.6990}$, find $\log \sqrt{x}$.

18. Find $\log \sqrt{10^{1.6990}}$.

19. If $\log x = a$ and $\log y = b$, express $\log \sqrt{xy}$ in terms of a and b.

20. Express the logarithm of $\dfrac{\sqrt[3]{a}}{b}$ in terms of $\log a$ and $\log b$.

21. Express $\log \dfrac{a}{\sqrt{b}}$ in terms of $\log a$ and $\log b$.

22. If $\log n = \dfrac{\log a + \log b - \log c}{3}$, express n in terms of a, b, and c.

In 23–25, if $\log n = a$, express the indicated logarithm in terms of a.

23. $\log \sqrt[3]{\dfrac{1000}{n}}$ **24.** $\log \sqrt[3]{1000n}$ **25.** $\log \sqrt[3]{100n^2}$

26. Given $\log 3 = x$ and $\log 5 = y$, (a) express $\log 45$ in terms of x and y and (b) express $\log \sqrt{\tfrac{3}{5}}$ in terms of x and y.

21. Applying Logarithmic Laws to More Difficult Problems

〰〰〰〰〰〰〰 *MODEL PROBLEMS* 〰〰〰〰〰〰〰

1. The velocity u of a bullet in flight is given by the formula $u = kd\sqrt{\dfrac{g}{R}}$.

Using logarithms, find the value of u, correct to three significant digits, if $k = 834$, $d = 19.8$, $g = 980$, and $R = 295$.

Solution:

$$u = kd\sqrt{\dfrac{g}{R}}$$

Substitute the given values.

$$u = 834 \times 19.8 \sqrt{\frac{980}{295}}$$

$$\log u = \log 834 + \log 19.8 + \tfrac{1}{2}(\log 980 - \log 295)$$

$$
\begin{array}{ll}
\log 834 = 2.9212 & \log 980 = 2.9912 \\
+\log 19.8 = 1.2967 & -\log 295 = 2.4698 \\
\hline
4.2179 & 2\overline{\smash{)}0.5214} \\
+\,0.2607 \;\longleftarrow & 0.2607 \\
\hline
\log u = 4.4786 & \\
u = 30{,}100 \quad Ans. &
\end{array}
$$

2. Using logarithms, find to the nearest degree the value of the acute angle x for which

$$\cos x = \frac{\sqrt[3]{0.064 \sin 22^\circ}}{0.932}$$

Solution:

Write the logarithmic equation for the given equation.

$$\log \cos x = \tfrac{1}{3}(\log .064 + \log \sin 22^\circ) - \log .932$$

$$
\begin{array}{l}
\log .064 = 8.8062 - 10 \\
+\log \sin 22^\circ = 9.5736 - 10 \\
\hline
18.3798 - 20 = 28.3798 - 30
\end{array}
$$

$$\log \text{numerator} = \tfrac{1}{3}(28.3798 - 30) = 9.4599 - 10$$

$$
\begin{array}{l}
\log \text{numerator} = 9.4599 - 10 = 19.4599 - 20 \\
-\log .932 = 9.9694 - 10 = 9.9694 - 10 \\
\hline
\log \cos x = 9.4905 - 10
\end{array}
$$

Hence, $x = 72^\circ$, to the nearest degree.

Answer: 72°

Exercises

In 1–13, write the logarithmic equation for the given equation.

1. $C = \pi D$ **2.** $S = 2\pi r h$ **3.** $S = 4\pi r^2$ **4.** $V = \tfrac{1}{3}BH$

5. $V = \frac{4}{3}\pi R^3$ **6.** $A = \frac{S^2}{4}\sqrt{3}$ **7.** $t = 2\pi\sqrt{\frac{l}{g}}$ **8.** $R = \sqrt{\frac{3V}{\pi H}}$

9. $a = \dfrac{b \sin A}{\sin B}$ **10.** $K = \frac{1}{2}bc \sin A$

11. $\tan \frac{1}{2}(A - B) = \dfrac{(a - b)\tan \frac{1}{2}(A + B)}{(a + b)}$

12. $\tan \frac{1}{2}A = \sqrt{\dfrac{(s - b)(s - c)}{s(s - a)}}$ **13.** $K = \sqrt{s(s - a)(s - b)(s - c)}$

14. Match the expressions in Column I with those in Column II.

Column I	*Column II*
1. $\log xy$	a. $\log x + 2 \log y$
2. $\log \dfrac{x}{y}$	b. $\dfrac{\log x + \log y}{2}$
3. $\log xy^2$	c. $\frac{1}{2}\log x - \log y$
4. $\log x^2 y$	d. $\log x + \log y$
5. $\log (xy)^2$	e. $\log y + \frac{1}{2}\log x$
6. $\log \sqrt{xy}$	f. $2(\log x + \log y)$
7. $\log \sqrt{\dfrac{x}{y}}$	g. $\dfrac{\log x + 2 \log y}{2}$
8. $\log \sqrt{\dfrac{y}{x}}$	h. $\log x - \log y$
	i. $\dfrac{\log y - \log x}{2}$
9. $\log \dfrac{x}{\sqrt{y}}$	j. $\dfrac{\log x - \log y}{2}$
10. $\log \dfrac{\sqrt{x}}{y}$	k. $\dfrac{\log x - 2 \log y}{2}$
11. $\log x\sqrt{y}$	l. $2 \log x + \log y$
12. $\log y\sqrt{x}$	m. $\log x + \frac{1}{2}\log y$
13. $\log \sqrt{xy^2}$	n. $\log x - \frac{1}{2}\log y$
14. $\log \sqrt{\dfrac{x}{y^2}}$	

In 15–29, find the value, using logarithms.

15. $\dfrac{7.34 \times (87)^2}{155}$ **16.** $\dfrac{83\sqrt{521}}{437}$ **17.** $\dfrac{5.94 \times 86.68}{\sqrt[3]{824}}$

18. $\sqrt[4]{\dfrac{82 \times 61.7}{.016}}$

19. $\sqrt[3]{\dfrac{7.98}{0.586 \times 84}}$

20. $\sqrt{\dfrac{17.4 \times 96.3}{27.8 \times 156}}$

21. $\dfrac{65 \sin 58°}{\sin 64°}$

22. $\dfrac{28.6 \sin 45° \, 50'}{\sin 64° \, 30'}$

23. $\dfrac{19.75 \sin 54° \, 13'}{\sin 48° \, 26'}$

24. $\dfrac{35 \tan 55°}{75}$

25. $\dfrac{18.4 \tan 48° \, 30'}{42.6}$

26. $\dfrac{175.3 \tan 61° \, 25'}{256.4}$

27. $\dfrac{79.6 \cos 74°}{\sqrt[4]{485}}$

28. $\dfrac{9.614 \times \tan 42°}{\sqrt[3]{.0618}}$

29. $\sqrt{\dfrac{37.8 \times (\sin 48°)^2}{1.25}}$

30. Using logarithms, find, to the nearest tenth, the value of L from the formula $L = \dfrac{t^2 g}{4\pi^2}$ when $t = 3.50$, $g = 32.2$, and $\pi = 3.14$.

31. If $V = \frac{1}{3}\pi r^2 h$, find V when $\pi = 3.14$, $r = 11.5$, and $h = 9.3$.

32. The volume, V, of a circular cylinder whose altitude is h and whose radius is r is given by the formula $V = \pi r^2 h$. Using logarithms, find, to the nearest tenth, the value of r if $V = 906$ and $h = 14.6$. (Use $\pi = 3.14$.)

33. Using logarithms, find, to the nearest integer, the value of $\dfrac{3.84^3 \times (1.82)^2}{\sqrt[3]{0.0870}}$.

34. Using logarithms, find, to the nearest hundredth, the value of $\dfrac{762 \times \sqrt[3]{0.364}}{94.4}$.

35. Given the formula $t = \pi\sqrt{\dfrac{L}{g}}$. Using logarithms, find, to the nearest hundredth, the value of t when $L = 1.38$, $g = 32.2$, and $\pi = 3.14$.

In 36 and 37, using logarithms, find, to the nearest integer, the value of:

36. $\dfrac{2.35 \times \tan 75°}{\sqrt[3]{.0376}}$

37. $\dfrac{47.9 \times \tan 34°}{\sqrt[3]{.0475}}$

In 38–40, find c, using logarithms, if $c = \sqrt{a^2 + b^2}$ and:

38. $a = 23.8$ and $b = 16.2$
39. $a = 350$ and $b = 485$
40. $a = 2340$ and $b = 5764$

41. Given the formula $s = \sqrt{\dfrac{3V}{e \sin x}}$. By means of logarithms, find, to the nearest tenth, the value of s when $V = 350$, $e = 8.30$, and $x = 70°$.

42. Given the formula $d = \sqrt{\dfrac{6V}{e \cos x}}$. Using logarithms, find, to the nearest tenth, the value of d when $V = 248$, $e = 6.50$, and $x = 72°$.

43. Given the formula $S = \sqrt{\dfrac{0.8V}{h \tan 54°}}$. Using logarithms, find S, to the nearest hundredth, if $V = 327$ and $h = 28.7$.

44. Using logarithms, find, to the nearest hundredth, the value of $\sqrt{\dfrac{94.7 \tan^2 59°}{3.14}}$.

45. Using logarithms, find, to the nearest hundredth, the value of $\sqrt[3]{\dfrac{87.2 \sin 43°}{1970}}$.

22. Using Logarithms To Solve Exponential Equations

Earlier in this chapter, exponential equations were solved by expressing both sides of the equation as powers of the same base. Exponential equations which cannot be solved by this method may be solved using logarithms. The following model problems show how the exponential equations are transformed into logarithmic equations by equating the logarithms of both sides of the given equation. The resulting equation is then solved for the unknown.

~~~~~~~~~ *MODEL PROBLEMS* ~~~~~~~~~

1. Solve for x, correct to the nearest tenth.
$$6^x = 19$$

2. Solve for x, correct to the nearest integer.
$$1.01^{2x} = 2$$

How To Proceed	*Solution*	*Solution*
1. Equate the logarithms of both sides of the given equation.	$6^x = 19$ $\log(6^x) = \log 19$	$1.01^{2x} = 2$ $\log(1.01^{2x}) = \log 2$
2. Solve the resulting equation for the unknown.	$x \log 6 = \log 19$ $0.7782x = 1.2788$ $x = \dfrac{1.2788}{.7782}$ $x = 1.6$ *Ans.*	$2x \log 1.01 = \log 2$ $2x(0.0043) = 0.3010$ $.0086x = .3010$ $x = \dfrac{.3010}{.0086}$ $x = 35$ *Ans.*

Exercises

In 1–16, solve the equation, giving the answer correct to the nearest tenth.

1. $2^x = 42$ **2.** $3^y = 15$ **3.** $5^y = 29$

4. $12^x - 87 = 500$ **5.** $22^m = 629$ **6.** $5^y = 37.6$

7. $15^x = 96.3$ **8.** $1.5^x + .4 = 4$ **9.** $1.04^x = 2$

10. $1.02^x = 3$ **11.** $5^{2x} = 72.5$ **12.** $1.2^{3x} - 25 = 27.25$

13. $1.01^{4x} = 2$ **14.** $3^{x+1} = 85.6$ **15.** $5^{3x-1} = 57.9$

16. $4^{3x} = 5^{x+1}$

In 17–19, the formula $A = e^{rt}$, has values of $A = 1.5$ and $e = 2.718$. Find t, to the nearest hundredth, when r has the given value.

17. $r = .01$ **18.** $r = .025$ **19.** $r = .0225$

23. Using Logarithms To Solve Problems Involving Compound Interest

If a sum of P dollars is placed at compound interest for a period of n years, interest being compounded annually at the rate of $r\%$, the sum of money to which it will amount at the end of this period of time, the *compound amount*, or *amount*, is given by the formula: $A = P(1 + r)^n$.

If interest is compounded semiannually (twice a year), $A = P\left(1 + \dfrac{r}{2}\right)^{2n}$; if quarterly (four times a year), $A = P\left(1 + \dfrac{r}{4}\right)^{4n}$; if t times a year, $A = P\left(1 + \dfrac{r}{t}\right)^{nt}$.

The interest which the principal has accumulated during the given period of years can be found by finding the difference between the compound amount and the original principal.

In problems, the expression "invested at $r\%$" means "invested at an *annual rate of $r\%$*."

~~~~~~~~~~ *MODEL PROBLEMS* ~~~~~~~~~~

1. How much money, to the nearest ten dollars, must be invested at 6% interest, compounded semiannually, to yield $1250 at the end of 10 years?

Solution:

$$A = P\left(1 + \frac{r}{2}\right)^{2n}$$

$A = 1250, r = .06, n = 10$

$$1250 = P \left(1 + \frac{.06}{2}\right)^{2 \times 10}$$

$$1250 = P(1.03)^{20}$$
$$\log 1250 = \log P + 20 \log 1.03$$
$$\log P = \log 1250 - 20 \log 1.03$$
$$\log 1250 = 3.0969$$
$$-20 \log 1.03 - 0.2560$$
$$\log P = \overline{2.8409}$$
$$P = \$690, \text{ rounded to tens}$$

Answer: $690

2. Find the number of years, correct to the nearest year, it will take $450 to amount to $590 if the principal of $450 is invested at 3%, compounded annually.

Solution:

$$A = P(1 + r)^n$$

$A = 590, P = 450, r = .03$

$$590 = 450(1.03)^n$$
$$\log 590 = \log 450 + n \log 1.03$$
$$n \log 1.03 = \log 590 - \log 450$$
$$0.0128n = 2.7709 - 2.6532$$
$$.0128n = .1177$$

$$n = \frac{.1177}{.0128} = 9, \text{ to the nearest integer}$$

Answer: 9 years

Exercises

In 1–6, find the amount and the interest, if interest is compounded annually on a principal of:

1. $250 for 5 years at 2%   **2.** $375 for 10 years at 3%
3. $600 for 20 years at 4%   **4.** $1500 for 15 years at 4%
5. $400 for 5 years at $2\frac{1}{2}$%   **6.** $750 for 10 years at $4\frac{1}{2}$%

In 7–12, find the amount and the interest, if interest is compounded semi-annually on a principal of:

7. $300 for 5 years at 4%   **8.** $550 for 10 years at 2%
9. $2500 for 6 years at 4%   **10.** $3000 for 4 years at 6%

11. $900 for 5 years at 3%

12. $1200 for 3 years at 5%

13. Find the principal that must be invested at 3%, interest compounded annually, in order that it amount to $800 in 5 years.

14. Find the principal that must be invested at 3%, interest compounded semiannually, to yield $2500 in 10 years.

In 15–19, find, to the nearest year, the time in which:

15. $750 will amount to $900 at 6% compounded annually.

16. $580 will amount to $650 at $2\frac{1}{2}$% compounded annually.

17. $300 will amount to $600 at 4% compounded annually.

18. $400 will double itself at 4% compounded annually.

19. $600 will amount to $725 at 4% compounded semiannually.

In 20–22, use $A = P(1 + r)^n$ and give your answer to the nearest year.

20. In how many years, n, will $570 amount to $965 if interest is compounded annually at 3%?

21. In how many years, n, will $350 amount to $498 if the money earns interest at the rate of 3% compounded annually?

22. Find n, to the nearest integer, when $r = .04$, $P = 1$ and $A = 3$.

23. For $375 it is possible to buy a bond that will be worth $500 in 10 years. Using the formula $A = P(1 + r)^n$, find, to the nearest tenth of a per cent, the rate of interest on this investment if interest is compounded annually.

24. Using Logarithms in Trigonometry Problems Involving Right Triangles

The solution of problems dealing with right triangles generally involves multiplication and division. Since logarithms may be used to perform these operations, their use may simplify the necessary computations, especially when the numbers involved have two or more significant digits.

~~~~~~~~~~~~~~ *MODEL PROBLEM* ~~~~~~~~~~~~~~

In an isosceles triangle, each of the equal sides is 18.7 and the measure of each of the equal angles is 41° 10′. Find, correct to the nearest tenth, the altitude drawn to the base.

Given: $AC = BC = 18.7$; $\angle A = \angle B = 41° 10′$, $\overline{CD} \perp \overline{AB}$. Find CD, or x.

632   Algebra Two and Trigonometry

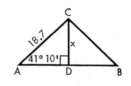

Solution: Since triangle ADC is a right triangle,

$$\sin A = \frac{DC}{AC}$$

$$\sin 41° 10' = \frac{x}{18.7}$$

$$x = 18.7 \sin 41° 10'$$
$$\log x = \log 18.7 + \log \sin 41° 10'$$
$$\log 18.7 = 1.2718$$
$$+\log \sin 41° 10' = 9.8184 - 10$$
$$\log x = \overline{11.0902 - 10} = 1.0902$$
$$x = 12.3, \text{ to nearest tenth}$$

Answer: 12.3

Exercises

1. In right triangle ABC, $\angle C = 90°$, $\angle A = 57° 30'$, and $AB = 176$ feet. Find BC, correct to the nearest foot.

2. In right triangle RST, $\angle T = 90°$, $\angle S = 38° 50'$, and $RT = 32.2$ feet. Find ST, correct to the nearest tenth of a foot.

3. In right triangle ABC, $\angle C = 90°$, $\angle B = 41° 30'$, and $AB = 60.8$ feet. Find BC, correct to the nearest hundredth of a foot.

4. At a point 275 feet from the foot of a flagpole, the angle of elevation of the top of the pole is $28° 40'$. Find, correct to the nearest foot, the height of the flagpole.

In 5–8, use isosceles triangle ABC as shown in the figure.

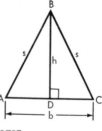

5. If $A = 35° 10'$ and $b = 486$, find h, correct to the nearest integer.

6. If $A = 38° 40'$ and $h = 173$, find b, correct to the nearest integer.

7. If $b = 483.8$ and $h = 154.5$, find A, correct to the nearest minute.

8. If $b = 37$ and $h = 12$, find s, correct to the nearest integer.

CHAPTER XIX

SOLUTIONS OF OBLIQUE TRIANGLES

The parts of triangles that are used to establish the congruence of triangles fix the size and shape of a triangle; that is, they *determine* the triangle. Hence, a triangle is determined by each of the following sets of data:

1. three sides (s.s.s.)
2. two sides and the angle included by these sides (s.a.s.)
3. two angles and the side included by these angles (a.s.a.)
4. two angles and a side not included by these angles (a.a.s.)
5. hypotenuse and either leg of a right triangle (hyp. leg)

To *solve an oblique triangle* means to use the measures of the given sides and angles that determine the triangle in order to find the measures of the remaining unknown sides and angles. To solve oblique triangles, we will make use of the law of sines, the law of cosines, and the law of tangents. Recall that, in Chapter XVII, these laws were limited to simple applications. The purpose of this chapter is to use these same laws to solve more difficult problems. We shall find that the law of sines, the law of tangents, and another set of formulas known as the *half-angle formulas* lend themselves to logarithmic computation. For that reason, these laws and formulas are useful in the solution of problems of more than average difficulty.

1. Using the Law of Sines When One Side and Two Angles of a Triangle Are Given   (a.s.a.) or (a.a.s.)

The law of sines can be used to solve an oblique triangle when the triangle is determined by two angles and the included side (a.s.a.) or by two angles and a side opposite one of the angles (a.a.s.). In either of these situations, the third angle can be found, if needed, by subtracting the sum of the two given angles from 180°.

You will find it useful to review simple applications of the law of sines in oblique triangles by referring to Chapter XVII.

~~~~~~~~~~~~~~~ *MODEL PROBLEMS* ~~~~~~~~~~~~~~~

1. In triangle ABC, $BC = 30$ feet, $A = 30° 10'$, and $C = 103° 20'$. Find AC to the nearest foot.

Solution:

Since two angles are given, the third angle may be found by subtracting the sum of the two given angles from $180°$.

$$B = 180° - (A + C)$$
$$= 180° - (30° 10' + 103° 20')$$
$$= 180° - 133° 30' = 46° 30'$$

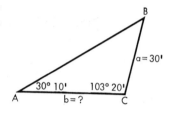

Use the law of sines to find AC, or b, as follows:

$$\frac{b}{\sin B} = \frac{a}{\sin A}$$

Multiply each side by $\sin B$.

$$b = \frac{a \sin B}{\sin A}$$

Substitute 30 for a, $46° 30'$ for B, and $30° 10'$ for A.

$$b = \frac{30 \sin 46° 30'}{\sin 30° 10'}$$

Method 1: *Natural Functions*

$$b = \frac{30(.7254)}{.5025} = 43.3 \approx 43$$

Method 2: *Logarithms*

Write the equation in logarithmic form.
Log $b = \log 30 + \log \sin 46° 30' - \log \sin 30° 10'$.

$$
\begin{aligned}
\log 30 &= 1.4771 \\
+\log \sin 46° 30' &= 9.8606 - 10 \\
\hline
\log \text{numerator} &= 11.3377 - 10 \\
-\log \sin 30° 10' &= 9.7012 - 10 \\
\hline
\log b &= 1.6365 \\
b &= 43.3 \approx 43
\end{aligned}
$$

Answer: The distance, AC, is 43 ft., to the nearest foot.

2. A lighthouse $\overline{DC}$ is sighted from two points, A and B, directly west of the lighthouse and on the same horizontal plane with its base C. At A the angle of elevation of D, the top of the lighthouse, is $13°\,30'$ and at B the angle is $31°\,45'$. If AB is 1156 feet, find the height of the lighthouse to the nearest foot.

Given: $\angle DAB = 13°\,30'$ Find: DC or x

$\angle DBC = 31°\,45'$

$AB = 1156$

Solution: First we will find BD or y in $\triangle ABD$ by means of the law of sines. Then we will find DC in rt. $\triangle DCB$.

$$\angle ADB = \angle DBC - \angle DAB$$
$$\angle ADB = 31°\,45' - 13°\,30' = 18°\,15'$$

In $\triangle ABD$, $\dfrac{BD}{\sin \angle DAB} = \dfrac{AB}{\sin \angle ADB}$

$$\frac{y}{\sin 13°\,30'} = \frac{1156}{\sin 18°\,15'}$$

$$y = \frac{1156 \sin 13°\,30'}{\sin 18°\,15'}$$

$$\log y = \log 1156 + \log \sin 13°\,30' - \log \sin 18°\,15'$$

$\log 1156 = 3.0630$

$+\log \sin 13°\,30' = 9.3682 - 10$

$\log$ of numerator $= \overline{12.4312 - 10}$

$-\log \sin 18°\,15' = 9.4958 - 10$

$\log y = \overline{2.9354}$

(We do not need to find y because the value of $\log y$ is used below.)

In rt. $\triangle DCB$, $\sin 31°\,45' = \dfrac{x}{y}$

$$x = y \sin 31°\,45'$$

$$\log x = \log y + \log \sin 31°\,45'$$

$\log y = 2.9354$

$+\log \sin 31°\,45' = 9.7212 - 10$

$\log x = \overline{12.6566 - 10}$

$\log x = 2.6566$

$x = 454$, to the nearest integer

Answer: The height of the lighthouse, to the nearest foot, is **454 ft.**

Exercises

1. In triangle ABC, $A = 66° 20'$, $B = 42° 40'$, and $c = 12$. Find a and b to the nearest integer.

2. In triangle ABC, $A = 44° 10'$, $C = 57° 30'$, and $AC = 62.5$ feet. Find BC, correct to the nearest tenth of a foot.

3. Two observers, A and B, at the ends of a level base line 1000 yards long, measure angles from the base line to a gun emplacement G. If angle $BAG = 37° 20'$ and angle $ABG = 62° 30'$, find BG, to the nearest yard.

4. In triangle ABC, $A = 69° 10'$, $b = 261$, and $C = 51° 40'$. Find c, to the nearest integer.

5. In triangle ABC, $AB = 35$, $A = 41° 30'$, and $B = 62° 30'$. Find, to the nearest integer, the altitude drawn from C.

6. In triangle ABC, $A = 42°$, $C = 115°$, and $AC = 32.6$. Find to the nearest tenth, the length of the altitude drawn from B to side $\overline{AC}$ extended.

7. From two points on level ground in line with the foot of a tree and on the same side of the tree, the angles of elevation of the top of the tree are $41°$ and $47°$. If the distance between the two points is 50 feet, find, correct to the nearest foot, the height of the tree.

8. A vertical tower stands at the top of a hill which is inclined $16°$ to the horizontal. At a point 95 feet down the hill from the base of the tower, the tower subtends an angle of $38°$. Find, correct to the nearest foot, the height of the tower.

9. Two observers 5280 feet apart on a straight horizontal road observe a balloon between them directly above the road. At the points of observation, the angles of elevation of the balloon are $60°$ and $75°$. Find, correct to the nearest foot, the height of the balloon.

10. A sign 50.7 feet high is put on top of a building. From a point on the ground the angles of elevation of the top and bottom of the sign are $42° 30'$ and $35° 20'$. Find the height of the building, correct to the nearest foot.

11. A tree is growing at the bank of a river. The angle of elevation of the top from a point directly across on the other bank is $37° 50'$. From a second point on the same bank, 125 feet from the first and in line with the first point and the tree, the angle of elevation of the top of the tree is $22° 30'$. Find, to the nearest foot, the width of the river.

12. From the top of a house 32 feet high, the angle of elevation of the top of a pole is $12° 10'$. At the ground level of the house, the angle is $40° 50'$. Find, correct to the nearest foot, the height of the pole.

13. From the top of a hill, a man observes that the angles of depression of two successive markers one mile apart in the horizontal plane below, in a straight line before him, are $14° 20'$ and $5° 30'$. Find, to the nearest foot, the height of the hill.

14. Engineers wish to build a bridge across a stream to join point C on one side with either point A or point B on the other side. The distance from A to B is 325 feet, angle ABC is $79° 30'$ and angle BAC is $72° 20'$. By how many feet does the distance from A to C exceed the distance from B to C?

15. Just as a plane flies over a level straight line segment joining two ground observation posts, 4680 feet apart, it is spotted by observers at both posts. If the angles of elevation of the plane from the two posts at this moment are $72° 20'$ and $51° 50'$ respectively, find, to the nearest ten feet, the height at which the plane is flying.

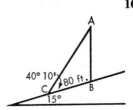

16. A vertical transmitting tower $\overline{AB}$, as shown at the left, is located on a slope that is inclined $15°$ to the horizontal. At a point C, 80 feet down the slope from the foot of the tower, the tower subtends an angle of $40° 10'$. Find to the nearest foot the height of the tower.

2. Determining the Number of Solutions Possible When Two Sides of a Triangle and an Angle Opposite One of Them Are Given: The Ambiguous Case (s.s.a.)

When two sides of a triangle and an angle opposite one of the sides are given, we cannot be sure that there is just one triangle which satisfies the given data. For this reason, this situation is referred to as the "Ambiguous Case." When such a set of data is given, it will be found useful to represent the given angle as A, the side opposite the given angle as a and the side adjacent to the given angle as b.

Using a, b, and $\angle A$ as the given parts, we can, in some cases, construct triangle ABC as follows: First construct $\angle A$. On one side of $\angle A$, lay off $\overline{AC}$ of length b. With C as a center, strike an arc whose radius is a, which will cut the other side of $\angle A$ in B. Triangle ABC is the required triangle.

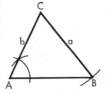

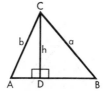

In triangle ABC, when a, b, and $\angle A$ are given, the altitude to the third side can always be found.

$$\sin A = \frac{h}{b} \quad \text{or} \quad h = b \sin A$$

Therefore, the altitude to the third side is equal to

the product of the sine of the given angle and the given adjacent side.

We will now discuss all the possible cases that occur when A is an acute, right, or obtuse angle. For each type of angle, the length of the opposite side a will be increased in proceeding from any situation to the next one. In each case, we will determine the number of possible solutions.

If the given angle A is an *acute angle*, the following situations 1 to 5 are possible:

1. If the opposite side, a, is less than h, the altitude to the third side, there is no solution. Hence, if A is acute and $a < b \sin A$, there is no solution.

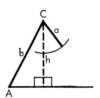

2. If the opposite side, a, is equal to h, the altitude to the third side, there is one solution, a right triangle ABC. Hence, if A is acute and $a = b \sin A$, there is one solution, a right triangle.

3. If the opposite side, a, is less than the adjacent side, b, but greater than h, the altitude to the third side, there are two solutions. Note that both triangles ABC and $AB'C$ contain acute angle A, opposite side a, and adjacent side b. Hence, if A is acute, $a < b$ and $a > b \sin A$, which may be written $b > a > b \sin A$, there are two solutions.

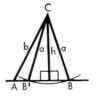

4. If the opposite side, a, is equal to the adjacent side, b, there is one solution, an isosceles triangle ABC. Hence, if A is acute and $a = b$, there is one solution, an isosceles triangle.

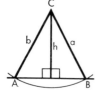

5. If the opposite side, a, is greater than the adjacent side, b, there is one solution, triangle ABC. Note that triangle $AB'C$ is not a solution because although it contains a and b, it does not contain $\angle A$. Hence, if A is acute and $a > b$, there is one solution.

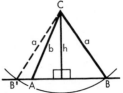

If the given angle A is a *right angle*, the following situations 6 to 8 are possible:

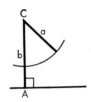

6. If the opposite side, a, is less than the adjacent side, b, there is no solution. Hence, if A is a right angle and $a < b$, there is no solution.

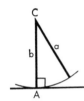

7. If the opposite side, a, is equal to the adjacent side, b, there is no solution. Hence, if A is a right angle and $a = b$, there is no solution.

8. If the opposite side, a, is greater than the adjacent side, b, there is one solution, right triangle ABC. Note that triangle $AB'C$ is not a different solution because it is congruent to triangle ABC. Hence, if A is a right angle and $a > b$, there is one solution, a right triangle.

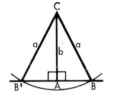

If the given angle A is an *obtuse angle*, the following situations 9 to 11 are possible:

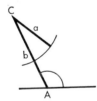

9. If the opposite side, a, is less than the adjacent side, b, there is no solution. Hence, if A is obtuse and $a < b$, there is no solution.

10. If the opposite side, a, is equal to the adjacent side, b, there is no solution. Hence, if A is obtuse and $a = b$, there is no solution.

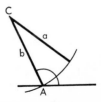

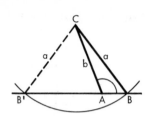

11. If the opposite side, a, is greater than the adjacent side, b, there is one solution, obtuse triangle ABC. Note that triangle $AB'C$ is not a solution because, although it contains a and b, it does not contain obtuse angle A. Hence, if A is obtuse and $a > b$, there is one solution.

Summary of the Ambiguous Case

I. When A is an obtuse angle or a right angle,
   1. if $a > b$, one solution
   2. if $a = b$, no solution
   3. if $a < b$, no solution

II. When A is an acute angle,
   4. if $a > b$, one solution
   5. if $a = b$, one solution
   6. is $a < b$ and $\begin{cases} a > h, \text{ that is, } b > a > b \sin A, \text{ two solutions} \\ a = h, \text{ that is, } a = b \sin A, \text{ one solution} \\ a < h, \text{ that is, } a < b \sin A, \text{ no solution} \end{cases}$

Remember that, in any problem, the number of solutions can be discovered by making a careful working drawing which represents the given data.

~~~~~~~~~~~~ *MODEL PROBLEMS* ~~~~~~~~~~~~

1. Find the number of different triangles that can be constructed if $A = 130°$, $a = 40$, and $b = 60$.

Solution: Since angle A is obtuse and the opposite side, a, is smaller than the adjacent side, b, there is no solution.

Answer: no solution

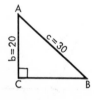

2. Using the data $c = 30$, $b = 20$, and $C = 90°$, there can be constructed (1) no triangle (2) one triangle (3) two triangles

Solution: Since C is a right angle and the opposite side, c, is greater than the adjacent side, b, there is one solution.

Answer: (2) one triangle

3. Answer *true* or *false*. Two different triangles can be formed when $A = 40°$, $a = 10$, and $c = 10$.

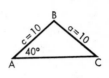

Solution: Since A is an acute angle and the opposite side, a, is equal to the adjacent side, c, there is one solution.

Answer: false

4. Using the data $a = 6$, $b = 10$, and $A = 50°$, it is possible to construct (1) only one triangle (2) two triangles (3) no triangle

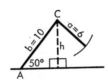

Solution: Since A is an acute and $a < b$, we must find the altitude to the third side.
$$h = b \sin A$$
$$h = 10 \sin 50° = 10(.7660) = 7.66$$
Since $a < b \sin A$ or h, there is no solution.
Answer: (3) no triangle

5. Find the number of different triangles that can be constructed when $A = 30°$, $b = 30$, and $a = 25$.

Solution: Since A is acute and $a < b$, we must find the altitude to the third side.
$$h = b \sin A = 30(.5000) = 15$$
Since $a < b$ and $a > b \sin A$ or h, there are two solutions.

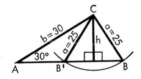

Answer: two solutions

Exercises

In 1–6, find how many different triangles can be constructed with the given parts.

1. $A = 135°$ $a = 40$ $b = 30$
2. $A = 90°$ $a = 25$ $b = 35$
3. $A = 60°$ $a = 12$ $b = 12$
4. $A = 55°$ $a = 30$ $b = 24$
5. $A = 30°$ $a = 9$ $b = 10$
6. $B = 150°$ $b = 10$ $a = 15$

7. How many different triangles may be formed in which $a = 14$, $b = 12$, and $A = 30°$?

8. How many different triangles may be formed in which $a = 6$, $b = 10$, and $A = 30°$?

9. Using the data angle $B = 60°$, $b = 10$, and $c = 9$, it is possible to construct (1) only one triangle   (2) two triangles   (3) no triangle

10. The number of different triangles that can be formed in which $A = 48°$, $a = 50$, and $b = 64$, is (1) two   (2) one   (3) none

11. Using the values $A = 40°$, $a = 10$, and $b = 8$, there can be constructed (1) no triangle   (2) only one triangle   (3) two triangles

12. Using the data $A = 35°$, $b = 3$, and $a = 4$, it is possible to construct (1) two triangles   (2) a right triangle   (3) no triangle   (4) an obtuse triangle

13. Using the data $A = 34°20'$, $a = 55.4$, and $b = 100.0$, it is possible to construct (1) no triangle   (2) a right triangle   (3) two triangles   (4) an obtuse triangle

14. Is the following statement *true* or *false*? If, in a plane triangle ABC, a is less than b but greater than $b \sin A$, then B must be acute.

15. Triangle ABC is determined if the given parts are A, a, and b, and if a is greater than b. (Answer *true* or *false*.)

16. In plane triangle ABC, angle A is acute. If a is less than b and a is greater than $b \sin A$, how many solutions has the triangle?

17. In triangle ABC, if $A = 30°$, $a = 15$, and $b = 12$, then triangle ABC must be   (1) acute   (2) obtuse   (3) right   (4) isosceles

18. Two different triangles can be constructed if, in triangle ABC, $b = 10$, $a = 6$, and A equals   (1) $35°$ (2) $40°$ (3) $45°$ (4) $50°$

3. Using the Law of Sines When Two Sides of a Triangle and an Angle Opposite One of These Sides Are Given (s.s.a.)

~~~~~~~~~~ *MODEL PROBLEM* ~~~~~~~~~~

In $\triangle AOB$, $OB = 270$, $BA = 50$, and $\angle OAB = 105°$. Find $\angle BOA$, to the nearest degree.

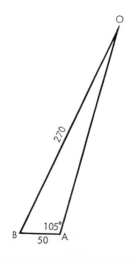

Solution: In $\triangle AOB$, we know two sides, $\overline{OB}$ and $\overline{BA}$, and an angle, $\angle OAB$, opposite one of the sides. Since $\angle OAB$ is an obtuse angle and $\overline{OB}$, the side opposite $\angle OAB$, is greater than $\overline{BA}$, the side adjacent to $\angle OAB$, there is only one solution possible.

We now use the law of sines in $\triangle AOB$ relating the known angle, $\angle OAB$; the unknown angle, $\angle BOA$; and their opposite sides, $\overline{OB}$ and $\overline{BA}$.

$$\frac{\sin \angle BOA}{BA} = \frac{\sin \angle OAB}{OB}$$

$$\frac{\sin \angle BOA}{50} = \frac{\sin 105°}{270}$$

$$\sin 105° = \sin 75°: \quad \frac{\sin \angle BOA}{50} = \frac{\sin 75°}{270}$$

$$\sin \angle BOA = \frac{50 \sin 75°}{270}$$

Method 1: *Natural Functions*	*Method 2:* *Logarithms*

Method 1:
Natural Functions

$$\sin \angle BOA = \frac{50(.9659)}{270}$$
$$\sin \angle BOA = .1789$$
$$\angle BOA = 10° \ 18' \approx 10°$$

Method 2:
Logarithms

$\log \sin \angle BOA = \log 50 + \log \sin 75° - \log 270$

$\log 50 = 1.6990$
$+\log \sin 75° = 9.9849 - 10$
$\log \text{numerator} = 11.6839 - 10$
$\log 270 = 2.4314$
$\log \sin \angle BOA = 9.2525 - 10$
$\angle BOA = 10° \ 18' \approx 10°$

Answer: $\angle BOA = 10°$, to the nearest degree.

Exercises

1. In the acute triangle ABC, $AB = 24$, $BC = 18$, and $A = 40°$. Find angle C, to the nearest degree.
2. In triangle ABC, $a = 190$, $b = 230$, and $B = 63° \ 10'$. Find angle A, to the nearest ten minutes.
3. In $\triangle ABC$, $c = 28.7$, $a = 36.3$, $A = 50° \ 20'$. Find C, to the nearest 10 minutes.
4. In triangle RST, $R = 58° \ 40'$, $r = 52.5$, and $s = 40.3$. Find S, to the nearest 10 minutes.
5. Two forces are to act on a body to produce a resultant of 125 lb. If the lines of action of the two forces form an angle of $70° \ 20'$ and one of the forces is 79 lb., find, to the nearest 10 minutes, the angle which the other force forms with the resultant.
6. Two forces are to act on a body to produce a resultant of 85 pounds. If the lines of action of the two forces form an angle of $62°$ and one of the forces is 52 pounds, find, to the nearest pound, the other force.
7. The diagonals of a parallelogram make an angle of $28° \ 20'$ with each other. The shorter diagonal is 38.6 in. and the shorter side is 20.4 in. Find the other diagonal, to the nearest tenth of an inch.

8. In order to measure the distance BC across a swamp, a surveyor measures $\overrightarrow{BA}$, $\overrightarrow{AC}$, and $\angle CBA$. If $\angle CBA = 48° \ 10'$, the length of $\overrightarrow{AC} = 4840$ ft., and the length of $\overline{BA} = 3470$ ft., find the length of $\overrightarrow{BC}$, to the nearest 10 feet.

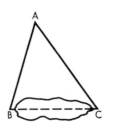

9. Two forces of 437 pounds and 876 pounds, respectively, act upon a body at an acute angle with each other. The angle between the resultant force and the 437-pound force is $41° \ 10'$. Find, to the nearest ten minutes, the angle formed by the 437-pound and the 876-pound forces.

4. Using the Law of Cosines When Two Sides and an Included Angle Are Given   (s.a.s.)

The law of cosines can be used to solve an oblique triangle when the triangle is determined by two sides and the angle included by these sides (s.a.s.). It is used effectively when the measures of the sides are limited to one or two significant digits.

You will find it useful to review simple applications of the law of cosines in oblique triangles by referring to Chapter XVII.

~~~~~~~~~~~ *MODEL PROBLEM* ~~~~~~~~~~~

Two forces act on a body to produce a resultant of 70 pounds. The 50-pound force makes an angle of $67° \ 40'$ with the resultant force. Find to the nearest pound the magnitude of the other force.

Solution:

Given: $\overrightarrow{AB}$ represents a force of 50 lb.

Resultant $\overrightarrow{AC}$ represents a force of 70 lb.

$\angle CAB$, or θ, equals $67° \ 40'$.

To Find: a, the magnitude of component force $\overrightarrow{AD}$, to the nearest lb.

How To Proceed: Since $ABCD$ is a parallelogram, $BC = AD = a$. Use the law of cosines in $\triangle I$.

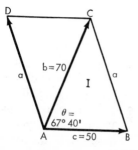

The resultant, $\overrightarrow{AC}$, is a diagonal of the parallelogram of forces $ABCD$.

In $\triangle\mathrm{I}$, $a^2 = b^2 + c^2 - 2bc\cos\theta$

$ = 70^2 + 50^2 - 2(70)(50)\cos 67°\,40'$

$ = 4900 + 2500 - 7000(.3800)$

$ = 7400 - 2660 = 4740$

$a = \sqrt{4740}$

$ = 68.8 = 69$, to the nearest integer

```
          6  8. 8
        √ 47 40.00
          36
   128 | 11 40
       | 10 24
  1368 | 1 16 00
       | 1 09 44
```

Therefore, the required force $= 69$ lb., to the nearest lb.

Answer: 69 lb.

Exercises

In 1–6, use the law of cosines to find the third side in the triangle, correct to the nearest integer.

1. $a = 15$ $b = 20$ $C = 75°$
2. $a = 24$ $c = 32$ $B = 64°\,20'$
3. $b = 55$ $c = 43$ $A = 38°\,40'$
4. $a = 35$ $b = 40$ $C = 140°$
5. $a = 28$ $c = 44$ $B = 108°\,30'$
6. $b = 31$ $c = 53$ $A = 132°\,50'$

7. In triangle ABC, $AB = 40$, $BC = 34$, and $B = 50°$. Find, to the nearest integer, the length of AC.
8. In order to find the distance between two points, A and B, separated by a swamp, a station C was chosen and the distances CA and CB were found to be 350 yards and 380 yards respectively. Angle ACB was found to be $62°$. Find, to the nearest yard, the distance from A to B.
9. Two forces of 38 pounds and 27 pounds are acting on a body at an angle of $48°$. Find the resultant, correct to the nearest pound.
10. Two forces of 55 pounds and 44 pounds are acting on a body at an angle of $64°\,20'$. Find the resultant, correct to the nearest pound.
11. The distances from an observer's eye to the summits of two hills are 10 miles and 28 miles. If the angle between his lines of sight is $104°$, find, to the nearest mile, the shortest distance from one summit to the other.
12. The diagonals of a parallelogram are 60 and 70 inches and intersect at an angle of $68°$. Find the shorter side of the parallelogram, correct to the nearest inch.
13. A triangular plot of ground measures 18 rods on one side and 24 rods on another side. The angle included between these sides is $72°$. Find, to the nearest rod, the amount of fencing required to enclose the plot.
14. Two sides of a triangular plot of ground whose lengths are 90 feet and 110 feet form an angle of $103°\,20'$. Find, to the nearest foot, the perimeter of the plot.

5. Using the Law of Cosines When Three Sides of a Triangle Are Given (s.s.s.)

The law of cosines can be used to solve an oblique triangle when the triangle is determined by three sides of a triangle (s.s.s.) and one or more angles of the triangle are to be found. It is used effectively when the measures of the sides are limited to one or two significant digits.

~~~~~~~~~~ *MODEL PROBLEMS* ~~~~~~~~~~

1. In triangle ABC, $a = 25$, $b = 31$, and $c = 14$. Find B to the nearest ten minutes.

Solution:

To find $\angle B$ of $\triangle ABC$ when the three sides of the triangle are given, use the following form of the law of cosines:

$$\cos B = \frac{a^2 + c^2 - b^2}{2ac}$$

Substitute 25 for a, 31 for b, and 14 for c.

$$\cos B = \frac{25^2 + 14^2 - 31^2}{2(25)(14)}$$

$$= \frac{625 + 196 - 961}{700}$$

$$= -\frac{140}{700}$$

$$= -\frac{1}{5}$$

$$= -.2000$$

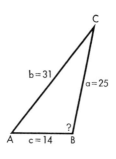

Since the cosine is negative, then B must be an obtuse angle in the second quadrant. As shown on the right, the supplement of B is found to be nearest to $78° 30'$.

Hence, $B = 180° - 78° 30'$
          $= 101° 30'$ *Ans.*

Angle	Cosine	
78° 20′	.2022	22
(180° − B)	.2000	
78° 30′	.1994	6

2. The diagonals of a parallelogram are 88 and 66 and the shorter side is 20. Find, correct to the nearest degree, the acute angle formed by the two diagonals.

Solution:

Given: $\square ABCD, AC = 88, DB = 66, BA = 20$

To Find: $\angle ATB$

How To Proceed: Since the diagonals $\overline{BD}$ and $\overline{AC}$ bisect each other, $BT = 33$ and $AT = 44$.

To find $\angle T$ in $\triangle ATB$, we can use the law of cosines which relates $\angle T$ with sides a, b, and t.

$$t^2 = a^2 + b^2 - 2ab \cos T$$
$$(20)^2 = (33)^2 + (44)^2 - 2(33)(44) \cos T$$
$$400 = 1089 + 1936 - 2904 \cos T$$
$$2904 \cos T = 2625$$
$$\cos T = \frac{2625}{2904} = .9039$$
$$T = 25° \quad Ans.$$

Exercises

1. In triangle ABC, $AB = 19$, $BC = 34$, and $AC = 49$. Find C, to the nearest degree.

2. In triangle ABC, $a = 78$, $b = 49$, and $c = 63$. Find B, to the nearest degree.

3. In triangle RST, $r = 7.5$, $s = 5.5$, and $t = 6.5$. Find R, correct to the nearest degree.

4. In triangle ABC, $a = 86$, $b = 41$, $c = 62$. Find A, correct to the nearest degree.

5. The diagonals of a parallelogram are 96 and 72 and the shorter side is 30. Find, correct to the nearest 10 minutes, the acute angle formed by the two diagonals.

6. The diagonals of a parallelogram are 54 and 64 and the longer side is 52. Find, correct to the nearest degree, the obtuse angle formed by the two diagonals.

7. Find, correct to the nearest ten minutes, the angle subtended by an object 72 feet long, if the eye of the observer is 57 feet from one end of the object and 81 feet from the other.

8. A body is acted upon by two forces of 30.0 pounds and 16.0 pounds. If their resultant is 40.0 pounds, find, correct to the nearest ten minutes, the angle at which the resultant is inclined to the 30-pound force.

9. A body is acted upon by two forces of 28 pounds and 42 pounds. If their resultant is 58 pounds, find, correct to the nearest degree, the angle at which the resultant is inclined to the 28-pound force.

10. The three sides of a triangular plot of ground are 50 feet, 70 feet, and 90 feet. Find, correct to the nearest degree, the largest angle of the plot.

11. Two straight railroad tracks intersect at J. Two trains traveling at rates of 40 and 48 miles an hour leave J at noon. At 2:30 P.M. the trains are 60 miles apart. Find, correct to the nearest minute, the angle at which the tracks intersect.

6. Using the Formula for the Tangent of Half an Angle When Three Sides of a Triangle Are Given (s.s.s.)

The formulas for the tangent of half an angle can be used to solve an oblique triangle when the triangle is determined by its three sides (s.s.s.) and one or more angles of the triangle are to be found. They are used effectively when the measures of the sides have more than two significant digits. Note in the model problem how a formula for the tangent of half an angle can be used to solve a triangle, using logarithmic computation.

STATING THE FORMULA FOR THE TANGENT OF HALF AN ANGLE

The sides of oblique triangle ABC are a, b, and c. The perimeter of $\triangle ABC$ is equal to $a + b + c$. If s represents half of the perimeter, or the semi-perimeter, then:

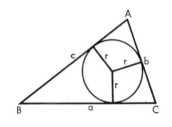

$$s = \tfrac{1}{2}(a + b + c)$$

In any triangle,

$$\tan \tfrac{1}{2}A = \sqrt{\frac{(s-b)(s-c)}{s(s-a)}} \quad \text{or} \quad \tan \tfrac{1}{2}A = \frac{r}{s-a}$$

$$\tan \tfrac{1}{2}B = \sqrt{\frac{(s-a)(s-c)}{s(s-b)}} \quad \text{or} \quad \tan \tfrac{1}{2}B = \frac{r}{s-b}$$

$$\tan \tfrac{1}{2}C = \sqrt{\frac{(s-a)(s-b)}{s(s-c)}} \quad \text{or} \quad \tan \tfrac{1}{2}C = \frac{r}{s-c}$$

The length of the radius, r, of the circle inscribed in triangle ABC is given by the formula

$$r = \sqrt{\frac{(s-a)(s-b)(s-c)}{s}}$$

PROVING THE FORMULA FOR THE TANGENT OF HALF AN ANGLE

In exercise 13, following, the formula for $\tan \frac{1}{2}A$ in terms of the sides of the triangle is derived, beginning with the formula $\tan \frac{1}{2}A = \sqrt{\dfrac{1 - \cos A}{1 + \cos A}}$. Note that the $\pm$ sign is omitted before the radical. Since A is an angle of a triangle, $\frac{1}{2}A$ must be an acute angle. Hence, $\tan \frac{1}{2}A$ is positive.

 MODEL PROBLEM

In triangle ABC, $a = 476$, $b = 344$, and $c = 438$. Find B, correct to the nearest degree.

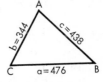

Solution:
Given: $a = 476$, $b = 344$, $c = 438$
To Find: B

How To Proceed: Since the three sides of the triangle are given and they are expressed in three digits, we can find B by using the formula for $\tan \frac{1}{2}B$.

$$
\begin{aligned}
a &= 476 \\
b &= 344 \\
c &= 438 \\
\hline
2s &= 1258 \\
s &= 629 \\
s - a &= 153 \\
s - b &= 285 \\
s - c &= 191
\end{aligned}
$$

Check: $s = 629$, by adding.

$$\tan \tfrac{1}{2}B = \sqrt{\frac{(s-c)(s-a)}{s(s-b)}}$$

$$\tan \tfrac{1}{2}B = \sqrt{\frac{(191)(153)}{(629)(285)}}$$

$$\log \tan \tfrac{1}{2}B = \tfrac{1}{2}[(\log 191 + \log 153) - (\log 629 + \log 285)]$$

$\log 191 =$ 2.2810	$\log 629 = 2.7987$
$+\log 153 =$ 2.1847	$+\log 285 = 2.4548$
$\log$ numerator $=$ 4.4657	$\log$ denominator $= 5.2535$
$\log$ numerator $=$ 14.4657 $-$ 10	Express $\log$ numerator as $14.4657 - 10$
$-\log$ denominator $=$ 5.2535	in order to subtract.
$\log$ fraction $=$ 9.2122 $-$ 10	Express $\log$ fraction as $19.2122 - 20$
or 19.2122 $-$ 20	in order to obtain a characteristic
2⌊19.2122 $-$ 20	ending in (-10).
$\log \tan \tfrac{1}{2}B =$ 9.6061 $-$ 10	

$$\tfrac{1}{2}B = 22° \; 0' \text{ to the nearest 10 minutes}$$
$$B = 44°, \text{ to the nearest degree } \quad Ans. \; 44°$$

Exercises

1. In triangle ABC, $a = 328$, $b = 321$, and $c = 295$. Find B, correct to the nearest 10 minutes.

2. The sides of a triangle are 36.8, 42.7, and 48.5. Find, to the nearest 10 minutes, the largest angle of the triangle.

3. In the triangle ABC, $a = 6.73$, $b = 4.52$, $c = 3.75$. Find B, correct to the nearest 10 minutes.

4. In triangle ABC, $c = 19.3$, $a = 32.9$, and $b = 18.4$. Find B, correct to the nearest 10 minutes.

5. In triangle ABC, $a = 32.5$, $b = 57.3$, and $c = 61.2$. Find B, to the nearest 10 minutes.

6. Given the sides of a triangle $a = 34.25$, $b = 52.45$, $c = 71.40$. Find the angles, correct to the nearest 10 minutes.

7. The sides of a triangle are 156, 248, and 336. Find, to the nearest ten minutes, the smallest angle of the triangle.

8. The sides of a triangular lot are 521 feet, 467 feet, and 208 feet. Find, to the nearest 10 minutes, the angle opposite the longest side.

9. In a certain air race, the course was a triangle with sides 143 miles, 224 miles, and 315 miles. Find, to the nearest degree, the angle at the turn between the 143-mile and 315-mile sides.

10. In the roof of a clubhouse, three steel girders, 27.4 feet, 39.7 feet, and 50.5 feet in length, are riveted into a triangle. Find, to the nearest 10 minutes, the angle at which the longest and shortest girders meet.

11. In parallelogram $ABCD$, $AB = 435$, $AD = 373$, and $AC = 684$. Find angle ABC, to the nearest 10 minutes.

12. A body is acted upon by two forces of 450 pounds and 368 pounds. If their

resultant is 524 pounds, find, to the nearest 10 minutes, the angle formed by the lines of action of the forces.

13. Beginning with the formula $\tan \frac{1}{2}A = \sqrt{\dfrac{1 - \cos A}{1 + \cos A}}$, obtain each of the following steps in order:

a. By substituting $\dfrac{b^2 + c^2 - a^2}{2bc}$ for $\cos A$, obtain

$$\tan \tfrac{1}{2}A = \sqrt{\frac{a^2 - (b^2 - 2bc + c^2)}{(b^2 + 2bc + c^2) - a^2}}.$$

b. By factoring, obtain $\tan \tfrac{1}{2}A = \sqrt{\dfrac{(a + b - c)(a + c - b)}{(a + b + c)(b + c - a)}}$.

c. By substituting $2s$ for $(a + b + c)$, $2(s - a)$ for $(b + c - a)$, $2(s - b)$ for $(a + c - b)$, and $2(s - c)$ for $(a + b - c)$, obtain

$$\tan \tfrac{1}{2}A = \sqrt{\frac{(s - b)(s - c)}{s(s - a)}}.$$

14. Beginning with the proof that $\triangle OAF \cong \triangle OAD$, obtain each of the following steps in order, keeping in mind that circle O is inscribed in $\triangle ABC$: (Let $AF = x$.)

a. $\triangle OAF \cong \triangle OAD$

b. $\tan \tfrac{1}{2}A = \dfrac{r}{x}$

c. The perimeter, $2s = 2x + 2(c - x) + 2(b - x)$.

d. $x = b + c - s$

e. $\tan \tfrac{1}{2}A = \dfrac{r}{s - a}$

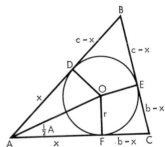

7. Using the Law of Tangents When Two Sides and an Included Angle of a Triangle Are Given (s.a.s.)

The law of tangents can be used to solve an oblique triangle when the triangle is determined by two sides and the angle included by these sides (s.a.s.) and the remaining two angles are to be found. Note in the model problem how the law of tangents can be used to solve a triangle using logarithmic computation.

You will find it useful to review simple applications of the law of tangents in oblique triangles by referring to Chapter XVII.

~~~~~~~~~~~~~ *MODEL PROBLEMS* ~~~~~~~~~~~~~

1. In triangle ABC, $a = 474$, $b = 346$, and $C = 50° 40'$. Find A, correct to the nearest degree.

Solution:
Given: $a = 474$, $b = 346$, $C = 50° 40'$
To Find: A
How To Proceed:

$A + B = 180° - C$
$A + B = 179° 60' - 50° 40' = 129° 20'$
$\frac{1}{2}(A + B) = \frac{1}{2}(129° 20') = \frac{1}{2}(128° 80') = 64° 40'$

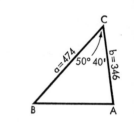

Since we know sides a and b, and $\frac{1}{2}(A + B)$, we can use the law of tangents as follows:

$$\frac{\tan \frac{1}{2}(A - B)}{\tan \frac{1}{2}(A + B)} = \frac{a - b}{a + b}$$

$$\frac{\tan \frac{1}{2}(A - B)}{\tan 64° 40'} = \frac{474 - 346}{474 + 346} = \frac{128}{820}$$

$$\tan \frac{1}{2}(A - B) = \frac{128 \tan 64° 40'}{820}$$

$\log \tan \frac{1}{2}(A - B) = \log 128 + \log \tan 64° 40' - \log 820$
$\log 128 = \quad 2.1072$
$+\log \tan 64° 40' = \underline{10.3248 - 10}$
$\log \text{numerator} = \overline{12.4320 - 10}$
$-\log 820 = \underline{\quad 2.9138}$
$\log \tan \frac{1}{2}(A - B) = \overline{\quad 9.5182 - 10}$
$\frac{1}{2}(A - B) = 18° 15'$
$\frac{1}{2}(A + B)$ or $\frac{1}{2}A + \frac{1}{2}B = 64° 40'$
$\frac{1}{2}(A - B)$ or $\frac{1}{2}A - \frac{1}{2}B = \underline{18° 15'}$
$\overline{A \qquad\quad = 82° 55'}$, by adding

Answer: 83°

2. Two forces of 62 pounds and 49 pounds, respectively, act on a body at an angle of 53° 20' with each other. Find to the nearest 10 minutes the angle formed by the resultant and the greater force.

Solution:

Given: $\overrightarrow{AD}$ represents a force of 49 lb. $\quad \overrightarrow{AB}$ represents a force of 62 lb.
$\angle DAB = 53° 20'$

To Find: Find to the nearest ten minutes $\angle x$, the angle between the resultant, $\overrightarrow{AC}$, and the force $\overrightarrow{AB}$.

How To Proceed: Use the law of tangents in $\triangle\text{I}$.

The resultant, $\overrightarrow{AC}$, is a diagonal of the parallelogram of forces $ABCD$.

In parallelogram $ABCD$, $\angle B = 180° - \angle DAB = 180° - 53°\,20' = 126°\,40'$.

Also, $BC = AD = 49$.

In $\triangle\text{I}$, since $\angle B = 126°\,40'$, then $x + y = 53°\,20'$. Hence, $\frac{1}{2}(x+y) = 26°\,40'$.

Use the law of tangents in $\triangle\text{I}$ as follows:

$$\frac{\tan\frac{1}{2}(y-x)}{\tan\frac{1}{2}(y+x)} = \frac{c-a}{c+a}$$

Substitute $26°\,40'$ for $\frac{1}{2}(y+x)$, 62 for c, and 49 for a.

$$\frac{\tan\frac{1}{2}(y-x)}{\tan 26°\,40'} = \frac{62-49}{62+49} = \frac{13}{111}$$

$$\tan\frac{1}{2}(y-x) = \frac{13\tan 26°\,40'}{111}$$

Write the equation in logarithmic form.

Log tan $\frac{1}{2}(y-x) = \log 13 + \log\tan 26°\,40' - \log 111$.

$$
\begin{aligned}
\log 13 &= 1.1139\\
+ \log\tan 26°\,40' &= 9.7009 - 10\\
\log\text{ numerator} &= \overline{10.8148 - 10}\\
- \log 111 &= 2.0453\\
\log\tan\tfrac{1}{2}(y-x) &= \overline{8.7695 - 10}
\end{aligned}
$$

Interpolate as shown on the right.

(1) $\frac{1}{2}(y-x) = \frac{1}{2}y - \frac{1}{2}x = 3°\,20'$
(2) $\frac{1}{2}(y+x) = \frac{1}{2}y + \frac{1}{2}x = 26°\,40'$

Subtract (1) from (2).

$x = 23°\,20'$ to the nearest ten minutes

Answer: $23°\,20'$

Angle	Log tangent	
3° 30′	8.7865 − 10	170
$\frac{1}{2}(y-x)$	8.7695 − 10	
3° 20′	8.7652 − 10	43

Since log tan $\frac{1}{2}(y-x)$ is nearer to log tan 3° 20′, then $\frac{1}{2}(y-x) = 3°\,20'$, to the nearest ten minutes.

Exercises

1. In triangle ABC, $a = 58$, $b = 36$, and $C = 42°$. Find A, correct to the nearest degree.

2. In triangle ABC, $b = 256$, $c = 378$, and $A = 63° \, 40'$. Find B, correct to the nearest 10 minutes.

3. Given triangle ABC with $a = 42$, $b = 24$, and $C = 64°$. Find A, correct to the nearest 10 minutes.

4. In triangle ABC, $a = 35$, $b = 42$, $C = 75° \, 28'$. Find A to the nearest 10 minutes.

5. A body is acted upon by two forces of 320 and 205 pounds acting at an angle of 80°. Find, correct to the nearest degree, the angle at which the resultant is inclined to the 320-pound force.

6. A body is acted upon by two forces of 210 pounds and 28 pounds. These forces act an at angle of 76° with each other. Find, to the nearest 10 minutes, the angle at which the resultant is inclined to the force of 210 pounds.

7. From a point 175 feet from one end of a wall and 264 feet from the other end, the wall subtends an angle of 50°. Find, to the nearest foot, the length of the wall.

8. A and B are points on opposite sides of a lake at its greatest width. A point C is 2820 feet from B and 2240 feet from A; the angle ACB is 64°. Find, to the nearest foot, the greatest width of the lake.

9. A triangular field is determined by three markers, A, B, and C. The length of AC is 142 ft., the length of AB is 192 ft., and $\angle CAB$ is $52° \, 10'$. Find the perimeter of the field, to the nearest foot.

10. A gun fired at A was heard at B and at C two seconds and three seconds respectively after it was fired. If angle $BAC = 110° \, 30'$ and the sound traveled 1150 feet per second, compute, correct to the nearest foot, the distance between B and C.

8. Solving Oblique Triangles: Summary of Methods of Solving Oblique Triangles

To *solve an oblique triangle* means to determine the missing sides and angles from the given data. The following procedure will be found helpful in performing the solution.

Procedure. To solve oblique triangles:
1. Read the problem carefully.
2. Determine the given data and what is to be found.
3. Make a working diagram.
4. Note the given data on the diagram.

5. Select the method of solution which relates what is to be found with the given data.
6. Perform the necessary computations.
7. Check the answers.

We will now summarize the various methods for solving oblique triangles:

SUMMARY OF METHODS OF SOLVING OBLIQUE TRIANGLES

Case		Methods of Solution
I s.a.a. or a.s.a		1. Find the third angle by subtraction. $$C = 180° - (A + B)$$ 2. Use the law of sines to find the second and third sides. $$\frac{a}{\sin A} = \frac{b}{\sin B} = \frac{c}{\sin C}$$
II s.s.a.		1. Determine the number of possible solutions. 2. Use the law of sines to find the second angle. 3. Find the third angle by subtraction. $$C = 180° - (A + B)$$ 4. Use the law of sines to find the third side.
III s.a.s.	Method 1	1. Use the law of cosines to find the third side. $$c^2 = a^2 + b^2 - 2ab \cos C$$ 2. Use the law of cosines to find the second angle. $$\cos A = \frac{b^2 + c^2 - a^2}{2bc}$$ 3. Find the third angle by subtraction. $$C = 180° - (A + B)$$
	Method 2	1. Use the law of tangents to find the remaining angles. $$\frac{\tan \frac{1}{2}(A - B)}{\tan \frac{1}{2}(A + B)} = \frac{a - b}{a + b}$$ 2. Use the law of sines to find the third side.

656   Algebra Two and Trigonometry

Case		Methods of Solution
IV s.s.s.	Method 1	1. Use the law of cosines to find each of the angles. $$\cos A = \frac{b^2 + c^2 - a^2}{2bc}$$ 2. The third angle may also be found by $$C = 180° - (A + B).$$
	Method 2	1. Use the formula for the tangent of half an angle to find each of the angles. $$\tan \tfrac{1}{2}A = \sqrt{\frac{(s-b)(s-c)}{s(s-a)}} \text{ or } \tan \tfrac{1}{2}A = \frac{r}{s-a}$$ 2. The third angle may also be found by $$C = 180° - (A + B).$$

In checking, use the following equations, known as **Mollweide's equations.**

$$\frac{a-b}{c} = \frac{\sin \tfrac{1}{2}(A-B)}{\cos \tfrac{1}{2}C}$$

$$\frac{b-a}{c} = \frac{\sin \tfrac{1}{2}(B-A)}{\cos \tfrac{1}{2}C}$$

The advantages of using Mollweide's equations are (1) they were not used in solving the problem, and (2) they involve all the parts of the triangle, those that were found as well as those that were given.

Exercises

In 1–5, solve the triangle, finding the remaining sides, correct to two significant figures, and the remaining angles, correct to the nearest degree.

1. $B = 38°$ $C = 56°$ $a = 64$
2. $A = 41°$ $a = 86$ $b = 59$
3. $A = 75°$ $b = 2.5$ $c = 4.5$
4. $a = 16$ $b = 12$ $c = 22$
5. $B = 114°$ $a = 32$ $c = 60$

In 6–13, solve the triangle, finding the remaining sides, correct to three significant figures, and the remaining angles, correct to the nearest ten minutes.

6. $B = 61° \ 30'$ $b = 58.7$ $c = 47.9$

7. $A = 28° \ 40'$ $B = 79° \ 30'$ $a = 43.6$

8. $a = 82.4$ $b = 64.2$ $c = 36.8$

9. $A = 84° \ 50'$ $C = 42° \ 30'$ $b = 231$

10. $C = 38° \ 10'$ $c = 524$ $a = 408$

11. $a = 404$ $b = 316$ $C = 46° \ 20'$

12. $a = 546$ $b = 348$ $c = 224$

13. $a = 93.6$ $b = 48.4$ $c = 66.8$

In 14–16, solve the triangle, finding the remaining sides, correct to four significant figures, and the remaining angles, correct to the nearest minute.

14. $A = 37° \ 18'$ $a = 46.72$ $b = 31.25$

15. $A = 54° \ 15'$ $b = 158.5$ $c = 278.5$

16. $A = 31° \ 52'$ $C = 71° \ 10'$ $c = 72.84$

17. A tree stands at the end of a straight road which is inclined at an angle of $14° \ 20'$ to the horizontal. At a point down the road 180 feet from the foot of the tree, the angle subtended by the tree is $23° \ 50'$. Find, correct to the nearest foot, the height of the tree.

18. $\overline{AB}$ is a tower 175 feet high situated on level ground. Two objects, M and N, are located on the ground on opposite sides of the tower and in line with the base B. From A, the top of the tower, the angle of depression of M is $32° \ 50'$ and the angle of depression of N is $28° \ 40'$. Find, correct to the nearest foot, the distance MN.

19. A body is acted upon by two forces, 345 pounds and 320 pounds. The angle between the lines of action of the forces is $68° \ 40'$. Find, to the nearest 10 minutes, the angle between the line of action of the resultant and the 320-pound force.

20. In a certain air race, the course was a triangle with sides 220 miles, 152 miles, and 310 miles. Find, to the nearest degree, the angle at the turn between the 220-mile and 310-mile sides.

21. From the top of a hill, the angles of depression of A and B, two points in a straight line from the foot of the hill, are $21°$ and $18°$. If A and B are in the same horizontal plane as the foot of the hill and are 250 feet apart, find the height of the hill. (Answer may be left to the nearest ten feet.)

22. A tower is situated on the top of a hill. The hill is inclined at an angle of $32° \ 20'$ to the horizontal. At a point 42.8 feet from the foot of the tower measured down the incline, the angle subtended by the tower is $16° \ 40'$. Find, correct to the nearest tenth of a foot, the height of the tower.

23. Two buoys are 650 feet apart, and a boat is 575 feet from one of them. The angle subtended by the line between the two buoys at the boat is 58° 40′. Find the distance from the boat to the other buoy, correct to the nearest foot.

24. When the altitude (angle of elevation) of the sun is 42° 50′, the shadow of a tower is 85 feet longer than when the altitude of the sun is 57° 10′. Find, to the nearest foot, the height of the tower.

25. In the diagram at the right, $\overline{AB}$ represents a tower and $\overline{CD}$ a monument standing on level ground. From A, the angle of elevation of C is 42° 40′. From B, the angle of elevation of C is 54° 30′. If the tower is 34 feet high, find:

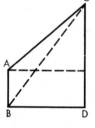

  a. the distance BC, to the nearest foot.
  b. the height of the monument, to the nearest foot.

CHAPTER XX

LITERAL PROBLEMS IN TRIGONOMETRY

1. Using Right Triangles To Derive Formulas

In the previous chapter, the formulas used to solve oblique triangles were the law of sines, the law of cosines, the law of tangents, and the formula for the tangent of one-half an angle. In this chapter, we will discover many other formulas that can be used to solve oblique triangles.

In the following model problems, note how the relationships that exist in right triangles may be used to derive new formulas. If an oblique triangle is given, right triangles may be formed by simply constructing one or more altitudes of the given triangle.

To derive a formula, it is helpful to plan your method of attack in advance. Note the planning in model problem 1. It is also helpful, as you proceed, to keep constantly in mind the formula to be derived so that each change is a change in the right direction.

By "literal problems," we mean problems in which formulas are to be derived; that is, problems in which the answer is literal rather than numerical in character.

~~~~~~~~~~ *MODEL PROBLEMS* ~~~~~~~~~~

1. *Given:* $\overline{AB} \parallel \overline{CD}$, $\overline{BC} \perp \overline{AC}$, $\overline{BD} \perp \overline{CD}$

$$AB = 1, \ \angle BAC = x, \ \angle ABC = y$$

To Prove: $CD = \sin^2 x$

Solution:

Since $\overline{BC} \perp \overline{AC}$, $\angle BCA = 90°$. Hence, $x = 90 - y$.

Since $\overline{BD} \perp \overline{CD}$, $\angle D = 90°$.

Since $\overline{AB} \parallel \overline{CD}$, $\angle ABD = 180° - \angle D = 180° - 90° = 90°$. Hence,
$\angle CBD = 90 - y = x$.

In $\triangle ABC$, $\sin x = \dfrac{BC}{AB} = \dfrac{BC}{1} = BC$. Hence, $BC = \sin x$.

In $\triangle BCD$, $\sin x = \dfrac{CD}{BC}$.

Substitute $\sin x$ for BC.

$$\sin x = \frac{CD}{\sin x}$$

Multiply each side by $\sin x$.

$$\sin^2 x = CD$$

2. Two ships at A and B are due west of a lighthouse and in line with its foot. The angles of elevation of the top of the lighthouse from the ships are a and b, with b greater than a. If the height of the lighthouse is h and the distance between the ships is d, show that $d = h(\cot a - \cot b)$.

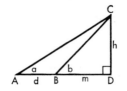

Solution:

Using rt. $\triangle ACD$, $\cot a = \dfrac{d + m}{h}$, or (1) $d + m = h \cot a$

From rt. $\triangle BCD$, $\cot b = \dfrac{m}{h}$, or   (2) $m = h \cot b$

Subtracting (2) from (1), $d = h \cot a - h \cot b$, or
$$d = h(\cot a - \cot b)$$

3. *a.* In $\triangle ABC$, in which angle A is an acute angle, prove that
$b = a \cos C + c \cos A$.
  b. Prove that this formula holds if angle A is a right angle.

Solution:

a. Since $\cos A$ and $\cos C$ appear in the formula to be proved, we will draw altitude $\overline{BD}$ to form right triangles which contain $\angle A$ and $\angle C$.
  1. Draw $\overline{BD}$, the altitude to side $\overline{AC}$.

  2. In rt. $\triangle$ I, $\cos A = \dfrac{m}{c}$, or $m = c \cos A$.

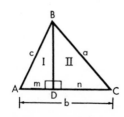

3. In rt. $\triangle$II, $\cos C = \dfrac{n}{a}$, or $n = a \cos C$.

4. Since $b = n + m$, $b = a \cos C + c \cos A$.

b. 1. If A is a right angle, $\cos A = \cos 90° = 0$.

2. The formula $b = a \cos C + c \cos A$ becomes $b = a \cos C + 0$, or $b = a \cos C$. This agrees with the fact that in right $\triangle ABC$, $\cos C = \dfrac{b}{a}$, or $b = a \cos C$.

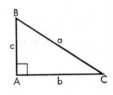

Exercises

In 1–3, in acute $\triangle ABC$, if $\overline{BD} \perp \overline{AC}$, prove that:

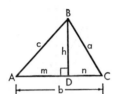

1. $b = h(\cot A + \cot C)$

2. $b = \dfrac{c \sec C + a \sec A}{\sec C \sec A}$

3. $b = \dfrac{h(\tan A + \tan C)}{\tan A \tan C}$

In 4–6, in right triangle ABC, if C is a right angle, prove that:

4. $\sin \frac{1}{2}A = \sqrt{\dfrac{c-b}{2c}}$

5. $\tan 2A = \dfrac{2ab}{b^2 - a^2}$

6. $\cos 2A = \dfrac{b^2 - a^2}{c^2}$

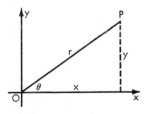

7. P is a point whose rectangular coordinates are represented by x and y, as shown in the drawing. The distance from the origin O to point P is represented by r, and the angle that $\overline{OP}$ makes with the positive portion of the x-axis is represented by θ.

a. Express x in terms of r and θ.

b. Express y in terms of r and θ.

c. Show that the equation $x^2 + y^2 - 2x = 0$ can be reduced to the form $r = 2 \cos \theta$.

8. The rectangular coordinates of the point P are represented by x and y. The distance from the origin O to P is represented by r, and the angle that $\overline{OP}$ makes with the positive portion of the x-axis is represented by θ.
   a. Express x in terms of r and a trigonometric function of θ.
   b. Express y in terms of r and a trigonometric function of θ.
   c. Using the results obtained in parts a and b, show that the equation $x^2 - y^2 = 4$ can be reduced to the form $r^2 \cos 2\theta = 4$.

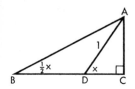

9. Using the figure, in which $AD = 1$, $\overline{AC} \perp \overline{BC}$, $\angle ABC = \frac{1}{2}x$, and $\angle ADC = x$, show that
$$\tan \tfrac{1}{2}x = \frac{\sin x}{1 + \cos x}.$$

10. A valley is crossed by a bridge $\overline{AB}$ whose length is d; C is a point in the valley directly below the bridge. The angles of depression of C at A and B are s and t, as shown in the drawing. In terms of s, t, and d, derive a formula for the height h of the bridge above C.

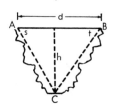

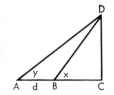

11. Given right triangle ADC, B any point on $\overline{AC}$, and $\overline{BD}$ drawn. Derive a formula for DC in terms of AB, angle x, and angle y.

12. Given in the figure: right $\triangle ABC$ with angle C the right angle. The bisector of angle BAC intersects $\overline{BC}$ at D. If angle DAC is represented by θ, show that
$$AD = \frac{AB(\cos^2 \theta - \sin^2 \theta)}{\cos \theta}$$

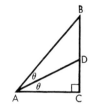

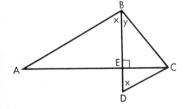

13. In the figure at the left, $\overline{BD}$ is perpendicular to $\overline{AC}$ at E, angle $ABD =$ angle $CDB = x$, and angle $DBC = y$. Using the letters given on the figure, show that $CD = AB \cot x \tan y$.

2. Using Oblique and Right Triangles To Derive Formulas

In the model problem that follows, note the use of the law of sines to derive a formula. Here, again, it is helpful to plan the method of attack in advance, keeping the formula constantly in mind so that each change will bring you closer to the goal of arriving at the formula to be derived.

~~~~~~~~~~~~~ *MODEL PROBLEM* ~~~~~~~~~~~~~

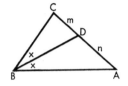

In $\triangle ABC$, the bisector of angle B meets $\overline{AC}$ in D. Using the letters that are shown in the diagram, prove $m \sin C = n \sin A$.

Solution: Since $\overline{BD}$ bisects $\angle B$,
$$\angle CBD = \angle DBA = x.$$

In $\triangle BCD$, $\dfrac{m}{\sin x} = \dfrac{BD}{\sin C}$.

Hence, $BD \sin x = m \sin C$.

In $\triangle BDA$, $\dfrac{n}{\sin x} = \dfrac{BD}{\sin A}$.

Hence, $BD \sin x = n \sin A$.
Since $m \sin C$ and $n \sin A$ are both equal to $BD \sin x$, $m \sin C = n \sin A$.

Exercises

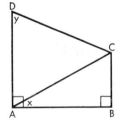

1. In quadrilateral $ABCD$, $\overline{DA}$ and $\overline{CB}$ are perpendicular to $\overline{AB}$. Using the letters indicated on the figure, show that
$$BC = DC \tan x \sin y$$

2. In triangle ABC, angle $C = 90°$. If angle DAC is x and angle ABC is $2x$, prove that $d = 2c \sin x$.

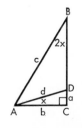

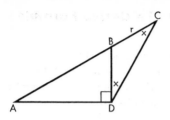

3. In triangle ADC, B is a point on $\overline{AC}$ such that $\overline{BD}$ is perpendicular to $\overline{AD}$, angles BDC and BCD are each represented by x, and BC is represented by r. Show that:

a. $DC = 2r \cos x$

b. $AC = \dfrac{2r \cos^2 x}{\cos 2x}$

4. Using the diagram, in which $\overline{AB}$ is perpendicular to $\overline{CB}$, show that

$$DA = \frac{CB \tan \theta}{\cos 2\theta}$$

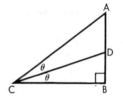

5. In triangle ABC, angle ACB is a right angle. Using the letters given on the figure, show that:

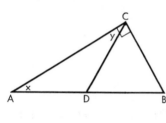

a. $BD = \dfrac{BC \cos y}{\sin(x+y)}$

b. $BD = \dfrac{AB \sin x \cos y}{\sin(x+y)}$

c. $BD = \frac{1}{2}AB$ if $x = y$
   (*Hint:* Use the relationship given in b.)

6. In triangle ABC, $\angle C = 90°$. Let $\angle BAC$ be represented by x and $\angle DAC$ be represented by y. Prove that

$$BD = \frac{AD(\sin x \cos y - \cos x \sin y)}{\cos x}$$

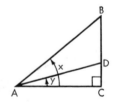

7. In the accompanying figure, ABC and ADC are right triangles, and a line through B intersects $\overline{AD}$ at E. Angles CAD, DAB, and DEB are represented by x, y, and z respectively. Show that:

a. $BD = \dfrac{BE \sin z}{\cos x}$

b. $BD = \dfrac{AE \sin y \sin z}{\cos x \sin(z-y)}$

8. Using the letters in the diagram shown, prove:

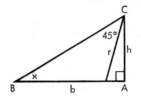

$a.$ $r = \dfrac{b \sin x}{\sin 45°}$

$b.$ $h = b \sin x(\sin x + \cos x)$

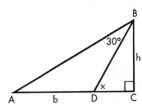

9. In the figure, $\overline{BC}$ is perpendicular to $\overline{AC}$, $AD = b$, $BC = h$, angle $ABD = 30°$, and angle $BDC = x$. Prove:

$$h = b \sin x(\sqrt{3} \sin x - \cos x)$$

10. In right triangle ABC, C is the vertex of the right angle and D is any point in $\overline{CB}$. Show that:

$a.$ $DB = AC(\tan CAB - \tan CAD)$

$b.$ $DB = \dfrac{AC \sin(\angle CAB - \angle CAD)}{\cos CAB \cos CAD}$

CHAPTER XXI

AREAS OF TRIANGLES AND OTHER POLYGONS

To *measure* or *find the area* of a region enclosed within the sides of a polygon means to find the number of units of area measure that are contained in the region, units such as square inches or square centimeters. For example, a rectangle whose area is 50 square inches encloses a region which is the same as the total area of 50 squares, each square being one inch on a side.

In this chapter, we will use trigonometry to find the measure of areas of triangles and other polygons.

1. Using Formulas To Find the Area of a Triangle When Two Sides and the Included Angle Are Given (s.a.s.)

In terms of any two sides of a triangle and their included angle (s.a.s.), the area of a triangle, K, can be expressed in any one of the following formulas (see the figure at the right):

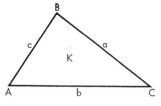

$$K = \tfrac{1}{2}ab \sin C \qquad K = \tfrac{1}{2}bc \sin A$$

$$K = \tfrac{1}{2}ac \sin B$$

These three formulas may be combined as follows:

$$K = \tfrac{1}{2}ab \sin C = \tfrac{1}{2}bc \sin A = \tfrac{1}{2}ac \sin B$$

Rule. The area of a triangle is equal to one-half the product of any two sides and the sine of the included angle.

Note. By "side" in an area problem is meant "the measure of a side" and by "angle" is meant "the measure of an angle."

For the proof of the formula for the area of a triangle when two sides and the included angle are given (s.a.s.), see page 741.

~~~~~~~~~~~~ *MODEL PROBLEMS* ~~~~~~~~~~~~

1. In triangle ABC, $a = 20$, $c = 9$, and $B = 30°$. Find the area of triangle ABC.

Solution:

$$K = \tfrac{1}{2}ac \sin B$$

Substitute 20 for a, 9 for c, and 30° for B.

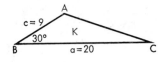

$$K = \tfrac{1}{2}(20)(9)\sin 30°$$
$$= 90(\tfrac{1}{2}) = 45 \quad Ans.$$

2. In $\triangle ABC$, $A = 50°$ and $B = 100°$. The area of the triangle is (1) $\tfrac{1}{2}ab \sin 50°$ (2) $\tfrac{1}{2}ab \sin 100°$ (3) $\tfrac{1}{2}ab$ (4) $\tfrac{1}{4}ab$

Solution:

$$K = \tfrac{1}{2}ab \sin C$$

Since $A = 50°$ and $B = 100°$, then $C = 180° - 150° = 30°$.

$\text{Sin } C = \sin 30° = \tfrac{1}{2}$. Substitute $\tfrac{1}{2}$ for $\sin C$.

$$\text{area of } \triangle ABC = \tfrac{1}{2}ab(\tfrac{1}{2}) = \tfrac{1}{4}ab$$

Answer: The correct choice is (4).

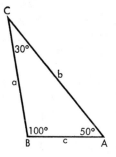

3. The area of $\triangle ABC = 15\sqrt{2}$ square feet, the length of $AC = 5$ ft., and $C = 45°$. Find the length of $\overline{BC}$.

Solution:

$$K = \tfrac{1}{2}ab \sin C$$

Substitute $15\sqrt{2}$ for K, the area; 5 for b; and 45° for C.

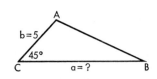

$$15\sqrt{2} = \tfrac{1}{2}a(5)\sin 45°$$
$$15\sqrt{2} = \tfrac{1}{2}(5)(\tfrac{1}{2}\sqrt{2})a$$

Divide each side by $5\sqrt{2}$.

$$3 = \tfrac{1}{4}a$$
$$12 = a$$

Hence, the length of $\overline{BC} = 12$ ft.   *Ans.*

~~~~~~

Exercises

1. Two sides of a triangle are a and b and their included angle is C. Express the area of the triangle in terms of a, b, and C.

2. The area of the oblique plane triangle ABC, having a, b, and C given, is
   (1) $\frac{1}{2}ab$ (2) $\frac{1}{2}ab \cos C$ (3) $\frac{1}{2}ab \sin C$

3. In $\triangle RST$, complete the following area formulas:
   a. $K = \frac{1}{2}rs$____   b. $K = \frac{1}{2}rt$____   c. $K = \frac{1}{2}st$____

4. In $\triangle ABC$, express $\sin A$ in terms of the area K, and the sides b and c.

5. In $\triangle ABC$, express the angle C, using inverse trigonometric notation, in terms of the area K and the sides a and b.

6. Two sides of a triangle are 3 and 4 and the angle between them is A. Express the area of the triangle in terms of $\sin A$.

In 7–9, in triangle ABC, side a is four times as long as side b. Express the area of the triangle in terms of b if:

7. $C = 30°$ 8. $C = 45°$ 9. $C = 60°$

In 10 and 11, in $\triangle ABC$, if $a = 12$ and $b = 16$, find K if:

10. $\sin C = \frac{5}{8}$ 11. $\sin C = .7$

12. What is the area of triangle ABC if $a = 5$, $b = 6$, $\sin C = 0.6$, $\cos C = 0.8$, and $\tan C = 0.75$?

13. In triangle ABC, $a = 18$, $b = 8$, and $\sin C = \frac{2}{3}$. Find the area of triangle ABC.

14. In triangle ABC, $a = 7$, $c = 8$, $\sin B = \frac{1}{4}$. Find the area of triangle ABC.

In 15–18, in $\triangle DEF$, if $d = 18$ and $f = 23$, find K if: (Answers may be left in radical form.)

15. $E = 30°$ 16. $E = 45°$ 17. $E = 60°$ 18. $E = 120°$

In 19–22, in $\triangle ABC$, if $K = 40$ and $a = 20$, find b if: (Answers may be left in radical form.)

19. $C = 30°$ 20. $C = 45°$ 21. $C = 120°$ 22. $C = 135°$

23. Find the area of triangle ABC if $a = 6$, $b = 13$, and $C = 30°$.

24. Find the area of triangle ABC if $a = 8$, $b = 11$, and $C = 150°$.

25. If the area of triangle $ABC = 150$, $a = 100$, and $b = 25$, find $\sin C$.

26. If the area of triangle $ABC = 72$, $c = 24$, and $a = 12$, find acute angle B.

27. If the area of triangle $RST = 120$, $s = 48$, and $t = 10$, find obtuse angle R.

28. If the vertex angle of an isosceles triangle is $30°$ and each leg is 6, the area of the triangle is equal to   (1) 9   (2) $9\sqrt{3}$ (3) 18   (4) $18\sqrt{3}$

29. In triangle ABC, $a = 10$, $b = 8$, and $C = 54°$. Find, to the nearest integer, the area of the triangle.

In 30–32, find, to the nearest integer, the area of triangle ABC in which $b = 2.38$ and $c = 8.19$ if:

30. $A = 40° 20'$ **31.** $A = 140° 10'$ **32.** $A = 105° 50'$

33. Using logarithms, find, to the nearest hundredth of an acre, the area of a triangular plot of ground if two sides of the plot are 19.35 rods and 14.90 rods and the included angle is $121° 20'$. (1 acre = 160 square rods.)

34. Show that the area of an isosceles triangle is given by $K = s^2 \sin A \cos A$, where K represents the area, s represents the length of a leg, and A represents a base angle.

35. A and C are angles of an acute plane triangle, b is the included side, h is the altitude upon b, and K is the area of the triangle.

a. Show that h is given by the formula

$$h = \frac{b \sin A \sin C}{\sin(A + C)}$$

b. Show that K is given by the formula

$$K = \frac{b^2 \sin A \sin C}{2 \sin(A + C)}$$

2. Using Formulas To Find the Area of a Triangle When Three Sides Are Given (s.s.s.)

If a, b, and c represent the three sides of a triangle, and s represents the *semiperimeter*, $s = \frac{1}{2}(a + b + c)$, the area K may be obtained through the use of the formula

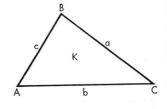

$$K = \sqrt{s(s - a)(s - b)(s - c)},$$

$$s = \tfrac{1}{2}(a + b + c)$$

This formula is called ***Heron's formula.***

When we use Heron's formula in a problem, such as model problem 1, where the measures of the sides have one or two significant digits, the computations can be done without logarithms. However, when the measurements have three or more significant digits, it is desirable to use logarithmic computation, as in model problem 2.

~~~~~~~~~~~~~~~~ *MODEL PROBLEMS* ~~~~~~~~~~~~~~~~

1. Find the area of $\triangle ABC$ if $a = 3$ ft., $b = 4$ ft., and $c = 5$ ft.

Solution:

$$a = 3 \qquad\qquad s - a = 3 \qquad\qquad K = \sqrt{s(s-a)(s-b)(s-c)}$$

$$b = 4 \qquad\qquad s - b = 2 \qquad\qquad\quad = \sqrt{6(3)(2)(1)}$$

$$c = 5 \qquad\qquad s - c = 1 \qquad\qquad\quad = \sqrt{36} = 6$$

$a + b + c = \overline{12}$ By adding,   Area of $\triangle ABC = 6$ sq. ft.   *Ans.*

$s = \frac{1}{2}(a + b + c) = 6$ $s = 6$ (Check).

Note. Since a triangle whose sides are in the ratio of $3:4:5$ is a right triangle, the area can be found readily by using $K = \frac{1}{2}bh$. Since the legs are 3 and 4, then $K = \frac{1}{2}(3)(4) = 6$.

2. The sides of a triangular lot are 32.8, 47.4, and 26.0 feet. Find the area, correct to the nearest square foot.

Solution:

$$a = 32.8 \qquad\qquad K = \sqrt{s(s-a)(s-b()s-c)}$$

$$b = 47.4 \qquad\qquad K = \sqrt{(53.1)(20.3)(5.7)(27.1)}$$

$$c = 26.0 \qquad\qquad \log K = \frac{1}{2}(\log 53.1 + \log 20.3 + \log 5.7 + \log 27.1)$$

$a + b + c = \overline{106.2}$

$$s = 53.1 \qquad\qquad \log 53.1 = 1.7251$$

$s - a = 20.3 \qquad\qquad \log 20.3 = 1.3075$

$s - b = 5.7 \qquad\qquad\; \log 5.7 = 0.7559$

$s - c = 27.1 \qquad\qquad \log 27.1 = 1.4330$

$$2\overline{)5.2215}$$

$$\log K = 2.6108$$

$$K = 408, \text{ to the nearest integer}$$

Hence, to the nearest square foot, the area is 408 sq. ft.   *Ans.*

~~~~~~

Exercises

1. Express the area of a triangle in terms of its sides a, b, and c and its semiperimeter s.

In 2–4, find the area of a triangle whose sides are:

2. 9, 12, and 15   **3.** 24, 26, and 10   **4.** 16, 34, and 30

In 5–7, find the area of a triangle whose sides are: (Answers may be left in radical form.)

5. 5, 7, and 9   **6.** 15, 25, and 30   **7.** 6, 8, and 9

8. Find the area of a triangle whose sides are 7, 8, and 9. (Answer may be left in radical form.)

In 9–11, find the area of the triangle to 3 significant digits.

9. $a = 5.37$ $b = 4.49$ $c = 8.98$
10. $a = 0.768$ $b = 0.352$ $c = 0.720$
11. $a = 2672$ $b = 1197$ $c = 2531$

12. A destroyer is ordered to patrol a triangular area whose sides are 46.8 miles, 81.4 miles, and 75.2 miles. Find, correct to the nearest square mile, the area to be patrolled.

3. Solving Area Problems Involving Parallelograms, Other Quadrilaterals, and Regular Polygons

If a and b represent two adjacent sides of a parallelogram and C represents their included angle, as shown, the area K can be obtained by using the formula

$$K = ab \sin C$$

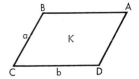

Rule. The area of a parallelogram is equal to the product of any two adjacent sides and the sine of the included angle.

Keep in mind that any two angles of a parallelogram are either equal or supplementary. Hence, the sine of any angle equals the sine of any other angle.

The area of quadrilaterals other than the parallelogram, and also the areas of other polygons, may be found by dividing these polygons into triangles.

~~~~~~~~~~~~ *MODEL PROBLEMS* ~~~~~~~~~~~~

1. In $\square ABCD$, $AB = 12$, $BC = 18$, and $A = 120°$. Find the area of $\square ABCD$ in radical form.

Solution:
The area of $\square ABCD$, $K = AB \cdot BC \cdot \sin B$.
Substitute 12 for AB and 18 for BC.

$$K = 12(18) \sin B$$

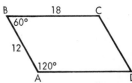

Since consecutive angles of a parallelogram are
   supplementary, $B = 180° - 120° = 60°$.
Hence, $\sin B = \sin 60° = \frac{1}{2}\sqrt{3}$.

Therefore, $K = 12(18)(\frac{1}{2}\sqrt{3}) = 108\sqrt{3}$ *Ans.*

2. Two adjacent sides of a parallelogram are 20 and 15 and the included angle is
123°. Find, correct to the nearest integer, the area of the parallelogram.

Solution:
   $K = ab \sin C$
Substitute 15 for a, 20 for b, and 123° for C.

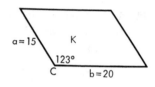

$\quad K = (15)(20) \sin 123°$
$\qquad = 300 \sin 57° \qquad (\sin 123° = \sin 57°)$
$\qquad = 300(.8387)$
$\qquad = 251.61$

Hence, the area of the parallelogram, to the nearest integer, is 252.   *Ans.*

3. The side of a regular polygon of 10 sides is 24.
   a. Find, to the nearest integer, the length of the
      radius of the inscribed circle.
   b. Using the value obtained in *a*, find the area of
      the regular polygon to the nearest integer.

Solution:
a. Let p be the perimeter of the regular polygon
   and r the radius of the inscribed circle, or
   apothem, of the regular polygon.

Since $AB = 24$, $p = 10(24)$ or 240.
Circumscribe a circle about the regular polygon.

Central $\angle AOB = \dfrac{360°}{10} = 36°$.

Since r bisects both central angle AOB and side $\overline{AB}$, $\angle DOB = 18°$ and
$DB = 12$.

In rt. $\triangle DOB$, $\dfrac{r}{12} = \cot 18°$
$\qquad\qquad r = 12 \cot 18°$
$\qquad\qquad\ = 12(3.0777)$
$\qquad\qquad\ = 36.9324 \approx 37$

Hence, the radius of the inscribed circle, to the nearest integer, is 37.

b. The area of a regular polygon equals one-half the product of its perimeter and its apothem; that is, $K = \frac{1}{2}$ pr.
Substitute 240 for p, and 37 for r.

$$K = \tfrac{1}{2}(240)(37) = 4440 \quad Ans.$$

Exercises

1. Express the area of a parallelogram in terms of the sides a and b and their included angle C.

In 2–4, find the area of a parallelogram if it has an angle of 30° and if the sides which include the angle are:

2. 24 inches and 30 inches   **3.** 8.6 feet and 7.3 feet   **4.** 140 yards and 78 yards

In 5–8, find the area of a parallelogram if its two adjacent sides are 25 and 36 and their included angle is: (Answers may be left in radical form.)

5. 45°   **6.** 60°   **7.** 120°   **8.** 135°

9. Two sides of a parallelogram are 20 and 12 and their included angle is 60°. Find the area of the parallelogram. (Answer may be left in radical form.)

In 10–13, find, correct to the nearest integer, the area of a parallelogram whose sides are 12 and 15 and whose included angle is:

10. 27°   **11.** 73°   **12.** 107°   **13.** 163°

14. The area of a parallelogram $ABCD$ is 60, $A = 30°$, and $AB = 12$. Find AD.
15. Two sides of a parallelogram are 24 inches and 10 inches and the area is 120 square inches. Find an acute angle of the parallelogram.
16. Prove that the area of any quadrilateral is equal to one-half the product of the two diagonals multiplied by the sine of the included angle.

In 17–20, find the area of quadrilateral $ABCD$, to the nearest integer, using the given data.

17. $AB = 6$, $BC = 8$, $\angle ACD = 65°$, $\angle ABC = 90°$, $CD = 20$
18. $AB = 10$, $BC = 24$, $BC \perp AB$, $\angle CAD = 72°$, $AD = 36$
19. $AB = 5$, $BC = 12$, $AC = 13$, $\angle CAD = 90°$, $AD = 24$
20. $AB = 9$, $BC = 12$, $AC = 15$, $\angle ACD = 56°$, $CD = 13$

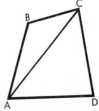

21. A plot of ground has the form of the quadrilateral *ABCD* shown at the right. $\angle DAB = 90°$, $\angle DBC = 50°$, the length of $\overline{AB} = 36$ rods, the length of $\overline{AD} = 48$ rods, and the length of $\overline{BC} = 28$ rods. Find the area of the plot, to the nearest square rod.

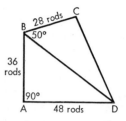

In 22–25, find, to the nearest integer, the area of a regular polygon if one side is 32 and the number of sides is:

22. 5   **23.** 6   **24.** 8   **25.** 10

In 26–28, find the area of a regular pentagon to the nearest integer if:
26. one side is 12.
27. the radius of the inscribed circle is 14.
28. the radius of the circumscribed circle is 20.

29. Find, to the nearest inch, the side of a regular pentagon whose area is 300 sq. in.

30. Prove that the area K of a regular polygon of n sides inscribed in a circle of radius R is given by the formula

$$K = \frac{nR^2 \sin \dfrac{360°}{n}}{2}$$

31. Prove that the area K of a regular polygon of n sides inscribed in a circle of radius R is given by the formula

$$K = nR^2 \sin \frac{180°}{n} \times \cos \frac{180°}{n}$$

CHAPTER XXII

TYPES OF VARIATION

In solving problems in mathematics and science, we very often apply formulas that have the same general structure, $z = xy$, a relationship among three variables in which one variable is the product of the other two.

Mathematical Formula	Scientific Formula	
Motion formula: $\quad D = RT$	Density × Volume = Mass	$DV = M$
Interest formula: $\quad I = PR$	Height × Density = Pressure	$HD = P$
Cost formula: $\quad C = NP$	Force × Distance = Work	$FD = W$
Area formula: $\quad A = LW$	Weight × Distance = Moment	$WD = M$
Percentage formula: $P = BR$	Current × Resistance = Voltage	$IR = V$

In this chapter, we shall study the manner in which the three basic types of variation are associated with formulas having the structure of $z = xy$. The basic types are *direct variation*, *inverse variation*, and *joint variation*.

1. Understanding Direct Variation: $y = kx$ or $\dfrac{y}{x} = k$

The values in the table at the right are those of the perimeters (p) and sides (s) of four squares, I, II, III, and IV. From the four pairs of corresponding values of p and s, we note that $\dfrac{p}{s} = \dfrac{4}{1} = \dfrac{8}{2} = \dfrac{24}{6} = \dfrac{240}{60}$. For the four squares, the formula $p = 4s$ states the relationships between the perimeter and a side of any one of the squares. By a transformation, $p = 4s$ becomes

VALUES OF SIDES
AND PERIMETERS
OF SQUARES

	I	II	III	IV
p	4	8	24	240
s	1	2	6	60

$\dfrac{p}{s} = 4$. The equations $p = 4s$ and $\dfrac{p}{s} = 4$ illustrate *direct variation*. If, instead of squares, we were to use equilateral triangles, our equations would be $p = 3s$ and $\dfrac{p}{s} = 3$; for regular hexagons, our equations would be $p = 6s$ and $\dfrac{p}{s} = 6$.

EXPRESSING DIRECT VARIATION IN EQUATION FORM BY USING A CONSTANT OF VARIATION

If $y = kx$ where x and y are variables and k is a constant, then we say that x and y vary *directly* as each other; that is, x varies directly as y, or y varies directly as x. The constant, k, $k \neq 0$, is called the **constant of variation.**

Note that k cannot have a value of 0. In this chapter, in all cases, assume that the constant of variation does not equal 0.

Thus, if $p = 4s$, then p and s vary directly as each other and the constant of variation is 4. In a motion problem, when there is a uniform rate of 30 miles per hour, then $D = 30T$. If $D = 30T$, then D and T vary directly as each other and 30 is the constant of variation.

If $y = kx$, then $\dfrac{y}{x} = k$. The equation $\dfrac{y}{x} = k$ also expresses direct variation.

The equation $\dfrac{y}{x} = k$ is exemplified in $\dfrac{p}{s} = 6$, $\dfrac{D}{T} = 30$, and $\dfrac{A}{L} = 35$. In this form of the equation, the constant of variation stands alone on one side and the two variables are on the other.

```
┌──────────── KEEP IN MIND ────────────

    If $y = kx$ or $\dfrac{y}{x} = k$, where $x$ and $y$ are variables and $k$

    is the constant, then $x$ and $y$ vary directly as each other
    and $k$ is the constant of variation.
└──────────────────────────────────────
```

EXPRESSING DIRECT VARIATION IN PROPORTION FORM

Direct variation is expressible in proportion form. In the figure, Square I and Square II are any two squares whose perimeters are p_1 and p_2 and whose corresponding sides are s_1 and s_2. Since the ratio of the perimeter of a square to its side is 4, then $\dfrac{p_2}{s_2} = \dfrac{p_1}{s_1}$. This proportion may be transformed

Square I
(perimeter $= p_1$)

Square II
(perimeter $= p_2$)

I

s_1

II

s_2

into $\dfrac{p_2}{p_1} = \dfrac{s_2}{s_1}$. In this form, we note that *the ratio of the perimeters directly equals the ratio of the corresponding sides.*

In general, if x and y vary directly as each other, then when x varies from x_1 to x_2 and y varies from y_1 to y_2, $\dfrac{x_2}{x_1} = \dfrac{y_2}{y_1}$.

Thus, in the table at the right, if two travelers A and B are traveling at 20 mph, A for 6 hours and B for 4 hours, the ratio of their times of travel, $\frac{6}{4}$, equals the ratio of their distances traveled, $\frac{120}{80}$. Note in the table that the time-ratio and the distance-ratio, each equal to $\frac{3}{2}$, have been placed alongside the values of time and distance.

TRAVELERS TRAVELING
AT A CONSTANT RATE
OF SPEED

	(mph)	(hr.)	(mi.)
	Rate	× Time	= Distance
A	20	$6 \rbrace \frac{3}{2}$	$120 \rbrace \frac{3}{2}$
B	20	$4 \rbrace$	$80 \rbrace$

If two travelers are traveling at the same rate of 20 miles per hour, then $D = 20T$ and D and T vary directly as each other. The constant of variation is 20.

MULTIPLICATION AND DIVISION OPERATIONS IN DIRECT VARIATION

If a man travels at a constant rate of speed, then when he travels *twice* as long, he will cover a distance *twice* as far. If the length of a rectangle is constant, dividing the width by 3, or taking a width that is one-third as long, will result in a rectangle whose area is one-third as great.

In general, if y varies directly as x:

(1) When x is *multiplied* by a number, y will be *multiplied* by the same number.

(2) When x is *divided* by a nonzero number, y will be *divided* by the same number.

THE GRAPH OF DIRECT VARIATION

If x and y vary directly as each other and k is the constant of variation, then $y = kx$. Recall that the graph of $y = kx$ is a straight line passing through the origin. In the figure are shown the graphs of $y = 4x$ and $y = -4x$, using 4 and -4 as constants of variation. Note in the case of $y = -4x$ that y and x vary directly; yet, when x increases, y decreases.

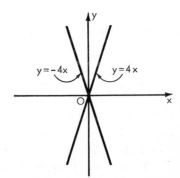

KEEP IN MIND

If y varies directly as x, then:

1. In equation form, $y = kx$ or $\dfrac{y}{x} = k$, where k is the constant of variation.

2. In proportion form, $\dfrac{y_2}{y_1} = \dfrac{x_2}{x_1}$ when x varies from x_1 to x_2 and y varies from y_1 to y_2.

3. Whenever x is multiplied by a number, y is multiplied by the same number.

4. Whenever x is divided by a nonzero number, y is divided by the same number.

5. The graph of the equation $y = kx$ is a straight line passing through the origin.

~~~~~~~~~~~~ **MODEL PROBLEMS** ~~~~~~~~~~~~

1. *a.* If $D = RT$, when will D vary directly as R?

  b. If $V = IR$, when will V vary directly as R?

Solution:

  a. D will vary directly as R when T is constant.

  b. V will vary directly as R when I is constant.

2. If y varies directly as x and if $y = 15$ when $x = 3$, find y when $x = 9$.

Solution:

Method 1	*Method 2*
($y = kx$ method)	(direct proportion method)

Method 1
($y = kx$ method)

Since y varies directly as x,
$$y = kx$$

If $y = 15$ when $x = 3$, $15 = 3k$.

Hence, k, the constant of variation, equals 5, and $y = 5x$. Therefore, when $x = 9$, $y = 5(9) = 45$. *Ans.*

Method 2
(direct proportion method)

$$\frac{y_2}{y_1} = \frac{x_2}{x_1}$$

$$\frac{y}{15} = \frac{9}{3}$$

	y	x
2nd values	y	9
1st values	15	3

$$3y = 135$$
$$y = 45 \quad Ans.$$

3. *a.* If a man triples his rate of speed, how many times as far will he go if his time of travel is the same?

  b. If the length of a rectangle of constant width is divided by 5, what happens to the area of the rectangle?

Solution:
a. If $D = RT$ and T is constant, then D varies directly as R. Hence, if the rate is multiplied by 3, the distance is also multiplied by 3. *Answer:* 3 times as far
b. If $A = LW$ and W is constant, then A varies directly as L. Hence, if the length is divided by 5, the area is divided by 5. *Answer:* The area is divided by 5.

Exercises

In 1–3, show that one variable in the table varies directly as the other and write an equation or formula that expresses the relationship between the variables.

1.

y	2	4	6
x	1	2	3

2.

C	5	10	15
n	1	2	3

3.

A	5	10	15
h	2	4	6

In 4–7, in the table, the ratio $\dfrac{y}{x}$ is constant. Find the missing numbers.

4.

y	3	12	?	27
x	1	4	5	?

5.

y	7	14	?	56
x	2	4	8	?

6.

y	−5	−10	?	−25
x	−1	−2	−3	?

7.

y	−8	−12	?	20
x	2	3	4	?

In 8–12, write an equation or formula that expresses the relationship between the variables, using k as the constant of variation.
8. The circumference of a circle, C, varies directly as the diameter, D.
9. The perimeter of an equilateral triangle, P, varies directly as a side, s.
10. The resistance, R, of a copper wire varies directly as its length, l.
11. The weight, W, of a circular pipe is directly proportional to its length, l.
12. Under certain conditions, the volume, V, of a gas varies directly as the absolute temperature, T.

13. If y varies directly as x and $y = 50$ when $x = 5$, find y when $x = 10$.
14. If C varies directly as n and $C = 6$ when $n = 4$, find C when $n = 12$.
15. If C varies directly as r and $C = 6.28$ when $r = 1$, find r when $C = 25.12$.
16. If A varies directly as h and $A = 72$ when $h = 8$, find A when $h = 5$.
17. If D varies directly as t and $D = 30$ when $t = \frac{1}{2}$, find t when $D = 20$.
18. If x varies directly as y and if $y = 27$ when $x = 6$, find y when $x = 8$.
19. If y varies directly as x and if $y = 8$ when $x = 4$, find the value of y when $x = -50$.

20. If r varies directly as s and if $r = 13$ when $s = 52$, find s when $r = 100$.

21. If 5 hats cost \$60, how much will 11 hats of the same kind cost?

22. If 3 men earn \$180 in a week, what will 15 men working at the same rate of pay earn?

23. If a boat travels 132 miles in 11 hours, how far can it travel in $38\frac{1}{2}$ hours, traveling at the same rate of speed?

24. A 20-acre field yields 300 bushels of wheat. At the same rate, how many bushels will a 50-acre field yield?

25. If one quantity varies directly as another, (1) their product is constant (2) their sum is constant   (3) their ratio is constant

26. Tell what happens to the area of a rectangle if its width is fixed and its length is (a) doubled, (b) divided by 3, and (c) halved.

27. How many times as far will a man travel if his time of travel is fixed and his rate of speed is (a) tripled, (b) divided by 5, and (c) halved?

28. How many times as far will a man travel if his rate of speed is fixed and his time of travel is (a) quadrupled, (b) divided by 10, and (c) halved?

29. D varies directly as R. What change takes place in D if (a) R is tripled (b) R is halved?

30. $A = LW$. (a) When will A vary directly as L? (b) When will A vary directly as W?

In 31–34, select two variables that may vary directly and state when this will occur.

31. $C = NP$ **32.** $I = PR$ **33.** $A = \frac{1}{2}bh$ **34.** $V = \frac{1}{3}Bh$

35. $V = LWH$. (a) When will V and L vary directly?   (b) When will V and W vary directly?   (c) When will V and H vary directly?

2. Understanding Inverse Variation: $xy = k$ or $y = \dfrac{k}{x}$

The values in the table at the right are those of the lengths (l) and widths (w) of four rectangles, I, II, III, and IV, having the same area. From the table, we see that for rectangle III, when the length is 8, the width is 3; for rectangle IV, when the length is 6, the width is 4. For the four rectangles, the formula $lw = 24$ states the relationships between the length, l, and the width, w, of any of the rectangles. The equation $lw = 24$ illustrates *inverse variation*.

VALUES OF LENGTHS AND WIDTHS OF RECTANGLES HAVING A CONSTANT AREA

	I	II	III	IV
l	24	12	8	6
w	1	2	3	4

EXPRESSING INVERSE VARIATION IN EQUATION FORM BY USING A CONSTANT OF VARIATION

If $xy = k$ where x and y are variables and k is a constant, then we say that x and y vary *inversely* as each other; that is, x varies inversely as y, and y varies inversely as x. The constant, k, is called the *constant of variation*.

Thus, if $lw = 24$, then l and w vary inversely as each other and the constant of variation is 24. In a motion problem where the distance traveled is 120 miles and this distance remains the same in several situations, then $RT = 120$. If $RT = 120$, then R and T vary inversely as each other and 120 is the constant of variation. In an interest problem, where $PR = I$ and I is fixed at 200 in several situations, then $PR = 200$. If $PR = 200$, then P and R vary inversely as each other and the constant of variation is 200.

KEEP IN MIND

If $xy = k$ or $y = \dfrac{k}{x}$, where x and y are variables and k is a constant, then x and y vary inversely as each other and k is the constant of variation.

EXPRESSING INVERSE VARIATION IN PROPORTION FORM

Inverse variation is expressible in proportion form. In the figure, Rectangle I and Rectangle II are any two rectangles whose lengths are l_1 and l_2 and whose corresponding widths are w_1 and w_2. When the areas of the rectangle are the same, $l_1 w_1 = l_2 w_2$, which, when transformed, becomes the proportion $\dfrac{l_2}{l_1} = \dfrac{w_1}{w_2}$.

In this form, note that *the ratio of the lengths is "inversely" equal to the ratio of the widths;* that is, the ratio of the lengths is the inverse or reciprocal of the corresponding ratio of the widths.

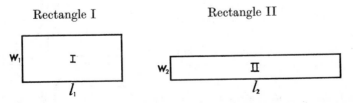

Rectangle I   Rectangle II

In general, if x and y vary inversely as each other, then $\dfrac{y_2}{y_1} = \dfrac{x_1}{x_2}$; that is, the ratio of two values of one variable *inversely* equals the ratio of the corresponding values of the other variable.

Thus, in the table at the right, if two travelers A and B are traveling the same distance, 120 miles, A at 20 miles per hour and B at 15 miles per hour, the ratio of their rates is $\frac{20}{15}$, and the ratio of their times of travel is $\frac{6}{8}$. Note in the table that the rate-ratio, $\frac{4}{3}$, and the time-ratio, $\frac{3}{4}$, have been placed alongside the values of rate and time.

	(mph)	(hr.)	(mi.)
	Rate $\times$	Time $=$	Distance
A	$20\big\}_{\tfrac{4}{3}}$	$6\big\}_{\tfrac{3}{4}}$	120
B	15	8	120

TRAVELERS TRAVELING A CONSTANT DISTANCE

If two travelers are traveling the same distance of 120 miles, then $RT = 120$ and R and T vary inversely as each other. The constant of variation is 120.

MULTIPLICATION AND DIVISION OPERATIONS IN INVERSE VARIATION

A man travels over a fixed distance in two trips. If he goes four times as fast, his time will be divided by 4; that is, he will travel only $\frac{1}{4}$ as long. If the price of an article is doubled, then if the cost of an entire purchase remains fixed, a purchaser can buy only one-half the original number of such articles.

In general, if x varies inversely as y:
(1) When x is *multiplied* by a nonzero number, y will be *divided* by the same number.
(2) When x is *divided* by a nonzero number, y will be *multiplied* by the same number.

THE GRAPH OF INVERSE VARIATION

If x and y vary inversely as each other and k is the constant of variation, then $xy = k$. Recall that the graph of $xy = k$ is an equilateral hyperbola. If k is positive, the branches of the hyperbola are in quadrants I and III, and if k is negative, the branches of the hyperbola are in quadrants II and IV, as shown in the figure. Note in the case of $xy = -4$ that x and y vary inversely; yet, when x increases, y increases also.

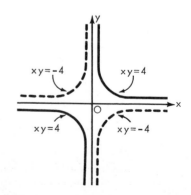

KEEP IN MIND

If y varies inversely as x, then:

1. In equation form, $xy = k$ or $y = \dfrac{k}{x}$, where k is the constant of variation.

2. In proportion form, $\dfrac{y_2}{y_1} = \dfrac{x_1}{x_2}$, when x varies from x_1 to x_2 and y varies from y_1 to y_2.

3. Whenever x is multiplied by a nonzero number, y is divided by the same number.

4. Whenever x is divided by a nonzero number, y is multiplied by the same number.

MODEL PROBLEMS

1. Express as an equation: The measure of the central angle, C, of a regular polygon varies inversely as the number of sides, n. *Answer:* $Cn = k$

2. If $D = RT$, when will R and T vary inversely? *Answer:* when D is constant

3. If y varies inversely as x and if $y = 3$ when $x = 12$, find y when $x = 4$.

Solution:

Method 1 ($xy = k$ method)	Method 2 (inverse proportion method)

Method 1
($xy = k$ method)

Since y varies inversely as x,

$$xy = k$$

If $y = 3$ when $x = 12$, $\quad (12)(3) = k$

$$36 = k$$

Hence, $xy = 36$

When $x = 4$,

$$4y = 36 \text{ or } y = 9 \quad Ans.$$

Method 2
(inverse proportion method)

$$\frac{y_2}{y_1} = \frac{x_1}{x_2}$$

$$\frac{y}{3} = \frac{12}{4}$$

$$4y = 36$$

$$y = 9 \quad Ans.$$

	y	x
2nd values	y	4
1st values	3	12

4. The expression $xy = z$ represents (1) direct variation of x with respect to y when z is constant (2) inverse variation of x with respect to y when z is constant (3) inverse variation of x with respect to z when y is constant

Solution:

Make the correct choice by applying the following principle:
If the product of two variables is constant, then either of the variables varies inversely with respect to the other.

In choice (2), the product xy equals z, which is given as constant. Hence, x varies inversely with respect to y.

Answer: The correct choice is (2).

〰〰〰〰〰〰〰〰〰〰〰〰〰〰〰〰〰〰〰〰〰〰〰〰

Exercises

In 1–3, show that one variable in the table varies inversely as the other and write an equation or formula that expresses the relationship between the variables.

1.

x	1	2	4
y	40	20	10

2.

R	2	4	10
T	50	25	10

3.

C	12	24	36
D	12	6	4

In 4–9, in the table, the product xy is constant. Find the missing numbers.

4.

y	36	18	8	9
x	2	4	?	?

5.

y	10	6	4	?
x	3	5	?	20

6.

y	2	$2\frac{1}{2}$	3	?
x	5	4	?	$2\frac{1}{2}$

7.

y	6	4	?	1
x	-2	-3	-6	?

8.

y	-4	-3	-2	?
x	-6	-8	?	4

9.

y	4	-2	$-\frac{1}{2}$	?
x	-1	2	?	-8

In 10–12, write an equation or formula that expresses the relationship between the variables, using k as the constant of variation where k is not given.

10. If the distance remains at 100, the rate, R, varies inversely as the time, T.

11. For a fixed sum of money, the number of articles, N, that can be bought varies inversely as the cost, C, of an article.

12. Under fixed conditions, the volume, V, of a gas varies inversely as the pressure, p.

13. If x varies inversely as y and $x = 4$ when $y = 5$, find x when $y = 10$.

14. If n varies inversely as c and $n = 20$ when $c = 10$, find c when $n = 50$.

15. If R varies inversely as T and $R = 40$ when $T = \frac{1}{2}$, find R when $T = 4$.

16. If y is inversely proportional to z and $y = 9$ when $z = 8$, find y when $z = 2$.

17. If x varies inversely as y and $x = 8$ when $y = 9$, find y when $x = 24$.

18. If s varies inversely as t, and if $s = 6$ when $t = 2$, find s when $t = 3$.

19. The speed of a gear varies inversely as the number of teeth. If a gear which has 36 teeth makes 30 revolutions per minute, how many revolutions per minute will a gear which has 24 teeth make?

20. If 8 printing presses can do a job in 6 hours, how many hours would it take 3 printing presses to do the same job, assuming the rate of work of each press is the same?

In 21–32, state whether the relationship is one of direct variation, inverse variation, or neither.

21. $bh = 40$ **22.** $RT = 80$ **23.** $P = \dfrac{60}{V}$ **24.** $b = 40h$

25. $R + T = 80$ **26.** $\dfrac{e}{i} = 20$ **27.** $h = 40b$ **28.** $R = 80T$

29. $t = \dfrac{100}{r}$ **30.** $b + h = 40$ **31.** $T = 80R$ **32.** $\dfrac{N}{C} = 4$

33. V varies inversely as P. (*a*) If P is tripled, what change takes place in V? (*b*) If P is divided in half, what change takes place in V?

34. $A = LW$. When will L and W vary inversely?

In 35–38, select two variables that may vary inversely and state when this will occur:

35. $C = NP$ **36.** $I = RP$ **37.** $A = \frac{1}{2}bh$ **38.** $V = \frac{1}{3}Bh$

39. $V = LWH$. (*a*) When will L and W vary inversely? (*b*) When will L and H vary inversely? (*c*) When will W and H vary inversely?

3. Understanding Joint Variation: $z = kxy$ or $\dfrac{z}{xy} = k$

The values in the table at the right are those of the areas (A), bases (b), and altitudes (h) of four triangles, I, II, III, and IV. From the table, we see that when the length of a base is 10 and the altitude is 4, then the area of triangle II is 20. For the four triangles, the formula $A = \frac{1}{2}bh$ states the relationships among the base, altitude, and area of any one of the triangles. By a transformation, $A = \frac{1}{2}bh$ becomes $\dfrac{A}{bh} = \frac{1}{2}$. Note in the table that the ratio of A to bh equals $\frac{1}{2}$ in each instance. The equations $A = \frac{1}{2}bh$ and $\dfrac{A}{bh} = \frac{1}{2}$ illustrate *joint variation*.

VALUES OF BASES, ALTITUDES, AND AREAS OF TRIANGLES

	I	II	III	IV
A	12	20	24	40
bh	24	40	48	80
h	3	4	4	5
b	8	10	12	16

EXPRESSING JOINT VARIATION IN EQUATION FORM BY USING A CONSTANT OF VARIATION

If $z = kxy$ where x, y, and z are variables and k is a constant, then we say that z varies jointly as the product of x and y, or, in simpler language, "z varies jointly as x and y." The constant, k, is called the *constant of variation*.

Thus, if $A = \frac{1}{2}bh$, we say that A varies jointly as b and h and the constant of variation is $\frac{1}{2}$. In the motion formula $D = RT$, D varies jointly as R and T and the constant of variation is 1.

The equation $z = kxy$, which expresses joint variation, can be transformed into $\dfrac{z}{xy} = k$. The latter equation is exemplified in $\dfrac{A}{bh} = \frac{1}{2}$, $\dfrac{C}{NP} = 1$, and $\dfrac{V}{BH} = \dfrac{1}{3}$.
In this form, the constant of variation stands alone on one side of the equation and the three variables are on the other side.

KEEP IN MIND

If $z = kxy$ or $\dfrac{z}{xy} = k$, where z, x, and y are variables and k is a constant, then z varies jointly as x and y and k is the constant of variation.

Note. The equation $z = kxy$ may be transformed into an equivalent equation $y = \dfrac{z}{kx}$. If $\dfrac{1}{k}$ is replaced by k', we obtain $y = k'\dfrac{z}{x}$. If $y = k'\dfrac{z}{x}$ where x, y, and z are variables, the expression is used, "y varies directly as z and inversely as x." It should be kept in mind that in such cases, the type of variation that is involved is that of joint variation.

EXPRESSING JOINT VARIATION IN PROPORTION FORM

Joint variation is expressible in proportion form. In the figure Triangle I and Triangle II are any two triangles whose bases are b_1 and b_2, whose altitudes are h_1 and h_2, and whose areas are A_1 and A_2. Since $A_2 = \frac{1}{2}b_2h_2$ and $A_1 = \frac{1}{2}b_1h_1$, then by division, $\dfrac{A_2}{A_1} = \dfrac{b_2 h_2}{b_1 h_1}$, eliminating the constant, $\frac{1}{2}$. This proportion may be transformed into $\dfrac{A_2}{A_1} = \left(\dfrac{b_2}{b_1}\right)\left(\dfrac{h_2}{h_1}\right)$. In this form, we note that *the ratio of the areas equals the product of the ratio of the bases and the ratio of the corresponding altitudes drawn to these bases.*

Triangle I   Triangle II

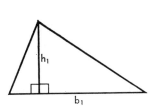

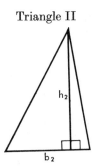

In general, if z varies jointly as x and y, then when z varies from z_1 to z_2 and x from x_1 to x_2 and y from y_1 to y_2, $\dfrac{z_2}{z_1} = \dfrac{x_2 y_2}{x_1 y_1}$ or $\dfrac{z_2}{z_1} = \left(\dfrac{x_2}{x_1}\right)\left(\dfrac{y_2}{y_1}\right)$; that is, the ratio of two values of z equals the product of the ratios of the corresponding values of x and y. In this case, (x_1, y_1, z_1) and (x_2, y_2, z_2) are ordered triplets of numbers that satisfy $z = kxy$.

Thus, in the table at the right, if traveler B goes twice as fast and three times as long as A, then B will go six times as far as A. The ratio of the distances, 6, equals the product of the ratio of the rates, 2, and the ratio of the times, 3. Note in the table that the three ratios, $\frac{2}{1}$, $\frac{3}{1}$, and $\frac{6}{1}$, are next to the values.

In the above example of two travelers, the motion formula, $D = RT$ applies. Hence, D varies jointly as R and T.

TRAVELERS TRAVELING AT VARYING RATES, TIMES, AND DISTANCES		
(mph)	(hr.)	(mi.)
Rate $\times$	Time $=$	Distance
B $\;30\big)_1^2$	$6\big)_1^3$	$180\big)_1^6$
A $\;15\big)$	$2\big)$	$30\big)$

MULTIPLICATION AND DIVISION OPERATIONS IN JOINT VARIATION

In a problem involving the area of a triangle, if the base is multiplied by 4 and the altitude is multiplied by 3, then the area of the new triangle is 12 times the area of the old triangle. In the motion problem shown in the preceding table, if a man travels twice as fast and three times as long, then he will go six times as far; that is, if the ratio of the speeds is 2 and the ratio of the times of travel is 3, then the ratio of distances traveled is 6.

In general, if z varies jointly as x and y:

When x is multiplied by a number a and y is multiplied by a number b, then z is multiplied by the product of these numbers ab. This is another way of saying that when the ratio of the x-values is a and the ratio of the y-values is b, then the ratio of the z-values is ab.

KEEP IN MIND

If z varies jointly as x and y, then:

1. In equation form, $z = kxy$ or $\dfrac{z}{xy} = k$, where k is the constant of variation.

2. In proportion form, $\dfrac{z_2}{z_1} = \dfrac{x_2 y_2}{x_1 y_1}$ or $\dfrac{z_2}{z_1} = \left(\dfrac{x_2}{x_1}\right)\left(\dfrac{y_2}{y_1}\right)$, where x varies from x_1 to x_2, y varies from y_1 to y_2, and z varies from z_1 to z_2.

3. When x is multiplied by a number a and y is multiplied by a number b, then z is multiplied by ab.

Note. If a number is divided by a nonzero number a, the number may be considered to be multiplied by $\dfrac{1}{a}$.

Hence, the division operation may be replaced by a multiplication operation in order to apply this principle. For example, if $z = kxy$, x is divided by 4, and y is multiplied by 3, then z is multiplied by $\frac{1}{4}(3)$ or $\frac{3}{4}$.

MODEL PROBLEMS

1. If $V = LWH$, when will V vary jointly as (a) W and H (b) L and H (c) L and W?

Solution:
(a) when L is constant   (b) when W is constant   (c) when H is constant

2. If z varies jointly as x and y, and $z = 120$ when $x = 8$ and $y = 5$, find z when $x = 15$ and $y = 4$.

Solution:
Since z varies jointly as x and y, $z = kxy$
If $z = 120$ when $x = 8$ and $y = 5$, $120 = k(8)(5)$
$$120 = 40k$$
$$3 = k$$
Substitute $x = 15$ and $y = 4$. $z = 3xy = 3(15)(4) = 180$ *Ans.*

Exercises

In 1–3, write an equation or formula that expresses the relationship between the variables, using k as the constant of variation.

1. The area of a parallelogram, A, varies jointly as its base, b, and altitude, h.
2. The volume of a pyramid, V, varies jointly as its base, B, and altitude, h.
3. The area of a rhombus, A, varies jointly as its diagonals, D and d.
4. If V varies jointly as B and h, and $V = 100$ when $B = 30$ and $h = 10$, find V when $B = 60$ and $h = 30$.
5. If I varies jointly as p and r, and $I = 8$ when $p = 100$ and $r = .04$, find I when $p = 400$ and $r = .06$.
6. D varies jointly as R and T. If R is doubled and T is trebled, what change takes place in D?
7. V varies jointly as l, w, and h. If l is multiplied by 4, w is multiplied by 5 and h is halved, what change takes place in V?
8. $I = PRT$. (a) When will I vary jointly as P and R? (b) When will I vary jointly as P and T?
9. If the base of a triangle is quadrupled and the height is tripled, then its area is multiplied by _____.

In 10–12, complete the statement, using $A = \frac{1}{2}bh$.
10. If the base and height are each doubled, the area of a triangle will be _____.
11. If the base and height are each halved, the area of a triangle will be _____.
12. If the area of a triangle is to be multiplied by 6 and the base is doubled, then its height must be _____.

13. $A = \frac{1}{2}nsr$. (a) When will A vary jointly as s and r? (b) When will A vary jointly as n and r? (c) If n and s are constant, how will A and r vary? (d) If A and n are constant, how will s and r vary?

4. Understanding Direct and Inverse Square and Square Root Variation

DIRECT SQUARE VARIATION: $y = kx^2$ or $\frac{y}{x^2} = k$

The values in the table at the right are those of the edges (e) and surfaces (S) of four cubes, I, II, III, and IV. From the four pairs of corresponding values of S and e^2, we note that $\frac{S}{e^2} = \frac{6}{1} = \frac{24}{4} = \frac{54}{9} = \frac{150}{25}$. For each of the four cubes, the formula, $S = 6e^2$ states the relationships between its surface, S, and its edge, e.

VALUES OF EDGES AND SURFACES OF CUBES

	I	II	III	IV
S	6	24	54	150
e^2	1	4	9	25
e	1	2	3	5

EXPRESSING DIRECT SQUARE VARIATION IN EQUATION FORM BY USING A CONSTANT OF VARIATION

─────────── *KEEP IN MIND* ───────────

If $y = kx^2$ or $\dfrac{y}{x^2} = k$, where x and y are variables and k is a constant, then y varies directly as the square of x, and k is the constant of variation.

In general, if y varies directly as the square of x, then when x varies from x_1 to x_2 and y varies from y_1 to y_2,

$$\frac{y_2}{y_1} = \left(\frac{x_2}{x_1}\right)^2 \quad \text{or} \quad \frac{y_2}{y_1} = \frac{x_2{}^2}{x_1{}^2}$$

Thus, if $S = 6e^2$, then S varies directly as the square of e, and the constant of variation is 6. Also, if $A = \pi r^2$, then A varies directly as the square of r, and the constant of variation is π.

If $y = kx^2$, then $\dfrac{y}{x^2} = k$. The equation, $\dfrac{y}{x^2} = k$ also expresses direct square variation. The equation $\dfrac{y}{x^2} = k$ is illustrated by $\dfrac{S}{e^2} = 6$ and $\dfrac{A}{r^2} = \pi$. In this form, the constant of variation stands alone on one side of the equation and the two variables are on the other.

The graph that is associated with direct square variation is the parabola, $y = kx^2$.

DIRECT SQUARE ROOT VARIATION: $y = k\sqrt{x}$ or $\dfrac{y}{\sqrt{x}} = k$

If $y = k\sqrt{x}$ or $\dfrac{y}{\sqrt{x}} = k$ where x and y are variables and k is a constant, then y varies directly as the square root of x, and k is the constant of variation.

If y varies directly as the square root of x, then when x varies from x_1 to x_2 and y from y_1 to y_2, $\dfrac{y_2}{y_1} = \sqrt{\dfrac{x_2}{x_1}}$ or $\dfrac{y_2}{y_1} = \dfrac{\sqrt{x_2}}{\sqrt{x_1}}$. To solve problems involving direct square root variation, procedures are used that are similar to those used in direct square variation.

INVERSE SQUARE VARIATION: $yx^2 = k$ or $y = \dfrac{k}{x^2}$

In the table of values at the right, h represents the altitude and s represents the side of the base of four prisms having a square base and a constant volume. From the four pairs of corresponding values of h and s^2, we note that $hs^2 = 18 \times 4 = 8 \times 9 = 2 \times 36 = \frac{1}{2} \times 144$. In each case, $hs^2 = 72$. For prisms having a square base and a constant volume, $hs^2 = k$ states the relationship between the altitude, h, and the side of the base, s.

VALUES OF BASES AND ALTITUDES OF PRISMS

	I	II	III	IV
h	18	8	2	$\frac{1}{2}$
s^2	4	9	36	144
s	2	3	6	12

EXPRESSING INVERSE SQUARE VARIATION IN EQUATION FORM, USING A CONSTANT OF VARIATION

——— *KEEP IN MIND* ———

In $yx^2 = k$ or $y = \dfrac{k}{x^2}$ where x and y are variables and k is a constant, then y varies inversely as the square of x and k is the constant of variation.

In general, if y varies inversely as the square of x, then when x varies from x_1 to x_2 and y varies from y_1 to y_2, $\dfrac{y_2}{y_1} = \left(\dfrac{x_1}{x_2}\right)^2$ or $\dfrac{y_2}{y_1} = \dfrac{x_1^2}{x_2^2}$. Thus, if $hs^2 = 72$, then h varies inversely as the square of s, and 72 is the constant of variation. Also, if $r^2h = \dfrac{100}{\pi}$, then h varies inversely as the square of r and the constant of variation is $\dfrac{100}{\pi}$.

INVERSE SQUARE ROOT VARIATION: $y\sqrt{x} = k$ or $y = \dfrac{k}{\sqrt{x}}$

If $y\sqrt{x} = k$ or $y = \dfrac{k}{\sqrt{x}}$ where x and y are variables and k is a constant, then y varies inversely as the square root of x, and k is the constant of variation.

If y varies inversely as the square root of x, then when x varies from x_1 to x_2 and y varies from y_1 to y_2, $\dfrac{y_2}{y_1} = \sqrt{\dfrac{x_1}{x_2}}$ or $\dfrac{y_2}{y_1} = \dfrac{\sqrt{x_1}}{\sqrt{x_2}}$. To solve problems involving inverse square root variation, procedures are used that are similar to those used in inverse square variation.

MULTIPLICATION AND DIVISION OPERATIONS IN DIRECT AND INVERSE SQUARE AND SQUARE ROOT VARIATION

If y varies directly as the square of x, then when x is multiplied by a number a, y is multiplied by a^2.

Thus, if S varies directly as the square of e, then when e is multiplied by 3, S is multiplied by 9.

If y varies inversely as the square of x, then when x is multiplied by a number a, y is divided by a^2.

Thus, if h varies inversely as the square of s, then when s is multiplied by 3, h is divided by 9.

If y varies directly as the square root of x, then when x is multiplied by a number a, y is multiplied by $\sqrt{a}$.

Thus, if the radius of a circle, r, varies directly as the square root of the area, A, then if A is multiplied by 9, r is multiplied by 3.

If y varies inversely as the square root of x, then when x is multiplied by a number a, y is divided by $\sqrt{a}$.

Thus, if r varies inversely as the square root of h, then when h is multiplied by 9, r is divided by 3.

$\sim\sim\sim\sim\sim\sim\sim$ *MODEL PROBLEMS* $\sim\sim\sim\sim\sim\sim\sim$

1. Express each sentence as an equation.
   a. The distance that a freely falling body falls, D, varies directly as the square of the time it falls, T.
   b. The force of attraction, F, of two bodies having constant masses varies inversely as the square of the distance between them, d.

Solution:

$$a. \ D = kT^2 \text{ or } \frac{D}{T^2} = k$$

$$b. \ F = \frac{k}{d^2} \text{ or } Fd^2 = k$$

2. Express each sentence as an equation.

   a. The radius of a circle, r, varies directly as the square root of the area, A.

   b. The radius, r, of a cylinder of constant volume varies inversely as the square root of the altitude, h.

Solution:

$$a.\ r = k\sqrt{A} \text{ or } \frac{r}{\sqrt{A}} = k$$

$$b.\ r\sqrt{h} = k$$

3. If x varies inversely as the square of y and if $x = 2$ when $y = 6$, find x when $y = 3$.

Solution:

Since x varies inversely as the square of y, then $xy^2 = k$.

Since $x = 2$ when $y = 6$, substitute 2 for x and 6 for y: $\quad 2(6^2) = k$

$$2(36) = k$$
$$72 = k$$

Hence, $xy^2 = 72$

To find x when $y = 3$, substitute 3 for y: $\quad x(3^2) = 72$

$$9x = 72$$
$$x = 8 \quad Ans.$$

4. Indicate the number by which T is to be multiplied if L is multiplied by 4 and:

   a. T varies directly as the square of L

   b. T varies inversely as the square of L

   c. T varies directly as the square root of L

   d. T varies inversely as the square root of L

Solution:

   a. If T varies directly as the square of L, then if L is multiplied by a, T is multiplied by a^2. Hence, if L is multiplied by 4, T is multiplied by 4^2 or 16. *Ans.*

   b. If T varies inversely as the square of L, then if L is multiplied by a $(a \neq 0)$, T is divided by a^2. Hence, if L is multiplied by 4, T is divided by 4^2 or 16. Since multiplying by $\frac{1}{16}$ is equivalent to dividing by 16, T is multiplied by $\frac{1}{16}$. *Ans.*

   c. If T varies directly as the square root of L, then if L is multiplied by a, T is multiplied by $\sqrt{a}$. Hence, if L is multiplied by 4, T is multiplied by $\sqrt{4}$ or 2. *Ans.*

  d. If T varies inversely as the square root of L, then if L is multiplied by
  a $(a \neq 0)$, T is divided by $\sqrt{a}$. Hence, if L is multiplied by 4, T is divided
  by $\sqrt{4}$ or 2. Since multiplying by $\frac{1}{2}$ is equivalent to dividing by 2, T is
  multiplied by $\frac{1}{2}$. *Ans.*

Exercises

  In 1–4, express the statement as an equation, using k as the constant of
variation.

1. The area of a circle, A, varies directly as the square of its radius, r.

2. The area of a square, A, varies directly as the square of its edge, e.

3. The surface area of a sphere, S, varies directly as the square of its radius, r.

4. The intensity of illumination, I, upon a surface varies inversely as the square
  of the distance, d, between the surface and the source of light.

5. If d varies directly as the square of t and if $d = 24$ when $t = 2$, find the value
  of d when $t = 5$.

6. If x varies directly as y^2 and if $x = 2$ when $y = 1$, find the value of x when
  $y = 2$.

7. If v varies directly as b^2 and $v = 45$ when $b = 3$, find the value of v when $b = 4$.

8. If x varies directly as the square of y and if $x = 200$ when $y = 5$, find the
  value of x when $y = 4$.

9. If x varies directly as the square root of y and if $x = 10$ when $y = 100$, find
  x when $y = 900$.

10. If S varies directly as the square of e and $S = 150$ when $e = 5$, find S when
  $e = 10$.

11. If I varies inversely as the square of d and $I = 400$ when $d = 5$, find I when
  $d = 20$.

12. If x varies inversely as the square root of y and $x = 4$ when $y = 25$, find
  x when $y = 4$.

13. If t varies directly as $\sqrt{x}$ and if $t = 2$ when $x = 25$, what is the value of t
  when $x = 100$?

14. If $y = 10$ when $x = 5$, find the value of y when $x = 20$ and:
  a. y varies directly as the square of x.
  b. y varies inversely as the square of x.
  c. y varies directly as the square root of x.
  d. y varies inversely as the square root of x.

15. If F varies inversely as the square of d, what change takes place in F when
  d is   (*a*) doubled   (*b*) trebled?

In 16 and 17, express the statement as an equation, using k as the constant of variation.

16. The volume of a sphere, V, varies directly as the cube of its radius, r.

17. The velocity, v, of sound in air varies directly as the square root of the absolute temperature, t, of the air.

18. $K = \frac{1}{2}mv^2$. (a) How do K and v vary when m is constant? (b) How do m and v vary when K is constant? (c) How do K and m vary when v is constant?

19. The surface area of a sphere varies directly as the square of its radius. If the surface area is 64π square inches when the radius is 4 inches, what is the surface area, in square inches, when the radius is 8 inches? (1) 128π (2) 32π (3) 64π (4) 256π

20. Indicate the number by which A is to be multiplied if B is multiplied by 9 and:

    a. A varies directly as the square of B.

    b. A varies inversely as the square of B.

    c. A varies directly as the square root of B.

    d. A varies inversely as the square root of B.

21. What is the graph of the relation between y and x when (a) y varies directly as x (b) y varies inversely as x (c) y varies directly as the square of x?

5. Simplifying the Rules in Variation by Means of a Symbol

THE RATIO SYMBOL, $+x)$

The rules in variation are simplified by the use of the symbol $+x)$ to represent the ratio of the second value to the first, as x varies from x_1 to x_2. We define the symbol $+x)$ as follows: $+x) = \dfrac{x_2}{x_1}$. Read $+x)$ as "x-ratio."

Also, $+D) = +R)+T)$ is read "The D-ratio equals the product of the R-ratio and the T-ratio." (Think of the hyphen across the left arm of the parentheses as representing the fraction line used in the ratio.)

THE MEANING OF THE SYMBOL $+x)$

$+x) = 3$ means that x is tripling in value. Do not confuse $+x) = 3$ with $x = 3$, since $x = 3$ means that x has a value of 3. In an area problem, $+L) = 4$ and $+W) = 5$ mean that the length is multiplied by 4 and the width is multiplied by 5. If L and W are the length and width of a rectangle, then $+A) = 20$ which means that the area is multiplied by 20.

COMPARING THE SYMBOL $+x)$ WITH THE SYMBOL Δx

Recall that $\Delta x = x_2 - x_1$. Hence, if x changes in value from 2 to 10, then $\Delta x = 10 - 2 = 8$. In this case, since $+x) = \dfrac{x_2}{x_1}$, then $+x) = \frac{10}{2} = 5$; that is, x becomes 5 times as great as it varies from x_1 to x_2.

If k is a constant, then $+k) = 1$, since a constant remains fixed in value. Hence, the ratio of any two values of a constant equals 1.

USING THE RATIO SYMBOL TO REPLACE FACTORS

We have learned that if $z = kxy$ and k is constant, then $\dfrac{z_2}{z_1} = \left(\dfrac{x_2}{x_1}\right)\left(\dfrac{y_2}{y_1}\right)$. Using ratio symbols, we may write $+z) = +x)+y)$, replacing $\dfrac{z_2}{z_1}$ with $+z)$, $\dfrac{x_2}{x_1}$ with $+x)$ and $\dfrac{y_2}{y_1}$ with $+y)$. In this way, we eliminate six subscripts and three letters, a total saving of 9 characters.

If $p = 4s$, we may write $+p) = +s)$ instead of $\dfrac{p_2}{p_1} = \dfrac{s_2}{s_1}$. If $RT = 120$, we may write $+R)+T) = 1$ instead of $\left(\dfrac{R_2}{R_1}\right)\left(\dfrac{T_2}{T_1}\right) = 1$.

Now we will prove that if $z = kxy$ and k is a constant, then $+z) = +x)+y)$.

Let x_1 and y_1 be values of x and y that correspond to z_1, a value of z. If z varies from z_1 to z_2, let x_2 and y_2 be values of x and y that correspond to z_2. Since $z = kxy$, then $z_2 = kx_2 y_2$ and $z_1 = kx_1 y_1$.

Hence, by division:

$$\frac{z_2}{z_1} = \frac{kx_2 y_2}{kx_1 y_1} = \frac{x_2 y_2}{x_1 y_1}$$

Using ratio symbols: $+z) = +x)+y)$

Observe that the equation $z = kxy$ is transformable into $+z) = +x)+y)$ by (1) replacing each variable factor with a ratio symbol involving the factor, and (2) replacing the constant factor with 1. (Recall that $+k) = 1$, if k is a constant.)

Thus, if $A = \pi r^2$ or $A = \pi rr$, then $+A) = +r)+r)$ or $+A) = +r)^2$. Also, if $V = \frac{4}{3}\pi r^3$ or $V = \frac{4}{3}\pi rrr$, then $+V) = +r)+r)+r)$ or $+V) = +r)^3$.

SUMMARY OF THE VARIATION FORMULAS

$$\left((\div x) = \frac{x_2}{x_1}, \ (\div y) = \frac{y_2}{y_1}, \ (\div z) = \frac{z_2}{z_1} \right)$$

Type of Variation	Equation	Equation with Subscripts	Equation with Ratio Symbols
direct	$y = kx$ or $\dfrac{y}{x} = k$	$\dfrac{y_2}{y_1} = \dfrac{x_2}{x_1}$	$(\div y) = (\div x)$
inverse	$y = \dfrac{k}{x}$ or $xy = k$	$\dfrac{y_2}{y_1} = \dfrac{x_1}{x_2}$ or $\dfrac{y_2}{y_1} = \dfrac{1}{\frac{x_2}{x_1}}$	$(\div y) = \dfrac{1}{(\div x)}$ or $(\div y)(\div x) = 1$
joint	$z = kxy$ or $\dfrac{z}{xy} = k$	$\dfrac{z_2}{z_1} = \left(\dfrac{x_2}{x_1}\right)\left(\dfrac{y_2}{y_1}\right)$	$(\div z) = (\div x)(\div y)$
direct square	$y = kx^2$ or $\dfrac{y}{x^2} = k$	$\dfrac{y_2}{y_1} = \left(\dfrac{x_2}{x_1}\right)^2$	$(\div y) = (\div x)^2$
inverse square	$y = \dfrac{k}{x^2}$ or $yx^2 = k$	$\dfrac{y_2}{y_1} = \left(\dfrac{x_1}{x_2}\right)^2$ or $\dfrac{y_2}{y_1} = \dfrac{1}{\left(\frac{x_2}{x_1}\right)^2}$	$(\div y) = \dfrac{1}{(\div x)^2}$ or $(\div y)(\div x)^2 = 1$
direct square root	$y = k\sqrt{x}$ or $\dfrac{y}{\sqrt{x}} = k$	$\dfrac{y_2}{y_1} = \sqrt{\dfrac{x_2}{x_1}}$	$(\div y) = \sqrt{(\div x)}$

Type of Variation	Equation	Equation with Subscripts	Equation with Ratio Symbols
inverse square root	$y = \dfrac{k}{\sqrt{x}}$ or $y\sqrt{x} = k$	$\dfrac{y_2}{y_1} = \sqrt{\dfrac{x_1}{x_2}}$ or $\dfrac{y_2}{y_1} = \dfrac{1}{\sqrt{\dfrac{x_2}{x_1}}}$	$\bumpeq(y) = \dfrac{1}{\sqrt{\bumpeq(x)}}$ or $\bumpeq(y)\sqrt{\bumpeq(x)} = 1$

~~~~~~~~~~ *MODEL PROBLEMS* ~~~~~~~~~~

1. Using ratio symbols, show that if the radius of a circle is tripled, the area of the circle becomes 9 times as great.

Solution:
Begin with the formula for the area of a circle, $A = \pi R^2$.
Replace each variable factor with a ratio symbol involving the factor and replace the constant with 1.

$$A = \pi R^2$$
$$\bumpeq(A) = 1 \bumpeq(R)^2$$
$$\bumpeq(A) = \bumpeq(R)^2$$

If the radius is tripled, then $\bumpeq(R) = 3$. Hence,

$$\bumpeq(A) = 3^2 = 9$$

Answer: The area of the circle becomes 9 times as great.

2. The volume of a sphere varies directly as the cube of its radius. If the volume becomes 64 times as great, what effect does this have on the radius?

Solution:
Let $V =$ the measure of the volume of the sphere and $R =$ the measure of the radius of the sphere.
Since the volume varies directly as the cube of the radius, then $\bumpeq(V) = \bumpeq(R)^3$.
If the volume becomes 64 times as great, then $\bumpeq(V) = 64$. Hence, $\bumpeq(R)^3 = 64$. Taking the cube root of each side, $\bumpeq(R) = 4$.

Answer: The radius of the sphere is quadrupled, or multiplied by 4.

3. $E = \frac{1}{2}mv^2$ expresses the scientific principle that the kinetic energy of a moving body equals one-half the product of its mass and the square of its velocity.

a. State the formula using ratio symbols.

b. State the formula using ratio symbols when the mass, m, is constant; state the type of variation involved.

c. State the formula using ratio symbols when the velocity, v, is constant; state the type of variation involved.

d. State the formula using ratio symbols when the kinetic energy, E, is constant; state the type of variation involved.

Solution:

a. Using ratio symbols, $\dotplus E) = \dotplus m)\dotplus v)^2$. (Recall that if k is a constant, then $\dotplus k) = 1$.)

b. Using ratio symbols, $\dotplus E) = 1\dotplus v)^2 = \dotplus v)^2$. Here, E varies directly as the square of the velocity.

c. Using ratio symbols, $\dotplus E) = 1\dotplus m) = \dotplus m)$. Here, E varies directly as the mass.

d. Using ratio symbols, $\dotplus m)\dotplus v)^2 = 1$ or $\dotplus m) = \dfrac{1}{\dotplus v)^2}$. Here, the mass varies inversely as the square of the velocity.

Exercises

In 1–3, the area of a rectangle is 25 and the area remains constant. Using ratio symbols, show that the statement is a true statement.

1. If the width is doubled, the length is divided in half.
2. If the length is multiplied by 5, the width is divided by 5.
3. If the width is multiplied by $1\frac{1}{4}$, the length is multiplied by $\frac{4}{5}$.

In 4–6, use ratio symbols to show that the statement is a true statement.

4. If the radius of a circle is doubled, its area becomes 4 times as much.
5. If the area of a circle becomes 100 times as great, its radius is 10 times as great.
6. If the diameter of a circle is multiplied by $2\frac{1}{2}$, its area is multiplied by $6\frac{1}{4}$.

In 7 and 8, the volume of a sphere varies directly as the cube of its radius. Complete the statement.

7. If the volume of a sphere becomes 125 times as great, then its radius_____.
8. If the radius of a sphere is tripled, then its volume_____.

In 9–14, z varies jointly as x and y. That is, $z = kxy$ where k is a constant.

9. State the equation, using ratio symbols.
10. When x is constant, state the equation, using ratio symbols, to show that the type of variation involved is direct variation.

11. If z is constant, show that $+x) = \dfrac{1}{+y)}$ and state the type of variation involved.

12. If $x = y$, show that $+x) = \sqrt{+z)}$ and state the type of variation involved.
13. If $+x) = 4$ and $+z) = 10$, find $+y)$.
14. If $+y) = 5$, $+z) = 20$, and $x_1 = 12$, find x_2.

In 15 and 16, state an equation or formula for the statement, using ratio symbols.
15. The volume of a sphere, V, varies directly as the cube of its radius, r.
16. The intensity of illumination, I, upon a surface varies inversely as the square of the distance, d, between the surface and the pinpoint source of light.

In 17–20: $A = \frac{1}{2}bh$, the formula for the area of a triangle of base, b, and altitude, h, may be written as $+A) = +b)+h)$, using ratio symbols. Complete each statement.
17. If the base of a triangle is doubled and its altitude is tripled, then its area_____.
18. If the area of a triangle remains constant, then tripling its altitude_____.
19. If $+A) = \frac{1}{4}$ and $+b) = 2$, then $+h) = ?$
20. If $+b) = \frac{3}{4}$ and $+h) = \frac{4}{3}$, then $+A) = ?$

In 21–24: $V = \frac{1}{3}\pi r^2 h$, the formula for the volume, V, of a cone of radius r and altitude h, may by written as $+V) = +r)^2 h$, using ratio symbols. Complete each statement.
21. If $+r) = 1.1$ and $+h) = 10$, then $+V) = ?$
22. If $+V) = 1$ and $+h) = 4$, then $+r) = ?$
23. If $+r) = 1$ and $+h) = 25$, then $+V) = ?$
24. If $+h) = 1$ and $+r) = 25$, then $+V) = ?$

In 25–27, apply the formula $+F) = \dfrac{1}{+d)^2}$ for Newton's law of gravitation in order to find what happens to the force of attraction between the bodies whose masses remain constant if the distance between them becomes:
25. 3 times as great   **26.** $\frac{1}{4}$ as much   **27.** $2\frac{1}{4}$ times as much

In 28–31, apply the formula $+F) = \dfrac{1}{+d)^2}$ for Newton's law of gravitation to find what happens to the distance between two bodies of constant mass if the force of attraction between them becomes:
28. 25 times as great   **29.** $\frac{4}{9}$ as much
30. $6\frac{1}{4}$ times as much   **31.** 3 times as much

CHAPTER XXIII

SEQUENCES AND SERIES

1. Understanding the Meaning of a Sequence

Observe that there is a simple pattern in the number arrangement 4, 8, 12, 16, ... If this pattern is extended, the next two terms are 20 and 24. A set of ordered numbers such as 4, 8, 12, 16, 20, 24 is called a **sequence**.

The sequence 4, 8, 12, 16 may be extended by setting up a one-to-one correspondence between the four terms of the given sequence and the first four members of the set of positive integers as follows:

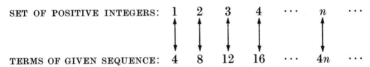

SET OF POSITIVE INTEGERS: 1   2   3   4 $\cdots$ n $\cdots$

TERMS OF GIVEN SEQUENCE: 4   8   12   16 $\cdots$ $4n$ $\cdots$

Observe that each term of the given sequence is 4 times the positive integer with which it is paired. If this pattern is applied to find new terms, the fifth term is 4(5) or 20; the sixth term is 4(6) or 24; and, in general, the nth term is $4n$.

A sequence such as 4, 8, 12, 16, which has a first term and a last term, is called a **finite sequence**. A sequence such as 4, 8, 12, 16, . . . in which, after each term of the sequence there is another term, is called an **infinite sequence**.

In the sequence whose terms are a_1, a_2, a_3, ..., a_n, ..., a_1 represents the first term, a_3 represents the third term, and a_n represents the nth term. The subscript in a term represents the place of the term in the sequence.

An infinite sequence may also be represented by $\{a_n\}$, the domain of n being the set of positive integers.

The expression that represents the general term of a sequence, a_n, is the rule that may be used to find any term of the sequence. For example, in the sequence 4, 8, 12, 16, . . . , $4n$, . . . , the nth term is represented by $4n$. Therefore, $a_n = 4n$ is the rule for forming the sequence. Each term of the sequence may be found by substituting a positive integer for n. For example, to find the 8th term, substitute 8 for n. Hence, the 8th term, $a_8 = 4(8)$ or 32. Since in the sequence 4, 8, 12, 16, . . . , the nth term $a_n = 4n$, the sequence may also be represented by $\{4n\}$.

~~~~~~~~~~~~~~~ *MODEL PROBLEMS* ~~~~~~~~~~~~~~~

1. *a.* Write a rule that can be used in forming a sequence 1, 4, 9, 16, ...
   b. Use the rule found in part *a* to write the next three terms of the sequence.

Solution:

   a. Set up a one-to-one correspondence between the members of the set of positive integers and the terms of the given sequence.

SET OF POSITIVE INTEGERS: 1   2   3   4   . . . n . . .

TERMS OF GIVEN SEQUENCE: 1   4   9   16   . . . n^2 . . .

Since each term of the sequence is the square of the positive integer with which it is paired, the rule $a_n = n^2$ is a rule that can be used to form the sequence.

Answer: $a_n = n^2$

   b. Use the rule which forms the sequence $a_n = n^2$ to find the next three terms of the sequence as follows:
   The fifth term, $a_5 = 5^2$ or 25.
   The sixth term, $a_6 = 6^2$ or 36.
   The seventh term, $a_7 = 7^2$ or 49.

Answer: 25, 36, 49

2. Write the first five terms of the sequence represented by $\{n + 2\}$.

Solution:

To find the first five terms of the sequence represented by $\{n + 2\}$: In $n + 2$, replace n by the positive integers 1, 2, 3, 4, and 5 respectively.

$$a_1 = 1 + 2 \text{ or } 3 \quad a_2 = 2 + 2 \text{ or } 4 \quad a_3 = 3 + 2 \text{ or } 5$$
$$a_4 = 4 + 2 \text{ or } 6 \quad a_5 = 5 + 2 \text{ or } 7$$

Answer: 3, 4, 5, 6, 7

~~~~~~

Exercises

In 1–16: *a.* Write a rule (that is, write a formula for the general term a_n) that can be used in forming a sequence. *b.* Use the rule found in part *a* to write the next three terms of the sequence.

1. 4, 5, 6, 7, . . .   **2.** 2, 4, 6, 8, . . .

3. $1, \frac{1}{2}, \frac{1}{3}, \frac{1}{4}, \ldots$

5. $3, 6, 9, 12, \ldots$

7. $6, 7, 8, 9, \ldots$

9. $1, \frac{1}{4}, \frac{1}{9}, \frac{1}{16}, \ldots$

11. $3, 5, 7, 9, \ldots$

13. $2 \cdot 3, 2 \cdot 3^2, 2 \cdot 3^3, 2 \cdot 3^4, \ldots$

15. $4, 12, 36, 108, \ldots$

4. $-1, 0, 1, 2, \ldots$

6. $-5, -10, -15, -20, \ldots$

8. $-2, -1, 0, 1, \ldots$

10. $\frac{1}{2}, \frac{2}{3}, \frac{3}{4}, \frac{4}{5}, \ldots$

12. $1, 4, 7, 10, \ldots$

14. $5, 5 \cdot 2, 5 \cdot 2^2, 5 \cdot 2^3, \ldots$

16. $-2, 0, 2, 4, \ldots$

In 17–25, write the first four terms of the sequence defined by the given rule.

17. $a_n = 5n$

18. $a_n = n + 5$

19. $a_n = 3n - 4$

20. $a_n = n^2$

21. $a_n = 3^n$

22. $a_n = 2^{n-1}$

23. $a_n = n(n + 1)$

24. $a_n = \dfrac{2n}{2n + 1}$

25. $a_n = (-1)^n \cdot 2n$

In 26–33, write the first four terms of the sequence that is defined.

26. $\{n + 6\}$

27. $\{4n - 3\}$

28. $\{n^2 + n\}$

29. $\dfrac{1}{\{n + 2\}}$

30. $\{n^3\}$

31. $\{4^n\}$

32. $\{3^{n-1}\}$

33. $\{2 \cdot 5^{n-1}\}$

2. Finding the General Term of an Arithmetic Sequence

In the sequence 2, 5, 8, 11, each term after the first term, 2, is the sum of the preceding term and a constant, 3. Such a sequence is an *arithmetic sequence*, or an *arithmetic progression (A.P.)*.

An arithmetic sequence is a sequence in which each term after the first is the sum of the preceding term and a constant.

Thus, in the sequence 2, 5, 8, 11, the term $5 = 2 + 3$ and the term $11 = 8 + 3$. Note that the constant 3 may be found by subtracting any term from its successor; for example, $5 - 2 = 3$, and $8 - 5 = 3$, also $11 - 8 = 3$. Hence, the constant 3 is the *common difference* in the arithmetic sequence 2, 5, 8, 11.

Procedure: To find the common difference in an arithmetic sequence, subtract any term from its successor.

Thus, in the decreasing arithmetic sequence 15, 12, 9, 6, the common difference is -3 since $12 - 15 = -3$.

In general, in an arithmetic sequence, if d represents the common difference, and a_{n-1} and a_n represent two consecutive terms, then $d = a_n - a_{n-1}$. Keep in mind that the common difference is positive in an increasing sequence such as 2, 5, 8, 11; it is negative in a decreasing sequence such as 15, 12, 9, 6; it is zero in the sequence 5, 5, 5, 5.

If a_1 represents the first term of an arithmetic sequence and d represents the common difference, then the sequence may be written as follows:

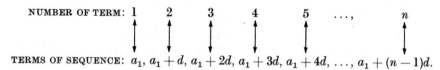

NUMBER OF TERM: 1   2   3   4   5   ..., n

TERMS OF SEQUENCE: a_1, $a_1 + d$, $a_1 + 2d$, $a_1 + 3d$, $a_1 + 4d$, ..., $a_1 + (n-1)d$.

Note that the fourth term of the sequence is $a_1 + 3d$ and the fifth term is $a_1 + 4d$. In general, the nth term $= a_1 + (n-1)d$; that is, the nth term is the sum of the first term and $(n-1)$ common differences.

In general, if the nth term of an arithmetic sequence is represented by a_n, then

$$a_n = a_1 + (n-1)d$$

For example, in the sequence 2, 5, 8, 11, ..., the 51st term is $a_{51} = 2 + 50(3) = 2 + 150 = 152$. Also, in the sequence 15, 10, 5, ..., the 25th term is $a_{25} = 15 + 24(-5) = 15 - 120 = -105$.

MODEL PROBLEMS

1. Find the 12th term of the arithmetic sequence 3, 8, 13, 18, ...

Solution:

First find the common difference by subtracting the first term from the second. Then find the 12th term.

$$d = 8 - 3 = 5$$
$$a_n = a_1 + (n-1)d \qquad a_1 = 3,\ n = 12,\ d = 5$$
$$a_n = 3 + (12 - 1)5$$
$$= 3 + (11)5$$
$$= 3 + 55 = 58$$

Answer: The 12th term is 58.

2. Write the first seven terms of an arithmetic sequence in which the third term is 7 and the seventh term is 15.

Solution:

$$a_n = a_1 + (n-1)d$$

When $n = 7$, $a_n = a_7 = 15$. Hence, $15 = a_1 + 6d$

When $n = 3$, $a_n = a_3 = 7$. Hence, $7 = a_1 + 2d$

Subtract: $\overline{8 = \qquad 4d}$

$$2 = d$$

Since the third term is 7: $\quad 7 = a_1 + 2d$
Substitute $d = 2$: $\quad 7 = a_1 + 2(2)$
$$7 = a_1 + 4$$
$$3 = a_1$$

Answer: The required terms are 3, 5, 7, 9, 11, 13, 15.

~~~~~~

Exercises

In 1–6, write the first four terms in an arithmetic sequence that has the given values for a_1 and d.

1. $a_1 = 2, d = 4$ **2.** $a_1 = -3, d = 2$ **3.** $a_1 = -5, d = -3$
4. $a_1 = 9, d = \frac{1}{3}$ **5.** $a_1 = 6, d = .5$ **6.** $a_1 = -2, d = -.7$

In 7–15, find the common difference of the arithmetic sequence. Then find the next two terms.

7. 5, 7, 9, ...   **8.** $x+1, x+4, x+7, \ldots$ **9.** 7, 2, −3, ...
10. $2\frac{1}{2}, 3, 3\frac{1}{2}, \ldots$ **11.** $2x, 3x, 4x, \ldots$ **12.** $5\frac{2}{3}, 5\frac{1}{3}, 5, \ldots$
13. .3, .5, .7, ...   **14.** 1.02, 1.04, 1.06, ...   **15.** $b-c, b, b+c, \ldots$

In 16–23, find the indicated term of the arithmetic sequence.

16. 7, 11, 15, ... (15th term)   **17.** 10, 7, 4, ... (13th term)
18. −5, −7, −9, ... (18th term)   **19.** $5\frac{1}{2}, 6, 6\frac{1}{2}, \ldots$ (40th term)
20. $9, 8\frac{3}{4}, 8\frac{1}{2}, \ldots$ (20th term)   **21.** 1.05, 1.10, 1.15, ... (12th term)
22. 7, 6.9, 6.8, ... (35th term)   **23.** $7x, 9x, 11x, \ldots$ (10th term)

24. Find the 17th term in the arithmetic sequence 3, 7, 11, ...
25. Find the 40th term of the arithmetic progression −26, −24, −22, ...
26. Write the 30th term of the arithmetic sequence $x - y, x, x + y, \ldots$.
27. Find a_7 in the arithmetic sequence 8, 5, 2, ...

In 28–31, find a_n in an arithmetic sequence which has the given values for a_1, d, and n.

28. $a_1 = 6, d = 4, n = 8$ **29.** $a_1 = 9, d = -2, n = 10$
30. $a_1 = \frac{5}{2}, d = -\frac{1}{2}, n = 7$ **31.** $a_1 = -\frac{4}{5}, d = -\frac{2}{5}, n = 28$

32. Find the first term of an arithmetic sequence in which $a_4 = 9$ and $d = 2$.
33. Find a_1 in an arithmetic progression in which $a_6 = 8$ and $d = -\frac{2}{3}$.
34. Find the first term in an arithmetic progression in which the sixth term is −2 and the seventh term is −7.
35. Which term of the arithmetic sequence 5, 8, 11, ... is 35?
36. Which term of the arithmetic sequence 15, 13, 11, ... is −13?

37. Which term of the arithmetic sequence 7, 13, 19, ... is 133?

38. If the first term of an arithmetic sequence is 7 and the 25th term is 79, what is the common difference?

39. The first term of an arithmetic progression is 10 and the thirtieth term is −77. Find the common difference.

40. In an arithmetic progression, $a_1 = \frac{2}{3}$ and $a_{12} = 19$. Find the common difference.

41. Find the number of terms in the arithmetic sequence 4, 7, 10, ... , 40.

42. Find the number of terms in the arithmetic sequence 84, 82, 80, ... , 20.

43. The second and fourth terms of an arithmetic sequence are 15 and 21. Find the third term.

44. Mr. Ward accepted a job which pays $8000 the first year with yearly increases of $400. Find his salary during his tenth year on the job.

45. In a theatre, the front row of the orchestra has 30 seats. Each row after the first row has 6 seats more than the previous row. Find the number of seats in the 15th row.

46. Miss Taylor saved $400 during 1965. In each of the following years, she saved $150 more than she had saved the previous year. During which year will her savings for the year amount to $1600?

47. *a.* Find x so that the numbers $4x − 1$, $2x + 2$, and $2x − 3$ are in arithmetic progression.

   b. Find the fifth term of the progression.

In 48–50, solve $a_n = a_1 + (n − 1)d$ for the indicated variable.

48. a_1 **49.** d **50.** n

In 51–53, if a_1, a_2, a_3, a_4, ... , a_n are in arithmetic progression, prove the stated relationship.

51. $a_1 + a_3 = 2a_2$ **52.** $a_1 + a_4 = a_2 + a_3$ **53.** $a_1 + a_n = a_2 + a_{n-1}$

3. Inserting Arithmetic Means

The terms between any two given terms of an arithmetic sequence are called the ***arithmetic means*** between those terms.

Thus, in the sequence 5, 7, 9, 11, 13, the terms 7, 9, 11 are the three arithmetic means between 5 and 13.

A single arithmetic mean between two given terms of an arithmetic sequence is called the ***arithmetic mean*** between the two terms.

Thus, in the sequence 5, 7, 9, the number 7 is the arithmetic mean between 5 and 9. Observe that the arithmetic mean, 7, is the average of the other terms 5 and 9; that is, $7 = \frac{1}{2}(5 + 9)$.

In general, if M represents the arithmetic mean between two real numbers a and b, then $M - a = b - M$

$$2M = a + b$$

$$M = \frac{a+b}{2}$$

Rule. The arithmetic mean between two real numbers is the average of the numbers.

~~~~~~~~~~ *MODEL PROBLEMS* ~~~~~~~~~~

1. Insert three arithmetic means between 19 and 11.

How To Proceed	*Solution*
1. Use spaces to represent the arithmetic means to be inserted between the given numbers.	1. 19, ___, ___, ___, 11
2. Determine the values of a_1, a_n, and n.	2. $a_1 = 19$, $a_n = 11$ Since there are five terms, $n = 5$.
3. Find d by substituting the values of a_1, a_n, and n in the following formula: $a_n = a_1 + (n-1)d$.	3. $a_n = a_1 + (n-1)d$ $11 = 19 + (5-1)d$ $11 = 19 + 4d$ $-8 = 4d$ $-2 = d$
4. Find the required means by successively adding the value of d to the value of a_1.	4. $19 + (-2) = 17$ $17 + (-2) = 15$, etc. 19, 17, 15, 13, 11 *Ans.*

2. Find the arithmetic mean between 8 and 14.

Solution: If M represents the arithmetic mean between 8 and 14, then 8, M, 14 is an arithmetic sequence.

Method 1	*Method 2*
Using a common difference:	Using an average:
$M - 8 = 14 - M$	$M = \dfrac{a+b}{2} \quad a = 8,\ b = 14$
$2M = 22$	$M = \dfrac{8+14}{2} = \dfrac{22}{2} = 11$ *Ans.*
$M = 11$ *Ans.*	

Exercises

In 1–3, write the arithmetic means between the given terms of the sequence
−12, −9, −6, −3, 0, 3, 6, 9.

1. −12 and 9   **2.** −9 and 0   **3.** −6 and 6

In 4–9, insert the indicated number of arithmetic means between the given
numbers.

4. 4, ..., 16 (3 means)   **5.** −5, ..., 10 (4 means)

6. 25, ..., 13 (5 means)   **7.** 6, ..., −6 (5 means)

8. 3, ..., 5 (7 means)   **9.** 1, ..., −2 (8 means)

In 10–13, find the arithmetic mean between the two given numbers.

10. 7 and 15   **11.** −9 and −5   **12.** $5\frac{3}{4}$ and $7\frac{1}{4}$ **13.** −6.4 and 8.4

14. Insert two arithmetic means between 8 and 23.

15. Find the arithmetic mean between −24 and 6.

16. The arithmetic mean between two numbers is $4\frac{1}{2}$. If one of the numbers is 3, find the other number.

17. Three numbers inserted between 4 and 6 form with these numbers an arithmetic progression. Find the common difference of this progression.

18. What four numbers inserted between 2 and 37 will form with these numbers an arithmetic progression of 6 terms?

19. The first term of an arithmetic progression is −4 and the fifth term is 20. Find the second term.

20. In a certain school system, a teacher's annual salary increases in arithmetic progression for six years. If a teacher's first-year salary is $6400 and his sixth-year salary is $9400, what is his salary during each of the other years?

21. Write an equation which shows that x is the arithmetic mean between a and b.

In 22–24, represent, in terms of x, the arithmetic mean between the given expressions.

22. $2x$ and $8x$ **23.** $3x + 4$ and $5x − 2$ **24.** $2x − 4$ and $7x + 4$

25. Prove that if M is the arithmetic mean between the real numbers p and q, then $M = \dfrac{p + q}{2}$.

26. Show that if a and b are both even integers, then their arithmetic mean, M, is an integer.

27. Show that if a and b are both odd integers, then their arithmetic mean, M, is an integer.

28. Show that if a is an odd integer and b is an even integer, then their arithmetic mean, M, cannot be an integer.

4. Finding the Sum of an Arithmetic Series

A series is the indicated sum of the terms of a sequence.

Thus, $2 + 5 + 8 + 11$ is an example of a *finite series*.

Also, $2 + 5 + 8 + 11 + \cdots$ is an example of an *infinite series*.

In general, $a_1 + a_2 + a_3 + \cdots + a_n$ represents a finite series.

Also, $a_1 + a_2 + a_3 + \cdots + a_n + \cdots$ represents an infinite series.

Be careful to note that a series is an *indicated sum* of the terms of a sequence, not the sum itself. Do not confuse the series $2 + 5 + 8 + 11$ with its sum, 26. The series $2 + 5 + 8 + 11$ cannot be represented by the numeral 26.

An *arithmetic series* is the indicated sum of the terms of an arithmetic sequence.

Hence, since 5, 8, 11, 14, 17 is an arithmetic sequence, then $5 + 8 + 11 + 14 + 17$ is an arithmetic series. Since $5 + 8 + 11 + 14 + 17 = 55$, we say that the *sum* of this series is 55.

In an arithmetic series, if a_1 is the first term, n is the number of terms, a_n is the nth term, and d is the common difference, then S_n, the sum of the arithmetic series, is given by the following formulas:

$$S_n = \frac{n}{2}(a_1 + a_n)$$

$$S_n = \frac{n}{2}[2a_1 + (n-1)d]$$

The derivations of these formulas appear on pages 745–746.

~~~~~~~~~~~ *MODEL PROBLEMS* ~~~~~~~~~~~

1. Find the sum of ten terms of an arithmetic sequence whose first term is 5 and whose tenth term is -13.

Solution:

$S_n = \frac{n}{2}(a_1 + a_n)$

$a_1 = 5, a_{10} = -13, n = 10$

$S_n = \frac{10}{2}[5 + (-13)]$

$\quad = 5(-8)$

$\quad = -40 \quad Ans.$

2. Find the sum of the first 50 terms of the arithmetic series $3 + 5 + 7 + 9 + \cdots$

Solution:

<table>
<tr><td align="center">Method 1</td><td align="center">Method 2</td></tr>
</table>

Method 1

Using $S_n = \dfrac{n}{2}(a_1 + a_n)$:

First, find the 50th term.

$a_1 = 3, d = 2, n = 50$

$a_n = a_1 + (n - 1)d$
$a_{50} = 3 + (50 - 1)2$
$\quad = 3 + (49)2$
$\quad = 101$

Then find the sum of 50 terms.

$S_n = \dfrac{n}{2}(a_1 + a_n)$

$S_{50} = \dfrac{50}{2}(3 + 101)$

$\quad = 25(104) = 2600 \quad Ans.$

Method 2

Using $S_n = \dfrac{n}{2}[2a_1 + (n - 1)d]$:

$a_1 = 3, d = 2, n = 50$

$S_n = \dfrac{n}{2}[2a_1 + (n - 1)d]$

$S_{50} = \dfrac{50}{2}[2(3) + (50 - 1)2]$
$\quad = 25[6 + (49)2]$
$\quad = 25(6 + 98)$
$\quad = 25(104)$
$\quad = 2600 \quad Ans.$

Exercises

In 1–6, find the sum of the terms of the arithmetic sequence which has the given data.

1. $a_1 = 7, a_{12} = 29, n = 12$ **2.** $a_1 = -14, a_5 = 30, n = 5$

3. $a_1 = 2, a_{14} = 54, n = 14$ **4.** $a_1 = 20, a_9 = -6, n = 9$

5. $a_1 = 5, d = 3, n = 15$ **6.** $a_1 = -12, d = -2, n = 10$

In 7–12, find the sum of the indicated number of terms of the arithmetic sequence.

7. $1, 8, 15, \ldots$ (first ten terms)   **8.** $20, 17, 14, \ldots$ (first 16 terms)

9. $8, 7\frac{1}{2}, 7, \ldots$ (first 20 terms)   **10.** $5, 1, -3, \ldots$ (first 13 terms)

11. $-3, -5, -7, \ldots$ (first 18 terms)   **12.** $-12, -10, -8, \ldots$ (first 12 terms)

13. Find the sum of all the positive odd integers less than 100.

14. Find the sum of all the even integers from 2 to 100 inclusive.

15. Find the sum of all the positive numbers less than 200 which are exactly divisible by 3.

16. Find the sum of all integers between 1 and 100 that are exactly divisible by 7.

17. An object falls 16.08 feet, 48.24 feet, 80.40 feet in successive seconds.
    a. How far will it fall in the tenth second?
    b. How far will it fall in 15 seconds?

18. In an arithmetic sequence, $S_n = 210$, $a_n = 24$, and $n = 14$. Find a_1.

19. In an arithmetic progression, $d = 5$, $n = 14$, $S_n = 651$. Find a_1 and a_n.

20. Prove that the sum of the first n positive integers $1 + 2 + 3 + \cdots$ is $\dfrac{n(n+1)}{2}$.

21. Prove that the sum of the first n positive odd integers $1 + 3 + 5 + \cdots$ is n^2.

22. Prove that the sum of the first n positive even integers $2 + 4 + 6 + \cdots$ is $n(n+1)$.

5. Solving Verbal Problems Involving Arithmetic Sequences

〜〜〜〜〜〜〜 *MODEL PROBLEMS* 〜〜〜〜〜〜〜

1. Three numbers are in the ratio of $3:4:7$. If 4 is added to the middle number, that resulting number will be the second term of an arithmetic sequence of which the other two numbers are the first and third terms. Find the three numbers.

Solution: Let $3x$, $4x$, and $7x =$ the original numbers.
Then $3x$, $4x + 4$, and $7x =$ the numbers which form an arithmetic sequence. In an arithmetic sequence of three terms, the middle term is the average of the first and the last terms. Hence,

$$4x + 4 = \frac{3x + 7x}{2}$$
$$4x + 4 = 5x$$
$$4 = x$$

If $x = 4$, then $3x = 12$, $4x = 16$, and $7x = 28$. *Answer:* 12, 16, 28

Note. The numbers in arithmetic sequence are 12, 20, 28.

2. A man wishes to pay off a debt of \$1160 by making monthly payments in which each payment after the first is \$4 more than that of the preceding month. According to this plan, how long will it take him to pay the debt if the first payment is \$20 and no interest charge is made?

Solution: Let $n =$ the number of payments.
The payments form an arithmetic progression 20, 24, 28, ...

$$S_n = \frac{n}{2}[2a_1 + (n-1)d] \qquad S_n = 1160, a_1 = 20, d = 4$$

$$1160 = \frac{n}{2}[40 + (n-1)4]$$

$$1160 = \frac{n}{2}(40 + 4n - 4)$$

$$1160 = \frac{n}{2}(4n + 36)$$

$$1160 = 2n^2 + 18n$$
$$0 = 2n^2 + 18n - 1160$$
$$0 = n^2 + 9n - 580$$
$$0 = (n+29)(n-20)$$

$$
\begin{array}{c|c}
n + 29 = 0 & n = 0 - 20 \\
n = -29 & n = 20 \\
\text{Reject} &
\end{array}
$$

Answer: 20 payments

Exercises

1. Three numbers are in the ratio of 4:5:7. If 3 is subtracted from the last number, the resulting number will be the third term in an arithmetic sequence of which the other two numbers are the first and second terms. Find the three numbers.
2. In an arithmetic sequence, the common difference is 2. If the sum of the first four terms of the sequence is divided by the third term, the quotient is 3 and the remainder is 5. Find the first term.
3. The sum of three numbers in arithmetic progression is 12. The sum of their squares is 56. Find the numbers.
4. Three numbers whose sum is 27 are in arithmetic progression. The square of the smallest number exceeds the largest by 12. Find the numbers.
5. In a certain school system, the salary scale for teachers starts at $6800 and provides for a yearly increase of $600 for the next 5 years. Miss A, starting at the minimum salary, plans to make $6000 cover her entire expenses for each year. How much will she be able to save if she stays five years? (Use a formula in the solution.)
6. The sum of a certain number of consecutive odd numbers is 180. The largest is three times the smallest.
   a. Find the smallest number.   *b.* Find the number of numbers.

7. The balcony in a theatre has 780 seats. If the first row has 36 seats and each succeeding row has four seats more than the previous row, find the number of rows in the balcony.

8. A man desiring to pay a debt of $340 finds that he can pay $25 the first month and thereafter increase each monthly payment $2 over that of the previous month. How long will it take him to pay the debt if the interest is not included?

9. Mr. Jones brought a machine costing $240. He arranged to pay $60 down and the rest in monthly installments. If he paid $33 the first month and each payment thereafter was $3 less than the preceding one, in how many months did Mr. Jones complete payment for the machine?

10. A sum of money is to be distributed among 10 prize winning contestants in such a way that each one after the first receives $10 more than the preceding person. The largest prize awarded is three times the smallest. Let a represent the smallest prize.

   a. Express the largest prize in terms of a.

   b. Using the formula for the last term of an arithmetic progression, find a.

   c. Find the amount distributed in prizes.

6. Summation Notation: Summation Symbol, Σ

The Greek capital letter *sigma*, written "Σ," which corresponds to the first letter of the English word "sum," is often used to abbreviate the representation of a series. For example:

1. $\displaystyle\sum_{i=1}^{9} i$ means $1 + 2 + 3 + 4 + 5 + 6 + 7 + 8 + 9$

2. $\displaystyle\sum_{y=5}^{8} y^2$ means $5^2 + 6^2 + 7^2 + 8^2$

3. $\displaystyle\sum_{z=7}^{9} \frac{1}{z}$ means $\dfrac{1}{7} + \dfrac{1}{8} + \dfrac{1}{9}$

Observe that in each of the above examples the summation symbol Σ generates a series that can be obtained by replacing the variable by a succession of consecutive integers beginning with the value of the variable below sigma and ending with the value above sigma. For example, in the third example above, the variable z is replaced by 7 first, then by 8, and finally by 9.

In general,

$$\sum_{i=1}^{n} a_i = a_1 + a_2 + a_3 + \cdots + a_n$$

The symbol a_i represents the terms being added. The letter i is called the *index of summation*, or the *summation variable.* The numbers 1 and n indicate the extremes of the domain of the summation variable. The summation variable may also be represented by a letter other than i.

See how the summation notation can be used to generate the series that indicates the sum of the first 500 positive consecutive even integers.

$$\sum_{i=1}^{500} 2i = 2(1) + 2(2) + 2(3) + \cdots + 2(498) + 2(499) + 2(500)$$

$$= 2 + 4 + 6 + \cdots + 996 + 998 + 1000$$

~~~~~~~~~~~~~ *MODEL PROBLEMS* ~~~~~~~~~~~~~

1. *a.* Write the series generated by $\sum_{i=1}^{9} (2i - 1)$.

   b. Find the sum of the series found in answer to part *a*.

Solution:

a. Beginning with 1, the value of i below sigma, and ending with 9, the value above sigma, substitute consecutive integers for the variable i in the expression $(2i - 1)$, to generate the required series:

$$1 + 3 + 5 + 7 + 9 + 11 + 13 + 15 + 17$$

For example, 17, the last term of the generated series, is found by substituting 9 for i in $(2i - 1)$: $2(9) - 1 = 18 - 1 = 17$

Answer: $1 + 3 + 5 + 7 + 9 + 11 + 13 + 15 + 17$

b. Since the series generated in part *a* is an arithmetic series, apply the formula $S_n = \dfrac{n}{2}(a_1 + a_n)$. Substitute 9 for n, 1 for a_1, and 17 for a_n:

$$S_9 = \tfrac{9}{2}(1 + 17) = \tfrac{9}{2}(18) = 81 \quad Ans.$$

2. Write the series $5 + 9 + 13 + 17 + 21$ using the summation notation.

Solution:

The sequence 5, 9, 13, 17, 21 is an arithmetic sequence in which the first term is 5 and the common difference is 4. Therefore, the representation of the general term, the nth term, found by using the formula $a_n = a_1 + (n-1)d$, is $5 + (n-1)4$ or $4n + 1$. The sequence is obtained by varying n from a lower limit of 1 to an upper limit of 5. The given series may be represented in summation notation as $\sum_{n=1}^{5} (4n + 1)$.   *Ans.*

Exercises

In 1–8, write the series generated by the summation symbol.

1. $\displaystyle\sum_{i=1}^{7} i$ **2.** $\displaystyle\sum_{z=4}^{9} 3(z+1)$ **3.** $\displaystyle\sum_{w=5}^{8} (3w-1)$ **4.** $\displaystyle\sum_{x=15}^{20} \frac{7}{x}$

5. $\displaystyle\sum_{i=1}^{5} (i^2-1)$ **6.** $\displaystyle\sum_{i=4}^{6} (i^2+2i-1)$ **7.** $\displaystyle\sum_{x=0}^{4} \frac{x-1}{x+1}$ **8.** $\displaystyle\sum_{i=2}^{5} 4\cdot 3^{i-1}$

In 9–22, represent the series using the sigma notation for summation

9. $10+20+30+40$ **10.** $5+8+11+14$
11. $1^2+2^2+3^2+4^2+5^2$ **12.** $5+25+125+625$
13. $1\cdot 3+2\cdot 4+3\cdot 5+4\cdot 6$ **14.** $\frac{1}{2}+\frac{2}{3}+\frac{3}{4}+\frac{4}{5}+\frac{5}{6}$
15. $10(12)+11(13)+12(14)$ **16.** $1+\frac{1}{3}+\frac{1}{9}+\frac{1}{27}$
17. $\frac{2}{7}+\frac{3}{7}+\frac{4}{7}+\frac{5}{7}+\frac{6}{7}$ **18.** $\sqrt{5}+\sqrt{6}+\sqrt{7}+\sqrt{8}$
19. $1+2+3+\cdots+49+50$ **20.** $6+9+14+21+30+41$
21. $-1+2-3+4-5+6$ **22.** $2-4+8-16+32-64+128-256$

In 23–25, use sigma notation to represent the series of:
23. the first 25 positive integers.
24. the first ten positive even integers.
25. the consecutive integers from -5 to 10.

In 26–29, (*a*) write the arithmetic series generated by the summation symbol and (*b*) find the sum of the series generated in part (*a*).

26. $\displaystyle\sum_{i=1}^{4} 4i$ **27.** $\displaystyle\sum_{y=2}^{6} 2(y-1)$ **28.** $\displaystyle\sum_{z=7}^{10} (3z+2)$ **29.** $\displaystyle\sum_{w=12}^{20} (1\tfrac{1}{2})(w+4)$

7. Finding the General Term of a Geometric Sequence

In the sequence 2, 6, 18, 54, each term after the first term, 2, is the product of the preceding term and a constant 3. Such a sequence is a *geometric sequence*, or a *geometric progression* (*G.P.*).

A *geometric sequence* is a sequence in which each term after the first is the product of the preceding term and a constant.

Thus, in the sequence 2, 6, 18, 54, the term $6=2(3)$ and the term $54=18(3)$. Note that the constant 3 may be found by dividing any term by its predecessor. Thus, $\frac{6}{2}=3$ and $\frac{18}{6}=3$. Also, $\frac{54}{18}=3$. Hence, the constant 3 is the *common ratio* in the geometric sequence 2, 6, 18, 54.

Procedure: To find the common ratio in a geometric sequence, divide any term by its predecessor, the term that immediately precedes it.

Thus, in the geometric sequence 5, -25, 125, -625, the common ratio is -5 since $\dfrac{-25}{5} = -5.$

In general, in a geometric sequence, if r represents the common ratio and a_{n-1} and a_n represent two consecutive terms, then

$$r = \frac{a_n}{a_{n-1}}$$

Note that the common ratio may be positive or negative, but not 0.

If a_1 represents the first term of a geometric sequence and r represents the common ratio, then the sequence may be written as follows:

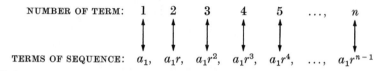

NUMBER OF TERM:	1	2	3	4	5	...,	n
TERMS OF SEQUENCE:	$a_1,$	$a_1r,$	$a_1r^2,$	$a_1r^3,$	$a_1r^4,$	...,	a_1r^{n-1}

Note that the fourth term of the sequence is a_1r^3 and the fifth term is a_1r^4. In general, the nth term $= a_1r^{n-1}$; that is, the nth term is the product of the first term, and the common ratio raised to the $(n-1)$ power.

Thus, the 9th term of 2, 20, 200, 2000, ... is $2(10^8) = 200{,}000{,}000$. In general, if the nth term of a geometric sequence is represented by a_n, then

$$a_n = a_1 r^{n-1}$$

For example, in the sequence 8, 4, 2, 1, ..., $a_6 = 8(\frac{1}{2})^5 = 8(\frac{1}{32}) = \frac{1}{4}$. Also, in the sequence 12, -6, 3, $-1\frac{1}{2}$, ..., $a_6 = 12(-\frac{1}{2})^5 = 12(-\frac{1}{32}) = -\frac{3}{8}$.

⁓⁓⁓⁓⁓⁓⁓⁓⁓ *MODEL PROBLEM* ⁓⁓⁓⁓⁓⁓⁓⁓⁓

Find the seventh term of the geometric progression 32, -16, 8, ...

Solution: First find the common ratio by dividing the second term by the first. Then find the seventh term.

$$r = (-16) \div (32) = -\tfrac{1}{2}$$
$$a_n = a_1 r^{n-1} \qquad\qquad a_1 = 32,\ n = 7,\ r = -\tfrac{1}{2}$$
$$= 32(-\tfrac{1}{2})^6$$
$$= 32(\tfrac{1}{64})$$
$$= \tfrac{1}{2} \quad Ans.$$

Exercises

In 1–9, find the common ratio of the geometric sequence and the next two terms.

1. 5, 10, 20, ...   **2.** −3, 6, −12, ...   **3.** −3, −9, −27, ...
4. 9, 3, 1, ...   **5.** $4x$, $16x$, $64x$, ...   **6.** $\frac{1}{2}$, $\frac{1}{2}y$, $\frac{1}{2}y^2$, ...
7. x^3, x^6, x^9, ...   **8.** 1, 1.05, $(1.05)^2$, ...   **9.** 2, 2, 2, ...

In 10–12, write the first four terms of a geometric progression in which a_1 and r have the given values.

10. $a_1 = 5$, $r = -2$ **11.** $a_1 = 6$, $r = \frac{1}{3}$ **12.** $a_1 = 4$, $r = x$

In 13–15, write the last four terms of a geometric progression in which a_n and r have the given values.

13. $a_n = 243$, $r = 3$ **14.** $a_n = 12$, $r = \frac{1}{2}$ **15.** $a_n = 368$, $r = -2$

In 16–21, find the indicated term of the geometric sequence.

16. 1, 2, 4, ... (7th term)   **17.** 12, 6, 3, ... (8th term)
18. −3, 6, −12, ... (6th term)   **19.** 4, 1, $\frac{1}{4}$, ... (5th term)
20. 3, $\frac{3}{2}$, $\frac{3}{4}$, ... (8th term)   **21.** $-\frac{3}{2}$, 3, −6, ... (9th term)

In 22–24, supply the missing term of the geometric sequence.

22. 4, 12, 36, ..., 324   **23.** 2, 3, $4\frac{1}{2}$, ..., $10\frac{1}{8}$ **24.** 6, −2, $\frac{2}{3}$, ..., $\frac{2}{27}$

25. What term of the sequence 4, 8, 16, ... is 128?
26. What term of the sequence 4, −12, 36, ... is 324?
27. What term of the sequence 36, 18, 9, ... is $\frac{9}{32}$?
28. Which of the following is *not* a geometric progression? (1) 16, 8, 4, ... (2) 3, −6, 12, ... (3) 2, 5, 8, ...
29. Find the missing term in the sequence 2, −6, 18, ..., 162.
30. Find the fifth term of the sequence 2, 3, $4\frac{1}{2}$, ...
31. What is the fifth term of the sequence 2, 6, 18, ...?
32. The first term of a geometric progression is 8 and the fourth term is 125. Find the common ratio.
33. The fourth term of a geometric progression is 125 and the sixth term is 3125. Find the common ratio and the first three terms.
34. In a culture, there are 200 bacteria. Every hour the number of bacteria in the culture doubles. Find the number of bacteria in the culture at the end of 8 hours.
35. In a lottery, the first ticket drawn paid a prize of $50,000. Every succeeding ticket paid half as much as the preceding one. Four tickets were drawn. How much did the fourth ticket pay?
36. A house which was built at a cost of $50,000 depreciates each year by an amount equal to 4% of its value at the beginning of the year. Find the value of this house at the end of 5 years.

8. Inserting Geometric Means

The terms between any two given terms of a geometric sequence are called the *geometric means* between those terms.

Thus, in the sequence 5, 10, 20, 40, 80, the terms 10, 20, 40 are the three geometric means between 5 and 80.

A single geometric mean between two given terms of a geometric sequence is called the *geometric mean* between the two terms.

Thus, in the sequence 5, 10, 20, the number 10 is the geometric mean between 5 and 20. Observe that the geometric mean 10 is the *mean proportional* between 5 and 20; that is, $\frac{20}{10} = \frac{10}{5}$.

In general, if G represents the geometric mean between two real numbers a and b, then $\dfrac{a}{G} = \dfrac{G}{b}$.

Rule. The geometric mean between two real numbers is their mean proportional.

Note. Since $\dfrac{a}{G} = \dfrac{G}{b}$, then $G^2 = ab$ and $G = \pm\sqrt{ab}$.

〜〜〜〜〜〜〜〜 *MODEL PROBLEMS* 〜〜〜〜〜〜〜〜

1. Insert three geometric means between $\frac{1}{9}$ and 9.

How To Proceed	*Solution*
1. Use spaces to represent the geometric means to be inserted between the given numbers.	1. $\frac{1}{9}$, ___, ___, ___, 9
2. Determine the values of a_1, a_n, and n.	2. $a_1 = \frac{1}{9}$, $a_n = 9$ Since there are five terms, $n = 5$.
3. Substitute the values of a_1, a_n, and n in the formula $a_n = a_1 r^{n-1}$ and then find r.	3. $a_n = a_1 r^{n-1}$ $9 = \frac{1}{9} r^4$ $81 = r^4$ $\pm 3 = r$
4. Find the required means by successively multiplying the value of a_1 by the value of r.	4. If $r = 3$, the resulting series is $\frac{1}{9}, \frac{1}{3}, 1, 3, 9$. If $r = -3$, the resulting series is $\frac{1}{9}, -\frac{1}{3}, 1, -3, 9$.

Answer: $\frac{1}{9}, \frac{1}{3}, 1, 3, 9$ or $\frac{1}{9}, -\frac{1}{3}, 1, -3, 9$

2. Find the positive geometric mean between $\frac{1}{2}$ and $\frac{1}{32}$.

Solution: If G represents the geometric mean between $\frac{1}{2}$ and $\frac{1}{32}$, then $\frac{1}{2}, G, \frac{1}{32}$ is a geometric sequence.

Method 1	*Method* 2
Using $\dfrac{b}{G} = \dfrac{G}{a}$:	Using $G = \pm\sqrt{ab}$:
	Since G is positive, then
$\dfrac{\frac{1}{32}}{G} = \dfrac{G}{\frac{1}{2}}$	$G = \sqrt{\left(\dfrac{1}{2}\right)\left(\dfrac{1}{32}\right)}$
$G^2 = \left(\dfrac{1}{32}\right)\left(\dfrac{1}{2}\right)$	$= \sqrt{\dfrac{1}{64}}$
$= \dfrac{1}{64}$	$= \dfrac{1}{8}$ *Ans.*
Since G is positive, then	
$G = \sqrt{\dfrac{1}{64}} = \dfrac{1}{8}$ *Ans.*	

Exercises

In 1–3, find the common ratio of a geometric sequence which has the given terms.

1. $a_1 = 5, a_3 = 45$ **2.** $a_1 = 36, a_3 = 9$ **3.** $a_1 = 4, a_4 = 500$

In 4–7, insert the indicated number of geometric means between the given numbers. Give all possible real answers.

4. 2 means between 8 and 64   **5.** 4 means between 1 and 32

6. 3 means between 2 and 162   **7.** 3 means between -6 and $-\frac{3}{8}$

8. Find the positive geometric mean between 2 and 50.

9. Find the negative geometric mean between 16 and 25.

10. The geometric mean between two numbers is 10. If one of the numbers is 4, find the other number.

11. Insert two geometric means between 2 and 54.

12. Insert a positive geometric mean between 2 and 6.

13. Two geometric means between 2 and 128 are (1) 16 and 64   (2) 44 and 86   (3) -8 and 32   (4) 8 and 32

14. Find the fifth term of a geometric sequence whose first term is 4 and whose fourth term is 32.

15. Find the first term of a geometric progression whose common ratio is 3 and whose fifth term is -162.

16. When $a > 0$, insert the positive geometric mean between a and $\dfrac{1}{a}$.

17. Represent in terms of x, when $x > 0$, the positive geometric mean between $2x$ and $8x$.

9. Finding the Sum of a Geometric Series

A *geometric series* is the indicated sum of the terms of a geometric sequence. Since 5, 10, 20, 40, 80 is a geometric sequence, $5 + 10 + 20 + 40 + 80$ is a geometric series. Since $5 + 10 + 20 + 40 + 80 = 155$, we say that the sum of this series is 155.

In general, a geometric series is represented by $a_1 + a_1 r + a_1 r^2 + \cdots + a_1 r^{n-1}$, in which a_1 is the first term, n is the number of terms, a_n is the nth term, and r is the common ratio. The sum of the geometric series, S_n, is given by the following formulas:

$$S_n = \frac{a_1 - a_1 r^n}{1 - r} \quad \text{or} \quad S_n = \frac{a_1 - a_n r}{1 - r}, \ r \neq 1$$

The derivation of the first formula appears on page 746.

〰〰〰〰〰〰 *MODEL PROBLEM* 〰〰〰〰〰〰

Find the sum of the first five terms of the geometric sequence 5, 15, 45, ...

Solution:
1. Find the common ratio, r, by dividing the second term, 15, by the first term, 5. $r = 15 \div 5$, or $r = 3$.
2. Find the sum of the first five terms of the series $5 + 15 + 45 + \cdots$.

$$S_n = \frac{a_1 - a_1 r^n}{1 - r} \qquad a_1 = 5, r = 3, n = 5$$

$$S_5 = \frac{5 - 5(3)^5}{1 - 3}$$

$$= \frac{5 - 1215}{-2} = \frac{-1210}{-2} = 605 \quad Ans.$$

Exercises

In 1–6, find the sum of the indicated number of terms of the geometric sequence. (In exercise 6, $y \neq 0$, $y \neq 1$.)

1. 1, 3, 9, ... (first 6 terms)

2. 8, 4, 2, ... (first 6 terms)

3. -3, -15, -75, ... (first 5 terms)

4. 3, -6, 12, ... (first 5 terms)

5. $\frac{1}{27}$, $\frac{1}{9}$, $\frac{1}{3}$, ... (first 5 terms)

6. 1, y, y^2, ... (first 10 terms)

In 7–10, find the sum of the indicated number of terms of the geometric series.

7. $8 + 16 + 32 + \cdots$ (first 5 terms)

8. $81 + 27 + 9 + \cdots$ (first 6 terms)

9. $\frac{1}{8} + \frac{1}{4} + \frac{1}{2} + \cdots$ (first 7 terms)

10. $1 - 5 + 25 - 125 + \cdots$ (first 8 terms)

In 11–14, (a) write the geometric series and (b) find the sum of the series.

11. $\sum\limits_{i=1}^{4} 2^i$

12. $\sum\limits_{i=1}^{3} (\frac{1}{3})^i$

13. $\sum\limits_{j=1}^{5} 2(3)^{j-1}$

14. $\sum\limits_{k=-1}^{3} (-5)(4)^{k+1}$

In 15–18, the values of a_1, n, and r of a geometric sequence are given. Find the sum of the terms of the sequence.

15. $a_1 = 6$, $n = 4$, $r = 3$

16. $a_1 = 5$, $n = 6$, $r = 2$

17. $a_1 = -3$, $n = 5$, $r = -2$

18. $a_1 = 18$, $n = 5$, $r = \frac{2}{3}$

19. The first term of a geometric progression is 1 and the common ratio is 2. Find the sum of the first ten terms.

20. The sum of the first eight terms of the progression 3, 12, 48, ... is
(1) $4^8 + 1$ (2) 4^{10} (3) $4^8 - 1$

21. Find the first term of a geometric sequence of five terms in which the sum of the five terms is 363 and the common ratio is 3.

22. Find the number of terms of a geometric progression whose first term is 8, whose common ratio is 2, and the sum of whose terms is 120.

23. Find the common ratio of a geometric sequence in which $a_1 = 25$, $a_n = 400$, and $S_n = 775$.

24. If there have been no intermarriages in your family, how many ancestors have you had in the eight generations preceding you?

25. One Sunday morning, Ted sent a letter to each of three different friends in which he asked each of them to send a similar letter to each of three of their friends on the following Sunday. If no one breaks the chain and there are no duplications among the friends, how many letters will have been sent in the first seven Sundays?

10. Solving Verbal Problems Involving Geometric Sequences

In the solution of verbal problems involving geometric sequences, the following may be helpful in writing the equations that can be used in solving the problems:

1. The ratio of any term of a geometric sequence to its preceding term is equal to the ratio of any other term to its preceding term.
2. Apply the formulas for a_n and S_n in a geometric sequence.

~~~~~~~~~~~~ *MODEL PROBLEM* ~~~~~~~~~~~~

There are three numbers such that the second is two more than the first and the third is nine times the first. The numbers form a geometric sequence. Find the numbers.

Solution:

Let $x =$ the first number. Then $x + 2 =$ the second number and $9x =$ the third number.

The numbers x, $x + 2$, $9x$ are numbers in a geometric sequence.

In a geometric sequence of three terms, the middle term is the mean proportional between the first and the last terms. Hence,

$$\frac{x}{x+2} = \frac{x+2}{9x}$$
$$9x^2 = (x+2)^2$$
$$9x^2 = x^2 + 4x + 4$$
$$8x^2 - 4x - 4 = 0$$
$$2x^2 - x - 1 = 0$$
$$(x-1)(2x+1) = 0$$

$$x - 1 = 0 \qquad \bigg| \qquad 2x + 1 = 0$$
$$x = 1 \qquad \bigg| \qquad x = -\tfrac{1}{2}$$

If $x = 1$, the geometric sequence is 1, 3, 9. If $x = -\tfrac{1}{2}$, the geometric sequence is $-\tfrac{1}{2}, 1\tfrac{1}{2}, -4\tfrac{1}{2}$.

Answer: $1, 3, 9$ or $-\tfrac{1}{2}, 1\tfrac{1}{2}, -4\tfrac{1}{2}$

~~~~~~

Exercises

1. Three numbers are in the ratio of $1:3:5$. If 12 is added to the third number, the resulting number will be the third term of a geometric sequence of which the other two numbers are the first and second terms. Find the three numbers.

2. Three integers are in the ratio of $2:5:8$. If 2 is subtracted from the middle integer, the resulting number will be the second term of a geometric sequence of which the other two integers are the first and third terms. Find the three integers.

3. How much must be added to each of the numbers 2, 9, 23 so that the resulting numbers should form a geometric progression?

4. How much must be subtracted from each of the numbers 6, 10, and 18 so that the resulting numbers will form a geometric sequence?

5. What number must be added to the first number of the sequence 15, 10, 5 so that the resulting numbers will form a geometric progression?

6. Three numbers are in arithmetic progression, the common difference being 3. If the first number is diminished by 2, the second is increased by 4, and the third is doubled and then increased by 2, the resulting numbers are in geometric progression. Find the original numbers.

7. The sum of three numbers in a geometric progression is 14. Their product is 64. Find the numbers.

8. The sum of three positive numbers in an arithmetic progression is 18. If the third number is increased by 8, the numbers then form a geometric progression. Find the numbers in the arithmetic progression.

11. Finding the Sum of an Infinite Geometric Series

We have learned that if the number of terms in a sequence increases without limit, the sequence is called an *infinite sequence*. Also, if the number of terms in a series increases without limit, we call the series an *infinite series*.

Thus, $1, \frac{1}{2}, \frac{1}{4}, \frac{1}{8}, \frac{1}{16}, \frac{1}{32}, \ldots$ is an infinite geometric sequence. Also, $1 + \frac{1}{2} + \frac{1}{4} + \frac{1}{8} + \frac{1}{16} + \frac{1}{32} + \cdots$ is an infinite geometric series.

Consider the infinite geometric series $1 + 2 + 4 + 8 + 16 + 32 + \cdots$.

Let us find the sums of different numbers of terms of this series.

$$S_1 = 1 \text{ (We define } S_1 \text{ as the first term, 1.)}$$
$$S_2 = 1 + 2 = 3$$
$$S_3 = 1 + 2 + 4 = 7$$
$$S_4 = 1 + 2 + 4 + 8 = 15$$
$$S_5 = 1 + 2 + 4 + 8 + 16 = 31$$

In general, $S_n = 1 + 2 + 4 + 8 + 16 + \cdots$ to n terms.

We can see that as we increase the number of terms that are being added in the series, the individual terms become larger and larger. Furthermore, the sums $S_1, S_2, S_3, \ldots$ also become larger and larger. In fact, we can make S_n as large as we please by adding a sufficiently large number of terms. There is no limit to the value of S_n. We say that the sum of the terms of this infinite series is not finite. Such an infinite series is said to be a ***divergent series.***

Other examples of infinite geometric series that are divergent are

$$-1 - 2 - 4 - 8 - 16 - 32 - \cdots \text{ and } 1 - 2 + 4 - 8 + 16 - 32 + \cdots$$

In general, an infinite geometric series is a divergent series if the absolute value of the common ratio, r, is greater than or equal to 1; that is, $|r| \geq 1$.

On the other hand, consider the infinite geometric series

$$1 + \tfrac{1}{2} + \tfrac{1}{4} + \tfrac{1}{8} + \tfrac{1}{16} + \tfrac{1}{32} + \cdots$$

Let us find the sums of different numbers of terms of this series.

$$S_1 = 1 \text{ (We define } S_1 \text{ as the first term, 1.)}$$
$$S_2 = 1 + \tfrac{1}{2} = 1\tfrac{1}{2}, \text{ or } 1.5$$
$$S_3 = 1 + \tfrac{1}{2} + \tfrac{1}{4} = 1\tfrac{3}{4}, \text{ or } 1.75$$
$$S_4 = 1 + \tfrac{1}{2} + \tfrac{1}{4} + \tfrac{1}{8} = 1\tfrac{7}{8}, \text{ or } 1.875$$
$$S_5 = 1 + \tfrac{1}{2} + \tfrac{1}{4} + \tfrac{1}{8} + \tfrac{1}{16} = 1\tfrac{15}{16}, \text{ or } 1.9375$$

In general, $S_n = 1 + \tfrac{1}{2} + \tfrac{1}{4} + \tfrac{1}{8} + \tfrac{1}{16} + \cdots$ to n terms.

We can see that as we increase the number of terms in the series, the individual terms are becoming smaller and smaller. Although the sums $S_1, S_2, S_3, \ldots$ are becoming larger, there is a limit to the value of S_n. The value of S_n gets closer and closer to 2, but is never equal to 2. We can obtain a value of S_n as close to 2 as we wish by adding a sufficiently large number of terms. For example, to obtain a value of S_n within $\tfrac{1}{1000}$ of 2, we would add 12 terms. However, there is no value of n for which the value of S_n is equal to 2. We say that the value of S_n "approaches" the number 2 as a limit, and for that reason we also say that the sum of an infinite number of terms of this series is 2. Such a series, in which the infinite sequence $S_1, S_2, S_3, \ldots$ approaches a limit, is called a ***convergent series.***

Other examples of infinite geometric series that are convergent are

$$-1 - \tfrac{1}{2} - \tfrac{1}{4} - \tfrac{1}{8} - \tfrac{1}{16} - \tfrac{1}{32} - \cdots \text{ and } 1 - \tfrac{1}{2} + \tfrac{1}{4} - \tfrac{1}{8} + \tfrac{1}{16} - \tfrac{1}{32} + \cdots$$

In general, an infinite geometric series is a convergent series if the absolute value of the common ratio, r, is less than 1; that is, $|r| < 1$.

In order to find the limit of the sum of an infinite convergent geometric series, we can use the following formula, whose derivation appears on pages 746–747:

$$S = \frac{a_1}{1-r}, |r| < 1$$

For example, in the series $1 + \frac{1}{2} + \frac{1}{4} + \frac{1}{8} + \cdots$, $a_1 = 1$ and $r = \frac{1}{2}$. Hence,

$$S = \frac{a_1}{1-r} = \frac{1}{1 - \frac{1}{2}} = \frac{1}{\frac{1}{2}} = 2$$

~~~~~~~~~~~~~~~ *MODEL PROBLEMS* ~~~~~~~~~~~~~~~

1. Find the sum of the infinite series $4 + \frac{4}{3} + \frac{4}{9} + \frac{4}{27} + \cdots$.

Solution:
First, find the ratio by dividing the second term by the first term. Then find the sum.

$r = (\frac{4}{3}) \div (4) = \frac{4}{3} \times \frac{1}{4} = \frac{1}{3}$

$S = \dfrac{a_1}{1-r}$ Substitute: $a_1 = 4, r = \dfrac{1}{3}$

$= \dfrac{4}{1 - \frac{1}{3}} = \dfrac{4}{\frac{2}{3}} = 6$ *Ans.*

2. Find the sum of the terms of the infinite geometric sequence $2, -1, \frac{1}{2}, -\frac{1}{4}, \ldots$.

Solution:

$$r = (-1) \div (2) = -\tfrac{1}{2}.$$

$$S = \frac{a_1}{1-r} \qquad a_1 = 2, r = -\frac{1}{2}$$

$$= \frac{2}{1 - (-\frac{1}{2})} = \frac{2}{1 + \frac{1}{2}} = \frac{2}{\frac{3}{2}} = \frac{4}{3} \quad Ans.$$

3. Find the value of the repeating decimal $.535353 \ldots$.

Solution:
$$.535353 \ldots = .53 + .0053 + .000053 + \cdots$$
In this infinite geometric series, the common ratio $r = .0053 \div .53 = .01$.

Since $a_1 = .53$ and $r = .01$, then $S = \dfrac{a_1}{1-r} = \dfrac{.53}{1 - .01} = \dfrac{.53}{.99} = \dfrac{53}{99}$.

Answer: $\frac{53}{99}$

Exercises

In 1–4, find the first term and the common ratio of the infinite geometric series and state whether the series diverges or converges.

1. $20 + 10 + 5 + 2\frac{1}{2} + \cdots$ **2.** $3 + 12 + 48 + 192 + \cdots$

3. $8 - 2 + \frac{1}{2} - \frac{1}{8} + \cdots$ **4.** $2 - 6 + 18 - 54 + \cdots$

In 5–10, find the sum of the terms of the infinite geometric sequence.

5. $4, 2, 1, \ldots$ **6.** $5, \frac{5}{2}, \frac{5}{4}, \ldots$ **7.** $3, -1, \frac{1}{3}, \ldots$

8. $12, 8, 5\frac{1}{3}, \ldots$ **9.** $.4, .04, .004, \ldots$ **10.** $.23, .0023, .000023, \ldots$

In 11–19, find the sum of the infinite series.

11. $6 + 2 + \frac{2}{3} + \cdots$ **12.** $12 + 3 + \frac{3}{4} + \cdots$

13. $200 + 50 + 12\frac{1}{4} + \cdots$ **14.** $8 + 4 + 2 + \cdots$

15. $\frac{7}{10} + \frac{7}{100} + \frac{7}{1000} + \cdots$ **16.** $\frac{1}{5} + \frac{1}{10} + \frac{1}{20} + \cdots$

17. $-2 - \frac{1}{4} - \frac{1}{32} \cdots$ **18.** $9 - 6 + 4 - \cdots$

19. $\frac{1}{2} - \frac{1}{3} + \frac{2}{9} - \cdots$

In 20–22, find the sum of the infinite geometric progression in which a_1 and r have the given values.

20. $a_1 = 7, r = \frac{1}{2}$ **21.** $a_1 = 8, r = -\frac{1}{4}$ **22.** $a_1 = .7, r_1 = .1$

23. Find the common ratio in an infinite geometric progression whose first term is 4 and whose sum is 8.

24. Find the first term in an infinite geometric progression whose sum is 10 and whose common ratio is $\frac{1}{2}$.

25. A rubber ball is dropped from a height of 18 feet. It rebounds $\frac{2}{3}$ of the distance from which it fell previously. This process continues until the ball comes to rest. Find the total distance through which the ball moved.

26. The sum of the first two terms of an infinite geometric series is $\frac{8}{9}$ and the first term is $\frac{2}{3}$. Find the sum of the series.

In 27–38, represent the repeating decimal as an equivalent fraction.

27. $.888888 \ldots$ **28.** $.131313 \ldots$ **29.** $.363636 \ldots$ **30.** $.484848 \ldots$

31. $.727272 \ldots$ **32.** $.838383 \ldots$ **33.** $.125125 \ldots$ **34.** $.431431 \ldots$

35. $.566666 \ldots$ **36.** $.844444 \ldots$ **37.** $.45151 \ldots$ **38.** $.326363 \ldots$

12. Expanding a Binomial by the Binomial Theorem

The binomial theorem provides a method for *expanding* any power of a binomial, without repeated multiplication. We shall consider only those cases of binomials which have positive integral exponents.

If we begin with $(x + y)^1 = x + y$ and repeatedly multiply by $x + y$, we obtain the following:

$$(x + y)^1 = x + y$$
$$(x + y)^2 = x^2 + 2xy + y^2$$
$$(x + y)^3 = x^3 + 3x^2y + 3xy^2 + y^3$$
$$(x + y)^4 = x^4 + 4x^3y + 6x^2y^2 + 4xy^3 + y^4$$
$$(x + y)^5 = x^5 + 5x^4y + 10x^3y^2 + 10x^2y^3 + 5xy^4 + y^5$$

These results suggest the following rules for expanding $(x + y)^n$ when n is a positive integer:

1. The exponent of x in the first term is n. In each succeeding term, the exponent of x decreases by 1. The last term does not contain x.
2. The first term does not contain y. The exponent of y is 1 in the second term and increases by 1 in each succeeding term until it is n in the last term.
3. The coefficient of the first term is 1; of the second, n.
4. If the coefficient of any term is multiplied by the exponent of x in that term, and the product divided by the number of the term, the quotient is the coefficient of the next term.

In the expansion of $(x + y)^n$, when n is a positive integer, the following statements are always true:

1. The number of terms in the expansion is $n + 1$.
2. The sum of the exponents of x and y in each term in the expansion is n.
3. The coefficients of terms "equidistant" from the ends are the same.

The binomial theorem stated in general terms is :

$$(x + y)^n = x^n + \frac{n}{1}x^{n-1}y + \frac{n(n-1)}{1 \cdot 2}x^{n-2}y^2 + \frac{n(n-1)(n-2)}{1 \cdot 2 \cdot 3}x^{n-3}y^3 + \cdots + y^n$$

~~~~~~~~~~ *MODEL PROBLEMS* ~~~~~~~~~~

1. Expand $(a + 1)^4$ by using the binomial theorem.

Solution:

If we write the terms of the expansion of $(x + y)^4$ without their coefficients, we have

$$(x + y)^4 = (?)x^4 + (?)x^3y^1 + (?)x^2y^2 + (?)x^1y^3 + (?)y^4$$

In this example, $x = a$ and $y = 1$. Hence,

$$(a + 1)^4 = (?)a^4 + (?)a^3(1)^1 + (?)a^2(1)^2 + (?)a^1(1)^3 + (?)(1)^4$$

To find the coefficients:

a. The coefficient of the first term is 1.

b. The coefficient of the second term is 4, the exponent of the binomial.

c. To find the coefficient of the third term, multiply 4, the coefficient of the second term, by 3, the exponent of a in the second term. Then divide the product, 12, by 2, the number of the second term. The result, 6, represents the coefficient of the third term.

d. To find the coefficient of the fourth term, multiply 6, the coefficient of the third term, by 2, the exponent of a in the third term. Then divide the product, 12, by 3, the number of the third term. The result, 4, represents the coefficient of the fourth term.

e. The coefficient of the last term, the fifth term, is 1.

Hence, $(a + 1)^4 = (1)a^4 + 4a^3(1)^1 + 6(a^2)(1)^2 + 4(a)^1(1)^3 + (1)(1)^4$.

Answer: $(a + 1)^4 = a^4 + 4a^3 + 6a^2 + 4a + 1$

2. Expand $(2c - d)^3$ using the binomial theorem.

Solution:

If we write the terms of the expansion of $(x + y)^3$ without their coefficients, we have

$$(x + y)^3 = (?)x^3 + (?)x^2y^1 + (?)x^1y^2 + (?)y^3$$

In this example, $x = 2c$ and $y = -d$. Hence,

$$(2c - d)^3 = (?)(2c)^3 + (?)(2c)^2(-d)^1 + (?)(2c)^1(-d)^2 + (?)(-d)^3$$

To find the coefficients:

a. The coefficient of the first term is 1.

b. The coefficient of the second term is 3, the exponent of the binomial.

c. To find the coefficient of the third term, multiply 3, the coefficient of the second term, by 2, the exponent of $(2c)$ in that term, and divide the product by 2, the number of the term. The result, 3, represents the coefficient of the third term.

d. The coefficient of the last term, the fourth term, is 1. Hence,

$$(2c - d)^3 = (1)(2c)^3 + (3)(2c)^2(-d)^1 + (3)(2c)^1(-d)^2 + (1)(-d)^3$$
$$= (1)(8c^3) + (3)(4c^2)(-d) + (3)(2c)(d^2) + (1)(-d^3)$$

Answer: $(2c - d)^3 = 8c^3 - 12c^2\,d + 6cd^2 - d^3$

Exercises

In 1–4, state the number of terms there are in the expansion of the expression.

1. $(a+b)^8$ **2.** $(3x-5y)^5$ **3.** $\left(a+\dfrac{1}{2}\right)^7$ **4.** $\left(\dfrac{b}{4}+\dfrac{4}{b}\right)^{10}$

5. The number of terms in the expansion of $(a+b)^n$, when n is a positive integer, is (1) n (2) $n+1$ (3) $2n$ (4) $n-1$

In 6–21, expand the expression using the binomial theorem.

6. $(a+b)^5$ **7.** $(r-s)^4$ **8.** $(m+n)^6$ **9.** $(x+2)^4$
10. $(d-2)^5$ **11.** $(a^2+b)^4$ **12.** $(c^2-d^2)^5$ **13.** $(m^2-1)^6$
14. $(2a+b)^5$ **15.** $(r-2s)^4$ **16.** $(2c-3d)^3$ **17.** $(1+x)^6$

18. $(2-b)^5$ **19.** $(x+\tfrac{1}{2})^4$ **20.** $\left(x+\dfrac{1}{x}\right)^3$ **21.** $(\tfrac{1}{2}-x^2)^3$

In 22–25, write the first two terms in the expansion of the expression.
22. $(a+b)^8$ **23.** $(x+y^2)^4$ **24.** $(2a+b)^4$ **25.** $(x+\tfrac{1}{2})^6$

In 26–33, write the first three terms of the expansion of the expression.
26. $(a+b)^6$ **27.** $(a-b)^7$ **28.** $(1+2a)^4$ **29.** $(x^2-y)^3$

30. $(c^2+1)^8$ **31.** $(a^2-2b)^{10}$ **32.** $\left(2-\dfrac{a}{2}\right)^5$ **33.** $\left(x+\dfrac{y}{3}\right)^7$

In 34–37, write the required term in the expansion of the expression.
34. the second term of $(a+b)^{12}$ **35.** the second term of $(2x-y)^4$

36. the third term of $(2-s)^5$ **37.** the fourth term of $\left(\dfrac{b}{3}+\dfrac{3}{b}\right)^6$

38. Find the middle term of $\left(\dfrac{x}{2}+\dfrac{2}{x}\right)^8$.

CHAPTER XXIV

PROOFS AND DERIVATIONS OF TRIGONOMETRIC AND ALGEBRAIC FORMULAS

Proofs and Derivations of Trigonometric Formulas

An asterisk (*) preceding the derivation of a formula indicates that the derivation may be called for on the Eleventh Year Regents Examination of the State of New York.

*1. LAW OF COSINES (FOR ALL VALUES OF THE ANGLE USING RECTANGULAR COORDINATES IN TRIGONOMETRIC FORM)

Prove: $c^2 = a^2 + b^2 - 2ab \cos \theta$

1. Let P be a point on the initial side of angle θ, which is in standard position. Let the distance from the origin O to P be denoted by a. The coordinates of P are $(a, 0)$. Let P' be a point on the terminal side of angle θ. Let the distance from the origin O to P' be denoted by b. The coordinates of P' are $(b \cos \theta, b \sin \theta)$.
Let the length of $\overline{PP'}$ be denoted by c.

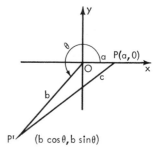

2. Using the distance formula, find the length of $\overline{PP'}$ as follows:
$PP' = \sqrt{(x_2 - x_1)^2 + (y_2 - y_1)^2}$

3. $c = \sqrt{(b \cos \theta - a)^2 + (b \sin \theta - 0)^2}$

4. $c^2 = (b \cos \theta - a)^2 + (b \sin \theta - 0)^2$

5. $c^2 = b^2 \cos^2 \theta - 2ab \cos \theta + a^2 + b^2 \sin^2 \theta$

6. $c^2 = a^2 + b^2 \sin^2 \theta + b^2 \cos^2 \theta - 2ab \cos \theta$

7. $c^2 = a^2 + b^2(\sin^2 \theta + \cos^2 \theta) - 2ab \cos \theta$ (Substitute 1 for $\sin^2 \theta + \cos^2 \theta$.)

8. $c^2 = a^2 + b^2 - 2ab \cos \theta$

730

Remarks. This formula is true for all values of θ. However, if θ is greater than $0°$ and less than $180°$, then the angle θ may be thought of as an angle C of a triangle ABC. Note that angle C is included between two sides of length a and b and opposite a remaining side of length c.

Forms of the Law of Cosines

$$c^2 = a^2 + b^2 - 2ab \cos C$$

$$a^2 = b^2 + c^2 - 2bc \cos A$$

$$b^2 = a^2 + c^2 - 2ac \cos B$$

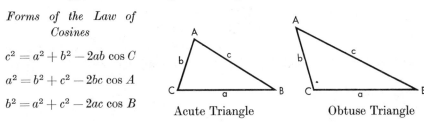

Acute Triangle   Obtuse Triangle

As in proof 1 and other proofs in this chapter, a letter such as θ may be used, unless otherwise stated, to represent the measure of an angle as well as the angle according to the context in which the letter is used. Also, a letter, unless otherwise stated, represents either a side of a geometric figure or the measure of the side according to the context in which the letter is used.

*2. COSINE OF THE DIFFERENCE OF TWO ANGLES (FOR ALL VALUES OF THE ANGLES USING RECTANGULAR COORDINATES IN TRIGONOMETRIC FORM)

Prove: $\cos(x - y) = \cos x \cos y + \sin x \sin y$

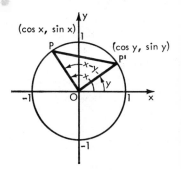

1. Let O be the center of a circle whose radius is 1. The equation of this circle is $x^2 + y^2 = 1$. Since $OP = OP' = 1$, the coordinates of P are $(\cos x, \sin x)$ and the coordinates of P' are $(\cos y, \sin y)$.

2. Using the distance formula, find the length of $\overline{PP'}$ as follows:
$$PP' = \sqrt{(x_2 - x_1)^2 + (y_2 - y_1)^2}$$

3. $PP' = \sqrt{(\cos x - \cos y)^2 + (\sin x - \sin y)^2}$

4. $(PP')^2 = (\cos x - \cos y)^2 + (\sin x - \sin y)^2$

5. Using the law of cosines, find the length of $\overline{PP'}$ as follows:
$$(PP')^2 = (OP)^2 + (OP')^2 - 2(OP)(OP')\cos(x - y)$$

6. $(PP')^2 = (1)^2 + (1)^2 - 2(1)(1)\cos(x - y) = 2 - 2\cos(x - y)$

7. Equating the right members of equations 4 and 6,
$$2 - 2\cos(x - y) = (\cos x - \cos y)^2 + (\sin x - \sin y)^2$$

8. $2 - 2\cos(x - y) =$
$$\cos^2 x - 2\cos x \cos y + \cos^2 y + \sin^2 x - 2\sin x \sin y + \sin^2 y$$
9. $2 - 2\cos(x - y) =$
$$(\sin^2 x + \cos^2 x) + (\sin^2 y + \cos^2 y) - 2(\cos x \cos y + \sin x \sin y)$$
10. $2 - 2\cos(x - y) = 2 - 2(\cos x \cos y + \sin x \sin y)$
11. Therefore, $\cos(x - y) = \cos x \cos y + \sin x \sin y$.

Remarks. The formula $\cos(x - y) = \cos x \cos y + \sin x \sin y$ may be used to prove $\cos(-y) = \cos y$ and $\sin(-y) = -\sin y$ for all values of y, as follows:

2a. Prove: $\cos(-y) = \cos y$

$\cos(x - y) = \cos x \cos y + \sin x \sin y$

Substitute $0°$ for x.

$\cos(0° - y) = \cos 0° \cos y + \sin 0° \sin y$
$\cos(-y) = (1)\cos y + (0)\sin y$
$\cos(-y) = \cos y$

2b. Prove: $\sin(-y) = -\sin y$

$\cos(x - y) = \cos x \cos y + \sin x \sin y$

Substitute $90°$ for x.

$\cos(90° - y) = \cos 90° \cos y + \sin 90° \sin y$
$\cos(90° - y) = (0)\cos y + (1)\sin y$
Substitute $(-A)$ for y.
$\cos(90° + A) = 0 + \sin(-A)$
$-\sin A = \sin(-A)$
Let $A = -y$.
$-\sin(-y) = \sin y$
$\sin(-y) = -\sin y$

2c. Prove: $\tan(-y) = -\tan y$

$$\tan A = \frac{\sin A}{\cos A}$$

Let $A = -y$: $\tan(-y) = \dfrac{\sin(-y)}{\cos(-y)}$

Hence, $\tan(-y) = \dfrac{-\sin y}{\cos y}$

$\tan(-y) = -\tan y$

*3. COSINE OF THE SUM OF TWO ANGLES

Remarks. To derive the formula for $\cos(x + y)$, we begin with the formula for $\cos(x - y)$ and use the identities $\cos(-y) = \cos y$ and $\sin(-y) = -\sin y$.

Prove: $\cos(x + y) = \cos x \cos y - \sin x \sin y$

1. $\cos(x - y) = \cos x \cos y + \sin x \sin y$.
2. In the above identity, replacing y with $(-y)$,
   $\cos[x - (-y)] = \cos x \cos(-y) + \sin x \sin(-y)$
3. Substituting $\cos y$ for $\cos(-y)$ and $-\sin y$ for $\sin(-y)$,
   $\cos(x + y) = \cos x \cos y - \sin x \sin y$

*4. SINE OF THE DIFFERENCE OF TWO ANGLES

Remarks. To derive the formula for $\sin(x - y)$, we begin with the formula $\sin A = \cos(90° - A)$ and then substitute $(x - y)$ for A.

Prove: $\sin(x - y) = \sin x \cos y - \cos x \sin y$

1. $\sin A = \cos(90° - A)$.
2. In the above identity, replacing A with $(x - y)$,
   $\sin(x - y) = \cos[90° - (x - y)]$.
3. $\sin(x - y) = \cos[(90° - x) + y]$
4. $\sin(x - y) = \cos(90° - x)\cos y - \sin(90° - x)\sin y$
5. Substituting $\sin x$ for $\cos(90° - x)$ and $\cos x$ for $\sin(90° - x)$,
   $\sin(x - y) = \sin x \cos y - \cos x \sin y$.

*5. SINE OF THE SUM OF TWO ANGLES

Remarks. To derive the formula for $\sin(x + y)$, we begin with the formula for $\sin(x - y)$ and use the identities $\cos(-y) = \cos y$ and $\sin(-y) = -\sin y$.

Prove: $\sin(x + y) = \sin x \cos y + \cos x \sin y$

1. $\sin(x - y) = \sin x \cos y - \cos x \sin y$
2. In the above identity, replacing y with $(-y)$,
   $\sin[x - (-y)] = \sin x \cos(-y) - \cos x \sin(-y)$
3. Substituting $\cos y$ for $\cos(-y)$ and $-\sin y$ for $\sin(-y)$,
   $\sin(x + y) = \sin x \cos y - (\cos x)(-\sin y)$.
4. $\sin(x + y) = \sin x \cos y + \cos x \sin y$.

*6. TANGENT OF THE SUM OF TWO ANGLES

Remarks. To derive the formula for $\tan(x+y)$, we begin with the identity $\tan A = \dfrac{\sin A}{\cos A}$, replace A by $(x+y)$, and then use the formulas for $\sin(x+y)$ and $\cos(x+y)$.

Prove: $\tan(x+y) = \dfrac{\tan x + \tan y}{1 - \tan x \tan y}$

1. $\tan A = \dfrac{\sin A}{\cos A}$

Let $(x+y) = A$.

2. $\tan(x+y) = \dfrac{\sin(x+y)}{\cos(x+y)}$

3. $\tan(x+y) = \dfrac{\sin x \cos y + \cos x \sin y}{\cos x \cos y - \sin x \sin y}$

Divide each term of the numerator and the denominator of the fraction by $\cos x \cos y$.

4. $\tan(x+y) = \dfrac{\dfrac{\sin x \cos y}{\cos x \cos y} + \dfrac{\cos x \sin y}{\cos x \cos y}}{\dfrac{\cos x \cos y}{\cos x \cos y} - \dfrac{\sin x \sin y}{\cos x \cos y}}$

5. $\tan(x+y) = \dfrac{\dfrac{\sin x}{\cos x} + \dfrac{\sin y}{\cos y}}{1 - \dfrac{\sin x}{\cos x} \cdot \dfrac{\sin y}{\cos y}}$

$\left(\dfrac{\sin x}{\cos x} = \tan x\right) \quad \left(\dfrac{\sin y}{\cos y} = \tan y\right)$

6. $\tan(x+y) = \dfrac{\tan x + \tan y}{1 - \tan x \tan y}$

*7. TANGENT OF THE DIFFERENCE OF TWO ANGLES

Remarks. To derive the formula for $\tan(x-y)$, we begin with the formula for $\tan(x+y)$, replace y with $(-y)$, and then use the identity $\tan(-y) = -\tan y$.

Prove: $\tan(x-y) = \dfrac{\tan x - \tan y}{1 + \tan x \tan y}$

1. $\tan(x+y) = \dfrac{\tan x + \tan y}{1 - \tan x \tan y}$

2. In the above identity, replace y with $-y$.

$$\tan[x + (-y)] = \dfrac{\tan x + \tan(-y)}{1 - \tan x \tan(-y)}$$

3. Since $\tan(-y) = -\tan y$,

$$\tan(x-y) = \dfrac{\tan x - \tan y}{1 + \tan x \tan y}$$

SEQUENCE OF PROOFS OF THE TRIGONOMETRIC FORMULAS FOR THE SINE, COSINE, AND TANGENT OF THE SUM OR THE DIFFERENCE OF TWO ANGLES

The following table lists the six trigonometric formulas proved in proofs 2 to 7. Learning the proofs of these formulas is made easier if you know the sequence of the proofs as well as the key ideas used in their derivation. The arrows in the table indicate the sequence of proofs of the formulas, that is, the order in which formulas are used to derive other formulas. Using the arrows, note that formula 2 is used to prove formula 3, which in turn is used to prove formula 4, etc.

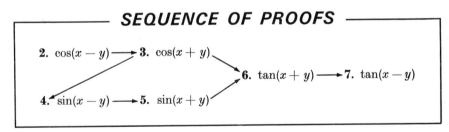

SEQUENCE OF PROOFS

2. $\cos(x-y)$ ⟶ 3. $\cos(x+y)$
4. $\sin(x-y)$ ⟶ 5. $\sin(x+y)$
6. $\tan(x+y)$ ⟶ 7. $\tan(x-y)$

Remarks Involving Proofs 8 to 10. Proofs 8 to 10 are the proofs of the formulas for the sine, cosine, and tangent of the double angle. In each case, we begin with the formula for the same-named function of the sum of two angles; for example, to prove the formula for $\sin 2x$, we begin with $\sin(x+y)$. In each proof, y is replaced with x.

*8. SINE OF THE DOUBLE ANGLE

Prove: $\sin 2x = 2 \sin x \cos x$

1. $\sin(x + y) = \sin x \cos y + \cos x \sin y$
2. In the above identity, replace y with x.
   $\sin(x + x) = \sin x \cos x + \cos x \sin x$
3. $\sin 2x = 2 \sin x \cos x$

*9. COSINE OF THE DOUBLE ANGLE

Prove: $\cos 2x = \cos^2 x - \sin^2 x$

1. $\cos(x + y) = \cos x \cos y - \sin x \sin y$
2. In the above identity, replace y with x.
   $\cos(x + x) = \cos x \cos x - \sin x \sin x$
3. $\cos 2x = \cos^2 x - \sin^2 x$

9a. Prove: $\cos 2x = 2 \cos^2 x - 1$

$\cos 2x = \cos^2 x - \sin^2 x$
Replace $\sin^2 x$ with $(1 - \cos^2 x)$.
$$\cos 2x = \cos^2 x - (1 - \cos^2 x)$$
$$= \cos^2 x - 1 + \cos^2 x$$
$$= 2 \cos^2 x - 1$$

9b. Prove: $\cos 2x = 1 - 2 \sin^2 x$

$\cos 2x = \cos^2 x - \sin^2 x$
Replace $\cos^2 x$ with $(1 - \sin^2 x)$.
$$\cos 2x = (1 - \sin^2 x) - \sin^2 x$$
$$= 1 - \sin^2 x - \sin^2 x$$
$$= 1 - 2 \sin^2 x$$

*10. TANGENT OF THE DOUBLE ANGLE

Prove: $\tan 2x = \dfrac{2 \tan x}{1 - \tan^2 x}$

1. $\tan(x + y) = \dfrac{\tan x + \tan y}{1 - \tan x \tan y}$

2. In the above identity, replace y with x.

   $\tan(x + x) = \dfrac{\tan x + \tan x}{1 - \tan x \cdot \tan x}$

3. $\tan 2x = \dfrac{2 \tan x}{1 - \tan^2 x}$

*11. SINE OF THE HALF ANGLE

Prove: $\sin \tfrac{1}{2}x = \pm\sqrt{\dfrac{1 - \cos x}{2}}$

*12. COSINE OF THE HALF ANGLE

Prove: $\cos \tfrac{1}{2}x = \pm\sqrt{\dfrac{1 + \cos x}{2}}$

1. $\cos 2A = \cos^2 A - \sin^2 A$
2. Since $\cos^2 A = 1 - \sin^2 A$,
   $\cos 2A = 1 - \sin^2 A - \sin^2 A$.
3. $\cos 2A = 1 - 2 \sin^2 A$
4. $2 \sin^2 A = 1 - \cos 2A$
5. $\sin^2 A = \dfrac{1 - \cos 2A}{2}$
6. $\sin A = \pm \sqrt{\dfrac{1 - \cos 2A}{2}}$
7. If we let $A = \frac{1}{2}x$, then $2A = x$.
8. Substituting $\frac{1}{2}x$ for A, and x for $2A$ in (6), we obtain

$$\sin \tfrac{1}{2}x = \pm \sqrt{\frac{1 - \cos x}{2}}$$

1. $\cos 2A = \cos^2 A - \sin^2 A$
2. Since $\sin^2 A = 1 - \cos^2 A$,
   $\cos 2A = \cos^2 A - (1 - \cos^2 A)$.
3. $\cos 2A = 2 \cos^2 A - 1$
4. $2 \cos^2 A = 1 + \cos 2A$
5. $\cos^2 A = \dfrac{1 + \cos 2A}{2}$
6. $\cos A = \pm \sqrt{\dfrac{1 + \cos 2A}{2}}$
7. If we let $A = \frac{1}{2}x$, then $2A = x$.
8. Substituting $\frac{1}{2}x$ for A, and x for $2A$ in (6), we obtain

$$\cos \tfrac{1}{2}x = \pm \sqrt{\frac{1 + \cos x}{2}}$$

*13. TANGENT OF THE HALF ANGLE

Remarks. To derive the formula for $\tan \frac{1}{2}x$, we begin with the identity $\tan \frac{1}{2}x = \dfrac{\sin \frac{1}{2}x}{\cos \frac{1}{2}x}$ and then we use the formulas for $\sin \frac{1}{2}x$ and $\cos \frac{1}{2}x$.

Prove: $\tan \tfrac{1}{2}x = \pm \sqrt{\dfrac{1 - \cos x}{1 + \cos x}}$

1. $\tan \frac{1}{2}x = \dfrac{\sin \frac{1}{2}x}{\cos \frac{1}{2}x}$

2. $\tan \frac{1}{2}x = \dfrac{\pm \sqrt{\dfrac{1 - \cos x}{2}}}{\pm \sqrt{\dfrac{1 + \cos x}{2}}} = \pm \sqrt{\dfrac{\dfrac{1 - \cos x}{2}}{\dfrac{1 + \cos x}{2}}}$

3. $\tan \frac{1}{2}x = \pm \sqrt{\dfrac{1 - \cos x}{1 + \cos x}}$

Note. $\left(\dfrac{1 - \cos x}{2}\right) \div \left(\dfrac{1 + \cos x}{2}\right) = \dfrac{(1 - \cos x)}{\cancel{2}} \cdot \dfrac{\overset{1}{\cancel{2}}}{(1 + \cos x)} = \dfrac{1 - \cos x}{1 + \cos x}$

*14. ALTERNATE PROOF OF THE FORMULA FOR THE SINE OF THE SUM OF TWO ANGLES

Prove: $\sin(x + y) = \sin x \cos y + \cos x \sin y$, when x, y and $(x + y)$ are positive acute angles.

Let $\angle AOC = x$, $\angle COB = y$, $\angle AOB = (x + y)$.
Angles x, y, and $(x + y)$ are positive acute angles.
O is the center of a unit circle.
Therefore, the length of radius $\overline{OB} = 1$ unit.
From B, draw $\overline{BF} \perp \overline{OA}$ and $\overline{BD} \perp \overline{OC}$.
From D, draw $\overline{DE} \perp \overline{OA}$ and $\overline{DG} \perp \overline{FB}$.
Since the sides of acute $\angle DBG$ are perpendicular
    to the sides of acute $\angle x$, $\angle DBG = x$.

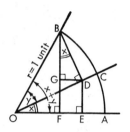

1. In right triangle FOB,

$$\sin(x + y) = \frac{FB}{OB} = \frac{FB}{1} = FB = FG + GB = ED + GB.$$

$$\sin(x + y) = ED + GB$$

2. In right triangle EOD, $\sin x = \dfrac{ED}{OD}$, or $ED = (\sin x)(OD)$.

3. In right triangle DOB, $\cos y = \dfrac{OD}{OB} = \dfrac{OD}{1} = OD$, or $OD = \cos y$.

4. From (2), $ED = \sin x \cos y$.

5. In right triangle DGB, $\cos x = \dfrac{GB}{DB}$, or $GB = (\cos x)(DB)$.

6. In right triangle DOB, $\sin y = \dfrac{DB}{OB} = \dfrac{DB}{1} = DB$, or $DB = \sin y$.

7. From (5), $GB = \cos x \sin y$,

8. Substituting the results of (4) and (7) in (1), we have
    $\sin(x + y) = \sin x \cos y + \cos x \sin y$

Remarks. Observe in the above proof 14, the formula for the sine of the sum of two angles is proved only for the case where each angle and also the sum of the two angles is an acute angle. In proof 5 (page 733), which involves the same formula, the formula is proved to be true for all values of the angles.

*15. ALTERNATE PROOF OF THE FORMULA FOR THE COSINE OF THE SUM OF TWO ANGLES

Prove: $\cos(x+y) = \cos x \cos y - \sin x \sin y$, when x, y and $(x+y)$ are positive acute angles.

Let $\angle AOC = x$, $\angle COB = y$, $\angle AOB = (x+y)$.
Angles x, y, and $(x+y)$ are positive acute angles.
O is the center of a unit circle.
Therefore, the length of radius $\overline{OB} = 1$ unit.
From B, draw $\overline{BF} \perp \overline{OA}$ and $\overline{BD} \perp \overline{OC}$.
From D, draw $\overline{DE} \perp \overline{OA}$ and $\overline{DG} \perp \overline{FB}$.
Since the sides of acute $\angle DBG$ are perpendicular to the sides of acute $\angle x$, $\angle DBG = x$.

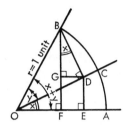

1. In right triangle FOB,

$$\cos(x+y) = \frac{OF}{OB} = \frac{OF}{1} = OF = OE - FE = OE - GD$$

$$\cos(x+y) = OE - GD$$

2. In right triangle EOD, $\cos x = \dfrac{OE}{OD}$, or $OE = (\cos x)(OD)$.

3. In right triangle DOB, $\cos y = \dfrac{OD}{OB} = \dfrac{OD}{1} = OD$, or $OD = \cos y$.

4. From (2), $OE = \cos x \cos y$.

5. In right triangle DGB, $\sin x = \dfrac{GD}{DB}$, or $GD = (\sin x)(DB)$.

6. In right triangle DOB, $\sin y = \dfrac{DB}{OB} = \dfrac{DB}{1} = DB$, or $DB = \sin y$.

7. From (5), $GD = \sin x \sin y$.
8. Substituting the results of (4) and (7) in (1), we have
   $\cos(x+y) = \cos x \cos y - \sin x \sin y$

Remarks. In the above proof 15, the formula for the cosine of the sum of two angles is proved only for the case where each angle and also the sum of the two angles is an acute angle. In proof 3 (page 733), which involves the same formula, the formula is proved to be true for all values of the angles.

*16. ALTERNATE PROOF OF THE SINE OF THE DIFFERENCE OF TWO ANGLES

Remarks. To derive the formula for $\sin(x-y)$ in the alternate proof, we begin with the formula for $\sin(x+y)$ and use the identities

$$\cos(-y) = \cos y \quad \text{and} \quad \sin(-y) = -\sin y$$

Prove: $\sin (x-y) = \sin x \cos y - \cos x \sin y$

1. $\sin(x+y) = \sin x \cos y + \cos x \sin y$
2. In the above identity, replacing y with $-y$:
   $\sin[x + (-y)] = \sin x \cos(-y) + \cos x \sin(-y)$.
3. Since $\cos(-y) = \cos y$ and $\sin(-y) = -\sin y$,
   $\sin[x + (-y)] = \sin x \cos y + (\cos x)(-\sin y)$.
4. $\sin(x-y) = \sin x \cos y - \cos x \sin y$

*17. ALTERNATE PROOF OF THE COSINE OF THE DIFFERENCE OF TWO ANGLES

Remarks. To derive the formula for $\cos(x-y)$ in the alternate proof, we begin with the formula for $\cos(x+y)$ and use the identities $\cos(-y) = \cos y$ and $\sin(-y) = -\sin y$.

Prove: $\cos(x-y) = \cos x \cos y + \sin x \sin y$

1. $\cos(x+y) = \cos x \cos y - \sin x \sin y$
2. In the above identity, replacing y with $-y$:
   $\cos[x + (-y)] = \cos x \cos(-y) - \sin x \sin(-y)$.
3. Since $\cos(-y) = \cos y$ and $\sin(-y) = -\sin y$,
   $\cos[x + (-y)] = \cos x \cos y - (\sin x)(-\sin y)$.
4. $\cos(x-y) = \cos x \cos y + \sin x \sin y$

Note. The proofs of the formulas for $\tan(x+y)$ and $\tan(x-y)$ are the proofs 6 and 7 on pages 734–735. There are no alternate proofs for these formulas.

ALTERNATE SEQUENCE OF PROOFS OF THE TRIGONOMETRIC FORMULAS FOR THE SINE, COSINE, AND TANGENT OF THE SUM OR THE DIFFERENCE OF TWO ANGLES

The following table sets forth an alternate sequence of the proofs of the six formulas proved in proofs 2 to 7. In this alternate sequence, note that any formula involving the difference of two angles is proved by beginning with the formula of the same-named function of the sum of two angles.

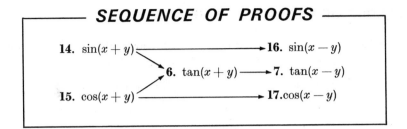

$$\text{SEQUENCE OF PROOFS}$$

14. $\sin(x + y)$ ⟶ **16.** $\sin(x - y)$

6. $\tan(x + y)$ ⟶ **7.** $\tan(x - y)$

15. $\cos(x + y)$ ⟶ **17.** $\cos(x - y)$

18. PROOF OF THE FORMULAS FOR THE AREA OF A TRIANGLE WHEN TWO SIDES AND THE INCLUDED ANGLE ARE GIVEN (s.a.s.)

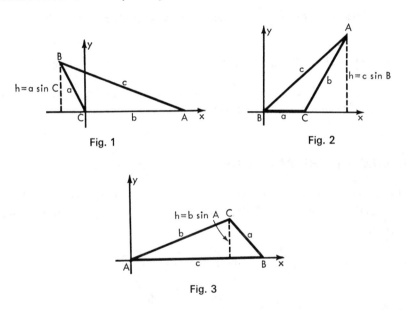

Fig. 1

Fig. 2

Fig. 3

In Figs. 1–3, a triangle is placed so that one vertex of the triangle is at the origin and, in each of the three figures, a different side of the triangle is along the positive half of the x-axis.

Beginning with the formula $K = \frac{1}{2}bh$ in each case, we derive:

1. $K = \frac{1}{2}ab \sin C$, using Fig. 1. Here, we replace h by $a \sin C$.
2. $K = \frac{1}{2}ac \sin B$, using Fig. 2. Here, we replace h by $c \sin B$.
3. $K = \frac{1}{2}bc \sin A$, using Fig. 3. Here, we replace h by $b \sin A$.

19. PROOF OF THE LAW OF SINES

If we begin with the combined formula for the area of a triangle and divide each member by $\frac{1}{2}abc$, the law of sines is derived as follows:

Area formula: $K = \frac{1}{2}ab \sin C = \frac{1}{2}bc \sin A = \frac{1}{2}ac \sin B$

$$\frac{\frac{1}{2}ab \sin C}{\frac{1}{2}ab \cdot c} = \frac{\frac{1}{2}bc \sin A}{\frac{1}{2}bc \cdot a} = \frac{\frac{1}{2}ac \sin B}{\frac{1}{2}ac \cdot b}$$

Law of sines: $$\frac{\sin C}{c} = \frac{\sin A}{a} = \frac{\sin B}{b}$$

Proofs and Derivations of Algebraic Formulas

20. ROOTS OF THE QUADRATIC EQUATION $ax^2 + bx + c = 0, a \neq 0$

The proof of the formula for the roots of the quadratic equation, by completing the square, is given on pages 410–411.

21. SUM OF THE ROOTS OF $ax^2 + bx + c = 0, \quad a \neq 0$

If the roots of the quadratic equation $ax^2 + bx + c = 0$ are represented by r_1 and r_2, derive the formula for the sum of the roots $r_1 + r_2$ in terms of a and b.

Solution:

1. $r_1 = \dfrac{-b + \sqrt{b^2 - 4ac}}{2a}$ and $r_2 = \dfrac{-b - \sqrt{b^2 - 4ac}}{2a}$

2. $r_1 + r_2 = \dfrac{-b + \sqrt{b^2 - 4ac}}{2a} + \dfrac{-b - \sqrt{b^2 - 4ac}}{2a}$

3. $r_1 + r_2 = \dfrac{-b + \sqrt{b^2 - 4ac} - b - \sqrt{b^2 - 4ac}}{2a}$

4. $r_1 + r_2 = \dfrac{-2b}{2a}$

5. $r_1 + r_2 = -\dfrac{b}{a}$

22. PRODUCT OF THE ROOTS OF $ax^2 + bx + c = 0$, $a \neq 0$

If the roots of the quadratic equation $ax^2 + bx + c = 0$ are represented by r_1 and r_2, derive the formula for the product of the roots $r_1 \times r_2$ in terms of a and c.

Solution:

1. $\quad r_1 = \dfrac{-b + \sqrt{b^2 - 4ac}}{2a}$ and $r_2 = \dfrac{-b - \sqrt{b^2 - 4ac}}{2a}$

2. $r_1 \times r_2 = \left(\dfrac{-b + \sqrt{b^2 - 4ac}}{2a} \right) \left(\dfrac{-b - \sqrt{b^2 - 4ac}}{2a} \right)$

3. $r_1 \times r_2 = \dfrac{b^2 - (b^2 - 4ac)}{4a^2}$

4. $r_1 \times r_2 = \dfrac{b^2 - b^2 + 4ac}{4a^2}$

5. $r_1 \times r_2 = \dfrac{4ac}{4a^2}$

6. $r_1 \times r_2 = \dfrac{c}{a}$

23. SLOPES OF PERPENDICULAR LINES

If the product of the slopes of two nonvertical lines is -1, prove that the lines are perpendicular to each other.

Solution:

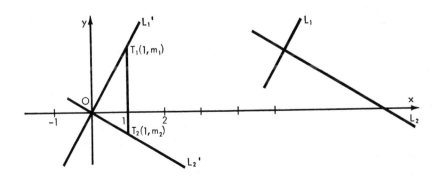

1. In the figure, lines L_1 and L_2 have slopes m_1 and m_2 respectively.

   Note. If these two lines are parallel, their slopes are equal and $m_1 \cdot m_2 \neq -1$. Thus we need to consider only the case in which L_1 and L_2 intersect.

2. Lines L_1' and L_2' are drawn through the origin and parallel to L_1 and L_2 respectively. Lines L_1' and L_2' have slopes m_1 and m_2 respectively.

3. The line whose equation is $x = 1$ is drawn, intersecting L_1' at point $T_1(1, m_1)$ and L_2' at point $T_2(1, m_2)$.

4. By the theorem of Pythagoras, triangle T_1OT_2 is a right triangle in which $\angle T_1OT_2$ is a right angle if and only if

$$(T_1T_2)^2 = (T_1O)^2 + (T_2O)^2$$

5.
$$(m_2 - m_1)^2 = (1^2 + m_1^2) + (1^2 + m_2^2)$$
$$m_2^2 - 2m_1m_2 + m_1^2 = 2 + m_1^2 + m_2^2$$
$$-2m_1m_2 = 2$$
$$m_1m_2 = -1$$

6. Therefore, if $m_1 \cdot m_2 = -1$, then the lines are perpendicular to each other.

24. EQUATION OF THE AXIS OF SYMMETRY OF A PARABOLA, $y = ax^2 + bx + c$

In the figure at the right, P_1 and P_2 are the points at which the graph of $y = ax^2 + bx + c$ intersects the x-axis. Therefore, both the ordinate of P_1 and the ordinate of P_2 are 0. That is, at P_1 and P_2, $y = 0$.

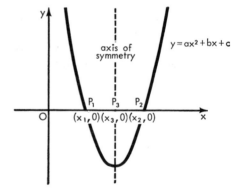

To obtain x_1 and x_2, the values of x at these points, we replace y with 0 in the equation $y = ax^2 + bx + c$. We thus obtain the equation $0 = ax^2 + bx + c$. We have learned that the roots of $ax^2 + bx + c = 0$ are

$$x = \frac{-b \pm \sqrt{b^2 - 4ac}}{2a}$$

Hence, $x_1 = \dfrac{-b - \sqrt{b^2 - 4ac}}{2a}$ and $x_2 = \dfrac{-b + \sqrt{b^2 - 4ac}}{2a}$.

Therefore, the coordinates of P_1 and P_2 are respectively $\left(\dfrac{-b-\sqrt{b^2-4ac}}{2a}, 0\right)$

and $\left(\dfrac{-b+\sqrt{b^2-4ac}}{2a}, 0\right)$.

If $P_3(x_3, 0)$ is the point at which the axis of symmetry intersects the x-axis, then P_3 is the midpoint of segment $\overline{P_1 P_2}$. Hence, x_3 is the average of x_1 and x_2.

$$x_3 = \tfrac{1}{2}(x_1 + x_2)$$

$$= \tfrac{1}{2}\left(\dfrac{-b-\sqrt{b^2-4ac}}{2a} + \dfrac{-b+\sqrt{b^2-4ac}}{2a}\right)$$

$$= \tfrac{1}{2}\left(\dfrac{-2b}{2a}\right)$$

$$= -\dfrac{b}{2a}$$

Since all points on the axis of symmetry of the parabola, $y = ax^2 + bx + c$, have the same abscissa, the axis of symmetry is the set of all points whose abscissa, x, is $-\dfrac{b}{2a}$. Therefore, the equation of the axis of symmetry is

$$\boldsymbol{x = -\dfrac{b}{2a}}$$

25. SUM OF AN ARITHMETIC SERIES

a. Derive the formula for the sum, S_n, of an arithmetic series in terms of the number of terms, n, the first term, a_1, and the nth term, a_n.

Solution:

1. $S_n = a_1 + (a_1 + d) + (a_1 + 2d) + \cdots + (a_n - d) + a_n$
2. $S_n = a_n + (a_n - d) + (a_n - 2d) + \cdots + (a_1 + d) + a_1$
3. $\overline{2S_n = (a_1 + a_n) + (a_1 + a_n) + (a_1 + a_n) + \cdots + (a_1 + a_n) + (a_1 + a_n)}$

Since there are n terms in the series, there will be n addends in (3), each of which is $(a_1 + a_n)$.

4. $2S_n = n(a_1 + a_n)$

5. $S_n = \dfrac{n}{2}(a_1 + a_n)$

b. Derive the formula for the sum, S_n, of an arithmetic series in terms of the number of terms, n, the first term, a_1, and the common difference, d.

Solution:

1. $S_n = \dfrac{n}{2}(a_1 + a_n)$ (Formula for the sum of an arithmetic series.)

2. $a_n = a_1 + (n-1)d$ (Formula for the nth term of an arithmetic sequence.)

In (1), substitute $a_1 + (n-1)d$ for a_n.

3. $S_n = \dfrac{n}{2}[a_1 + a_1 + (n-1)d]$

4. $S_n = \dfrac{n}{2}[2a_1 + (n-1)d]$

26. SUM OF A GEOMETRIC SERIES

Derive the formula for the sum, S_n, of a geometric series in terms of the first term, a_1, the common ratio, r, and the number of terms, n.

Solution:

1. $S_n = a_1 + a_1 r + a_1 r^2 + a_1 r^3 + \cdots + a_1 r^{n-1}$
2. M_r: $rS_n = \qquad a_1 r + a_1 r^2 + a_1 r^3 + \cdots + a_1 r^{n-1} + a_1 r^n$
3. Subtract: $S_n - rS_n = a_1 \qquad\qquad\qquad\qquad\qquad\qquad\qquad - a_1 r^n$
4. Factor: $(1-r)S_n = a_1 - a_1 r^n$
5. D_{1-r}: $S_n = \dfrac{a_1 - a_1 r^n}{1-r}$

27. SUM OF AN INFINITE GEOMETRIC SERIES

Derive the formula for the sum, S, of an infinite geometric series in terms of the first term, a_1, and the common ratio, r, whose absolute value is less than 1.

Solution:

1. The formula for the sum of a geometric series is $S_n = \dfrac{a_1 - a_1 r^n}{1-r}$, or

$$S_n = \dfrac{a_1}{1-r} - \dfrac{a_1 r^n}{1-r}$$

2. When $|r| < 1$: As n becomes greater and greater, r^n becomes smaller and smaller and, in so doing, the value of r^n comes closer and closer to 0. A value of n can always be found that will make the difference between r^n and 0

smaller than any arbitrarily selected value, no matter how small this selected value may be. Hence, we say that r^n approaches 0 as a limit. If r^n approaches 0 as a limit, then $\dfrac{a_1 r^n}{1-r}$ must also approach 0 as a limit. Hence, we may replace $\dfrac{a_1 r^n}{1-r}$ with 0 in step 1, if the geometric series is an infinite series.

3. Therefore, if $\dfrac{a_1 r^n}{1-r}$ is replaced by 0 in step 1, we see that

$$S = \frac{a_1}{1-r}$$

if $|r| < 1$ and the geometric series is an infinite series.

Note that we have replaced S_n with S for the reason that n can only be used to represent a finite number. The above formula applies only to an infinite series, the number of whose terms is not a finite number.

28. LOGARITHM OF A PRODUCT

Prove: $\log(A \times B) = \log A + \log B$

1. Let $\log A = x$ and $\log B = y$.
2. Then $A = 10^x$ Changing $\log A = x$ to exponential form.
3. And $B = 10^y$ Changing $\log B = y$ to exponential form.
4. $A \times B = 10^{x+y}$ Multiplying powers with the same base.
5. $\log (A \times B) = x + y$ Changing $A \times B = 10^{x+y}$ to logarithmic form.
6. $\log (A \times B) = \log A + \log B$ Substituting.

29. LOGARITHM OF A QUOTIENT

Prove: $\log \dfrac{A}{B} = \log A - \log B$

1. Let $\log A = x$ and $\log B = y$.
2. Then $A = 10^x$ Changing $\log A = x$ to exponential form.
3. And $B = 10^y$ Changing $\log B = y$ to exponential form.
4. $\dfrac{A}{B} = 10^{x-y}$ Dividing powers with the same base.
5. $\log \dfrac{A}{B} = x - y$ Changing $\dfrac{A}{B} = 10^{x-y}$ to logarithmic form.
6. $\log \dfrac{A}{B} = \log A - \log B$ Substituting.

30. LOGARITHM OF A POWER

Prove: $\log A^b = b \log A$

1. Let $\log A = x$.
2. Then $\quad A = 10^x \qquad$ Changing $\log A = x$ to exponential form.
3. $\qquad A^b = (10^x)^b \qquad$ Raising both sides of (2) to the bth power.
4. $\qquad A^b = 10^{bx} \qquad$ Power of a power rule.
5. $\quad \log A^b = bx \qquad$ Changing $A^b = 10^{bx}$ to logarithmic form.
6. $\quad \log A^b = b \log A \quad$ Substituting.

31. LOGARITHM OF A ROOT

Prove: $\log \sqrt[b]{A} = \dfrac{\log A}{b}$

1. Let $\log A = x$.
2. Then $\quad A = 10^x \qquad$ Changing $\log A = x$ to exponential form.

3. $\qquad A^{\frac{1}{b}} = (10^x)^{\frac{1}{b}} \qquad$ Finding the bth root of both sides of (2).

4. $\qquad A^{\frac{1}{b}} = 10^{\frac{x}{b}} \qquad$ Power of a power rule.

5. $\quad \log A^{\frac{1}{b}} = \dfrac{x}{b} \qquad$ Changing $A^{\frac{1}{b}} = 10^{\frac{x}{b}}$ to logarithmic form.

6. $\quad \log \sqrt[b]{A} = \dfrac{\log A}{b} \qquad$ Substituting.

CHAPTER XXV

SUMMARY OF IMPORTANT ALGEBRAIC AND TRIGONOMETRIC FORMULAS

KEEP IN MIND

Throughout this chapter it is understood that the denominator of any fraction in a formula cannot equal 0; that is, any fraction must be defined.

Algebraic Formulas

I. LAWS OF EXPONENTS

1. $x^m \cdot x^n = x^{m+n}$ **2.** $x^m \div x^n = x^{m-n}$ **3.** $(x^m)^n = x^{mn}$

4. $(xy)^m = x^m y^m$ **5.** $\left(\dfrac{x}{y}\right)^m = \dfrac{x^m}{y^m}$ **6.** $x^0 = 1$

7. $x^{-m} = \dfrac{1}{x^m}$ **8.** $x^{\frac{1}{n}} = \sqrt[n]{x}$ **9.** $x^{\frac{m}{n}} = \sqrt[n]{x^m} = (\sqrt[n]{x})^m$

II. LAWS OF LOGARITHMS

1. $\log (A \times B) = \log A + \log B$ **2.** $\log \dfrac{A}{B} = \log A - \log B$

3. $\log A^b = b \log A$ **4.** $\log \sqrt[b]{A} = \dfrac{\log A}{b} = \dfrac{1}{b} \log A$

III. THE QUADRATIC EQUATION $ax^2 + bx + c = 0$
WHERE $a \neq 0$ AND a, b, AND c ARE REAL NUMBERS

If the roots of $ax^2 + bx + c = 0$ are represented by r_1 and r_2, then:

1. $r_1 = \dfrac{-b + \sqrt{b^2 - 4ac}}{2a}$ and $r_2 = \dfrac{-b - \sqrt{b^2 - 4ac}}{2a}$

2. $r_1 + r_2 = -\dfrac{b}{a}$

3. $r_1 r_2 = \dfrac{c}{a}$

4. $x^2 - (r_1 + r_2)x + r_1 r_2 = 0$

Using the discriminant to determine the nature of the roots of $ax^2 + bx + c = 0$:

5. If $b^2 - 4ac$ is zero or positive, the roots are real.

6. If $b^2 - 4ac$ is negative, the roots are imaginary.

7. If $b^2 - 4ac$ is zero, the roots are equal.

8. If $b^2 - 4ac$ is not zero, the roots are unequal.

9. If $b^2 - 4ac$ is a perfect square, the roots are rational numbers.

10. If $b^2 - 4ac$ is positive and not a perfect square, the roots are irrational numbers.

IV. GRAPHS (a, b, c, m, AND r ARE REAL NUMBERS)

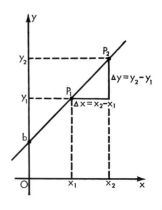

1. The slope of a line that passes through two points $P_1(x_1, y_1)$ and $P_2(x_2, y_2)$, $x_1 \neq x_2$:

$$m = \text{slope of } \overleftrightarrow{P_1 P_2} = \frac{y_2 - y_1}{x_2 - x_1} = \frac{\Delta y}{\Delta x}$$

2. Equation of a straight line: $y = mx + b$ where $m = $ slope of the line and $b = y$-intercept.

3. Equation of a parabola: $y = ax^2 + bx + c$ or $x = ay^2 + by + c$, $a \neq 0$.

4. Equation of a circle: $(x - h)^2 + (y - k)^2 = r^2$ where center is (h, k) and radius is r, $r > 0$.

5. Equation of a circle: $x^2 + y^2 = r^2$ where center is at the origin and radius is r, $r > 0$.

6. Equation of an ellipse: $ax^2 + by^2 = c$ where center is at the origin; a, b, and c are positive; $c \neq 0$.

7. Equation of a hyperbola: $ax^2 - by^2 = c$, $ay^2 - bx^2 = c$ where center is at the origin; a and b are positive. Also, $xy = k$, k is a constant.

8. At the turning point of the parabola $y = ax^2 + bx + c$, $x = -\dfrac{b}{2a}$.

9. The graph of the parabola $y = ax^2 + bx + c$ opens upward and has a minimum turning point when a is positive, $a > 0$.

10. The graph of the parabola $y = ax^2 + bx + c$ opens downward and has a maximum turning point when a is negative, $a < 0$.

V. ARITHMETIC SEQUENCES AND SERIES

In an arithmetic sequence, if a_1 represents the first term, a_n represents the nth term, d represents the common difference, n represents the number of terms, and S_n represents the sum of the terms:

1. $a_n = a_1 + (n-1)d$ **2.** $S_n = \dfrac{n}{2}(a_1 + a_n)$ **3.** $S_n = \dfrac{n}{2}[2a_1 + (n-1)d]$

4. The arithmetic mean, M, between two real numbers, a and b, is the average of the two numbers; that is, $M = \dfrac{a+b}{2}$.

VI. GEOMETRIC SEQUENCES AND SERIES

In a geometric sequence, if a_1 represents the first term, a_n represents the nth term, r represents the common ratio, n represents the number of terms, and S_n represents the sum of the terms:

1. $a_n = a_1 r^{n-1}$ **2.** $S_n = \dfrac{a_1 - a_1 r^n}{1-r}$, $r \neq 1$ **3.** $S_n = \dfrac{a_1 - a_n r}{1-r}$, $r \neq 1$

4. The geometric mean, G, between two real numbers, a and b:

(1) $\dfrac{a}{G} = \dfrac{G}{b}$ **(2)** $G^2 = ab$ **(3)** $G = \pm\sqrt{ab}$

5. The sum, S, of an infinite geometric series in which the absolute value of r is less than 1; that is, $|r| < 1$: $S = \dfrac{a_1}{1-r}$.

VII. VARIATION FORMULAS

For a summary of the variation formulas and the use of ratio symbols, refer to the table on pages 697–698.

Trigonometric Formulas

VIII. TRIGONOMETRY OF THE RIGHT TRIANGLE

$$\sin A = \frac{\text{opposite leg}}{\text{hypotenuse}} \qquad\qquad \csc A = \frac{\text{hypotenuse}}{\text{opposite leg}}$$

$$\cos A = \frac{\text{adjacent leg}}{\text{hypotenuse}} \qquad\qquad \sec A = \frac{\text{hypotenuse}}{\text{adjacent leg}}$$

$$\tan A = \frac{\text{opposite leg}}{\text{adjacent leg}} \qquad\qquad \cot A = \frac{\text{adjacent leg}}{\text{opposite leg}}$$

Note. In the context of an equation, the terms "leg" and "hypotenuse" are understood to mean "the length of the leg" and "the length of the hypotenuse" respectively.

IX. THE SIX TRIGONOMETRIC FUNCTIONS

$$\sin \theta = \frac{y}{r} \qquad\qquad \csc \theta = \frac{r}{y}$$

$$\cos \theta = \frac{x}{r} \qquad\qquad \sec \theta = \frac{r}{x}$$

$$\tan \theta = \frac{y}{x} \qquad\qquad \cot \theta = \frac{x}{y}$$

X. SUMMARY OF VALUES FOR FUNCTIONS OF 0°, 30°, 45°, 60°, AND 90°

	0°	30°	45°	60°	90°
sin	0	$\frac{1}{2}$	$\frac{1}{2}\sqrt{2}$	$\frac{1}{2}\sqrt{3}$	1
cos	1	$\frac{1}{2}\sqrt{3}$	$\frac{1}{2}\sqrt{2}$	$\frac{1}{2}$	0
tan	0	$\frac{1}{3}\sqrt{3}$	1	$\sqrt{3}$	*∞
cot	*∞	$\sqrt{3}$	1	$\frac{1}{3}\sqrt{3}$	0
sec	1	$\frac{2}{3}\sqrt{3}$	$\sqrt{2}$	2	*∞
csc	*∞	2	$\sqrt{2}$	$\frac{2}{3}\sqrt{3}$	1

Note. Refer to page 354 for an understanding of the use of "∞" in the case of functions such as tan 90° and cot 0°, whose values are undefined.

XX. SUMS AND DIFFERENCES OF LIKE FUNCTIONS

$$\sin A + \sin B = 2 \sin \tfrac{1}{2}(A + B) \cos \tfrac{1}{2}(A - B)$$
$$\sin A - \sin B = 2 \cos \tfrac{1}{2}(A + B) \sin \tfrac{1}{2}(A - B)$$
$$\cos A + \cos B = 2 \cos \tfrac{1}{2}(A + B) \cos \tfrac{1}{2}(A - B)$$
$$\cos A - \cos B = -2 \sin \tfrac{1}{2}(A + B) \sin \tfrac{1}{2}(A - B)$$

XXI. FUNDAMENTAL LAWS OF OBLIQUE TRIANGLES

1. Law of sines: $\dfrac{a}{\sin A} = \dfrac{b}{\sin B} = \dfrac{c}{\sin C}$

2. Law of cosines:

$$a^2 = b^2 + c^2 - 2bc \cos A \text{ or } \cos A = \frac{b^2 + c^2 - a^2}{2bc}$$

3. Law of tangents:

$$\frac{a - b}{a + b} = \frac{\tan \tfrac{1}{2}(A - B)}{\tan \tfrac{1}{2}(A + B)} \text{ or } \frac{b - a}{b + a} = \frac{\tan \tfrac{1}{2}(B - A)}{\tan \tfrac{1}{2}(B + A)}$$

4. Half-angle law of tangents:

$$\tan \tfrac{1}{2}A = \sqrt{\frac{(s - b)(s - c)}{s(s - a)}} \text{ or } \tan \tfrac{1}{2}A = \frac{r}{s - a}$$

where $s = \tfrac{1}{2}(a + b + c)$ and $r = \sqrt{\dfrac{(s - a)(s - b)(s - c)}{s}}$

XXII. AREA FORMULAS

1. Area of triangle:
$$K = \tfrac{1}{2}ab \sin C$$
$$K = \sqrt{s(s - a)(s - b)(s - c)} \qquad [s = \tfrac{1}{2}(a + b + c)]$$
2. Area of a parallelogram:
$$K = ab \sin C$$

XXIII. AMPLITUDE, FREQUENCY, AND PERIOD

If the equation of a curve is of the form $y = a \sin bx$ or $y = a \cos bx, a > 0$, $b > 0$:

1. The amplitude of the curve $= a$.

2. The frequency of the curve in $360°$ or 2π radians $= b$.

3. The period of the curve $= \dfrac{360°}{b}$ or $\dfrac{2\pi}{b}$ radians.

Squares and Square Roots

No.	Square	Square Root	No.	Square	Square Root	No.	Square	Square Root
1	1	1.000	51	2,601	7.141	101	10,201	10.050
2	4	1.414	52	2,704	7.211	102	10,404	10.100
3	9	1.732	53	2,809	7.280	103	10,609	10.149
4	16	2.000	54	2,916	7.348	104	10,816	10.198
5	25	2.236	55	3,025	7.416	105	11,025	10.247
6	36	2.449	56	3,136	7.483	106	11,236	10.296
7	49	2.646	57	3,249	7.550	107	11,449	10.344
8	64	2.828	58	3,364	7.616	108	11,664	10.392
9	81	3.000	59	3,481	7.681	109	11,881	10.440
10	100	3.162	60	3,600	7.746	110	12,100	10.488
11	121	3.317	61	3,721	7.810	111	12,321	10.536
12	144	3.464	62	3,844	7.874	112	12,544	10.583
13	169	3.606	63	3,969	7.937	113	12,769	10.630
14	196	3.742	64	4,096	8.000	114	12,996	10.677
15	225	3.873	65	4,225	8.062	115	13,225	10.724
16	256	4.000	66	4,356	8.124	116	13,456	10.770
17	289	4.123	67	4,489	8.185	117	13,689	10.817
18	324	4.243	68	4,624	8.246	118	13,924	10.863
19	361	4.359	69	4,761	8.307	119	14,161	10.909
20	400	4.472	70	4,900	8.367	120	14,400	10.954
21	441	4.583	71	5,041	8.426	121	14,641	11.000
22	484	4.690	72	5,184	8.485	122	14,884	11.045
23	529	4.796	73	5,329	8.544	123	15,129	11.091
24	576	4.899	74	5,476	8.602	124	15,376	11.136
25	625	5.000	75	5,625	8.660	125	15,625	11.180
26	676	5.099	76	5,776	8.718	126	15,876	11.225
27	729	5.196	77	5,929	8.775	127	16,129	11.269
28	784	5.292	78	6,084	8.832	128	16,384	11.314
29	841	5.385	79	6,241	8.888	129	16,641	11.358
30	900	5.477	80	6,400	8.944	130	16,900	11.402
31	961	5.568	81	6,561	9.000	131	17,161	11.446
32	1,024	5.657	82	6,724	9.055	132	17,424	11.489
33	1,089	5.745	83	6,889	9.110	133	17,689	11.533
34	1,156	5.831	84	7,056	9.165	134	17,956	11.576
35	1,225	5.916	85	7,225	9.220	135	18,225	11.619
36	1,296	6.000	86	7,396	9.274	136	18,496	11.662
37	1,369	6.083	87	7,569	9.327	137	18,769	11.705
38	1,444	6.164	88	7,744	9.381	138	19,044	11.747
39	1,521	6.245	89	7,921	9.434	139	19,321	11.790
40	1,600	6.325	90	8,100	9.487	140	19,600	11.832
41	1,681	6.403	91	8,281	9.539	141	19,881	11.874
42	1,764	6.481	92	8,464	9.592	142	20,164	11.916
43	1,849	6.557	93	8,649	9.644	143	20,449	11.958
44	1,936	6.633	94	8,836	9.695	144	20,736	12.000
45	2,025	6.708	95	9,025	9.747	145	21,025	12.042
46	2,116	6.782	96	9,216	9.798	146	21,316	12.083
47	2,209	6.856	97	9,409	9.849	147	21,609	12.124
48	2,304	6.928	98	9,604	9.899	148	21,904	12.166
49	2,401	7.000	99	9,801	9.950	149	22,201	12.207
50	2,500	7.071	100	10,000	10.000	150	22,500	12.247

Common Logarithms of Numbers*

N	0	1	2	3	4	5	6	7	8	9
10	0000	0043	0086	0128	0170	0212	0253	0294	0334	0374
11	0414	0453	0492	0531	0569	0607	0645	0682	0719	0755
12	0792	0828	0864	0899	0934	0969	1004	1038	1072	1106
13	1139	1173	1206	1239	1271	1303	1335	1367	1399	1430
14	1461	1492	1523	1553	1584	1614	1644	1673	1703	1732
15	1761	1790	1818	1847	1875	1903	1931	1959	1987	2014
16	2041	2068	2095	2122	2148	2175	2201	2227	2253	2279
17	2304	2330	2355	2380	2405	2430	2455	2480	2504	2529
18	2553	2577	2601	2625	2648	2672	2695	2718	2742	2765
19	2788	2810	2833	2856	2878	2900	2923	2945	2967	2989
20	3010	3032	3054	3075	3096	3118	3139	3160	3181	3201
21	3222	3243	3263	3284	3304	3324	3345	3365	3385	3404
22	3424	3444	3464	3483	3502	3522	3541	3560	3579	3598
23	3617	3636	3655	3674	3692	3711	3729	3747	3766	3784
24	3802	3820	3838	3856	3874	3892	3909	3927	3945	3962
25	3979	3997	4014	4031	4048	4065	4082	4099	4116	4133
26	4150	4166	4183	4200	4216	4232	4249	4265	4281	4298
27	4314	4330	4346	4362	4378	4393	4409	4425	4440	4456
28	4472	4487	4502	4518	4533	4548	4564	4579	4594	4609
29	4624	4639	4654	4669	4683	4698	4713	4728	4742	4757
30	4771	4786	4800	4814	4829	4843	4857	4871	4886	4900
31	4914	4928	4942	4955	4969	4983	4997	5011	5024	5038
32	5051	5065	5079	5092	5105	5119	5132	5145	5159	5172
33	5185	5198	5211	5224	5237	5250	5263	5276	5289	5302
34	5315	5328	5340	5353	5366	5378	5391	5403	5416	5428
35	5441	5453	5465	5478	5490	5502	5514	5527	5539	5551
36	5563	5575	5587	5599	5611	5623	5635	5647	5658	5670
37	5682	5694	5705	5717	5729	5740	5752	5763	5775	5786
38	5798	5809	5821	5832	5843	5855	5866	5877	5888	5899
39	5911	5922	5933	5944	5955	5966	5977	5988	5999	6010
40	6021	6031	6042	6053	6064	6075	6085	6096	6107	6117
41	6128	6138	6149	6160	6170	6180	6191	6201	6212	6222
42	6232	6243	6253	6263	6274	6284	6294	6304	6314	6325
43	6335	6345	6355	6365	6375	6385	6395	6405	6415	6425
44	6435	6444	6454	6464	6474	6484	6493	6503	6513	6522
45	6532	6542	6551	6561	6571	6580	6590	6599	6609	6618
46	6628	6637	6646	6656	6665	6675	6684	6693	6702	6712
47	6721	6730	6739	6749	6758	6767	6776	6785	6794	6803
48	6812	6821	6830	6839	6848	6857	6866	6875	6884	6893
49	6902	6911	6920	6928	6937	6946	6955	6964	6972	6981
50	6990	6998	7007	7016	7024	7033	7042	7050	7059	7067
51	7076	7084	7093	7101	7110	7118	7126	7135	7143	7152
52	7160	7168	7177	7185	7193	7202	7210	7218	7226	7235
53	7243	7251	7259	7267	7275	7284	7292	7300	7308	7316
54	7324	7332	7340	7348	7356	7364	7372	7380	7388	7396
N	0	1	2	3	4	5	6	7	8	9

* This table gives the mantissas of numbers with the decimal point omitted in each case. Characteristics are determined by inspection from the numbers.

N	0	1	2	3	4	5	6	7	8	9
55	7404	7412	7419	7427	7435	7443	7451	7459	7466	7474
56	7482	7490	7497	7505	7513	7520	7528	7536	7543	7551
57	7559	7566	7574	7582	7589	7597	7604	7612	7619	7627
58	7634	7642	7649	7657	7664	7672	7679	7686	7694	7701
59	7709	7716	7723	7731	7738	7745	7752	7760	7767	7774
60	7782	7789	7796	7803	7810	7818	7825	7832	7839	7846
61	7853	7860	7868	7875	7882	7889	7896	7903	7910	7917
62	7924	7931	7938	7945	7952	7959	7966	7973	7980	7987
63	7993	8000	8007	8014	8021	8028	8035	8041	8048	8055
64	8062	8069	8075	8082	8089	8096	8102	8109	8116	8122
65	8129	8136	8142	8149	8156	8162	8169	8176	8182	8189
66	8195	8202	8209	8215	8222	8228	8235	8241	8248	8254
67	8261	8267	8274	8280	8287	8293	8299	8306	8312	8319
68	8325	8331	8338	8344	8351	8357	8363	8370	8376	8382
69	8388	8395	8401	8407	8414	8420	8426	8432	8439	8445
70	8451	8457	8463	8470	8476	8482	8488	8494	8500	8506
71	8513	8519	8525	8531	8537	8543	8549	8555	8561	8567
72	8573	8579	8585	8591	8597	8603	8609	8615	8621	8627
73	8633	8639	8645	8651	8657	8663	8669	8675	8681	8686
74	8692	8698	8704	8710	8716	8722	8727	8733	8739	8745
75	8751	8756	8762	8768	8774	8779	8785	8791	8797	8802
76	8808	8814	8820	8825	8831	8837	8842	8848	8854	8859
77	8865	8871	8876	8882	8887	8893	8899	8904	8910	8915
78	8921	8927	8932	8938	8943	8949	8954	8960	8965	8971
79	8976	8982	8987	8993	8998	9004	9009	9015	9020	9025
80	9031	9036	9042	9047	9053	9058	9063	9069	9074	9079
81	9085	9090	9096	9101	9106	9112	9117	9122	9128	9133
82	9138	9143	9149	9154	9159	9165	9170	9175	9180	9186
83	9191	9196	9201	9206	9212	9217	9222	9227	9232	9238
84	9243	9248	9253	9258	9263	9269	9274	9279	9284	9289
85	9294	9299	9304	9309	9315	9320	9325	9330	9335	9340
86	9345	9350	9355	9360	9365	9370	9375	9380	9385	9390
87	9395	9400	9405	9410	9415	9420	9425	9430	9435	9440
88	9445	9450	9455	9460	9465	9469	9474	9479	9484	9489
89	9494	9499	9504	9509	9513	9518	9523	9528	9533	9538
90	9542	9547	9552	9557	9562	9566	9571	9576	9581	9586
91	9590	9595	9600	9605	9609	9614	9619	9624	9628	9633
92	9638	9643	9647	9652	9657	9661	9666	9671	9675	9680
93	9685	9689	9694	9699	9703	9708	9713	9717	9722	9727
94	9731	9736	9741	9745	9750	9754	9759	9763	9768	9773
95	9777	9782	9786	9791	9795	9800	9805	9809	9814	9818
96	9823	9827	9832	9836	9841	9845	9850	9854	9859	9863
97	9868	9872	9877	9881	9886	9890	9894	9899	9903	9908
98	9912	9917	9921	9926	9930	9934	9939	9943	9948	9952
99	9956	9961	9965	9969	9974	9978	9983	9987	9991	9996
N	0	1	2	3	4	5	6	7	8	9

* This table gives the mantissas of numbers with the decimal point omitted in each case. Characteristics are determined by inspection from the numbers.

Angle		Sin	Cos	Tan	Cot		
0°	00′	.0000	1.0000	.0000	—	90°	00′
	10	.0029	1.0000	.0029	343.77		50
	20	.0058	1.0000	.0058	171.89		40
	30	.0087	1.0000	.0087	114.59		30
	40	.0116	.9999	.0116	85.940		20
	50	.0145	.9999	.0145	68.750		10
1°	00′	.0175	.9998	.0175	57.290	89°	00′
	10	.0204	.9998	.0204	49.104		50
	20	.0233	.9997	.0233	42.964		40
	30	.0262	.9997	.0262	38.188		30
	40	.0291	.9996	.0291	34.368		20
	50	.0320	.9995	.0320	31.242		10
2°	00′	.0349	.9994	.0349	28.636	88°	00′
	10	.0378	.9993	.0378	26.432		50
	20	.0407	.9992	.0407	24.542		40
	30	.0436	.9990	.0437	22.904		30
	40	.0465	.9989	.0466	21.470		20
	50	.0494	.9988	.0495	20.206		10
3°	00′	.0523	.9986	.0524	19.081	87°	00′
	10	.0552	.9985	.0553	18.075		50
	20	.0581	.9983	.0582	17.169		40
	30	.0610	.9981	.0612	16.350		30
	40	.0640	.9980	.0641	15.605		20
	50	.0669	.9978	.0670	14.924		10
4°	00′	.0698	.9976	.0699	14.301	86°	00′
	10	.0727	.9974	.0729	13.727		50
	20	.0756	.9971	.0758	13.197		40
	30	.0785	.9969	.0787	12.706		30
	40	.0814	.9967	.0816	12.251		20
	50	.0843	.9964	.0846	11.826		10
5°	00′	.0872	.9962	.0875	11.430	85°	00′
	10	.0901	.9959	.0904	11.059		50
	20	.0929	.9957	.0934	10.712		40
	30	.0958	.9954	.0963	10.385		30
	40	.0987	.9951	.0992	10.078		20
	50	.1016	.9948	.1022	9.7882		10
6°	00′	.1045	.9945	.1051	9.5144	84°	00′
	10	.1074	.9942	.1080	9.2553		50
	20	.1103	.9939	.1110	9.0098		40
	30	.1132	.9936	.1139	8.7769		30
	40	.1161	.9932	.1169	8.5555		20
	50	.1190	.9929	.1198	8.3450		10
7°	00′	.1219	.9925	.1228	8.1443	83°	00′
	10	.1248	.9922	.1257	7.9530		50
	20	.1276	.9918	.1287	7.7704		40
	30	.1305	.9914	.1317	7.5958		30
	40	.1334	.9911	.1346	7.4287		20
	50	.1363	.9907	.1376	7.2687		10
8°	00′	.1392	.9903	.1405	7.1154	82°	00′
	10	.1421	.9899	.1435	6.9682		50
	20	.1449	.9894	.1465	6.8269		40
	30	.1478	.9890	.1495	6.6912		30
	40	.1507	.9886	.1524	6.5606		20
	50	.1536	.9881	.1554	6.4348		10
9°	00′	.1564	.9877	.1584	6.3138	81°	00′
		Cos	Sin	Cot	Tan	Angle	

Angle		Sin	Cos	Tan	Cot		
9°	00′	.1564	.9877	.1584	6.3138	81°	00′
	10	.1593	.9872	.1614	6.1970		50
	20	.1622	.9868	.1644	6.0844		40
	30	.1650	.9863	.1673	5.9758		30
	40	.1679	.9858	.1703	5.8708		20
	50	.1708	.9853	.1733	5.7694		10
10°	00′	.1736	.9848	.1763	5.6713	80°	00′
	10	.1765	.9843	.1793	5.5764		50
	20	.1794	.9838	.1823	5.4845		40
	30	.1822	.9833	.1853	5.3955		30
	40	.1851	.9827	.1883	5.3093		20
	50	.1880	.9822	.1914	5.2257		10
11°	00′	.1908	.9816	.1944	5.1446	79°	00′
	10	.1937	.9811	.1974	5.0658		50
	20	.1965	.9805	.2004	4.9894		40
	30	.1994	.9799	.2035	4.9152		30
	40	.2022	.9793	.2065	4.8430		20
	50	.2051	.9787	.2095	4.7729		10
12°	00′	.2079	.9781	.2126	4.7046	78°	00′
	10	.2108	.9775	.2156	4.6382		50
	20	.2136	.9769	.2186	4.5736		40
	30	.2164	.9763	.2217	4.5107		30
	40	.2193	.9757	.2247	4.4494		20
	50	.2221	.9750	.2278	4.3897		10
13°	00′	.2250	.9744	.2309	4.3315	77°	00′
	10	.2278	.9737	.2339	4.2747		50
	20	.2306	.9730	.2370	4.2193		40
	30	.2334	.9724	.2401	4.1653		30
	40	.2363	.9717	.2432	4.1126		20
	50	.2391	.9710	.2462	4.0611		10
14°	00′	.2419	.9703	.2493	4.0108	76°	00′
	10	.2447	.9696	.2524	3.9617		50
	20	.2476	.9689	.2555	3.9136		40
	30	.2504	.9681	.2586	3.8667		30
	40	.2532	.9674	.2617	3.8208		20
	50	.2560	.9667	.2648	3.7760		10
15°	00′	.2588	.9659	.2679	3.7321	75°	00′
	10	.2616	.9652	.2711	3.6891		50
	20	.2644	.9644	.2742	3.6470		40
	30	.2672	.9636	.2773	3.6059		30
	40	.2700	.9628	.2805	3.5656		20
	50	.2728	.9621	.2836	3.5261		10
16°	00′	.2756	.9613	.2867	3.4874	74°	00′
	10	.2784	.9605	.2899	3.4495		50
	20	.2812	.9596	.2931	3.4124		40
	30	.2840	.9588	.2962	3.3759		30
	40	.2868	.9580	.2994	3.3402		20
	50	.2896	.9572	.3026	3.3052		10
17°	00′	.2924	.9563	.3057	3.2709	73°	00′
	10	.2952	.9555	.3089	3.2371		50
	20	.2979	.9546	.3121	3.2041		40
	30	.3007	.9537	.3153	3.1716		30
	40	.3035	.9528	.3185	3.1397		20
	50	.3062	.9520	.3217	3.1084		10
18°	00′	.3090	.9511	.3249	3.0777	72°	00′
		Cos	Sin	Cot	Tan	Angle	

Angle	Sin	Cos	Tan	Cot	
18° 00′	.3090	.9511	.3249	3.0777	**72° 00′**
10	.3118	.9502	.3281	3.0475	50
20	.3145	.9492	.3314	3.0178	40
30	.3173	.9483	.3346	2.9887	30
40	.3201	.9474	.3378	2.9600	20
50	.3228	.9465	.3411	2.9319	10
19° 00′	.3256	.9455	.3443	2.9042	**71° 00′**
10	.3283	.9446	.3476	2.8770	50
20	.3311	.9436	.3508	2.8502	40
30	.3338	.9426	.3541	2.8239	30
40	.3365	.9417	.3574	2.7980	20
50	.3393	.9407	.3607	2.7725	10
20° 00′	.3420	.9397	.3640	2.7475	**70° 00′**
10	.3448	.9387	.3673	2.7228	50
20	.3475	.9377	.3706	2.6985	40
30	.3502	.9367	.3739	2.6746	30
40	.3529	.9356	.3772	2.6511	20
50	.3557	.9346	.3805	2.6279	10
21° 00′	.3584	.9336	.3839	2.6051	**69° 00′**
10	.3611	.9325	.3872	2.5826	50
20	.3638	.9315	.3906	2.5605	40
30	.3665	.9304	.3939	2.5386	30
40	.3692	.9293	.3973	2.5172	20
50	.3719	.9283	.4006	2.4960	10
22° 00′	.3746	.9272	.4040	2.4751	**68° 00′**
10	.3773	.9261	.4074	2.4545	50
20	.3800	.9250	.4108	2.4342	40
30	.3827	.9239	.4142	2.4142	30
40	.3854	.9228	.4176	2.3945	20
50	.3881	.9216	.4210	2.3750	10
23° 00′	.3907	.9205	.4245	2.3559	**67° 00′**
10	.3934	.9194	.4279	2.3369	50
20	.3961	.9182	.4314	2.3183	40
30	.3987	.9171	.4348	2.2998	30
40	.4014	.9159	.4383	2.2817	20
50	.4041	.9147	.4417	2.2637	10
24° 00′	.4067	.9135	.4452	2.2460	**66° 00′**
10	.4094	.9124	.4487	2.2286	50
20	.4120	.9112	.4522	2.2113	40
30	.4147	.9100	.4557	2.1943	30
40	.4173	.9088	.4592	2.1775	20
50	.4200	.9075	.4628	2.1609	10
25° 00′	.4226	.9063	.4663	2.1445	**65° 00′**
10	.4253	.9051	.4699	2.1283	50
20	.4279	.9038	.4734	2.1123	40
30	.4305	.9026	.4770	2.0965	30
40	.4331	.9013	.4806	2.0809	20
50	.4358	.9001	.4841	2.0655	10
26° 00′	.4384	.8988	.4877	2.0503	**64° 00′**
10	.4410	.8975	.4913	2.0353	50
20	.4436	.8962	.4950	2.0204	40
30	.4462	.8949	.4986	2.0057	30
40	.4488	.8936	.5022	1.9912	20
50	.4514	.8923	.5059	1.9768	10
27° 00′	.4540	.8910	.5095	1.9626	**63° 00′**
	Cos	Sin	Cot	Tan	Angle

Angle		Sin	Cos	Tan	Cot		
27°	**00′**	.4540	.8910	.5095	1.9626	**63°**	**00′**
	10	.4566	.8897	.5132	1.9486		50
	20	.4592	.8884	.5169	1.9347		40
	30	.4617	.8870	.5206	1.9210		30
	40	.4643	.8857	.5243	1.9074		20
	50	.4669	.8843	.5280	1.8940		10
28°	**00′**	.4695	.8829	.5317	1.8807	**62°**	**00′**
	10	.4720	.8816	.5354	1.8676		50
	20	.4746	.8802	.5392	1.8546		40
	30	.4772	.8788	.5430	1.8418		30
	40	.4797	.8774	.5467	1.8291		20
	50	.4823	.8760	.5505	1.8165		10
29°	**00′**	.4848	.8746	.5543	1.8040	**61°**	**00′**
	10	.4874	.8732	.5581	1.7917		50
	20	.4899	.8718	.5619	1.7796		40
	30	.4924	.8704	.5658	1.7675		30
	40	.4950	.8689	.5696	1.7556		20
	50	.4975	.8675	.5735	1.7437		10
30°	**00′**	.5000	.8660	.5774	1.7321	**60°**	**00′**
	10	.5025	.8646	.5812	1.7205		50
	20	.5050	.8631	.5851	1.7090		40
	30	.5075	.8616	.5890	1.6977		30
	40	.5100	.8601	.5930	1.6864		20
	50	.5125	.8587	.5969	1.6753		10
31°	**00′**	.5150	.8572	.6009	1.6643	**59°**	**00′**
	10	.5175	.8557	.6048	1.6534		50
	20	.5200	.8542	.6088	1.6426		40
	30	.5225	.8526	.6128	1.6319		30
	40	.5250	.8511	.6168	1.6212		20
	50	.5275	.8496	.6208	1.6107		10
32°	**00′**	.5299	.8480	.6249	1.6003	**58°**	**00′**
	10	.5324	.8465	.6289	1.5900		50
	20	.5348	.8450	.6330	1.5798		40
	30	.5373	.8434	.6371	1.5697		30
	40	.5398	.8418	.6412	1.5597		20
	50	.5422	.8403	.6453	1.5497		10
33°	**00′**	.5446	.8387	.6494	1.5399	**57°**	**00′**
	10	.5471	.8371	.6536	1.5301		50
	20	.5495	.8355	.6577	1.5204		40
	30	.5519	.8339	.6619	1.5108		30
	40	.5544	.8323	.6661	1.5013		20
	50	.5568	.8307	.6703	1.4919		10
34°	**00′**	.5592	.8290	.6745	1.4826	**56°**	**00′**
	10	.5616	.8274	.6787	1.4733		50
	20	.5640	.8258	.6830	1.4641		40
	30	.5664	.8241	.6873	1.4550		30
	40	.5688	.8225	.6916	1.4460		20
	50	.5712	.8208	.6959	1.4370		10
35°	**00′**	.5736	.8192	.7002	1.4281	**55°**	**00′**
	10	.5760	.8175	.7046	1.4193		50
	20	.5783	.8158	.7089	1.4106		40
	30	.5807	.8141	.7133	1.4019		30
	40	.5831	.8124	.7177	1.3934		20
	50	.5854	.8107	.7221	1.3848		10
36°	**00′**	.5878	.8090	.7265	1.3764	**54°**	**00′**
		Cos	Sin	Cot	Tan		Angle

Angle		Sin	Cos	Tan	Cot		
36°	00′	.5878	.8090	.7265	1.3764	54°	00′
	10	.5901	.8073	.7310	1.3680		50
	20	.5925	.8056	.7355	1.3597		40
	30	.5948	.8039	.7400	1.3514		30
	40	.5972	.8021	.7445	1.3432		20
	50	.5995	.8004	.7490	1.3351		10
37°	00′	.6018	.7986	.7536	1.3270	53°	00′
	10	.6041	.7969	.7581	1.3190		50
	20	.6065	.7951	.7627	1.3111		40
	30	.6088	.7934	.7673	1.3032		30
	40	.6111	.7916	.7720	1.2954		20
	50	.6134	.7898	.7766	1.2876		10
38°	00′	.6157	.7880	.7813	1.2799	52°	00′
	10	.6180	.7862	.7860	1.2723		50
	20	.6202	.7844	.7907	1.2647		40
	30	.6225	.7826	.7954	1.2572		30
	40	.6248	.7808	.8002	1.2497		20
	50	.6271	.7790	.8050	1.2423		10
39°	00′	.6293	.7771	.8098	1.2349	51°	00′
	10	.6316	.7753	.8146	1.2276		50
	20	.6338	.7735	.8195	1.2203		40
	30	.6361	.7716	.8243	1.2131		30
	40	.6383	.7698	.8292	1.2059		20
	50	.6406	.7679	.8342	1.1988		10
40°	00′	.6428	.7660	.8391	1.1918	50°	00′
	10	.6450	.7642	.8441	1.1847		50
	20	.6472	.7623	.8491	1.1778		40
	30	.6494	.7604	.8541	1.1708		30
	40	.6517	.7585	.8591	1.1640		20
	50	.6539	.7566	.8642	1.1571		10
41°	00′	.6561	.7547	.8693	1.1504	49°	00′
	10	.6583	.7528	.8744	1.1436		50
	20	.6604	.7509	.8796	1.1369		40
	30	.6626	.7490	.8847	1.1303		30
	40	.6648	.7470	.8899	1.1237		20
	50	.6670	.7451	.8952	1.1171		10
42°	00′	.6691	.7431	.9004	1.1106	48°	00′
	10	.6713	.7412	.9057	1.1041		50
	20	.6734	.7392	.9110	1.0977		40
	30	.6756	.7373	.9163	1.0913		30
	40	.6777	.7353	.9217	1.0850		20
	50	.6799	.7333	.9271	1.0786		10
43°	00′	.6820	.7314	.9325	1.0724	47°	00′
	10	.6841	.7294	.9380	1.0661		50
	20	.6862	.7274	.9435	1.0599		40
	30	.6884	.7254	.9490	1.0538		30
	40	.6905	.7234	.9545	1.0477		20
	50	.6926	.7214	.9601	1.0416		10
44°	00′	.6947	.7193	.9657	1.0355	46°	00′
	10	.6967	.7173	.9713	1.0295		50
	20	.6988	.7153	.9770	1.0235		40
	30	.7009	.7133	.9827	1.0176		30
	40	.7030	.7112	.9884	1.0117		20
	50	.7050	.7092	.9942	1.0058		10
45°	00′	.7071	.7071	1.0000	1.0000	45°	00′
		Cos	Sin	Cot	Tan	Angle	

Angle	L Sin	L Cos	L Tan	L Cot	
0° 00′	—	10.0000	—	—	90° 00′
10	7.4637	10.0000	7.4637	12.5363	50
20	7.7648	10.0000	7.7648	12.2352	40
30	7.9408	10.0000	7.9409	12.0591	30
40	8.0658	10.0000	8.0658	11.9342	20
50	8.1627	10.0000	8.1627	11.8373	10
1° 00′	8.2419	9.9999	8.2419	11.7581	89° 00′
10	8.3088	9.9999	8.3089	11.6911	50
20	8.3668	9.9999	8.3669	11.6331	40
30	8.4179	9.9999	8.4181	11.5819	30
40	8.4637	9.9998	8.4638	11.5362	20
50	8.5050	9.9998	8.5053	11.4947	10
2° 00′	8.5428	9.9997	8.5431	11.4569	88° 00′
10	8.5776	9.9997	8.5779	11.4221	50
20	8.6097	9.9996	8.6101	11.3899	40
30	8.6397	9.9996	8.6401	11.3599	30
40	8.6677	9.9995	8.6682	11.3318	20
50	8.6940	9.9995	8.6945	11.3055	10
3° 00′	8.7188	9.9994	8.7194	11.2806	87° 00′
10	8.7423	9.9993	8.7429	11.2571	50
20	8.7645	9.9993	8.7652	11.2348	40
30	8.7857	9.9992	8.7865	11.2135	30
40	8.8059	9.9991	8.8067	11.1933	20
50	8.8251	9.9990	8.8261	11.1739	10
4° 00′	8.8436	9.9989	8.8446	11.1554	86° 00′
10	8.8613	9.9989	8.8624	11.1376	50
20	8.8783	9.9988	8.8795	11.1205	40
30	8.8946	9.9987	8.8960	11.1040	30
40	8.9104	9.9986	8.9118	11.0882	20
50	8.9256	9.9985	8.9272	11.0728	10
5° 00′	8.9403	9.9983	8.9420	11.0580	85° 00′
10	8.9545	9.9982	8.9563	11.0437	50
20	8.9682	9.9981	8.9701	11.0299	40
30	8.9816	9.9980	8.9836	11.0164	30
40	8.9945	9.9979	8.9966	11.0034	20
50	9.0070	9.9977	9.0093	10.9907	10
6° 00′	9.0192	9.9976	9.0216	10.9784	84° 00′
10	9.0311	9.9975	9.0336	10.9664	50
20	9.0426	9.9973	9.0453	10.9547	40
30	9.0539	9.9972	9.0567	10.9433	30
40	9.0648	9.9971	9.0678	10.9322	20
50	9.0755	9.9969	9.0786	10.9214	10
7° 00′	9.0859	9.9968	9.0891	10.9109	83° 00′
10	9.0961	9.9966	9.0995	10.9005	50
20	9.1060	9.9964	9.1096	10.8904	40
30	9.1157	9.9963	9.1194	10.8806	30
40	9.1252	9.9961	9.1291	10.8709	20
50	9.1345	9.9959	9.1385	10.8615	10
8° 00′	9.1436	9.9958	9.1478	10.8522	82° 00′
10	9.1525	9.9956	9.1569	10.8431	50
20	9.1612	9.9954	9.1658	10.8342	40
30	9.1697	9.9952	9.1745	10.8255	30
40	9.1781	9.9950	9.1831	10.8169	20
50	9.1863	9.9948	9.1915	10.8085	10
9° 00′	9.1943	9.9946	9.1997	10.8003	81° 00′
	L Cos	L Sin	L Cot	L Tan	Angle

Angle		L Sin	L Cos	L Tan	L Cot		
9°	**00′**	9.1943	9.9946	9.1997	10.8003	**81°**	**00′**
	10	9.2022	9.9944	9.2078	10.7922		50
	20	9.2100	9.9942	9.2158	10.7842		40
	30	9.2176	9.9940	9.2236	10.7764		30
	40	9.2251	9.9938	9.2313	10.7687		20
	50	9.2324	9.9936	9.2389	10.7611		10
10°	**00′**	9.2397	9.9934	9.2463	10.7537	**80°**	**00′**
	10	9.2468	9.9931	9.2536	10.7464		50
	20	9.2538	9.9929	9.2609	10.7391		40
	30	9.2606	9.9927	9.2680	10.7320		30
	40	9.2674	9.9924	9.2750	10.7250		20
	50	9.2740	9.9922	9.2819	10.7181		10
11°	**00′**	9.2806	9.9919	9.2887	10.7113	**79°**	**00′**
	10	9.2870	9.9917	9.2953	10.7047		50
	20	9.2934	9.9914	9.3020	10.6980		40
	30	9.2997	9.9912	9.3085	10.6915		30
	40	9.3058	9.9909	9.3149	10.6851		20
	50	9.3119	9.9907	9.3212	10.6788		10
12°	**00′**	9.3179	9.9904	9.3275	10.6725	**78°**	**00′**
	10	9.3238	9.9901	9.3336	10.6664		50
	20	9.3296	9.9899	9.3397	10.6603		40
	30	9.3353	9.9896	9.3458	10.6542		30
	40	9.3410	9.9893	9.3517	10.6483		20
	50	9.3466	9.9890	9.3576	10.6424		10
13°	**00′**	9.3521	9.9887	9.3634	10.6366	**77°**	**00′**
	10	9.3575	9.9884	9.3691	10.6309		50
	20	9.3629	9.9881	9.3748	10.6252		40
	30	9.3682	9.9878	9.3804	10.6196		30
	40	9.3734	9.9875	9.3859	10.6141		20
	50	9.3786	9.9872	9.3914	10.6086		10
14°	**00′**	9.3837	9.9869	9.3968	10.6032	**76°**	**00′**
	10	9.3887	9.9866	9.4021	10.5979		50
	20	9.3937	9.9863	9.4074	10.5926		40
	30	9.3986	9.9859	9.4127	10.5873		30
	40	9.4035	9.9856	9.4178	10.5822		20
	50	9.4083	9.9853	9.4230	10.5770		10
15°	**00′**	9.4130	9.9849	9.4281	10.5719	**75°**	**00′**
	10	9.4177	9.9846	9.4331	10.5669		50
	20	9.4223	9.9843	9.4381	10.5619		40
	30	9.4269	9.9839	9.4430	10.5570		30
	40	9.4314	9.9836	9.4479	10.5521		20
	50	9.4359	9.9832	9.4527	10.5473		10
16°	**00′**	9.4403	9.9828	9.4575	10.5425	**74°**	**00′**
	10	9.4447	9.9825	9.4622	10.5378		50
	20	9.4491	9.9821	9.4669	10.5331		40
	30	9.4533	9.9817	9.4716	10.5284		30
	40	9.4576	9.9814	9.4762	10.5238		20
	50	9.4618	9.9810	9.4808	10.5192		10
17°	**00′**	9.4659	9.9806	9.4853	10.5147	**73°**	**00′**
	10	9.4700	9.9802	9.4898	10.5102		50
	20	9.4741	9.9798	9.4943	10.5057		40
	30	9.4781	9.9794	9.4987	10.5013		30
	40	9.4821	9.9790	9.5031	10.4969		20
	50	9.4861	9.9786	9.5075	10.4925		10
18°	**00′**	9.4900	9.9782	9.5118	10.4882	**72°**	**00′**
		L Cos	L Sin	L Cot	L Tan	Angle	

Angle	L Sin	L Cos	L Tan	L Cot		
18° 00′	9.4900	9.9782	9.5118	10.4882	72°	00′
10	9.4939	9.9778	9.5161	10.4839		50
20	9.4977	9.9774	9.5203	10.4797		40
30	9.5015	9.9770	9.5245	10.4755		30
40	9.5052	9.9765	9.5287	10.4713		20
50	9.5090	9.9761	9.5329	10.4671		10
19° 00′	9.5126	9.9757	9.5370	10.4630	71°	00′
10	9.5163	9.9752	9.5411	10.4589		50
20	9.5199	9.9748	9.5451	10.4549		40
30	9.5235	9.9743	9.5491	10.4509		30
40	9.5270	9.9739	9.5531	10.4469		20
50	9.5306	9.9734	9.5571	10.4429		10
20° 00′	9.5341	9.9730	9.5611	10.4389	70°	00′
10	9.5375	9.9725	9.5650	10.4350		50
20	9.5409	9.9721	9.5689	10.4311		40
30	9.5443	9.9716	9.5727	10.4273		30
40	9.5477	9.9711	9.5766	10.4234		20
50	9.5510	9.9706	9.5804	10.4196		10
21° 00′	9.5543	9.9702	9.5842	10.4158	69°	00′
10	9.5576	9.9697	9.5879	10.4121		50
20	9.5609	9.9692	9.5917	10.4083		40
30	9.5641	9.9687	9.5954	10.4046		30
40	9.5673	9.9682	9.5991	10.4009		20
50	9.5704	9.9677	9.6028	10.3972		10
22° 00′	9.5736	9.9672	9.6064	10.3936	68°	00′
10	9.5767	9.9667	9.6100	10.3900		50
20	9.5798	9.9661	9.6136	10.3864		40
30	9.5828	9.9656	9.6172	10.3828		30
40	9.5859	9.9651	9.6208	10.3792		20
50	9.5889	9.9646	9.6243	10.3757		10
23° 00′	9.5919	9.9640	9.6279	10.3721	67°	00′
10	9.5948	9.9635	9.6314	10.3686		50
20	9.5978	9.9629	9.6348	10.3652		40
30	9.6007	9.9624	9.6383	10.3617		30
40	9.6036	9.9618	9.6417	10.3583		20
50	9.6065	9.9613	9.6452	10.3548		10
24° 00′	9.6093	9.9607	9.6486	10.3514	66°	00′
10	9.6121	9.9602	9.6520	10.3480		50
20	9.6149	9.9596	9.6553	10.3447		40
30	9.6177	9.9590	9.6587	10.3413		30
40	9.6205	9.9584	9.6620	10.3380		20
50	9.6232	9.9579	9.6654	10.3346		10
25° 00′	9.6259	9.9573	9.6687	10.3313	65°	00′
10	9.6286	9.9567	9.6720	10.3280		50
20	9.6313	9.9561	9.6752	10.3248		40
30	9.6340	9.9555	9.6785	10.3215		30
40	9.6366	9.9549	9.6817	10.3183		20
50	9.6392	9.9543	9.6850	10.3150		10
26° 00′	9.6418	9.9537	9.6882	10.3118	64°	00′
10	9.6444	9.9530	9.6914	10.3086		50
20	9.6470	9.9524	9.6946	10.3054		40
30	9.6495	9.9518	9.6977	10.3023		30
40	9.6521	9.9512	9.7009	10.2991		20
50	9.6546	9.9505	9.7040	10.2960		10
27° 00′	9.6570	9.9499	9.7072	10.2928	63°	00′
	L Cos	L Sin	L Cot	L Tan	Angle	

Angle		L Sin	L Cos	L Tan	L Cot		
27°	**00′**	9.6570	9.9499	9.7072	10.2928	**63°**	**00′**
	10	9.6595	9.9492	9.7103	10.2897		50
	20	9.6620	9.9486	9.7134	10.2866		40
	30	9.6644	9.9479	9.7165	10.2835		30
	40	9.6668	9.9473	9.7196	10.2804		20
	50	9.6692	9.9466	9.7226	10.2774		10
28°	**00′**	9.6716	9.9459	9.7257	10.2743	**62°**	**00′**
	10	9.6740	9.9453	9.7287	10.2713		50
	20	9.6763	9.9446	9.7317	10.2683		40
	30	9.6787	9.9439	9.7348	10.2652		30
	40	9.6810	9.9432	9.7378	10.2622		20
	50	9.6833	9.9425	9.7408	10.2592		10
29°	**00′**	9.6856	9.9418	9.7438	10.2562	**61°**	**00′**
	10	9.6878	9.9411	9.7467	10.2533		50
	20	9.6901	9.9404	9.7497	10.2503		40
	30	9.6923	9.9397	9.7526	10.2474		30
	40	9.6946	9.9390	9.7556	10.2444		20
	50	9.6968	9.9383	9.7585	10.2415		10
30°	**00′**	9.6990	9.9375	9.7614	10.2386	**60°**	**00′**
	10	9.7012	9.9368	9.7644	10.2356		50
	20	9.7033	9.9361	9.7673	10.2327		40
	30	9.7055	9.9353	9.7701	10.2299		30
	40	9.7076	9.9346	9.7730	10.2270		20
	50	9.7097	9.9338	9.7759	10.2241		10
31°	**00′**	9.7118	9.9331	9.7788	10.2212	**59°**	**00′**
	10	9.7139	9.9323	9.7816	10.2184		50
	20	9.7160	9.9315	9.7845	10.2155		40
	30	9.7181	9.9308	9.7873	10.2127		30
	40	9.7201	9.9300	9.7902	10.2098		20
	50	9.7222	9.9292	9.7930	10.2070		10
32°	**00′**	9.7242	9.9284	9.7958	10.2042	**58°**	**00′**
	10	9.7262	9.9276	9.7986	10.2014		50
	20	9.7282	9.9268	9.8014	10.1986		40
	30	9.7302	9.9260	9.8042	10.1958		30
	40	9.7322	9.9252	9.8070	10.1930		20
	50	9.7342	9.9244	9.8097	10.1903		10
33°	**00′**	9.7361	9.9236	9.8125	10.1875	**57°**	**00′**
	10	9.7380	9.9228	9.8153	10.1847		50
	20	9.7400	9.9219	9.8180	10.1820		40
	30	9.7419	9.9211	9.8208	10.1792		30
	40	9.7438	9.9203	9.8235	10.1765		20
	50	9.7457	9.9194	9.8263	10.1737		10
34°	**00′**	9.7476	9.9186	9.8290	10.1710	**56°**	**00′**
	10	9.7494	9.9177	9.8317	10.1683		50
	20	9.7513	9.9169	9.8344	10.1656		40
	30	9.7531	9.9160	9.8371	10.1629		30
	40	9.7550	9.9151	9.8398	10.1602		20
	50	9.7568	9.9142	9.8425	10.1575		10
35°	**00′**	9.7586	9.9134	9.8452	10.1548	**55°**	**00′**
	10	9.7604	9.9125	9.8479	10.1521		50
	20	9.7622	9.9116	9.8506	10.1494		40
	30	9.7640	9.9107	9.8533	10.1467		30
	40	9.7657	9.9098	9.8559	10.1441		20
	50	9.7675	9.9089	9.8586	10.1414		10
36°	**00′**	9.7692	9.9080	9.8613	10.1387	**54°**	**00′**
		L Cos	L Sin	L Cot	L Tan	Angle	

Angle		L Sin	L Cos	L Tan	L Cot		
36°	**00'**	9.7692	9.9080	9.8613	10.1387	**54°**	**00'**
	10	9.7710	9.9070	9.8639	10.1361		50
	20	9.7727	9.9061	9.8666	10.1334		40
	30	9.7744	9.9052	9.8692	10.1308		30
	40	9.7761	9.9042	9.8718	10.1282		20
	50	9.7778	9.9033	9.8745	10.1255		10
37°	**00'**	9.7795	9.9023	9.8771	10.1229	**53°**	**00'**
	10	9.7811	9.9014	9.8797	10.1203		50
	20	9.7828	9.9004	9.8824	10.1176		40
	30	9.7844	9.8995	9.8850	10.1150		30
	40	9.7861	9.8985	9.8876	10.1124		20
	50	9.7877	9.8975	9.8902	10.1098		10
38°	**00'**	9.7893	9.8965	9.8928	10.1072	**52°**	**00'**
	10	9.7910	9.8955	9.8954	10.1046		50
	20	9.7926	9.8945	9.8980	10.1020		40
	30	9.7941	9.8935	9.9006	10.0994		30
	40	9.7957	9.8925	9.9032	10.0968		20
	50	9.7973	9.8915	9.9058	10.0942		10
39°	**00'**	9.7989	9.8905	9.9084	10.0916	**51°**	**00'**
	10	9.8004	9.8895	9.9110	10.0890		50
	20	9.8020	9.8884	9.9135	10.0865		40
	30	9.8035	9.8874	9.9161	10.0839		30
	40	9.8050	9.8864	9.9187	10.0813		20
	50	9.8066	9.8853	9.9212	10.0788		10
40°	**00'**	9.8081	9.8843	9.9238	10.0762	**50°**	**00'**
	10	9.8096	9.8832	9.9264	10.0736		50
	20	9.8111	9.8821	9.9289	10.0711		40
	30	9.8125	9.8810	9.9315	10.0685		30
	40	9.8140	9.8800	9.9341	10.0659		20
	50	9.8155	9.8789	9.9366	10.0634		10
41°	**00'**	9.8169	9.8778	9.9392	10.0608	**49°**	**00'**
	10	9.8184	9.8767	9.9417	10.0583		50
	20	9.8198	9.8756	9.9443	10.0557		40
	30	9.8213	9.8745	9.9468	10.0532		30
	40	9.8227	9.8733	9.9494	10.0506		20
	50	9.8241	9.8722	9.9519	10.0481		10
42°	**00'**	9.8255	9.8711	9.9544	10.0456	**48°**	**00'**
	10	9.8269	9.8699	9.9570	10.0430		50
	20	9.8283	9.8688	9.9595	10.0405		40
	30	9.8297	9.8676	9.9621	10.0379		30
	40	9.8311	9.8665	9.9646	10.0354		20
	50	9.8324	9.8653	9.9671	10.0329		10
43°	**00'**	9.8338	9.8641	9.9697	10.0303	**47°**	**00'**
	10	9.8351	9.8629	9.9722	10.0278		50
	20	9.8365	9.8618	9.9747	10.0253		40
	30	9.8378	9.8606	9.9772	10.0228		30
	40	9.8391	9.8594	9.9798	10.0202		20
	50	9.8405	9.8582	9.9823	10.0177		10
44°	**00'**	9.8418	9.8569	9.9848	10.0152	**46°**	**00'**
	10	9.8431	9.8557	9.9874	10.0126		50
	20	9.8444	9.8545	9.9899	10.0101		40
	30	9.8457	9.8532	9.9924	10.0076		30
	40	9.8469	9.8520	9.9949	10.0051		20
	50	9.8482	9.8507	9.9975	10.0025		10
45°	**00'**	9.8495	9.8495	10.0000	10.0000	**45°**	**00'**
		L Cos	L Sin	L Cot	L Tan	Angle